CW00522026

THE REPAIR AND
MAINTENANCE OF HOUSES

THE REPAIR AND MAINTENANCE OF HOUSES

by
Ian A. Melville, F.R.I.C.S.
and
Ian A. Gordon, F.R.I.C.S.

with illustrations to Chapter 1 by
E. Moira Stephenson

and the remaining illustrations
by the authors

THE ESTATES GAZETTE LIMITED
151 Wardour Street London
W1V 4BN

First published 1973
Reprinted 1979
Reprinted 1984
Reprinted 1988

ISBN 0 900361 43 3

Printed in Great Britain at The Bath Press, Avon

Preface

THERE are at present a number of excellent books available which deal with new constructional work and which are revised from time to time so as to focus on contemporary building methods and modern detailing. As these books are revised, however, so the older forms of construction become less well documented and are lost to the student and the practitioner. There is a lack of books dealing with the repair and maintenance of structures and yet in any one year a third of the total expenditure on building work is devoted to these purposes. There are various factors which suggest at the present time that this proportion might increase in the future. The country's stock of existing buildings is receiving increasing attention and the tendency now is to preserve them.

In our previous book, "Structural Surveys of Dwelling Houses", we endeavoured to develop three themes in the examination of existing buildings. Firstly to view the structure as a whole and to relate it to the period when it was built. Secondly to describe the defect and yet also diagnose its cause and thirdly, where possible, to prescribe a remedy. It was recognised that within the ambit of the previous book it was not always possible to diagnose accurately the cause of complicated defects within the time, of necessity, available for a structural survey on behalf of a prospective purchaser. Correspondingly the full treatment of the third theme, to prescribe a remedy, could not always be presented without further investigation. It is thought therefore that a second volume giving consideration to the further investigation envisaged in such circumstances and dealing with the repairs that may be found to be necessary would be of value. Maintenance, the neglect of which gives rise to many of the repairs which will be found described in this volume, is included, as a necessary corollary and preventative measure.

As this book is directed towards the investigation of the structure as a necessary part of the repair of buildings, which may involve the question of professional negligence, it is not directed to the small builder or do-it-yourself handyman. On the contrary it is intended for the practising surveyor and architect, both in the private and public sector, and to the student who has already acquired a basic

v

knowledge of building construction. For this reason some of the more routine items of repair and maintenance are deliberately excluded.

As in our previous book the field has been restricted to houses but even so in the broadest possible terms as including large and small, old and the relatively new, together with houses now used for other purposes. It may be that much of the information contained within will be found to be applicable to other types of building but the specific problems of these would involve a book of a different nature.

The form which the book should take was given much consideration before the present layout was adopted. In the field of repair so many factors may be involved that it is difficult to categorise items in watertight compartments. It was therefore considered appropriate after setting the scene to provide Chapter 1 as historical background and to devote a section of Chapter 2, Brick Walls, to a study of the investigations which may have to be undertaken to diagnose the cause of defects, information derived from this section, broadly speaking, being of common relevance to Chapters 3, Stone Walls and 4, Foundations. Chapters 2 to 4 should therefore be considered together as forming the basic structural section of the book. The remaining Chapters can be considered as units but again only in the broadest sense. By the provision of a full table of contents and a detailed index we have endeavoured to make the book useful as one of reference without hampering the continuity of the text.

In regard to the drawings, these must be considered as typical examples only and each building requiring repair must be treated on its merits. There are, after all, in this particular field many diverse but satisfactory methods of dealing with the same problem. Enshrined within the drawings are numerous examples of incorrect constructional detail and some atrocious design. It should not be necessary to point out that this is deliberate!

It is anticipated that the book will be ready for publication at about the same time as the building industry is in the middle of the change from measurement in British units to SI metric units. Particularly in the context of the repair of old buildings the change over period is likely to prove a difficult one and a conscious decision has been taken to present the information in both British and SI metric units, the British units being printed first. It has been necessary however in the preparation of the drawings to adopt scales appropriate to the metric system. For example to eyes familiar with working drawings some of the figures, at first glance, may appear to be at a scale of $\frac{1}{8}$th of an inch to 1 foot, i.e. 1:96. Closer examination will show however that they are drawn to a scale of 1:100 and similarly other figures will be found to be drawn at 1:200, 1:50, 1:20 and 1:10 instead of the more familiar scales of the past.

It will be noted throughout that no proprietary products or systems are mentioned by name but this is not for want of admiration for many of those available on the market. It is not, however, possible to do justice to all the various products and systems in this book and it was therefore considered essential to omit all names. The Building Centres are available to issue information provided by manufacturers and the owners of proprietary systems and it is considered that every professional adviser should form his own opinion on the information given. Some of the systems mentioned may be recognisable to the more assiduous readers of articles and advertisements in the technical journals, a method whereby most practitioners can keep up to date. The authors however hold to the view that it is not for them to recommend or advise upon particular proprietary brands or methods. Where possible British Standards should be invoked and where necessary reference made to the Building Research Establishment.

With a book of this nature it is no easy matter to make proper acknowledgment to all the sources of material used in its compilation. Much reference is made in the text to Government publications in particular to those of the Building Research Establishment, to which all members of the building team owe a heavy debt since its inception and to those of the British Standards Institution. We have drawn freely on these and on the various books and publications set out in the Bibliography at the end, to which due acknowledgment is made. For the form which the book has taken together with many of the views expressed and any errors which may have crept in undetected, we must however claim full responsibility!

Our sincere thanks are due to Mr. J. H. Whittaker, B.Eng., B.Sc., M.I.C.E., M.I.Struct.E., sometime District Surveyor for Kensington for kindly consenting to read through the manuscript of Chapters 2 to 6 and for providing much useful criticism based on his wide experience of old buildings. Our warm thanks are also extended to Mr. P. H. Wikramaratna for his valuable suggestions on the treatment of certain matters in Chapters 2 and 5.

London
August 1972

IAN A. MELVILLE
IAN A. GORDON

Contents

A paged list of contents appears at the beginning of each Chapter.

Illustrations

Figure   Page

Figure   Page

Joints for the overhang on sides and
at corner. Main beam and floor joists.
Joint for top plate, main post, tie beam
and principal rafter. Scarf joints.

Construction of narrow and square
wattle and daub panels.
Mathematical or brick tiles. The
correct position of moisture and
vapour barriers on repair to cladded
buildings.

Older types of trussed partitions, their
design and uses. Improvements to sub-
floor ventilation in floor repairs.

Diagrams to illustrate section on
calculations to check the strength of
floors and improvements thereto.

To a leaning and bulged four storey
wall.

Where building heights differ.
Single and double flying shores.

Figure	Page

Introduction

THERE is undoubtedly a great interest by the public in the subject matter of this book. This interest has grown remarkably in recent years and if it seems strange to state such an obvious fact the answer is that it was not at all obvious just after the Second World War. At that time, rows of shabby, peeling and neglected houses were a depressing sight in all urban areas. Few houses had received attention for some six years and the only hope of a coat of paint very often lay in a successful war damage claim. At that time everyone thought in terms of urban redevelopment. It is only now with the restrictions on the spread of existing towns, a quite new departure since the end of the Second World War, that urban redevelopment has proved incapable of keeping pace with the demand, particularly at a time of continually rising costs and an increase in the population. The unpopularity of flats among families with young children, the increasing affluence in most sections of the population and the difficulty of the public transport system to provide a reliable and comfortable service to the commuting public due to congestion, have all served to point out the difficulties of sole reliance on new development in outer areas. In recent years the attractions of retaining the older houses have been born in populace and national and local politician alike with the accolade, in 1968, of a White Paper to prove it[1] and subsequent legislation to back it up. Recent legislation has endorsed the principle that the Englishman's home is his castle by providing that at least it's capital appreciation in value shall not, unlike other investments, be taxed. This is a trend that may seem retrograde and be received with a resigned shrug by the Architect or Town Planner but is nevertheless a trend that is a peculiarly modern one and that makes something of a departure in the work of the urban surveyor as against his type of work in earlier periods. The point can be illustrated.

When John Clutton and Edward Ryde sat down to their by now well-known dinner at the Westminster Palace Hotel in Victoria Street on 23rd March 1868 and formed a resolution to establish an Institute of Surveyors, the Battle of Waterloo was within living memory just as the First World War is within living memory today. The population of England however, consisting of thirteen million

[1] Old Houses into New Homes (H.M.S.O. 15 p nett).

1

people, was to double between 1815 and 1871. The Surveyors
Institution was formed on the occurrence of immense changes that
were taking place and that were to follow. The Victorian age was to
see not only the immense steps in Sanitary and Building legislation
that were to enable vast urban complexes to function without disease, fire or collapses, but was to see also the enormous building
boom that was to follow on the steps of the enlarging railway system
carried forward by the wealth and optimism of the time. Indeed, it
is due to the railways in no small measure that the profession of
surveyor as we know it today was formed from a number of rather
dissimilar types of occupation. The Land Agent and the Surveyor
of constructional work closely allied to the building industry, whose
origins went back to Tudor times, met the need for the new skills
involved in assessing the amount of compensation that should be
paid to an aggrieved citizen who had been deprived of his land as a
result of new railway development. Many of the old established
firms of surveyors in the country were formed at this particular time
and for such a reason. The surveyor then developed new skills in
laying out estates, valuing assessing and acting as agent in the disposal or letting of the newly built houses that followed the railway
development.

At the time the Surveyors Institution was formed, England had
only recently become a largely urban community. The Georgian
building boom had ended and its long period of duration was due
to the fact that war in earlier periods only absorbed part of the resources of the population and enabled building to be reasonably
continuous since, although there were periods of slump and unemployment due to shortages of money and materials the whole of the
labour force had not trooped off to battle. All this was, however, to
change. Two enormous building booms, the first between about
1880 and 1914 and the second between 1925 and 1939 were to
follow. The total industrial and social commitment of the people to
the First and Second World Wars entailed an almost complete
stoppage of building activity at these times but the effect of the late
19th and early 20th centuries was to change for ever the average
Englishman into a town dweller. By the outbreak of the Second
World War the pattern was set. Every urban area was covered by
acre upon acre of houses set out in a controlled, rigid pattern
separated by shopping or commercial centres and by only the
occasional park or recreation ground. To the traveller returning to
Britain who flies into any of the main airports at the present time, it
might seem as if these areas have not changed very much. It is true
that tall blocks now stand in land previously covered by a web of
small streets but residential development since the Second World

War has generally taken place in the outer periphery of cities, where permitted, or in fact, in new towns that have been formed elsewhere. The inner residential areas remain generally intact apart from cities such as Coventry where the new development is, unhappily, the product of war. The inner Victorian and Edwardian houses and, to a large extent their Georgian predecessors, remain, to a large degree.

It is clear then that the function of the urban surveyor was largely bound up with redevelopment until quite recent times. It is now that the private practice urban surveyor becomes familiar as the Estate Manager. Instead of development he becomes responsible for conservation. The development of substantial estates of Council homes also led to local authorities employing surveyors to be responsible for their maintenance and repair. Many of the earlier houses on these estates are now showing the ravages of time and although well maintained, are becoming due for major renovation. Many local authorities are now also seeing in the older properties in their areas a useful addition to their own schemes of redevelopment. It is often only they who have the necessary source of capital to bring such properties up to the standards required by the Housing Acts so that many authorities buy these when they become available or when a private owner cannot afford to do the work required. Authorities who do this find that they can sometimes house more people in the renovated older houses than they can in a scheme which would involve demolition and rebuilding. What has come as a surprise to the Councils is that the tenants are often happier as a result. As the trend also grows in the private sector for people to purchase rather than rent houses the surveyor is consulted on questions of repair and condition by a wider and wider section of the community. But it is a sobering reflection that many Victorian houses will be one hundred years old when this book is published. It is extremely doubtful if the builders of the urban houses of the past ever remotely contemplated that their lives should have to extend to the lengths now considered acceptable. Indeed it is not clear if any "life" of a building was ever calculated. It is under the circumstances therefore remarkable, particularly after one or in other cases the neglect of two World Wars, that the existing stock of houses is serviceable or can be rendered so. However some parts of houses, like parts of motor cars, wear out quicker than others. Timber when exposed to damp in unventilated places will become affected by dry rot. Badly made bricks will crumble. Certain materials exposed to polluted atmospheres will have disconcertingly short lives. This of course is not to be wondered at particularly since the new mass-produced materials of the Victorian age were never subjected to scientific analysis, nor as mentioned earlier, was any particular "life" ever contemplated. In any event, like parts of a motor car, parts of house structures can surely be renewed. There comes a time however, even with motor cars where the straightforward renewal of a part is not the answer. Time and the elements will take their toll leaving very little of the basic structure in places remaining. The question will then arise as to whether it is worth proceeding further with repair work. In the answer to this question a lot will depend on the quality of the original vehicle. If good it might be worth it. So it is with houses and in advocating the need for a full investigation before embarking on repair work, the following cases might be cited.

The first case concerns a Georgian end of terrace cottage. At first sight it was evidently neglected but constructed of sound 9 in. stock brickwork, bulged to be true, but no doubt adequate. The problem appeared to resolve itself therefore into working out an overall figure of cost for the repair of the building. Close investigation, however, and cutting away revealed the depressing fact that each external wall consisted of two separate skins of brickwork laid against each other with no bond between. The writers thought it remarkable and devious of the original bricklayers that they had taken the trouble to use snapped headers on each elevation to simulate solid brickwork and to fool a trusting surveyor nearly 150 years later. Discussion more recently with colleagues revealed however that this practice was widespread since due to the irregularities in common bricks notwithstanding the regulations of the time, many bricklayers scorned a 9-inch solid wall to give both a regular inner and outer face and the practice of stretchers and snapped headers set up in two skins was carried on even into the 20th century. In the building in question, however, what would have been acceptable bulges in a 9-inch solid wall proved to be very different as the brick skins had separated and there was not sufficient structural strength left to form a sound basis for repair work and the property had to be demolished. The second case concerns a large detached early Georgian house. Once the internal plaster was removed in places, bonding timbers were found in all the external brick walls. All of these due to particular and unusual conditions were sodden with dampness, and rot and weevil had removed any strength. The internal structure of the property, composed mainly of timber, not brick, did not assist the stability of the brick walls already rendered unstable by the defect mentioned. The same fate befell this property. The final case concerns a large Victorian semi-detached house. This stood on a hill slope and the downhill flank wall after some 85 years of indecision had finally made up its mind to depart from the main structure. Cutting away however showed that the cracking in the return of the front elevation had allowed moisture to penetrate and rot the wood lintel over the front bay window thus rendering the brickwork above, to the front elevation, unsafe and in need of rebuilding. In consequence not only the whole of the flank wall but a substantial portion of the front wall was rebuilt. Now the remarkable feature of these cases, to the authors, is that there were facilities and time for full investigation and time to ascertain what was wrong. Not only was the possibility of superficial repairs avoided and money saved but the client was able to know the full extent of his liability in advance in the latter case rather than being asked for more money at an inconvenient later stage. It is hardly to be wondered at, therefore, if the authors advocate the need for investigation before any work is carried out. It is true, perhaps, to say that given sufficient time and a sufficient budget of money that a surveyor should be able to repair most types of dwelling houses but conditions are rarely ideal. In some cases a telephone call from a client to his surveyor to repair a house that has already been structurally surveyed will send the surveyor scurrying to his filing cabinet to find out what he said about it. This at least gives a convenient starting point but in other cases the surveyor stands the risk of commencing work without proper investigation, for example where he is engaged to plan alterations to a house and where he is more concerned to get his plans out against time rather than know about the state of the structure. The writers therefore advocate the need for a structural survey in the case of alterations and repairs affecting the fundamental structure. All offices are busy nowadays and conditions may arise where the surveyor stumbles across some serious fault in the structure only when the work has commenced and where there may not be sufficient funds to neet the extra liability. The surveyor may be more than adequately equipped with the technical knowledge required under such circumstances but may be trapped into error by over anxiety to please the client. This introduces another point; the question of money. Money will always loom large in the repair of dwelling houses since the sums involved are often substantial and will form a large part of the resources of most people, in some cases having to be raised by way of mortgage on the property that is to be the subject of the repair work. The desire of a surveyor to risk an inexpensive answer to a problem may at first seem to be laudable but may later be termed incompetence. It is not the object of this book to suggest cheap and risky solutions to difficult problems. However, the practical problems of the surveyor with a client of restricted means can well occupy a brief space, for there are often a number of different solutions to a particular problem. The choice of the one to be adopted will depend in some cases entirely on the client's resources but at other times on the future life of the building.

Consideration of the question of the appearance of the building when repaired will also enter into the decision.

A word might now be said on the subject of the maintenance of dwelling houses. It is perhaps a truism to say that maintenance becomes more difficult according to the age of the structure, but the quality of the original building is also an important factor, coupled with the degree of maintenance in the past. Surveyors in both the public and the private sector have similar problems to face in arranging for work to substantial estates of buildings. The problems of the public service surveyor are perhaps a little easier in that in a particular purpose built estate most of the properties will be of a similar age and possess similar characteristics. On the other hand, budgetary control can be strict and with such estates quite major renewals might arise at the same time throughout; for example the the roof of almost every house may need reslating within a short space of time. Generally however if the estate was purpose built for the local authority it is likely to have fewer of the basic structural defects that can be found in the estates of the private sector. Private estates often consist of a diverse range of properties from different periods and matters are often complicated by the varying nature of the tenancies and the income derived from them. As an example we might consider therefore, a common instance in private practice, that of a terrace of houses in a suburban street where the dwellings may be occupied by controlled or regulated tenants and will, it is hoped, be painted neatly in good oil paint, although, forgivably in rather uniform colours. A vivid contrast may, however, compensate for this uniformity in the case of one or two houses in the same street which, having been purchased by their tenants under the stimulus of local loans schemes, may reflect their new owners' sense of self-expression in bright primary colours. In one case the brick joints may be picked out in white with infinite care. In another case the writers can recall, lilac paint coupled with a revolving porch light that flashed out alternate tones of crimson, green and amber presented an impression both impressive and distinctive in the true sense.

If all the houses have the same structure, apart from extraneous local difficulties such as tree root damage or defects caused by, say, variable sub-soil, each house should have the same fundamental defects in structure and materials as its neighbour. The only exceptions to this are the two end of terrace houses which may be expected to have other possible defects due to the differing strains to which these are subjected. In accepting instructions for the management and maintenance of the properties however the surveyor must exercise some care. Lack of maintenance in the past may breed a surprising crop of defects and initial expenditure may well be required before recurrent items of expenditure can be budgeted for at appropriate periods and a repairs fund set aside from rents so that the client can be certain of receiving a regular net income. Where the surveyor on the other hand is asked to look after a single house occupied by two elderly pensioners and owned by a third, he may be presented with an insoluble task to meet the bills for maintenance that are to be expected at the present time.

It is clear then the surveyor in both the public and private sector has a wide responsibility for the maintenance of many different types of residential buildings. It is not even true to say that Local Authority surveyors are restricted to the dwellings built this century. Acquisitions of older properties has meant these in turn have been placed in the care of surveyors in the public service both from the point of view of maintenance as well as repair.

To look after these older properties and to repair them successfully when something goes wrong requires a knowledge of the way they were built in the first place and knowledge of the way the materials available at that time were used in the constructional process. The buildings in the past had to fulfil a need which existed at the time they were built just as buildings put up today. As times were different, so the shape and type of house erected was quite different to what is required at the present time. Similarly the way available sites have been used has changed over the years. A number of factors have influenced the design and construction of dwelling houses and the layout of the towns and cities of Britain in which the majority of them are situated. Most people will be familiar with the pattern of concentric rings which surround many of our major cities from the daily drive or the journey by public transport to the place of work. Approaching a city centre the seemingly endless leafy suburbs eventually give way to the closer packed dwellings of earlier periods. Suddenly the centre is reached and those fortunate enough to live in the quieter parts of the country may find this still consisting of gracious buildings from an age prior to the Industrial Revolution and perhaps even dating back to late mediaeval times.

Few however will have given much consideration to the social, economic and the legislative factors that have influenced the pattern of town development, let alone the layout of individual sites and the type of buildings erected on them. Part of each Chapter in this book will be devoted to a detailed consideration of the constructional features of the past and their repair and maintenance based on a knowledge of their significance and the historical use of the materials employed. Much repetition however will be avoided if the overall picture is dealt with separately so as to provide a broad frame

7

INTRODUCTION

within which the constructional features can be considered and Chapter 1 will be devoted to this purpose. As the majority of the population are now town dwellers consideration, albeit briefly, will be given to building types, sites and their relation to town patterns as a whole. The rural dwelling house will not be entirely forgotten however. It is hoped that the Chapter will enable the surveyor to relate older buildings to their particular era and, in conjunction with the material from the remaining Chapters, assist in providing a historical understanding on which to base suitable schemes for maintenance and repair.

Britain is very rich in surviving houses from previous centuries and a fortunate freedom from invasion has made her better endowed than most other countries in this respect. It is somewhat disconcerting, however, to realise that it is necessary to look back over quite so many years. The houses of the early Britons do not form part of this account as they are, mercifully, now in the province of the archaeologist rather than the surveyor. The same applies to the houses of the first alien civilisation to come to Britain. This is a pity as it would be rather pleasant to consider Roman villas as part of the existing stock of houses.

Chapter 1
Historical Background

CONTENTS

*"All wallis, whether they be of stone
or of brycke or of claye with straw
or mudde, must be made levell and plumme,
orels they be ready to fall."*

HORMAN, C. 1500

FOLLOWING the sack of Rome in A.D. 410, the Emperor Honorius was obliged to tell his British subjects to make what arrangements they could for their own safety and with the abrupt departure of the legions little was left for the occupying Saxons except some fine brick and rendered villas with tiled roofs and cultivated gardens, a fortress system and a magnificent network of roads that was to endure, practically untouched, until the time of Macadam. Subsequent excavation has revealed the curious fact that the villas, once left by their Roman owners, were never again reoccupied but merely fell into decay. Ealdred, the 8th Abbot of St. Albans is recorded as having used the bricks from the ruins of Verulamium in building his church and Abbot Paul his successor followed his example, but generally the structures appear to have been ignored completely. To the Saxons it is probable that the sophisticated buildings left behind, although elementary when compared with the concrete vaulting and stone columns of Rome, did not resemble dwellings at all. The use of glass, the intricate mosaics and the advanced hypocaust central heating systems would appear utterly incomprehensible to the invaders, who were essentially countrymen and who had no experience of towns in any case. The use of plaster in conjunction with brick therefore returned to Italy not to be seen again for a long time. The Saxons then proceeded to build not only their own social system, but their own houses, and only the Roman road and fortress system was found to be of value. Ultimately, however, the Saxon influence was to be the greater for in spite of four centuries of Roman occupation ours is an Anglo-Saxon tongue today. Thus while Chester is familiar as a Roman legacy the modern home is now known as a dwelling (stead), a cottage (cot), or a farm (ham). "Ing" is a common element in Anglo-Saxon place names. Wokingham, for example, is the farm of Wocc's people. Most of our villages owe their origins to the Saxons.

The Anglo-Saxons formed settlements each known as a "tun". The buildings were grouped inside the "tun", surrounded by strong wooden stockades with one small entrance, and were formed of wood and thatch. The largest building belonged, naturally, to the Lord of the Tun. Outside, the arable land was tilled on the open field system, a third being left fallow every year. Later the complex of buildings grew larger and the subsequent grouping of the hundred or shire took place being still recognisable in units of local government today. At the same time the Anglo-Saxon dwelling house was to grow and assume a more recognisable character with the improved use of wood.

From excavations it has been possible to obtain a clear impression of the average type of early dwelling house of the time following the Roman departure. A reconstruction in the British Museum of a Saxon weaver's hut unearthed at Bourton-on-the-Water in the Cotswolds shows us a dwelling of oval plan. It has a sunken interior and levelled earth floor. Above this a cob and stone plinth forms the base for timber rafters which are arranged to meet at a ridge piece. The rafters are covered with branches and interwoven twigs, smeared with clay and termed wattle and daub.

In these primitive houses the framing of the wall and roof was continuous. A series of pairs of poles were set in line with their thicker ends in the ground and their thinner ends pegged at the apex. Smaller horizontal branches or sticks between the poles supported the covering of thatch and the ends of the inverted "V" were filled with wattle and daub and possibly contained a window. The inconvenience of a narrow headroom was soon overcome, however, with the appearance of the "Cruck" built house. This type of structure was known about in Roman times and regarded by Vitruvius as obsolete. Nevertheless it had an astonishingly long life in Britain. The "Cruck" was formed from a selected piece of oak with a branch growing at an angle of about 45 degrees which was cut and squared, with the vertical portion above the joint being severed. The angled timber so provided was then cut in half along its length and one side reversed. Both timbers were then set up in the ground, meeting at the top, each pair of crucks being steadied by a horizontal tie beam pegged into each member. The series of crucks then carried a squared ridge in their overlapping ends. The rectangular space between two pairs of crucks, a length often about 16 feet, was known as a bay, and became the acceptable unit of measurement and, later the mediaeval basis of taxation. The cruck was often known as a fork or gavel and this latter word eventually later became gable. Cruck construction remained in use for many hundreds of years for the smaller type of dwelling and although most have long since disappeared some examples still exist from later mediaeval times, see Figure 1(a). However the size and shape of the

11

Anglo-Saxon house was to change eventually under the influence of an alien society imposed from without.

Under the rule of Ethelred renowned to every school boy as the "Unready", Danish raids started in earnest in 978 and the Danish invasion quickly followed. The Norman conquest took place shortly afterwards and the imposition of Feudalism changed the old Anglo-Saxon way of life. Society was now arranged according to a man's relation to the land, so that if a man was a great lord it was because he held many fields. If he were a villein it was because he was tied to the soil. The lord held the land and the peasant tilled it. All land was held in theory from the King and the baron, knight, or tenant in chief to whom a manor or indeed manors were granted, which might consist of whole villages or a single farm, expected to have his own central residence and his surrounding fields tilled by the compulsory labour of the villeins in exchange for the right to cultivate strips of their own. The system of cross barter and payment in kind became more complex and the estates and houses reflected this. The lord, the freeman, the villein and the collar (cottager) owned or worked on land in a complicated inter-relationship to each other. The arable land was set out in oblong acre strips and the records of a Manor Court of the time reveal that the alteration of a boundary stone (marking the end of one strip and the beginning of another) was a serious offence.

Nearly all the mediaeval towns originated in Saxon times and developed from villages which, owing to some happy accident of a favourable position such as a good harbour, exceptionally good communications or a great monastery nearby, possessed more than ordinary consequence. In the early days a town was indistinguishable from a village or manor. As the town grew the townsmen were able, by increasing affluence from trade, to buy themselves free from feudal burdens. Many towns later gained their Charter of freedom, particularly from King John, who always had an eager eye for a financial bargain, and York, Norwich and Winchester are examples.

The development of the English house owes much to the Normans and to their use of stone. At first the invaders built castles for their own protection. The rectangular castle keep which was to provide such a strong influence often consisted of an arrangement of vertical storeys. The entrance was at first floor level and was reached by narrow stone steps or a ladder. Above the entrance floor was the hall with the "solar" or private room for the Lord and Lady on the floor above in the case of a Tower keep, or on the same level partitioned from the hall by a curtain or screen in the case of a hall keep. The vaulted ground floor was used for storage. As the Norman invaders became established and the need for the severe castle keep

Early mediaeval
forms

(a) Timber framed
house of cruck
construction

(b) Stone town house

(c) Timber house of box frame construction

1

13

grew less, modifications were made. The rectangular castle keep was replaced by a complex of buildings surrounded by a wall with a small gatehouse. The hall, however, still occupied the main building at first floor level with storage space below. The "solar" was now established at one end and to the side of the hall and a kitchen block was provided at the other end, but not at first linked to the hall for fear of fire. Later the linked "L" shaped house with combination of hall, solar, chapel and kitchen was to lead to further development, which will be referred to at a later stage in. this Chapter. It should be noted that in addition to large stone manor houses of this type however the Normans built a handful of small houses in the towns some of which are with us still. These are only some 20 feet by 40 feet, of rectangular shape, with the traditional living room and solar at first floor level. Often known as "Jew's houses", see Figure 1(b), the dwellings are supposed to have belonged to Norman debt collectors who were unpopular at the time and needed a measure of protection, which would not have been afforded by the more usual timber house of the period.

The great achievement of the Normans was, of course, the building of churches and cathedrals in stone and the massive extent of these dwarfed their other building both in cost and scale. It is a disconcerting fact however that mediaeval stone buildings were very prone to collapse. In the mists of mediaeval England the silence was all too often broken by a sudden crack followed by the sound of falling masonry and no doubt an ensuing hubbub of Anglo-Saxon or Norman voices. "Nothing is more common than to find that churches built in the eleventh century fell soon after their building or by the end of the century", says one source[1] and the great church towers of the Norman period were particularly prone to failure due to insufficient foundations, even although footings were often provided, and piles are recorded in marshy ground. There was much unskilful handling of materials and bad and scamped workmanship and gales took a dreadful toll of all buildings, rich and poor alike. It is however to the Normans that we are largely indebted for the introduction of stone, since although stone Saxon church towers still exist, all domestic and most other construction was in timber. Over the same period during which the Norman castle diminished in scale to a manor house the timber Saxon house increased in stature, evolving to much the same shape into a hall, sometimes aisled, with wings. It is now necessary therefore to deal briefly with the improving timber structure. There will be more to say about stone later on.

---

[1] Quiechrat: Melanges 434 quoted by Mortet 5 (Salzman).

The cramped early timber dwelling houses still accommodated the majority of the Saxon population. The infilling to the walls might vary from stones to trampled earth or mud or cob, which was a mixture of earth and straw, while the roofs might be of turf, heather or straw depending on the locality. The inverted "V" shaped house structure, however, was incapable of further expansion and accordingly as the ability of the carpenters of the Middle Ages increased, further developments took place so that the framing of the walls and roofs became separate. The framing for the walls was now set up on a rectangular base of massive timbers known as ground cills, morticed at the corners. These timbers were usually set on a low wall of stone or set level on stone bases. Underpinning was the term used for driving in wedges to correct irregularities in the base framing. John Loose was paid at Cambridge in 1457 for setting stone under the "ground sillys". Upright principal posts were then morticed into the corners and were carried up, unbroken, to the full height of the walls where they then carried the horizontal wall plates which supported the roof timbering, see Figure 1(c) on the hall section. Intervening spaces between doors and windows and between the posts and any horizontal stiffeners were filled with wattle and daub (also known as stud and mud), which provided a satisfactory material for weatherproofing, suitably light in weight. Accordingly wattling grew into an established building method to reduce the need for an excess of framing timbers over that required for the necessary strength to support the roof. The term was given to a row of upright stakes, the spaces in between being filled with inter-weaving small branches such as hazel rods, oziers or reeds. Earth, clay, mortar or plaster was thrust into the interstices, the surface then being smoothed with plaster and whitewashed. Torching was the term first used in the middle of the 13th century for plastering with mud, although its use survives until this day in a rather different sense. Daubing was the term used for both plastering and whitewashing alike.

Once the house frame was erected the roof structure was formed. This at first consisted of pairs of rafters placed on the wallplates, the upper ends being halved and pegged together. Each pair of rafters was known as a "couple". To provide stability each couple was pegged together horizontally one third of the length from the ridge by a "wind beam" now known as a collar. The roof was finally covered with "thack" the term given to the outer layer of the roof covering which was usually of straw or reed.

The early form of box frame timber house structure which usually consisted of one room serving as kitchen, living room and bedroom, was common until the end of the 13th century and was astonishingly

15

strong and adaptable. Houses could be moved as a whole or taken down and re-erected. The manufacture was efficient and organised. The cutting and preparation of the timber was often carried out some way away and all the timbers were then delivered to the site. They would have been previously marked by the master carpenter and were then erected without undue difficulty. The whole structure was loosely held in place by hookpins which were long tapering pegs which could be easily seized and withdrawn when the permanent joints were formed with oak pegs.

Further development of the house structure came about when it became possible to increase the span of roofs. Desirable in itself this may also have been brought about by the need to economise in timber. Thicker principal rafters at intervals permitted more slender common rafters to be used. The principal rafters were prevented from spreading by a tie beam morticed to the wallplates and the introduction of a Crown post and braces led to the formation of types of trusses, which, by supporting purlins, enabled even more slender common rafters to be used. It was later found that posts on corbels with pendants could serve as added support to the tie-beams themselves, which enabled enriched bosses to become decorative features and lead ultimately to the rare but renowned "hammer beam" roof. It was now possible to form practically any size of roof to a pleasing shape. Struts from the lowest point of the principal rafters to a high collar could be curved in the form of sous-laces (braces) so that a pointed arch could be formed and the roof structure thus given a high and lofty appearance, suitable for an imposing hall, the centre of domestic life at the time.

Construction and design was now being influenced by a man's desire for more comfort and his aim to display with a degree of pride his status in the community. The Norman and later examples in stone, see Figure 2(a), led to the development of the aisled hall in timber. By carrying the roof structure on a series of posts, the roof-slopes could sweep down to low eaves which permitted aisles to be provided on each side of the central area as in Figure 2(b). This allowed a large floor area to be formed to the main hall. Annexe wings were formed at each end of the hall to contain solar and kitchen, and as the need for ancillary chambers grew, the wings became the most complicated part of the structure and were usually two storeys in height. This was partly due to Norman influence in the social sense and partly for technical reasons. For two-storey structures in small spans, up to say 15 feet, joists for first floors were carried across from wallplate to wallplate. If the span was longer it would be necessary to introduce one or more summers (heavy timbers) which were morticed to the principal posts and to which the joists were generally morticed or laid over them where an overhanging storey was required. It was accordingly desirable to limit the size of the two-storey wings to reasonable limits and thus the hall with separately roofed cross wings became very much the standard design for larger timber houses as shown at Figure 2(b). In due course the wings were to become extended into the H-shaped plan, but for a time the Norman stone house and the timber house merged into a similar pattern and indeed cases are known where they merged in fact, a two-storey rectangular block in stone having a timber aisled hall attached. Later when the need for a large communal hall declined many of the old houses were altered by the provision of an additional floor over the hall making the central block two storey, see Figure 2(c).

The wood in universal use in mediaeval times was, of course, oak. Every virtue was expected of this tough wood. The early mediaeval carpenters had no hesitation about using green timber and merely used larger scantlings to avoid warp and twist. The desirability of seasoning was recognised but not usually regarded as of major importance. This is not to be wondered at as even the English ships that shattered the combined fleet at Trafalgar some five hundred years later were riddled with dry rot due to the use of green oak in their construction. Fortunately, however, the slow progress of building operations in mediaeval times allowed some time for drying out. Thus heart of oak was specified with prodigal waste and even in these times the price soared. Eventually however with the increased demand for oak and a shortage in some areas of timber by this time also being imported from the Baltic, not by any means the last time that this was to slow down house building, home grown oak became very expensive indeed. This had some benefit however, since the design of structures had to be improved and became more intelligent as a result.

Timber buildings began to cluster thickly in the towns and cities of England. The merchants required carpenters to provide two or more storeys in timber framed walls to make better use of limited space and to emulate the stone houses of the nobility and richer traders. The traditional box frame construction was unstable for this purpose but the answer was found in jetty construction whereby each storey, by means of summers and joists, was built to overhang the one below without any danger of collapse. Later the development of the dragon beam enabled jettied construction to be used all round the house where space permitted, see Figure 3(a). At the same time the development of roof construction based on the Queen Post design permitted space in the roof to be better utilised and enabled the introduction of dormer windows to give added light.

17

The hall with cross wings

(a) In stone with added entrance porch

(b) In timber framed construction with aisled hall

(c) In timber framed construction but with later
addition of extra floor over hall

2

18

With the passing of the Normans to the Plantagenets the mass of the people led lives that were unchanged. Many factors were soon to provide a new social structure for the country but Magna Carta at this time was basically a charter of the Barons, and Simon de Montfort, known as the founder of the English Parliament, merely seized the nearest means to hand of gaining advantage over the party of the King.

It was, however, the growth of trade that was mainly responsible for producing the wealth to enable a rich merchant to build a more elaborate dwelling, although it was the strong rule of the Plantagenets that enabled him to depart from a fortress structure outside the towns. The self-governing town on the other hand with Mayor, Aldermen and Burgesses saw the full flowering of the mediaeval builder. Informed and interested patronage was given by the trader and his elected representatives alike. The Merchant Guilds which were primarily set up to exclude "foreigners" from competition and regulate prices for the benefit of the community extended to the setting up of "craft guilds" which established the apprentice and craftsman system. These were fiercely parochial and extended only to the craftsmen's own town. It is accordingly not surprising that in building, the trades of mason and carpenter were most strongly represented and formed strong bonds and traditions, and it is worth perhaps looking back at the most powerful guild of all; that of the early masons.

"Free stone" is a term used in connection with blocks of stone that is worked, being carved or laid in courses, i.e. ashlar as opposed to rubble. Fre Maccons are first contrasted with ligiers (layers) in 1396. The Free Masons worked the stone while the setters, rough-layers and hardhewers placed it in position. From earliest times the mason stood at the shoulder of the building employer. The mediaeval "architect" was often a master mason or carpenter capable of drawing plans and details for others to work from, but also not above copying or drawing inspiration from the work of others. In the majority of instances he superintended the execution of his own designs and took an active part in carrying out the more skilled or artistic part of the work. "The Master of the Masons, carrying a rod[1] and glove in their hands say to others 'cut it for me thus'" said Nicholas de Biard preaching in 1261 and there is little doubt that the Master Masons were men of high standing. They often entered into contracts worth hundreds of pounds and a commensurate responsibility. Early manuscripts bear many references to the fact that mason's robes were supplied as part of the contract so that the

---

[1] Large pair of compasses for setting out often depicted in mediaeval drawings.

19

Later mediaeval forms

(a) Timber framed
town house with jettied
construction on adjacent sides

(b) Brick built small country house

3

20

Master Mason should be dressed in accordance with the dignity of his office. And the dignity grew. The Master Masons considered themselves to be a race apart in the primitive state of the mediaeval building industry and set up stringent regulations for themselves.

"No one who has not served his time as a craftsman or been employed in a lodge and does not know how to execute carved or designed stonework from the ground plan shall undertake such work: If he does, no fellow shall assist him."

"No craftsman warden or fellow shall teach anyone that is not of our craft to make extracts from the ground plan or other usages of masonry."[1]

Even when the Statute of Labourers was passed it was loftily disregarded by the Masons, much to the disgust of Wycliffe, but on the other hand the whole of the apprentice system formed primarily by Master Masons and carpenters was to benefit the mediaeval building industry very greatly. By this system an apprentice served for seven years. He could then become a mason if the opportunity arose from patronage when, under the London regulations of 1356, he was bound to produce four masons of standing to guarantee his capability. There was of course one difference between the mediaeval masons and any other building tradesmen of the time. Stone buildings were relatively few and widely scattered. There were not many guilds for masons as against carpenters and the masons had to form, largely, their own organisations to look after their members as they travelled from town to town. It accordingly became the custom for a travelling mason to visit the nearest large site of a building in stone and make his temporary accommodation in the mason's hut. This was the beginning of the mason's lodge. It is accordingly to the Master Masons and Carpenters that we must look for the beginnings of organisation in the building industry. Early building contracts from 1250 onwards, of which there are a number in existence, record a statement of the building, i.e. the dimensions and an enumeration of doors, windows and fireplaces (sometimes in great detail) the sum of money to be paid and a penalty clause. It is largely due to the Master Masons and Master Carpenters that so many contracts were possible. Records relating to stonework are the more prolific in mediaeval times due to the fact that patrons of the few stone buildings were among the most learned and wealthy in the community. We know that Kentish rag was used by the Romans for the walls of London and by the mediaeval builders, but the Surrey quarries of Reigate and Merstham were preferred for better work.

[1] Rules of the Strassburg Masons drawn up in 1459. (Gould; History of Freemasonry.)

The use of Purbeck marble dates from the 12th century and Bath stone has its first reference in 1237. Portland stone was known from 1303. Caen stone was imported and used after the Norman conquest and had a glittering white brilliance that was much admired for the major buildings. It remains a fact however that while the principle of bedding and grain were understood by the foremost masons many examples of the wrong use of stone are in evidence to this day.

The growth of the towns leads us to consider the first steps in building legislation that were brought in to control the congested development in the largest city of all, namely London. Buildings were erected against each other in a most haphazard fashion and the disputes between the adjoining owners proved to be so troublesome that in 1189 the first ordnance was passed relating to party walls. This was known as Fitz-Ailwyn's Assize of Buildings under Richard the First. This most remarkable document forms the first basis for all party wall negotiations over which surveyors have been happily quarrelling ever since. It was passed under the jurisdiction of the then Mayor, Henry Fitz-Ailwyn for allaying contentions that arose between neighbours touching boundaries. An assize meant that 12 men were elected in a court in order to decide a dispute. Under this ordnance each of two neighbours were required to give one foot and a half of his land on which they were to build at their joint cost a stone wall three feet in thickness and sixteen feet in height. It was then set out in considerable detail how points of difficulty were to be dealt with. Arches used as aumbries (cupboards) could only be one foot in depth. An adjoining owner who could not afford the cost was to give to him who decided to build three feet of his land. Building owners were then to build at their own cost but adjoining owners could then have the right to use half of the wall and utilise this for supporting timber joists and roof members. Other stipulations were made. An obstruction to a view from a window could not be objected to unless some document could be produced by the objector showing his right to the light and other matters, such as requirements for carrying off water and the provision of corbels and the construction of pits for receiving clean and foul water in the vicinity, were all dealt with. In the case of an objection, when the work was stopped, the Mayor and his twelve men promptly attended on an appointed day and heard and settled the matter. One often wishes that the procedure was as straightforward as this today.

In about 1100 London was divided into wards, and a stream of edicts were issued by the wardmotes. The penthouses and jetties of houses should be so high, they decided, that persons on horseback might ride underneath them and they should be of the height of nine feet at the very least. No stall should project out from a house beyond the width of two feet and a half and the same should be movable and flexible for the convenience of neighbours. In addition to regulations such as these, the edicts covered a wide range of subjects. They covered the manufacture of tiles, the positioning of furnaces and reredos (open fireplaces) which were not to be erected near laths, partitions or boards, and also dealt with the rates of wages of crafts-men and labourers ordained by the Common Council of the City.

Fire, however, was the greatest problem and the danger from this source was overwhelming. It is difficult for later generations to realise the fear of fire that existed from the 12th century onwards. Fire could arise in a flash and engulf towns. Fire engulfed part of London in 1136 and subsequently again and again while succeeding edicts endeavoured to deal with the matter. Simon de Montfort's plan to burn London by liberating cocks with burning brands tied to their feet presented a real threat. The edicts of the wardmotes were continually extended to cover fire precautions. All persons who lived in great houses within the ward were to have a ladder or two ready and to be prepared to help their neighbours in case of fire. They were also to have in summer time and in particular periods, a barrel full of water before their doors. Later it was laid down that roofs were to be covered with lead, tile or stone during the reign of Edward III in 1345. The encroachment of buildings on the high-ways was guarded against and the question of fire risk returned to again in this edict. Each ward was required to provide a strong iron hook with a wooden handle, two chains and two strong cords for the removal of burning houses. This equipment was to be left with the beadle of the ward who was also to be provided with a good horn "loudly sounding". It is a terrible irony that it was in fact the Black Death not fire that swept through the City in 1348.

With the increase in the production of wool, the manufacture of cloth and the general upsurge of trade including the ability to export to other countries the rate of town growth increased. Even so England was a bitter discontented country at the time of the Peas-ant's Revolt which endured until Richard II faced his rebellious subjects over the body of Wat Tyler. With the uneasy peace that followed, the old system of servile labour slowly vanished during the 15th century. It was therefore with horror that the inhabitants of the prosperous towns faced the advent of the Wars of the Roses. However, surprisingly, the war had comparatively little effect on daily life, trade and economic circumstances. The rate of growth in the towns continued, brick making was introduced and the number of brick and timber buildings increased particularly in parts of Yorkshire and East Anglia, this being proof enough that the bankers, traders and the rising middle class were becoming more established and little concerned with the struggles of the contenders for the throne.

With the Tudors and the passing of the Middle Ages the great transitional period followed. The old order changed and while the middle class continued to become stronger in the towns Henry VII's ruination of the old nobility resulted in the estates being broken up and the establishment of a strong yeoman farming community in rural areas. The procedure was accelerated by the dissolution of the monasteries under Henry VIII and both actions resulted in a vast increase of better and more substantial timber buildings during the 16th century, in the first instance in the villages, but later by way of farmhouses as well when the yeoman farmer began to live on the land rather than the village street. The discovery of the New World and the continuing increase of trade under the protection of sea power led to the conditions that were to pave the way for the Italian Renaissance to reach Britain in the 16th century. Even with the invention of printing by moveable type, however, there was still a long time lag in the flow of ideas. The educated man became aware of Michaelangelo although Renaissance Architecture did not establish itself until after Elizabeth's reign. Palladio (1518–1580) experimented with cheap brick and stucco in Vicenza, but it was not until the 17th century that the English house came so greatly under the influence of his architecture. Part of this was, of course, due to the conservative nature of the Burgesses of England. These out-did each other with prodigious feats of carpentry and resisted with vigour all new ideas.

The difference at this period in the larger English country house was limited in that brick became fashionable and more readily available. The large diaper patterned brick Tudor mansions with flat arches, mullioned windows and elaborately worked chimney pots as architectural features still had the rather undisciplined pre-Renaissance shapes of central hall with separately roofed cross blocks at each end. Although the hall had ceased a long time in the past to have a prime social function in the day to day order of events, the nobility and richer merchants still considered it an essential requirement for the larger house of the period both for entertaining and as a measure of their self esteem. Much of the ostentation of the time can be attributed to the monarch's practice of indulging in a "progress" through various parts of the country each year, staying overnight in a chosen subject's house and at that subject's expense. The hall provided ample space for the necessary entertainment expected by the monarch and there would seem to be good reason to suppose that many elaborate halls were built in hopeful anticipation of such a visit. Those without such aspirations but who could still afford a substantial house would dispense with the hall in which case the central portion could be made two storey. Towards the end of the 16th century in the smaller houses the projection of the wings tended to diminish and a single roof would be carried across from the hall to cover the wings. Yet the feeling of the earlier three part shape persisted when bay windows and gables were included in the elevation as in Figure 3(b). Perhaps the biggest innovation at the time however was in the standard of internal finishings. Panelling and plaster work became desirable in themselves to warm the interiors of the larger houses and to add a sense of humanity. Although only small pieces of glass could be produced, which explains the diamond lattice pattern of the Tudor period, glazed panels were leaded and set up in the frame by being soldered to the iron saddle bars. Often the windows were purchased ready made and their value was such that they were often treated as tenant's fixtures. In a Chancery court hearing of 1470, William Smith of London, a tailor, was prevented from taking away "certayn his goodes that is to witte glas wyndowes latices etc.". It is worth noting however that it is at this period that the formal garden came into being, proof, if further proof is needed, of the increasing wealth and leisure of the merchants.

As houses multiplied under the Tudors the over-crowding and rise in land values caused something like panic. A London Act of 1562 restricted the wages of craftsmen and labourers, which was probably the first instance of a prices and incomes policy. Confusion increased however and by a proclamation issued on 7th June 1580 in London the public were required "to desist and forebeare from any new buildings of any house or tenement within three miles from any of the gates of the sayd Citie of London . . . where no former house hath bene known to have been . . .". This has since been cited as Elizabeth's attempt at Town Planning and if it seems inexplicable at first sight the reason for it is a sensible one. It was fear of the spread of any "plague or popular sickness". There were, however, other reasons as the large acres in and around towns previously occupied by the monasteries were gradually divided up, sold off and the land was redeveloped with house property at a high density as part of the Elizabethan housing boom.

A further proclamation in 1589 again returned to the thorny problem of restricting residential development and restrictions were extended by further proclamations, each normally stimulated by a fresh outbreak of plague, until in June 1602 Elizabeth's temper finally ran out with an Act worded more tersely than ever . . . "it falleth out, partly by the covetous and insatiable dispositions of some persons, . . . that the said mischiefs and inconveniences do daily increase and multiply". The edict gave clear indication that the monarch's patience was exhausted as houses not built on a previous foundation but on new ground which were not finished were to be "plucked down" and a penalty was inserted for builders under certain circumstances to appear in the Star chamber.

The year 1600 provides a suitable point at which to pause and take stock in this brief account of the origins of the towns, the story of their growth and the social and economic factors which have influenced the development of domestic buildings both in town and country. It almost coincides with the death of Elizabeth and the accession of James I. Elizabeth's own strong personality and popularity had to a great extent staved off the upheavals which were to take place in the next century. She could ignore her own Parliaments and get away with it, but even so the testiness of the wording of her last Proclamation dealing with London suggest those of an ailing monarch with little idea of what to do about the problems which the years of peace and relative prosperity and security which followed the defeat of the Armada had produced.

Although the great majority of the population were still engaged in rural pursuits, the towns, London in particular, were crammed with buildings, the vast majority in timber, of all shapes and sizes along the lines seen in Figure 4. The outbreaks of plague resulting from the absence of sanitary provisions, both for water supply and the disposal of waste, and the continual hazard of fire gave rise to the essentially negative endeavour to impose restrictions on new building. Yet the pressure to build was tremendous as more and more people could afford a house as against a hovel and it was left to James to hint at a more positive solution. James, used to the impressive multi-storey stone buildings of his own capital, was horrified by London and to him it must have looked like a shanty town. His reign started with high hopes as likely to bring a breath of fresh air to many problems, but his autocratic manner of imposing his ideas ran counter to the alliance that was forming between the traders, farmers and small-scale manufacturers making up the middle class and the artisan community.

Subsequent events have removed much of what would have met our gaze in 1600. The mediaeval heritage of buildings was largely destroyed in the extensive fires of the following two centuries which engulfed many towns, notably London, Marlborough, Northampton, Bury St. Edmunds, Blandford, Tiverton and Wincanton among others. Whereas the rebuilding had previously been carried out in timber following a fire, there was now to be not only a great scarcity of good quality timber but legislation in many instances to prevent

4

the use of timber as the structural element in external walls for houses in towns. The exhaustion of the extensive oak forests in the preceding century had already resulted in a marked reduction in the standard of timber buildings and the abandonment of jettied construction. The endeavour to construct two or more storeys on the box frame principle with inferior timber had not been successful and had led to a number of collapses. Fortunately the manufacture of bricks was increasing and as a result they were becoming cheaper for now new timber framed buildings were to be banned first in London and then in many other towns. Timber framed construction was to continue until the 19th century in country areas, but only for the humbler type of dwelling and generally in a different wood, usually softwood, the frames being covered over with tiles, boarding or sometimes even brick. In the towns the lesson of the fires was being learnt and this, coupled with the shortage of suitable timber, led to the almost total abandonment of the half-timbered building in the form traditionally associated with the name.

There still remain many half-timbered houses in existence, particularly from the 15th and 16th centuries and the first half of the 17th century. In some instances these form the nucleus of old market towns that escaped the worst ravages of fire and remained quiet backwaters of life at the time of the Industrial Revolution. There are many others in country areas and villages.

Half-timbered buildings therefore drop out of the account at this stage having reached their peak in design and construction at about the middle of the 16th century. The examples that remain represent an extremely interesting and unique feature in English domestic construction, the use of a separate frame with infilling panels, which was not to be seen again expressed in such a confident and assured manner.

James I ascended the throne in 1603 and at once continued to tackle the all too familiar problem of overcrowding in London. His first proclamation, given in this same year, was to restrict "inmates and multitudes of dwellers . . . in and about the city" and to enable certain newly erected buildings to be pulled down, but James, as his ordnance of 1607 wistfully hints, also had ideas to improve London. If buildings were erected on old foundations, the only new development allowed, they should "both adorne and beautifie his Sayde Citie" and an interesting variation in the general prohibition was that a person enlarging his own dwelling house was regarded as not being an offender against the Proclamation if the enlargement did not exceed more than one third of the old building. The difference between the proclamations of James and Elizabeth was however that any building allowed was to be of brick or stone and the fronts had to be of a uniform variety prescribed by the Aldermen of the Ward. James, who would have dearly liked to have become a paternal ruler and who had the Stuart love of building, published a self-congratulatory decree in 1615 setting out the works carried out during the twelve preceding years of his reign. "Wee could desire . . . that wee . . . might be able to say . . . that wee had found our Citie and Suburbs of London of Sticks and left them of Bricks being a Meteriall farre more durable, safe from fire, beautiful and magnificent." To his exasperation, however, his subjects remained rather deaf to his wishes. In 1619 we find that James, incensed with violations against his edicts, set up a Commission later to be known as "The Commission for Building" to deal with offences against the Proclamations and in the same year we have the Proclamation which is considered to this day as the birth of the Building Acts. This proclamation set out that every storey height of new buildings and each one of the rooms in the storey was to be 10 ft. high at least and every half storey 7 ft. 6 in. (i.e. attic rooms) and that the outer walls and "Jambs Heads and Soyles" had to be of brick or stone and were to be set up before the windows were installed—presumably a point to combat weak construction at the time, due to reliance being placed on the window framing to support the walling above. For the first time wall thicknesses were set out in detail. Bay windows were forbidden and uniform house elevations were required with windows higher than their width "to the end the roomes may receive ayre for health" and a sensible structural requirement enacted that there must be sufficient "peere of bricke between the windows for strength". There were, in conclusion, some requirements governing shop fronts. It is possible however that continuing structural trouble was experienced with house elevations since, in 1620, a new proclamation, while confirming the earlier standards, required piers between windows to be not less than one-half the breadth of the windows themselves.

In 1624 King James died, still threatening dire penalties to those who disobeyed the rules, and the first Proclamation of Charles I on the 2nd May 1625 was to ratify the old prohibitions against new buildings within two miles of the city (except on old foundations) and to confirm the use of brick as an approved building material. The use of brick was by now gaining ground and it is interesting to see that in 1625 the size, method of manufacture and the price of bricks is set out in a new proclamation in minute detail.

The growing popularity of brick as a building material was not received with universal acclaim by any means. Bitter animosity grew up from the craft guilds dependent upon the use of timber as the staple structural requirement for houses and new proclamations encouraging the use of brick were looked upon with suspicion by many. It should however be remembered this was an urban problem but not confined only to London. Throughout the country buildings of all types and periods by now displayed the astonishing variety and dissimilarity that the natural resources of the regions and individual skill could provide. It is true that earlier on the Flemish influence encouraged a few brick elevations with Dutch gables, see Figure 11(c), to appear in English trading ports but the high cost of carriage and the indifferent 17th-century roads discouraged too many experiments of this sort. The main building materials were indigenous to the locality concerned and these were mainly, of course, timber and the many varieties of stone. Cottages of cob, Figure 5(c), were however by now common, clustering more thickly in the south-west, but in the Welsh border counties of Cheshire, Shropshire, Worcester and Hereford, timber framing flourished over a much longer period than in the south though eventually even those large forests became depleted. Thick beams were easy to come by and jettied storeys and complex gables clustered in the nearby county towns, the dark timbers contrasting with the white daubed infilling which became an accustomed style along the upper Severn Valley into Wales. Although elsewhere in the eastern and southern counties half-timbering was common, it was also the custom in certain districts for both frame and panels to be covered and "pargetted" as shown on Figure 9(b) in complex relief decoration relying much on the inspiration and to a large extent the idiosyncracies of the craftsman concerned. Covering both frame and panels with plaster, see Figure 9(a), became increasingly useful when the shortage of timber, more pronounced in the south, necessitated the use of misshapen sections in the late 16th and 17th centuries. Tile hanging served the same purpose and began to be used about the same time, see Figure 6(c) and later still softwood weather boarding, Figure 6(b).

As is to be expected the hard ancient rock districts of Scotland, Wales, the North of England and Cornwall had over the years produced stone cottages, in many cases little more than hovels, formed of rough granite. It was only however in the poorest areas, such as the Scottish Highlands, that life was so harsh that even the rough refinement of a squared face to the stonework or a coat of whitewash was a luxury too costly to be added. It is however to Edinburgh that we have to look for a curious development in regional style which made this city unique in Europe. In the early 16th century the boundary of the city had been defined by a wall. As the density increased it became the custom to build upwards to as much as ten storeys and these enormous stone tenements with staircase turrets and crow stepped gables present the extraordinary appearance

Regional Styles

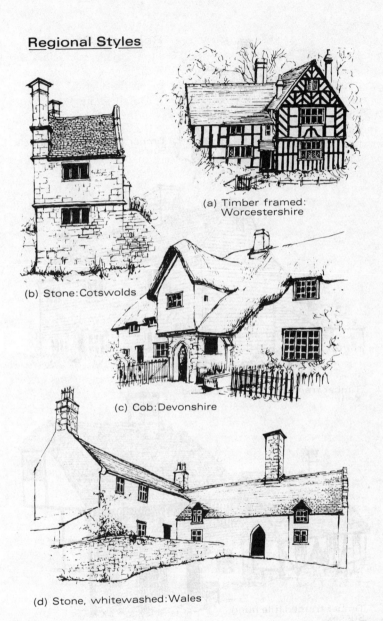

(a) Timber framed: Worcestershire

(b) Stone: Cotswolds

(c) Cob: Devonshire

(d) Stone, whitewashed: Wales

5

Regional Styles

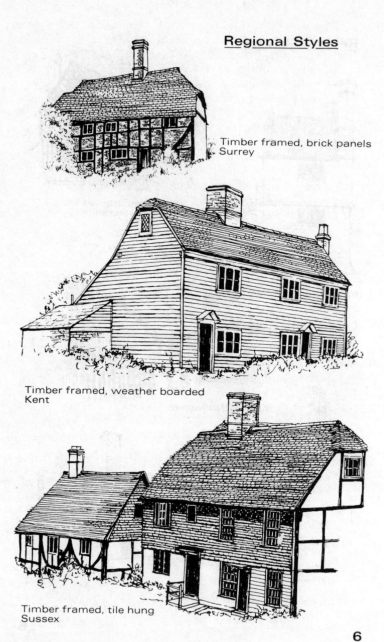

Timber framed, brick panels
Surrey

Timber framed, weather boarded
Kent

Timber framed, tile hung
Sussex

6

shown on Figure 7(c). It is not this fact however which makes them unique. It is the fact that each tenement contained as many families as there were floors, living horizontally and using communal stair-cases and, later, lavatories. These dwellings were called "lands" since they took the place of land for building and the tenement system grew and flourished in Edinburgh for years ahead. The main feature of this system initially was that the noble and artisan lived on different floors under the same roof and the diverse way of life of the different tenants gave variety to the community.

The regional characteristic of the larger Scottish house is also interesting. The need for the stone tower house in country areas re-mained long after the need for a fortified dwelling had lapsed in England and the strong influence from France resulting in corbelled angle turrets and stepped gables, see Figure 8(a), together with the coating to the stonework externally of "harl" or roughcast of granite chips led to the development of the Scottish house being carried out on quite different lines to its English counterpart.

In the great central areas of Warwickshire, Derbyshire and York-shire the local sandstone has been used for house building for centuries. The hard characteristics of Derbyshire stone permits of squared and disciplined elevations, bold ornament to the details and large stone slabs for roof covering giving a shallow pitch. To the South of England a belt of oolitic limestone runs across the country from Somerset to the Wash, and a recognisable style of building grew up in the Cotswolds, see Figures 5(b) and 8(b), the earlier examples based on single-storey construction in view of bonding difficulties but utilising the roof space for accommodation and making much use of gabled dormer windows, fine detailing on mouldings and chimneys and small stone slates for roofing at a steep pitch.

In Norfolk there is a complete departure with the use of flint, see Figure 9(c), clunch (hard chalk) and clay lumps for walling. All these local skills flourished in the 16th and 17th centuries to diminish gradually in the 18th century, see Figure 10, until submerged by the Industrial Revolution of the 19th century, which enabled mass produced building materials to be transported with ease to most parts of the country.

However, the impact of the idea that was to change the shape and style of the English dwelling house down to the smallest detail can be dated accurately. It started in 1615 when Inigo Jones was appointed Surveyor General to the King at the age of 44. The small group of noblemen and artists who found in the Courts of Florence and Venice an ideal of taste in the poetry and drama of Italy which contrasted with the phlegmatic Court of James I, immediately accepted Inigo Jones, a man well versed in Italian design. Inigo

Regional Styles

(a) Stone: County Durham

(b) Stone: Lancashire

(c) Stone, early 17th cent.
tenement, Edinburgh

(d) Stone, harled:
Scotland

7

Regional Styles

(a) Stone: Scotland

(b) Stone: Cotswolds.

8

35

Jones built the Queen's House at Greenwich and the Whitehall Banqueting House under court patronage and it is easy to see that in the case of the latter the reaction to a purely Italian building among the timber gables of Jacobean London must have been one of stupefaction and possibly outrage. Inigo Jones was responsible for the building of Covent Garden and his influence resulted in "the first regular street in London", Great Queen Street, both subsequently destroyed. This put an end to individual gables and provided a discipline that was to set the pattern for a long time to come. The new architectural canon in design was to reduce a house façade to the terms of a classical order raised on a podium, the ground floors representing the podium, the upper floors the column. Inigo Jones is also thought to have built Nos. 59–60 Lincolns Inn Fields, see Figure 11(a), but little else in London.

The Civil War ended building in London and the Palladian ideal for a hundred years until Lord Burlington's influence brought it back in full measure under George II. In the interim, a debased classical influence provided the basis for the architecture of public buildings but even the influence of Sir Christopher Wren never extended to the streets of Britain in the same way as the Palladian influence was eventually to spread to the humblest bricklayer in the land.

The Civil War between Charles and the Parliamentarians dragged on for eight years and the struggle involved most parts of the country. Peace came to a population weary of war and in the period of the Commonwealth some building commenced again. It is a sign that matters were returning to normal that yet a further Act was necessary in 1656 "preventing the multiplicity of buildings in and about the suburbs of London".

With the restoration of the Stuarts under Charles II, a disturbed reference to the ever present danger of fire in London can be seen in the first proclamation of 16th August 1661. This was amply justified by events. Following the plague of London in 1665 when 100,000 people are estimated to have died, a fire commenced in the early hours of Sunday morning the 2nd September 1666. It swept through the wooden houses and the warehouses of Thames Street and raged widespread for four days. In this fire described by Samuel Pepys as "a most horrid malicious bloody flame, not like the fine flame of an ordinary fire" four-fifths of the city was destroyed. There were dark rumours of plots by foreigners and one unfortunate Frenchman was even hanged.

The King and his ministers acted quickly. A well-intentioned measure to compile a survey on information supplied by the populace failed through inertia but one of the members of the body set up

Regional Styles

(a) Above: timber framed,
plastered, Essex

(b) Above left: pargetting,
East Anglia

(c) Left: Stone flints and
brick, Norfolk

(d) Timber framed wattle
and daub panels,
Suffolk

9

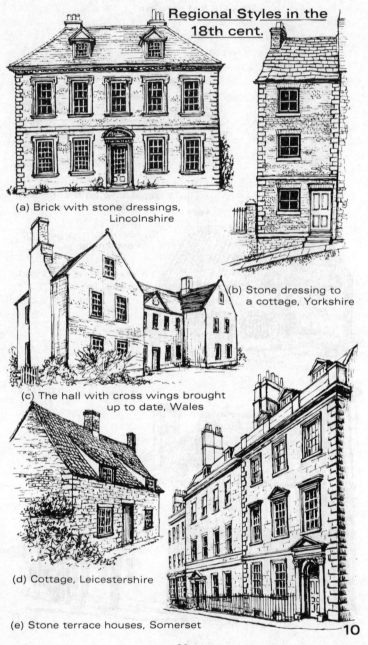

Regional Styles in the 18th cent.

(a) Brick with stone dressings, Lincolnshire

(b) Stone dressing to a cottage, Yorkshire

(c) The hall with cross wings brought up to date, Wales

(d) Cottage, Leicestershire

(e) Stone terrace houses, Somerset

10

to deal with the survey, Dr. Wren, was appointed to a group of six technical advisers, including three surveyors, which resulted in the first comprehensive Building Act for London, although it was said acidly at the time that Dr. Wren, a Professor of Astronomy, had the least qualification for the job.

The Act for the rebuilding of the City of London in 1667 set a standard which subsequent Acts unfortunately did not maintain. The Act was a comprehensive one. It cleaned up and straightened out bad parts of the existing city and set up a system of rules and penalties for non-compliance with the Act. Surveyors or supervisors were appointed to see that the requirements were carried out and a detailed complex of instructions was laid down to deal with fire prevention. The outsides of all new buildings had to be of brick or stone and brickwork above windows or openings had to be carried by brick or stone lintels or arches except in the case of shops. There were detailed provisions in the Act for foundations, timber near chimneys, bearing and spacing of joists, summers and girders, and the need for oak in roofs, window frames, cellar floors and tile pins. A careful machinery was laid down for foundations and party walls to be set out by and agreed with the surveyor appointed under the Act before building, in order to avoid disputes and even the payment of the surveyor's fees was provided for. By far the most outstanding proposal however was the standardisation of house building and Section V (2) deserves repeating:

"Be it enacted:—that there shall be only four sorts of buildings and no more:—and that all manner of houses to be erected shall be one of those four sorts of buildings and no other; (that is to say)
(a) The first or least sort of house fronting by-lanes
(b) The second sort fronting streets and lanes of note
(c) The third sort fronting high and principal streets
(d) The fourth and largest sort, of mansion houses for citizens or other persons of extraordinary quality not fronting either of the three former ways.
the roofs of each of the said first, second and third sorts of houses respectively shall be uniform."

The number of storeys for each of the types of building and the thicknesses of the external and party walls were set out in a table to the Act. Categories (c) and (d) could have balconies and "pent houses" under certain conditions and even rainwater downpipes were specified in the Act.

The Act of 1667 was completely new in scope. Never before had an Act contained such far reaching provisions and, indeed, consequences. It could be more correctly termed a replanning Act rather

The 17th century

(a) Classical influence,
    Inigo Jones, mid
    17th century

(b) The 'Queen Anne' house,
    late 17th century

(c) Dutch influence, brick ornamental
    gables common in Kent to Humber
    coastal ports from mid 17th to
    mid 18th centuries

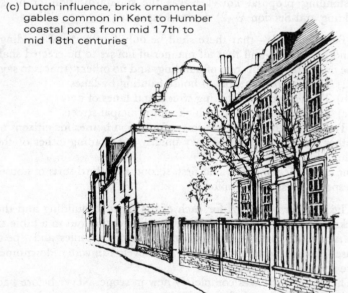

11

40

than a rebuilding Act and the relationship of house sizes to streets was one of the main reasons why Georgian urban development is considered a success today.

It should be remembered however that the Act was simply the product of the best experience in building at the time and was the result of the deliberations of able and interested men directly influenced by the King whose patronage was all important. The consequences of the Act have been very wide. It would be an error to suppose that the provisions of the Act are only of interest to a London surveyor. The great spate of Georgian urban architecture throughout the length and breadth of this island directly resulted from it, as London was now to set a pattern for the replacement of the near squalor of the previous centuries.

In country areas, although half-timbered buildings continued to be built, particularly in the first half of the century, there was a considerable increase matching that in the towns in the use of stone and brick for the larger houses. To an increasing number of wealthy men who encouraged the Huguenot settlers to make fine linen and silk there was room for taste and time to be receptive to new ideas from abroad. The Renaissance had had a profound effect and the central house block with enlarged wings which until the beginning of the 17th century was familiar as the Elizabethan "E" plan for the larger houses gave way to trim symmetry in fenestration around a central door and a plan of rectangular shape providing importance to all four sides of the house. In effect the wings merged together so that the central portion of the house increased in depth. This enabled the house to be covered by a roof consisting of two identical couples running parallel to the main frontage and separated by a valley gutter through which rose the central chimney stacks as shown on Figure 3(b), a house built about 1600. This gutter and the joints with the stacks gave continual trouble and a solution was evolved in the development of hipped end slopes, covering over the central section and later moving the stacks to the side. This development which provided a level eaves line to all sides of the house coincided with the influence of Inigo Jones and Sir Christopher Wren and enabled them to treat the eaves lines as a cornice, see Figures 10(a) and 11(b), to complete the classical treatment which was now lavished on the elevations.

The reign of Queen Anne is more thought of now as a time of good design and considerable quality in the larger houses, than as a time of change. This is odd, as the period produced comparatively few buildings of the style known as "Queen Anne" but did produce further legislation that was also to govern the design and set the character of the urban house throughout the Georgian building

41

boom that was to follow. The changes were still made necessary from the fear of fire owing to the continued exposure of much timber in proximity to adjacent buildings. The Building Act of 1707 started with the arrangements for providing Fire Brigades and then dealt with party walls. These were henceforward to be 18 inches thick at basement and ground floor levels, $13\frac{1}{2}$ inches above and project 18 inches above the roof. Also "No mundillion or cornish of timber or wood under the eaves . . . shall hereafter be made or suffered" said the Act and in this measure abolished for ever in London the wide elegant timber cornices and sweeping roof pitches which had only recently become fashionable, in favour of an abrupt brick parapet with perhaps a cornice of stone above the top floor window heads as an architectural detail rather than the natural outcome of the shape of the structure, see Figure 12(b) and (c) in contrast to Figures 12(a) and 11(b). A further Act in 1709 confirmed the former arrangements for fighting fires and the provisions for party walls and required that no beams or rafters be built into the brickwork of gable ends. Chimney jambs and backs were to be 9 inches thick with $4\frac{1}{2}$ inch "withs" plastered internally. Timbers near flues were further dealt with in detail. Section XIII of the Act however required the fixing of door and window frames into the wall four inches from the outer face. This comparatively simple change altered the appearance of buildings substantially and gave walls a heavy structural impression, Figure 15, instead of the rather frail character apparent in earlier houses, Figure 12. At this time the sash window, a Dutch invention, ousted the casement, many of which were removed and replaced with this very latest of fashions.

In 1700 England was still a land of small towns and villages and the population, including Wales, was about $5\frac{1}{2}$ million people. Although agriculture was still the occupation of the vast majority of the people, the strip system of cultivation was not only antiquated but wasteful, and the improving landlords of the 18th century were busy enclosing the old common fields. Hundreds of Enclosure Acts were passed culminating in the General Enclosure Act 1801, changing the face of the country beyond recognition. The disappearance of the "open field" system which had endured from Saxon times meant that land could be better used, but transformed the lesser yeomen into mere labourers with a barely sufficient standard for survival. Such rights as to graze on waste land and to collect fuel were also lost. By 19 out of 20 Enclosure Acts said Young, "the poor are injured and most grossly". The mechanical seed sower of Jethro Tull, the system of rotation of crops introduced by Lord "Turnip" Townshend who retired from politics in 1730 to devote time to experiments with his Norfolk estate, and the gradual introduction of cattle in place of crops changed the traditional agricultural structure and with it the appearance of rural England. Also, it began the change that within 200 years was to transform England from a rural to an urban society. The handsome stone farm houses, as in Figure 10(a), built by the new farmers about 1700 were the first signs that the whole social structure was about to alter.

In 1700, however, building was proceeding apace in London following the great fire. Brick or stone were now a statutory requirement and the former material was enthusiastically adopted once it was found that houses with brick load bearing walls were just as cheap, if not cheaper, than timber framed construction. This combined with, as we have seen, an enlightened period of legislation under informed and interested patronage formed the nature of the building boom. At the beginning of the century more than 1,600 houses were under construction in London and by the time George I ascended the throne in 1714 the number was increasing fast. The houses built were what is known as the "terrace" house, a product of the need to get as many houses as possible into one street. The site of a typical London house therefore consists, at this period, of a long strip of ground with the house covering the front part, the middle part consisting of a garden, and at the back, in the cases of the larger types of house set out under the Act of 1667, a coach-house and stable served from a minor parallel road. The feature that was to distinguish London and most cities in Britain was that practically the whole population was eventually to live in one or other version of these houses, rich and poor alike, see Figures 10(e), 12(b) and the houses on Figures 13 and 14.

The unusual feature of the different levels of the terrace house is explained by the fact that the roadway at the front is partly made up while the garden at the rear is at the normal ground level. This means that a shallow basement can look into what appears to be a deep "area". The custom of building vaults under houses is a very old one and the basement is the descendent of the mediaeval vaulted cellar, used as either a store or as a shop entered by steps from the street. Later, basements generally became kitchens, and inside the house, the entrance floor plan, which generally consists of two rooms in houses of each classification, provided in addition a hall, with ancillary rooms and closets in a back addition. The Palladian façade of a podium or base with the classical column above resulted naturally in the drawing room, the most important room in 18th-century society, being placed at first floor level, and above this the number of bedrooms and servants' bedrooms was worked out according to the number of floors envisaged in the classification of the house. Sir John Summerson[1] shows how the Georgian terrace house is capable of ingenious variation within the inflexible limits of party walls, from the largest house with a great hall, columns, double doors, recesses and niches to give the house a formal architectural character which carries through from front to back, to the smallest house with the simplest of decoration and the most rudimentary facilities.

The building trade in the 18th century was still based on the mediaeval pattern. The craftsmen, such as carpenters, joiners and bricklayers were apprenticed for seven years, worked as journeymen and later graduated to become tradesmen. The trades had however lost their close mediaeval organisation, although the City of London Companies still exercised control over the city itself. As in the Middle Ages, the leading tradesman, whether bricklayer or mason, could make a ground plan of a small building and this led to the introduction of the "master builder" who, perhaps a bricklayer or carpenter by training, would undertake the construction of a few houses for the speculative market. At this time there was still no architectural profession as such and this only emerged in its present form later on. The surveyor was an integral part of the building scene at the time however, either as a land surveyor or increasingly concerned with supervising building work under the Building Acts or to measure it for pricing.

Speculative building was the goal of success in the building trade and this helped by the willingness of the craftsman to educate himself and the increasing later flow of cheap but excellent books copied from Vitruvius Britannicus, launched by the Earl of Burlington, explains to a large extent the dominance of the Palladian ideal. The speculative builder was content to copy his designs from books and, more often than not, the result was astonishingly good. An individual might agree a lump sum with a master builder or might negotiate separate sums with a number of tradesmen to build a house of his own choice if he were a man of some means, otherwise he would be more likely to purchase one of a number of completed or half completed houses built for the speculative market. In this case a master builder would agree to enter into a building lease with a ground landlord for a 60- or 99-year term at a peppercorn rent for the first year or two. He would then erect the shell of the house and sell it within the peppercorn period to a customer for a lump sum which was to include constructional cost and profit. The attraction of the arrangement was that little capital was necessary although the cycles of boom and slump recurrent in the economy led to a great many bankruptcies.

[1] Georgian London.

44

Early 18th century products of
the Georgian building boom

(a) West Country terrace on large scale

(b) Small scale London
terrace

(c) Country mansion

12

45

In the early part of the 18th century the newly built London terrace house had reached a planned pattern. Built to the pre-ordained layout of the Act of 1667 of grey or brown stock bricks of specified size (yellow only became widespread at the end of the century) with red rubbing brick window arches set in putty, with Portland stone dressings and tiled roofs, the terraces must have presented a pleasing sight particularly with the churches of Sir Christopher Wren rising above their red roofs. From about 1770 with the success of Lord Penrhyn's Welsh quarries the use of slate became widespread. Sashes, although set back in the brickwork by 4 in. as prescribed by law, had not yet the thin glazing bars of the latter part of the century but were glazed with Crown glass, the laborious method of manufacture leaving faint concentric rings on the surface to provide an attractive texture. Each house had lead rainwater pipes and a closet connected to the brick drain which discharged into a sewer or cesspool. It was not until Joseph Bramah's valve closet in 1778 that the closet became a "water closet", although this invention had to await another hundred years before it came into general use.

In 1724 a further Act was passed confirming and strengthening the regulations relating to party walls and precautions to avoid the spread of fire from one house to another. In 1760 the procedure on rebuilding of party walls was altered and the prescribed thicknesses were increased to $22\frac{1}{2}$ inches at basement level and 18 inches above. There were further provisions as to land acquisition for widening streets on payment of compensation and new regulations for dealing with dangerous structures. In 1757 an Act was passed to empower building frontages to be set back to form a new highway from London's Edgware Road to Islington. The provisions were unhappily abandoned in 1822. Further Acts were passed between 1764 and 1772 which again confirmed and strengthened the position relating to party walls and finally required bond timbers to be abolished. One of these Acts required the inspection of an independent surveyor and for the surveyor to say on oath that new work inspected complied with current legislation. It is interesting to see that it is at this stage also that Insurance Companies became authorised to require the insurance money to be laid out upon rebuilding the damaged property as a defence against fraud in the case of houses being wilfully burned down. The repair of drains and sewers was set down in these statutes and in addition the paving cleaning and lighting of streets and alleys.

The year 1774 saw a long, complex and to some extent revolutionary Act passed. This Building Act confirmed all the previous legislation affecting party walls and not only the use of fireproof

46

materials but fireproofing measures as well. It set out a complicated table dividing buildings into seven rates or classes with the thickness of walls, both party and external, for each class. It is a significant pointer to the fact that trade had flourished in London during the century that warehouses and factories were included in the table separately for the first time. The flaw in the Act however was that heights were not restricted in any way so that streets, the development of which would have been regulated by the Act of 1667, ended by becoming under the 1774 Act gloomy and cavernous tunnels. The restrictive nature of the Act, applied to the bottom classes of houses, tended to produce uniformity, while the absolute prohibion of wood ornament to the exteriors of houses for fear of fire tended to make smaller façades appear repetitive, see Figure 15(a). One significant inclusion in the Act however was the provision for the first time of surveyors to administer the Act not only in the City of London but in Westminster and the suburbs. The surveyors who were to be "discreet persons skilled in the art of building" had to take an elaborate oath and register their address with the clerks of the peace. They had a complex schedule of duties and a detailed scale of fees ranging from the supervision of the erection of a first class building (£3 10s.) to alterations to less than a seventh class building (5s.). Modern surveyors, philosophically aware that fee scales rarely change, will be interested, if not surprised, to learn that this particular one remained in operation unaltered for 81 years.

In the 18th and early 19th centuries houses in the towns and cities throughout the land multiplied under the influence of the increased demand, and elegant and disciplined Palladian mansions and trim double-fronted houses, see Figure 12(c), owing much to the classical influence, were built in country or suburban districts. It is worth remembering, however, that the towns and cities of Britain have grown haphazardly and have been built with private wealth, not public funds. London grew upon the speculative instinct of the trader and craftsman within the guiding lines of intermittent legislation unlike, for example, Paris, which was set out mainly in one particular period under strong patronage. The Stuart kings would have liked to confer such patronage, but the people, suspicious of their belief in the divine right to rule, regarded any advances in this direction with coldness. Speculative building flourished more easily under the constitutionally appointed Hanoverian Monarchs. Building therefore in the 17th and 18th centuries and particularly in London proceeded with many hitches and setbacks due to the trade slumps and booms following periods of warfare. The Civil War in the 17th century halted building and while the Great Fire of London that followed became the opportunity for new ideas of construction

47

to blossom there was a time lag for these to reach the rest of the country. In 1720 a depression following the bursting of the South Sea Bubble halted building again. In the early years of the following century the threatened invasion, before Waterloo finally ended the threat of Napoleon, nevertheless caused a further building slump which is tended to be forgotten in the activities of the Prince Regent and John Nash.

Town planning was unknown at this period. It has been seen how urban and rural dwellings have so far grown from a web of circumstances that owe nothing to an overall plan for towns, let alone cities. London, the largest city of all, has been described as a collection of villages and although the most attractive town square developments of Hanover Square, the Grosvenor Estate and later the Cavendish Harley Estate which was envisaged as a residential unit with squares, streets, churches and markets are certainly town planning in one sense, they are planned enclaves within the city, rather than of the city. It is however now worth examining the steps taken in town planning, even if these are only partial and the most important first development was by John Wood at Bath. Wood was a surveyor turned architect, a disciple of Palladio who worked out his designs for Bath between 1725 and 1750. By a combination of square and crescent Wood linked Queen Square, the Circus and Royal Crescent sufficiently informally to give the houses a human residential quality but contrived at the same time to achieve a strictly classical style that prevented dullness. It was an impressive achievement; see Figure 13.

For the next most notable attempt we have to turn to Scotland. This seems surprising now but would have been even more astounding at the beginning of the 18th century. At this time Scotland was "a small country on the fringe of civilised Europe, poor, little known and of little account".[1] By the middle of the century however the tide of economic and intellectual life was beginning to flow. Adam Smith published "The Wealth of Nations", James Watt arrived in Edinburgh to join Boulton, and in 1761 Robert Adam was appointed Architect to the Crown, an event which was to leave a decisive influence upon Georgian architecture. This upsurge of energy came about within a very short time. The Union of 1707 which had been accomplished in the face of considerable opposition was not popular. Emotional patriotism together with envy of a more prosperous England was difficult for a Parliament and Privy Council to overcome when the members themselves had moved to London and no longer thought it worthwhile to maintain homes in Scotland.

[1] A. J. Youngson.

48

18th century town planning, Bath

(a) The Circus and Royal Crescent

(b) Terrace houses in the Circus, Bath

13

Matters improved, however, by increased trade with the West Indian and American colonies and England herself offered a growing market for the sale of Scottish cattle. The new ideas from Norfolk regarding the planting of crops and artificial grasses came to Scotland during the early years of the century and afforestation was also improved enormously. The Jacobite Rebellion of 1745 nearly upset matters but failed to do so. It had in fact, the opposite effect, for after Culloden no-one could think of the restoration of the Stuarts as a practical possibility and traders and bankers no longer had to make allowances in their plans for political revolution on a large scale. Accordingly trade began to flourish. Communications improved rapidly with the introduction of coach services and turn-pikes and the Tay Bridge at Perth was completed in 1771 which improved access to the north. Canals, the effective drainage of land for agriculture, better crops and cattle and the introduction of sheep farming all made their mark in this very short space of time.

The growth of wealth gave favourable conditions for the develop-ment of Edinburgh and the Banks helped to finance the schemes of the Town Council. In April 1766 an advertisement appeared in-viting "plans of a new town, making out streets of a proper breadth, and by-lanes, and the best situation for a reservoir and any other public buildings which may be thought necessary". The competition was won after some scuffling behind the scenes by Mr. James Craig from six competitors. "Craig's plan has been fervently eulogised and contemptuously derided. The truth is that the plan is entirely sensible and almost painfully orthodox."[1]

Planning new towns was a familiar occupation in the 18th century. Wren's plan for London, however, was never put into execution after 1666. This plan connected significant buildings by straight avenues so that they terminated in impressive monumental vistas, but it had no influence whatsoever on the subsequent development of London which grew in the 18th century by the building of formally discon-nected residential squares. There was enthusiasm for replanning towns in most countries at this period. In Paris an architectural com-petition under Louis XV led to a partial development on the site of the Place de la Concorde. Pierre Patte compiled the proposals of the competitors in a master plan for the whole city and published it in 1765. It is interesting to note that continental squares are quite differ-ent from London squares. The former employ large open spaces with possibly a statue, surrounded by an imposing palace-like façade. The Baroque "place" was entirely dramatic in conception forming an effective vista with entrance, approach and climax.

[1] Youngson.

Nancy, built in 1750, is a particularly interesting example of 18th-century town planning. The essence of the design (by Heré) is the close juxtaposition of two open spaces, the Place Stanislas, and what is in effect a large forecourt to the Palais du Gouvernement joined by a triumphal arch and the wide and tree lined Place de la Carrière. Such a description however gives no idea of the variety of ornateness and charm of Heré's town. The buildings in the Place Stanislas are of varying heights, the whole square is balustrated at the roof line and decorated with urns and figures and in each corner are intricate gilded screens of wrought ironwork, masterpieces of the metal-worker's art of the 18th century. In two of the corners ornate monumental rococo fountains play in the shadow of the over arching chestnut trees.[1] The space and scale of the buildings at the wide tree-lined Place de la Carrière give style and charm.[2]

Craig's plan for Edinburgh on the other hand was mechanical and symmetrical but the chief differences are found in the buildings. Craig had no control over these under the way in which the development was financed. The plan consisted of two squares joined by a straight central street flanked by two others. Craig ignored the idea of a circus and the use of varying heights but the result is nevertheless pleasing due to the excellent use of the site. The proportions are good generally and the feeling is one of spaciousness.

Due to the speculative nature of the venture, the Town Council did not build the houses but created conditions for others to do so. In 1767–68 they laid down pavement widths and lines of frontage and agreed to lay sewers, whereupon Craig was sent packing to London to "remain there as long as necessary for learning everything relative to these Shores" (Sewers). More Acts were passed in 1782 and 1785 regulating height and roof lines but the control was loose. Sir Laurence Dundas, a man of influence, got hold of the land earmarked for the church at the east side of the development and persuaded Sir William Chambers to build a house. The Town Council provided St. Andrew's Church but otherwise did not interfere. David Kay's attractive church therefore had to be built in George Street. It was, however, due to the Town Council's decision to try to introduce some quality into the houses which in Princes' Street and George Street tended to be undistinguished that Robert Adam was asked to provide a design for a unified scheme of frontages. He was already at the height of his powers. In 1791 he produced his plans and elevations for Charlotte Square and it is there now for all to see mainly as it was planned, except for Robert Reid's

[1] Youngson.
[2] It is possible that other sources contributed. Plans of linked squares were well known.

51

rather unfortunate Portico to St. George's Church. Charlotte Square is a rectangle with a central garden and streets entering at each corner. The frontages are unified in treatment and the north side is a replica of the south. Each side is three storeys high with attics and basements in addition and each have a pediment mounted on four Corinthian pillars of a classical order with recessed and arched doors and windows with swags and balustrades to decorated parapets above as shown at (a) on Figure 14. The square is visually satisfying and has been described as "one of the major achievements" in European civic architecture.

The Napoleonic war, however, broke out shortly after building commenced and the Square was only completed some time later, well after Robert Adam's death in 1792. It was indeed some considerable time before the Town Council could be confident that the venture would be a success for there was a sharp initial loss which, with the usual trade cycles and slumps due to the American and Napoleonic wars, protracted development into the 19th century. Later, however, William Playfair with his scheme for the north of Calton Hill and further development in the 19th century by Reid leaves a pattern for the "new town" of Edinburgh that is at least distinguished even if the original opportunity for an overall plan could not be wholly achieved. The second example shown at (b) on Figure 14 is part of a development commenced in 1816 on a more modest scale but still providing a unified street frontage with, somewhat unusually for the time, front gardens. The dormer window added later in the century is of a type very common in Scotland, but seldom seen in England.

Meanwhile in London in the latter part of the 18th century squares and terraces grew rapidly, see (a) and (b) on Figure 15. Robert Adam provided new standards of taste and revolutionised the use of ornament to a fundamental degree which also influenced furniture, pottery and textiles. While accepting traditional symmetries he began to treat ornament freely. "We have adopted" he said, "a beautiful variety of light mouldings, gracefully formed, delicately enriched and arranged with propriety and skill." His delicate swags and slim enriched pilasters certainly came to take London by storm but were disliked by the academic and traditional weight of established architectural opinion behind Sir William Chambers, who, with Robert Adam, was one of the separate leaders of the taste of the period. It was Adam, however, on the Portman Estate, followed later by builders such as Burton in Bloomsbury who probably had more influence on the development of the English dwelling house.

In 1811 the Prince of Wales became Prince Regent. This fortu-

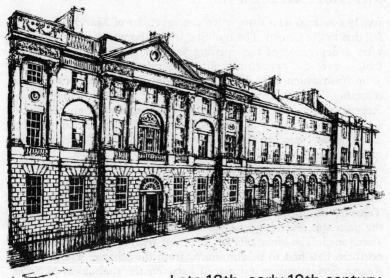

Late 18th, early 19th century town planning, Edinburgh

(a) Charlotte Square

(b) Ann Street

14

nately occurred at a time when the reversion of Marylebone Park fell due to the Crown. The building trade also was picking up again after a depression of the opening years of the century, and these factors gave the opportunity for the third achievement of note to John Nash which most nearly approaches our modern idea of town planning. The plan, with the enthusiastic backing of the Prince Regent, which was worked out by Nash envisaged an elaborate scheme for Regent's Park with villas in wooded groves, lakes and a canal, great crescents and terraces of houses with a working-class quarter complete with markets and shops.

The boldest feature was that Regent Street should form a "Royal mile" from the Park to Carlton House. The final scheme however was rather disappointing compared with the original plan. The Treasury clamped down on the cost so that the number of villas in the park was severely restricted and the great central crescent was abandoned. The lessee of Park Crescent went bankrupt so that the northern half had to be eliminated from the scheme. The plan for Regent Street, cunningly placed between the shabbiness of Soho and the elegance of the West End ran into trouble almost at once. The only persons interested in participating had conflicting ideas and wishes regarding plans and elevations, but Nash not only finally managed to reconcile the various demands in order to provide architectural unity but even stepped in at an awkward stage to take the offending land in his own name. He then formed a group of speculating tradesmen and achieved the necessary link in the development. His eye for the overall unity of the scheme was unerring. All Souls' Church which forms a pivot to the "Royal mile" at Langham Place is a fine little building in itself. Nash was content to accept a certain loss of detail provided that the main plan could be saved. Working at great speed the old gentleman handed sketches to his draftsmen which, when built by the speculating builders, often suffered from poor detailing and construction. The overall achievement however was a remarkable one and it is a pity that so little of it can be seen today. It owed much not only to the ability of Nash as a planner but also to his considerable powers of persuasion. John Nash's "plaster palaces" consolidated the success of stucco as an external coating for brickwork and established the use of it as adopted by Adam, that is to say carefully scored and finished to accurately resemble stone. Certainly Adam's buildings in Edinburgh were stone faced, but it is probably due largely to Nash that nothing odd was seen in brick buildings being disguised as stone ones. Subsequent painting of the stucco has tended to obscure the original intention and the buildings are now accepted for what they are. By this time speculative building had become a very large-scale business

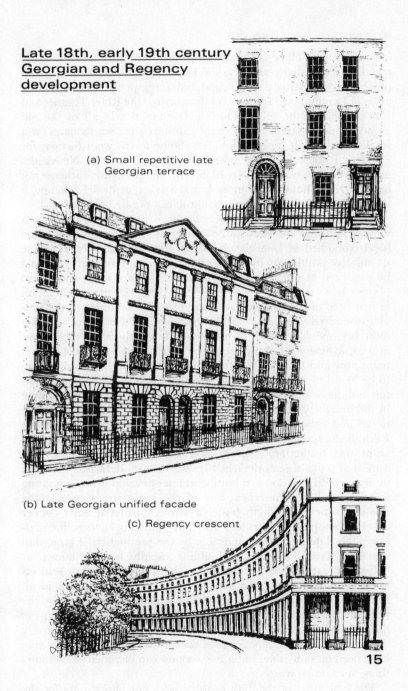

Late 18th, early 19th century Georgian and Regency development

(a) Small repetitive late Georgian terrace

(b) Late Georgian unified facade

(c) Regency crescent

15

55

in some hands. Thomas Cubitt, remembered mainly for substantial tracts of Bloomsbury and also for Eaton Square, developed many other areas and latter day Georgian buildings spread over increasing areas of London, into Islington to the north of the River Thames and Camberwell to the south. Outside London nearly all of the old cathedral and market towns could exhibit their own schemes on a smaller scale built by local builders. Some towns went further, for example Robert Grainger rebuilt the central area of Newcastle-upon-Tyne between 1826 and 1836. This comprehensive scheme not only provided houses and shops but a market, central Exchange, a theatre, a music hall, chapels, banks and a public house as well.

Robert Adam and John Nash between them brought about a sense of lightness and it might be said frivolity to the strict Palladian ideal embodied in Georgian building. The appeal of Nash to the speculative builder lay in the fact that quite impressive effects could be produced at remarkably low cost using cheap bricks and stucco plaster. Even the new look of stucco found favour with a generation grown tired of the straight laced appearance of houses of the previous hundred years. Besides, the brickwork of Georgian buildings soon became blackened in the sooty atmosphere of the towns. Stucco, as was soon found, could be brightened up with a coat of paint now and then. At this time the wealthy and fashionable were to be found increasingly in spas such as Cheltenham and Leamington and the coastal town of Brighton. Much of the new development in the first forty years or so of the 19th century carried out in these towns and other "watering places" was faced entirely in stucco. Even the long reign of the terrace house with the tyranny of uniform plans was beginning to crack and in some developments there appeared pairs of semi-detached houses or even detached villas, all finding a ready market and hinting at later developments in housing for the wealthy. The cheapness of the basic structure adopted allowed money for trimmings such as wrought iron balconies, copper covered canopies, shutters and broad overhanging eaves to the shallow pitch slate roofs, made possible by the production of large thin sheets of slate. The style of building rapidly became known as "Regency", see Figure 16, and although attractive in many respects is often thought of as the decadent end to the Palladian ideal. Buildings in the style were essentially a matter of fashion for the relatively wealthy in towns unaffected by the current rumblings of the Industrial Revolution which was to sweep it aside in a relatively short space of time. Canons of good taste, restrictive though they may have been on individual initiative were now to be replaced by something very much worse.

The first years of the 19th century were not happy ones for the

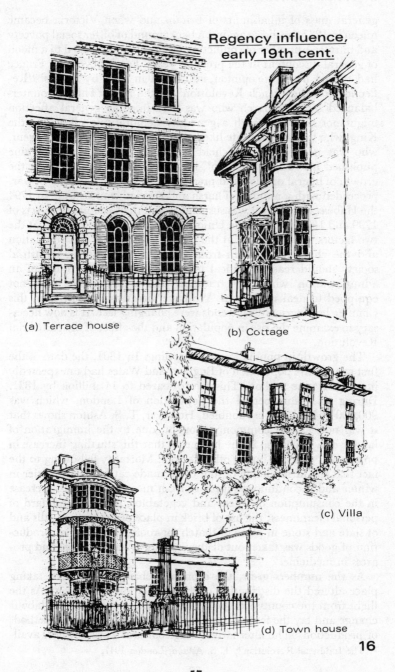

Regency influence, early 19th cent.

(a) Terrace house

(b) Cottage

(c) Villa

(d) Town house

16

57

general mass of inhabitants of Britain and when Victoria became queen in 1837 she did so against a background of bitter social poverty and unrest. A number of conflicting circumstances had led to a mood of general discontent in the previous years. Fear of events in France had turned moderate opinion, influenced in 1790 by Burkes' "Reflections on the French Revolution" to the right. This, if counterbalanced by a Monarch who was held in some general affection might not have had such a generally demoralising effect but the King, who was at first quite liked, was mad, and the Prince Regent, who was not liked at all, held the power. In 1791 Tom Paine published his "Rights of Man" but the Government, ignoring the growth of liberal opinion and preoccupied with the demands of war, proceeded with a number of harsh and restrictive measures. In 1794 the Habeas Corpus Act was suspended and the Combination Acts of 1799 and 1800 made Trade Unions illegal. It is unfortunate that the two factors least regarded at the time, the growth of the population and the change in Britain from an agricultural to an industrial society should reach a critical peak against the background of an administration which by tradition and temperament was not equipped to deal with them. We have already seen earlier in this Chapter how agricultural trends were changing fast. It is now necessary to examine the rise in population and the effect of the Industrial Revolution.

The growth in population was startling. In 1801, the date of the first census, the population of England and Wales had unexpectedly jumped to nine million. This figure soared to 14 million by 1831. During this same period the population of London, which was 900,000 in 1801, almost doubled. However, T. S. Ashton shows that it was not, as was commonly thought, due to the immigration of labour or a sharp rise in the birth rate that this startling increase in population was due but to other factors. Mortality fell owing to the fact that the introduction of root crops made cattle rearing easier in winter and a continuous supply of fresh meat possible; an increase in the consumption of wheat and vegetables; a higher standard of personal cleanliness; the use of brick in place of timber for walls and of slate and stone in place of thatch for roofs; the fact that production of goods was taken out of the workers' own dwellings and progress in medicine.

As the numbers grew, the economic changes that were taking place altered the distribution of the population completely. As the flight from the countryside began, so did the organisation of labour change and lay the foundation for a complete alteration in methods of production.[1] The alternative to agricultural work not now avail-

[1] "The Industrial Revolution", T. S. Ashton, London 1947.

able owing to the Enclosure Acts was industrial work, in particular weaving, which had a rapidly expanding market. The old family method of production in the worker's home where the thread was spun, woven and dyed and from where the finished product was sold was hopelessly incapable of expansion. Traders began to use groups of specialist workers as competition demanded a further saving in costs and therefore increased production. Further competition acted as a powerful spur to invention. In 1773, John Kay, of Bury, invented his "flying shuttle" which increased the speed of the weaver's operation and heralded the death knell of the old hand loom. In 1764 Hargreaves' "spinning jenny" was introduced which enabled a single worker to manage several threads and seven years later R. Arkwright, a barber from Preston, invented the "water frame", the spinning machine worked by water which was replaced eight years later by Crompton's "mule". This combined the benefit of all the earlier machines. In 1784 the Reverend E. Cartwright displayed that fertility of invention which has been found in a surprising number of clergy of the Church of England and set up the first mechanical looms. In the closing years of the century however the steam engine, patented by James Watt, a cross grained, melancholy instrument maker from Glasgow, revolutionised the whole pattern of the industry. The workshops moved to be near coal mines and to places where the damp climate suited the thread. Liverpool with the Mersey river, convenient for importing and exporting, and the climate of Lancashire suitable for production, was the main supplier of cotton goods to the world for 150 years. Lancashire imported 25,000 tons of raw cotton in 1800 and 300,000 tons in 1861.

In 1783 H. Cort discovered how to utilise coal in forging and rolling metal. Abraham Derby and later his son had been using coke in furnaces in Shropshire but it was only when James Watt persuaded "Iron mad" Wilkinson to try a Watt's engine in his blast furnace at Bilston in Staffordshire that the real change occurred. Blast furnaces and foundries moved from wooded regions to coal-producing areas and unlimited production became possible. From a production level of 17,000 tons in 1740 the level jumped to 650,000 tons in 1830.

With these enormous changes, whole agricultural districts to the south of the country were depleted. Families moved to the cramped districts near the factories and coalfields of the Black country, South Wales, South Yorkshire, Lancashire and Scotland. Manchester, which was a half-timbered village of 12,000 people in the middle of the 18th century jumped in population to 400,000 in 1850 and the population of Glasgow and Leeds increased tenfold within one hundred years. The insatiable appetite for production meant that coal and iron ore had to be transported and this in turn led to an overhaul of the networks of communication. After the middle years of the 18th century new turnpikes replaced the rough parish roads and a "flying coach" service could soon reach Manchester from London in four and a half days. Metcalfe and Telford built new roads and bridges and John Macadam invented his new process of roadmaking in 1810. "No stone" he said sternly "shall be larger than the road mender can put in his mouth." After the Duke of Bridge-water's first commercial experiment near Manchester in 1761 a boom in canals and sea transport followed and communications further improved after Stephenson's locomotive had completed its first run between Stockton and Darlington in 1825, although it was not until some time later, with the adoption of the standard gauge, that the real impact of railways was felt.

The trade routes converged on the main towns which became the financial and administrative pivots of the new methods of production. All this revolutionised the use of land and changed the appearance of the countryside. In the half century in which Britain lost the 13 American Colonies and helped to defeat Napoleon, the new Industrial Britain came into being.

Economic and political thought at the time was concerned mainly with opposition to any institution or restriction on free expansion. In 1776 Adam Smith published his "Wealth of Nations". He held that all government interference was bad for trade. His advocacy of *laissez-faire* was made at a time when industry and trade were hampered at all points by a mass of Government restrictions (the Mercantilist System) but it was unfortunate that the book should have had such far reaching influence at that particular juncture. His suggestions even disagreed with the old Guild system of the Middle Ages and the Acts in Tudor and Stuart times regulating hours of work and rates of labour. During the famine of 1797 Malthus put forward the depressing theory that in the absence of war, disease and famine which had kept down the growth of population in the past, the population of the country would grow too large for the means of subsistence. He received much abuse but many people interpreted this to mean the uselessness of laws for the relief of the poor.

At the end of the 18th century progressive inflation had arrived and between 1790 and 1813 the cost of living doubled. The Luddite riots against the use of machines were in full swing by 1820 and at a time when the soldiers had returned and arms manufacture was ended the disastrous protectionist Corn Laws pushed up the price of bread. The unhappy Speenhamland system whereby deficiencies in wages were supposed to be made up by local rates but in fact had the effect of sending wages down came at a particularly bad time and with the benefits of the Reform Bill of 1832 not yet in sight, it is not altogether surprising that the period reached the point of dreadful frustration and mutual suspicion culminating in Peterloo.

The houses that sprang up round the centres of production under the system of *laissez-faire* to house the industrial workers were small and of poor quality. *Laissez-faire* held sway in the field of housing as it did in production and labour conditions. There were no controls whatever and indeed in many of the centres of production springing up, there were no representative local authorities at all to provide those services which are almost taken for granted today. In many of the newer centres of production remote from existing towns, mill and colliery owners built their own workers' housing for as little outlay as possible on sites which had, by their very nature, to be cramped, much of the best available land for building being taken up by the works. The rents of such "tied" houses were often linked to the wages paid and were accordingly low so that the capital cost of each house had to be kept to a minimum. In established centres or where older towns were being extended local traders, builders and professional people would dabble in a speculation of low cost workers' houses to let as an investment. The pressure for accommodation was so great from the massive influx of labour to the new industries that a high proportion of a worker's wage could be extracted by way of rent for even the meanest unit of accommodation, with the result that fantastic rates of return could be earned by the investor in boom times. Added to this, much development took place during the Napoleonic wars when timber imported from the Baltic countries was scarce, labour costs were increasing and when interest rates on capital were unstable. Although the houses were usually somewhat better than the previous country dwellings, by being constructed of slate and brick rather than wood and thatch and were used as dwellings only instead of being cluttered up with the machines of trade, nevertheless they were rudimentary and the new problems presented by the lack of proper sanitation and refuse collection, pollution from smoke and waste and general congestion were overwhelming. The following extract is from the well-known account of Manchester in 1845 written by Engels. It referred to the old part of the town and highlights how the existing owners of property capitalised on the demand for accommodation.

". . . the streets, even the better ones are narrow and winding . . . the houses dirty, old and tumbledown and the construction of the side streets utterly horrible . . . But all this is nothing in comparison with the courts and lanes which lie behind, to which access can be gained only through covered passages, in which no two human beings can pass at the same time. Of the irregular cramming together of dwellings which defy all rational plan, of the tangle in which they are crowded literally one upon the other, it is impossible to convey an idea. And it is not the buildings surviving from the old times of Manchester which are to blame for this; the confusion has only recently reached its height when every scrap of space left by the old way of building has been filled up and patched over until not a foot of land is left to be further occupied."

Engels continues and refers to a terrible description of Allen's Court by Dr. J. P. Kay at a time of widespread cholera when it was ordered to be evacuated, swept and disinfected with chloride of lime by the sanitary authorities. He continues to describe the Irk, a narrow foul smelling stream.

". . . In dry weather a long string of the most disgusting, blackish-green slime pools are left standing on this bank, from the depths of which bubbles of miasmic gas constantly arise and give forth a stench unendurable even on the bridge forty or fifty feet above the surface of the stream. But besides this, the stream itself is checked every few paces by high weirs, behind which slime and refuse accumulate and rot in thick masses. Above the bridge are tanneries, bone mills and gasworks from which all drains and refuse find their way into the Irk, which receives further the contents of all the neighbouring sewers and privies. It may easily be imagined, therefore, what sort of residue the stream deposits."

Engels also describes the housing of the new parts of the town.

"The space between two streets is divided into . . . courts . . . they were built this way from the beginning and communicate with the streets by means of covered passages. If the totally planless construction (by this he refers to the old part of the town) is injurious to the health of the workers by preventing ventilation, this method of shutting them up in courts surrounded on all sides by buildings is far more so. The air simply cannot escape . . . Moreover, the houses surrounding such courts are usually built back to back, having the rear wall in common and this alone suffices to prevent any through ventilation."

"More recently" said Engels "another different method of building was adopted:
"Working men's cottages are almost never built singly, but always by the dozen or score; a single contractor building up one or two streets at a time. These are then arranged as follows:—One front

The Industrial Revolution

(a) Terraced houses in a Northern steel town

(b) Miners' cottages in a colliery village

17

is formed of the best class, so fortunate as to possess a back door and small court and these command the highest rent. In the rear of these cottages runs a narrow alley, the back street, built up at both ends, into which either a narrow roadway or a covered passage leads from one side. The cottages which face this back street command least rent and are most neglected. These have their rear walls in common with the third row of cottages which face a second street, and command less rent than the first row and more than the second."

Engels went on to describe the back alleys of the poorest districts and said that there were cottages "whose outer walls were but one half brick thick, lying not sideways but lengthwise, their narrow ends touching". The object of this said Engels was to save money and materials but he blames the system of building leases and speculative housing for profit that encouraged such construction. He finally ends up with a harrowing description of the dilapidated cottage quarters of the city.

In the 17th century the hardship of life was taken for granted as being unalterable and part of an unavoidable destiny. The horrors of the man-made industrial town were, however, something new. Professor Benevolo[1] puts forward the analysis that the origins of modern town planning are to be sought at that moment in time when circumstances had crystallised sufficiently not only to cause the discomfort but also to provoke the protest of the people involved. The birth of modern town planning did not coincide with the technical and economic movements which created the industrial town; it emerged later when these changes began to be felt to their full effect and when they began to conflict, making some kind of corrective intervention inevitable. He traces the first attempts to right the evils of the industrial town and which found expression in two schools of thought. One adhered to the view that planning must start again from scratch; the other that each problem must be dealt with and each defect remedied separately, without taking into account their inter-relationship, and without having any overall vision of the town as a single organism. The "Utopians" such as Robert Owen, himself a mill owner, who when he left England set up a group in Indiana at a village named New Harmony, a venture which however collapsed in discord, formed the first group. The second group included the specialists and officials who sought to introduce new regulations and services into the towns and who, because they had to find the technical and legal means to implement these improvements, laid the real foundations of modern town-planning legislation.

[1] The Origins of Modern Town Planning.

The beginning of the age of reform can be dated quite accurately. The passing of the Reform Act of 1832 spread political power over a much wider area by giving parliamentary representation to many areas inadequately represented before and led to much subsequent legislation. The moving spirit behind the new factory legislation which by stages was to abolish the worst aspects of working conditions such as the employment of children in the mines, was the Earl of Shaftesbury. He had already been responsible for ending the employment of children as chimney sweeps and in 1834 he was asked to turn his formidable talents to the reform of the Poor Law. One of the Commissioners under the new legislation was Edwin Chadwick, the former assistant of Jeremy Bentham the reformer. Chadwick became intensely interested in housing and when the Poor Law Commission was asked to enquire into the origins of an epidemic in Whitechapel, Chadwick's report made a wide impression. This gave him the opportunity to compile a similar report covering the whole of the country.

In 1835 the Municipal Corporations Act, a Whig reform, introduced a standard type of elected Town Council. The ultimate benefit which was to be felt from this and the repeal of the protectionist Corn Laws provided the conditions for a great step forward in the Public Health and building legislation that was to come. Three large Public Health Acts were to follow. The preparatory work to produce the necessary climate for them was speeded up by terrible and repeated outbreaks of cholera in the cities and a growing feeling that plague was not merely a natural disaster that had to be endured but that it was rather due to man-made conditions which should be stopped. Accordingly, when the first Act in 1848 was passed it had wide powers framed on the principle that the Government should not be prohibited from interfering with the actions of individuals. This principle of course was not accepted by a large section of the community who had seen the success and had benefited from the results of "*laissez-faire*" in trade and manufacture from afar and who had little knowledge of slum or working conditions. It was perhaps unfortunate also that this principle had to be fought out in the field of Public Health where the general knowledge of the subject at the time was low and the sympathy for the science was equivocal. The radical Economist in 1848 refused to go into details of the Public Health Act since it dealt with "a great variety of matters which we cannot even enumerate without crowding our space with a catalogue of somewhat offensive words". Nevertheless the Act was passed and it was a vast one. It not only set up a Public Health Board in London but Local Boards in many other places as well. It covered a wide field—not only such matters as sewers and rubbish disposal but the inspection and regulation of lodging houses (the accommodation of migrant labour being a particular problem at the time) and sanitary requirements for new houses as well. Its range extended to burial grounds, roads, public gardens and water supply. The Public Health Act of 1875 set up a completely new basis for the layout of houses and streets (although London retained its own Act) and by the time that the Public Health Act of 1891 had been passed a vast pattern of health legislation was in existence which set the pattern for future house building. Sanitary rules for new houses were stringent and exact, and the appointment of Medical Officers of Health had been made in all districts to ensure that they were carried out. Joseph Chamberlain, the radical Mayor of Birmingham completely improved the city in a remarkably short time. The Public Health legislation and the Artisans Dwellings Act of 1875 which permitted local authorities to purchase slum dwellings, enabled many improvements to be made.

In London, meanwhile, the Building Act of 1844, made in anticipation of the growth of the capital, extended the control of the previous Acts over a wider area and created the official title of "District Surveyor" with wider powers and duties under this post than in the past. It dealt again with party walls, dangerous structures, drains and sewers. It dealt with open areas to houses and underground rooms and provided that every new street had to be a minimum of 40 feet wide and that new buildings were to be limited in height to the width of the street. Buildings were divided in the Act into three classes; Dwellings, Warehouses and Public Buildings. The Act restated wall thicknesses and set out four standards for houses of varying heights. It was however a curious ommission in the Act that while a maximum height for buildings in new streets was laid down there was no height limitation for new buildings in old streets. It is with this Act that stone stairs in dwelling houses had to be supported henceforth by fireproof construction.

The Metropolis Local Management Act of 1855 improved the system of local government in London and not only created the post of Superintending Architect but strengthened the powers of District Surveyors. It provided for new frontage lines to the primary roads in order to prevent indiscriminate building over the front gardens of existing Georgian houses, although much building of this nature had already been carried out. There were also a number of minor amending Building Acts between 1855 and 1882. It is of interest to note that the Act of 1878 provided for a minimum concrete foundation depth of 9 inches and an oversite layer of concrete 6 inches thick. It also required damp proof courses to be incorporated in new houses. It is therefore in buildings erected after this date that damp

proof courses can be expected to be found in London and later elsewhere. Towards the end of the century a scandal arose over the actions
of some members of the Metropolitan Board of Works and its duties
in the administration of the London Building Acts were taken over by
the London County Council in 1889. Much of the subsequent legislation for London while consolidating previous rules for the construction of buildings concentrated on street widths, open space around
buildings and height limitations showing increasingly how attention
was being turned on to aspects of layout and planning before the
legislation split into two separate branches.

There is a tendency to believe that all Victorian towns and cities
suffered from the same evils and grew in the same way. True some
trends were common, the exodus of not only the wealthier classes but
clerks and warehousemen vacating their houses in central areas
which were absorbed for business purposes and which resulted in the
suburbs spreading wider with the benefit of cheap rail travel. In
cities such as London and Newcastle-upon-Tyne, the older districts
became more closely packed than ever as a result of railway and
warehouse construction. Professor Asa Briggs, however, shows that
Victorian cities were not "insensate" ant heaps. They were never
"mere collections of individuals" some weak, some strong. They had
large numbers of voluntary organisations, covering a far wider
range of specialised interests than were possible in either the village
or the smaller town. They were more free of "aristocratic influence".
They allowed room for middle-class initiative and for greater independence and organisation of the "lower ranks of society" than did
smaller places. By the end of the century both organisation and independence were being reflected in new policies and genuine transfer
of power. Moreover the cities possessed in their newspapers what
were extremely effective propaganda agencies focusing attention on
local issues and through competitive rivalry stimulating the development of articulate opinion.

Not all cities however followed the same process of growth. Some
grew from the nucleus of smaller and older towns. Other cities were
amalgamations of towns fused into a new urban area such as Newcastle and Gateshead. A few Victorian towns were new and had
a genuine Victorian character. Manchester and Birmingham di-
verged strongly in their economic life, their social structure and their
politics. Birmingham depended on the Black Country but it had a
quite different social and political structure from its region. Manchester was the business capital of a whole constellation of textile
towns and villages.

Some towns evolved for quite different reasons. Bournemouth was
the model for middle class residential areas in the mid-19th century.

Scarborough was formed into the town it later became by the enter-
prise of the Cliff Bridge Company which took the Spa from the Corporation and formed shops, promenades, a theatre and a carriage
road. Liverpool Corporation promoted the planned extension of the
town, and in 1871 a private Act enabled the worst part of Dundee
to be cleared. Philanthropic housing associations such as the Peabody
Trust founded in 1862 which raised housing standards and charged
less than the market rents were not uncommon.

As to the buildings, in architecture the lightening and whimsi-
calities brought to the strict Palladian ideal in the Regency period
were succeeded by a flood of buildings in architectural styles
drawing inspiration from all parts of the world, China, Egypt, Italy
and Switzerland among others. Principally, however, a battle was
fought in the profession between the upholders of classicism and the
devotees of Romanesque and Gothic and architects developed personal styles based on historical examples. Fierce arguments would
arise as to whether this or that building of the Industrial Revolution
should be clothed in one or other of these styles. There were Vic-
torians who wanted a style of their own based on a sensitive and
imaginative use of new materials but these were in a minority, as
were those who continued to wish for towns to be planned on formal
18th-century lines, despite the totally changed circumstances. In the
heyday of Palladianism there were sufficient numbers of wealthy
educated men with ample time to devote to a cultivation of the arts
and architecture so as to provide an interested patronage and to act
as arbiters of taste. The fundamentals of design were laid down and
the small builder and craftsman were happy to be guided. The
wealthy, but hard working, middle class produced by the Industrial
Revolution had no wish for arbiters of taste and the self-made man
wanted something "imposing" with "pretentions" to reflect his
success. The architectural profession satisfied these requirements
with exuberance, see Figure 18(b), even mixing styles if the result
could be made more imposing. Even so the profession was over-
whelmed by the rapidity of events and the vast bulk of middle
class, let alone working-class housing, was left to speculative builders
who, lacking any guidance, plundered with gay abandon any particular style or detail that took their fancy and seemed at the time a
current selling point. Developments of detached "villas" for the
upper middle class proliferated and the term even became applicable
to semi-detached houses for the lower middle class, see Figure 18(a).
Where land was more expensive terraces continued to be built with
limited frontages but these might now be decked out with porticos,
bay windows, a riot of moulded brickwork in multi-colours, stucco
mouldings of overpowering effect, terra-cotta and even crenellations,

Upper class Victorian houses

(a) Early Victorian semi-detached houses, usually called villas

(b) Victorian pretensions. Late 19th century mansion

18

69

gables, gargoyles and carved barge boards. The mass manufacture of many materials and standardised elements for the construction of buildings, their cheapness and the ability of the railways to transport them to almost any part of the country meant that local traditions and skills were rendered obsolete. Speculative building commenced in Victorian times to have the same general appearance wherever it was carried out, a factor which has continued ever since to affect the appearance of our towns. It became a luxury reserved to a few with pronounced individual views to build in the local manner.

As we have seen from the description by Engels of conditions in Manchester, an account particularly of the newer parts of the town which could be applied with equal effect to most of the industrial connurbations, the housing for the workers produced appalling slums. The worst and indeed most of these have now been cleared and, although a lot of sub-standard dwellings incapable of improvement do still remain, have become part of history. Even so at the end of the 19th century the Victorian age had seen a growth of housing development unparalleled till then in history. The rectangular terraces of houses stood in street after street, row after row, structurally sound in the main and healthy as to drainage, lighting and water supply but in the last analysis, depressing, see Figures 19 and 20. What, then, had gone wrong? Part of the answer is to be found in the legislation. Well intentioned, having been produced under the auspices of the reforming Tories under Disraeli to curb the worst excesses, it concentrated largely on the plumbing rather than the planning. What planning there was, more by accident than design, created minimum street widths and lengths rigidly adhered to and seldom exceeded by the builders and which resulted in a dreary rectangular uniformity. Part of the answer also is to be found in the economic conditions which grouped the new development in concentric rings round existing cities and towns and which enabled suburbs by means of the railways, to be formed at further distances away from the centres of the cities and towns. Such development, coupled with the indiscriminate application of ornamental detail to the houses unrelated to the shape or structure was no substitute for the squares and varying scale of Georgian town development. Part of the answer lay also in the system which relied almost solely on the law of supply and demand to fulfil housing needs. Whereas much development in the 18th century had been controlled both in layout scale and detailed design by the ground landlord and his surveyor or architect, no such controls were exercised over the former agricultural land brought in for housing purposes in Victorian times. The prime purpose was to build as many houses with as little open

Low and middle class Victorian terrace houses, mid 19th century

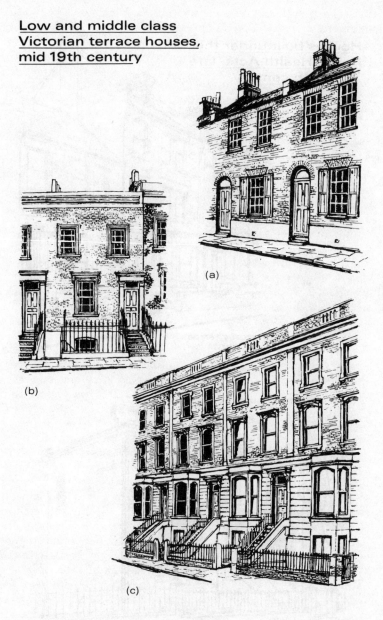

(a)

(b)

(c)

Houses built under the Public Health Acts, late 19th century

(a) Two and three storey terrace houses of about 1870

(b) A detatched house, 1875

20

space as absolutely necessary for access, or as necessary to comply with the law as it existed.

The overpowering effect of Victorian development produced its own reaction in due course and a desire for the relative simplicity fostered by the arts and crafts movement. In building this took the form of a return to an idealised cottage style, blown up as necessary to produce the desired accommodation, see Figure 21. In the private field the pioneer development was that commenced in about 1876 at Bedford Park, Chiswick, where moderately sized villas were laid out with gardens in an entire suburb of winding roads, as many of the existing trees being preserved as possible and the houses being of a remarkable simplicity for the period. Enlightened employers were next in the field, W. H. Lever of Lever Brothers commencing the setting out of Port Sunlight for his employees in 1888 as a garden suburb and George Cadbury at Bourneville from 1894, both businessmen combining success in their field with a strong social conscience. The buildings in both towns tended to be varied in size and scale and were intended for working, administrative and managerial staff, many being faithful copies externally of mediaeval buildings. These three developments had a far reaching influence which has extended to the present time and their devotees proved a vocal, though comparatively ineffective, force initially in the first half of the present century. The immediate effect however was to bring about a certain simplification in both the external and internal design of the speculative built houses erected between 1900 and 1914, though the layout of the estates and the basic plans adopted were not really very much different from those adopted prior to 1900. Gone however from the speculative estates were the large multi-storey family houses which envisaged a staff of servants to run them and there was a great concentration on the building of two and three storey dwellings of a reasonable size, a pattern foreshadowing post-1914 developments. Basements by this time were distinctly out of fashion for new buildings and since at this period good quality relatively cheap materials were still available and the houses were built with the full benefit of the legislation requiring site concrete and damp proof courses, they provide dwellings which have attractions not to be found in much mass-produced housing built immediately before 1900 and after 1914. The early part of the century was a period of excitement among the town planning supporters of the principles put into practice at Port Sunlight and Bourneville of whom Ebenezer Howard was one. "Garden Cities Tomorrow" was published in 1898. The Town Planning Act of 1909 enabled those local authorities that wished to do so to prepare town planning schemes for land about to be developed and this saw the start of the

73

Early 20th century cottage style houses

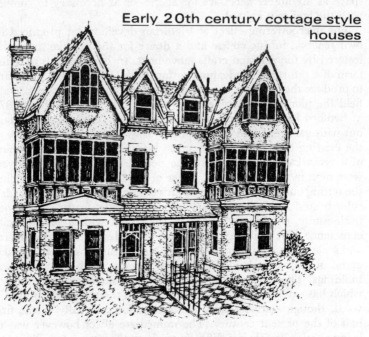

21

new legislation to be devoted solely to this field. It was an "adoptive" Act only and many local authorities still considered the principles expressed repugnant and had no intention of ever adopting any of the powers permitted to be used. Unfortunately it was the first of a number of such Acts relating to planning as the central authority still felt shy of telling reluctant local authorities what they had to do. At once however discussion turned to the subject of who should play the leading role in this new field. Architects, naturally, felt that they should play the main part aided by the surveyor, the engineer, the valuer, the economist, the sociologist and the antiquarian. Others felt that this would result in the emphasis being on the outward appearance of things not on the satisfaction of social needs, although it was a growing awareness of social shortcomings that had created a demand for statutory town planning. The view prevailed however that a vast spread of new building was inevitable and that the design factor was of major consequence. It was thus that the principle of low density planning of the kind advocated by Unwin established itself in practice. Low density housing on the garden city principle, with groups of suburbs round a central nucleus, with tree lined streets and ample gardens before and behind became normal for new suburban estates, whether built by private development or otherwise, see Figure 22, in general. In the First World War the Tudor Walters Committee on the construction and layout of working-class houses built by local authorities recommended that future house building should be regulated by town planning schemes controlling density and design instead of rigid by-laws controlling street widths and open space around buildings. It proposed the construction of large numbers of two storey, 3 bedroom houses which paved the way for the later low density council housing estate, see Figure 22(a). There were misgivings however as to whether this constituted town planning in its full sense. In 1914, C. B. Purdom declared that the Garden City Association ought not to support the extension of large towns and the multiplication of suburbs. Mr. Trystan Edwards, the year before, had already pointed out that low density housing was spoiling too much of the countryside and denounced the garden suburb as possessing neither the crowded interest of the town nor the quiet charm of the country and involving as much unnecessary travelling. P. Geddes tried to cure town planning of its now simplified idea. He took it for granted that town planning was concerned with the whole range of life and activity in a town on a much more fundamental basis, but it was many years before all these ideas were really considered. In 1912 the Town Planning Institute was formed and in 1919 the statutory basis of town planning was changed so that local authorities were empowered to prepare town planning schemes

75

without seeking the prior approval of the Ministry of Health, which had succeeded the Local Government Board. Moreover, most boroughs and urban districts were supposed to prepare town planning schemes by a certain date but this did not prove effective as few did so.

In 1918 the formation of the New Town group was to result in the development of Welwyn, see Figure 22(d), and the idea of separate garden cities attracted some support. It was later, in the 1920s, that the idea of controlled large-scale decentralisation of industry and population was first thought out. The idea was gaining ground that individual towns could not be planned in isolation and the principle of decentralisation was gradually extended to cover not only regional but also national planning.

The various ideas of town planners, diverse though they may have been, had little influence on the central or local authorities or on the mass of the population and in spite of the increased powers in the Town and Country Planning Act 1932, the difference made in practice was small. The nature of British urban development between the wars was simply a reinforcement of what had occurred before 1914 and the enormous multiplication of low-density residential suburbs with two storey three bedroomed detached, semi-detached and terrace houses, (b) and (c) Figure 22, resulted in consequence. The built up area of London for example quadrupled between the two World Wars. Many of the largest local authorities developed such estates themselves. The London County Council developed part of South Essex in the Becontree estate although it was obvious that there were not enough schools. Statutory town planning was merely suburban estate planning in practice, unrelated to the problems of town life. Private estate development was no better, concerning itself with residence and amenity unrelated to other factors, and spurred on by the cheapness and extensive improvements in the rail and roadway public transport systems, which usually preceded the development of new estates. This is what the public wanted and there was a massive exodus from the central areas, which became increasingly places for work, while the inner suburbs continued however to house the poorer workers who could not afford to move. Legislated town planning moreover paid little attention to the problem of road traffic and congestion on the main roads and city streets increased, particularly in districts long built up. Such improvements as were made to roads were outside formal town planning as central responsibility was vested in the Ministry of Transport. This body failed to exercise its powers to acquire land each side of new arterial roads with the result that ribbon development became common and unsightly. This led to the Restriction of

The spread of suburbia between the two World Wars

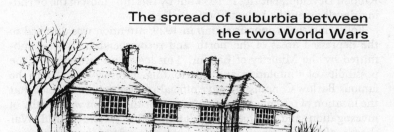

(a) A group of three Council houses of the 1920s

(b) and (c) Two versions of the private speculative house of the period 1920–1940

(d) Welwyn Garden City

22

Ribbon Development Act in 1935 but by this time most of the offending development had already taken place.

Following the economic slump in 1929, attention was directed to the depressed areas of the north and recommendations were submitted by the Ministry of Labour. This led to an awareness of the possibility of stimulating and distributing industry and, later, the famous Barlow Commission gave official recognition to the fact that the location of settlements of population for the nation was worthy of investigation and, perhaps, regulation. The Second World War shortly afterwards prevented anything being done, but evacuation in time of war and the new factories for war production gave unexpected experience to some and also gave rise to a feeling for the value of rural land. The greatest stimulus to town planning brought by war was, however, the rebuilding of shattered cities and a new generation of planners began to set up schemes based on a far wider range of data than ever before. A real effort was made at the end of the war to lessen administrative obstacles to town and country planning. The location of new industry became the province of the Board of Trade and a separate Ministry of Town and Country Planning was formed in 1943. A New Towns Committee was also set up. The general legal structure for town and country planning at national and local level was completely changed by the Town and Country Planning Act 1947 which made planning an obligatory function and made the county council the local planning authority with wide ranging powers.

After 50 years or so of much talk but little action, town planning at last became a real influence on town development and seems likely to continue to be so. The immediate problem at the end of the Second World War concerned the rebuilding of destroyed city centres and the overdue need for clearing slum areas but the restriction on the spread of towns by the imposition of Green Belts was an important decision taken shortly afterwards. Town planning at the present time may have acquired a reputation for the negative rather than the positive, but it has at least saved us from a further vast uncontrolled expansion of towns and cities over the last 25 years. The consequences of such restriction are however serious and coupled with increased congestion on the roads and a substantial deterioration in the public transport system have led to a revived interest in redeveloping the inner worn-out residential areas. The local authority method of high rise blocks of flats to replace the cramped terraces has recently produced profound misgivings as being an architectural solution rather than one fulfilling social needs. On the other hand the private sector solution, being more attuned to demand, of producing modern variants of the 18th-century town house on

Mid 20th century houses

(a) Houses for a New Town authority

(b) A private detached house

(c) The re-emergence of the terrace house

23

restricted sites has had some success, see Figure 23(c), despite the paucity of good design exhibited by most. In addition the demand for the older type of house suitable for modernisation in the inner areas has increased so that properties considered only 35 years ago, at the time of the flight to the suburbs, as being almost ripe for demolition are now given a very much longer life. In consequence of the green belt policy land values have soared where development is permitted and it has proved necessary to convert the large older type of multi-storey house into flats where single unit redevelopment is not possible.

Away from the old towns and cities the development of new towns has proceeded along lines which have not been universally acclaimed. There has been a tendency to produce suburban estates, see Figure 23(a), as before around an inadequate centre and occasionally even to build blocks of flats in almost open country.

However twenty years is too short a time to judge an experiment in satisfying basic human needs, particularly at a time when the absence of serious unemployment has produced an affluence tending rapidly to change peoples' viewpoints and requirements. Already there are new ideas in the planning of neighbourhood units with pedestrian precincts and ideas of forming residential areas on an extension of democratic rule in a more fundamental way than before. There is little doubt that the remaining years of this century will show radical departures from the past and it may well be that the buildings will follow suit.

However the buildings of the future are not the concern of this account and the problems posed in the upkeep of the existing stock of houses are likely to keep the surveyor fully occupied for many years to come. Furthermore at a time when many new materials are being introduced, labour lacks the skills of the past and initial cost is often considered all important, it is however an unfortunate axiom that what is new today may well need repair tomorrow, be it in the public or private sector.

Chapter 2
Brick Walls

CONTENTS

PART 1. OLD WALLS AND NEW WALLS

The art of construction in brickwork is as old as the earliest civilisations of Mesopotamia where the clay deposits of the rivers were dug out, sun dried and assembled into buildings. From that time onwards brick construction has flourished, spreading throughout the Mediterranean and Europe wherever suitable clays occurred, impetus arising from the discovery that clay when burnt was practically indestructable. By the 14th century brick was in great demand on the continent for major buildings including the largest of the churches in the Hanseatic ports around the shores of the Baltic and the North Sea and in the Netherlands. Despite the knowledge of these that must have been brought back by travellers and seamen there remained in these islands sufficient supplies of two natural building materials, timber and stone, to satisfy all requirements and it was not until the early part of the 14th century that bricks began to be made in East Yorkshire for the construction of new buildings.

By this time however, a very fair standard of building construction had been reached in both timber and stone. Both of these materials lent themselves to the principle of framed construction where the weight of roof and floors was transferred through columns in either material to a base, usually of stone, and thence to the ground, infil panels of walling being kept relatively light but sufficient to keep out the weather. Alongside these framed buildings, however, military structures, manor houses, barns and the like had been constructed with walls of stone blocks bonded and jointed together with mortar to form a monolithic structure, transferring the loads from roof and floors uniformly through the walls to the ground below. The degree of skill required to set out and construct the large framed ecclesiastical structures at this time was considerable and although skill to the same degree was not required for the monolithic structures, the remains of the enormous multi-storeyed keeps of the castles of the period are sufficient evidence to show that the standard was by no means far below. The principles of bonding between blocks and at the angles, thicknesses depending on length and height were sufficiently well understood to enable these structures to survive assaults at the time of the Civil War, subsequent dismantling and nearly three hundred years more of exposure to the elements. It can be imagined therefore that these skills could easily be turned to the use of brick, so much so that within a hundred years or so at least two new castles, or more properly fortified houses, had been built almost

83

entirely of brick, the clay provided by digging out the moat probably being used to make the bricks. Even the main tower of Canterbury Cathedral about the end of the 15th century was built of brick, although in this instance given a casing of stone.

The cheapness and ease of building in brick must have provided, to a substantial degree, a help to its increased use. Whereas formerly it took the labour of many men to quarry, dress, transport and get into position the stones required for building, once the bricks were ready the craft depended on the skill of one man, the bricklayer, with the help of one other to fetch and carry for him. Being a manu-factured product, bricks could be made to a size suitable for one man to handle and lay and, indeed, it has been this principle that has always governed the size of bricks. Although slight variations in size have occurred at all times according to individual preferences, even before the general standardisation in 1625 at $9'' \times 4\frac{3}{8}'' \times 2\frac{1}{4}''$ in thick-ness, the variations were slight. Correspondingly brickwork has always been thought of in terms of brick units even from the earliest of times. A Proclamation issued by James I in 1619, makes this point abundantly clear. Among other things it said:

"And if the saide Buildings doe not exceed two stories in height, then the walles thereof shall bee of the thickness of one bricke and halfe a brickes length from the ground unto the uppermost part of the said walles. And where the building shall be (over) the height of two stories, the walles of the first storey shall bee of the thickness of two brickes length and from thence to the uppermost part of the walls of the thickness of one bricke and half a brickes length."

Before the issue of this Proclamation and even subsequently as there existed little or no means to secure compliance with it, most brick walls would be built to a thickness governed purely by the experience of the bricklayer. This experience would generally mean that about the right thickness would be chosen and it is greatly to the credit of these early bricklayers that their buildings show few of the faults that arise from inadequate thickness exhibited by later structures. The reader might well say at this point that if they all built to the standard of James I's Proclamation this is hardly sur-prising!

Standards however did subsequently decline and brick buildings erected on estates for selling at a profit from about the middle of the 17th century were sometimes pared down in wall thickness to the detriment of their stability. Whereas for buildings in early Stuart times one might expect to find, even for two-storey work, walls of $1\frac{1}{2}$ brick thickness, for four storeys in later times it is likely to be down to 1 brick thickness for the upper floors and even a ½ brick thickness is not unknown at top floor level. Considerations of weather-proofing however have usually entered into a decision on wall thickness so that it is not often that ½ brick walls will be found, unless there is some particular reason for keeping the weight down, for example in a panel wall carried on a timber beam, in projecting windows or in the desire to achieve the ultimate in cheapness, as Engels found in Manchester.

Thickness is not, of course, the only criteria for stability in brick walls, which among other things, depends on suitable bonding, suitable mortar and sufficient restraint. This latter point seems to have received inadequate consideration in the past and whereas the by-laws which have been in force in various amended forms since the latter part of Victoria's reign have concentrated on establishing adequate thickness, the modern tendency is for more concentration to be paid to this aspect enabling a reduction to be made on what are now considered to be excessive requirements for thickness in domestic buildings. Loads, always assuming that they are uniformly distributed, are so light in domestic construction that given sufficient restraint and reasonable construction one brick thickness is adequate for more than was formerly realised. The weatherproofing aspect has, of course, in new construction been taken care of by the development and increasing use of cavity walling in this century.

Bearing in mind that in the field covered by this book it is existing walls that are being considered it is nonetheless of interest to see what is permitted under the two documents which govern construction in England and Wales at the present time, the metric Building Regulations 1972, superseding the 1965 edition which was in British units, for all areas other than the Inner London area which is covered by the London Building (Constructional) Amending By-Laws (No. 1) 1964, which are still in British units with exact metric equivalents and to study these in addition to the British Standard Code of Practice C.P.121.101 1951, entitled "Brickwork", which takes the form of recommendations representing a standard of good practice.

Both the Building Regulations 1972 and the London By-Laws of 1964 permit the thickness of brick walls to be determined by reference to their lengths and heights in certain circumstances. In the Building Regulations 1972 these circumstances are set out (Rule 7, Schedule 7) as follows (the British units being taken from the 1965 edition) for an external or separating wall which forms part of:

(a) (i) a building of one storey; or
    (ii) a building of two storeys or more, if the imposed load on

85

each floor above the ground storey when determined in accordance with the provisions of regulation D2 is less than 60 lbs. per square foot (3 kilonewtons per square metre) and (*b*) does not exceed 40 feet (12 metres) in height.

The limitation on loading to 60 lbs. per square foot (3 kilonewtons/m²) includes for all forms of normal domestic construction. The London By-Laws provide a table for buildings other than buildings of the warehouse class and no account is taken of floor loading. Therefore the section caters for domestic buildings as well as offices and retail shops when the permissible loading may be as much as 80 lbs. per square foot (3·83 kN/m²), although we are not concerned with these classes of building here. The thicknesses set out in both sets of rules are identical in their general effect even apart from the fact that the Building Regulations 1965 used the measurement of 12 inches (304·8mm) while the by-laws use 13 inches (330·2mm) both taken to represent a wall 1½ bricks in thickness. For convenience the thicknesses are set out as shown in the Building Regulations, the metric values being as shown in the 1972 edition which are rounded off and not the exact equivalents of the British units used in the earlier edition of 1965 (see table on next page).

In the Code of Practice there are no tables but Clause 301 (as amended in 1956) instructs that reference is to be made to the relevant by-laws when thicknesses are to be determined on the basis of length and height. On the other hand the Code states that where brickwork is to be designed on the basis of specified permissible stresses reference should be made to Code of Practice C.P.3 "Code of Functional Requirements in Buildings" Chapter V "Loading" and Code of Practice C.P.111:1964 "Structural Recommendations for Loadbearing Walls". Brickwork constructed in accordance with Code of Practice C.P.111:Part 2:1970, the metricised edition of C.P.111:1964 referred to in the Building Regulations 1965, will also satisfy the requirements of the Building Regulations 1972 under regulation D8, but the London By-Laws provide their own set of rules for determining the thickness of walls by calculation.

A cautionary note perhaps should be inserted at this stage as it must not be forgotten that all the rules discussed above are hedged by various qualifications. We are concerned here with the general rather than the particular for the purposes of comparison and it must be assumed that the reader will have, as part of his stock-in-trade, a copy of at least one or other of the publications already mentioned for controlling construction as ready reference. Although mention has been made of determining wall thicknesses by calculation it is not considered appropriate in dealing with old buildings to

(1) Height of Wall	(2) Length of Wall	(3) Thickness of Wall
Not exceeding 12 ft. (3·6m)	Any length	8 in. (200mm) for the whole of its height
Exceeding 12 ft. (3·6m) but not exceeding 30 ft. (9m)	Not exceeding 30 ft. (9m)	8 in. (200mm) for the whole of its height
	Exceeding 30 ft. (9m)	12 in. (300mm) from the base for the height of one storey and 8 in. (200mm) for the rest of its height
Exceeding 30 ft. (9m) but not exceeding 40 ft. (12m)	Not exceeding 30 ft. (9m)	12 in. (300mm) from the base for the height of one storey and 8 in. (200mm) for the rest of its height
	Exceeding 30 ft. (9m)	12 in. (300mm) from the base for the height of two storeys and 8 in. (200mm) for the rest of its height

rely on these methods for checking the strength of old walls. The methods are somewhat refined and pre-suppose accurate knowledge of the materials being used, usually on the basis of current British Standards, coupled with ideal modern conditions for construction. It may be that the methods will be found useful in particular cases when due allowance has been made for the conditions as found on site following exhaustive enquiry but then probably only in consultation with an engineer and after tests on samples of the bricks and mortar have been carried out to establish compressive strength.

Use of the rules for determining the thickness of walls by reference to length and height in the type of buildings envisaged provides a sizeable factor of safety and pre-supposes only return walls at each end. Although there is an over-riding minimum thickness for walls in terms of a fraction of the storey height in both the Building Regulations (one sixteenth) and the London By-Laws (one eighteenth) it is unlikely that the lateral restraint normally provided in domestic buildings would qualify as adequate in the case of the London By-Laws. For example the mere building in of floor joists would not satisfy the definition of lateral support set out in the by-laws which is identical to that set out in the Code of Practice C.P.111:1964. In the case of the Building Regulations, however, there is no reference to lateral restraint whatsoever and provided a wall is built no less than the minimum thickness it would be satisfactory.

To qualify as lateral support timber floors have to be tied securely to walls by means of metal anchors, irrespective of whether the joists are at right-angles or parallel to the wall. This requirement is hardly surprising perhaps as most readers will be familiar with the condition arising when a wall moves outwards thus depriving floor joists or roof timbers of some, if not most, of their support. In other words the mere bearing of floor joists on a wall is not necessarily sufficient to act as lateral restraint, although spiking joists to a wallplate may well do so in older types of construction where the horizontal wallplate formed part of a rigid frame at floor level.

The reader may well ask what all this has got to do with the repair of old brick walls, but it has to be stressed that an understanding of what has gone before, coupled with a sound knowledge of modern principles and theory, is the fundamental requirement for an intelligent examination of old walls which are out of repair. With this knowledge the problems encountered can be carefully considered, a diagnosis made of the cause of defects and a correct remedy prescribed. All too often one sees and hears of repairs being carried out which are not successful and more often than not this is due to a faulty diagnosis. The tendency to attribute defects in walls to foundation inadequacy is common and frequently expensive schemes of underpinning are carried out which are quite unnecessary and do nothing to cure the basic cause. It is for this reason that an investigation of the existing walls and the visible defects comes first in this book and solutions for foundation problems are dealt with later. Often the need to consider foundations will not arise as an effective and cheaper repair can be successfully carried out without disturbing work below ground.

In examining old buildings one must expect to encounter every degree of quality and type. At times one will encounter the cheap-jack, where the original builder has taken a chance on one brick thickness when one and a half would have been advisable or one and a half brick thickness when two brick thicknesses would have been better and so on. There is little use bemoaning the fact that whatever statutory control existed at the time was inadequate. There are plenty of instances where the risk was justified, by the mere fact that after the elapse of anything from 50 to 400 years nothing much is wrong. On the other hand there are many buildings where the thicknesses of brick walls are in excess of modern requirements. Problems are then rare but occasionally do arise for reasons other than those simply connected with wall strengths.

In any event one is able with the aid of the current regulations to compare the length and height of the existing wall with the appropriate thicknesses set out in the table and to establish initially whether the sizes are adequate by modern standards. In this comparison one must take account of the rules for the measurement of height and lengths as set out in slightly different form in both the Building Regulations and the London Constructional By-Laws and also the rules for dividing long walls into sections for the purpose of determining their thicknesses with the aid of buttressing walls, piers or chimney breasts. In this connection it may be necessary to cut away sections of plaster internally to see whether partitions are bonded to external walls so as to qualify as buttresses. In many cases, however, where partitions are hollow sounding, probably of timber framing, they will have to be discounted for this purpose and the wall considered as though it had no buttressing.

With the above comparison the surveyor will now know a little more about the wall and be able to add this knowledge to his perhaps previous subjective thoughts on the problem. He will in effect now know if the wall under consideration were to be built today whether it would be approved under current regulations on the basis of thickness in relation to height and length.

There are other factors involved of course, apart from height and length. The London By-Laws provide for all bricks to have a minimum compressive strength of 1,500 lbs. per square inch (10·34 newtons per square millimetre) for external and internal load-bearing purposes except between damp course and eaves level when it may be reduced to 400 lbs. (2·75 N/mm²) in single- and two-storey dwelling houses. The Building Regulations 1972 allow 400 lbs. per square inch (2·75 N/mm²) for one- and two-storey dwelling houses throughout and only require an increase to 1,500 lbs. (10 N/mm²) in other buildings. B.S. 3921:1965 requires a minimum strength of 750 lbs. per square inch (5·17 N/mm²) for bricks but this is only to ensure that bricks are sufficient for the low loadings in houses and to ensure that they survive handling. In addition both By-Laws and Regulations require that brickwork be properly bonded and solidly put together with mortar, the London By-Laws going further and requiring a mortar of not less strength than 1:1:6 cement lime and sand or 1:3 if lime mortar is used, both by volume.

Accordingly to make a comparison between an old wall and current regulations valid the surveyor must use a certain amount of historical sense related to the age and quality of the building. In regard to compressive strength it is probably very rare indeed to come across facing bricks built into a wall which are below the current requirements although there may be present the odd under-burnt brick not fulfilling the minimum requirements, but this is unimportant. What did happen sometimes in the past however is that walls were built as a facing skin applied to virtually a rubble backing consisting of underburnt and broken bricks, bats and some-times broken stone and wood all very roughly put together with a liberal lacing of lime mortar of dubious quality. A few headers might be passed through from the facing skin but more often than not snapped headers would be used to save cost on the facing bricks. Great reliance would be placed in Stuart, Restoration and Georgian periods on the incorporation of continuous timber plates to support wood floors and roofs and continuous bonding timbers at about 3 feet (9·14mm) vertical intervals to bind the whole lot together. Even in Victorian times bonding timbers continued to be used although the quality of the brickwork had often improved by then.

Accordingly comparisons with current requirements can be made more reasonably with Edwardian or later buildings, with the better quality Victorian and Georgian house, particularly if it should be an individual building and not one of an estate, than with Stuart or Restoration brick buildings and with the poorer Victorian estate building. There are therefore circumstances which may indicate that although on basis of length and height the thickness of a wall is satisfactory, the age of the building and the quality of the workman-ship may be such as to reinforce a suspicion that the wall is defective notwithstanding. The components making up an old wall can be highly suspect after a long period of years have elapsed. Age alone can indeed alter the bearing capacity of a wall.

The introduction to this Chapter has discussed, by way of com-parison, old walls with what might be expected to be built at the present time. The point that old walls by their very nature and con-struction can become defective has been made, but this point should not be exaggerated. It remains an astonishing fact that poor bricks flung together in a haphazard fashion with the aid of a weak and sloppy mortar still stand after three hundred or more years have

elapsed. The fact that most well burnt clay bricks are almost inde-
structible by ordinary weathering processes and the ability of the
joints to adjust and take up all manner of small movements is remarkable evidence of the soundness of brick as a building material
even ignoring its long history and its use in other countries, where it
has found equal favour. It is far more likely that the defective brick
wall on which advice is required will be affected by other factors
which have introduced defects by subjecting the wall to pressures
which it was never intended to withstand. This Chapter will therefore continue by describing the steps necessary to investigate the
defects and with a description of the faults likely to arise in an old
wall. The point will be made repeatedly that there can be no successful repair without a correct initial diagnosis of the problem.
Repair may well involve correcting faults in other parts of the
structure and these will have to be dealt with in other Chapters. But,
initially, the surveyor will commence with the pattern of defects in
the brickwork itself and eventually after such other work as is
necessary has been carried out the defects in the brickwork will
remain for repair.

PART 2. THE DIAGNOSIS OF DEFECTS

A. THE INVESTIGATION

Mention has been made in the Introduction to some of the steps
necessary to ascertain the cause of defects in buildings and an initial
point has also been made in the introduction to this Chapter in
regard to defects in brick walls. In order to suggest the scope that
such an investigation may entail it is necessary to envisage substantial defects in a valuable property with an owner prepared to
pay for the right sort of repair and with the patience and purse to
pay for and allow a proper investigation, if necessary over a period.
Repairs costing perhaps two to three thousand pounds to many
existing buildings can well be justified on economic grounds in view
of the high cost of land and new construction works at the present
time. Provided that a building owner can be assured that there is
no danger in living with cracks and bulging walls that may look
alarming, he will normally be prepared to allow the surveyor sufficient time to make a proper investigation, particularly if the surveyor
is forthright enough to stress the danger of hasty work, perhaps at
much cost, proving ineffective and the possibility that a properly
thought out scheme based on correct deductions being not only
successful but costing a great deal less.

91

The writers consider it is essential for a surveyor following his initial inspection of the building and its defects to report on his findings and clarify his instructions and authority at that point. Initially the building owner is almost sure to be worried by the question of safety and he will wish to have the surveyor's advice on this aspect at once. The surveyor must therefore on accepting instructions to inspect and report put himself out to arrange at an early date to view the premises with this sole object in mind. To the trained surveyor this presents little difficulty in regard to brick walls as his experience will tell him almost at once whether there is a danger of collapse. To the newly qualified or less experienced some difficulty may be presented but if the wall appears dangerous and there is not the time available to plumb walls or take the measurements recommended at the beginning of the section of this Chapter entitled "Whole Wall Movements" no chances should be taken and instructions should be given as a matter of urgency on behalf of the building owner to shore or strut the defective wall or feature. Most contractors will respond to an urgent call for such work with alacrity, but if difficulties are experienced in getting hold of a firm to take the necessary steps most local authorities can help, as they usually retain a contractor specially for such work should an emergency arise. It may also be possible to make an informal approach and enlist the aid of the District Surveyor in London or the Building Inspector outside London as these officials are responsible for taking steps to deal with dangerous structures. As they cannot see every building and all round every building in their area, they rely extensively on information being placed before them.

When there is a danger to life by way of possible collapse it is far better to look a little foolish by ordering shoring that may subsequently prove to be unnecessary than to hazard people's lives. On accepting instructions to advise on the aspect of safety the surveyor takes on an onerous responsibility and should a death arise by way of dilatoriness or incorrect advice he will have failed in his duty and the coroner's remarks are likely to ruin the surveyor's reputation. He is also likely to find himself in court not only answering a claim from the owner for damages in negligence but also from the personal representatives of the deceased.

Shoring is dealt with in Chapter 6 but while on the subject of negligence it might be as well to stress that a surveyor is responsible for the design and satisfactory nature of all shoring which he orders. The subject is of vital importance both from the point of view of knowing when the need for shoring arises and for ensuring its effectiveness when erected. Claims have successfully been made against both architects and surveyors in cases of deaths arising from a failure to order shoring when needed[1] and for the collapse of features inadequately shored.

Shoring provides the necessary breathing space for a consideration of the correct repairs necessary in the same way that an assurance given that there is no danger allows time for diagnosis. The writers consider that instructions following the initial advice should be correctly dealt with at this stage. Often the need for further investigation will not arise, the reason for the defects being all too apparent, in which case advice can be given and authority obtained to proceed with specifications, drawings if necessary, and the obtaining of competitive estimates. If the reasons are not apparent and the best interests of the building owner will be served by a period of waiting coupled with further investigation, the surveyor should say so. This advice will often conflict with other advice given to the building owner, usually by a contractor who, perhaps with a slack period on his hands, is all for pulling down a wall and rebuilding or underpinning it at substantial cost and who is sure that such work is required. To some building owners the contractor's advice is more acceptable for the simple reason that he is probably tired of living with unsightly and alarming looking cracks and wants to get his house in order again. Beware the building owner's wife in such cases as she is probably the one exerting a degree of pressure on the owner and will give short shrift to the surveyor with the "wait and see" approach, however correct it may be.

If the building owner is prepared to accept the contractor's advice, and many will do so however persuasive the surveyor's arguments because it is "action" the building owner wants and an end to a problem that he has lived with for sometime, then the writers suggest that it is time for the surveyor to withdraw. Diplomacy suggests that he should not withdraw in a huff muttering or committing to paper dire warnings of what will happen if the contractor's proposals are followed, as he may be asked to eat his words at a later date. However on no account should he accept instructions to supervise the contractor's operations simply for the reason that he has not had the opportunity of deciding whether these are likely to provide the correct answer. It would be unwise to supervise such operations and should they prove to be an incorrect solution, the surveyor will not be helped later by saying that he did not really believe in them. At best the opprobium will rub off on him and at worst the building owner will actually blame him, having conveniently forgotten what went on before.

We will now assume therefore that the building owner has

[1] *Clay v. A. J. Crump and Sons Ltd. and others.* Estates Gazette 21st September 1963, page 835.

overruled his wife, taken the surveyor's advice and has agreed to wait and to pay for the costs of a proper investigation. Since the defects are going to have a cause which requires this further investigation the stages will be set out in detail covering as many aspects as are likely to arise as is possible. Obviously in many cases suspicions will be aroused at an early date and these confirmed so that the investigation will fall far short of that necessary to cover all the possibilities. Even in the most difficult of problems it is to be hoped that the light may shine at some point along the course leaving the rest unnecessary.

The writers hold strictly to the view that in most cases it is not sufficient to view the damage and the surrounding areas in isolation. The first thing to do after viewing the damage is to get to know the house. The advice given in the Introduction to carry out an investigation of the structure along the lines of a structural survey should be followed, so that the surveyor knows how the roof is constructed and supported, what work is done by the respective walls and the details of their construction, how floors are constructed and supported and so on. From his knowledge of house types he will be able to make intelligent assumptions as to conditions behind plaster and in other hidden parts of the structure and decide whether it is necessary to expose certain areas for further examination. The position of defects when viewed in relation to drain runs might suggest that the drains should be tested, a relatively simple operation when compared with the necessary digging to expose foundations. If the house is of simple design and construction it may be an easy matter to assemble this information by way of notes but if the property is more complicated and involves say split-levels or differing forms of construction it may be easier to prepare drawings both in plan and section to a reasonably large scale, 2 feet to 1 inch (1:24 or later 1:20), if possible as this enables much structural detail to be shown. If the building is fairly new plans prepared at the time of building may be still in existence, if not with the owner, probably deposited with the local authority for by-law approval. Copies can sometimes be obtained in the circumstances but plans prepared at the time of building should always be treated with a certain amount of reserve and the information shown on the drawings checked at the property. It is not unknown and indeed quite common for details, particularly those below ground, to be altered at the time of construction but not amended on the drawings. An interview with the Building Inspector in charge of the area in which the building is situated can be invaluable not only on this point but also to glean any facts that might be of interest concerning site conditions before and during building. Dates of construction can also be checked at the same time together with details of any similar work in the same area. Past history of this and adjoining properties, soil characteristics in the district, details of made up ground and sundry snippets of local information and history that can sometimes be invaluable might also be obtained. Often an informal conversation on the capabilities of local contractors can be enlightening and this may be particularly useful if the building owner has a nomination in mind. It should also not be forgotten that a study of old Ordnance Survey maps will often reveal features on a site from a time before the building under consideration was even built. Local authority offices often possess a stock of these older maps which are useful for showing sites of ponds, orchards, wells, ballast pits, quarries, old brickworks, possibly coal mines or other mineral workings and areas of brine pumping, signs of which may have long since disappeared but which may still affect the sites of buildings. Local authority records can also be searched with effect for evidence of wartime bomb craters, disused drainage systems, landslips, floods and so on.

Not only should the building be looked at in detail but also the surrounding site and adjacent sites. Evidence of the type of sub-soil may well be visible in the locality if not already known by the surveyor, otherwise geological maps can usually be consulted in the area's central library or museum. In this respect the Geological Museum in South Kensington, London has a good set of large-scale geological maps with ink annotations on sub-soil conditions when excavations of interest have taken place in the area and information has been reported to the museum. The surveyor should take note of the position of any trees on the site or in neighbouring gardens or on the highway. It is always useful in this respect to check with the building owner whether any trees have recently been cut down in the immediate vicinity. This enquiry could be extended at the same time to include any other changes in the vicinity, possible excavations, undue vibration or new drain laying.

General conditions in the area can often be judged from a walk in the neighbourhood of the building. Broken ground in hilly areas may be caused by soil creep particularly when slopes exceed 1 in 10. This can often be gauged by the presence of tilted fences, walls and trees. Low lying flat areas in predominately hilly country may suggest the presence of soft silty soils and peats, as these may have been lakes or ponds at one time. Naturally growing poplar, willows or reeds may confirm this view. On the other hand bracken and gorse in the area usually indicate a well drained soil. In chalk and limestone areas small craters or gentle depressions can indicate the presence of "swallow holes", which will be referred to again later, where the top soil of sand or loam has collapsed into a cavity below. In built up areas broken pavings and curb stones particularly near trees suggest that the soil may well be shrinkable. If the inspection is being made during a dry summer a pattern of polygonal cracks in the surface of lawns and flower beds, about an inch wide, with shallow depressions around large trees would also confirm this view. Often the almost total absence of the vegetation typical of the surrounding neighbourhood is indicative of made up ground.

Away from the coast and tidal rivers and depending on the season, the level of water in nearby ponds, streams and ditches may give good guidance as to the level of water in the adjoining ground. Along river valleys and in coastal regions it would be necessary to establish highest flood levels from local sources of information with possibly the assistance of Admiralty charts.

Finally on looking round the area, should the building in question be one of a terrace of similar properties or there be semi-detached or detached buildings nearby forming part of an estate it is imperative to have a look at the other houses as well. By doing this one can sometimes see similar defects in existence either in a lesser or a more advanced stage. On other occasions one may even be lucky enough to find a similar building where works of making good have already been carried out. This would indeed be good fortune as with the co-operation of the owner of the repaired building one might be allowed to examine the repairs, find out what the cause of the trouble was and, into the bargain, ascertain whether the works were successful or not. The building owner might consider the surveyor a bit of a charlatan if the works proposed to his house were based on "cheating" from up the road but he will be saved the cost of part at least of the investigation and ought to have the grace to acknowledge that the surveyor had used common sense if nothing else!

The damage and its history must of course be recorded at the time the investigation is commenced. In this respect plans, sections and elevations in particular are useful for recording the position and size of cracks and whether they taper to one end or are uniform throughout. Leans and vertical bulges in walls can be measured and plotted on the sections of the drawings and horizontal bows in walls measured and plotted on the plans. In the roof any pulling apart of joints can be noted and any sagging in timbers. The surveyor will also have to obtain the best information he can on the history of the troubles. The building owner might be able to say when he first noticed the damage or when he found it necessary to do repairs, redecoration or patching. This may not be, of course, when the damage first occurred but if the date can be related in time fairly closely to a particular period of weather, for example a very long hot summer or a particular period of exceptionally heavy rainfall, it may be a very useful pointer to the cause. Confirmation on weather conditions can be obtained by reference to the daily, monthly and annual records of the Meteorological Office.

The question of whether there is any evidence to suggest that movements are progressive or not will have to be considered. Old making good might conceivably exist in the cracks. Unless of mastic this is sure to shrink over a period but the surveyor may be able to form an opinion as to whether the gaps now visible are more than would arise on mere shrinkage having regard to when the making good was carried out. This is not always easy to decide and unfortunately the evidence provided by the building owner, his family, tenants or contractors who may have been brought in is often conflicting. Usually unless something sudden and dramatic has happened the evidence will be insufficient to formulate an opinion. This is not too serious if the time is available for further investigation as the surveyor will wish to verify points of this nature for himself.

The use of glass tell-tales bedded on pats of cement either side of a crack in brickwork has little to commend it, as for one reason the glass is easily damaged and for another they give no idea of the amount of movement. The building owner can also be alarmed if he sees that they have broken and will worry about movement which he will always think of as getting worse. Far better on internal plaster walls is to mark at fairly frequent intervals a measurement of an inch or more at right-angles across the crack. Externally, and internally as well if required, small holes can be cut in the brickwork on either side of the crack and non ferrous square section pegs about 2 to 3 inches (about 50 to 75mm) long can be carefully set in cement mortar so as to enable accurate measurements to be taken either between the inner faces of the pegs, or across the pegs to their outer faces. The use of a micrometer is essential to ensure that accurate measurements are taken and quite small movements can thereby be detected. These may of course show an increase but the surveyor should not be surprised if, according to the season, movements are in the form of a recovery.

It is often difficult to show in accurate detail by way of drawings or notes the precise size and run of cracks. In this connection photographs can be of assistance provided care is taken to identify the photograph accurately at the time it is taken. By comparing cracks with the photograph at a later date quite small changes can be detected which would not be noticed if reliance was placed solely on notes, measurements and sketches.

The need for accuracy in taking these measurements and the need for keeping all records very carefully and safely should be obvious otherwise the work undertaken is pointless. In addition they should be retained for reference after repairs are completed. The interval before the need to attend again at the property will depend on circumstances but for reassurance of the building owner it might well be within a month, even if the surveyor considers that nothing much is likely to happen in that period. Subsequently visits might well be made at monthly or two monthly intervals and after a year or so a pattern of movement, or for that matter non-movement, might emerge. Further movement might suggest the need for more conclusive evidence on a particular aspect, for example settlement suspected might suggest the taking of a series of levels on a particular brick course all round the building, damp course level if the building has a damp course, coupled with some excavation to examine the foundations. Complicated settlements might indicate a more thorough study of the sub-soil involving the employment of a soil mechanics specialist. This could possibly be extended to include the area within the building if it has hollow wood floors and if not it might well be worthwhile drilling through the site concrete for this purpose.

Whatever the line taken by the further studies they should be continued until the surveyor is reasonably satisfied that he has found the cause and that his proposed scheme of repair will prove effective. As long as there is no danger of collapse there is no reason why this should not take as long as necessary to form the correct conclusion. Mrs. Building Owner will however rapidly lose patience, assuming she had any to begin with, and the surveyor will face much chiding on his inability to find an answer following his successive visits. Some sympathy must be extended to the lady, however, as she will be putting up with massive inconvenience by her way of it (all those cracks and pencil marks) but the surveyor must resist the persuasion to come to a conclusion on evidence which he may consider flimsy, tempted though he may be to do so if the lady complains forcefully about the inaction. Fortunately most cases in fact resolve themselves fairly quickly and we must turn attention to the symptoms which will be exhibited in brick walls and other building components which will guide the surveyor to his conclusion. We will commence with those visible above ground and which owe their origin to forms of construction and the materials involved in building, leaving those associated with foundations and ground movements to the subsequent section. Movements originating above ground are usually easier and cheaper to remedy and it is therefore logical to deal with them first, particularly as the investigation involved can normally be completed fairly quickly.

B. Defects arising from conditions above ground level concerning Types of Construction and Materials Involved

Symptoms arising from defective conditions above ground can be divided into four separate groups, the first two groups being perhaps more important with buildings erected before 1900 and probably being the more commonly encountered while the second two groups arise more frequently in post 1900 buildings but even more so are applicable to houses shortly after they have been erected. It is, however, unwise to be too dogmatic about this.

(1) *Movements Arising from Inadequate Design, Faulty Construction or Overloading*

(a) *Inadequate Thickness in Walls*

As we have mentioned before, long tall slender walls were often built in the past which have proved incapable of sustaining even the light loads of domestic building. As such they can develop leans if subject to no restraint, vertical bulges if subject to some horizontal restraint and horizontal bows if provided with vertical restraint at the corners or from intermediate partitions. Vertical fractures may occur at the corners if the bonding is poor or some short distance along the wall from the corners if the bonding is sound, see Figure 24. Thin tall chimney stacks can be included in this category, together with unsupported gables and tall thin parapets as shown on the top three examples on Figure 25. Even walls of normally adequate thickness for their length and height but not provided with adequate vertical restraint at the ends or horizontal restraint from floors and roofs can develop leans, bulges and horizontal bows as described above. In parapet walls vertical leans and horizontal bows often arise owing to this lack of horizontal restraint at the top. Internally evidence of these defects in walls will be seen by way of diagonal cracks to ceilings in the corners of rooms and, in particular, at the junction of ceiling and walls and also in corners of rooms where partitions meet the wall in question. Often an examination in the roof space will reveal a fracture not visible from elsewhere, where one wall parts company from another.

(b) *Faulty Construction*

Inadequate bonding in brickwork at corners or to party walls can lead to whole walls leaning outwards with the same results as in (a) above. Poor bonding between leaves of brickwork may result in the whole leaf being shaken free and loose areas of brickwork becoming

Typical defects arising from conditions above ground level
(1) (a) Inadequate thickness and lack of restraint in walls

Section of tall thin wall
with no restraint
'A'

Rear elevation
'A'

Section of tall thin wall
with partial restraint
'B'

Scale throughout 1 : 200

In 'A' if bond at angles
is weak a vertical
fracture could develop
at 'C' and 'D' on key
plan. If the bond is
sound the panels of
brickwork on the
rear wall will tend to
pull away and fractures
will approximately
follow the line of the
window reveals and
the flank wall displace-
ment may take the
form of a horizontal
bow (see rear elevation
'A' above and key plan
'B' on right).

Key plan for 'A'
Top floor

Key plan for 'B'
First floor

In 'B' partial restraint from the roof and floor joists at first
floor level might restrict the movement to a vertical bulge
coupled with the horizontal bow if the bond at the angles
is sound. The defects illustrated are common to pre-1900
semi-detached and end of terrace houses particularly when
the staircase is positioned on the exposed flank wall.

24

100

Typical defects arising from conditions above ground level
(1) (a) Inadequate thickness and lack of restraint in walls

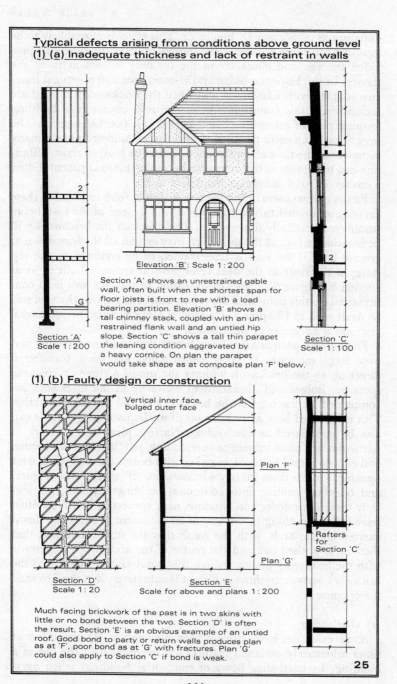

Section 'A'
Scale 1:200

Elevation 'B': Scale 1:200

Section 'A' shows an unrestrained gable wall, often built when the shortest span for floor joists is front to rear with a load bearing partition. Elevation 'B' shows a tall chimney stack, coupled with an un-restrained flank wall and an untied hip slope. Section 'C' shows a tall thin parapet the leaning condition aggravated by a heavy cornice. On plan the parapet would take shape as at composite plan 'F' below.

Section 'C'
Scale 1:100

(1) (b) Faulty design or construction

Vertical inner face, bulged outer face

Section 'D'
Scale 1:20

Section 'E'
Scale for above and plans 1:200

Plan 'F'

Plan 'G'

Rafters for Section 'C'

Much facing brickwork of the past is in two skins with little or no bond between the two. Section 'D' is often the result. Section 'E' is an obvious example of an untied roof. Good bond to party or return walls produces plan as at 'F', poor bond as at 'G' with fractures. Plan 'G' could also apply to Section 'C' if bond is weak.

25

apparent as on Section D, Figure 25. This effect is more likely to be localised but some cutting away should confirm the diagnosis provided the age and character of the building is such as to fit the theory. In this respect a bulge on the outer face and a vertical inner face coupled with a hollow sound when the brickwork is tapped are indicative of this condition. As to age and character a building forming part of an estate of any period is a possible suspect. The urge to make an extra profit on the brickwork, undetectable in many instances at the time of construction, would be hard to resist. Vibration can be a cause of this symptom becoming more apparent. Often a change in road use makes the defect worse.

Faulty construction or inadequate design in roofs can lead to these exerting an angled thrust on top of a wall instead of the load being transferred vertically downwards. The effect on the brickwork will be to induce a lean at the top which may extend all the way down to ground level if the wall is unrestrained or be confined to the top storey if the floor at the next level down is securely built in as at Section E, Figure 25. Close examination in the roof will help confirmation on this point and the repair aspect as regards the roof will be dealt with in Chapter 5. Horizontal bows can also be induced if restraint is adequate at the corners.

Point loads particularly, from heavy floor and roof beams and over large openings in older construction are often transferred direct on to the brickwork without the use of a stone or concrete spreader. Bulges and displacement can arise in the brickwork accompanied by fractures if the brickwork is well restrained nearby. This is included here as an example of inadequate design but it can also be considered as overloading. Narrow piers in brickwork in particular are often subject to overloading, see "A" on both section and elevation on Figure 26, together with beams carrying walls over openings such as those for bay windows, see "B" on the same Figure, and openings leading into additional buildings. Arches, particularly those over doors and windows near corners of buildings often have little or nothing in the way of an abutment to resist the thrust exerted by the arch, with the result that the small abutment that there is, is pushed out and the centre of the arch drops sometimes with the brickwork above, though this is not always the case as the brickwork above may have sufficient tensile strength in itself to span the opening.

(c) Overloading

Some examples have already been included in (b) above but at times adequately designed features are overloaded in the use of a building. In particular floors of residential buildings when over-

Typical defects arising from conditions above ground level
(1) (b) Faulty design or construction and (c) Overloading

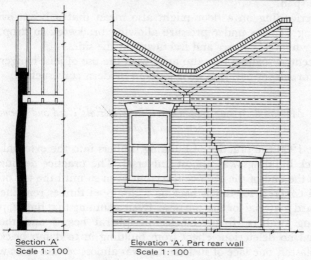

Section 'A'
Scale 1 : 100

Elevation 'A'. Part rear wall
Scale 1 : 100

The section and elevation above show bulging and fracturing
resulting from a gutter beam carrying one quarter of total
roof load bearing on a relatively narrow pier of brickwork.
The condition is often aggravated by settlement in the partition, usually of timber, parallel to frontage and carrying half the
roof load throwing further load on front and rear walls.
In the example below, also in section and elevation, about one
quarter of total loading above ground floor level is carried
on the beam over the bay window, often inadequate for the
purpose. Deflection in the beam produces the effect shown.

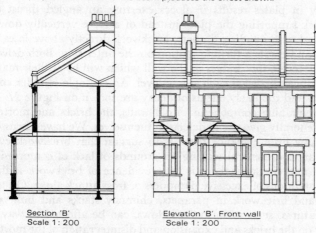

Section 'B'
Scale 1 : 200

Elevation 'B'. Front wall
Scale 1 : 200

26

103

loaded can exert an angled eccentric thrust on walls producing bulges in the brickwork, particularly if the overload is in the centre of the span.

Overloading on a floor might also mean that a beam over an opening deflects under pressure allowing brickwork to drop, producing uneven courses and fracturing at the sides.

Eccentric loading can also arise with the use of joist hangers and iron corbels for carrying floor joists in modern construction.

(2) *Movement Arising from Defects in Materials Used and Chemical Action on Materials*

Before 1900 the practice of building timbers into the external walls of brick buildings was almost universal. The practice declined towards the end of the 19th century but even so until the use of reinforced concrete for lintels became widespread timber remained the standard material for this purpose. Even assuming that lintels, plates, bonding timbers, fixing blocks, peripheral beams and the like suffered no deleterious effect from building in to damp brickwork and plaster, one face of such timber was almost certain to be within 4–5 inches (102–127mm) of the exterior. Rainwater penetrates this thickness of brickwork with ease but far more so when pointing is defective or where there are cracks and loose areas to external rendered surfaces. It is not surprising therefore that few such timbers when exposed nowadays are found to be sound and extensive dry or wet rot and almost total decay to the timber is what is usually found.

Decay in plates results in floors exerting an angled thrust on brickwork supporting the plate instead of a force vertically downwards and with bonding timbers, brickwork directly above loses its support and exerts a turning motion on the outer skin. Both defects are likely to produce bulges in the wall which will be at their maximum halfway between each storey level. An example of older construction and the likely effects of decay are shown on Figure 27.

The remaining components of old walls, the bricks and mortar, do not generally give rise to defects in themselves. We have discussed before how little evidence there is to suggest that brickwork ever fails in areas of general walling on grounds of lack of compressive strength and similarly there is little evidence of brickwork failing under conditions of excessive dampness or frost attack alone. On the other hand brickwork in parapets, chimney stacks and built up brick features, such as dormer windows, can be affected by way of spalling on the bricks and expansion and disintegration of the mortar due to the action of frost or soluble salts or both. For example the leaning chimney stacks shown on Figures 25 and 28, although in the examples given specific causes, could equally well on unrendered brickwork have been caused by rain saturation on one side of the stack being followed by frost, particularly if the pointing had been neglected. To a lesser extent brickwork below damp proof course can also be affected but principally such damage is confined to brickwork in the very exposed positions mentioned above, together with retaining walls and free standing walls, all subject to periodic saturation.

As to mortar much of the lime mortar used in old buildings was originally of very poor quality and if employed for thick walls usually failed to set properly. As such, however, if the wall is otherwise sound the mortar is unlikely to cause a failure on its own account but it may well be a contributory factor in many other cases of failure as part of a general weakness in the wall. In buildings of this century where a cement based mortar is used in conjunction with bricks containing soluble salts there is a danger of the mortar being attacked if brickwork becomes wet. The slow but steady expansion of the mortar can produce cracks and bulged sections of brickwork which can eventually impair stability, particularly if the brickwork is restrained. The danger arises primarily if brickwork is rendered when the attack on the rendering allows continual moisture penetration and long periods of saturation in the brickwork. In such cases expansion has increased the height of the outer leaf of a cavity wall by as much as two inches disrupting the setting of the wall ties as shown at Section "A" on Figure 28. If the wall was restrained at top and bottom, the bulge would be sufficient to dislodge the wall-ties completely as shown at Section "B". A further effect of sulphate attack on an exposed parapet is shown at Elevation "D".

A by now well-known defect involving sulphate attack concerns domestic boiler flues which are unlined. Many inter-war houses were provided with solid fuel domestic boilers, the chimney stacks being built in cement or cement lime mortar. A change in the post-war years to slow burning or gas-fired boilers meant that the flue gases, containing quantities of sulphates, condensed into liquids attacking the cement in the mortar causing it to expand. Chimney stacks are subject to much soaking from rain which dilutes the acid but carries it to all parts of the brickwork. Unequal drying according to orientation produces the dramatic tilts which can sometimes be seen, such as that at Elevation "C" on Figure 28. This type of defect has been well publicised but it must be remembered that it is only brickwork constructed with a mortar containing Portland cement that is affected in this particular way. A rebuilt stack on an old building could be affected of course if it were rebuilt in cement mortar at the

(2) Movement arising from defects in materials used and chemical action on materials

Decay of built in timber

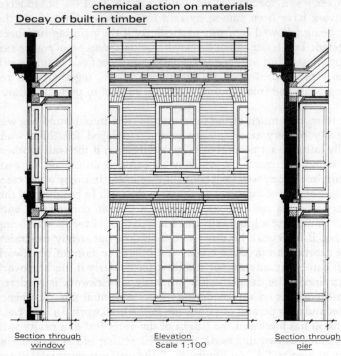

Section through window

Elevation
Scale 1:100

Section through pier

Below Section 'C'
Scale 1:20

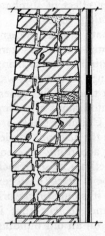

The nature of much brickwork of the 17th and 18th centuries can be gauged from the two sections through the windows and piers of the part house shown above. Continuous wood lintels and main floor beams built in at each level as work proceeded provided a rigid frame to stiffen the brickwork confined in the main to narrow piers. Timbers built in at intervals helped to bond the rough brick backing together, leaving the facing half brick skin with a few headers as a tie to the backing. Lack of maintenance to parapet gutters, flashings to projections and pointing may allow damp penetration and induce fungal attack. Decay in the peripheral beam forming the lintels produces fractures similar to those shown on the elevation above, while the effect on the brickwork of decay in just one bonding timber is shown on the left. Note the sagging brickwork, bulging on the facings and the breaking of the headers. Bond timbers also provided a fixing for battens and panelling shown here and also later for lath and plaster.

27

(2) Movement arising from defects in materials used and chemical action on materials
Sulphate attack on brickwork

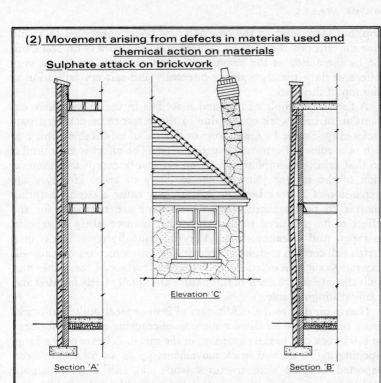

Section 'A'

Elevation 'C'

Section 'B'

Absence of a d.p.c. below the coping and shrinkage on the rendering can allow much damp penetration to the brickwork shown in Sections 'A' and 'B'. If the brickwork contains a high proportion of salts expansion will occur increasing the height of the outer leaf in 'A' where there is no restraint and causing a bulge in 'B' where the concrete roof bears on both leaves. Sulphate attack on the typical semi-detached kitchen boiler flue is shown on Elevation 'C'. Note the different pattern of ordinary shrinkage cracking to the rendering on the house wall compared with that on the stack, where the original shrinkage cracks have enlarged on the line of the brick joints as sulphate attack progresses. On Elevation 'D' the exposed parapet has expanded in length on the asphalt d.p.c., which forms a slip joint, to oversail at the corners.

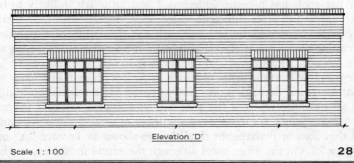

Elevation 'D'

Scale 1:100   28

107

top, but more often in the case of a new boiler connected to an old flue the effect on the parging, mortar and brickwork of the stack will be by the action of the heavy acidic condensation producing very offensive dark treacly staining internally and salt crystallisation at the top of the stack.

A further example of unsound materials in use arises where expansion of brickwork occurs due to the presence of unslaked particles of quicklime in the mortar or the use of unsuitable clinker or ash in a coloured cement gauged mortar. The effect is very similar to that arising in sulphate attack on brickwork except that lamination of the mortar joints is not so likely to arise. However the expansion of a weak bedding mortar may cause a strong pointing mortar to be displaced. Damp conditions are necessary for the effect to be produced so that the defect is more likely to arise in parapets and chimney stacks. Very occasionally some bricks in a batch will contain nodules of unhydrated lime which on wetting will expand to such an extent as to shatter the surface of the bricks and split the interiors. Effects of this nature are usually fairly isolated and easily distinguishable.

Corrosion due to the oxidisation of iron or steel built into brickwork can produce localised symptoms of cracking and displacement of brickwork due to the expansion in the metal. A beam over a large opening may rust and brick movements up to an inch have been reported coupled with fractures while old cast iron stanchions embedded in brick piers on rusting have caused substantial vertical fractures.

(3) Movements Arising from Temperature Changes

Movements arising from temperature changes are not often encountered in domestic construction and certainly not in old buildings with pitched roofs or those with flat roofs covered with lead or zinc on a timber structure. In recent years however the use of concrete for flat roofs has become widespread and although unlikely to be encountered in sizes sufficient to introduce measurable movement the surveyor should be familiar with the possibility of expansion thrusting over a parapet so that it leans or a similar effect arising at the top of a wall immediately below a flat roof. The movement in the concrete is to the order of $\frac{1}{3}$ inch in 50 feet (8·5mm in 15·2m) so that structural damage is only likely to arise in substantial buildings or for example where a flat roof cast as one unit, without proper expansion joints, is carried over a number of smaller domestic units be they flats or perhaps the small houses shown as Terrace "A" on Figure 29. On the other hand although the actual movement in the

(3) Movement arising from temperature changes
Expansion of long concrete roof slab

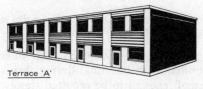

Terrace 'A'

Section through top of flank
wall in terrace 'A'. Scale 1:40

The post Second World War terrace house may have problems
typical of current methods of construction and the use of materials.
Terrace 'A' above has a long continuous concrete roof with screed
and asphalt but a lack of expansion joints and insulation. Hot weather
will cause expansion in the concrete which will push the top of the
flank walls and parapets outwards resulting in a long horizontal
crack near the top of the wall, cracks in plasterwork near the
ceiling of top floor rooms and possibly cracks in the asphalt.
Terrace 'B' below if built of sand lime or concrete bricks with a high
initial shrinkage rate will rapidly develop vertical cracks at about
6 foot (2 metre) intervals particularly between ground and first
floors in the long panel. Crack might extend to d.p.c. level but not below.
In the construction of the stepped terrace 'C', the new clay brickwork has expanded on becoming wet for the first time causing
vertical fractures to appear on the short return walls as shown
on the plan. A common feature of both examples below is that
the movement is of a "once and for all" nature.

(4) Movement arising from shrinkage on drying or expansion on wetting of materials

Shrinkage in long lengths
of sand lime or concrete
bricks

Terrace 'B'

Expansion of new clay brickwork

Terrace 'C'

Part plan terrace 'C'
Scale 1:200

29

concrete is relatively small the continual expansion and contraction as the weather changes can lead to defects arising in the roof covering of even quite small buildings. As a result water penetrates and the damage can eventually prove to be quite extensive.

(4) Movements Arising from Shrinkage on Drying or Expansion on Wetting of Materials

All building materials alter in size on changes in their moisture content and everyone is familiar with the usual drying shrinkage. Normally movements are small enough to be repaired simply and it is seldom that anything serious arises.

Two examples in modern construction of damage arising from drying shrinkage are fairly common and concern brickwork built in sand lime or concrete bricks. Rapid drying under a hot sun can produce shrinkage cracks particularly at window or door openings in long walls, for example in continuous terrace construction, see Terrace "B", Figure 29. This is usually because the bricks were not matured before laying and were bedded in too strong a mortar mix. Once the cracking occurs and it is usually sudden, it will not occur again. It is a point to remember in diagnosis that shrinkage cracks in brickwork usually occur at regular intervals, with sand lime bricks about 6 feet (1·8m), but do not extend below damp course level where bricks remain wet and do not taper. Inner leaves of cavity walls built of the same type of brick, or concrete or breeze blocks can shrink and this can affect an outer leaf of clay bricks causing cracking where the two are bonded together around openings or in the areas of the wall tie fixings.

The Building Research Establishment has, however, recently established that some clay bricks expand when they are first wetted on leaving the kiln and that this has caused a substantial movement in newly built brickwork. Two instances are quoted showing vertical bulging in a brick panel restrained at top and bottom, the bulge being so severe that stability was impaired and the panel had to be rebuilt, and vertical cracking on new brickwork where two long walls were bonded to a short return, for example as in Terrace "C" on Figure 29.

Once the expansion has taken place, and it is safe to allow three months for this after construction, the movement will not increase and will not be repeated. It is a feature that cracks caused both by shrinkage on drying or expansion on wetting in brickwork tend to be of uniform size throughout and do not taper, unlike cracks due to other causes.

It is also considered that initial moisture expansion of this nature is probably the cause of oversailing at the corners at damp course level that sometimes takes place in new buildings and can fairly often be seen on older houses with an asphalt damp proof course which provides an ideal slip-joint for the purpose of overall movement of this nature. Clearly if there is restraint some cracking will occur and in new building with an initial severe crack and no subsequent movement the conclusion might be drawn that initial moisture expansion has been the cause.

As will be seen from the foregoing sections the symptoms of many of the causes are similar and it will be found in turn that they are similar to the effects produced by the movements described in the next section. This can make diagnosis difficult but not so difficult as it may seem at first sight because the symptoms have to be related to the age, character and quality of the building under review and the locality in which it is situated, information on which will give the necessary assistance towards the correct diagnosis. On the other hand the similarities will reinforce the advice given previously that even if a building has to be shored up, the necessary time should be taken to arrive at the correct diagnosis before repairs are commenced.

C. Defects Arising from Foundation Failures or Ground Movements

Initially all new buildings settle to a greater or lesser degree. The very operation of digging out the ground, compacting it in a manner which may be uniform or may not and then placing a substantial load on it is enough to induce slight movement as the ground below is compacted to a uniform degree to resist the loading. The aim in building is that the ground should be loaded to the same extent consistent with its bearing capacity throughout. For this reason loads are usually spread uniformly in the domestic construction under consideration on strip foundations in order to achieve this aim to limit such settlement to the initial compaction only. This is not always as simple to achieve as it sounds and the fact that buildings move and crack after they are built is hardly surprising in view of all the factors that can arise in soil conditions and constructional features.

Defects which arise in foundations or ground movements cause settlement which involves a subsidence of some sort. The settlement may be uniform, which is what normally happens for a short period after a building has been erected but unless it is very large it remains undetected and not important, or it may be differential where one part of the structure moves to a greater extent than the remainder. It is the differential settlement which causes most of the trouble with its tearing effect at the junction between the slower moving or stable portion and that portion really on the move. Differential settlement may occur to a recently constructed building or to an old building but in either case it is always essential to establish whether it is of a continuing nature or not or whether it is intermittent. If it is continuing something must be done to stop it. If it has stopped the damage can be examined with a view to repair. If it is intermittent it might be tolerated provided it is limited or alternatively steps may be taken to stop it.

Settlement is only the symptom and the cause must be found if satisfactory steps are to be taken to arrest a continuing or intermittent movement. If movement has ceased it is still often more than a matter of interest to know the cause.

Consideration of settlement has been deferred to this section because it is normally more expensive to deal with than other defects. It is suggested therefore that unless there are extremely good grounds for considering it to be involved the surveyor should first conclude on his investigation that none of the factors previously noted are at the root of the trouble. Cracks arising on settlement do sometimes take an identifiable form but so many other causes can give rise to cracks that it is highly inadvisable to jump to conclusions.

Most of this section will deal with settlement but it must not be forgotten that soil movements can involve an upward thrust, sometimes of an equally disturbing nature.

The principal causes of foundation defects and ground movements can be divided into five groups each covering a different aspect.

(1) *Overloading of Foundations*

The foundations of completed buildings are never seen until special digging is carried out and unless the building owner is a keen gardener he will not care a hoot what the sub-soil is like below his house. As long as everything is fine it does not matter whether a building has foundations in the modern sense of the term or not. It is sufficient that the walls stand up and support floors and roof. It comes as a surprise therefore to find that most buildings put up before the late 19th century have very little in the way of foundations apart from a couple of courses of footings laid on the earth.

Whatever foundations the building has, however, can become overloaded and this often happens when some form of alteration is carried out, a window is enlarged or a door formed which may result in a section of wall being removed and a consequentially larger load is transferred on to an adjacent section of brickwork which in itself might be in the form of a narrow pier. The foundation below as a result is overloaded and the pier settles. Courses of brickwork drop in relation to work on either side. Above the area affected the courses may take on a visible dip and window or door openings distort in a downwards direction towards the pier. If the condition progresses cracks may eventually appear.

Many other instances of overloading can be cited, for example the design of many 17th- and 18th-century buildings is based on fairly large windows divided by narrow piers, the foundations of which are often inadequate for the load. Again, the weight of the front wall of a Victorian terrace house is often carried on a beam over a bay window. The load is then transferred down through a pier between the bay window and the entrance door. The result is often settlement not only in the region of the entrance door but above the bay window as well.

(2) *Differential Settlement in Foundations*

When parts of a building are provided with different foundations and these foundations are probably at a different level it is inevitable that differential settlement will arise between the two parts. In many cases the difference is so slight as to be barely noticeable but many instances occur where fractures arise at the junction between the two sections.

The most common example concerns the bay window so beloved of estate developers since mid-Victorian times. These are often provided with such inadequate foundations and brickwork and with no tie at the top that they tilt forward to the extent of being a danger and large fractures are found at the junction of the bay and the front wall.

Another instance concerns the back additions also very popular in pre-1930 houses. At one time these were often built after the main part of the house had been allowed to settle particularly when a large estate was being developed, but with smaller estates there was not always time for this. If main building and back addition are well bonded together fractures appear and situations arise where part of the back addition side wall remains attached to the rear wall of the main part of the building, the fracturing taking place at the window and door openings in the back addition. As the party wall between terrace and semi-detached houses was usually built as one long length, very often the effect is more pronounced and dramatic on the party wall line between the two back additions.

On other occasions it may be found that there is either no bond between addition and main building and only a straight joint or alternatively the addition wall is built into a chase left in the rear wall of the main building with stout hoop iron cramps at every sixth course. The effects of differential settlement are much less damaging in such circumstances.

(3) *Undermining of Foundations*

Foundations can be undermined by various means, some natural and some induced by man.

Underground streams can wash away part of the soil below foundations causing extensive damage involving leaning walls and severe fractures. The same effects can arise from excessive leakage from drains, particularly if these run parallel and close to the base of a wall. Localised defects can arise from a severe leak in a gulley. In addition the layout of soakaway drains can cause problems in this respect and may need to be investigated. Sandy soils in particular are prone to this form of disturbance.

In areas with chalk and limestone forming the sub-strata, cavities in the ground can be formed by the action of underground water dissolving the rock. The top layer of soil then collapses into the cavity, particularly likely if the top soil is of sand, causing foundations to drop. The cavities are known as "swallow holes" and as water movement is necessary for their formation, drains for buildings in areas with this geological formation must be watertight and soakaway arrangements made well away from the building and below the level of the house should the house be on a hill.

Surveyors in mining regions will be familiar with the large settlement problem which exists in such areas as the ground subsides over the workings below. The approach of subsidence is heralded by a tilt of the property towards the area of the workings followed by a true settlement downwards when the ground subsides below the building. Considerable horizontal and vertical pressures will be encountered but sometimes a recovery to the near vertical, at a lower level occurs, providing the initial tilt is not too severe. Houses on reinforced rafts are likely to withstand the pressures best but those on strip foundations are likely to be severely affected. It is considered however that this problem will be so common in the area in which it occurs that there will be no problem in the diagnosis. The repair of the houses affected will be another matter however.

Excavation near a house can cause disturbance below ground to foundations in two ways. The sides of the excavation can be inadequately shored depriving the existing foundations of their support from adjoining ground. They may settle to one side causing a whole wall to lean out at an angle. In another way water flowing from below a building into an excavation nearby can carry the finer particles away allowing the soil below the existing foundations to compact at a lower level resulting in a differential settlement.

New foundation construction and building following excavation nearby may bring about troubles with the existing foundations of a building. Loads on the soil will increase and with clay soils further consolidation may occur. This could cause settlement to take place on the side of the house nearest the new building apart from differential settlement in the new building itself. Excavation and new foundations within 10 feet and 20 feet (3·04m and 6·1m) of an existing building are covered by the provisions of the London Building Acts (Amendment) Act 1939 Part VI Section 50, but outside London, Common Law applies so that a surveyor may well be called in after the work adjacent has been completed to investigate cracks and other matters.

The two preceding paragraphs involve questions of support and the rights of building owners to the support formerly existing to their buildings. The Common Law is reasonably clear on this aspect and it is doubtful that the building owner will fail to take the point that someone else is responsible for the damage to his house and should be made to pay for it. However, the surveyor may have to be prepared to contribute evidence to any action that might arise and assist the matter to a successful conclusion. His diagnosis, however, will need to be correct in the first place.

(4) Consolidation of Soil below Foundations

Ground below foundations can consolidate by its very nature if it consists of peat or silt containing a lot of organic matter which varies greatly in volume according to its water content. Such soils are very compressible and settle even without loading from strip foundations. Filled up ground is suspect unless it is known to have been filled in thin layers, carefully placed, of good material and well consolidated. Unfortunately such knowledge is usually lacking and uncontrolled and unconsolidated tipping arises leaving pockets which can settle under their own weight. Substantial differential settlements can arise in the foundations of houses built on made up ground if the foundations are of the strip type, a particular hazard at the present time when sites previously considered unsuitable are being brought into use.

The filling of ponds and ditches on a site used for building can give rise to similar difficulties if the material is not well consolidated.

(5) *Movement of Soil Below Foundations*

The most familiar instance of soil movement arises with shallow foundations placed in firm shrinkable clay soil. The clay expands when wet and shrinks in dry weather but site conditions govern the extent of the movement in that vegetation, particularly large bushes and trees, and the presence or absence of paving near the house affect the size of the seasonal change. As clay shrinks and expands both horizontally and vertically and the house itself protects the clay from drying immediately below, the tendency is for foundations to settle both downwards and away from the building resulting in the typical pattern of diagonal fractures occurring at window and door openings and the dropping away of corners and external walls. In wet seasons the cracks have a tendency to recover partially when the clay expands but they seldom close up completely as differential movement of other features and the accumulation of debris in the cracks prevents this.

The effect of normal shrinkage of firm clays is greatly enlarged by the presence of fast growing trees with shallow root systems such as poplars and elms. If such trees singly are within their height by way of distance from a building or within $1\frac{1}{2}$ times their height if in clumps or rows very serious seasonal movements can be expected. The pattern of cracks in the building remains the same however as for the movements normally associated with clay soil, although often substantially greater.

If mature trees on firm shrinkable clay have been felled to provide a cleared site for building and a house is subsequently erected on the site near to where they were originally, i.e. within the distances mentioned in the previous paragraph, there is a serious danger of a continuous swelling of the clay over a period of years. If the house is on strip foundations even at a depth of 3 ft. 6 in. (1·067m) normally considered satisfactory for this type of soil in the absence of vegetation other than grass, it is likely that the foundations will be lifted and differential movements will be apparent in the house, resulting in cracks and fractures. The Building Research Establishment found after seven years in such circumstances a movement upwards to the order of $1\frac{1}{2}$ inches (38·1mm). Cracking in such circumstances will take a reversed form as walls and corners are forced upwards. In a brick house the diagonal cracks may still be from the corners of windows but likely only below ground floor sill level and in the opposite direction to those which arise on settlement.

Building on sloping sites has its hazards and when sites are of clay there is danger of soil movement. It has been verified that clay soils tend to move downhill when the slope exceeds 1 in 10 even though the movement may be very slow indeed. However in old buildings evidence can exist of both total movement and differential settlement from this cause. The movement may be in part horizontal, for example in a building with an asphalt damp proof course, the structure below damp course level may move, leaving the remainder in its original position if restrained by adjoining structures, the damp course forming the slip joint.

Fairly recent research has indicated two further forms of movement which might affect external walls and prove difficult to diagnose satisfactorily. The first concerns new buildings and might arise before they are occupied. With buildings erected on fine sands, silt and chalk where the water table is close to ground level there have been cases of "frost heave" in the soil in very severe winters. The ground below floor slabs has lifted and expanded sideways causing the walls to crack horizontally and to tilt where the lower section is forced outwards. It is not considered that this could happen in an occupied dwelling or one newly built where the windows are glazed, but unheated garages, entrance porches and outhouses of existing occupied buildings could be affected if the conditions were right as these may only have concrete slabs to support the external walls or if foundations are provided, they are often at a much shallower depth than the foundations of the house. The second form of movement concerns the use of colliery shale or other sulphate containing hardcore or filling used below concrete slabs. Colliery shale while not only containing sulphates may also be incompletely burnt so that when wetted, it expands. The sulphates present in the hardcore or filling combined with the water present will attack the cement in the concrete slab causing it to expand. The slab may arch and crack but even so pressure will be exerted at the base of the external walls causing horizontal cracks and tilting as the base of the walls are forced out.

The similarity of the damage caused by "frost heave" and sulphate attack on a concrete floor slab will be obvious to the reader but the timing of the defect and the parts of the building affected should make correct diagnosis a reasonably straightforward matter for the surveyor.

We have now examined a wide range of possible causes for damage to brick walls and the similarity of many of the symptoms will be noted, all tending to confuse the diagnosis of the cause in some circumstances. The lines that the investigation will take depend on the circumstances but it is to be hoped that the reasons for suggesting the need for measurement of cracks, consideration of site conditions and the surrounding area, further investigation of sub-soil, drains and the like are now abundantly clear.

The symptoms of all these causes as we have seen are limited to leans, bulges, displacement and fractures in brickwork. Many causes but the symptoms falling into only four categories. Some symptoms can however be associated with a particular group of causes and this is perhaps truer in the case of settlements than with causes which arise above ground level. The pattern of symptoms for settlement and soil recovery with notes on the particular features of each are shown on Figures 30 and 31 with references to paragraphs (1) to (5) in this section for the possible causes. Two types of settlement are further related to buildings on Figures 32, 33 and 34. It is hoped that these figures might assist in reducing the scope of the investigation in certain circumstances. They can do no more than this as the surveyor must keep his mind open to all possibilities even if some can be dismissed early on in the investigation. There is great danger in, for example, taking a crack pattern in isolation and ascribing a cause to it without taking into account the other considerations which it is hoped have been stressed.

An analogy with the practice and of the terms used in the medical profession is considered to be particularly suitable in these circumstances. The structural survey might be likened to the medical examination before an insurance contract is agreed, the end product being the report on the building in the former case and the report on the person in the second. In the situation covered by this book however the patient is bothered by some trouble and seeks advice. The surveyor, as the doctor does, will ascertain the symptoms by examination and questioning and may have to undertake a further investigation, in the surveyor's case perhaps digging or cutting away, in the doctor's case possibly a minor exploratory operation, in order to diagnose the cause. Once this has been ascertained a prescription by the doctor and a specification by the surveyor can be prepared for a remedy.

In the case of damage to brick walls we have seen that the cause can be attributed more often than not to factors other than those concerned with the wall itself and remedies for these will be considered in the appropriate Chapters, for example roof spread in Chapter 5 on "Timber" and tree root damage on clay soil in Chapter 4 on "Foundations". With brick walls however we have now reached the stage of considering the repairs to be specified. Before these are examined in detail another medical analogy seems appropriate, depressing though it may sound. Is there any hope? Is the patient beyond the stage when a remedy can be prescribed or should he just be allowed to carry on his usual activities until he

Defects arising from foundation troubles or ground movements. Types of settlement. 1

References on possible causes to paragraphs in text

A. Uniform settlement

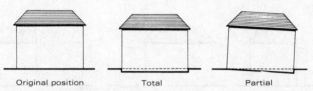

Original position   Total   Partial

Possible causes: see paragraphs (3), (4) and (5).
This form of settlement, when slight, often remains undetected
as there is no fracturing in the structure. Uniform settlement
usually occurs in all new buildings to some extent.

B. Differential settlement
   (1) Within a single structural unit

Original positon (a) Settlement in the ends (b) Settlement in the centre
                  of a wall with the centre of a wall with the ends
                  stable (see Figure 32).   stable (see Figures 33 and 34).
Possible causes: See paras (3), (4) and (5) See paras (1) and (3)

Differential settlement within a single structural unit always causes
fracturing giving rise to vertical or diagonal cracks. It is sometimes said that the origin of the settlement lies below the highest
point of a diagonal crack but while this is very often the case it is
not invariably so and confirmation must be sought elsewhere.
Cracks tend to follow a pattern consistent with the movement
of a part of the building as a whole and there is often a
rotational effect in panels of brickwork as they move about an
axis. With settlement in the ends of a wall cracks increase
in width with the height but with settlement in the centre of
a wall the cracks diminish in width with height. The formation
of cracks in an actual building is complicated by the planes
of weakness introduced by windows, doors and other constructional features so that careful consideration must
be given to the pattern of cracks and damage to ascertain
how the building would have had to move for such a pattern
to be produced. Note however the similarity in B (1) (a) above
and Figure 32 to cracks produced by defects in walls, particularly lack of restraint, or roof thrust, and in B (1) (b) and
Figures 33 and 34, the similarity to cracks produced by
soil recovery as shown at the foot of Figure 31.

30

Defects arising from foundation troubles or ground movements (continued)

Types of settlement 2

B. Differential settlement
   (2) Between structional units

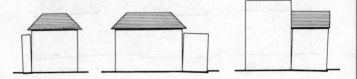

Possible causes: see paragraph (2).

Many houses are made up of more than one structural
unit. There is often a main structure with an addition
frequently of inferior design and construction. The connection
between the two units governs the type of damage which
results when differential settlement occurs and more use
of flexible joints rather than rigid connections would help to
reduce the fracturing commonly arising. Bonding, while it
provides some restraint, is not sufficiently strong to prevent
settlement occurring and although the bond might hold,
fracturing will occur at the first plane of weakness
usually in the addition at window openings but sometimes
in the main structure. Bay windows although often appearing to form part of the main structure are usually in the
form of a separate structural unit with thin walls and
shallow foundations.

Soil recovery
See paragraph (5)

Althou h the reverse of settlement, movement due to
soil recovery bears a marked resemblance in the pattern
of cracks formed to differential settlement in the ends
of a wall. There could be confusion between the two if no
account is taken of site conditions. As the ground swells
parts of a building are forced upwards and the
cracks which form diminish in width as the height
increases.

Examples of settlement 1

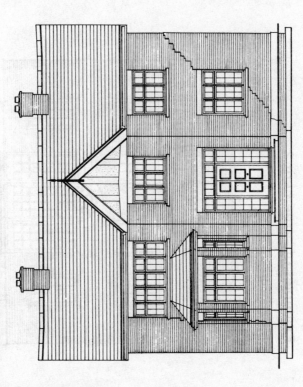

B (1) Differential settlement within a single structural unit
(a) Settlement in the ends of a wall with the centre stable.

In this example the flank walls have settled to an equal amount but the pattern of cracks varies at each end of the front wall. The crack on the right is merely interrupted by the window, but in fact extends round the opening as a gap between frame and brickwork. On the left however the large opening for the bay weakens the structure and allows the whole pier to move, resulting in a vertical fracture from bay to first floor window. There will probably be appreciable loss of bearing for the purlin in the roof space where the movement is at its maximum. Note that fractures increase in width with height.

Examples of settlement 2

B (1) Differential settlement within a single structural unit
(b) Settlement in the centre of a wall with the ends stable.

The removal of the central pier at ground floor level to form an enlarged opening has thrown additional weight on the piers on either side, the foundations as a result settling. Note that with this type of settlement, cracks diminish in width with height. In this example the cracks below the enlarged opening would not be visible unless the ground was excavated. A slate or blue brick d.p.c. if present would be fractured.

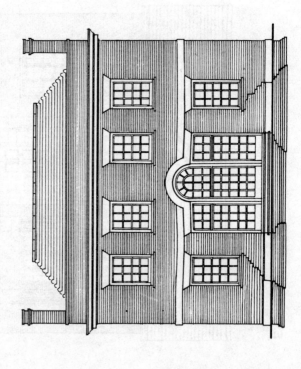

33

Examples of settlement 3

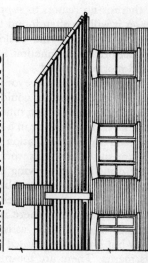
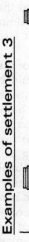

B (1) Differential Settlement within a single structural unit
(b) Settlement in the centre of a wall with the ends stable.

The provision of a large window and a door opening at ground floor level in the original construction of this example took little account of the loading from the roof and wall above. The pier between door and window is heavily overloaded. An asphalt d.p.c. provides a slip joint and in contrast to the previous examples the cracks appear in two separate sections, above and below the d.p.c. level and there is oversailing at the corner as a result of the movement. A badly leaking main drain running below the pier could produce the same result in an otherwise sound structure.

collapses? With buildings a collapse cannot be allowed to happen in view of the danger to all concerned, but economics may dictate a patching operation short of the ideal of demolishing and rebuilding a section and in extreme cases it may be necessary to demolish and clear a whole building. First however we must consider whether the brick wall that is being dealt with can be saved or whether it is in such an impaired state of stability that there is no alternative but to pull it down and rebuild.

PART 3. REPAIRS TO BRICK WALLS

A. Repairs to Solid Walls

(1) *Whole Wall Movements*

To establish whether a wall is in danger of collapse or not is not always an easy matter but the position of a surveyor called in for advice is such that he should be in no doubt in his own mind on the correctness of his decision.

In many cases it will be obvious that despite the presence of a lean or bulge the wall has been in that condition for many years and that provided no alterations likely to aggravate the position have been recently carried out or are proposed there is no reason to suppose that any change will occur. In such cases it will be often found that although some movement has occurred, features in the building providing restraint have continued to perform their function satisfactorily and the condition of bricks and mortar is sound.

On other occasions it will be perfectly obvious to the surveyor that if something is not done very quickly the consequences could be serious indeed in which case urgent steps to provide shoring must be taken at once. The presence of a substantial lean or bowing in a wall coupled with large fractures are perhaps an obvious indication and in such circumstances it will not only be the surveyor who is worried.

Other cases however present greater difficulty in arriving at a decision and to a great extent experience in these matters is probably the best guide. It is for this reason that the young and inexperienced surveyor should never hesitate to seek further advice. There is no disgrace in this. However some methods which might assist in forming a conclusion are discussed below but it must be stressed that each case should be considered on its merits. There are too many variable factors involved for hard and fast rules to be laid down.

If it has not already been done it is necessary in the first instance to raise ladders and plumb the wall from top to bottom at various intervals along its length and then to measure its total height and thickness at each floor level. This information will enable a scale section to be drawn through the wall at its worst point. If appropriate it may also be valuable to prepare a plan, if the wall is bowed horizontally, and to show on this the line of the bow also at its worst point. Information may also be noted on the drawings of the restraint, if any, provided by floors, the roof or intersecting partitions.

On considering the section of wall at its worst point and having very full regard to all the factors of age and condition which will be discussed more fully in this section coupled with the absence or presence of fractures some guidance might be obtained from the degree of lean. If this should exceed in the full height of the wall an amount equal to one third of the thickness at the base of the wall there are good grounds for considering that the wall is in danger of collapse. Applying this principle to a two-storey house with one-brick walls it can easily be appreciated and would be obvious on site that a lean of 3 inches (76mm) or more at the top of the wall would be distinctly alarming. In such circumstances demolition of the leaning wall must be advised in which case it would have to be rebuilt including foundations if necessary, in accordance with current requirements.

In many instances of damage to a building of the above order rebuilding will involve the whole wall but there are circumstances where it might be only necessary to rebuild the wall in part. Often it is in the thinner sections of a high wall towards the top where the greatest lean occurs in which case possibly only the top storey or two requires rebuilding. Similarly in a fairly long wall, the bond to walls at each end might act as sufficient restraint, leaving only the central section in need of rebuilding with, perhaps, a section at the top.

In considering the possibility of partial rebuilding in the Inner London area the authority of the District Surveyor under Section 138, Part XII of the London Building Acts (Amendment) Act 1939 must not be forgotten. This section provides that if a wall is demolished to an extent exceeding half its area, the District Surveyor can require the whole wall to be pulled down and rebuilt in accordance with the by-laws, if he considers it necessary. The District Surveyor will probably not make such a requirement if the remainder of the wall is satisfactory and on adequate foundations, but his authority is absolute in this respect, subject only to an appeal to the Superintending Architect of Metropolitan Buildings. The writers have never found a decision of the District Surveyor on this section other than absolutely reasonable in all respects and indeed a word here in regard to the District Surveyor might well be appropriate. The District Surveyors in London owe their authority to the Building Act of 1774 passed in George III's reign although they were not known by that title until the London Building Act of 1844. They are responsible for the safety of both new and old buildings in the Inner London area. Originally they were quite independent being answerable to Parliament only and although now housed and financially supported by the Greater London Council still exercise an independent control over all buildings and building operations, the only exclusions being the premises of the Council itself, those of the Crown, Sessions Houses and of the Inns of Court. As such they possess the widest of powers and a unique fund of knowledge covering the construction and the defects likely to arise in buildings of the London area. Accordingly it is very advisable for anyone dealing with structural repairs on buildings in London to approach the District Surveyor at an early date to discuss the problem. It is not the task of the District Surveyor to solve problems and prepare schemes of repair for owners and their advisers but a discussion of the problem with a viewpoint put forward on possible methods will often elicit valuable information based on the District Surveyor's wide experience. By the very nature of things the busiest private practitioner is unlikely to have anything like the same experience covering the repair of structures. In any event whatever method of structural repair is adopted it must have the District Surveyor's approval and it is far better to have this in principle well in advance than to be involved in alterations to the working programme at a later date. Such alterations are likely enough in the usual course of events, without omitting to take this elementary precaution.

Outside London, local authorities have a statutory duty under the Public Health Acts where the safety of a building is in question, for deciding what needs to be done and seeing that it is carried out in a similar manner as the District Surveyors under the Dangerous Structures procedure in London. It may well be that the same form of assistance can be obtained now in deciding what needs to be done but certainly in the past this was not always the case on repairs except in the largest and most progressive towns.

In considering whether a wall needs total rebuilding or not there is not much doubt in regard to the degree of leans and bulges. These affect the stability of a wall far more than extensive cracking. Stepped or slanting cracks impair stability in general far less than might be supposed, and it is considered that a crack of this type up to about 1-inch (25mm) wide does not reduce a wall's ability to carry vertical loads by more than about 30 per cent provided there is no more than a minimal amount of sideways movement. Even when damage appears to be severe, provided the bulk of the brick-work is soundly bonded together, the mortar is good and there is little transverse movement, repairs rather than rebuilding should be all that is necessary. The important factor to be considered is the function of the wall and its suitability to perform that function when viewed in relation to the building as a whole. It is always necessary to distinguish the function of the various walls in a building, which ones carry the bulk of the weight and whether the remainder merely enclose. Are those that carry the weight soundly designed and constructed or does the arrangement of the window and other openings mean that the weight is transferred to small disconnected lengths of brickwork? If so what can be done to even the load across the wall in relation to other repairs or is it possible to transfer some of the load elsewhere? What sort of support is given to the wall by other features such as chimney stacks, abutting walls and partitions?

In rebuilding a whole wall it must not be forgotten that the provision of foundations to comply with current regulations might have an effect on foundations to the walls that remain. The effect of the additional excavation should be considered; shoring of existing walls, even apart from the question of shoring to take the weight of features formerly supported by the wall to be demolished, should be carefully investigated. In the design of foundations for the new wall an endeavour should be made to avoid the need for under-pinning adjacent walls which would arise if the new foundations are at a lower level than the old. This can sometimes be achieved by putting in wider foundations to spread the load over a greater area of the sub-soil but this may not always be possible if the sub-soil is poor, leaving no alternative but to underpin the remaining walls.

The re-use of old bricks in rebuilding a wall or part of a wall has much to commend it as there is nothing worse than seeing rebuilt walls or sections of old mellowed buildings patched up with Fletton bricks. Tests carried out on sections of walls built with re-used bricks show that the completed work is at least equal in strength to that of work with new bricks of a similar type. In order to re-use the old bricks it is usually necessary for the original wall to have been built in lime mortar, as cleaning off cement mortar is difficult and usually involves too much damage to the bricks. If old bricks from elsewhere have to be brought in, care should be taken to match up as near as possible to the existing bricks elsewhere in the building. Bricks with unequal suction, any contaminated by soot, old plaster unless this can easily be cleaned off, chemicals or those marked by efflorescence should be avoided. In laying, the re-used bricks should be wetted and mortar, whatever that used on the existing walls, should not be stronger than 1:1:6 cement, lime, sand by volume. A stronger mortar is likely to lead to cracking between old and new work and a weaker mortar may compress to permit courses to settle in relation to existing work, besides being more liable to excessive weathering on the outer face.

Admittedly at a time when labour costs are high in relation to the cost of materials and the work of cleaning old bricks both hard and boring, the temptation to buy new bricks will be considerable, particularly when the contractor is consulted, who will immediately think of the effect on his labour force of instructions to clean off vast quantities of old bricks. However the surveyor should persevere for the effect of the completed work will be much more satisfactory, even if the cost is a little more.

We are now left in this section with a decision on what to do with a whole wall that has a tilt of something less than the maximum that can be allowed for safety. If the lean is something to the order of less than half the maximum then there is good authority for suggesting leaving things as they are as no repair is usually needed on structural grounds alone, always provided of course that any thrust from above or movement below ground causing the tilt has been remedied. This might be expressed in regard to a 9-inch (229mm) wall in the average two-storey house on the same basis as previously set out as a lean of about $\frac{3}{4}$ inch (19mm) over a storey height or $1\frac{1}{2}$ inches (38mm) overall. The Building Research Station have expressed the view that no repair is normally needed on walls that are out of plumb by no more than 1 inch (25·4mm) in the average storey height so that there would certainly seem to be no risk in leaving a wall with this degree of tilt. On the other hand walls can have a tilt in excess of this amount although still not be in danger of collapse in which case some form of strengthening is necessary.

Before considering the type of strengthening or tieing-in which is to be adopted, some additional factors need to be taken into account as they might well influence a decision in view of the limited number of methods which are available for this purpose and the inherent character of each. These factors are as follows:

(a) The condition of the wall:
If there are cracks, loose areas of brickwork or a preponderance of poor bricks tieing-in or strengthening might involve more disturbance and make these conditions worse so that rebuilding might prove more advisable.

(b) The possibility of vibration:
Should the building be particularly subject to vibration, unlikely in the ordinary course of events for domestic premises but possible where domestic buildings are in use for other purposes, such as a hotel, club or as offices, or there is severe vibration from passing

128

traffic or underground railways, tieing-in for example to floors would be unwise and would be likely to cause much displacement subsequently around the fixing of the ties in the brickwork.

(c) The effect of the appearance of the proposed work:
It is an undoubted fact that the appearance of a leaning wall and ties will put off many a purchaser and even more likely the Building Society surveyor, even if the tieing-in is successful. This is particularly so in areas where subsidence is not normal and tieing-in relatively rare. There are times when a client looking to the future might decide that it was well worthwhile to pay the additional cost of rebuilding if the leaning or bulged wall and the proposed work were to stand out like a sore thumb. This might be particularly so if there was the slightest element of doubt as to the success of the proposals.

Similar appearance considerations also apply to the other methods of supporting a leaning or bulged wall set out below, namely with a buttress or piers or by thickening. It is very seldom indeed that a buttress or piers can be so arranged that they look naturally part of the building or "fit in" as an architectural feature. There is the difficulty also of matching bricks so that more often than not an applied buttress or piers stand out brightly for all to see and form the unfortunately correct conclusion. It might well be considered that the use of methods for tieing-in or propping up are more appropriate to extending for perhaps a reasonably foreseeable time a building the days of which are numbered in any event on grounds of future clearance or redevelopment.

There are available only two recognised methods of supporting a leaning brick wall and these are as follows:

(1) To tie in the wall with a system of metal tie rods and plates or channels, or to form concrete anchorages in the wall for tie rods, the tie rods passing through floors and the roof structure to be securely anchored to a wall on the opposite side of the house which is stable or tending to move in the opposite direction, or alternatively to a sound structural member internally.

(2) To strengthen the wall either (a) by building a buttress, or buttresses provided that these can be founded on stable ground and be securely tied in to the leaning wall so that any thrust exerted by the buttress can be certain to be against the direction of lean of the wall. At all costs the building of a buttress which settles away from the wall must be avoided as this will only aggravate the trouble. Alternatively (b) a wall can be strengthened by the provision of piers or by thickening.

As to (1) above there is a long tradition of tieing-in buildings with rods and metal plates and many readers will be familiar with the

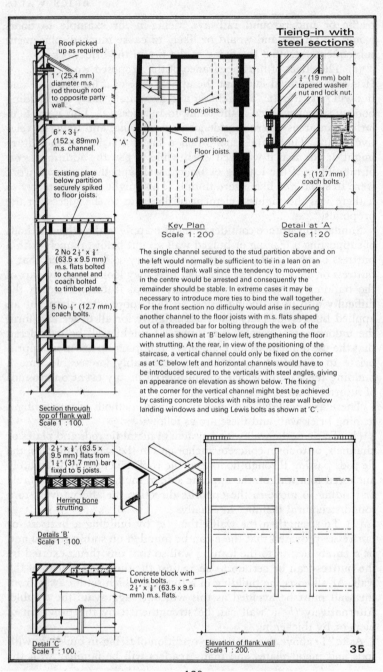

Tieing-in with steel sections

Roof picked up as required.

1″ (25.4 mm) diameter m.s. rod through roof to opposite party wall.

6″ x 3½″ (152 x 89mm) m.s. channel.

Existing plate below partition securely spiked to floor joists.

2 No 2½″ x ⅜″ (63.5 x 9.5 mm) m.s. flats bolted to channel and coach bolted to timber plate.

5 No ½″ (12.7 mm) coach bolts.

Section through top of flank wall.
Scale 1 : 100.

Key Plan
Scale 1 : 200

Floor joists.

Stud partition.

Floor joists.

'A'

Detail at 'A'
Scale 1 : 20

¾″ (19 mm) bolt tapered washer nut and lock nut.

½″ (12.7 mm) coach bolts.

The single channel secured to the stud partition above and on the left would normally be sufficient to tie in a lean on an unrestrained flank wall since the tendency to movement in the centre would be arrested and consequently the remainder should be stable. In extreme cases it may be necessary to introduce more ties to bind the wall together. For the front section no difficulty would arise in securing another channel to the floor joists with m.s. flats shaped out of a threaded bar for bolting through the web of the channel as shown at 'B' below left, strengthening the floor with strutting. At the rear, in view of the positioning of the staircase, a vertical channel could only be fixed on the corner as at 'C' below left and horizontal channels would have to be introduced secured to the verticals with steel angles, giving an appearance on elevation as shown below. The fixing at the corner for the vertical channel might best be achieved by casting concrete blocks with nibs into the rear wall below landing windows and using Lewis bolts as shown at 'C'.

2½″ x ⅜″ (63.5 x 9.5 mm) flats from 1¼″ (31.7 mm) bar fixed to 5 joists.

Herring bone strutting.

Details 'B'
Scale 1 : 100.

Concrete block with Lewis bolts.
2½″ x ⅜″ (63.5 x 9.5 mm) m.s. flats.

Detail 'C'
Scale 1 : 100.

Elevation of flank wall
Scale 1 : 200.

35

discs, crosses and "S" shaped features in cast or wrought iron on old buildings. The tendency nowadays is to favour the use of steel rods and channel sections, used horizontally and also vertically if conditions warrant as shown on Figure 35. Undoubtedly these exert a greater restraining influence than the older plates but it must be remembered that the principle is to tighten the ties securely in position and not to overtighten. There must be no pressure on the brickwork as the intention is not to pull it back into position but merely to restrain it. The suspicion that originally plates were overtightened is sometimes aroused when one finds plates put in some years ago which have tended to pull through the brickwork. On no account should steel cables be used in lieu of tie-rods as these can be extremely dangerous if overtightened.

The method of passing the tie-rods through a floor is more practicable when the floor joists are running in the same direction as the run of the rods but more often the need arises to tie in a wall where the joists are parallel to the wall. Also one of the most frequent cases arises in the end of terrace house where the exposed flank wall is the one that needs attention. It is not usually possible in the circumstances to tie in to the opposite party wall as apart from the disturbance involved to the neighbour who may not even allow it let alone welcome it, invariably joists in houses of this type are running from front to rear. Figure 35 shows the fixing of steel channels in such circumstances but in some cases the methods of anchoring walls shown in British Standard Code of Practice C.P.111:1964 are also useful. These involve the use of steel flats with a minimum section of $2\frac{1}{2}$ by $\frac{3}{8}$ inches (63·5 by 9·5mm) securely fastened to at least four joists or if joists are let into the wall for a distance of about 3 to 4 feet (0·9 to 1·2m). The ends of the steel flats are ragged or otherwise securely fixed and set in a concrete block 9 inches (229mm) deep and about 2 ft. 3 in. (686mm) long which is cast in a section of the wall cut away for the purpose. The Code of Practice recommends that such anchors be provided for restraint purposes at intervals of about 6 feet (1·8m) in buildings of one or two storeys and at intervals of 4 feet (1·2m) in all storeys for buildings exceeding two storeys. The form of tie illustrated on Figure 36 is suitable also for use with flat roofs and also with pitched roofs subject to suitable conditions.

The use of ties of the type recommended by the Code of Practice for repair work requires precautions to ensure that the floor joists to which the anchors are fixed are themselves secured in position. With joists at right-angles to the wall there is little point in screwing the anchors to joists unless these in turn are well secured to a wallplate at their far ends, and thus adequately built in. If joists are parallel to the wall then the surveyor should be satisfied that the

131

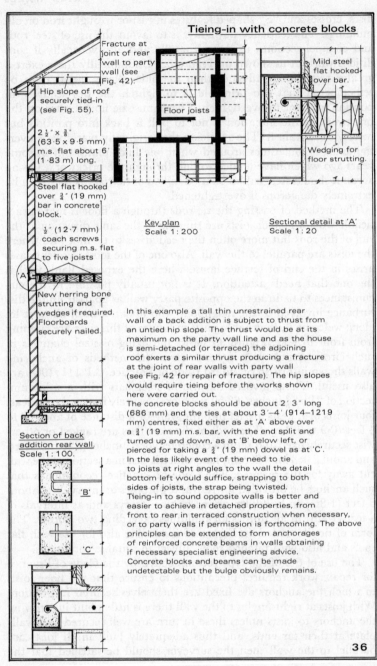

Tieing-in with concrete blocks

Fracture at joint of rear wall to party wall (see Fig. 42).

Hip slope of roof securely tied-in (see Fig. 55).

$2\frac{1}{2}'' \times \frac{3}{8}''$ (63·5 x 9·5 mm) m.s. flat about 6' (1·83 m) long.

Floor joists

Mild steel flat hooked over bar.

Steel flat hooked over $\frac{3}{4}''$ (19 mm) bar in concrete block.

$\frac{1}{2}''$ (12·7 mm) coach screws securing m.s. flat to five joists

'A'

New herring bone strutting and wedges if required. Floorboards securely nailed.

Wedging for floor strutting.

Key plan
Scale 1: 200

Sectional detail at 'A'
Scale 1: 20

Section of back addition rear wall.
Scale 1: 100.

'B'

'C'

In this example a tall thin unrestrained rear wall of a back addition is subject to thrust from an untied hip slope. The thrust would be at its maximum on the party wall line and as the house is semi-detached (or terraced) the adjoining roof exerts a similar thrust producing a fracture at the joint of rear walls with party wall (see Fig. 42 for repair of fracture). The hip slopes would require tieing before the works shown here were carried out.

The concrete blocks should be about 2' 3" long (686 mm) and the ties at about 3'–4' (914–1219 mm) centres, fixed either as at 'A' above over a $\frac{3}{4}''$ (19 mm) m.s. bar, with the end split and turned up and down, as at 'B' below left, or pierced for taking a $\frac{3}{4}''$ (19 mm) dowel as at 'C'. In the less likely event of the need to tie to joists at right angles to the wall the detail bottom left would suffice, strapping to both sides of joists, the strap being twisted.

Tieing-in to sound opposite walls is better and easier to achieve in detached properties, from front to rear in terraced construction when necessary, or to party walls if permission is forthcoming. The above principles can be extended to form anchorages of reinforced concrete beams in walls obtaining if necessary specialist engineering advice.

Concrete blocks and beams can be made undetectable but the bulge obviously remains.

36

joists themselves are in good condition and of sufficient size. It will usually be necessary to introduce herring bone strutting if this is not present to stiffen the floor for the purpose.

The Code of Practice indicates that a wall may be assumed to be provided with adequate lateral restraint if the construction providing the support is capable of resisting the sum of the following assumed lateral forces:

(i) The simple static reactions to the total applied horizontal forces at the point of lateral support.

(ii) $2\frac{1}{2}$ per cent of the total vertical load that the wall is carrying at the point of lateral support.

If there is any doubt that the proposed anchorage does not fulfil this requirement then the services of an engineer should be engaged to investigate the matter and make the necessary calculations.

The use of the metal anchors secured to floor joists and set in concrete blocks in the wall means that these are at least not visible although of course the tilt on the wall may be still very obvious. On the other hand this form of tieing-in is probably not so effective as the use of long tie-rods fixed to another wall and channel sections. The latter are the most economical as for the smaller cost a more effective tieing-in can be achieved. With judicious arranging in regard to position, wrapping the channels in expanded metal lathing and rendering over, they can sometimes be disguised so that on an old property they appear as moulded band courses, pilasters and cornices.

There are occasions when tieing-in can be very difficult to arrange and in extreme cases impossible. A case presenting particular difficulties arises in a weak flank end of terrace wall where the staircase is positioned against the flank wall. Usually the front half of the wall can be tied as rooms are usually arranged across the property at the front but towards the rear where the staircase rises, it often is very difficult to tie in to floors because of headroom difficulties. A possible solution is shown on Figure 35, but much would depend on suitable circumstances and in such cases the combination of tieing-in the front section and providing a buttress at the rear may be all that can be done short of rebuilding. Often however there will be insufficient room even for a buttress and rebuilding may be the only alternative.

Mention has been made in the previous paragraph of insufficient room for a buttress and this is more often than not the reason why the provision of a buttress or buttresses has to be discounted. When occasions arise when they can be employed they require proper design and detailing, careful selection of the bricks and the provision of a good foundation to ensure that the buttresses provide an

133

inclined support against the defective wall and a counter-thrust. They are, however, expensive.

Proper bonding of the new buttress to an old wall is most essential. There are a number of different ways in which this can be done, governed to a great extent by the bond and the condition of the existing wall. Block bonding can be carried out at intervals or if the old brickwork and jointing is soft, alternate courses can be cut away. If the buttress is to be built at a rake, as shown on Figure 37, where the new bricks enter the old wall at an angle great care must be taken to fill up the spaces with mortar well rammed in. The top of the buttress should be finished by one or other of the traditional methods either by bonding in flush at the top, by splayed off-sets or by "tumbling" the top courses.

In building up a buttress it is important that the work should not proceed too fast as there is bound to be some settlement in the new work. The slower it is carried out the less will be the amount of settlement. Reinforcement by the use of galvanised iron or steel cramps is desirable if the work has to be completed quickly, together with the use of quick setting mortar.

Raking buttresses and buttresses in stepped form are often found to be more useful for dealing with bulged conditions in retaining walls rather than in supporting leaning or bulged walls in buildings, being cheaper than thickening the wall. The same considerations apply however in their design and construction as described above.

Occasionally it will be found possible in the case of two neighbouring properties which are similarly defective to provide a form of flying buttress spanning between the two. This will often be satisfactory where insufficient room exists to buttress one building only. Sometimes adjoining owners can be persuaded to co-operate in such repair work to the advantage of both and this solution is particularly appropriate where an estate of houses is in one ownership. Flying buttresses of this sort with archways and some care and attention to detailing on the front elevation can often be made to "fit in" very suitably with the general design of the buildings.

The principle of the flying buttress is also usefully adapted to provide support for the pavement retaining wall of the front area of many inner suburban houses with basements of the 18th and 19th centuries. Swelling of old wood block road construction and heavy traffic often forces these walls out of upright and provided they are not unduly cracked and fissured, when rebuilding would be more appropriate, they are capable of support from a series of arches spanning between the main wall of the building and the top of the retaining wall.

We have considered the methods of dealing with whole wall

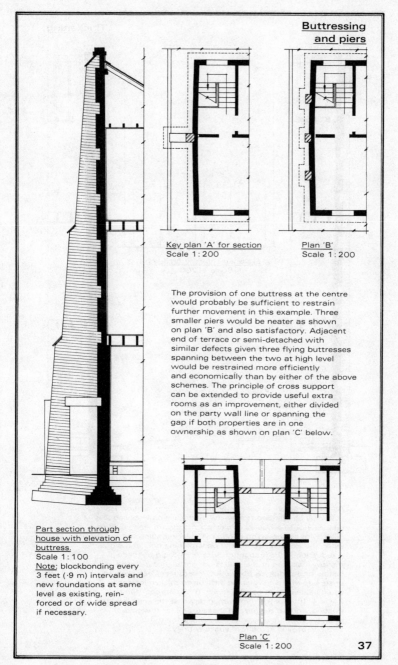

Buttressing and piers

Key plan 'A' for section
Scale 1 : 200

Plan 'B'
Scale 1 : 200

The provision of one buttress at the centre would probably be sufficient to restrain further movement in this example. Three smaller piers would be neater as shown on plan 'B' and also satisfactory. Adjacent end of terrace or semi-detached with similar defects given three flying buttresses spanning between the two at high level would be restrained more efficiently and economically than by either of the above schemes. The principle of cross support can be extended to provide useful extra rooms as an improvement, either divided on the party wall line or spanning the gap if both properties are in one ownership as shown on plan 'C' below.

Part section through house with elevation of buttress.
Scale 1 : 100
Note: blockbonding every 3 feet (·9 m) intervals and new foundations at same level as existing, reinforced or of wide spread if necessary.

Plan 'C'
Scale 1 : 200

37

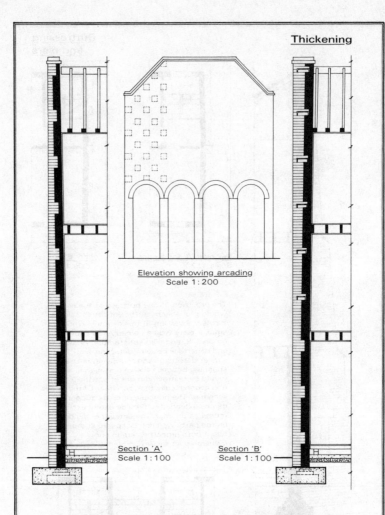

Elevation showing arcading
Scale 1 : 200

Section 'A'
Scale 1 : 100

Section 'B'
Scale 1 : 100

As an alternative to demolition and rebuilding, a badly leaning
wall may be restored to stability by thickening involving less
disturbance to occupied property. An outward lean could be
dealt with as shown on Section 'A', blockbonding to the existing
as on the elevation above and underpinning new and old work.
A reduction in the amount of brickwork could be made if
the lower section of the wall is upright by using piers and
beams or arcading as above. An inward lean, less likely to
arise, but where it would be difficult to thicken internally,
could be dealt with as on Section 'B'. Rustproof cramps,
$2\frac{1}{2}$" × $\frac{3}{8}$" (63·5 × 9·5 mm) turned down at the ends hold the
existing work to the new. In these examples it would
probably be more convenient to rebuild the top
sections of wall in the roof space entirely.

38

movements which involve a lean or tilt over most of the area of the wall but there are occasions where whole walls move but where they remain upright. This can happen where there is horizontal movement on the damp proof course and occurs in particular where buildings are provided with asphalt for this purpose. The movement can involve a slip of the whole structure above damp proof course level of an even amount all round leaving the foundations and walls below damp proof course level in their original position. The opposite can happen in certain circumstances of soil movement as we have already stated. Often the movement is sufficiently slight not to warrant any action beyond raking out the joint where movement has taken place and repointing. The Building Research Establishment suggest that where movement of this nature exceeds $1\frac{1}{2}$ inches (38mm) new brickwork bonded to the existing below damp course level can be added and taken down to foundation level. This is illustrated at the top of Figure 39, and as shown can be done whichever way the direction of the slip occurs.

Tests carried out by the Building Research Establishment have indicated that where a wall moves transversely, the load bearing capacity of the wall remains proportional to the area still actually loaded. Accordingly a one brick wall moving 3 inches (76mm) off its support below damp course level would still retain about two-thirds of its original strength. As has been mentioned before, the loads carried in normal two storey domestic construction are very low and one brick thickness is usually required only because of the need for weather-proofing and heat insulation. As such, movements up to $1\frac{1}{2}$ inches (38mm) are of no consequence structurally and even above this amount it is considered that from the pure aspect of vertical loading the suitability of the wall to carry the loads in domestic construction is hardly impaired. However the appearance of movement to the order of or in excess of $1\frac{1}{2}$ inches (38mm) can be alarming and the visual re-assurance of the repair illustrated will be a comfort to the owner. Movement of this nature usually arises in houses built after 1900 when asphalt began to be used as a damp proof course, so that the repair is entirely suitable having regard to the fact that such houses usually have adequate foundations and consequently the whole of the loading can be transferred back on to those foundations.

It is of course seldom that the upper part of the house will move entirely in this way without causing other damage. Cracking in brickwork may well arise, the tie of roof timbers may be damaged and floors partially deprived of their support. Accordingly much other work will probably have to be carried out which will be covered by the other chapters of this book.

137

Repair to the base of a wall where movement takes place on "slip" joint of asphalt or sheet d.p.c.

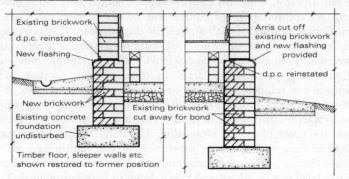

Existing brickwork

d.p.c. reinstated

New flashing

New brickwork

Existing concrete foundation undisturbed

Timber floor, sleeper walls etc. shown restored to former position

Arris cut off existing brickwork and new flashing provided

d.p.c. reinstated

Existing brickwork cut away for bond

Failure in the abutment of an arch

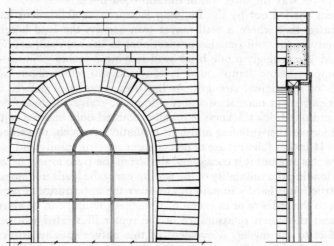

A semi-circular arched opening near a corner requires an abutment of about three quarters the span. In this example the inadequate abutment is showing signs of progressive failure. Rebuilding the abutment as before alone will not suffice. Sometimes the abutment can be enlarged by a buttress but this is not always possible or acceptable. In the same way that rough relieving arches were used over stone lintels in the past so a reinforced concrete lintel can be introduced to assist this brick arch. Built in above the arch and tailed down into the abutment it will transfer the load above the arch vertically downwards and so stabilise the construction. The lintel need not show if a rustproof angle is built in to support the facing skin of brickwork.

Scale 1 : 40

39

138

There are specialist firms who are prepared to undertake work which involves the jacking up and returning to their original position of whole buildings which have moved. If the subsidiary damage is relatively slight such a method might well warrant consideration. Specialist engineering advice, however, would be necessary and it would be preferable for this to be obtained on an independent consultant basis. Clearly with a building not based on framed construction the difficulties of such a method are considerable and much would depend on the soundness of the brickwork in general and its bonding and jointing material. Such work, however, has been successfully carried out.

(2) *Subsidiary Wall Movements*

Movements in parts only of walls present somewhat different problems but again before repairs or renewals are carried out to the brickwork, full steps must be taken to ascertain the cause and the brickwork must be relieved of the thrust or pressure which is causing the lean or bulge or adequately supported from below if the cause of the movement is a settlement of some sort depriving the brickwork of its support.

The causes of subsidiary movements in walls are basically the same as those for whole wall movements although of course the effects are limited either in extent or confined to particular sections of the wall. There are however some additional causes which will effect localised areas only. In repeating the list which appeared in Part 2 of this Chapter, comments will be added as appropriate for more localised situations.

Defects arising from Conditions above ground level concerning Types of Construction and Materials Involved

Localised defects arising from inadequacy of design might again consist of roof thrust if limited to only part of a wall, overloading from beams and other point loads, decay failure of wood lintels in pre-20th-century buildings, failure of arches due to inadequate abutments, eccentric loading from heavy ornamental members, poor bonding between walls and poor bonding between thicknesses in a wall, differential movements caused by shrinkage of materials drying out and expansion of materials on becoming wet and movements arising out of chemical changes, usually expansion on corrosion of metals and sulphate attacks on mortar.

Defects Arising from Foundation Troubles or Ground Movements

In this connection localised defects might occur where inadequate foundations are provided below a pier or a bay window. Differential settlement resulting from shrinkage of clay sub-soils below shallow foundations can arise according to ground conditions and the action of vegetation. See Part 2 of this Chapter and Chapter 4 for a sub-division of the various categories and remedies.

Although remedies for movements below ground level can satis-factorily be left for detailed study as a group in Chapter 4 it will be necessary to deal with some of the items relating to construction in this section of Part 3 of this Chapter as the components involved in the movement are incorporated in the brick walls and when defective have to be replaced sometimes in a different form. First of all however there is the basic factor of safety to consider in relation to the subsidiary wall movements which govern whether the wall is capable of repair, whether the defective section needs complete rebuilding or whether it can be left alone. We have already men-tioned the Building Research Establishment's advice that a wall no more than one inch out of plumb in a storey height can be considered satisfactory on the grounds of stability but this advice is extended to include a bulge in a wall of not more than $\frac{1}{2}$ inch (12mm) in the same height. This may sound as though it is not very noticeable but when it is seen as a gap at the side of a window opening between the brickwork and the frame it can appear quite large and is probably where most owners first notice a bulge, usually seen when windows are being cleaned. A word of warning is appropriate here so as to avoid any confusion between a true defect in the wall and one merely arising from displacement of the window frame due to war-time blast from a bomb explosion. An examination of the frame and architrave from the interior will often distinguish the two symptoms. In the case of war damage the effect will be noticeable on other windows of the building as well.

There are many cases where bulges of this extent exist and owners become worried. More often than not they occur in rela-tively narrow piers between windows or sometimes below point loads which are not adequately distributed. Provided the bulge is not progressively increasing and in old buildings it is often not, then nothing need be done except for repointing the gap to keep the weather out and to prevent damp attacking the window frame. It would only be necessary to investigate further if the gap should open more but even then provided the cause of the movement was dealt with promptly little further would be required apart from additional pointing which might then be completed with an oil-based mastic applied with a gun. It is important in such pointing that the whole of the gap between frame and brickwork be filled as otherwise constant use of the window will cause the pointing to fall out.

A further cause of bulging arises with the use of bonding timbers in buildings erected before 1900. The theory behind bonding timbers is sensible enough in that besides providing a fixing for panelling their use, in combination with continuous wallplates, often of substantial size supporting both floors and roof, provided a continuity of framing which tended to hold a wall together. Unfortunately most of these timbers, particularly those at high level, are near the outer face of the wall and, as a result, over the years, being buried in the brickwork and covered over by plaster or panelling, they become damp and eventually disintegrate. The courses of brickwork above the bonding timber as a result are partially deprived of their support and sag and any through bricks before snapping tend to cause a disruptive influence on the remaining sections of the outer leaf. Defective bonding timbers must obviously be cut out but renewal must be carried out in different material to avoid a repetition of the trouble. Replacement of the bonding timbers in brick, without reinforcement, which is so convenient and which is so often done, takes no account of the continuity formerly provided. Replacement in reinforced concrete is far more appropriate in the circumstances. With heavy beams supporting floors and roofs, the tieing-in to cross beams, partition walls and at angles is vitally important to re-establish continuity. Suggested methods to achieve these aims are shown on Figure 40.

Again, in buildings dating from before 1900 the use of timber lintels over window and door openings was almost universal. Although more substantial timbers were used than those for bonding purposes such timbers are even more often within $4\frac{1}{2}$ inches (119mm) of the external wall face and as such liable to decay through moisture penetration and sometimes, in addition, to woodworm and weevil attack. Settlement in the arches, cracks or uneven courses of brickwork above the windows are invariably due to a defective wood lintel which on failing transfers some of its burden to the arch which in turn fails. Sometimes the brickwork above if not unduly loaded itself will act as an arch for a while provided also that the opening is not too wide but in the end this will settle downwards. The substitution of reinforced concrete is once again the remedy with the provision of a metal angle to support the arch if it is flat or a curved arch bar if the arch is of gauged construction. If the arch has settled badly it may be necessary to dismantle the arch and reset the bricks.

Sometimes the failure of an arch is due to the failure of the abutment which is inadequate to take the thrust. A typical example is a

141

Reinforced concrete as a replacement for built in timber

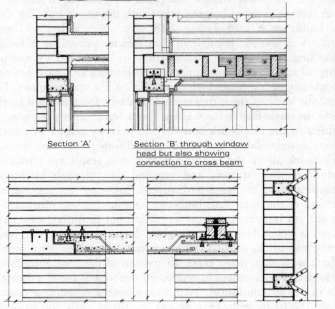

Section 'A'

Section 'B' through window
head but also showing
connection to cross beam

Elevation with facing brick skin removed.

Section 'C'

In houses built since about 1850 the replacement of defective
timber lintels with concrete is a relatively simple matter as
shown at Section 'A'. The arch may need taking down and resetting
if badly fractured and settled. Figure 24 shows construction
typical of many houses built prior to 1850 where much
reliance was placed on a rigid horizontal frame built in at
each floor level to stiffen the external walls, the peripheral
beam forming a continuous lintel above the windows. The
replacement of sections of the peripheral member with concrete
lintels and new brickwork in the piers would break the continuity of the frame. Either the whole frame has to be renewed
in concrete with continuous joints or alternatively a lengthening
joint must be made between remaining sections of the beam and
the new concrete with top and side metal plates as shown above left
on the elevation. The connection between the peripheral and
cross beams must also be maintained and a method is shown
on Section 'B' and on the right of the elevation above. The
end of the cross beam is assumed also defective and shown
repaired.
Defective bond timbers should also be replaced with reinforced concrete in earlier construction, to a larger size if
necessary, all joints being continuous and steel straps
cast in to be attached to timbers of partitions abutting
external walls as shown on Section 'C'.

Scale 1:40

40

door or window opening too near the corner of a building. The brickwork on the corner is pushed out and the arch drops as a result, see Figure 39. More often than not the condition is not serious as the movement relieves the pressure. However, if it is desired to effect a repair in more serious cases or for the sake of appearance then there is little point in restoring previous conditions by rebuilding in an identical form. In this case it would be more suitable to replace the arch with a reinforced concrete lintel. If it is essential to replace the arch, however, then it would be necessary to provide a buttress on the corner so as to strengthen the corner sufficiently to take the thrust exerted by the reinstated arch. If the opening is at ground floor level a buttress of this nature might be provided in the form of a screen wall or gate pier as an architectural feature. Another different method of overcoming this problem, more satisfactory in many respects, is by the provision of a reinforced concrete relieving lintel positioned above the arch so as to transfer the load formerly carried by the arch vertically on to the abutment, as illustrated at the bottom of Figure 39.

In replacing timber lintels the rule of thumb sizes can be adopted, 6 inches (152mm) deep for openings up to 4 feet (1·2m) and 9 inches (229mm) deep for openings not exceeding 6 feet (1·8m) wide with a $\frac{3}{8}$ inch (9·5mm) mild steel bar hooked and cranked at the ends for each $\frac{1}{2}$ brick wall thickness. For openings in excess of 6 feet (1·8m) it may be necessary to calculate the size of the lintel and the amount of reinforcement required. A more than usual bearing on each side is often helpful to tie the sides of the brick opening together. Mention of reinforced concrete lintels introduces the case where such components are badly made as they often are on estate work in modern housing with little or no control over site conditions. Concrete for both in-situ and pre-cast units can be mixed and placed in such a way that the mix at the top of the lintel or beam is far richer than that at the soffit. Differential shrinkage can cause some distortion both in the lintel and the surrounding brickwork and subsequent wetting can increase the movement. Such movements are relatively slight, however, and not likely to be progressive so that cracks and displaced brickwork can be made good as described subsequently in Section C of this part of the Chapter. There is however a possibility of further movement if the mix to the lower section of concrete allows damp to penetrate setting up some corrosion in the steel reinforcement. Eventually the concrete may crack and spall and it may be thought that this is serious when it is seen that the reinforcement is rusty. However the strength of the lintel is unlikely to be affected and it is sufficient to remove all loose sections of concrete including any that look as though they will probably be

143

affected in the same way, coat the reinforcement with cement paint and reform using a stiff mix of 1:2 cement and coarse sand mixed to a stiff paste. All dirt should be well washed from the old concrete and the surface hacked or undercut to form a key. In addition 12-gauge copper wire can be twisted round the existing reinforcement to improve the key, the ends being set and bedded in holes cut for the purpose in the old concrete. Calcium chloride at 2 per cent by weight of cement can be added to the mixing water to increase the speed of set but the patching should be covered and protected for seven days to allow it to cure. The possible attack of the calcium chloride on reinforcement in these circumstances is considered a reasonable chance to take as such attack is not progressive and an early set is required for patching work of this nature in order to be at all useful for dealing with such defects in concrete. If there is undue wetting of the lintel by rain, however, it would be advisable to reduce the incidence of this if possible. In the case of a lintel the provision of some form of hood mould along the top exposed edge is useful. Patching of this nature to concrete work is a little unsightly, so that it may be desirable to apply a coat of cement paint to the whole of the exposed surface of concrete on completion.

Iron and steel sections which are embedded in brickwork require exposing if there is deformation or loosening of the brickwork in the area. Providing the metal remaining is substantial enough for stability it should be thoroughly wire brushed and primed with a rust inhibiting primer. Painting with bitumen paint should be followed by rebonding of brickwork and repairs to fractures and cracks as described in Section C of this part of the Chapter. Particular attention should be paid to the ends of sections if only these are built in and the socket at this point should be well caulked with a bituminous compound. Again with sections built in, close attention should be paid to ensure that as far as possible rain does not penetrate the brickwork. Rendering or silicone solution (see Section B of Part 4 of this Chapter) might be useful for this purpose, but more often the provision of a projecting flashing above the detail will help to throw water clear of the wall. Water running down a wall and soaking in is often the cause of corrosion in embedded structural elements.

We have seen in two examples where the use of reinforced concrete is useful for replacing features of timber built into brick walls. The usefulness of reinforced concrete can be extended to include building in spreaders to relieve brickwork from overloading by point loads or where thin narrow piers are found to be overloaded in the ordinary course of events. Examples where the use of reinforced concrete is advantageous are illustrated throughout but these are by no means exhaustive and many other instances could be cited.

While reinforced concrete is useful for the purposes mentioned above we must return to metal to provide ties and bonding anchors in various other circumstances, for example the heavy ornamental cornice inadequately tailed down so that it is pulling over a parapet above. A repair which has proved effective in such circumstances and could be adapted to tie in the top section of a wall if no other simpler method proved to be available, consists of spanning between the flank walls above roof level a steel channel section and bolting to this with tapered washers long mild steel hooks passed over the cornice section. By careful cutting and fixing the work can be made nearly invisible from below. In the example illustrated on Figure 41 for a mid-Victorian house of about 18 feet (5·5m) frontage, 5 hooks were used and no movement has been observed for over ten subsequent years.

In old buildings there are many circumstances that can arise which will cause the bond between two sections of brickwork either to fracture or to pull apart. After deciding on the cause and taking steps to remedy this, there remains the problem of the gap at the junction. A suitable method of dealing with this is to take down the brickwork on either side of the gap or fracture, removing all fractured bricks and to bond in new brickwork building in at every 3 foot (0·9m) vertical intervals 2½ by ⅜ inch (63·5 by 9·5mm) galvanised wrought iron or steel flat bars turned up and down at the ends and built in as far as possible into sound brickwork, up to 3 feet (0·9m) if possible. Such strengthening at the joint will help by introducing a material strong in tension well bedded and hooked over a length of brickwork to prevent subsequent slight pulling away which is bound to happen to a minor extent whichever repair is carried out to stop the cause. A repair of this nature where one wall has pulled away but no bricks have fractured is shown on Figure 42.

The use of metal anchors as described above is of course, similar to the use of galvanised hoop iron in the past to reinforce brickwork at quoins and along the length of walls where the original builders suspected pockets of weak ground below foundations. The practice seems to have died out but the type of reinforcement is still mentioned in British Standard Code of Practice C.P.121.101 (1951) "Brickwork". In many circumstances foundations are better designed now than in the past particularly for major building projects which on many occasions nowadays include domestic buildings, but on the other hand smaller developments are still carried out by builders often without professional advice. Though the suspicions may be there in regard to weak ground the chance is taken and nothing special is done about reinforcing the brickwork. The practice, which might well be adopted in repair work, consisted of building in lengths of

Provision of restraint to a leaning parapet and cornice

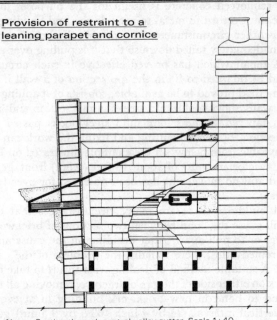

Above: <u>Section through central valley gutter.</u> Scale 1 : 40.
Below Left: <u>Plan at roof space level.</u> Scale 1 : 100.
Below Right: <u>Plan above slating.</u> Scale 1 : 100.

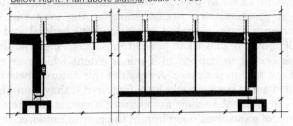

Section 'C', Figure 25 showed a tall, thin, virtually unrestrained leaning parapet wall, the condition aggravated by a heavy cornice. In the example the cornice was based on a stone slab cantilevered out from the parapet and then built up with tiles and stucco. The outer edge of the stone slab provides a suitable point from which to restrain further movement and here a 6″ x 5″ (152 x 127 mm) R.S.J. is built in to the party walls and three 1″ (25·4 mm) mild steel rods hooked over the slab and secured to the web of the steel with a tapered washer, nut and locknut. Two further rod ties are provided near the party walls through the roof space. These are each in two sections with a tightening linkage, the ends ragged and built in to concrete blocks set in the party walls. All steel should be thoroughly treated against rust and the top of the cornice weatherproofed on making good.

41

hoop iron 1 by $\frac{1}{16}$ inch (25 by 1·5mm) one row for every $\frac{1}{2}$ brick thickness of wall. The hoop iron should always be galvanised and hooked at all angles and junctions but being thinner in section than the type of reinforcement mentioned in the preceding paragraph it should be built in at every fourth course.

Finally in this section dealing with tieing-in we must consider the cause of a fault in the construction of walls themselves. In speculative development of the past it is sometimes found that in order to save on facing bricks little or no bond was provided between the outer $\frac{1}{2}$ brick skin of facing bricks and the backing of common bricks. Snapped headers were all too often used instead of a through brick to bond front section to rear. Sometimes all remains well and it is only when there is some disturbance and movement that the lack of bond becomes apparent. Provided that the backing is sound, or can easily be repaired if there is anything wrong with it, a suitable method is to reface the wall with a skin of bricks tied to the backing with wall-ties, used in the same manner as in cavity walls. The use of non-ferrous cramps (or at least well galvanised ties) is essential in the circumstances and there are a number of suitable anchors now available for the purpose.

If the backing to the wall is a little suspect but is not in such condition as to warrant rebuilding, once all timber has been removed from the wall and replaced, it is possible, following the stripping of all old plaster, to reinforce the wall by stapling heavy gauge expanded metal to the brickwork and then rendering over with a medium strength cement lime sand mix 1:1:6 by volume taking care to use sulphate resisting cement if there is any possibility of sulphate attack. Plastering or the refixing of panelling can then be carried out. This is not, however, a practical method of repair for the exterior of walls in view of the risk of shrinkage cracks in the rendering allowing damp to penetrate and cause corrosion in the lathing, even apart from the aspect of appearance.

The method of tieing a new leaf of brickwork to old brickwork is one that is increasingly popular now that adequate non-ferrous or galvanised anchors are more readily available. It avoids the considerable disturbance involved by block bonding a new leaf to old. Admittedly there is some disturbance in cutting away for the anchors but although it involves more frequent cutting the scope is much less extensive in each position.

The subject of tieing-in a leaf of brickwork brings up the matter of cavity walls which are dealt with separately, different principles being involved, both in their construction and repair.

147

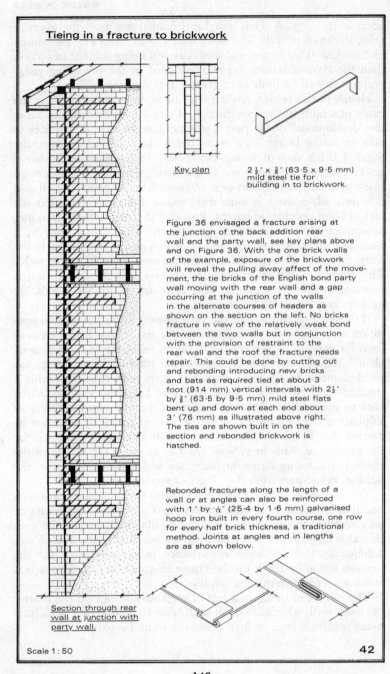

Tieing in a fracture to brickwork

Key plan

$2\frac{1}{2}" \times \frac{3}{8}"$ (63·5 x 9·5 mm) mild steel tie for building in to brickwork.

Figure 36 envisaged a fracture arising at the junction of the back addition rear wall and the party wall, see key plans above and on Figure 36. With the one brick walls of the example, exposure of the brickwork will reveal the pulling away affect of the movement, the tie bricks of the English bond party wall moving with the rear wall and a gap occurring at the junction of the walls in the alternate courses of headers as shown on the section on the left. No bricks fracture in view of the relatively weak bond between the two walls but in conjunction with the provision of restraint to the rear wall and the roof the fracture needs repair. This could be done by cutting out and rebonding introducing new bricks and bats as required tied at about 3 foot (914 mm) vertical intervals with $2\frac{1}{2}"$ by $\frac{3}{8}"$ (63·5 by 9·5 mm) mild steel flats bent up and down at each end about 3" (76 mm) as illustrated above right. The ties are shown built in on the section and rebonded brickwork is hatched.

Rebonded fractures along the length of a wall or at angles can also be reinforced with 1" by $\frac{1}{16}"$ (25·4 by 1·6 mm) galvanised hoop iron built in every fourth course, one row for every half brick thickness, a traditional method. Joints at angles and in lengths are as below.

Section through rear wall at junction with party wall.

Scale 1 : 50

42

148

B. Repairs to Cavity Walls

Cavity wall construction is a comparatively recent innovation in building although examples dating from Victorian times are found. It owes its origin to the fact that ordinary two-storey house construction requires nothing more than 9-inch brickwork on the ground of load bearing, yet such work is not always proof against driving rain and does not provide a good degree of heat insulation. Cavity walls were developed either with a brick inner leaf or one comprising concrete blocks to provide an answer to this problem. There is however a radical departure from traditional construction in that the stability of the wall depends essentially on the wall-ties, particularly when the load from the roof and floors is carried on the inner leaf only. Accordingly any disruption to the brickwork from whatever cause can lead to more serious defects and require more radical repair than would be the case with a solid wall.

There is good reason to suppose, in view of the short distance that wall-ties are built in, that a cavity wall with a bulge or lean in excess of 1 inch (25mm) in a storey height is in danger of the collapse of the outer leaf, particularly if there are indications of disturbance in the areas where wall-ties can be expected or if the mortar of the wall suggests that the ties have been loosened free. In such circumstances there is little alternative to taking down the outer leaf and rebuilding. Should this be necessary and the roof is bearing wholly or partly on the outer leaf it must not be forgotten that the roof will require shoring.

The cause of an outer leaf moving independently from the inner leaf might be due to roof thrust, sulphate attack on the mortar and brickwork or excessive drying shrinkage of an inner leaf constructed of concrete or sometimes, in the case of earlier examples, coke breeze blocks. Should minor movements from overloading by way of poor design or faulty construction suggest that cracked bricks or sections of the outer leaf be taken down and rebuilt, this can normally be done fairly easily particularly if all loads are carried on the inner leaf. Where cracks and movement are present it should always be done.

If there has been merely an increase in height in an outer leaf due, say, to sulphate attack on the mortar alone, involving a loosening of the ties it should be possible to cut out sections of the brickwork from outside and reset the ties. If this might be considered unsightly it should be possible to work from the interior provided the building owner prefers the disturbance involved with this method to the patchy appearance of the repair from outside.

If defects arise from disturbance of soil or faulty foundations this is

149

a more serious matter and it is almost certain in such circumstances that both leaves will require rebuilding. Inner leaves in modern cavity construction are able to resist most of the damage arising from defects above ground as they are steadied by reason of roof loading, their support of floors and the fact that most modern houses have brick or block partitions instead of timber partitions and these help considerably. Unfortunately these steadying factors are of little or no help when the cause emanates from below ground level.

C. Repair of Cracks in Brickwork

Cracks in facing brickwork can be separated into two types, those passing diagonally through brick joints and leaving the bricks undamaged and those which are more or less vertical and involve the cracking of individual bricks. Pointing of cracked bricks in facing work is very unsightly and whether bricks need to be cut out and renewed depends mainly on the size of the crack, whether it is unsightly or not and whether if it is left it will permit water to penetrate to the interior. To determine the latter point it is necessary to give some consideration to the porosity of the brickwork concerned.

To determine whether brickwork is porous or not, about a cupful of water should be thrown on to the brickwork when dry. If the water runs down the wall face and is not absorbed then there is a serious risk that if a fine crack in a brick, in an exposed position, is left, rain will be drawn through by capillary action to cause dampness inside. If on the other hand the water does not run far down the face and is fairly rapidly absorbed the brickwork can be considered porous and there is little risk in leaving a fine crack in brickwork, say up to $\frac{1}{16}$ inch (1·5mm) even in exposed positions.

In dense non-porous brickwork in exposed positions, however, even if the crack was pointed and the unsightliness tolerated there is a danger of shrinkage in the mortar which might still allow damp penetration. The only reasonable repair in these circumstances is for the cracked bricks to be cut out and renewed with bricks to match the existing. It is essential in carrying out this work to ensure that good adhesion is obtained between the new bricks, the mortar and existing work, otherwise with non-porous bricks shrinkage may permit water penetration as described before to the interior. The procedure to adopt for fine cracks is therefore to leave them in porous brickwork in any situation, but for dense brickwork to leave only those in sheltered positions. For fine cracks in dense brickwork in exposed positions however, all cracked bricks should be removed, the joints raked out along which the crack occurs, the area rebonded with stretchers where bricks have been cut out, using a cement lime

150

sand mortar 1:1:6 by volume, the cracked joints filled with mortar as far as possible and repointed.

For medium-sized cracks in both joints and bricks, say between $\frac{1}{16}$ to $\frac{3}{8}$ inch (1·5 to 10mm) wide it will generally be necessary for these to be repaired but the method to be adopted will depend on the nature of the mortar in the existing brickwork. With old and weak lime mortar and cracks in the joints only, joints should be raked deeply on both sides of the wall and filled and pointed with cement lime sand mortar no stronger than 1:3:12 by volume. With stronger mortar joints, either the bricks on both sides of the wall could be cut out and rebonded using a medium strength mortar 1:1:6 cement lime and sand, or alternatively the joints could be pointed up on the face and the cracks behind filled with grout as described below. However, if cracks of this order occur in the bricks themselves it will always be necessary to cut out and re-bond using a mortar mix to match as near as possible that in the existing wall.

Cracks above $\frac{3}{8}$ inch (5mm) up to say 1$\frac{1}{2}$ inch (31mm) should always be cut out and re-bonded with a mortar mix to match the existing work.

In repairing cracks with mortar it is essential to avoid the use of strong cement mortars which are so subject to shrinkage themselves and in order to achieve good adhesion to existing work vital that porous brickwork should be well wetted before the mortar is applied.

It should be obvious that repairing cracks should not be carried out until all movement has ceased. If there is evidence to suggest that movement is continuing either involving opening or closing of the cracks then the use of an oil based mastic applied with a gun will keep out the rain until such time as a permanent repair can be affected.

In cutting out cracks and re-bonding bricks some thought should be given to the eventual appearance as, however well done, the work is bound to show. If the bulk of the existing pointing is poor it may be the ideal time to repoint walls generally if the building owner can be persuaded to the additional expense. On the other hand, if pointing is in reasonable condition it is possible with care and by trial and error and the use of coloured cement, to match up existing work. Much damage to bricks can be done however by raking out strong pointing which is sound, so that this should be avoided whenever possible.

If a cracked wall is to be rendered or plastered it will not normally be necessary to do more than rake out loose mortar and debris as far in to the wall as possible and repoint from both sides of the wall both cracked bricks and joints. Mortar must be pressed firmly into cracks, but this is difficult where walls are thick so that the use of grout is recommended in such circumstances. For example party walls have been repaired by shooting fine concrete into wide cracks by means of a cement gun and cracks and fissures in quite massive walls have also been satisfactorily filled by high pressure air grouting. However these methods would not be possible if the joints are of friable lime mortar or other mortar that is disintegrating. In such cases low pressure gravity grouting must be resorted to as follows and as shown on Figure 43.

The appliance required for low pressure gravity grouting can be made up simply with a section of 4-inch (102mm) steel tube about a foot long (305mm) with a reducing piece down to $\frac{1}{2}$ inch (12·5mm) on one end with a nozzle. About 5 feet (1·524m) of ordinary rubber or plastic garden hose is required to connect the hopper with a further nozzle made from a section of $\frac{1}{2}$-inch (12·5mm) steel tube, which is inserted into an access hole near or at the lower end of the crack to be grouted.

The whole of the main crack, any subsidiary cracks and open joints must then be pointed with a quick setting mortar, the addition of 5 per cent calcium chloride of the dry weight of the cement to the mix giving the required effect, and a boss must be formed round the access hole. The hopper should be securely positioned about 1 foot (305mm) above the top of the crack it is intended to fill. When the pointing has set, the nozzle on the hose may be inserted into the access hole and the joint made watertight with plasticine. Water poured in through the hopper in the first instance should be used to test that the pointing is sound, that there is a free passage for the grout and to wet the brickwork to secure good adhesion. If the access hole is not at the lowest end of the crack a small drainage hole should be formed at the end so that any surplus water can be drained off and this should be plugged with plasticine as soon as grout can be seen to flow through on commencing the grouting operation.

The grout should be a mixture of neat cement and water in the proportion of 2 to 1 by weight. It must be well stirred before use. As soon as it has been poured so that it reaches and appears at the top of the crack, the nozzle must be withdrawn and the access hole plugged. The appliance should then immediately be washed through with water.

The use of a neat cement mix for grouting is necessary to ensure a proper flow but such a mix is liable to shrink and for cracks more than $\frac{1}{8}$-inch (3mm) wide a second application of grout may be necessary.

Grouting a crack in brickwork

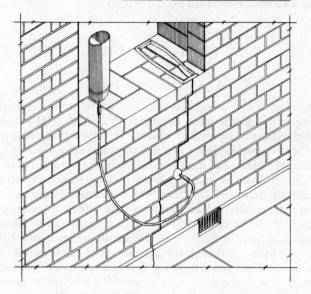

Cracks in facing brickwork of this order would normally be dealt with by cutting out fractured bricks, their renewal and rebonding. In the backing or in a wall where the appearance does not count or which is to be covered over, low pressure grouting can be used to restore the joint provided the remaining pointing is not too friable and after pointing up the crack both sides with quick setting mortar, leaving only an access hole and air vents for the grouting operation, see text.

Types of maintenance re-pointing

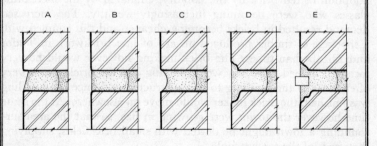

A   B   C   D   E

43

In dealing with long cracks the procedure is always to start at the base of the crack and to work upwards in lifts of about 3 feet (914 mm) at a time so as to avoid excessive pressure.

PART 4. BRICKS

A. CHARACTERISTICS

The burning of clay as against mere sun-drying to make bricks for building is thought to have commenced around 3000 B.C. in the Near East. Burnt clay tablets provide archaeologists with most of their documentary evidence of the past, apart from inscriptions on stone and the earliest of inscribed clay tablets date from about this time. The Romans introduced brick making to this country and there are still many bricks dating back to Roman times in existence but now incorporated in later buildings. They are easily distinguished from later bricks being usually only 1 to 2 inches (25 to 50mm) in thickness and more in the form of a thick tile rather than a brick as we know it today. Although the production of bricks continued on the continent it remains a puzzling fact that none were produced in this country until the early part of the 14th century at about the same time as they were also imported from the Netherlands and Northern Europe, perhaps as ballast in ships returning from voyages as part of the flourishing export trade in wool.

In the early stages of the industry, brick making was confined to the Eastern counties and during the 14th and 15th centuries brick remained as expensive as stone so that it was only in important buildings where it was employed. Exceptions to this general consideration however arose where there was little local building stone. The adoption of red brick by the Court for palaces such as that at Hampton Court in the 16th century provided great impetus for the adoption of red brick by the nobility, emulated by the mercantile classes who were becoming increasingly wealthy. The increased demand resulted in bricks becoming cheaper and this coupled with a shortage of timber produced an era of fine brickwork in Tudor and Elizabethan times. The brick making however would be very localised indeed. The clay would be dug and the bricks made very often close to the building to be constructed and once the building was finished, the brick maker would move on elsewhere. At the same time however the towns were growing in size, so that the area surrounding a town might be dotted with small brickfields, supplying the needs of the townspeople.

At this time reliance would be placed solely on the experience of the brick maker for the selection of suitable clay for the making of the bricks and for the firing. Often for important buildings a brick maker of experience would be brought over from the continent and entrusted with this task. Even so by the beginning of the 17th century much evidence of poor bricks must have existed and it was probably to provide some protection to the purchaser that the first Proclamation of Charles I issued on the 2nd May 1625 dealt with the manufacture of bricks. Directions were given for the method and timing of digging the clay, weathering, moulding, drying, and firing, and the finished size was to be length 9 inches, breadth $4\frac{3}{8}$ inches, thickness $2\frac{1}{4}$ inches. Even the price was regulated, a factor which not even the latest British Standard covers.

The fashion for brick continued through the 17th century greatly assisted in London by the Act of Rebuilding in 1667 following the Great Fire which forbade the use of timber for external walls and in other towns by the fear of similar fires which, notwithstanding, occurred all too frequently. Bricks in any event were by now much cheaper than stone so that with timber disallowed in towns, for most people, the choice between brick and stone hardly arose. Up until about 1750 the wealthiest and those whose task it was to design or commission the larger buildings such as Guildhalls, Customs Houses, Libraries, Colleges, Chapels, etc., often chose brick in preference to stone, always provided that a suitable clay was available locally and it was surprising how often it could be found. Once, however, the members of the circle of fashion took to the Grand Tour and brought back with them the idea that red brick was common and distasteful, stone became the fashion for the Age of Taste and at the very least a dullish grey brick only was acceptable as had been used by Vitruvius and Palladio in Italy. Even so brick continued in demand as being the only material that most could afford. The tax on bricks imposed at the end of the eighteenth century made little difference to the demand although it was a factor tending to increase the thickness of bricks from $2\frac{1}{4}$ inches to about 3 inches. Those who had aspirations but who could not rise to stone fell to the expediency of stucco to cover the brick and to give it a pale imitation of stone. In those days the stucco was left unpainted. At the same time there was a substantial demand for the grey bricks in preference to those of a reddish hue to reflect current ideas of taste. In the middle of the 19th century the abolition of the tax on bricks virtually coincided with the mechanisation of brickmaking and the spread of the railways. The production of bricks accordingly increased to vast proportions to satisfy the demands of the Industrial Revolution and the railways enabled them to be carried to areas of the north and west where suitable clays for hand-made bricks had not been found in the past.

155

Even so the introduction of new machinery eventually enabled the harder clays of the Midlands and the North to be processed into bricks and it became possible to produce the wide range of mass produced, hard, smooth, accurately dimensioned and identically coloured bricks that are the main hall-mark of the Victorian era, many very good as bricks but almost uniformly deplorable in appearance. It was only in those areas not affected by industry and with a local stone tradition that managed to hold out against the invasion but the 20th century has seen even these areas succumb to the all-embracing brick, road transport having seen to it that hardly anywhere is inaccessible. Now even in areas where brick seems totally incongruous the products of the neighbourhood south of Peterborough (where one of the villages, Fletton, has given the generic name of "Flettons" to the bricks produced over a large area) can be seen everywhere and the country can now truly be termed a land of brick.

In the production of bricks from whatever age two factors govern the characteristics of the individual brick, namely the suitability of the clay used and the firing. In the past, the brick maker travelled the countryside testing the clay and setting up where he considered it suitable. From his point of view it would be the workability of the clay that would be the prime consideration in the process of hand moulding. Secondly the hardness of the finished product would be on his mind but this would be governed by his skill in firing. In this consideration comes the factor of compressive strength covered by the building codes at the present time. It is doubtful however if the original brick makers gave any thought to the chemical composition of the clay which governs the durability of the brick in use. Due thought is given to this nowadays by the makers for the benefit of the users, but the point is not governed by the building codes and the users are left to make their own choice.

Of the two characteristics of individual bricks which we have noted above, compressive strength is of the least importance in domestic building although this is not necessarily the case in other forms of construction. Certainly as long as bricks are reasonably well fired and if they are not they would probably be rejected in any event by the maker or layer, their compressive strength is adequate in normal walling. Defects due to inadequacy of compressive strength in bricks in dwelling houses are extremely rare but may arise where point loads occur and which are not adequately distributed. If danger point has been reached in such circumstances then the only method to adopt would be to support the load temporarily by shoring and demolish and rebuild the section of brickwork affected with a stronger brick. More often than not, however, the trouble will be diagnosed before this point is reached. In such a case it may be possible to relieve the brickwork of some of the load by transferring it elsewhere or alternatively by building in a concrete spreader to distribute the load over a greater area of brickwork. Some idea of the unlikeliness of compressive strength being a factor in general areas of walling can be gathered from current requirements. The Building Regulations both in the 1965 and 1972 editions and the London By-Laws of 1964 require bricks or blocks to have a resistance to crushing of 1,500 lbs. per square inch (10·34 N/mm²) for external and internal load bearing purposes. For two-storey houses this can be reduced to 400 lbs. per square inch (2·75 N/mm²) under the Building Regulations but this only applies above damp proof course level in London under the by-laws. British Standard 3291:1965 for bricks has only one requirement in regard to compressive strength and that is for a resistance to crushing of 750 lbs. per square inch (5·17 N/mm²). Although unsafe to generalise, since the strength can vary widely in a batch, it is generally considered that Flettons, Red Wire Cuts and Hard Stocks are satisfactory for 3,000 lbs. per square inch (20·68 N/mm²) Ordinary Stocks, Cavity Flettons and Red Facings for 1,500 lbs. per square inch (10·34 N/mm²).

Clearly although there may be many individual bricks in old structures with a strength not even up to 400 lbs. per square inch (2·76 N/mm²) these are amply compensated for in general walling by the majority well in excess of this figure.

The other main factor in individual bricks to be considered before we proceed to bricks incorporated structurally in walls concerns their durability. The two main causes of failure in individual bricks occur through frost damage and the presence of an excessive amount of salts within the bricks themselves or in the mortar in which they are embedded. In both cases water is required to produce the disintegration which occurs and the degree of exposure often governs the extent of the damage, coupled with the quality of the brick itself, soft underburnt bricks being more prone to failure, together with bricks made with a hard impervious skin over a soft interior.

The Building Regulations and the London By-Laws give no guidance on the selection of bricks suitable for different degrees of exposure but the British Standard Code of Practice C.P.121.101 (1951) provides general advice and British Standard 3921:1965 classifies bricks into "varieties", common, facing and engineering and "qualities", internal, ordinary and special and defines the positions suitable for each. The Building Research Establishment in its Digests (in particular Nos. 65 and 66 of the Second Series) also provides much useful information, further comment and cautionary criticism on the limitations of test results when related to bricks. This guidance is indispensable when it is necessary to select a type of brick for replacing bricks which are disintegrating or where it has become necessary to rebuild features which have become dangerous such as parapets or chimney stacks. If such conditions arise and it is necessary to rebuild such features the opportunity can be taken to incorporate damp proof courses immediately below the top of stacks and directly above the junction with roofs. It may also be necessary to redesign the tops of stacks which it is necessary to retain and also copings so as to provide sufficient overhangs and throatings to afford a degree of protection to the brickwork below. These aspects are discussed more fully in Chapter 8 on Dampness.

B. Repairs and Maintenance

(1) *Repairs in connection with Defective Bricks and Jointing*

In examining a property where disintegration is occurring on the face of the bricks one will be governed in the choice of treatment by the extent of the defects. Should the flaking of the bricks occur mainly in parapets and chimney stacks and in localised areas between the damp proof course and the tops of walls then a study of the building during heavy rainfall will often show the areas which are particularly prone to severe wetting. These areas, more often than not, will correspond with the areas of defective bricks and it should be possible to see how and why water tends to become concentrated at particular points. An examination in dry conditions is of little assistance as only when it is raining heavily can one see water actually coursing off copings, cornices, band courses and other architectural features and running down and soaking into the brickwork. Similarly it is only during or immediately after heavy rain that the patches of damp below cracks in sills or copings can be easily seen.

A detailed study of the symptoms, causes and remedies for damp penetration through walls is deferred to Chapter 8 and it will be appreciated with this section that the primary concern is only saturation of the facing brickwork giving rise to an acceleration in the process of disintegration. That penetration to the interior may follow eventually is very probable but the main consideration at this stage is the failure, from whatever cause, on the face of the structural element. Accordingly the overlapping between this Chapter and Chapter 8 is more apparent than real even although it will eventually become clear that the remedies available for dealing with areas of very poor bricks as against for example a problem of damp penetration arising from the inappropriate use of hard, impervious bricks in general walling are the same.

In such cases where the flaking of bricks is localised then it is considered that the best way of dealing with the trouble is to cut out and renew individual bricks with a suitable "special" quality brick according to B.S.3921:1965 matching as near as possible for colour and texture. The remainder of the brickwork not too seriously affected can then be protected by altering and improving the detailing which allows water to penetrate. In this respect the reforming of defective edges and mouldings to cornices, string courses and the like and the covering of the top of such projecting architectural features with a lead, copper or zinc flashing with at least a 6-inch turn-up into the brickwork above to prevent splashing and a suitable drip mould on the lower edge to ensure that water falls clear of the brickwork below, can do much to alleviate the condition. Cracks in sills are a further important feature that require attention and in this respect a new sill with a damp proof course is preferable to repairing the crack. In particular the provision of damp proof courses to tops of walls is most important bearing in mind that for this purpose two courses of slates or tiles have been shown many times to be an inadequate barrier to moisture penetrating downwards. Occasionally it may be necessary to provide a gutter around a door casing, window, or some other feature which allows water to soak into adjacent brickwork.

If the disintegration of bricks is severe and general then a more radical treatment is necessary than that outlined above. It is not always practical or even economic to cut out and renew vast areas of brickwork so that some method of protecting the defective brickwork may have to be evolved. A method of protection much favoured in the past and one which always comes first to mind, that of rendering the brickwork, is a possibility but may cause far more trouble in certain circumstances. The reason for this is that should a rendering based on ordinary Portland cement be applied over bricks containing a high proportion of soluble salts any entrapped moisture or any subsequent moisture entering (almost inevitable with such rendering but not necessarily always of consequence) will carry the salts into the rendering and these will attack the tricalcium aluminate constituent of the cement, causing the rendering to expand and bulge, loosening the key and causing cracks to appear. The cracks allow further moisture to penetrate and the cycle to continue probably resulting in the eventual complete failure of the rendering and much worse damage to the brickwork below. However carefully specified and applied, rendering external walls has its limitations and the maintenance by painting if this is applied and

159

the continual need to watch for hair cracks, loose areas and damp penetration make the attractions of other methods of protecting external brickwork more pronounced. The other methods available are unfortunately all more expensive and, in descending order of cost at the present time, are; refacing with an entire new skin of brickwork secured to the old with non-ferrous cramps or ties, slate or tile hanging or weatherboarding. Since all involve applying a surface over the existing bricks and all involve a thickness considerably in excess of rendering it is not hard to see why rendering is more often selected. With a new brick face much alteration is usually required to eaves details and very often doors and windows if it is desired to maintain the former appearance. For a house of quality where expense is not a prime consideration this method is, however, probably the best.

Slate or tile hanging are probably the most frequently used alternatives to rendering and both, if well carried out, look more attractive than rendering, require less maintenance and are more durable. Careful detailing and attention is required at angles and around openings, the aim being to make the house look as though it has always been slate or tile hung. In some cases the appearance of the original house can even be improved upon and the worry of crumbling bricks can be forgotten by the owner. On the other hand problems can arise in regard to the change in appearance, as it can also with the addition of weatherboarding, if the house being dealt with owes its particular character to its original construction or where the house forms one of a group of similar houses in a street. Clearly a change in external appearance will involve a planning application and the owner is possibly going to be up against a body of opinion that will oppose the proposed change. It may well be that the planning authority will prefer a refacing of the original building in new brick of a variety similar in appearance to the old. If such a scheme can be shown to be uneconomic and if it can be shown that if something is not done at reasonable cost the building will fail, it is thought that opposition could be overcome to a change in appearance provided a scheme is sensitively handled and the application intelligently pursued.

Applying battens and weatherboarding is of course similar in character to slate or tile hanging as a protection for disintegrating bricks, but there are, of course, problems in urban areas in regard to the general use of this method which would have to be cleared with the local authority as regards fire resistance. In addition painted weatherboarding adds to maintenance costs so that it is not always a repair that usually comes to mind in these circumstances, although of course it should not be overlooked on this account since initial cost and maintenance may present a favourable balance. Fairly recently self-coloured P.V.C. panels giving the appearance of white painted weatherboarding have become available. These may prove most useful once experience has been gained with them.

In this section methods of dealing with defective areas of bricks through a lack of durability in certain positions and, in cases where necessary, over whole wall surfaces, have been described. The same methods can be adopted for an inadequacy which does occur on occasions in brickwork as built, depending on the degree of exposure. Normally in domestic construction one brick thickness is perfectly adequate for keeping out rain but in sections of walls at high level and on the elevations of buildings exposed to prevailing winds even if pointing is well maintained this thickness can permit dampness to penetrate. In the circumstances tile or slate hanging or rendering may be necessary, although a far cheaper palliative can be the application of a silicone solution in accordance with the manufacturer's directions. This however needs renewal every few years to be effective, so that even although the initial cost is a great deal cheaper, in the long run it may prove more expensive particularly as the ratio of labour costs to materials continues to increase unabated.

The need for additional protection to 9-inch brickwork presupposes that steps have been taken to ensure that the pointing is sound. Soft and loose pointing is a frequent source of damp penetration in old walling and obviously if this is found it must be assumed initially to be a contributory cause of damp penetration even if not the sole cause. Accordingly steps should be taken to repoint the brickwork before any more expensive works are carried out and this at least given a fair trial, over say two years, to prove whether or not defective pointing is the only reason for the damp penetration.

As mentioned earlier problems of damp penetration both involving diagnosis and remedies will be discussed much more fully in Chapter 8. Some of these remedies, adding a brick skin, slate and tile hanging, weatherboarding and the application of silicones have been mentioned briefly here as constituting appliable treatments to walls in particular circumstances. Maintenance repointing will be dealt with as the penultimate section of this Chapter but there remains the other method of repair, that of rendering, which requires consideration in detail. This will be dealt with in the next section of this Chapter and not in Chapter 8 since rendering becomes an integral part of the wall and factors which apply to it do not apply to other methods of repair. As we have seen rendering can be severely affected by the constituents both of the backing and within the mix itself. It is accordingly for these reasons more convenient to dispose

entirely of the subject of rendering on brick walls as a repair together with the subject of repairs to existing rendering at this stage.

(2) *Repair by the Application of a Rendered Finish*

The sight of disintegrating brickwork or trouble from damp penetration through brick walls has invariably brought to mind the idea
of applying a few coats of rendering as an immediate cure. As long
as the rendering mix was based on naturally occurring lime and sand
the cure would probably be reasonably effective. Even if the repair
was carried out in the 19th century using one of the earlier patent
cements it would also probably be satisfactory, but in this century
the widespread use of Portland cement has led to many shortcomings in rendered finishes through a failure to appreciate the
strength of this type of cement. In addition the indiscriminate use of
Portland cement rendering by the speculative builder to cover up
poor cheap bricks in the period 1920–1940 and its use by the jobbing
builder for every conceivable form of repair has led to a revulsion
against the use of Portland cement for this purpose by the more
informed.

This is probably only a temporary set-back for a method of
treatment to brick walls which has a long history. The failures and
the opprobriation resulting from these has however led to an intensive study of the subject, the results of which are set out in British
Standard Code of Practice C.P.221:1960 "External Rendered
Finishes", a document of some forty pages devoted exclusively to
the subject. Where an external rendered finish is to form a part of
new work the Code must be considered a very necessary guide at
the design and specification stage, so much so that a copy should be
in every surveyor, architect and builder's office. For repair work
where the rendered finish is being considered for application to
existing brickwork much of the contents of the Code still of course
apply but have to be varied according to the circumstances found.

Existing backgrounds and their position in the building must be
considered from various points of view in relation to the number of
coats of rendering to be applied, the composition of the mixes and
the type of finish but it is a waste of time even to consider these
aspects if it has not first been ascertained that the background is
suitable. On page 159 it has already been briefly mentioned what
might happen if a rendering based on Portland cement is applied
over bricks containing soluble salts. It might be said that the use of
sulphate resisting Portland cement in all cases should overcome this
problem but it is not, unfortunately, as simple as this. Properties
built in the last seventy years or so will have been constructed in all

probability with a jointing and pointing mortar containing Portland
cement so that unless the brickwork backing both before and after
rendering is kept absolutely dry, expansion could still occur in the
joints of the bricks thereby causing cracking, loss of adhesion and
probably spalling of the rendering after a period of about two years.
If the backing could be kept absolutely dry after application then
rendering would be satisfactory, but even this is almost impossible
to achieve as however well rendering is specified and applied, its
very nature and the slight imperfections which do arise are likely
to allow penetration of moisture into the brickwork in a manner as
will be described later. Bearing in mind that it is rendering on
old brickwork that is under discussion the difficulty of getting it dry
in the first place is formidable and items such as chimney stacks,
parapet walls, high walls in exposed positions, free standing and
retaining walls and walls below damp course level must be ruled out
for a start as it is impossible to make and keep these dry. It might be
possible to dry out general walling between damp course and eaves
level so that one can be sure that the bricks and mortar are satisfactory but it is extremely difficult to be able to tell for certain
whether the interior of a wall is dry. For one thing the level of dampness in a wall built partly of dense impervious facing bricks will
remain high for long periods, probably for the duration of the interval between one shower of rain and the next, unless there is an
exceptional period of drought. There would be good grounds therefore for considering the success of rendering to be dubious in these
circumstances and other methods of protection might have to be
considered.

It will be found, as it will be in so many cases of repair work, that
much assistance can be gained in the first place by considering the
age of the building. It is known that soluble salts, unfortunately
contained in most bricks, water and Portland cement are needed to
cause the trouble of sulphate attack. Thus if Portland cement can
be discounted in the original construction there is a possibility still
for the successful use of rendering. Portland cement was only
patented in 1824 so that anything built before this is bound to be
satisfactory from this limited point of view. On the other hand the
general use of Portland cement for jointing and pointing did not
really commence until very much later, so that the vast majority of
the substantial volume of early, middle and late Victorian houses
still remaining will have no Portland cement in their make up.
Probably the vast majority of Edwardian houses fall into the same
category but here one cannot be so sure and it may be necessary to
carry out analytical tests of the mortar in order to be certain.

It will of course be said immediately that any house more than

163

BRICK WALLS

say 50–70 years old will almost certainly have been repointed within that period and in such repointing Portland cement must have been used. This is true but a moments thought will confirm that this need not be of consequence. Even if the combination of salts in the bricks and Portland cement in the repointing has caused expansion in the joints this can be simply eliminated in the future by the sufficient raking out of joints that will be necessary before a rendering is applied. All the more reason in this case to ensure that the raking out is carried out thoroughly and sufficiently deep and to take the necessary precaution to ensure that no ordinary Portland cement is used in the mix for rendering.

With houses built since 1920 however the surveyor must look very carefully indeed into the condition of both the brickwork and the mortar for here it is almost certain that both jointing and pointing will have been carried out in a mix based on ordinary Portland cement. Substantial water penetration dissolving the inevitable salts in the bricks will be likely to produce evidence of sulphate attack. It is just this evidence that the surveyor, examining a house built since 1920 should watch for at times when new rendering for any reason comes to mind. It is probably best for the surveyor to select for his examination one of the areas of brickwork most severely affected and although sulphate attack has been described in Part 2 Section B (2) of this Chapter in its more serious forms as affecting structural stability, it is as well here to set out some of the less pronounced indications of its presence.

Apart from the expansion in the joints which causes deformation, bulging and cracking in facing brickwork, sulphate attack will also often cause the edges of individual bricks to spall. As the attack develops, the mortar joints take on a whitish appearance particularly on the edges nearest the bricks and a fine crack in the centre of the joint may appear as a prelude to the surface of the joint falling off leaving a disintegrating mush behind. If there is any doubt in the surveyor's mind as to whether the defects in the brickwork are due to sulphate attack and it is quite often likely that a doubt will arise, then a sample of bricks of sufficient size to be representative should be removed and sent for testing under B.S.3921:1965. If the soluble salt limit does not exceed that laid down for "special" quality bricks then it would seem that the damage has been caused by frost action alone or general poor quality of the brick in the first instance. In selecting a representative sample it is also probably as well to include some bricks which have remained dry since it is the salt content of a dry brick that is more pertinent to this enquiry than that of a brick which has been constantly saturated and from which most of the salts have already been leached. In practice not many

164

bricks are able to meet the requirement of sulphate limitation of the "special" quality classification of B.S.3921:1965 so that even though there might not be indications of sulphate attack present on the facing brickwork the risk of it arising if the brickwork were to be rendered would still exist where all bricks were not up to the appropriate "special" quality standard. The difficulty and the reason for this is that light porous renderings, for example, let the water through into the brickwork so that when it evaporates it does so through the joints and the rendering while, on the other hand, dense impervious renderings invariably shrink and develop hair cracks to allow moisture into the brickwork by capillary action. With all types of rendering including those at both extremes of the range as described above moisture will inevitably remain longer in contact with the brickwork when it is rendered than would otherwise be the case if rendering were omitted.

To summarise therefore on the first important factor as to whether rendering is a possible method of repair it is found that:

(a) Rendering should never be applied to brickwork built entirely (not merely pointed) in ordinary Portland cement since there is a grave risk of continuing expansion in the brickwork joints disrupting the adhesion of any rendered finish. The only exception is where the bricks can be shown to have a limited salt content and this is unlikely to be found very often in practice. Nearly all houses built since 1920 will come within this category and a few from earlier times so that analysis of the mortar may be necessary to determine its constituents.

(b) Rendering may be applied as a finish to brickwork only when it is built entirely in lime mortar apart from any pointing and then only when a cement resistant to sulphate attack, for example sulphate resisting Portland cement, Supersulphate cement or High Alumina, is used. The only exception is the unlikely one as in (a) above in which case ordinary Portland cement may be used in the mix.

Rendering therefore is a suitable form of repair for most houses built before 1900 and for a good proportion of those built between 1900–1920. But if there is doubt a sample of the bedding mortar (not the pointing mortar since this must be raked out in any event if rendering is to be applied) should be taken for analysis of the tricalcium aluminate content.

Chemical action between a rendering and its background has probably been the cause of more failures in rendered finishes on brickwork than any other, particularly since the almost universal use of Portland cement began. For this reason the need to consider the background in this respect has been put first. There is however one other important aspect which might indeed often determine the answer without the need to consider chemical interactions and this concerns the strength of the background. Frequently when rendering is being considered the surveyor will be faced with areas of disintegrating bricks. If these areas are general and on exposed or moderately exposed walls and the bricks are showing a soft weak underburnt interior there is really no point in considering rendering. To be effective in these positions at least two and preferably three coat work is required and the first coat should be relatively impervious. Old soft underburnt bricks will just not be strong enough to support such a rendering. There would be little adhesion generally to the powdery surfaces and even where adhesion was obtained the weight of the rendering would be likely to pull off further sections of the brick. It is sometimes recommended in these circumstances that a framework set out from the face of the brickwork and covered with metal lathing or wire netting should be used but with very poor bricks the difficulty of securing such a framework can be formidable. In addition there is eventual danger of cracking, from whatever cause, in the rendering with the severe consequences of corrosion in the metal lathing. On the whole it is considered that this method is indeed one of very last resort and to be avoided, even if secure fixings can be obtained, whenever possible. One of the other forms of repair would be far superior in these circumstances.

One of the rare occasions, however, when the method described in the above paragraph might be considered is where the problem of damp penetration through external walls arises through the use of hard, dense impervious bricks. The defect and cause will be described in more detail in Chapter 8 but even supposing good adhesion can be obtained by raking out brick joints, hacking the surface of the bricks to form a key or other means such as the application of a spatterdash coat there is still a danger that any moisture passing through the rendering will immediately be drawn by capillary action through the brick joints to the interior. The moisture would be prevented by the character of the bricks from being soaked up by them. In such a way the old problem of dampness could recommence, whereas setting the rendering forward on a securely fixed system of battening, well proofed against rot, and built up with two coats of a relatively porous texture over an impervious undercoat could solve the problem. The completion with an oil painted finish would make the repair even better.

For considering rendering as a repair on brickwork the background can indeed be categorised into three separate groups of which the two extremes have already been touched upon. The three groups are:

(i) *Dense strong brickwork* generally has low porosity, little suction and a smooth surface that affords no mechanical key. Although it may not suffer from the same defects and same forms of efflorescence as more porous brickwork, by its nature and because of the capillarity existing in the joints, it is often far from weather resistant. Methods of dealing with rendering are as described above in view of this factor.

(ii) *Moderately Strong and Porous Brickwork* which will be found in the vast majority of cases. This has relatively high suction, and in general provides a good mechanical key and good adhesion for rendering. Being porous however it is particularly prone to sulphate attack and, in accordance with the points already made, may not always be suitable to take rendering if of relatively recent construction. Even if suitable it will usually need the use of sulphate resisting Portland cement or Supersulphate cement rather than ordinary Portland cement in the mix. If the suction of this type of background is high, a spatterdash treatment is recommended and there must always be care not to exceed the strength of the background with the first coat of rendering even in exposed positions. If the surface of the brickwork has already been treated with oil paint, distemper or water repellents that destroy the natural key then hacking by hand or bush hammer to remove one third of the surface to a depth of $\frac{1}{8}$ inch (3·2mm) will be necessary.

(iii) *Moderately Weak and Porous Brickwork.* Although more rare than that in group (ii) above, some brickwork of relatively low strength needs much more care in the selection of rendering particularly because of the need to avoid exceeding the strength of the bricks. If a mistake is made and strong rendering is applied over weak bricks, shrinkage in the rendering will remove by sheer stress the surface of the bricks. The difficulty and well nigh impossibility of rendering over soft and disintegrating bricks on exposed positions has already been discussed. The greater attraction of other methods of protecting the brickwork loom very large in this example and increasingly warrant consideration as the bricks decline in quality and condition.

Exposure conditions and the degree of protection afforded by over-hanging features should govern the selection of mixes and the number of coats of rendering to be applied, bearing in mind that it has been found by long experience that a rough textured and porous rendering gives the most effective resistance to water penetration.

167

Overhanging eaves in particular give protection to any wall, whether rendered or not, the higher the wall the greater the over- hang needed while projecting verges on gables also provide good protection in exposed positions along with cornices, string and band courses, provided these are of reasonable projection and can be given a suitable throating in relation to new rendering. If it is necessary to render a parapet wall it is probable that a new larger coping properly throated and with a damp proof course below will be required. The most important aspect however is to leave the inner face exposed or at least properly ventilated, to allow for the evaporation of any penetrating moisture. Defects often commence in parapets and ideally if reconstructed they should be in cavity work with damp proof courses at the base as well as at the top if more than six courses of brickwork high.

As to a decision on the number of coats and their character, exposure conditions can be divided into three grades:

(a) *Severe conditions* of exposure arise where the wall face is liable to exposure to a moderate gale of wind accompanied by persistent rain. Brickwork at high level and that which projects well above surrounding buildings should be classed as severely exposed as well as most buildings on hillsides and on the coast. Three coats of rendering should be used, the first relatively impervious, with porous second and third coats. A water repellent added to the first coat is desirable, bearing in mind that a rendered solid wall is not really now a recommended form of construction for this degree of exposure and accordingly the finish is being pressed and extended to its extreme limits.

(b) *Moderate conditions* of exposure exist in the vast majority of situations and it is safest to consider all cases of repair work either on this or that of severe exposure basis, since it is almost bound to be first floor brickwork or brickwork above this level which is under con- sideration. Two coat work is recommended in these conditions, the first coat being relatively impervious and the second coat being porous.

(c) *Sheltered Conditions* occur in districts of moderately low rainfall where brickwork is protected from the weather by the proximity of buildings of similar or greater height. The first two storeys above ground of buildings in the interior of towns in such districts are usually considered to come within this group as far as new work is concerned. In regard to rendering as a repair it is considered that there will be relatively few occasions where the two coat work both coats of a porous nature, considered suitable for sheltered conditions will be used except perhaps where appearance only is the factor in deciding on rendering or where the backing is relatively weak.

The final consideration governing the mix of the various coats to be applied is the type of finish selected. While some finishes are superior to others in weather resisting and durability characteristics it is probable that aesthetic considerations will loom fairly prominently in making a decision. It is difficult to give suitable guidance on this aspect even although experienced surveyors will have seen plenty of examples of downright bad selection. So much will depend on the age and character of the existing building but the best guide must surely come from local practice or by study of rendered finishes on similar buildings elsewhere. The finishes available can be classified in the following manner.

(a) *Plain Finishes*: Steel trowelled finishes are not recommended for external cement renderings and a wood floated finish requires a very high standard of workmanship to avoid or minimise the risk of cracking, crazing and irregular discoloration. There is little justification for the use of a wood floated finish even when it is to be decorated with a cement or emulsion paint. Its decoration with an oil paint unfortunately makes it no match for the old smooth stucco finishes and if such finishes are to be matched by new rendering, steps must be taken to obtain the texture of rendering used in earlier times, realising that a mix to produce such a smooth surface while ideal for this limited purpose, relies upon a dense impervious oil paint for protection against the weather and for its ultimate durability. This matching is dealt with more fully in the next section on the repair of existing rendered surfaces but appropriate mixes might be selected for trial from the following alternatives:

(i) 1 part of hydraulic lime to 2 to 3 parts by volume of sand in places where a 1 part of Portland cement, 2 parts of non-hydraulic lime, 8 to 9 parts sand by volume would now be recommended.
(ii) 1 part of High Alumina cement, $1-1\frac{1}{2}$ parts of ground chalk (whiting), 5–6 parts of sand where the corresponding mix based on Portland cement, lime and sand would be $1:1-1\frac{1}{2}:5-6$. Also equivalent would be a mix of 1 part of Roman cement to $2-2\frac{1}{2}$ parts of sand but at the time of writing no manufacturer of Roman cement remains in business.

Even so with these mixes it will be necessary to use a steel trowel or float to produce the smooth finish and there is accordingly a slight risk of crazing, although this is substantially less than would be the case if Portland cement were to be used. It is essential however to allow ample time for drying before painting is put in hand and, because of this, any fine cracks can be stopped as part of the decoration process. One of the advantages of High Alumina cement is that it can be painted at a fairly early stage without the use of special primers, but it is difficult to use in view of its rapid set.

(b) *Scraped or Textured Finishes*: Scraped or textured finishes are generally less liable to crack and craze than plain finishes and are easier to bring to a uniform appearance, which is important if coloured renderings are being used. Successful effects, however, depend on the artistry as well as the skill of the craftsman as the surface skin of the mortar is removed to expose the aggregate. The texture obtained depends mainly on the grading of the aggregate. Horizontal or vertical ribbed textures, the fan texture, the torn texture and the English Cottage texture are some of the ornamental patterns produced by treatment of the freshly applied final coat with various tools. Although these finishes offer more lodgement for dirt, a rough texture tends to an evenness of discoloration which is less apparent than with a smoother finish. The rough texture also breaks up the flow of rainwater over the surface so reducing the risk of penetration. Although scraped and textured finishes are of long standing and have been used for centuries, some of the more fanciful designs are particularly associated with suburban developments of the period 1920–1940 and are related to similar effects produced on internal plaster.

(c) *Hand Thrown Finishes*: The hand thrown finishes can in turn be divided into two groups. In the first place there are those finishes known as dry-dash, pebble-dash or spar-dash where small pebbles or crushed stones of suitable size are thrown on to the freshly applied final coat of rendering and, although lightly pressed in, are left exposed. The difference between this process is that although the pebbles in order to secure good adhesion have to be thrown on wet, they are in the form of an applied finish whereas with rough-cast, wet-dash or harling, as it is known in Scotland, the whole final coat, containing a proportion of fairly coarse aggregate is thrown on as a wet mix and is left as thrown, the texture being governed by the size of the coarse aggregate. The hand thrown finishes have all the advantages of scraped and textured finishes and are indeed more satisfactory from the points of view of weatherproofing, durability and resistance to crazing and cracking under conditions of severe exposure. Although pebble-dash in the same way as some of the more extreme designs for scraped and textured finishes is particularly associated with the cheaper speculative suburban building, rough-cast has for long been traditional as a covering for rubble stonework of the less attractive kind so its use in repair work could be quite considerable. The particular advantage of roughcast, and to an almost similar extent pebble-dash, is now well recognised and lies in the far greater adhesion obtained by throwing on the mix (or in the case of pebble-dash, the pebbles) than is the case when it is merely laid on with a trowel. This advantage is pronounced in many of the finishes more recently developed which are applied by machine and it is also the principle behind spatterdash coats applied over smooth backgrounds where adhesion would be difficult.

(*d*) *Machine Applied Finishes*: Various methods have now been developed to apply a final coat to rendered treatments by hand- or power-operated machines which spatter or throw the material on to the wall. The roughness of the finished surface depends on the material used and the type of machine but interesting textures of a fluffy nature can be obtained quite unlike those achieved by any other method, coupled with integral colouring. Most of the processes are proprietary using proprietary ready mixed materials and are operated by specialists. Two of the types are as follows:

(i) The first type has an open porous structure behaving similarly to hand applied scraped finishes but is equal in general to the waterproof qualities, durability and resistance to cracking and crazing of hand thrown finishes. The particles are thrown on by machine.

(ii) Another type also applied by means of a cement gun produces a finish with a mix of cement and sand only, somewhat similar in appearance to rough-cast but less attractive. It is, however, generally more dense and therefore gives very effective protection, usually being used in circumstances where this is the main consideration. Machine applied finishes, reducing the amount of time and labour required on the finishing coat together with some, but by no means all, of the skill provide a useful alternative range of finishes to those available by traditional means.

As will be seen from the foregoing there is a wide range of finishes available from which, given satisfactory conditions in the background etc. for rendering, a suitable choice ought to be able to be made. As will have been seen, rendering is not a method of repair to be adopted without thought but given that thought, care in the selection of finish, in specifying the materials and good and conscientious workmanship the result can look good and be extremely durable, even if a little more maintenance by way of external painting is sometimes involved.

It remains in this section to suggest various mixes suitable for repair work in accordance with conditions found on the background, exposure conditions and the type of finish required. These

171

are best set out in the form of the table on page 173 which has been adapted from British Standard Code of Practice C.P.221:1960 "External Rendered Finishes" and to which reference should be made for further study in regard to materials and workmanship.

It will be noted from the Table that alternative mixes are given at certain points. The mix shown first is to be preferred in most circumstances but the following considerations should be borne in mind:

(a) the mix for each successive coat should never be richer in cement than that of the previous coat, though it may of course be the same.

(b) the mix richer in cement is to be preferred when it is applied under winter conditions.

It will be noted that Mix Type 1, which can be considered as a pure cement and sand mix with the lime added merely to improve plasticity, is seldom used. Such mixes have a high drying shrinkage and consequently high risk of cracking and are really too strong for most purposes. Their use should therefore be restricted to:

(i) Roughcast or dry-dash finishes (pebble-dash or spar-dash) providing the backing is strong.

(ii) On metal lathing or expanded metal for the first undercoat but only when those backgrounds form a very rigid base. The lighter gauges of metal lathing of the plain expanded type should not be expected to cope with the shrinkage stresses involved with Mix Type 1 and accordingly undercoats of Type 2 or 3 only should be used on the less rigid backgrounds. Second undercoats should obviously be restricted always to Types 2 or 3.

As already mentioned a spatterdash coat is useful to provide good adhesion for a rendering on a non-porous surface and the mix in this case should be of 1 part Portland cement to 1½ to 2 parts sand by volume. If a spatterdash coat is used to overcome uneven suction on porous brickwork the sand ratio should be increased to 2 to 3 parts by volume.

Where there is no danger of expansion in the brickwork but still the likelihood of salts being present, it was recommended earlier that sulphate resisting Portland cement should be used in the mix in lieu of ordinary Portland cement. This is used exactly in the same way so that the mix proportions given in the Table still apply except that where alternatives are given the mix richer in sulphate resisting cement should be used. In severe conditions where there is pronounced evidence of salts in the bricks or the old lime mortar, the

Recommended Portland cement based mixes for hand applied External Renderings on existing brickwork or new Metal Lathing

Mix Type 1. 1 part Portland cement : 0 to ¼ part lime : 3 parts sand by volume
Mix Type 2. 1 part Portland cement : ½ part lime : 4 to 4½ parts sand by volume
Mix Type 3. 1 part Portland cement : 1 part lime : 5–6 parts sand by volume
Mix Type 4. 1 part Portland cement : 2 parts lime : 8–9 parts sand by volume

TYPE OF MIX RECOMMENDED FOR THE GIVEN EXPOSURE CONDITION

Background	Type of finish	First and subsequent undercoats			Final coat		
		Severe	Moderate	Sheltered	Severe	Moderate	Sheltered
Dense, strong and smooth brickwork	Wood float	3 or 2	4 or 3	4 or 3	3	4 or 3	4 or 3
	Scraped or textured	3	4 or 3	4 or 3	3	4 or 3	4 or 3
	Roughcast	3 2 or 1	3 2 or 1	3 2 or 1	3 or 2	3 or 2	3 or 2
	Pebble-dash	2 or 1	2 or 1	2 or 1	2	2	2
Moderately strong and porous brickwork	Wood float	3 or 2	4 or 3	4 or 3	3	4 or 3	4 or 3
	Scraped or textured	3	4 or 3	4 or 3	3	4 or 3	4 or 3
	Roughcast	3 or 2	3 or 2	3 or 2	3 or 2	3 or 2	3 or 2
	Pebble-dash	2	2	2	2	2	2
Moderately weak and porous brickwork	Wood float	3	4 or 3	4 or 3	3	4 or 3	4 or 3
	Scraped or textured	3	4 or 3	4 or 3	3	4 or 3	4 or 3
	Roughcast	3	3	3	3	3	3
	Pebble-dash	2 or 3	2 or 3	2 or 3	2 or 3	2 or 3	2 or 3
Metal lathing or expanded metal	Wood float	1 2 or 3	1 2 or 3	1 2 or 3	3	3	3
	Scraped or textured	1 2 or 3	1 2 or 3	1 2 or 3	3	3	3
	Roughcast	1 2 or 3	1 2 or 3	1 2 or 3	3	3	3
	Pebble-dash	1 or 2	1 or 2	1 or 2	2	2	2

NOTE: The preferred finishes for particular backgrounds are shown in italics, and the mix to be preferred in most circumstances is given first. The table should be read in conjunction with the text, particularly as to undercoats on metal lathing.

173

use of High Alumina cement was recommended. This cement how-ever cannot be used in combination with lime and accordingly in place of the mixes given in the Table the following must be used in substitution:

In place of Type 1: 1 part High Alumina cement to 3 parts sand by volume.

In place of Type 2: 1 part High Alumina cement to $\frac{1}{2}$ to $\frac{3}{4}$ parts ground chalk (whiting) to 4 to $4\frac{1}{2}$ parts sand, all by volume.

In place of Type 3: 1 part High Alumina cement to 1 to $1\frac{1}{2}$ parts ground chalk (whiting) to 5 to 6 parts sand, all by volume.

For spatterdash coats 1 part High Alumina cement to $1\frac{1}{4}$ to 2 parts sand is suitable.

Finally in the Table it will be noted that alternative sand contents are noted for three of the mixes. The principle to be followed is that the higher sand content should be used if the sand is well graded, but the lower sand content should be used if the sand is coarse or uniformly fine.

(3) *Repairs to Existing Rendered Finishes*

Rendering in the form of a daub on the wattle infilling of timber framed buildings comprised the normal method of weatherproofing such buildings in mediaeval times. The treatment was also extended to some of the smaller stone buildings of rubble work both for the weatherproofing aspect and also for the sake of appearance. The re-introduction of brick making enabled this applied treatment to external surfaces to be omitted on the new brick buildings of mono-lithic construction. Weatherproofing and appearance would be en-tirely satisfactory particularly when, as we have seen, the tendency was to build at first to a higher standard of thicker walls. Indeed the use of rendering on brickwork was comparatively uncommon until Renaissance styles of building were well established in the 18th century. Even then the rendering was not so much applied as an essential structural element but as an imitation of stone for archi-tectural effect. Whereas the walls of the mansion were hewn out of stone, or at least faced with real stone on a brick backing, the middle classes made do with plain brickwork faced up in lime and sand, the wall surfaces incised and colour washed to provide a pale imitation of the more expensive stone. The limes used would probably be of the hydraulic type, such as Blue Lias, but even so this has compara-tively little strength or resistance to frost when wet or to the penetration of rain unless protected by coats of lime wash applied at frequent intervals.

The fairly regular treatment which was necessary to maintain lime and sand renderings led to various developments to improve the water resistance of the materials. The first of these, patented in 1773, was Liardet's cement used by the Adam brothers (sometimes accordingly known as "Adam's cement") and also by the architect Thomas Leverton both responsible for fairly large-scale developments in Portland Place and Bedford Square, London. This cement was of a type known as "oil mastic" and later variations and improvements included "Dihl's cement" (also spelt as Dahl or even Dehl) patented in 1815 and 1816 and "Hamelin's cement" patented in 1817. Dihl's cement was said to consist of linseed oil rendered dry by boiling with litharge and mixed with porcelain clay in fine powder and coloured with ground bricks or pottery. The addition of a little oil of turpentine to thin the cement was said to aid its adhesion to the bricks covering the fronts of buildings. Hamelin's cement was said to consist of fifty measures of siliceous sand, fifty of lime wash and nine of litharge ground up with linseed oil. The interesting fact making for difficulty in repair work is that in the application of these oil mastics it was necessary for the brickwork to be first brushed over with linseed oil before the mastic was applied and floated smooth in one coat. In addition to the Adam brothers and Thomas Leverton, Nash is also known to have specified oil mastic for covering walls and chimney stacks and for outside mouldings in the Regent's Park and Carlton House Terraces. The last reference to oil mastic however was in 1854 for repair work, so that although given good and skilful workmanship it was said to produce excellent results, it might be said to have lost out to the success of the "natural" cements which were undergoing parallel development in the early part of the 19th century.

The first of the "natural" cements was patented by James Parker in 1796 and was produced by burning calcareous clay nodules from the Essex coast. It became known as Parker's Roman cement and had properties which were intermediate between a hydraulic lime and ordinary Portland cement, which is an artificial cement and which was not patented until 1824. Atkinson's cement was of a similar type made from argillaceous limestone found in Yorkshire but was said to be inferior to Parker's.

In many ways the availability of Parker's cement, with its relatively good hardening properties, made possible the type of architecture favoured by Nash and known in general as "Regency". Up to that time work of the same class as was envisaged for Park Crescent and the Regent's Park Terraces had been carried out using

Bath stone as a facing. By the time the former were being built Parker's Stucco cement, as it was then called, was being specified by Nash to cover up the rather cheap brickwork and to be "coloured and jointed in imitation of Bath stone". This requirement was carried forward in the lease documents and the finish was to be renewed every four years without variation. Bath stone does not look particularly bright and cheerful so that the terraces must have looked much duller than they do today in their brilliant off-white shade of shiny oil paint. Oil paint, however, for the stucco work was not mentioned until about 1840, probably because by that time it was realised that a superior finish and longer durability could be obtained by the use of oil paint as against the lime washes formerly used.

No doubt the success of Parker's cement on the Crown properties helped towards its popularity for use on many other similar developments of residential properties throughout the middle and later Victorian periods in many towns throughout the country. Certainly for painted stucco Roman cement provided all the hallmarks for success and it was not until the turn of the century and a change in social and architectural fashions that Portland cement began to make real headway as against Roman cement for rendering purposes. Whereas for stucco work on Victorian terraces a smooth painted finish was required the tendency towards "cottage" styles of building started a revival in textured renderings which it was thought should be of a hard and dense nature to keep the rain out since they were usually left unpainted or at best finished with a cement paint. From this time onwards stucco went out of favour and Roman cement was displaced almost entirely by Portland cement, a position which has remained constant ever since. Undoubtedly the use of very hard strong renderings rich in Portland cement was the cause of many failures in the early part of this century, particularly when this richness was combined with attempts to produce either a very smooth finish with a steel float or even the slightly rougher finish produced by the wood float. As we have seen from the section on the use of rendering as a repair, there is a better understanding now in regard to the use of Portland cement and a greater appreciation of techniques used in the past which produced sound work over a wide range of finishes.

In dealing with the subject of repairs to rendered surfaces it will be convenient to deal first with general principles applicable to all surfaces leaving the rather special problems of repairs to painted stucco and oil mastic to the end, even although repairs to painted stucco will account for a considerable volume of the work in this field.

The surveyor presented with areas of cracked and defective rendering would be well advised not to jump to conclusions as to the cause of the defects. As always with repair work an investigation, albeit brief perhaps, is necessary to establish the true cause of defects since the scope of repair work will be governed by these. To carry out the investigation satisfactorily it may be necessary to raise ladders so that quite substantial areas of rendering can be checked for loss of adhesion. Coupled with establishing the cause of the defects will be the decision as to whether the rendering is to be totally renewed, in which case the advice given in the previous section of this Chapter should be followed, or whether it is a question of repairs confined to cracks or patches. Both the extent of the defects and the causes will have a bearing on this decision.

The need for repairs to rendering may arise from neglect, damage, use of unsuitable materials or workmanship or unsatisfactory design of the building. Neglect alone not coupled with any other defect is of course normally a case for renewal, although possible methods of lengthening the life or improving appearance by the addition of further rendering coats or paint treatments will be discussed later. Physical damage is usually confined to specific areas so that defects from this cause can be dealt with under repairs to damaged areas. The remaining causes of defects involve much more complex considerations. A simple example however is of rendering affected by severe diagonal cracks but with no other damage occurring. This might well, on investigation of the house as a whole and particularly of the interior, transpire to be a matter of structural movement. Possibly defects in the rendering might be the least of the house owner's worries, but if the stage of proving the cessation of all movement has been reached and patching up is now the order of the day, there are the indications of how this should be done in the next section. If this stage has not yet been reached then obviously some time may elapse before the structural problems are solved, in which case a temporary pointing in building mastic might be indicated to keep damp at bay in the meantime.

"Map" patterns on rendering, as shown below eaves level on Elevation "C" of Figure 28 are invariably caused by the use of mixes too strong in cement particularly when combined with floated finishes. The difficulty is that if left, much dampness eventually penetrates the cracks in exposed positions leading to the much more serious defect of loss of adhesion due to frost action and, if circumstances permit, sulphate attack in the mortar joints of the brickwork giving rise to the horizontal cracks in the rendering as appear on the chimney stack. We have already seen in discussing the use of rendering as a repair that a rendered finish is not really

177

suitable for chimney stacks and clearly in this example rebuilding the stack in brickwork in accordance with good current practice is necessary, paying particular attention to the flue lining and choice of brick.

Pursuing the example at "C" on Figure 28 and bearing in mind the advice given in the previous section, one would expect sulphate attack to develop below eaves level in due time, since it is almost certain in this typical example that Portland cement has been used in both the jointing mortar and the mix of the rendering. From the pattern of cracking shown, it would seem that no such attack has started so that provided dampness can be kept out of the cracks and away from the brickwork all should be well. Painting with a cement or oil paint might do just that and obviate the need for further work to the rendering as there is hardly any likelihood in the design of a two-storey semi-detached house such as this of water penetration except through the face.

If matters have progressed a little further however and there is evidence of some loss of adhesion and dampness getting into the rendering then a decision on what to do could be a little more difficult. The strictly correct advice as set out in the previous section would be that here is a situation where rendering should not be applied and indeed the evidence points to such a view being correct in the long run. On the other hand the failure so far is due more to shrinkage and an unsuitable finish, not sulphate attack, and the building is two storey and has a projecting eaves all round. In the circumstances if the old rendering is removed, everything allowed to dry out thoroughly, a good key provided by raking out and a two coat (the first coat impervious) render of sulphate resisting cement with a rough cast pebble-dash or a machine applied finish provided would not all be satisfactory? The answer strictly in these circumstances is probably "Yes", because the defect has been caught and dealt with in time, although the slight risk of taking this action ought, it is considered, to be explained to the client. The risk lies in that the drying out of brickwork may not be complete and further slight expansion might take place in the joints, disrupt the new rendering, however well applied, and start the process all over again.

In the above example it is of course assumed that the brick backing contains soluble salts as it is almost certain to do though it may be necessary to carry out a test to be certain. If matters have progressed very much further then the map pattern of crazing may well turn into the pattern emphasised by strong horizontal cracks typical of sulphate attack, in which case no tests will be needed. Sections of rendering will then probably be very loose and it may be possible to find sulphate crystals on the back of detached sections. Sulphate attack as advanced as this requires removal of the rendering and the brickwork left exposed to act as an unrendered wall or alternatively if this is not possible in view of the condition or appearance of the bricks some form of covering other than rendering applied, such as tile or slate hanging or weather-boarding. Refacing with a new skin of bricks is of course another possibility but normally not feasible on account of expense.

The example above related specifically of course to the elevation at "C" on Figure 28, a portion of what might be said to be a typical semi-detached house of the period 1920–1940. As discussed under the section dealing with rendering as a repair the problems of houses of different periods are not necessarily the same. For example a later house of cavity construction might take a new leaf of brickwork at fairly reasonable cost whereas with a house of pre-1900 construction there might be no problem of sulphate attack in the brick joints at all.

It must not be forgotten also that much damp penetration into rendering can be caused by poor design, for example the omission of damp proof courses below copings on parapet walls and below sills. Such causes obviously need dealing with before the repair of the rendering is undertaken. The areas of rendering affected in these circumstances require cutting off and the background allowed to dry out thoroughly before reinstatement is carried out.

The making good of Cracks and Defective Areas. It is not an easy matter to repair cracks and defective areas of rendered walls without making it rather obvious that such work has been carried out. For this reason on unpainted work small cracks which are inconspicuous and which remain dry are best left as they are. If such cracks are more numerous and more noticeable a coating of cement paint or one of the reputable textured paints may well be sufficient to close and conceal the cracks. In painted work of course, the "repair" can in some circumstances be treated as part of the decorative process, the cracks to be filled every time the paintwork is renewed.

Deeper cracks which penetrate right through the rendered finish but do not penetrate into the background of brickwork can usually be attributed to a failure of adhesion in the vicinity of the crack and if hollowness is confirmed it will be necessary for the loose areas to be cut out and made good as described shortly. If there is no sign of hollowness then the crack should be cut out to a total width of not less than 3 inches (76mm). The disturbance of cutting out is likely to cause, in some cases, a certain loss of adhesion in the vicinity of the crack and in these circumstances it may be necessary to cut beyond this distance. The edges of the cut areas should be left square or preferably undercut and the background should be well brushed

179

and washed so as to remove any dust or loose material. Larger sections of making good should preferably be cut to rectangular shape.

Making good should be carried out according to the nature of the background and the type of finish as described in the previous section dealing with rendering as a repair. Obviously the colour and texture of the insertions should be matched as closely as possible to the original work and for this purpose the sand requires to be carefully selected and the Portland cement can either be coloured with pigments or coloured cement used. It is often necessary and well worthwhile to prepare test panels if the work is on a large scale and the original work was unpainted. Even so it must be acknowledged that however carefully the making good is carried out it will almost certainly stand out in contrast to the old work and accordingly the desirability of coating the whole of surfaces with a cement or other paint on completion of the repairs is considerable.

Where cracks penetrate through the background of brickwork then of course it is desirable to ascertain the cause and to deal with this first before tackling the repair of the cracks in the rendering. This is of course a counsel of perfection and if for any reason it is not possible to ensure that all further movement in the brickwork has ceased then the following method is useful in lessening the severity of further cracking. The principle in this case is to cut out the crack in the rendering for a distance of 6 inches (152mm) on either side of the crack and to fix light expanded metal to the background and embedded in the undercoat of the rendering. If it is necessary to repair a crack which has arisen in old rendering due to differential movement between dissimilar types of background, it may be necessary in a similar way to cut away and carry out a repair using metal lathing as described above. Alternatively if the crack is fairly straight and the differential movement is of some order then it may be preferable for the crack to be left as a movement joint and sealed with a building mastic of suitable colour.

Repairs to General Surfaces. Occasionally although a wall with a rendered finish will not exhibit cracks or loose areas it will still allow water to penetrate possibly through undue exposure coupled with an inadequate number of coats, all of a porous nature. If there is some resistance by the owner to hacking off the old rendering and renewing in accordance with the previous section on rendering as a repair, or if economics do not permit this then it would be worthwhile to treat the wall with one of the colourless water repellents available for the purpose, based either on wax or silicones, the latter probably producing a more lasting effect. Even so all such colourless treatments, applied strictly in accordance with the manufacturer's directions, require renewal after a period of some years. This is also necessary with an alternative treatment, that of applying a suitable paint film. A proper oil or other waterproof paint film satisfactorily maintained and applied originally in accordance with the current British Standard Code of Practice C.P.231 is an effective means of preventing rain penetration through external rendered finishes. Obviously however the successful use of these treatments depends on correct diagnosis as they will not be effective if the damp penetration in fact is from some other point and likely to soak not only inwards but also outwards, to blow off either a water repellent or paint treatment from behind.

A paint treatment is also effective for improving the appearance of rendering when this is desired. When there is no question of waterproofing as well the choice of paint is much wider of course and can be extended to include cement and emulsion paints of appropriate types. Not of course that renderings cannot just be cleaned; washing down with water applied through a fine jet at mains pressure is effective but it is important that all cracks, however fine, and damaged areas are made good first in view of the danger of capillary action.

Another method of changing the appearance of a rendered finish can be adopted in certain circumstances. This consists of applying a further rendering coat over the existing work. It can only be done if the adhesion of the whole area of old rendering is satisfactory and if the old work is sound and dense and not soft and friable and so long as the thickness of the old work is not in excess of ¾ inch (19mm). Before applying the new finishing treatment the existing surface will require cleaning down, hacking to form a key and care is required to ensure that the new coating is not stronger than the existing. The amount of hacking may have to be increased if the old surface has been treated with water repellents as adhesion may be difficult in these circumstances.

Repairs to Painted Stucco. Repairs to painted stucco can be divided into two categories in view of the fact that over the years a paint film of something approaching ⅛ inch (3mm) in thickness has very often been built up. Accordingly in the first category it may only be cracks in the paintwork, with curling along the edge of the cracks, which require repair. In other words the defects may be limited entirely to within the thickness of the paint layer.

Where cracks occur only in the paint layer all curled or loose paint should be removed and the wall carefully rubbed down when wet. Cracks and crazes should be primed with an alkali-resistant primer and filled with hard stopping or a non-bleeding mastic. Broad areas requiring filling should be similarly primed and filled

181

with an oil based filler suitable for either knife or brush application. Where the paintwork is thick and it is desired to fill the area flush, then the filling should be applied in several coats. The filling should be primed and brought forward with undercoating prior to the application of the general undercoat and the whole of the stucco should then be repainted in accordance with Code of Practice C.P.231. It must however be acknowledged that repairs carried out as described above over extensive areas of stucco may not be entirely satisfactory either in appearance or durability and where there is much cracking it is preferable, although obviously much more costly, to strip all the old paintwork, make good the stucco if necessary and repaint the whole.

Where cracking is severe, has penetrated to an appreciable extent into the backing and hollowness can be detected by tapping, the defective areas should be cut out in the same manner as previously described and the background cleaned down by brushing and washing to remove dirt and loose material. If oil mastic has been used as the rendering material originally, the brick backing will be found to be contaminated by oil which will make adhesion of a new rendering coat difficult. In these circumstances it is necessary to provide a mechanical key in addition to thorough cleaning and this is best done by hacking or drilling to form at least two holes to every brick, ¾ inch (19mm) in depth. This can be done either by hand or by machine tool and is generally considered cheaper to do than deep raking of the old brick joints, although this too would be an added safeguard to secure better adhesion in critical cases. Before making good is carried out a spatterdash coat should be applied to the brick backing, thrown on in the usual way ⅛ to ¼ inch (3 to 6mm) in thickness again to improve adhesion.

The choice of mix to be used in the making good does not depend, as with unpainted work, upon the appearance required as the stucco is to be re-painted. On the other hand, however, the suitability of the mix for early painting is important and accordingly a mix of 1 part of High Alumina cement to 1–1½ parts of ground chalk (whiting) to 5–6 parts of sand by volume is to be preferred as this can be painted at an early stage without the use of special primers. Special primers are also not really necessary if it is possible to use a mix of 1 part of Roman cement to 2–2½ parts of sand should Roman cement become available again provided the mix is allowed thoroughly to harden. The mix frequently used incorporating 1 part of Portland cement, 1–1½ parts of lime and 5–6 parts of sand does of course require the use of an alkali-resisting primer in view of the high alkali content of Portland cement. A further suitable mix for making good but likely to be variable and much weaker in quality is 1 part of hydraulic lime to 2–3 parts of sand but this should be reserved for very sheltered positions and matching very weak existing renderings. Although this mix, as with the Roman cement mix, is not really likely to require the use of a special primer it is considered a wise precaution to specify the use of such a primer in all cases except where High Alumina cement is used. There is nothing worse than patches of flaking paint on newly repaired and decorated stucco work when they can be avoided so easily by the thorough application of primer.

The mixes for making good should be applied in the same way as for new work, usually in two coats and brought flush with the surface of the existing rendering. With oil mastic as the original rendering there is no possibility of a bond between the old work and new patches so that an undercut edge on the old work rather than a square edge is much to be preferred. If only small patches of oil mastic require repair then it might be possible to consider making up a mix roughly corresponding to the original. One such mix consists of 50 parts of sand, 50 parts of ground chalk (whiting) and 9 parts of litharge mixed to a stiff paste with linseed oil immediately before use. The brick backing is primed with linseed oil, which should be allowed to dry and the mastic is pressed into position and finished with a trowel. One advantage of using an oil mastic such as this is that it can be brought up flush with the level of the existing paintwork. To achieve a match for existing surfaces it is usually necessary, whatever the mix, to finish with a steel float rather than a wood float with the consequent risk of slight crazing and shrinkage cracks.

The final operation of painting should be delayed for as long as possible so as to allow for complete drying and for the development of any fine cracks which may arise between new and old work. Such cracks should be stopped before painting and in cases where oil mastic forms the original material this might well be done by using a suitable oil mastic mix thinned with linseed oil or a filled oil paint, well worked into the cracks and allowed to harden before painting as a whole. The painting operation should of course be carried out in accordance with the current Code of Practice.

(4) Maintenance Repointing

As already indicated under the heading of Repairs to Existing Rendered Finishes, before 1824 when a patent was granted for the manufacture of the first artificial cement, known as Portland cement and made from burning together finely ground limestone and clay, all mortars for jointing, pointing and rendering were based on

183

naturally occurring lime. It is true that during the previous fifty years or so a number of "natural" hydraulic and oil mastic cements had been patented, but these together with Portland cement which eventually superseded them had been developed as a media for rendering rather than pointing, possessing improved water proofing qualities. It was not until the present century that Portland cement came to be used for mixing with sand for pointing. Nobody can regret the invention of Portland cement since without it the rediscovery of concrete, lost since Roman times, would have been impossible but its indiscriminate use has been a mixed blessing so far as mortar for pointing is concerned. The trouble lies in the great strength which can be produced when it is mixed with sand, for example in the proportion by volume of 1:3. Areas of brickwork laced with fat strong joints in the depressing colour produced with Portland cement are unsightly and to a great extent ruin the pleasant effect which can be produced by the texture of the bricks. The pointing itself probably has a compressive strength of something like twice the bricks themselves and the result is quite inappropriate for the purpose.

Admittedly, in maintenance work old lime mortar when it has become soft and has lost its key must be thoroughly raked out and joints cleared of dust and debris at least to a depth of $\frac{3}{4}$ inch (19mm) to provide a key for new pointing, but in addition some care should be taken to specify the mortar for repointing to suit the brickwork and in particular on domestic construction the cement content should be kept as low as possible consistent with the degree of weather resistance required. Gauging with lime to produce a 1:3:12 cement lime sand mix to replace lime mortar is strongly recommended and the judicious use of a colouring element has much to commend it. As is so often the case, the Building Research Establishment and the former Ministry of Public Building and Works have issued pamphlets containing much good advice in regard to mixes for various varieties and qualities of bricks (for example 1:2:9 cement lime sand for soft bricks, 1:1:6 for medium and hard bricks) and for the various positions in the building, i.e. stronger mixes are recommended for work up to damp proof course level and in chimney stacks and parapet walls where the degree of exposure is greater. If repointing is being carried out on brickwork containing soluble salts then sulphate resisting Portland cement should be used and if on porous brickwork it is important to remember the need to wet the brickwork first.

As to the type of pointing the temptation to use a recessed joint should be resisted unless it can be seen that a joint of this type previously used has not caused damage to the brickwork. Replacement of a flush or struck weathered joint by a recessed joint can be dangerous unless one is sure that the bricks are sufficiently hard and of a homogenous type so that there is little or no danger of water penetration through the top edge of the brick freezing and causing damage. Three types of joint only are considered satisfactory and these are the flush, the struck weathered joint and the keyed joint, even the latter being slightly suspect as introducing a shape which can, if not carefully carried out, introduce a ledge for water. Care in the selection of a suitable type of pointing according to the characteristics and condition of the brickwork will be repaid by the appearance of the completed work. For instance if one of the suitable types has been employed previously, was considered to look satisfactory and the condition of the brickwork is still appropriate for its use, there is no point in changing it. Generally it can be said that a struck weathered joint, as at "A" on Figure 43, is more suitable for machine made smooth surfaced bricks of fairly uniform colour as the mechanical regularity of the joint is apt for these characteristics. On the other hand a rubbed flush joint, "B" on Figure 43 or a keyed joint "C", is more appropriate for dappled sand faced brickwork of good texture and the unrubbed flush joint as left from the trowel for rustic work. The opportunity will therefore sometimes arise to select a joint on repointing so as to improve on the appearance of that used previously. The difficulty arises when the brickwork has been neglected over a long period and the arrises of the bricks are badly damaged. Flush jointing as shown at "D" on Figure 43 is normally recommended as the only remedy in these circumstances but the appearance can be dreadful unless the pointing material is carefully blended to tone with the colour of the brickwork and even then the effect is flat and uninteresting. Although tuck pointing is now frowned upon and hardly merits mention in books on a new construction, it served a distinct purpose to match ordinary facing brickwork to the finer gauged brickwork of arches, quoins, band courses etc. on the principal elevations of many houses of the 17th, 18th and early 19th centuries. Repointing general areas of brickwork in some other thicker joint can ruin the appearance of such houses and a client on seeing alternative trial panels might well be persuaded to the extra cost of tuck pointing, despite its reputed lack of durability compared with other forms of pointing. Tuck pointing is also useful and was much used as such in the past, as shown at "E" on Figure 43, for repointing where the edges of bricks are damaged since all the material, apart from the nib, can be coloured to match the brickwork and accordingly the objection to flush pointing in these circumstances can be overcome and an enhanced appearance over the original achieved.

In maintenance work repointing should be carried out in good time and not left until a whole wall is totally in need of it, as by this time decay in the bricks at the top of the wall may be extensive and costly to cure.

PART 5. THE REINSTATEMENT OF FIRE DAMAGE

The reinstatement of fire damage has been kept separate from the rest of this Chapter since it involves no problem, for obvious reasons, in diagnosing the cause.

Following a fire, however, an accurate assessment of the damage must be made before steps for reinstatement can be put in hand. Occasionally the damage will be so great that the building must be considered a total loss but more often the damage varies from the superficial upwards and it is economical to reinstate rather than demolish and rebuild.

Most fires in houses seldom involve temperatures which can cause damage to the already well burnt clay bricks of walls, but concrete or sand lime bricks may be seriously affected. Mortar may be damaged but this is usually superficial and repointing of brick-work is often sufficient. Cement mortar powders under the effect of fire and raking out is accordingly made easier. In cavity construc-tion the cavities between leaves may act as flues exposing the mortar to prolonged and very high temperatures virtually destroying it and severely damaging the ties. Rebuilding of walls becomes a necessity in such circumstances.

Should temperatures reach a high level in a part of the house there is a possibility of unequal expansion inducing cracks and bulges in the wall, particularly if metal in any form is built into the wall, but the affects of this may well be capable of remedy by the same methods as described in this Chapter for subsidiary wall movements, bearing in mind that it is damage caused by movement above ground level so that no foundation problems are involved.

The action of the fire, sudden quenching with water or any small explosion which it may induce could cause holes or spalling to the face of the brickwork, in which case it will be necessary to cut out and rebond with new bricks the section affected. If this is only small, cutting back need only be taken a half brick depth and the making good carried out with stretchers and half brick bats. If large then metal anchors can be used or alternatively block bonding in the traditional manner.

Cleaning of smoke stains from brickwork should be carried out by spraying with water and rubbing with a stiff bristle brush. The use of chemicals must be avoided as these will only leave deposits of salts or alkalis in the pores to cause subsequent trouble. Steam cleaning may be used if the circumstances require, but it should be borne in mind that with brickwork the process of continuous spraying with water over a period before brushing, while labour saving, can saturate right through to the back face and in the circumstances should be avoided.

The mention of saturation in the previous paragraph highlights one of the most important factors in the reinstatement of fire damage. Following the quenching of a fire by hoses the brickwork is saturated and the drying out process is very slow. So much so that it may take a year or so for the level of moisture to reach that favourable for the propagation of dry rot. In the meantime the reinstatement may well have been completed as far as physical features are concerned. It is therefore very vital to ensure that all embedded timbers in walls are removed including all bonding timbers, lintels, plates, fixing blocks, panels, shutter boxes and the like and replaced in concrete, brickwork or plaster as appropriate, having particular regard to the remarks made previously in this Chapter on maintaining continuity in respect of built in timbers in pre-1900 buildings. Provision at the same time should also be made for adequate through ventilation to such timber features as floors and roof structure that remain, or adequate means for easy inspection at a later date. If these precautions are not followed there is every danger of a virulent attack of dry rot following one to two years after a fire has occurred. In addition to the replacement of all timber possible, the treatment against rot of all new timber is essential and items such as door and window frames, skirtings etc., in contact with brickwork should be separated by a fungicidal and moisture barrier. If drying out by forced means is necessary it is preferable to install a dehumidifying system, which extracts moisture into containers to be thrown away, rather than industrial heaters which tend to increase the relative humidity of the air in the building.

Chapter 3
Stone Walls

Contents

STONE WALLS

Page

CLASSIFICATION OF BUILDING STONES 226

THE CHARACTERISTICS OF BUILDING
STONES 227

Factors affecting weathering and decay 229
Atmospheric pollution 229
Soluble salts 231
Vegetation and other organisms 232

REPAIR OF DEFECTIVE STONE

Refacing with new stone 233
Redressing to a new face 234
Plastic repairs 235
Prevention of dampness 239

MAINTENANCE OF STONEWORK

Pointing 240
Stone preservatives 241
Water repellents 241
Painting 242
Limewash 242
Cleaning and removal of stains 243

REINSTATEMENT OF FIRE DAMAGE

Colour changes 246
Calcination 246
Shattering effect of sudden temperature
changes 247

INTRODUCTION

ALTHOUGH in early times stone might be used for the foundations and base of timber dwellings it has always been, apart perhaps for a short period in the early part of the 17th century, expensive in contrast to other building materials. As a result stone houses have nearly always been for the favoured few with the wealth to afford them. This was no less true of mediaeval times and there are, perhaps, no more than 100 or so stone houses surviving from the period up to the end of the 14th century. There are of course many times this number of ecclesiastical and military structures of stone with dates prior to this period but this fact only points to where the resources of the country were deployed at the time. With the growth of the wool trade, stability and increasing wealth, house building in stone increased in the 15th century and included a number of relatively small size houses. The pace increased in the 16th century, although at this time brick was beginning to make an impact owing to its adoption in areas suitable for brickmaking by those in the Court circle for the more important buildings. On the other hand, the dissolution of the Monasteries made available much ready quarried and worked stone suitable for plunder and considerable advantage was taken of this.

By the end of the 16th century, timber had become very scarce and expensive and for the next fifty years or so, before brickmaking became really established and bricks became cheaper, to build in stone was only a little more expensive than in either of the other two materials available. By this time there were a vast number of small local quarries in areas where suitable outcrops of stone occurred, but particularly through the broad limestone belt stretching north-eastwards across the country from the south Dorset coast to the estuary of the Humber. By the end of the 17th century in this broad belt, stone was very much the accepted building material even for the more humbler dwellings, so much so that whole towns and villages were built with the product of the local quarry. Taste and fashion for those who could afford to indulge it, decreed at this time that the man of substance should have a stone house and for the 150 years following 1700 stone was supreme for the larger house. Those whose ancestors had mistakenly built in brick were almost forced by the power of fashionable opinion to rebuild or at the very least encase the family home in stone so that not a vestige of brick remained to be seen. It was a real mark of wealth and standing if you happened to live in an area of brickmaking, to be able to afford to have stone transported many miles for the purpose of building. Those who could not afford to do this, made do with brick and disguised it with stone. Eventually with the mechanisation of brickmaking around the middle of the 19th century, bricks became so cheap that coupled with improved transport facilities, few people in any part of the country, except the most isolated would even consider stone for house building. Many quarries were forced to close and this trend continued almost to the present time. With the development of new types of electric saw since the end of the Second World War there has been a revival of interest in the use of stone as a facing material, mainly confined to public buildings. However, additional subsidies have been offered to certain local authorities in the endeavour to encourage the use of stone where brick has a tendency to look too bizarre in the surroundings. Stimulation of interest in the nation's historical past has also encouraged those in charge of buildings to undertake schemes of repair and restoration to many stone ecclesiastical and public buildings as well as private houses. The establishment of a full scale modern mason's shop by the authority responsible for Chichester Cathedral on a business footing is a sign of the revived interest and that it can take the form of an economically viable proposition. This organisation imports stone almost exactly similar in every respect to the Caen stone from northern France popular in mediaeval times and not only runs apprenticeship and training schemes for masons to be employed on the long-term renovation plan for the Cathedral but also undertakes contracts of repair for other organisations or building owners where the use of such stone would be suitable. There is thus a possibility of a revival of the mason's craft and the stone industry even if only on a very limited scale. This should assist the surveyor's task in arranging for suitable repairs to be carried out when the need arises and to go some way towards helping to avoid the many mistakes that have been perpetrated on the restoration of stone buildings in the last century or so. Some of these have undoubtedly been due to the lack of suitable material and skilled labour as much as to ignorance of sound procedures and lack of the appropriate historical knowledge, much of which has been unearthed comparatively recently.

It is inappropriate to talk of the development of construction in stone through the ages in the field of domestic buildings. In discussing the development of brick construction in Chapter 2 it has already been mentioned that by the time bricks began to be used again in this country, there already existed highly sophisticated stone buildings from the technical point of view. Prodigious feats of engineering had been accomplished in the construction of both the framed churches and the monolithic buildings for military purposes. In addition a high degree of skill had been obtained in cutting and working the stone both to produce accurately faced blocks for building the walls but also in carving to enrich moulded details for window and door openings, arcading walls and for decorating the bases and caps of columns. Structurally these feats had been achieved by building walls of two skins, an outer and an inner, of accurately cut and jointed face work and filling the space in between with stone rubble, pouring in lime mortar to complete the operation. Openings were spanned by arches as it was realised that stone, in contrast to timber, was weak in tension. There was no lack of skill when it came to the expenditure on the larger buildings and stone was often transported long distances by water for the purpose.

When it came to the few domestic buildings it was not a matter of skill as to how they were to be built but a matter of cost. As far as the labour is concerned it costs much the same to build a wall in cheap bricks as it does in expensive bricks. With stone walls, however, much of the cost lies in fashioning the stone so that the more the stone can be used as near its natural state as possible the cheaper the finished wall becomes. For this reason most of the domestic buildings from mediaeval times are built of rubble, as by this means more of the available stone could be used in the most economical fashion. By the end of the 16th century, however, the increased prosperity had enabled quite a few of the richer nobility and merchants to rise to ashlar for their houses. Even so the use of ashlar depended on the availability of the good quality freestone of fine grain and suitably homogenous quality to enable it to be cut easily in any direction with a saw or a mallet and chisel, and still retain a smooth surface and a sharp arris. In Scotland and Wales for both geological and economic reasons ashlar has always been a relatively unfamiliar luxury and even in the limestone belt there are, of course, still an enormous number of buildings in rubble, built this way purely for economic reasons.

The situation as regards construction remained constant until fashion dictated the encasement of some brick buildings in stone. It was not long before those living in areas where bricks were plentiful and cheap found themselves able to have the best of both worlds, a building of composite structure, the bulk of it in brick but beautifully faced in ashlar, thus avoiding the need for transporting two to three times as much stone, let alone the cost of quarrying and dressing. This system of construction also enabled plastering to be carried out much more easily, brick producing a ready keyed flat surface internally. From about 1700 onwards wherever bricks were readily available composite construction was generally adopted for ashlar work and occasionally in areas far beyond. After 1850 composite construction became even more general throughout the country, apart from cottages and small houses in the more isolated stone-producing areas. The trend continued through to the first half of the present century, reducing the demand for stone drastically and limiting its use to virtually an expensive facing material for public buildings of framed construction, often no more than 2 inches (51mm) thick. Apart from restoration work it seems unlikely that it will ever be used in any other way again and excellent fixing systems have now been developed for this purpose.

As indicated in Chapter 2, the great merit found in brick on its re-introduction was the uniform size of the block, easier to handle and lay in a number of different ways to secure a proper bond. Reliance is certainly placed on the bricklayer for a proper job but generally not quite so much as in the case of masonry. The mason often has to deal with stones of all different sizes and it is very much up to him to select those stones most suitable for bonding purposes, particularly in rubble work which is very much a local craft. Because of the irregular shape of stones in rubble work, there is a greater amount of mortar and also a greater reliance placed on the mortar for bonding purposes and these factors necessitate stone walls being thicker than brick walls to fulfil the same function. Books on building construction, certainly the earlier editions of the standard works, devote considerable attention to masonry details and it is not the purpose of this volume to repeat substantial amounts of the information that can be obtained by reference to these. The criticism levelled at the standard works for the last 40 years or so is that the original authors or their successors were almost dwelling in cloud-cuckoo land and the sort of work illustrated was highly unlikely to be required from all but the most limited number of practitioners, let alone students. However, reference to these earlier editions is often most essential in dealing with repairs and it is to be hoped that no-one mistakenly throws such volumes away as being out of date. Basic skills can so often be forgotten and require relearning from one age to the next and this applies in particular to the use of stone.

The fact that stone has almost ceased to be considered as a structural building material is reflected in current legislation. In London for example, never in any event noted for its stone buildings, the London Building (Constructional) Amending By-Laws (No. 1) 1964 deal with the material in one paragraph, so short as to be worth quoting in full.

By-Law 4.11 states that "Stone shall:

(a) possess a resistance to crushing of at least 1500 lbs per square inch (10·342 N/mm²)

(b) to the satisfaction of the District Surveyor, be free from cracks sand holes and any other defects likely to affect adversely its strength or permanence and

(c) if of laminated formation and to be subjected to pressure, be so laid that the natural bed will be at right angles to the direction of pressure."

All very sensible but not much help, for example, if one wished to design a small stone building following rules for wall sizes and thicknesses as one could do in the case of brickwork. On the other hand the use of the word "permanence" in paragraph (b) is interesting and the rule set out in paragraph (c) is undoubtedly a wise one enunciated by all authorities. It is clear that an architect or surveyor would have to convince the District Surveyor in London of the soundness of the proposals but it is thought that those who compiled the by-laws do not really anticipate receiving much in the way of such proposals. One can almost imagine a huddle of District Surveyors examining some masonry to see whether rule (c) is being fulfilled. The evidence of the past suggests that it is not always easy to decide which way to bed some types of stone. However at least this point is made in the by-laws whereas the Building Regulations 1972 ignore it!

On the other hand the Building Regulations are clearly prepared to encounter proposals to build in stone. As they are designed for application to the whole country this is not perhaps surprising. Chapter 2 set out the requirements for the thickness of brick walls according to their height and length for ordinary domestic buildings, as set out in the Building Regulations under the all-embracing terms of Regulation D8 and the "deemed to satisfy" provisions of Regulation D15. The regulation following, D16, covers stone as follows:

"Deemed-to-satisfy provision for walls of stone, flints or clunches of bricks.

D16. The requirements of regulation D8 shall be deemed to be satisfied as to any wall constructed of stones, flints, clunches of bricks or other burnt or vitrified material if such a wall is one to which Schedule 7 applies and it is constructed in accordance with the rules of that Schedule."

Schedule 7 is one that has already been fairly fully dealt with in Chapter 2 on Brickwork culminating in the Table for Rule 7 setting out wall thicknesses which was assumed in that Chapter to apply to brick walls only. In fact paragraph (4) of Rule 7 extends the Table to Rule 7 reprinted on page 87 to stone walls as follows:

(4) In the case of a wall constructed of stone, flints, clinker or other burnt or vitrified material, the thickness of the wall shall not be less than one-and-one-third times the thickness required by this rule for a wall of bricks or blocks.

There is an important qualification however at the commencement of Schedule 7 in case one should consider that the one-and-one-third thickness category should apply generally to those walls falling within the scope of the Schedule. This qualification is that the wall "is constructed of stones, flints, clunches of bricks or other burnt or vitrified material laid *otherwise* than in horizontal beds or courses and jointed". In other words the application of Rule 7 envisages only uncoursed random or squared rubble, Kentish rag, flint walling or other uncoursed local variations of techniques including those where a "watershot" or tilting of the bed from the horizontal is adopted.

The minimum thickness required is interesting as it is usually considered that one-and-one-half to two-times the thickness of a brick wall in comparable circumstances is required for such work. What of coursed work? It might be thought the same thicknesses as for brick might be considered satisfactory but blocks of stone certainly do not come within the definition of bricks or blocks set out in Rule 4 of Schedule 7 and indeed the use of coursed stonework does not appear to be envisaged at all. A curious omission.

Furthermore the Building Regulations give no consideration to the quality of stone or any direction as to methods of construction. This is also strange as it would have been a simple matter, and indeed desirable, to have extended the deemed to satisfy Regulation D16 to include reference to the two British Standard Codes of Practice dealing with Masonry as is done with Brickwork, Reinforced Concrete and Timber. Admittedly there is reference in general terms under Regulation B2 to materials or standards of workmanship being deemed to satisfy the Building Regulations if in accordance with British Standard Codes of Practice, but so much more ground could have been covered without adding to the already large bulk of the Regulations by simple reference to those Codes. It is not as though they were new. Both date from 1951.

Code of Practice C.P.121.202 is entitled "Masonry-Rubble Walls" and C.P.121.201 "Masonry Walls Ashlared with Natural Stone or With Cast Stone" and both follow the usual form of the Codes by setting out recommendations for good practice. To dispose of one point already mentioned it is of interest by cross reference to

Code of Practice C.P.111:1964 "Structural Recommendations for Load Bearing Walls", to note that for a random rubble wall the permissable stresses should be taken as 75 per cent of the corresponding stresses for coursed walling of similar materials (Clause 314a). By straightforward proportion the thicknesses of random rubble walls should therefore be one-and-one-third times the thickness of the corresponding thickness for coursed walling, so that it is reasonably clear how this rule came to be included in the Building Regulations. Unfortunately the straightforward application of this rule runs counter to some extent of the Code of Practice on Rubble Walls which recommends that on no account should solid walls be of lesser thickness than 16 inches (407mm). Difficulties of bonding will be encountered if walls are less than this on account of the fact that the width on bed of most building stones varies from 6 to 12 inches (152 to 305mm). This recommendation also applies to walls with a brick or block backing and it is also indicated that if the wall is to be fair-faced both sides there will be considerable extra labour in dressing the stones in an endeavour to produce a wall less than 16 inches (407mm) in thickness. If a hollow wall is proposed it is suggested that the outer leaf should be a minimum thickness of 16 inches (407mm) the cavity not less than 3 inches (76mm) and the inner leaf whether of bricks, concrete blocks or clay hollow blocks not less than 3 inches (76mm). Continuing the clause on the thickness of walls the Code recommends that on no account should the hearting exceed 6 inches (152mm) on the average. If, for strength or for any other purpose a greater thickness than 16 inches of rubble walling is required wider stones should be utilised.

In two-storey domestic building where in corresponding brick construction one would expect to find 9-inch (229mm) work or 11-inch (280mm) cavity work it is likely that stone walls will be to the order of 16 inch (407mm) solid or 22 inch (558mm) if in cavity work. Such walls, provided the bond and workmanship is of a suitable standard should be satisfactory but any lesser thickness might be viewed with suspicion in view of the difficulties of construction described above.

The Codes of Practice are of course mainly intended for use in connection with new work. They provide detailed information on the factors to be taken into account in the selection of stone for building and other materials for use in conjunction with stone, for example materials for use as damp proof courses and metal flashings and suitable mortars. The Codes also set out the considerations which need to be taken into account as far as design is concerned from a purely constructional and technical viewpoint. The Code on rubble walling is illustrated with photographs and descriptions of different types of wall construction and both Codes contain diagrams covering typical satisfactory detailing at critical points. The information contained in the Codes can be supplemented by reference to standard works of building construction, although it may be necessary to turn to some of the earlier editions for architectural detailing. New designs and shapes, departing perhaps from traditional details, can be checked back with the typical details in the Codes to see whether the functional requirement of the element is satisfactorily fulfilled.

The Codes of Practice provide a standard to which older buildings can usefully be related to ascertain whether they can be said to measure up to current recommendations. They can be of use in assisting towards the recognition of poor construction and enabling this to be dealt with. Where replacement of stone or rebuilding is necessary they will be found to give valuable guidance and assistance towards avoiding some of the mistakes of the past. Needless to say the recommendations should be followed where appropriate and all the factors to be considered duly weighed.

In a comparison between construction in stone as against brick, one factor stands out prominently. Bricks being of a uniform size require much less mortar and correspondingly a brick wall can be built much more efficiently. This is particularly so in comparison with rubble work. Stone walls may give the impression of solidity and strength but this may prove to be an erroneous impression. On the other hand, because of the difficulties of construction already described and which results in stone walls being usually about twice the thickness of comparable brick walls, they do have a substantial degree of mass and weight about them which can be advantageous in domestic construction. In comparison with brick, the components in a stone wall for a normal two-storey dwelling will be subjected to a stress of only something like half. In Chapter 2 it was indicated that a lack of compressive strength in the bricks themselves was seldom, if ever, a cause of failure in a brick wall and it was exceptional to find weakness in the mortar the cause of failure except after a very long period of time. Provided loads are suitably distributed the same considerations apply in general terms to the stone in a wall and also to the mortar, in view of the much lower stresses involved. Correspondingly it is not always appropriate to view the mortar in a stone wall with the same critical eye as one would view it in a brick wall. What would be considered very poor mortar for brickwork may, within reason, be perfectly adequate for a stone wall. Age is more important usually than the initial quality.

With the massive nature of stone walling, restraint is a further factor which is not quite so important in domestic construction in

comparison with brickwork. Stone walls in view of the more favourable relation of width to height will stand on their own a great deal
better than comparable brick walls. In other words the slenderness
ratio is usually far less. There is abundant evidence of this fact in
the many derelict stone buildings which dot the countryside. Roofs
and floors have gone but the walls remain standing, sometimes for
centuries.

Despite the favourable considerations which have been outlined
above in relation to stone walls as against brick, it still remains that
construction in brick is more efficient and provides a more economic
use of material. Bonding both transversely in the width of the wall
and longitudinally on the face of the wall is much easier to achieve.
It is this factor of difficulty in bonding coupled with the use of
rubble filling that provides the chief source of weakness in stone construction. In addition although poor bricks break down in time,
brick is in many respects the more durable of the two materials.
Stone, being a natural material, has to be taken as it is found and
although selection can permit rejection of the poorer and defective
strata there are still wide variations within veins which affect both
compressive strength, working characteristics and in particular
weathering qualities.

DEFECTS IN STONE WALLS

When confronted with a stone building that is out of repair the same
procedure as outlined in Chapter 2 must be followed in regard to the
investigation into the cause of defects before repair work is put in
hand. In the first place it is essential to establish whether the building
is constructed wholly of stone or is of composite construction. This
can usually be done by obtaining a sight of the interior wall face in
a part of the structure which is not plastered, either in the roof space
or below floor levels. The causes of structural failure are, in general,
precisely the same as those for brick walls which are dealt with in
detail in Chapter 2, so that too much need not be made of them here.
However, stone being a different material reacts to these causes in a
slightly different way and these manifestations need consideration.
It is convenient to follow the same headings as used in Chapter 2
and consider, albeit briefly, these differences.

DEFECTS ARISING FROM CONDITIONS ABOVE GROUND
LEVEL CONCERNING TYPES OF CONSTRUCTION AND
MATERIALS INVOLVED

(1) *Movements arising from inadequate design, faulty
construction or overloading*

(*a*) *Inadequate thickness in walls*

In domestic construction inadequate thickness in stone walls is less likely to be encountered in view of the factors that arise in the methods of building. Having regard to the minimum thickness normally required for satisfactory bonding even a reduction from this standard would not be too important as far as physical strength is involved. Should inadequate thickness be found, however, it is almost certain to manifest itself in a lack of bond and correspondingly a separation of the inner and outer skins from the hearting. This is true whether the wall is wholly of stone or is of composite construction. In the latter case there may well be no bond at all between the backing and the stone facing if the backing is a mere $4\frac{1}{2}$ inches (115mm) in thickness.

However in the larger multi-storey domestic buildings inadequate thickness can introduce the same type of defects in regard to leans and bulges as occur in brick construction. In addition tall parapets and chimney stacks are likely to be affected in the same way as already described in Chapter 2.

(*b*) *Faulty Construction*

With stone walls defective bonding will manifest itself by displaced sections of walling, localised leans and bulges and fissures but is less likely, in comparison with brickwork, to give rise to whole wall movements.

Faulty construction or inadequate design in roofs leading to an angled thrust at the top of walls will of course have the same effect as on brick. One is perhaps more likely to come across roofs deliberately designed to exert such a thrust with stone buildings. Many buildings from past eras may well have a hall or gallery with an open timber roof, the thrust from this being intended to be taken on buttresses. If the buttresses are inadequate, whole wall movements may be induced.

Arches with inadequate abutments will introduce localised movement in the abutments themselves and also in the stonework above the arch.

Sedimentary stones such as limestones and sandstones, in contrast to brick, are of laminated construction and it is important in normal

200

walling that the stone should be "natural bedded", that is laid with the laminations horizontal as in the quarry and correspondingly at right-angles to the pressure. This is desirable not so much from the point of view of compressive strength, although most stones do in fact exhibit a greater strength when laid this way, but from the weathering aspect. An exception arises in connection with cornices and string courses where natural bedding would tend to permit mouldings and throatings to be eroded too rapidly. For this reason "joint" or "edge" bedding is permissible in these circumstances, that is when the laminations are vertical but at right-angles to the face of the wall. Even so there is obvious difficulty in arranging for this at the corners and, at this point, it is desirable to choose stone carefully and to natural bed corner or angle stones. Arch stones should be carefully selected and arranged so that the laminations are at right-angles to the thrust.

One difficulty however is that it is not always an easy matter with some stones, particularly those which are not normally seasoned for a winter or so before use, to determine the natural bed. As a result many examples of "face bedding" will be found, that is where the laminations are vertical and parallel to the face of the wall. In general walling, this is not too important from the point of view of strength, always provided it is not too extensive, but in parapets, cornices, mullions in windows and in other projecting and free standing features it can lead to dangerous conditions, possibly involving the fall of large masses of stone from a building, and often at least settlement and fractures in features adjacent.

(c) Overloading

The effect of overloading on stone walls, whether from point loads on narrow piers, in beams carrying walls over openings or in floors is precisely the same as that in brick construction.

(2) Movement Arising from Defects in Materials Used and Chemical Action on Materials

Nothing further need be said here over and above that in Chapter 2 in regard to the decay of built-in timbers. The effects of such decay become apparent in the same way as in brickwork.

However, as has been mentioned previously, stone being a material which has to be taken in its natural state, is subject to correct selection for its use. It is possible, accordingly, for a stone of poor compressive strength to be selected but even so in domestic construction this is unlikely to be critical in regard to stability. Far more likely is that such a stone will exhibit poor weathering qualities

201

which prove critical in an exposed, free standing or projecting feature.

With some sedimentary stones, the quarry may contain beds of different structure and characteristics. These are often widely separated and easily apparent so that selection enables the bad to be rejected. On the other hand it is sometimes very difficult indeed to differentiate the various strata in the quarry so that occasionally whole blocks are taken out and eventually reveal markedly different weathering properties from the remainder. Within a single stone "soft" and "hard" beds may occur. Both sandstones and limestones may be subject to this defect but, again as previously described, the effect will not be particularly serious except in special features where the unequal weathering can cause trouble.

A further natural defect that can cause the same type of trouble arises with the presence of small fissures in the stone. These are usually attributed to earth movements causing a fold in the strata but they are not always apparent in the newly quarried stone. Sometimes the fissures are resealed naturally by the deposit of calcite from solution so that they only become apparent when the stone is subjected to the weather over a period. In this case the fissure opens again and the block is found to be in fact in smaller sections than originally believed. When defects of this order arise causing a weakness the term "vents" is applied, but when no fissure occurs in the folding of the strata the term "shake" is used. Vents can be a source of considerable trouble on a building with much ornamental detailing, loosening substantial features but in plain ashlar walling the effect is not severe, affecting appearance and weatherproofing qualities only.

Whereas vents and shakes arise naturally, the use of explosive charges in the quarry has been known to produce similar cracks which are not noticeable at the time of quarrying but only become apparent later. These cracks can allow the penetration of water and thus accelerate decay. Blocks affected in this way when used, for example, as lintels, can lead to failure.

It is reputed that bruising often occurs to stone when it is being worked, particularly sandstone. A sharp knock not causing damage at the time can result in loosening of the cementing material between the particles. This will cause an initial speedy erosion of the area when exposed to the weather and may result in sections becoming loosened. It is also reputed that machine dressing can result in similar defects arising if too heavy pressure is brought to bear on the stone by carelessness. Mouldings and details formed in these circumstances are liable to rapid disintegration and possible loosening.

While stone, as found in a natural state, may prove to be defective when used and may also have defects induced by methods of quarrying and working, its use in building renders it liable to decay to a greater extent than usually arises with bricks. Bricks are made for a purpose and, although as has been indicated in Chapter 2, poor bricks can be and are made and incorporated in buildings they are not normally a source of structural weakness in ordinary walling except in very exceptional cases. The same is generally true of most building stones but the problems of decay due to atmospheric pollution, chemical attack and chemical reactions are very much greater. Appearance and waterproofing characteristics are more likely to be severely affected, rather than the structure, but since many stone dwellings tend to have more ornamental features than those built in brick mention should be made of these causes even though they will be dealt with in greater detail later in this Chapter when types of stone are considered, coupled with a consideration of the differing effects of weather and contamination. Exposed features such as chimney stacks, parapets, cornices, free standing features and the like will be effected initially and, if the decay is allowed to continue, a structural problem may well arise involving a danger of collapse.

It has long been a practice in much stone construction for metal to be used for dowels and cramps, particularly to secure ornamental features. Rusting of wrought iron in particular, because of its laminated construction, has caused considerable trouble in the past. The knowledge of the difficulties likely to arise with the use of iron have been well known for centuries and many attempts have been made to overcome the problem. In the time of Edward II tinned iron was used in the Palace of Westminster. Wren is said to have specified that no iron should be used within 9 inches of the air, but his instructions were not always followed and much damage has resulted in his buildings from the corrosion of iron. However it has been found that in St. Paul's some of the iron had been completely encased in copper and had escaped corrosion. This procedure was adopted on some later buildings but unfortunately without the same success, corrosion necessitating much repair. It is known that in one church built in the 18th century steel was used for cramps and, when examined fairly recently, these were found to be free of corrosion. However, steel used on much more modern buildings has become seriously corroded and the material is not recommended now except in an alloyed state. Much of the trouble in the Houses of Parliament has been due to the use of iron in conjunction with a stone, Anston, particularly prone to vents. The need for restoration has arisen principally in the ornate decorative and free-standing features which became structurally unsound, although in some positions the iron had been galvanised in an effort to avoid the corrosive effects of the atmosphere. It is interesting to note that a building erected at about the same time in the same stone has suffered little, the reason being that the design was in a strict classical style as against the ornate neo-Gothic of the Houses of Parliament. Corrosion of embedded metal is a problem which affects stonework to a considerable extent and usually involves the replacement of both stone and the fixings. Nowadays the development of non-corrosive alloys of steel, copper or nickel should have overcome the problem, but even so pilfering of copper cramps is not unknown and their substitution by iron could remain unnoticed until troubles arise.

Finally in this section of the causes of defects attributable to materials used in stone walls mention must be made of the mortar. As mentioned previously, there is much more of this in most stone walls than in brick walls, although in the case of ashlar or good coursed work on both faces this may not be readily apparent. Also, as mentioned before, the mortar itself need not be so strong as in brickwork for comparable domestic structures. Notwithstanding this fact, however, the mortar of the hearting fulfils a vital function and its deterioration over the years can lead to substantial structural defects. This is true of both true stone walls and those of composite construction. In the latter case there can be a complete separation of the stone facing from the brick backing. In ashlared stone walls, the deterioration of the mortar can lead to the collapse of the hearting so that the smaller rubble stones of the interior settle to the base of the wall leaving the upper part as two unbonded skins. This can arise particularly where an old building is now subjected to the vibration of modern traffic. As a result, large masses of facing masonry can become separated from the core of the wall, stones displaced and leans and bulges arise either affecting the whole of the wall or a localised part only. More often than not the condition of the hearting can only be surmised from the symptoms and it is necessary usually to cut away a section of the base to examine the interior. This should always be done with care on a limited scale at any particular point, otherwise there is a danger of a considerable amount of friable mortar and rubble escaping from the hole which might result in a much more serious danger of collapse. Failure of the hearting, defective bonding and movements arising from foundation troubles or ground movements are probably the most frequent causes of structural defects in stone walls.

(3) *Movements Arising from Temperature Changes*

As for brickwork, movements of a serious nature due strictly to temperature changes are unlikely to be found in domestic buildings of stone construction. Long lengths of stone walls may show signs of slight cracking from this cause but generally the walls are divided up by window and door openings so that any movement is more likely to be taken up in these areas and probably extend to no more than a slight opening of the joints. The more extreme damage from this cause which has been reported, such as blocks being loosened out of place, shattering of blocks and spalling on the edges, is more likely to arise in buildings of other than the domestic type. In parapets however of long length where, of course, there are no openings a troublesome effect of temperature changes arises with coping joints which have a tendency to crack and, as a result, fail to remain watertight. Cracks in the parapet itself can also arise and sometimes a certain amount of oversailing at the corners of the building.

In modern composite construction where thin stone slabs are fixed as a cladding to brickwork or concrete, differential movements can arise on the expansion of the cladding under hot sunshine. These can be particularly severe if the expansion of the cladding is accompanied by a shrinkage of the brick backing as the construction dries out shortly after building. If these movements are not allowed for, by way of expansion joints in the design, then serious fractures can arise very often depriving substantial portions of the cladding of all support and introducing a danger of collapse.

(4) *Movements Arising from Shrinkage on Drying or Expansion on Wetting of Materials*

Movements arising from shrinkage on drying are less likely to be as serious in stone construction as in brick except in new buildings of composite construction, as described in the previous section, where the stone is used merely as a cladding. In these cases the differential movements are the main cause of the trouble.

Stone which becomes very wet is not likely to expand to any great degree so as to cause structural damage, but of course if the wetting is followed by a sharp frost there is serious danger of surface damage and fracturing of the stonework due to the substantial expansion of water as it turns into ice. Not all building stones in use are affected by frost damage. Most sandstones and the better quality limestones are safe from this danger and it is rare that stone used in the walls of buildings will be affected. Copings, string courses, cornices, parapet walls, sills, steps, free standing and retaining walls

205

are more likely to suffer from frost damage and the effects on these features will probably be more severe if it does arise than in comparable brick construction. The reason for this is that stone is used in larger unit sections, so that the expansion tends to fracture the stones whereas in brick the effect of the expansion is more often taken up in the more frequently occurring face joints.

Defects Arising from Foundation Troubles or Ground Movements

The symptoms arising from defects owing their origin to conditions above ground level in stone walls, as discussed, are different in some respects from those arising in brickwork but, as with brickwork, it is necessary to eliminate these causes from the investigation before proceeding with the next stage. All those causes set out previously can give rise to cracks and displaced sections of walls which can easily be confused with settlement. If, however, all these causes can be discounted, then it may well be that the symptom will be the result of a defect owing its origin to conditions below ground level. In considering this type of defect in relation to stone walls nothing need be added here that is not already fully dealt with in Part 2C of Chapter 2 and in order to determine into which of the five possible groups a defect falls, the reader is advised to turn to page 111 and read through to the conclusion of Part 2 on page 124. The symptoms of these causes are just the same for stone walls as for brick walls and the confirmatory evidence will have to be ascertained and found in the same manner. Again, however, before proceeding with the repair of the stone wall it may well be necessary to complete a repair elsewhere to eliminate the cause of the trouble if this is due to some factor other than conditions in the wall itself. For example it may be necessary to underpin and it may be advisable for this work to be carried out before the work to the wall is commenced.

REPAIRS TO STONE WALLS

WHOLE WALL MOVEMENTS

Consideration is given at the beginning of Part 3 of Chapter 2 to the problem of safety and whether a structurally defective brick wall can be tied in or repaired or whether it is necessary to demolish and rebuild it entirely. It is unnecessary to repeat the advice contained in that section of Chapter 2 as the considerations apply equally to stone walls and the procedure to determine what is required should be followed in the same manner, subject only to the following comments.

From the earlier parts of this Chapter where the characteristics of brick and stone walls have been contrasted, it will be apparent that in the domestic construction envisaged in this book the need to re-build is probably far less likely to arise with stone walls than with brick. Their greater thickness in relation to their height means that generally they will be able to tolerate a lean or bulge with far less danger of collapse. Providing the conditions giving rise to these symptoms have ceased or can be cured so that movement will not continue, it is more than likely that the problem will remain as one of repair rather than rebuilding. However, before any decision can be taken all the factors of age, quality, degree of lean or bulge, dis-placement of stone, cracks and fissures, whether bonding is satis-factory, the condition of the mortar and, of course, the function of the wall must be considered. Even if the condition of the wall is not so serious as to warrant rebuilding but it is still necessary to take some steps to arrest a movement due to conditions in the wall itself, the effect of the restraining work should be taken into account in conjunction with the estimated cost, the client's views and having regard to the effect on appearance of the finished work. As dis-cussed in Chapter 2 the client may well feel disposed to go to the additional expense of rebuilding if the restraining works are to appear very obvious, though with stone walls, as will be seen, there are probably more opportunities for making these unobtrusive than with brick.

Should it be necessary to rebuild then, of course, the opportunity will arise to comply with current recommendations, not only those in respect of legal obligations, but those also contained in the appro-priate Code of Practice to which reference should be made. Provided that the stone in the old wall is not too badly weathered it should be possible in the case of most old buildings which were originally built in lime mortar to re-use the stone from the demolished wall. There is no reason against the re-use of old stone and indeed, if it is neces-sary to make up the quantity, the most likely and suitable source of the required material may be from a ruined or demolished building nearby or perhaps by the demolition of an outbuilding on the same site, always provided that the stone is of a similar kind. The only trouble likely to arise in the re-use of old stone is that if it is light coloured and has been exposed to a smoke laden atmosphere it might develop light brown stains on newly cut surfaces.

If new stone has to be purchased great care should be taken over its selection. It should be as close to the original in colour, texture and type as possible and limestone should always be matched with limestone and sandstone with sandstone. The two should never be mixed for reasons which will be discussed later. If stone of the same

207

kind is no longer available from the quarries then even greater care is necessary in the selection of an alternative and this is particularly so if the unduly weathered condition of the existing stone suggests that in any event this is desirable. It may be necessary in these circumstances to take specialist advice and it is most important to ensure that supplies are sufficient to maintain a reasonably uniform quality in the deliveries to correspond with the samples on which the decision is based. When using new stone in contact with old blocks, it is always advisable to coat the back, sides and bed faces with two coats of a heavy bituminous paint so as to avoid the danger of any contamination from soluble salts from either the old stone adjoining or from a brick backing.

A sound idea to adopt in connecting new work to old, particularly where ashlar is involved, is shown at "A" on Figure 44. This is to rebate slightly the toothing left on the old work so as to provide an extra thick compressible joint at the point of contact. By this means an allowance will be made for the inevitable slight settlement on the new work and a fracture should be prevented from occurring near the joint of new work to old. Even so, it may still be necessary to carry out some repointing after about two years and after it has been established that all settlement in the new work has ceased.

Stone walls can become displaced horizontally in whole or in part without a lean or bulge being involved in the same way as with brickwork. If the movement is slight it is often of no consequence and it is usually sufficient to rake out the joint where the movement occurs and repoint. There is the additional advantage with stone, in view of the extra thickness involved in the walls and the inherent nature of the material, in that it can normally be dressed back to a new face with no loss of strength. This factor is of assistance in dealing with a problem of this kind.

Displacement on the damp proof course can be dealt with in a similar manner to that shown on Figure 39, for brickwork, by taking new stone down to the foundation level. In other circumstances where the condition of the wall itself is satisfactory it may be possible to jack the wall horizontally back into its proper position, provided it can be relieved of all load by shoring up the roof and floors. This method has been adopted with success on a number of ancient buildings but the need for a specialist engineer's advice is essential in the circumstances, preferably of an independent nature. Walls which are in a satisfactory condition but which through foundation failures or thrust from other features have developed a substantial lean can also be jacked back into position by relieving the wall of all loads and erecting a system of triangulated braced shores and plankings so that the pressure from the jacks is exerted evenly

Various methods of repair to stone walls

'A'. Joint of new work on right to old.

'B'. Jacking a wall back to the original position.

'C'. Flying buttress.

'D' & 'E'. Building a buttress using jacks.

Unlike the trussed rafter roof at 'B' which exerts a uniform thrust along the top of supporting walls, the collar braced roof at 'C' and 'D' exerts a thrust only where principal rafters and collars occur and accordingly a wall may need strengthening at these points. Buttresses are notorious for aggravating existing troubles by settling in themselves. To avoid this difficulty flying buttresses as at 'C' can be used or alternatively attached buttresses either carefully built (see text) or incorporating reinforced concrete bonders and jacking, shown at 'D', until all settlement in the new work has ceased before completing as at 'E'. Typical methods only are shown and all work of this nature requires calculation.

Scales 1:40 & 1:200

44

209

throughout the whole wall face. To obtain the required leverage it is necessary to jack from solid ground and such work may have to be carried out in conjunction with either underpinning or other works to ensure that the conditions giving rise to the lean are not repeated. Once again the services of an engineer would be essential. An example of a typical operation of this nature is shown at "B" on Figure 44. The trussed rafter type of roof, when the collar is placed too high, exerts a uniform thrust along the whole length of the top of the supporting walls. A consistent lean throughout the height in an otherwise sound wall could be corrected by using jacks after independently supporting all roof loads and cutting the ends of the wall from its connection with return walls. Obviously there would be no point in the operation unless something was done by way of alterations to the roof structure to prevent the uniform thrust continuing either by the insertion of ties or trusses. If the character of the roof was to remain entirely unchanged then the wall once back in its vertical position would have to be strengthened to resist the thrust, a possible case for the introduction of piers along the length of the wall.

Early stone houses with open roofs exerting an angled thrust at the top of the walls may lend themselves to the provision of external support in the form of buttresses, either to strengthen the wall generally or to take the thrust from open trusses. In so called Gothic architecture there is a long tradition of such features and new buttresses will fit in perfectly well if sensitively handled. As mentioned already in regard to the addition of buttresses to brick buildings, there is a considerable danger if the work is not done well of aggravating troubles already in existence. The buttress must be designed and built so as to exert a counter thrust otherwise it will be useless. In this connection a flying buttress as shown at "C" on Figure 44 is more satisfactory since by its design it will lean against the wall to be supported even if the foundations on which it stands do settle a little. A buttress attached to the wall which it is to support can however be successful provided certain precautions are taken. Excellent foundations must be provided at the same level as those for the existing wall and the size calculated carefully to avoid overloading the sub soil, new work must be thoroughly bonded to the old, and work must proceed slowly using quick setting cement so as to avoid compression before it is set. For very old and valuable buildings the method shown at "D" on Figure 44 has been suggested whereby a connection between new and old work is deferred for some time until any initial settlement in the new work has ceased. This is done by building reinforced concrete bonders into the old wall projecting outwards at suitable intervals and building up the new buttress in such a way as to leave spaces where adjustable jacks can be positioned under the bonders. These jacks are screwed up from time to time so that the new work is compressed under the weight of the old and which it will be expected to support when completed. It is only when movement in the new work has ceased that the jacks are removed, the new work pinned up to the old and the buttress completed as at "E" on Figure 44. It might be said that the same effect could probably be achieved at far less expense by the provision of metal tie-rods to the roof structure. This may be so but tie-rods would probably destroy the character of the roof, however unobtrusively arranged and for this reason a client might perhaps prefer to indulge in the additional outlay. It should not be forgotten that in respect of buildings of architectural and historical interest assistance in the form of grants can be obtained in certain circumstances towards the cost of works of repair, see Chapter 11.

Whereas buildings in the Gothic style might satisfactorily lend themselves to the addition of buttresses stone buildings of classical design generally do not and the addition of such features would be highly incongruous. There would appear to be very few ways in which such features could be disguised, except perhaps in conjunction with an extension to the existing building.

Though the condition is much rarer there are occasions when walls lean inwards rather than outwards. In these circumstances the provision of cross walls might be a solution which could be easily overlooked, but is clearly one which would only be a possibility on the rare occasion when internal re-arrangement was being carried out in conjunction with repairs.

The use of iron rods fixed to cast iron plates on the exterior of walls to tie them in has been as much used on stone construction in the past as it has with brickwork. It must be admitted, however, that the method has tended to be abandoned in the best class of work over the years for the same reasons as on brickwork. The plates are disfiguring and rusting of the iron has caused serious damage to the stonework. The method is probably now only considered in cases where a building has a known life of a fairly limited number of years and yet it is worthwhile to do something to preserve it to fulfil its function for even that length of time. If metal is used the sections within the stonework should be of a non-rusting material. When the rods are subjected to stress, the plates need to be fixed very securely as there is considerable danger that the stones on which they bear will pull out or alternatively that circular cracks will form around the plates. As such they are more suitable for walling of the ashlar type, still in sound condition but which may have developed a lean, for example due to mining subsidence. The effect of tightening up rods for plates on an ashlar wall with a defective core, however, can

211

well be imagined. Rubble walling because of its relatively poor bond in a longitudinal direction is not very satisfactory for tieing-in by this method, although on a wall soundly constructed and in reasonably good condition much could be achieved by packing out to the back of a steel channel, for example, as a means of providing additional support. If rods are used they should be adjustable so that they can be tightened up, but only just to take up the strain and no more.

Notwithstanding the foregoing comments on the use of tie rods and plates it must be acknowledged that the introduction of metal can cause more harm than it cures and it must not be forgotten that long metal rods can expand and contract according to changes in temperature and that this factor needs to be taken into account when they are in excess of about 30 feet (about 9m). They are perhaps more appropriate as ties to timber features where the resilience in the material will accommodate such changes. Shorter metal rods and straps set in concrete blocks as described in the Chapter on brickwork and illustrated on Figure 36 can be used however in stone walls with much greater scope as ties linked to sound and substantial floor structures. In view of the greater mass of stonework such ties have to be disposed more frequently than in brickwork to achieve the same effect. On the other hand the addition of turned down or cranked ends and nibs to the sides of the concrete can be made more easily in the greater thickness of stone walls so as to secure a good bond. Ties of this nature can serve the dual purpose of preventing an outward movement in the wall and, as will be seen shortly, of providing a longitudinal tie or "stitch" along the length of the wall. They can also be made quite invisible from both outside and inside, thus eliminating one of the principal objections to long metal tie rods and external plates or steel sections.

However, as already mentioned previously in connection with stone walls, there is far less likely to be a need for rebuilding, tieing-in or supporting a wall by buttresses in domestic construction than there is with brickwork. Indeed most authorities dealing with the repair of ancient buildings with historical associations have gone so far as to say that such methods are quite unnecessary and inappropriate and that repair section by section can always be effected so that as much as possible of the old work can be retained and preserved in its original state entirely consistent with safety. This is perhaps a counsel of perfection in regard to all stone buildings, for there are many that have neither historical connections or outstanding architectural qualities, or even simple age, to warrant the heavy expenditure which would be involved by the use of the labour consuming methods recommended. The economics of the situation may vitally affect the decision and indeed in many cases may be the prime consideration. However the method of repairing a wall part by part undoubtedly forms the ideal and even if it is not possible in all circumstances for it to be put into practice in respect of whole walls in very poor condition, it will certainly be necessary to carry out repairs of the same type, but on a more limited scale, if there are serious fractures or fissures in a wall otherwise sound, but perhaps with sections of displaced stonework. In conjunction with the repair of cracks and displaced sections grouting is also useful to help to bind an old wall together, at a time when age has resulted in a general decay of the mortar of the hearting, giving rise to extensive voids in the interior of the wall. Grouting on its own, however, is not considered satisfactory unless coupled with other repairs as it is far more likely to cause further movement and displacement.

The object of the repair of a fracture is to unite the two portions of the wall so that it becomes a unified whole as originally built. It presupposes, in the case of the first example of cross-bonding in stone that the original cause of the movement and fracture has ceased to operate or the cause has already been dealt with, for example by underpinning, otherwise the operation will be a waste of time. Cross-bonding in stone leaves the wall no stronger than before but merely unifies the two parts. The work is begun from the bottom of a vertical fracture and a hole is cut into the wall up to the back of the stones on the opposite face, taking care at this stage not to jar or disturb these. The size of the hole will be governed by the amount of masonry that can be considered self-supporting, and the general state of the wall. Obviously the work above must be strutted and shored while the work is being carried out. Loose walling only should be removed unless it is necessary to remove sound walling to secure a proper bond. When the hole is formed in the wall it should be carefully washed out and any crevices hand grouted together with flinging grout on to the back and sides of the wall, where it will adhere far more securely than by trowelling. The hole can then be built up again as for new work utilising the old stones when they have been cleaned off. In very special cases where such attention warrants the face stones can be set in the same positions as they existed originally. In this case the stones are marked when they are removed and detailed photographs taken of the wall before the works are commenced. The rebuilding is carried out in heights of about 1 foot (300mm) to 1 foot 6 inches (450mm) at a time, the lower courses being tailed back as far as possible. The core of the wall can then be filled with concrete well packed in and to which can be added clean stone, tile or broken brick provided this is entirely free from salts. The top of the concrete can be finished with a flat stone or layer of tiles to form a bed for the next and similar stage of the operation until the hole is filled and the stonework boned on either side. If the crack does not extend to the full height of the wall or runs in a diagonal manner, great care must be taken to pin up to sound work in the usual manner with a dry mix of concrete, well rammed in, but only after the rebuilt work has properly set.

Both fractures and loose sections of walling can be dealt with in this manner and, by a careful system of planning before the work is started, long lengths both vertically and horizontally can be repaired in alternate sections in the same manner as underpinning coupled with the necessary re-arrangement of shoring. Generally with a repair of a fracture as described above it is usually possible to do the work from one side of the wall only, selecting the side which is most seriously affected. If it is possible to avoid disturbance on the opposite side of the wall so much the better. It may not be entirely necessary to rebuild along the whole length of a vertical crack provided sections can be reunited and properly tailed in on either side to sound work. The remainder can be dealt with by grouting and pointing.

The difficulty in regard to the method of cross-bonding in stone as described above is that it is essential to ensure that the wall will not be subjected to the stresses originally giving rise to the fractures. At one time this form of cross-bonding was used even when there was no certainty that the cause had been eliminated and, because the wall as repaired is no stronger than before, there was a tendency for the new work at one end or the other to pull away from the old and the crack to re-appear. If there are suspicions of this nature, and the cost element precludes expensive investigations and works to entirely eliminate the cause or, alternatively, where by the nature of the cracks such works are hardly warranted the method of tile stitching is preferably adopted. This is a most adaptable method since the tile is small and easy to handle, but the tiles used should be of sound hard quality and if with nibs should be laid in a thick bed of cement mortar so that the nibs do not touch. In the case of a wall plastered internally it is considered that a tile stitch should always be used in preference to cross-bonding in stone. The method of working in the case of wall affected by a long vertical fracture is as follows and is illustrated on Figure 45. Commencing fairly near the lower end of the fracture and working from the inside face a section of stonework about 18 inches high (457mm) and for a distance of at least 30 inches (762mm) on either side of the crack should be removed, if necessary in short lengths, extending right to the back of the facing. A level bed is prepared and the opportunity should be taken to grout up the remainder of the crack below the selected point as will be described

Tile stitching

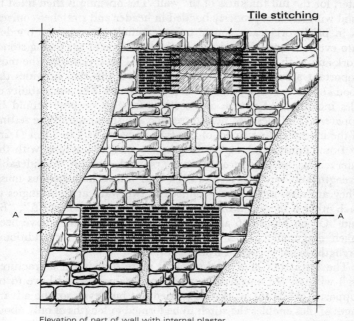

Elevation of part of wall with internal plaster
cut away for repairs.

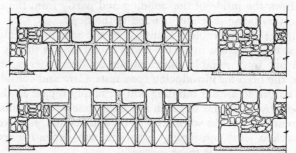

Plans of alternate courses of tile stitching on
Line A-A.

The elevation shows a random rubble wall built to courses
with a diagonal fracture in process of repair by tile stitching and grouting. The lower stitch has been completed
and the fracture above has been pointed and grouted
from the opening formed for the upper stitch, about two
thirds of which has also been completed. Temporary supports have been omitted for clarity. Stitches are usually
formed about 4 to 5 feet apart (1·22 to 1·52 m) and are about
5 feet (1·52 m) long and 18 inches (0·46 m) deep. Note from the plan
how, with pieces of tile, all the spaces can be filled in
right to the back of the outer face of the wall.

Scale 1 : 40   **45**

215

later, for the full thickness of the wall. The opening is then filled in solid with the tiles properly bonded in header and stretcher courses, as in brickwork, each course being carefully threaded or bonded into every irregularity existing in the back face of the facing stonework and to the stonework on either side. This is probably the most important aspect of the operation since it is this that provides the good key for the attachment of new work to old. The adaptability of tiles including, of course, cut sections for this purpose should be apparent. The tiles also help to reduce any shrinkage in the setting of the mortar. Tile stitches of this type disposed at 4 to 5 feet (1·2m to 1·5m) intervals along the length of a vertical fracture, with the intervening sections grouted and pointed, exhibit considerable strength and serve to re-unite the wall into a homogenous mass. They are also useful for re-connecting two walls at right-angles to each other if there is a fracture in the angle as shown at "A", "B" and "C" on Figure 46 and in these circumstances they have been taken diagonally across the angle to good effect for additional strength, being corbelled from below.

The formation of a tiled stitch is more difficult in a fractured wall with an old and friable rubble core which would have to be supported while the work was carried out but, even so, the advantages of tiles enables the stitch to be formed in lengths of only about 2 feet (610mm) at a time. In the worst cases a stitch can be inserted partly from the inside of the building and partly from the outside, each portion being carefully bonded to the next.

A further considerable advantage of tile stitching and gravity grouting to a fracture in an otherwise sound wall is that it can be carried out by a reliable conscientious builder under supervision without the need for introducing specialists. Care and consideration of this nature to an old building will be amply repaid in the satisfaction of knowing that so much has been done with a minimum of interference to the old work. It will be appreciated, however, that such work is time consuming, laborious and expensive requiring close supervision if it is to be successful.

A slightly cheaper method than using tile stitches is to form stitches in reinforced concrete but this form of stitching is by no means so adaptable and it is often difficult to arrange for the positioning of the reinforcement and to ensure that it has adequate cover. If there is a danger that the cover might be inadequate to prevent the metal rusting then it should consist of non-ferrous incorrodable metal, such as delta metal. The method of inserting reinforced concrete stitches is similar to that of tile stitches and the reinforcement should be positioned at top and bottom of the beam and connected by stirrups. If the stitch has to be inserted in short lengths then a suitable mesh reinforcement should be used which can be unrolled as the work proceeds and yet still be continuous from length to length. Alternatively it would seem perfectly feasible to use the method of cutting away and inserting patent stools so as to form the basis for an in-situ concrete beam as shown in the three stages at "D" on Figure 46 and on the section and which will be described in greater detail in the next Chapter for underpinning works. A further difficulty arising with reinforced concrete stitches is to ensure that a good bond is arranged both to existing work at either end and also to the back of the facing stonework. At the ends this can usually be arranged by the provision of nibs on the beam but it is more difficult to arrange a bond to the facing skin. As concrete shrinks on setting and unreinforced work is weak in tension there is some danger of nibs being broken off unless they in turn are reinforced. However, near horizontal cracks in stonework have been successfully repaired by the use of reinforced concrete stitches where stresses are more likely to be tensional and where the horizontal reinforcement can be satisfactorily placed to resist these. Horizontal bands of this nature amounting to the provision of beams tieing the wall together have the effect of redistributing stresses over the whole length of the wall. They are certainly more useful than tile stitches when placed near the top of a wall, as to be efficient a tile stitch must have a sufficient mass of wall above to provide rigidity.

In the case of ashlar on a brick backing it is usually possible to work in a similar way so as to avoid disturbing the stone face. If all movement has ceased the repair can be carried out by introducing as many new bricks as necessary to provide an adequate bond across the heart of the wall and to bond in on either side of the crack. With a brick backing, it is also probably more satisfactory to stitch in with brickwork for the full height of a wide fissure, but if the crack tails off then sections only need be dealt with in this manner the remainder being repaired by gravity grouting. If it is suspected that there is still a risk of movement then the introduction of wire mesh or hoop iron reinforcement in the joints, as described in Chapter 2 will help to resist tensional stresses.

The procedure for gravity grouting a crack in a stone wall when used in conjunction with stitching, in one or other of the various forms, but where the core of the wall is otherwise sound is as follows and as illustrated at "A" and "B" on Figure 47. A start is made at the lower end of the crack and work is carried out in lengths of about 4 feet (1·3m) at a time. A hole is opened up to the centre of the wall at the top of the section and the crack where visible on both faces is stopped up with clay. The interior of the crack is then washed out with clean water by introducing the water through a clay cup

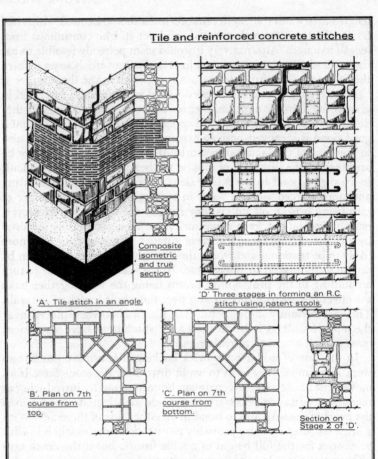

Tile and reinforced concrete stitches

Composite isometric and true section.

'D' Three stages in forming an R.C. stitch using patent stools.

1

2

3

'A'. Tile stitch in an angle.

'B'. Plan on 7th course from top.

'C'. Plan on 7th course from bottom.

Section on Stage 2 of 'D'.

The adaptability of tiles for stitching can be appreciated from 'A', 'B' and 'C' above where two walls fractured at the angle but otherwise sound can be united by tile stitches inserted in short lengths with a minimum of temporary support.
Patent precast concrete stools can provide the temporary support required for the insertion of R.C. stitches, which on concreting are incorporated in the stitch. Holes are formed for the insertion of the stools which are positioned on a prepared bed and the stone to be supported is pinned up with a stiff mix of 1:3 cement and sand (Stage 1). The spacing of the stools depends on the length of stonework which can safely be considered self supporting. If the weight of wall to be carried above the stool exceeds 2 tons per foot run (3333 kg/m), the stools used would be of steel. Stage 2 and the section at 'E' show the reinforcement in position, bars top and bottom with stirrups, and a spatterdash coat applied to the back of the facing stonework to form a key. Shuttering is then fixed and the concrete poured and tamped, the final operation being the pinning up, in a stiff mix, between the stools.

Scale 1:50

46

formed at the top of the section and allowed to run out at the bottom. When all loose particles have been washed out the hole at the bottom is then plugged with clay, the interior again filled with clean water which is left and allowed to seep into the surrounding wall. The grout, consisting of equal proportions of Portland cement and coarse sand mixed with enough water so that it runs easily, is then prepared, kept well stirred, and introduced through the clay cup until it appears out of the bottom hole. The bottom hole is then stopped and a further hole made about 1 foot (300mm) higher. More grout is introduced until it appears from this hole which in turn is stopped up and another hole higher up formed. The process is repeated until the whole crack is filled when the grout is allowed to set. It is advisable to repeat the whole operation once again to ensure that all cavities have been filled as the success of the method depends on the correct opening of the vent holes so as to prevent the formation of air-locks. Much also depends on the adequate saturation of the stonework and existing mortar within the crack as, on setting, a mix as rich and wet as that necessary to ensure a proper flow, is bound to shrink considerably if setting is accelerated by loss of the water in the mix to surrounding absorbent material. The penetrative power can be increased adopting the method of low pressure grouting described in Chapter 2 for cracks in brickwork by pouring the grout into a funnel attached to about 5 feet (1·6m) of garden hose and introducing the nozzle into a hole at the bottom of the section of crack being dealt with, the funnel being supported about 1 foot (300mm) above the top section of crack. By this method the grout can be forced into cavities which might not be reached by the normal method of gravity grouting, but as before the avoidance of air-locks is vital to the success of the work. Once again it is necessary to stress that grouting up a crack will not check an active source of movement and it can only be considered a method of consolidating the results of past weakness.

Stitching and gravity or low pressure grouting of cracks will normally repair a wall that is affected by cracks or fissures, which may also have given rise to loose and displaced sections of stonework, but where the core of the wall is generally sound. Walls which are dislocated and friable and where the core consists of little more than loose material, full of small and dusty cavities, really need the attention of specialists and high pressure grouting after the repair by stitching has been carried out. The extent of the cavities in these circumstances would be sufficient to short circuit gravity grouting by producing too many air locks.

However, before proceeding to describe the operation of high pressure grouting as carried out by specialists, it is useful to point out

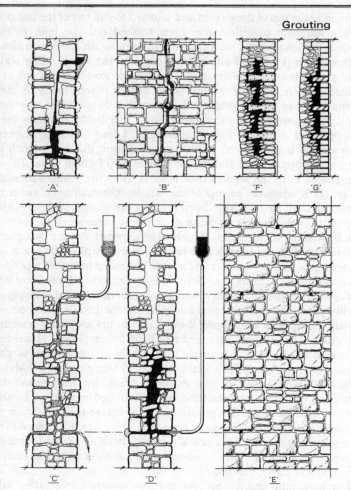

Grouting

'A'   'B'   'F'   'G'

'C'   'D'   'E'

Section 'A' and elevation 'B' show a crack in process of gravity grouting.
The grout is poured into a cup formed in clay at the top and has just
reached holes left in the temporary clay pointing about a quarter of
the way up the section being dealt with and is beginning to appear at
the hole on the left, the right hand hole already having been plugged.
Washing out for low pressure grouting is shown at section 'C' where
the whole core of a wall is friable. Holes are left for the operation
after pointing the wall both sides at about 3 foot (1 m) staggered
centres as shown on elevation 'E', while section 'D' shows the first
stage completed. Providing the facing is unbroken, grout can be
applied to hold the flintwork in place, if becoming separated from
the core or backing. Section 'F' shows dovetailed concrete bonders
built in from the back and section 'G' extra headers built in to a brick
backing.

Scale 1 : 50

47

that the low pressure method of grouting cracks can be extended to deal with the whole core of a wall if this has become friable if the the circumstances are appropriate. The conditions envisaged are where the economics of the job, the size of the walls involved and the remoteness of the property do not warrant the bringing of specialists to the site with the necessary high pressure air machinery. Provided pressures of no more than about 4 to 5 lbs. per square inch (0·028 to 0.034 newtons per square millimetre) equivalent to about a 10 foot (about 3m) maximum head are adopted, a reliable general contractor should be able to grout a whole wall, tackling small sections at a time as shown at "C", "D" and "E" on Figure 47 without the need to close shutter the wall as is normally necessary with high pressure grouting. Obviously, however, the wall must be pointed on both sides before the operation is commenced and holes are left at about 3 foot (1m) staggered centres for access, the sequence of procedure being as described below for high pressure grouting. With relatively thin rubble walls, however, it is not usually necessary to drill to form the holes for access as these can be made at joints. If it is necessary to drill however, the drills used should be of the helical type which withdraw the material as they penetrate the wall and water should be fed to the heads the whole time they are in operation as there is a serious risk otherwise of fracturing the stone.

Even the grout used for high pressure grouting, which since the introduction of improved apparatus after the Second World War can now be of two parts of coarse sand to one part of Portland cement without danger of clogging the nozzles, will not set or bond to dirt and, if pumped into a dusty wall, will in any event lose part of its water content to the dust or porous stone. For this reason it is essential, as in the case of gravity grouting, to wash out the section to be grouted before the operation is commenced. In cases where the hearting is very loose care is necessary to ensure that only dust and dirt is washed out and excessive washing must be avoided otherwise there is danger of complete collapse of the hearting. It is essential to maintain all shoring during the entire operation of grouting. The washing out process is commenced at about 6 feet (2m) from the bottom of the wall and when this and the interior has been saturated as previously described the grout is introduced under pressure through a nozzle held by hand with a lump of clay, initially at not more than 25 lbs. per square inch (0·172 newtons per square millimetre) from the base of the wall. Leaks are stopped with wooden plugs hammered in but when the level reaches about 3 feet (1m) within the wall the grout is left to set. The operation is then repeated over the same section twice more under higher pressures rising to a maximum of 40 lbs. per square inch (0·276 newtons per square millimetre) and the grout again left to set before the adjacent section directly above is dealt with. The sequence is carried out in much the same way as in underpinning in alternate lengths until the whole wall from bottom to top is filled with new grout. It must be appreciated of course that the new grout cannot replace old poor material that is still adhering soundly to the stonework inside the wall but at least all the voids will be filled and as such the transverse bond between faces can be restored. It is considered however unlikely that grouting alone can be relied upon to secure a defective stone wall. A wall that needs grouting almost certainly will need a considerable amount of other repairs to cracks and bulged and loose areas. Conversely a wall not requiring other works of this nature probably does not require grouting just for the sake of it, even if a trial hole shows that the mortar is in a relatively poor condition. As stated before, a stone wall, being thicker and therefore stiffer than a comparable brick wall, does not need mortar of the same strength and if the wall is reasonably sound in general terms and has been so for some years there is no point at all in disturbing it. The only circumstances where grouting might be resorted to as an insurance is where alterations to the building involve redistribution and perhaps a concentration of loads on the wall or improvements might necessitate the formation of new openings in walls. A loose or bulged facing of stonework can cause particular difficulties in regard to pressure grouting and this fault is likely to be found on just those walls that need grouting because of the poor condition of the core. If the condition is fairly general it would undoubtedly be cheaper, rather than taking down and rebuilding the face, to tie it in position with temporary bands or strut and plank it from a strengthened scaffolding, followed by pressure grouting which will then reunite the loose face to the core and the backing. It is on these occasions that a reverse of the usual process might have to be adopted and the grouting carried out before dealing with the more serious areas of displaced stonework. Much temporary filling will have to be carried out in these circumstances which will add to the cost, but it may be the only way to save an old wall from destruction.

With a facing of flint it is common to find the whole face detached from the core and bulging progressively forward. It is sometimes possible to avoid the need for complete refacing by inserting stone or precast concrete dove-tailed bonders set to project well into the core at intervals to anchor back the face and then grouting up the cavities in the core under pressure, two examples being shown completed at "F" and "G" on Figure 47. This is only possible if the flint face is unbroken and it is even more essential in these circumstances to shutter the face while the grouting operation is in progress and to leave the support in position until the grout is set so as to prevent complete separation. If sections of the flint face have to be re-set it is essential to build in long flints at intervals so as to bond the new work back to the core. Alternatively this can be done by building in pieces of worked stone at irregular intervals. Working with flints is nowadays practically a forgotten art, but the need for repairs continues particularly in East Anglia where a fair amount of buildings with flint facing or with flint panels exist. The difficulty of bonding the facing to the backing has always existed particularly with uncut or knapped flints normally built up without coursing to any bond on the face at all and accordingly much weaker structurally than squared flints built to courses. If sections of flint walling have to be rebuilt it is usual now to provide a brick backing, to build up sections no more than 12 inches (305mm) high at a time and to leave ample projections from both the flint face and the brickwork into the core and towards each other, filling the core with a cement lime concrete. Flints have one advantage over stone in being almost imperishable so that it is invariably the mortar and the core of the wall which decays. In repointing it should not be forgotten that flints are non-absorbent and therefore a cement lime mortar should be used and the mix kept fairly dry. The joints are by the very nature of the construction very wide with uncut or knapped flints and are often galleted with smaller pieces of flint.

Finally in this section dealing with movements in stone walls mention must be made of another method which combines the repair of fractures with grouting in one operation. Delta metal rods with hooked ends are threaded through small holes in alternate directions across a crack from side to side and from interior to exterior. These rods are then fixed in position by pressure grouting, the wall again being shuttered during the grouting operation. This method involves cutting away far less stonework than does the insertion of a tile stitch and is considered useful for uniting the two skins of a bulged wall. The result however is not very strong in resisting any of the tensional stresses that may arise in the wall and under certain circumstances it has been known for the rods merely to pull away at the ends. Although on the face of it this method may sound more attractive it is considered probably wise to anticipate some further movement, however slight, in most circumstances, in which case the method of tile stitching is more reliable and has been proved over many years in the repair of stone buildings.

Subsidiary Wall Movements

The causes of subsidiary movements in stone walls are the same as those which arise in connection with brick walls and nothing additional needs to be added here over that set out in Chapter 2. Many of the remedies are the same too, particularly those concerning other materials built into walls, timber for example in the form of lintels and bonding members. Much of the repair work to cracks and sections of loose walling has also been described in the previous section of this Chapter dealing with whole wall movements and need not be repeated again. There remain, however, one or two matters which require a few additional comments at this point. One of these concerns arch construction which in old stone buildings can present difficulties. There is an old saying that an "arch never sleeps" which is perfectly true since it always exerts a spreading tendency on its abutments. This tendency is known to those who have the care of old churches in their hands as "drift". The problems in domestic construction are nothing compared with those likely to be encountered in ecclesiastical work but even so with domestic buildings sufficient abutments were not always provided and the slow movement outwards of those provided will induce the arch to sag and cause movement above. Abutments can sometimes be stabilised by adding to the vertical load above the haunches of the arch, rather on the same principle as that adopted by the mediaeval builders with their flying buttresses by the provision of heavy pinnacles. However this is not often practical and a more likely solution will lie in transferring the load from the wall above the arch by means of a reinforced concrete lintel beam inserted a short distance above as shown for similar circumstances arising with brickwork on Figure 39. By this means the arch is relieved of the bulk of its load, will cease as a result to exert a thrust on the abutments, which will instead now be supporting a load acting vertically downwards. Once again there would appear to be every possibility of cutting away for a long beam and arranging for its casting by the use of the patent stools of the type described in the next Chapter on Foundations, provided loads are suitably calculated, as they would have to be in any event to establish the size of the beam and its reinforcement.

Abutments to arches can, of course, now be calculated, but a suitable rough rule of thumb useful for checking is that with semicircular arches there should be an abutment on each side equal to three-quarters of the span of the arch. This can be reduced to about half the arch span for pointed arches of the "gothic" style and increased to an amount equal to the arch span for shallower arches. An error of design frequently made in the past is that of providing

224

insufficient abutment at the ends of an arcade. Failure in the end abutment can introduce a serious danger of progressive collapse if steps are not taken to restrain the movement. In view of the inter-dependence of one arch upon another in an arcade a similar danger can arise if a single pier fails.

On the same principle, failure can also arise in a line of inverted arches below ground level used to distribute the load from a series of piers between a row of windows along the total length of foundation. In these circumstances, underpinning and rebuilding of the arch would probably be necessary but if it occurred at a corner abutment then it is likely that the services of an engineer would be required to deal with the problem of re-arranging the end arch and strengthening the abutment.

Stone buildings have a tendency to be provided with features such as oriel windows and staircase turrets which may project from the general line of the wall face. If these are showing indications of moving away from the main part of the building much can often be done with the use of gunmetal or delta metal straps. These can be looped round such features, preferably just above mouldings so that they are less likely to be visible and securely anchored back into sound and solid masonry on the main wall. Often the stonework in such features is of relatively thin construction and not suitable for the use of tile stitches.

Many of the subsidiary movements encountered in stone con-struction, on the other hand, are associated with the characteristics of particular types of building stone and their weathering qualities. These have been touched on briefly in regard to the causes of defects but it is now necessary before dealing with the types of repair possible to parts of walls to devote some attention to stone and its characteristics together with the effects upon it of various agencies. This subject is dealt with very fully in textbooks on new construc-tion and much invaluable information has been published by the Building Research Establishment. There have been a tremendous number of different types of stone used in building through the ages usually from small local quarries which have long since vanished. Within the classification of types of stone there have also been the wide varieties in quality from the different beds in each quarry. Until recently there has been little other than past experience on which to base a decision on the selection of stone and from an ex-amination of stone used in buildings it will be found that many cases arise of incorrect selection for a particular purpose as well as improper workmanship. For these reasons it is considered that a surveyor faced with extensive decay in the stonework of a building will need to carry out a certain amount of investigation not only to

STONE WALLS

establish the type of stone used but also to establish its characteristics before a suitable repair can be effected. The latter point can
of course be partially covered by the examination of the stone in the
building itself but it may be necessary to take samples for testing. In
most cases much information can normally be obtained from local
sources but the surveyor must be prepared to carry out this investigation and also to do some further research into characteristics once
the stone has been identified.

CLASSIFICATION OF BUILDING STONES

Geologists classify rocks into three main divisions according to the
way the rock was formed in the first place. These main divisions
are:

(1) *Igneous rocks* are formed by the cooling and solidification of
molten material, granite being most commonly used for building
purposes together with basalt.

(2) *Sedimentary rocks* are of secondary origin formed either from
the disintegration of igneous rocks, from organic matter or by precipitation from solution. Their essential nature is one of layers compressed by consolidation and cemented together with material
brought down by means of percolating water. Sedimentary rocks
are known normally by their main constituent, thus limestone consists mainly of carbonate of lime and sandstone mainly of grains of
sand. The sedimentary rocks form the main group of building stones.
There are many subdivisions depending largely on the amount of
secondary material.

(3) *Metamorphic rocks* are either igneous or sedimentary rocks
which have been changed from their original form either by heat or
pressure or a combination of both during movements in the earth's
crust. The character of the metamorphosed rock depends on the
composition of the original and the pressure to which it has been
subjected. Limestone turns into marble, sandstones into quartzites
and clays into slates. A characteristic of many of the metamorphic
rocks is their foliated structure, particularly pronounced in slate
which together with marble are the two principle rocks of this
division used in building. They are not, however, generally in use as
a walling material in domestic buildings in this country. Indeed the
stones which we know as marble in this country are not true marbles
at all but limestones having the ability to take a good polish.

226

CHARACTERISTICS OF BUILDING STONES

The character and composition of the stones used in a wall are two of the governing points affecting its weathering properties.

Granite, used primarily for domestic buildings in the areas where it is quarried, namely in Scotland, Cornwall and the Lake District is heavy, hard, dense and extremely strong although slight fissuring often occurs giving it a small degree of porosity. Being insoluble in water it has exceptional weathering qualities and durability although it will develop a skin of sooty deposits in polluted atmospheres which is difficult to remove when it is desired to clean a building. Problems of decay do not really arise in the case of granite even in the one time heavily polluted atmospheres of Scottish industrial towns.

Sedimentary rocks however depend to a large degree on their constituents for their resistance to weathering and decay. As mentioned above some consist of the more resistant constituents of igneous rocks such as quartz, which is pure silica and extremely hard, with subsidiary amounts of felspar and mica. These crystals are cemented together with some other material and it is the composition and chemical stability of the cement which is important in weathering. Sandstones are classed as siliceous, ferruginous, calcereous or argillaceous according to whether silica, iron oxide, calcium carbonate or clay form the main constituent of the matrix. Clearly the siliceous group of sandstones represent the most durable, not being attacked by water or gasses in the atmosphere. Sandstones with a cement of iron oxide are reasonably good but often the iron oxide is mixed with other less resistant materials and these stones are notably not good weathering stones. The calcereous sandstones being cemented with carbonate of lime and the dolomitic, cemented with magnesium carbonate, are also not good weathering stones as the cementing material is dissolved by rainwater and it is attacked by carbon dioxide and other acids in the air. This results in the loosening of the quartz grains. Clay itself is a poor cementing material and accordingly these sandstones in the argillaceous class are very poor indeed for building purposes and erode rapidly.

The limestone group of sedimentary rocks consist essentially of calcium carbonate. As with sandstones the original deposits consisted of loose particles but these were later cemented together, the chief agency in this process being the percolation of water carrying calcium carbonate in solution. Living organisms played a part in the formation of some limestones and it was originally thought that the oolitic group were formed in this way. This theory has now been

227

abandoned and it is generally accepted that they were formed by chemical precipitation and consist of small rounded particles of crystalline calcium carbonate. Their appearance resembles the structure of the roe of a fish from which the term oolite (egg stone) is derived. The size of the grains vary and generally they possess a concentric structure, layer upon layer of calcium carbonate being deposited around a nucleus which may be of sand. The oolitic grains vary too in their degree of porosity. The structure of oolitic limestone also varies in that in some, for example, Portland, Ketton, Casterton and Weldon the grains are cemented together simply at their points of contact. In other limestones the oolites are set in a continuous dense non-porous crystalline calcite. In these examples water can only penetrate through the grains of oolite and not through the cementing material. The oolitic Bath stones are of this type.

In most oolitic limestones shell fragments occur. In some stones they occur infrequently but in others they predominate, in Barnack stone for example. In the majority of limestones other constituents form a very small proportion of the composition, the remainder being pure calcium carbonate. The foreign constituents, however, may consist of silica and if this forms a significant proportion the stone is referred to as a siliferous limestone. It may consist of clay in which case the term argillaceous is used but these stones are not used for building purposes, being however a useful source of hydraulic lime for the building industry. In the case of magnesium carbonate as a constituent in any substantial proportion the stones are referred to as magnesian limestones and if these contain the double salt formed by the combination of calcium and magnesium carbonate they are referred to as dolomites, Anston and Mansfield being important examples much used as building stone, but being variable in weathering qualities.

The principal factor in regard to weathering in limestone is that calcium carbonate is slightly soluble in water but much more so in water carrying carbon dioxide or sulphur dioxide in solution. The former is a natural constituent of the air and the latter being a product of combustion is widely present in polluted atmospheres. The wide variety in the structure of limestones and the degree of porosity renders some stones much more durable than others despite the fact that most can be dissolved in acids.

Factors Affecting Weathering and Decay

(a) Atmospheric Pollution

Carbon dioxide in solution is not considered to be of particular consequence in affecting weathering and durability but sulphur dioxide is. In limestone buildings the effect of clean rainwater on the stone is to slowly dissolve it away. This may result in a certain softening of details and the exposure of fossil fragments in the coarser textured stones but in general walling surfaces the slight differences in hard and soft beds are often revealed and the wall given a textured and more interesting appearance. More often than not the calcium carbonate dissolved by clean rainwater is redeposited in a slightly different place on the surface of the stone on evaporation of the water so that the actual loss of material is slight. There is a possibility however that the redeposited material may be more susceptible to attack by sulphur dioxide as it is likely to be in a more powdery form than the original.

However, with calcareous sandstones as mentioned previously the effect of clean rainwater will be to dissolve the cementing material and this may result in quite large areas of stone being loosened in projecting features when the calcium carbonate is redeposited on the outer edge leaving the sections further back without any cementing material, a defect frequently occurring in sills, copings and cornices.

However, when the atmosphere and rainwater are polluted by smoke and sulphur dioxide in solution (sulphurous acid) as it is in many urban areas there is a reaction between the calcium carbonates in limestones and dolomites and the calcareous sandstones to produce calcium sulphate which in sheltered positions forms a hard dark smooth skin and which eventually causes blistering, scaling and loss of cohesion of the surfaces. The cause of exfoliation in these circumstances is probably due to a combination of crystal formation near the surface immediately behind the skin and also the fact that the calcium sulphate so formed on the surface has a different coefficient of expansion from that of the stone behind. In positions where the stone is exposed to the washing action of the rain the formation of the hard skin of calcium sulphate is prevented, as the rain washes away both the soluble compounds which would otherwise form the skin and also the deposited soot.

The form of blistering which occurs on limestones, dolomites and the calcareous sandstones in polluted atmospheres does not occur with granite or with silicaeous and ferruginous sandstones as the constituents of these do not produce the same reactions. On the other hand, buildings constructed of these stones collect a film of

STONE WALLS

firmly adherent black sooty deposits which unlike those in sheltered
positions on limestone buildings are insoluble in water and correspondingly much more difficult to remove. Although spoiling the
appearance of the building the deposits do not harm granites and
sandstones of the particular types mentioned. Construction utilising
these types of sandstone can usually be recognised by the fact that
there is usually little difference between rain washed surfaces and
those sheltered from the rain.

Atmospheric pollution is no new problem by any means and even
as far back as 1273 the burning of "sea cole" was prohibited in
London on account of the disfigurement of the decorated colour
wash applied to many mediaeval buildings. A similar proclamation, as might be expected, was issued in Elizabeth I's reign and in
1648 a petition was presented to Parliament asking for the importation of coal from Newcastle to be prohibited. Evelyn, the diarist, in
Charles II's reign wrote a pamphlet on the evil of smoke pollution
and even had a Bill prepared but this did not become law. Considering that coal was the only form of heating available it is hardly
surprising that legislation was lacking and it was not until the
Industrial Revolution that steps to prevent the worst excesses were
taken. A select committee in 1843 recommended the introduction of
a Bill to prohibit the production of smoke from furnaces and steam
engines and in consequence requiring these to be so built as to
consume the smoke from the fuel used. Acts to this effect for the
London area were passed in 1853 and 1856 but these became in
effect merely a prohibition against the emission of black smoke in
respect of the whole country under the Public Health Act 1875 and
the Public Health (London) Act 1891 which are identical. Even so
the domestic fire and certain other industrial processes were exempted.

The difficulty of proving nuisance in regard to smoke emission
meant that the Acts were ineffective and it is only with the passing
and adoption by some local authorities of the Clean Air Act 1956
that much improvement has taken place. Even so this Act coincided
with the increasing use of gas, electricity and oil both for domestic
heating and industrial uses and therefore the improvement is not so
much due to the Act as to other factors and in some areas still there
is little attempt at implementing its provisions. One can anticipate
that it is in the course of most legislation to be of the character of
"too little and too late" and it may well be a long time before all
smoke emission is controlled. No measure whatever, to date, has
been promulgated to deal with the increasing pollution from
vehicle exhausts, which are considered to be equally harmful to both
human beings and buildings, and the vast quantities of sulphur
dioxide emitted.

(b) Soluble Salts

Decay in porous stonework will be caused by contamination with salts which are soluble in water. The salts may originate from various possible sources and their effects will depend on their type and the ability of the particular stone to resist them. Crystallisation of the salts is probably the main cause of decay in the stonework both on the surface but principally a little further back from the outer face. Changes in volume also probably have an effect according to conditions of humidity. Efflorescence can be a preliminary indication of trouble.

There is little evidence to suggest that salts occur naturally in stone to cause the type of decay envisaged or for that matter the efflorescence common in some types of new brickwork. Most stone is relatively free from harmful salts despite the nature of the formation of sedimentary rocks and it is thought that rainwater leached out harmful salts during the formation process. Furthermore most stonework is built in lime mortar, even nowadays, so that salts derived from Portland cement are usually absent. Should old stonework, however, be mistakenly repointed in Portland cement there is a danger of soluble salts evaporating from the surface of the stone particularly if the cement is trowelled hard and smooth.

Brick backing to stonework is a common source of soluble salts. The salts can be carried back through to the face of the stone by the evaporation of rainwater after it has penetrated to the brickwork through porous stonework, or the joints, or by entry through defective sills, copings, string courses or other mouldings. If concrete lintels are used behind stone mouldings, decay can arise in the stonework if water penetrates the top of the moulding, soaks into the lintel and then evaporates through the stonework immediately above the window.

It has already been mentioned that in selecting new stone for rebuilding purposes where it will be in contact with old stone how essential it is to match the stone in type, colour, texture and porosity. The need for this will be clear if old buildings are examined which contain a mixture of different types of stone, either as part of the original design or as a result of repairs at a later date. This mixing of stones is liable to cause considerable trouble particularly in the case of sandstones mixed with limestones. Often a sandstone plinth or steps are provided to a building built otherwise in limestone and it will be observed that the sandstone becomes badly decayed due to the action of calcium sulphate on the sandstone, probably by crystallisation, sandstones being more susceptible to this form of attack. The same effect can often be seen below a limestone feature, such as a sill, on an otherwise brick building where salts carried into

231

the brickwork from the stone cause blistering on the face of the bricks.

It is not often realised however that it is not only a downward movement of salts that can occur when stones of different characteristics are used together. If the pore structure of the stones is different, and in this respect the pore structure in sandstones is much finer usually than in limestones, a movement of water will arise from the more open textured stone to the finer. This is due to the greater capillary action through the finer channels and in consequence there can be a transfer of salts in any direction on evaporation, even upwards. A new limestone, therefore, selected as a replacement for decayed blocks on an existing building because of its superior weathering qualities might well be the cause of a rapid deterioration in the old work should its pore structure be more open than the existing stone. Of course the reverse condition may arise and consideration must therefore always be given to the effect that new stone might have on the old stone, or vice versa, before a final decision on selection is taken.

Stonework in contact with the soil is frequently contaminated by soluble salts, particularly in older buildings where there is an absence of a damp proof course. It can also arise where buildings are provided with a damp proof course but where this is bridged or where for the sake of appearance it has not been taken through for the full width of the wall. Retaining walls built in stone are particularly prone to be affected by salts from adjoining ground.

Buildings in coastal areas may also be affected by the chlorides in sea spray and sea mists, but this defect is not particularly common. On the other hand washing and cleaning buildings with chemicals has been known to cause decay to begin shortly afterwards. Caustic soda, the soda ash contained in household scouring powders and modern detergents are all materials harmful to natural stone.

(c) Vegetation and Other Organisms

There are one or two other factors which are thought at times to cause decay in stonework and which deserve to be mentioned. Mosses and lichens have only occasionally been found to cause any perceptible harm to stonework and, since they are very susceptible to the noxious substances in the air of towns, only then in rural areas. The fact they tend to keep stone more damp than it would be if they were absent suggests that they are undesirable and some types have been known to extend hyphae below the surface of stone. On the other hand much of the charm of old buildings in country areas is due to the presence of these living organisms and it is considered that there should be real cause to suspect their presence as being damaging before they need to be removed. Other forms of vegetation present a different aspect and the contrast between ivy and Virginia creeper should by now be well known. Virginia creeper is relatively harmless, attaching itself to a wall by suckers, though it does keep the wall damp in the process but ivy, by rooting in the joints, can cause severe damage dislodging stones in the process.

Pigeons are considered to provide a possible source of soluble salts from their droppings besides causing much disfigurement of stonework and even some slight erosion from continual pecking. The droppings also encourage bacteria to form which at one time was thought to be a factor in the decay of stonework but now it is not considered that bacteria are of any prime importance in this process.

REPAIR OF DEFECTIVE STONE

Some consideration of the methods available for dealing with decayed stonework must now be made for a number of alternatives present themselves and there are a number of factors which need to be taken into account before decisions are taken on the method to be adopted. Most of these factors are aesthetic and economic rather than technical. From the technical point of view the methods available are all of long standing, but much argument has raged over the propriety of certain of them when used in relation to old stone buildings of character and those that may have historical associations. In the case of a private owner the financial situation may be paramount and this might dictate a form of repair which might not otherwise be considered appropriate. The extent of the damage will also be a governing factor in the choice of the method to be adopted.

It should be borne in mind that surface decay of stonework is a long-term process and it needs to be very advanced indeed to give rise to structural damage except in such features as parapets projecting cornices, string courses and mouldings and free standing features. If it has occurred in these features then there is no alternative but to renew the stone if there is any danger of structural collapse. This is particularly so in the case of parapets and copings where the decay may be operating from both sides of the wall. In general areas of walling it may also be necessary to renew the stone if for example a relatively shallow stone is so far decayed as to deprive adjoining stones of their support.

Where structural danger does not arise in general walling or for that matter in mouldings and projecting features but there is merely decay to a substantial proportion of the stone face and erosion on moulded features, replacement with new stone is not necessary on strictly technical grounds and indeed there are certain disadvantages in this method. The disadvantages are that the removal of the old stone may loosen or damage adjoining stone, less of the original work is preserved, the insertion of a new stone will show as a patch and will probably be far more noticeable than a repair by other means. In the case of mouldings the stone cannot be easily worked to conform with old surfaces adjoining which although worn are still basically sound and there will be a temptation to remove these worn features until a good moulded shape is reached and, finally, a new stone cannot be as tightly set in a wall as the original. On the other hand, although the carrying out of plastic repair work to stone in various materials has a long history the method is repugnant to many who consider it to be inappropriate to a building of any character, even although such methods if skilfully carried out may remain for a time almost undetectable and will avoid disturbing surrounding work.

The decision will therefore be governed to a great extent by these aesthetic considerations and of course by the extent of the decay as, clearly, plastic repairs cannot be considered a feasible method if for example three-quarters of a wall needs attention. In these circumstances refacing with new stone is desirable as the most ideal method. In this connection it should be remembered that it is undoubtedly a mistaken policy to leave only a few of the old stones that are not affected in the newly faced work. It is better to renew the whole face in these circumstances as the weathering of the old stone will probably be accelerated by the operation and this will quickly mar the appearance of the new stone, even apart from the likely effect of salts in the old stone contaminating the new stonework. New stone must in any event be protected on all faces in contact with the backing by applying two coats of a heavy bitumastic paint. Selection of the new stone is of course vital as already discussed earlier in this Chapter on rebuilding in part.

Another method of dealing with general surface decay which might well be investigated concerns redressing the whole of the wall faces back to a sound surface, as is often done on weathered and eroded cornices and string courses. The Building Research Establishment cites an example where this was carried out 40 years or so ago on a building constructed of limestone of poor durability. The new face is still hardly blemished and the need for replacement with new stone has been deferred for a period already sufficiently long to make the operation well worth while. Clearly this operation presents difficulty where there are elaborate mouldings and complications can arise around window and door openings and such features as columns or mullions of windows may need replacement in new stone at the same time. With plain wall surfaces in soft stone, however, the method represents a satisfactory solution to the problem of general surface decay and the restoration of a good surface at a reasonable cost.

On the smaller domestic building and where considerations of aesthetic value are not so important, cutting back the surface of the stone and applying a textured rendering may be necessary as a bold step to combat extensive surface decay. This treatment is particularly appropriate in areas where, owing to the nature of the local stone and the general quality of buildings, smooth coursed ashlar faces are virtually unknown and it was therefore considered quite normal to render the surface. This is particularly so in Scotland where many, though not all, building stones needed protection to be weather resistant by a coat of rendering or "harling" as it is called. Nowadays this can be produced with a mix of one part of cement, two parts of lime and eight parts of a coarse aggregate consisting of sharp sand graded up to very coarse and mixed with 10 per cent of pebbles or gravel up to $\frac{3}{8}$ of an inch (10mm). The mix has to be wet enough to spread when thrown against the wall and not too wet that it won't stand out to produce a crisp and interesting texture. Many of the stone buildings originally intended to be harled have raised margins and quoins in squared stone so as to provide a stop as a finish to the edge of the harling which would subsequently be lime washed or colour washed. There may be some reluctance in a building owner nowadays to cover up stone work in this way, but as stated it has been a common practice for a long time in the past in certain areas and it should be recognised that the appearance of much rubble stonework and certain types of stone are in many respects not particularly attractive and covering them up is no loss.

It can probably be said, however, that a combination of plastic repair and replacement with new stone fulfils most requirements in the restoration of badly weathered and decayed stone walls, the new stone being confined to those areas where structural stability has been impaired. On general walling surfaces it may not even be necessary to renew whole stones even, as if the decay extends to a depth of say 2 to 3 inches (say 50 to 70 mm) it will be sufficient to cut back the old stone to a vertical face, provide a key either by grooving old and new stones or drilling the old stone and providing non-corrosive dowels as an aid to securing the new stone, which may be in the form of a facing slab 3 to 4 inches (76 to 102mm) in thickness as shown on Figure 48 at "A" and "B".

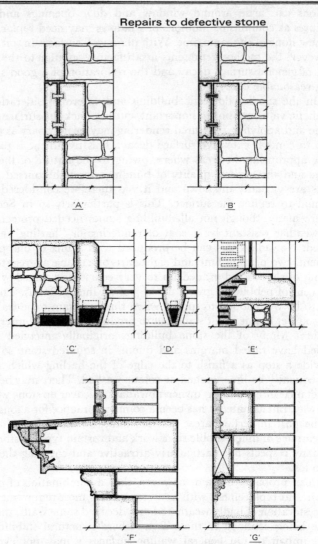

Repairs to defective stone

'A'   'B'

'C'   'D'   'E'

'F'   'G'

A single badly decayed stone in ashlar might well be cut back
and refaced with a new slab. To provide a key grooves should be
cut in both old and new stone, 'A', or as at 'B' non-ferrous dowels
let in. 'C', 'D', and 'E' show plastic repairs to dressings in a rubble
wall utilising tiles, the edges left exposed on the rubble work
and every third course built into a chase cut in sound stone. 'F'
shows a plastic repair to a cornice built up on non-ferrous reinforcement grouted in to sound stone. A combination of new
stone and plastic repair to ashlar is shown at 'G'.

Scale 1:20   48

The main advantage put forward for plastic repair is that it is only necessary to cut away sound stone in order to provide a key for the filling, so that much disturbance and loss of the original work is avoided. The filling material is chosen because of its plastic nature, enabling it to be married up to adjoining old surfaces, for its durability, adhesion and the fact that by trial it can be made up to match the surrounding old surfaces in texture, strength, porosity and colour. A long time in the past lime-hair mortars were used, secured with iron nails and in the 19th century, Roman cement. Since then various mixes have been adopted but since each repair has to be matched to particular circumstances no hard and fast rules can be given. Broadly speaking however the following types of mixes have proved suitable:

(*a*) Mortars based on the use of Portland cement with an aggregate of sand or crushed stone or a mixture of both and the addition of lime putty to the mix. Where light coloured stone is to be matched the use of white or tinted Portland cement is recommended.

(*b*) Mortars based on the use of zinc (or magnesium) oxychloride cement again with a sand or crushed stone aggregate. These mortars involve the use of acid solutions and need experience and special care in handling.

(*c*) Mortars of crushed stone or sand with an organic binder such as a special grade of silicone ester or cellulose acetate.

In carrying out the work it is essential to follow certain guide lines if the work is to be successful and restore rather than mar the appearance of the building.

(1) The decayed stone must be entirely removed until a sound surface is reached.

(2) Thin superficial patches must be entirely avoided.

(3) Repairs must not be worked to a feather edge and sound stone must be undercut to form a satisfactory keyed edge.

(4) Good adhesion must be secured between the filling and the sound stone. All dust must be removed from surfaces in the cavity and the surfaces well wetted before the material is placed if mortars based on Portland cement are used.

(5) The repair must be adequately keyed to the sound stone. For light repairs this can be done by drilling holes in the sound stone, forming grooves in the back of the cavity or alternatively drilling holes and grouting in brass screws or copper nails. Larger and deeper cavities can be provided with bronze, nickel or other non-corrosive metal dowels secured to the stone and a system of reinforcement in the same material of rods or metal wire. Another system advocated and used successfully in the past and particularly

useful for reforming window dressings and similar ornamental mouldings is based on the use of good quality hand-made clay tiles. These are cut roughly to the shape of, but slightly smaller than the cross section of the moulding to be restored and then set horizontally in chases cut in the sound stone. The moulding is then built up with the chosen mortar, the tiles forming a mechanical key and a reinforcement for the repair thus reducing advantageously the amount of mortar required. By this means quite substantial sections can be built up.

(6) The larger repairs should be built up gradually step by step allowing each stage to set before proceeding with the next and always providing an adequate key for the next stage.

(7) In order to avoid the risk of crazing excessive trowelling must be avoided. A wood float should always be used, never a steel float. In the case of mouldings these are more often best formed roughly to the required shape and then finished with a chisel when the mortar has set. Even with small straightforward patches a floated finish is not satisfactory and it is always necessary to remove the laitance. There are various ways of doing this. One is to use a wet brush on the patch before the mortar has set. Another is to brush the freshly set mortar with a stiff dry brush and a third is to rub or dress down the fully set mortar to the required texture, which, it is considered, should be somewhat rougher than the surrounding stone so that it should look right from a distance.

(8) Portland cement mixes should not be allowed to dry out quickly and should be covered with damp cloths for several days or occasionally sprayed with water.

(9) Patches must not be carried over from one adjacent block to another and the joint formed on the face by incision. Patches should be confined to one stone only and the normal joint formed and pointed to match the rest of the building.

When the above principles are followed and the work is carefully carried out and well supervised there is every chance that the repairs will be successful. It is possible by this method to match the appearance of the original stone so closely that the repair cannot be distinguished from the original except by the closest inspection. On the other hand work conscientiously carried out in some cases has tended to alter in appearance over the years, either lightening or darkening in comparison with the original stone or altering in texture. In unsympathetic hands such repairs have been highly unsuccessful so that the indications are that at the present time they should be entrusted to specialists in this field rather than the general contractor. As such the cost may not be much less than replacement with new stone so that the decision between the two methods may not be an easy one to take. The principles and various examples of plastic repair are shown on Figure 48.

A careful diagnosis of the cause of the defects which have been discussed will have been essential to decide the pattern of the repairs but while these are being completed the opportunity will arise and should be taken to carry out those additional works to the building which will help to ensure that so far as is possible the defects will not arise again. As is so often the case with buildings much of the decay in stonework is due to excessive water lodgement or penetration. The precautionary steps to be taken in regard to this problem are the same as those for buildings constructed in other materials but can well stand repetition. Many of the stone buildings will exist from a time when the precautions which are incorporated nowadays as a matter of course were unknown. Damp proof courses in parapet walls can be incorporated if parapets are rebuilt but if not, the tops of parapets can be covered with a metal flashing. It is also advantageous at times to cover the inner face of a parapet with a metal sheath so that water penetration does not occur from both faces.

Cornices, in particular, need covering on the top along with the tops of string courses, window and door mouldings, in fact any surface that can allow water to lodge or drive downwards through joints or through porous stone. Such details should also be weathered in the physical sense so as to throw water clear and attention must always be paid to the formation of suitable drip mouldings on the outer lower edge to prevent water running back and down the face of the wall. Sills may also need attention in that if renewed a damp proof course will be required but if not a covering of sheet lead may be desirable.

At the base of the wall the opportunity should be taken whenever possible to install a damp proof course if none exists, otherwise the lower courses of stone will be re-affected by the action of soluble salts. If it is considered undesirable to allow the damp proof course to show on the external face then it may be necessary to install a granite plinth although in many instances this will look more unsightly than allowing the damp proof course to show. If the building has a damp proof course then it may be necessary to lower ground or paving levels if these are the cause of bridging. If it is not possible to install a damp proof course then other palliative measures may be taken such as drastic lowering of the ground level outside to the top of the footings and ensuring that the ground above foundation level is well drained. These methods may well need to be weighed against the cost of inserting a damp proof course and having regard to the unlikely success of the palliatives, the insertion of a moisture barrier

239

to rising damp may well be considered the better alternative even at a greater cost.

On completion of all the repairs the final operation is likely to be the repointing. This can be discussed in the penultimate section of this Chapter as part of maintenance, regular attention to which in regard to stone buildings is likely to repay handsome dividends in the long run.

MAINTENANCE OF STONEWORK

(a) Pointing

Pointing of stonework whether as the final operation of a repair scheme, or for maintenance purposes, is an important matter and requires a slightly different approach from that involved in brickwork. The general principle however is the same in that the pointing, as for the jointing, should be neither denser nor stronger than the stone. The use of rich cement mixes make the structure unnecessarily rigid and strong dense pointing with such mixes is highly likely to be a substantial factor in accelerating decay in the stonework itself, a point which has been established when old soft lime-mortar in the past has been raked out and renewed in cement. In many cases it would have been better to have left the old soft and loose mortar. The matter is made even worse when cement mixes are heavily trowelled.

Experience in the locality may well be a useful guide in selecting a mortar mix both for bedding and pointing and if a particular mix can be shown to be satisfactory for a local stone then there is no valid reason for changing it. Where there is evidence that local practice is unsatisfactory or where there is no particular viewpoint, a lime mortar gauged with Portland cement will give good results.

Strength and density can be adjusted in the mortar by choosing either sand or crushed limestone for the aggregate according to the character of the stone. If sand is used it must be clean, sharp and well graded up to coarse. It is all the better if it contains small pebbles and other irregular particles such as broken shells. Attention should also be paid to colour.

For bedding and pointing dressed masonry it is not usually necessary to use a stronger gauged mortar than 1 cement 3 lime 10 aggregate. This is best prepared in advance using dry hydrated lime or lime putty in the proportion of 1:3 to the aggregate and mixing 10 parts of this mix with one part of cement, the volume of lime in the mortar mix occupying the interstices in the aggregate and being ignored in computing the volume used for gauging. For rubble walling where the joints are thicker and correspondingly more exposed to the weather and for pointing dressed masonry in the autumn or winter when frost might damage a weak mortar before it has had time to harden a stronger mix of $1:2:9$ or $1:1:6$ is more suitable, the latter when exposure conditions are particularly severe. These mixes are made by gauging 9 parts of $1:4\frac{1}{2}$ lime mortar with 1 part of cement or 6 parts of $1:6$ lime mortar with 1 part of cement. Each batch of cement lime mortar must be used within two to three hours of mixing before the cement has set so that small quantities only should be mixed at a time.

At one time recessed pointing was popular for restoration work perhaps as a marked reaction against the "strap" pointing which had held sway for some time before. Both methods are open to criticism from the point of view of appearance and for technical reasons as both provide ledges for water. It is now usual to finish pointing flush with the stone particularly the top edge but it must be kept back from the face of the stone so that the shape stands out if the edges are rounded or irregular. In these circumstances a very slight recessing of say no more that $\frac{1}{8}$ of an inch (3mm) may be necessary. The finish of the pointing is important and the correct procedure is to apply a dry medium soft bristle brush when the setting has begun in order to expose the sand and give a crisp finish.

All the attention given to the material, type of joint and finishing will be wasted unless the usual precautions and methods are adopted. Joints must be well raked out of all loose material and cleared of dust to a depth preferably of 1 to 2 inches (25 to 50mm) or at least twice the thickness of the joint. The stone in the joint should be thoroughly wetted before and during the pointing operation and when this is completed too rapid drying should be prevented, either by strong sun or wind and the work protected from frost if there is any danger of this arising.

(b) Protecting Stonework

With the repairs and pointing completed, it might be considered a suitable time for considering if any further steps can be taken to preserve the restored surfaces for the future. Liquid stone preservatives might be suggested as a means of providing a colourless protective treatment, but the Building Research Establishment is very clear in its advice on this point and suggests that there is no evidence to justify the use of any such liquids. In their application they just do not penetrate far enough and do not last long enough to have any appreciable effect as preservatives. On the other hand good quality British Standard silicone-based water repellents for masonry will serve to provide a temporary cure for rainwater penetration through thin porous walls. They will need renewal at suitable intervals if intended to effect a lasting cure for this type of defect but there is a difference between a water repellent and a stone preservative. It must also be recognised that water repellent liquids are not designed to bridge cracks and fissures and are therefore ineffective on dense impervious stone surfaces such as granite and some sandstones. The common occurrence of rain penetration in walls constructed of such impervious materials is often due to a crack or fissure allowing water to penetrate but not to evaporate, so that it runs through to the interior. This condition is usually aggravated by a hard dense pointing to the joints so that the remedy normally lies in repointing joints in cement lime mortar as previously described and seeking, finding and pointing up any cracks or fissures in the stone in the same manner.

A good method of preventing surface decay on stone walls is to paint them with an oil paint in the usual manner, using primer, undercoat and finishing coat on dry sound surfaces. Although the pattern of the stone will remain unmistakably visible, this is not the method found to be very attractive by most owners but it is perhaps suitable for smaller buildings where it is not important to retain the natural appearance of the stone. Stone textured paints are also available which simulate the appearance of stone and these can be used as a finishing coat if desired. In the past a strong belief was held by certain authorities on the efficiency of lime wash as a preservative for stonework although there is no chemical evidence or theory to suggest that it really is of any value. Those who favoured its use relied on evidence from mediaeval buildings that it was much employed then, both externally and internally and, as already discussed, pollution of the atmosphere was a problem even in those days. It is thought that limewash fills the small interstices and hinders the entry of moisture which in itself carries the agents of decay and that this was recognised a long time ago in the past as a means of preserving stone. It is physically and chemically similar to renderings based on lime and contains none of the injurious salts present in cement based paints which can react with the constituents of the stone. Limewash is made by adding animal or vegetable fat or oil to quick lime slaked with water while it is still hot, roughly in the proportion of ten pounds (4·5 kilos) of tallow for example, or a gallon (4·5 litres) of linseed oil, to a hundredweight (50·8 kilos) of lime. Some of the oil reacts with the alkaline of the lime to form an insoluble calcium soap and the remainder of the oil is emulsified by this soap and binds the mixture together. The mixture is allowed to stand for at least a day and can then be thinned with water to the desired consistency for application to clean dry stonework in at least two coats, the first being thin and well brushed in. Limewash becomes somewhat transparent when wet but it can be coloured using earth colours because these are stable in lime, or made a more opaque white in a mixture of two parts of limewash, two parts of whiting and one of zinc oxide. Limewash properly applied allows the texture of the stone to remain and can be suitable for the smaller building particularly in country areas. Reasonably frequent applications are neccessary, however, which can introduce a problem when many successive layers of limewash are built up over the years. There is no easy way of stripping old limewash as a preparation for a new coating since paint removers, whether of the alkaline or solvent type, have no effect. Mechanical scraping, wire brushing or steam strippers would probably do the work but normally it is only necessary to brush down by hand to remove loose or powdery material. If water is used in this process to keep down the dust the surface should be allowed to dry out in the main although limewash will tolerate slight dampness being present. The Building Research Establishment indicate that formulations for limewash containing glue, cassein or skimmed milk, being liable to shrinkage, should be avoided and that those containing tallow, as described above, or salt are to be preferred.

(c) Cleaning Stonework

If stonework is not protected by rendering, painting or limewash, then it is essential, as part of the normal maintenance programme, for buildings constructed in limestone to be regularly cleaned to prevent the accumulation of harmful deposits. The cleaning should be carried out by brushing or rubbing with water alone and no cleaning agents such as caustic soda, soda ash, soap, detergents or scouring powders should be used, as these can all introduce harmful agents which can be left behind as deposits to cause damage at a later date. There are various methods in use to bring the water to the surface of the stone. Steam cleaning has the advantage of bringing warm water to the surface of the stone and there is little risk of water penetration through the stone to cause internal damage. Lightly discoloured surfaces will be cleaned by the warm steam alone but heavy discoloration and deposits will need the use of bristle or non-ferrous wire brushes or rubbing with carborundum blocks. In the latter instance the work should only be entrusted to competent operatives.

Delicate surfaces and elaborate carvings on limestone buildings are best treated with water sprays if they will not stand heavy brushing. However the heavier deposits which are bound together with calcium sulphate and calcium carbonate may need prolonged

243

spraying before they can be appreciably dissolved and although nozzles to produce fine sprays are used there is more risk of water penetration to the interior than with steam cleaning and the disposal of the water can be a problem. The spray method is also useful for removal of iron stains and is preferable to any chemical treatment for this purpose. It has been observed with the use of sprays that brownish stains sometimes become apparent subsequently on Portland stone due to soluble matter from soot becoming widely deposited at depth in the pores of the stone and coming to the surface again on evaporation. These sometimes disappear of their own accord but may need repeated rinsing off with water on old stone.

Sandstones are more difficult to clean than limestones but some will respond to a steam and abrasive treatment. The majority however resist even this method and it is often necessary to resort to a chemical. Dilute hydrofluoric acid has a solvent action on sandstone and has been successfully used having the advantage of leaving behind no harmful salts. This acid can be dangerous, however, in use and work of this nature should definitely be left to specialist firms with operatives experienced in its use. The acid will etch glass, destroy polish on marble and granite and leave unsightly marks on pavings if spilled hence the extreme care needed in its use. One other chemical only is recommended in addition by the Building Research Establishment, ammonium bifluoride, but this should be confined solely to cleaning granite with the same elaborate precautions being adopted.

In Scotland the use of power tools with grinding discs and rotary brushes has largely been adopted for cleaning sandstone and granite, supplemented by the usual brushes and abrasive blocks for moulded work.

Grit blasting has also been used for cleaning sandstones and granites for some time and has recently, by adjusting pressures and the type and grade of grit, also been used on limestone. The abrasives used are sands, ground slags, ground coconut shell and even rice husks have been used on soft stone. The surfaces of smooth stone may be roughened by this method and it is necessary to protect glass and paintwork. There is also a considerable dust nuisance which can be allayed by the use of water sprays in conjunction with this method but as before, with the use of water sprays there is a danger of water penetration and the mixture of water debris and grit can cause a blockage in drains if special care is not taken.

The increasing popularity of grit blasting as a method of cleaning limestones has given rise to a certain amount of controversy recently. The method provides effective and quick results but which tend to be rather even overall producing a somewhat flat appearance on

244

completion coupled with a roughened texture to the softer stones. Since, in effect, the stone surface is redressed, the criticism that the characteristics of the stone are damaged seem ill-founded and there is little doubt in time that the flat appearance will improve on further weathering. It is only when old buildings are seen afresh almost as originally completed, that we realise it is age, the effects of moderate dirt deposits and weather which sometimes enhances their appearance. On the other hand the roughened texture produced on softer stone will probably attract much more dirt than would have been the case had the smoother surface of the original sawing been restored by washing. Undoubtedly there is a need for care in selecting pressure and the types and grades of grit to suit the stone to be cleaned and for scheduled buildings such advice is available on request from the Ancient Monuments Branch of the Department of the Environment. Owners of buildings scheduled under the Ancient Monuments Acts are required to give notice to the Branch before embarking on extensive cleaning, but in the case of listed buildings advice on the advisability of cleaning and on methods should initially be sought from the Local Planning Officer.

The removal of stains from stonework is a problem which often arises on the maintenance of buildings when they are being cleaned. As previously mentioned iron stains can be removed from Portland stone by water spraying, accompanied by bristle or wire brushing if the stains are deep seated. This method is to be preferred to any that would involve the use of a chemical. On the other hand, copper staining requires the use of a solution of ammonia for its removal or the application of a poultice of whiting moistened with ammonia solution, allowing this to dry and then brushing off. Several repeats of the operation may be desirable and it is also necessary to wet the stone before applying the poultice and to rinse down thoroughly afterwards with clean water. Oil stains require the use of a volatile organic solvent, preferably carbon tetrachloride as this is non-inflammable. Sponging may suffice to remove the stain but it may be necessary to adopt the poultice method. Care is very necessary in the use of carbon tetrachloride and with trichlorethylene, white spirit and benzene which are also useful for the removal of oil stains and which do not harm the stone.

If it is considered essential to remove lichens or moss from stonework in rural areas toxic solutions such as a 1 per cent solution of sodium pentachlorphenate in water or a 4 per cent solution of zinc or magnesium silicofluoride in water can be used. The concentration at this level of salts is considered unlikely to cause any harm to the stonework but even so the need for the removal should be really established in the first instance.

REINSTATEMENT OF FIRE DAMAGE

As has been indicated in the corresponding section on the reinstatement of brickwork damaged by fire, the temperatures of fires in domestic buildings are comparatively low. Stone nevertheless, unlike brick which is fired in the process of manufacture, is subjected to considerable stresses due to the way the temperature of the stone at the surface is raised in comparison with the temperature at even a shallow depth within the stone. This heat can of course be rapidly dissipated on dousing by fire hoses. Cracking or spalling of the stone then occurs often on a considerable scale. Before this happens however colour changes occur in most building stones when they are subjected to heat. The brown or buff coloured limestones and sandstones become pink or reddish brown due to the chemical reaction of hydrated iron oxide with other constituents of the stone. Those stones free of iron oxide, such as Portland or Huddlestone, a white magnesian limestone, do not show this colour change but the effect of heat is such as to make the stone become greyish in colour. The change of colour under heat is by no means a recently observed phenomena and many ancient buildings show such evidence of past fires without any other indications of damage. It can be concluded therefore that if there are no other signs of damage apart from a colour change then there is no fear that the durability or strength of the stone has been affected.

It is well known that limestone (calcium carbonate) when heated to a fairly high temperature (about 700 to 800°C) loses carbon dioxide and becomes calcium oxide or quicklime. The Building Research Establishment found on investigation that although calcination, as this process is called, may occur on arrises of door and window frames and sharp edges of mouldings it is unlikely to be a significant factor in limestone affected by fire. If it does occur it should be fairly apparent on close examination as in contrast to the colour change which will be observed on neighbouring surfaces, the arrises will be dull and earthy in appearance and be accompanied by crazing of the surface. A test can be carried out to resolve any doubt by the application of an alcoholic solution of phenolphthalein to the suspected area which will develop a pink colour if calcination has taken place. It is necessary to do this test fairly quickly after the fire has taken place otherwise the lime will have recarbonated by absorption of carbon dioxide from the air.

Most of the damage caused to stonework in a fire however arises in connection with the playing of water from fire hoses. The sudden cooling produces a shattering effect on the stone even when the

246

intensity of the fire is not very great. The features most likely to be affected are window jambs and mullions, columns, door casings, sills, cornices and other mouldings where more than one surface is exposed to the heat. All types of stone are affected by this in a similar way. Generally the outside of the walls are not affected except around the door and window openings but it has been known for the outside of a neighbouring building to be affected in this way, even though the fire has not spread to that building. To a lesser extent general disintegration may occur in some types of sandstone and granite due to a differential expansion in the constituent crystals. In view of the comparative low temperatures attained within the body of a wall the extent of this friability is usually limited.

The Building Research Establishment carried out experiments with various types of stone recovered from fire damaged buildings during the Second World War and from these has deduced in respect of stone used in general walling that there was no appreciable loss of compressive strength even where occasional cracks had developed and there was spalling and colour changing on the faces which had been exposed to the fire. The Research Establishment concluded that there was therefore a sufficient factor of safety in respect of masonry buildings to compensate for any slight loss of compressive strength that may have occurred. The Research Establishment, however, was not able to give similar advice in respect of stone where tensional stresses occur such as in a staircase and in this respect recommended that any stone staircase that had been subject to fire should be rebuilt, unless subjected to comprehensive loading tests to establish its safety.

In the repair of a fire damaged stone building it is necessary to consider structural safety in the first instance in the same way as with a brick building. Lateral movement may be induced however in contrast with most brick buildings by thermal expansion and also in the usual way resulting from the total or partial collapse of the roof or walls. Structural repairs of this character will depend on the particular circumstances of each case and the methods of repair have been dealt with previously.

The most serious problem which usually arises however is in ensuring that no danger will arise subsequently from falling fragments of stone. Every section of the stonework will need careful examination in order to detect all loose fragments and any hidden flaws. In particular projecting features such as cornices and string courses will require more thorough close examination and it will be necessary to "sound" each stone to detect possible hidden flaws. If these are detected, consideration must be given to the removal of the affected stones and their replacement or alternatively whether they can safely be allowed to remain. This will depend to a great extent on whether there has been any other movement in the vicinity that might affect stability, whether the stone was grossly overloaded in the first instance and whether its bearing surface is considerably reduced by spalling. Even if a certain amount of rebuilding proves necessary at the top of walls it would normally be considered satisfactory, subject to the results of the close examination, to rebuild on existing walls and to re-use any blocks that could be salvaged in a suitably sound condition.

The superficial damage caused by a fire can be repaired in much the same way as the defects in the surface of stone caused by other factors is repaired. Unflawed loose fragments can be keyed back into position using non-corrosive alloys and patch repairs can be carried out using the process of plastic repair as described previously. If necessary new blocks of stone can be inserted or a new stone facing fixed to the old stone, also in the ways previously described.

Chapter 4
Foundations

CONTENTS

249

OLD FOUNDATIONS AND NEW FOUNDATIONS

OUR forefathers appreciated the need for an adequate foundation to buildings from very early times and there are plenty of references to the subject in mediaeval documents. They also learnt no doubt from many mistakes involving collapse to relate the foundation to the condition of the sub-soil as witness the references and existence to this day of wood piles and rafts to support important structures near rivers. The very great number of variations in type and design to provide "adequate" foundations no doubt account for the lack of legislation on the subject until comparatively recently. It was considered, perhaps wisely in certain circumstances, that such a basic requirement would receive due attention by the mason designer or builder if only for the reason that a failure shortly after construction would reflect badly on the reputation of those concerned. At a time when most houses of brick and stone were the result of individual commissions this was no doubt very true and even in the times of great estate development a sense of responsibility could no doubt be assumed in the majority of cases. Such proclamations or Acts that there were referred to foundations merely to the extent that they "should rest on solid ground". This phraseology was included in the Metropolitan Building Act of 1855 but shortly after this came into effect a furore arose over the collapse of three houses which were in course of construction and this resulted in the formulation of by-laws which came into operation on the 6th October 1879. These provided for walls to have a concrete foundation 9 inches in thickness and specified the composition of foundation concrete.

From the passing of the 1879 By-Laws, requirements have been retained for foundations to the extent that probably many buildings have foundations somewhat in excess of their true need, particularly those in the field of two-storey domestic construction. However in the circumstances this has probably been no bad thing as unfortunately the corollary has also applied in that buildings with foundations in compliance with the by-laws have very often exhibited just those symptoms of foundation defects which occur in some buildings erected before 1879.

The problem of suitable foundation design is a complicated one even with the benefits of modern knowledge for examining and testing soils, the use of reinforced concrete and improved techniques in establishing the performance of materials in various conditions. It ill-behoves us therefore to criticise those designers or builders whose foundations fail on account of inadequate design, particularly when the cause is more likely due to subsequent changes entirely beyond their control. Even now there are still many symptoms of foundation failure in relatively new buildings and a vast body of older buildings showing little or no sign of trouble from this source. One would clearly like to see the foundations that support these sturdy buildings but unfortunately the opportunity for this seldom arises.

When foundations to old houses are examined therefore it should not come as a surprise to find very many variations. What one may find will range from a complete absence of a foundation in the modern sense we have come to expect, through the practice of spreading the load on brick footings in the older buildings. Later buildings may have a strip footing of an inferior form of lime concrete usually with brick footings as well. There is little point therefore in making comparisons between new and old types of foundations as the crucial point is only whether they succeed in their purpose. Even when they fail to do this it is probably not the fault of the original foundation itself. Although a comparison between new and old is of little value there is however some point in considering modern practice as this will have a bearing on any new work to be provided in lieu of old.

Current regulations in regard to foundations have a bearing on repair work to dwelling houses insofar as the need to rebuild a wall necessitates new foundations up to present-day standards and any work of a structural nature involving underpinning or piling would require notice being given to the local authority who would then consider the proposals for the purpose of approval.

In the Inner London area the application in certain circumstances of set rules for foundations has been totally abandoned and the London Building (Constructional) Amending By-Laws (No. 1) 1964 now give the District Surveyors complete discretion in dealing with all foundation matters. Part V of the By-Laws provides that every building shall be supported on concrete or reinforced concrete foundations of such thickness and projection as may, to the satisfaction of the District Surveyor, be necessary to transmit all the dead and imposed load without exceeding the appropriate limitations of permissible stresses imposed by the By-Laws (By-Law 5.06). Underpinning is specifically mentioned (By-Law 2.08) as to be of adequate load bearing capacity and in all other respects suitable to the satisfaction of the District Surveyor. The onus is therefore put directly on the surveyor, architect or contractor to prepare a scheme for foundations based on the relevant information as to materials, loading and the condition of the sub-soil and for this to be checked

251

FOUNDATIONS

and approved by the District Surveyor having regard to his specialised knowledge of conditions in the particular area. This system can
be advantageous in that there are probably cases where the strict
application of the rules set out in the earlier 1952 By-Laws would be
wasteful and expensive and also provides for those circumstances
where the use of the rules, although complying with the by-laws
then in force, did not in all the circumstances fully meet the standard
of a suitable foundation.

Over the last twenty years or so there have been marked improvements in the techniques of soil sampling and indeed in the science of
soil mechanics generally. Developments in foundation design have
also taken place and these were not only reflected in the change in
the London By-Laws of 1964 but also in the first edition of the
Building Regulations in 1965. The tendency now is for a much
closer attention to be paid to foundation design according to the type
of building and paying much greater attention to soil characteristics
than formerly. The Building Regulations 1965 and 1972 do however
still provide a schedule of minimum widths (Regulation D7) for
strip foundations of plain concrete situated centrally under the walls,
but these are based on soil conditions as well as on the loading
factor, not merely the thickness of the walls. In addition these
minimum widths can only be adopted if:

(a) There is no made ground or wide variation in the type of
sub-soil within the loaded area and no weaker type of soil exists
below the soil on which the foundations rest within such a depth as
may impair the stability of the structure.

(b) The width of the foundations is not less than the width specified in the Table to the regulation in accordance with the related
particulars specified in the Table.

(c) The concrete is composed of cement and fine and coarse
aggregate conforming to B.S.882:1954 in the proportion of 112 lbs.
of cement (50 kg) to not more than $3\frac{3}{4}$ cubic feet ($0.1m^3$) of fine
aggregate and $7\frac{1}{2}$ cubic feet ($0.2m^3$) of coarse aggregate.

(d) The thickness of the concrete is not less than its projection
from the base of the wall or footing and is in no case less than 6 inches
(150mm).

(e) Where the foundations are laid at more than one level, at
each change of level the higher foundations extend over and unite
with the lower foundations for a distance of not less than the thickness of the foundations and in no case less than 12 inches (300mm).

(f) Where there is a pier, buttress or chimney forming part of a
wall, the foundations project beyond the pier, buttress or chimney
on all sides to at least the same extent as they project beyond the wall.

252

An adaptation of the Table to Regulation D7 (Minimum widths of strip foundations) is set out on pages 254 and 255 with the metric figures taken from the Building Regulations 1972 where the wording both for the Table and for paragraphs (*a*) to (*f*) above is identical with the 1965 edition of the Regulations, apart from minor variations in column (3) and a rationalisation of loads and widths in column (4) reducing the number of sub-columns from seven in the 1965 edition to six in the 1972 edition. It should be noted that the metric figures are *not* equivalent values to the British units and, of course, in new or replacement work only the metric values will have legal effect.

Strip foundations under Regulation D7 have to be considered further in regard to Regulation D3 which provides that the foundations of a building shall (*b*) be taken down to such a depth, or be so constructed, as to safeguard the building against damage by swelling, shrinking or freezing of the sub-soil and (*c*) be capable of adequately resisting any attack by sulphates or any other deleterious matter present in the sub-soil.

Paragraph (*a*) of this Regulation is the all-embracing requirement that foundations shall

safely sustain and transmit to the ground the combined dead load and imposed load in such a manner as not to cause any settlement or other movement which would impair the stability of, or cause damage to, the whole or any part of the building or of any adjoining building or works.

Strip foundations constructed in accordance with the Table are deemed to satisfy the requirements of paragraph (*a*) of Regulation D3.

When it is considered that a typical two-storey house of approximately 900 square feet (93·7 square metres) with cavity wall construction of brick, timber floors and a tiled roof weighs about 100 tons (101·6 metric tons) and the load per lineal foot or metre, i.e. the force per unit length on front and rear walls is about 0·8 tons (26·15 kN/m) at ground level, for the party wall about 1·5 tons (49·04 kN/m) and for the gable wall 1·2 tons (39·23 kN/m), it can be seen that, even when the weight of the foundations are added, on strictly load considerations Regulation D7 should provide adequate foundations for most ordinary two storey domestic construction. There always remains however the factor of depth and the constitution of the sub-soil from the point of view of chemical attack on the concrete to be considered.

Should the building under consideration involve loads in excess of those set out in the Table to Regulation D7 the Building Regulations provide, in addition, that foundations for buildings other than

Table to Regulation D7 (Minimum width of strip foundations)

(1)	(2)	(3)	(4) Minimum width in inches or millimetres for total load in tons per lineal foot or kilonewtons per lineal metre of load bearing walling of not more than:—						
Type of sub-soil	Condition of sub-soil	Field test applicable	½ton/ft. 20kN/m	¾ton/ft. 30kN/m	1ton/ft. —	1¼ton/ft. 40kN/m	1½ton/ft. 50kN/m	1¾ton/ft. 60kN/m	2ton/ft. 70kN/m
I Rock	Not inferior to sandstone, limestone or firm chalk	Requires at least a pneumatic or other mechanically operated pick for excavation	In each case equal to the width of wall						
II Gravel Sand	Compact Compact	Requires pick for excavation. Wooden peg 2 inches (50mm) square in cross section hard to drive beyond 6 inches (150mm)	9 250	9 300	12 —	15 400	18 500	21 600	24 650
III Clay Sandy Clay	Stiff Stiff	Cannot be moulded with the fingers and requires a pick or pneumatic or other mechanically operated spade for its removal	9 250	9 300	12 —	15 400	18 500	21 600	24 650

254

Type	Soil	Consistency	Field test							
IV	Clay Sandy Clay	Firm Firm	Can be moulded by substantial pressure with the fingers and can be excavated with graft or spade	10½ 300	13 350	15 —	18 450	22½ 600	27 750	30 850
V	Sand Silty sand Clayey sand	Loose Loose Loose	Can be excavated with a spade. Wooden peg 2 inches (50mm) square in cross section can be easily driven	12 400	18 600	24 —	Note: In relation to types V, VI and VII foundations do not fall within the provisions of Regulation D7 if the total load exceeds 1 ton per lineal foot or 30 kilonewtons per lineal metre.			
VI	Silt Clay Sandy clay Silty clay	Soft Soft Soft Soft	Fairly easily moulded in the fingers and readily excavated	14½ 450	21 650	27 —				
VII	Silt Clay Sandy clay Silty clay	Very soft Very soft Very soft Very soft	Natural sample in winter conditions exudes between fingers when squeezed in fist	18 600	27 850	36 —				

255

factories or storage buildings may be deemed to satisfy Regulation D3(a) if such foundations are constructed in accordance with British Standard Code of Practice 101:1963 "Foundations and Substructures for Non-Industrial Buildings of not more than Four Storeys". This document represents a standard of good practice in relation to buildings of not more than four storeys where the foundation loads are dispersed evenly on the ground and where ground conditions can be proved to be adequate. The emphasis in this document is again on the selection of a proper type of foundation having regard to site and soil conditions. In addition to indicating the matters which should be checked before foundation design is considered for new building operations some order is brought to the classification of the main soil types for near surface foundations together with a table for typical bearing capacities. The use of the table depends on the correct identification of the particular soil and a basis for field identification is given in terms of the predominant size of soil particle and those strength features which have an important influence on foundation behaviour. Soils are divided into two categories, non-cohesive and cohesive and the sub-divisions of these categories are set out below with additional comments and applicable elements for field assessment tests for structure and strength.

Non-cohesive soils

These are defined as soils such as sands and gravels which include the coarser and largely siliceous and unaltered products of rock weathering. They possess no plasticity and tend to lack cohesion, especially when in the dry state.

Gravel

A natural deposit consisting of rock fragments in a matrix of finer and usually sandy material. Many of the particles are larger than $\frac{1}{16}$ inch (1·5mm) in size and may reach to 3 inches (75mm) being retained in a No. 7 BS sieve. If the gravel is loose it can be easily removed by a shovel and 2 inch (51mm) stakes can be driven well in. If compact the deposits require a pick for their removal and a 2-inch (51mm) peg is hard to drive for more than a short distance.

Sand

A natural sediment consisting of the granular and mainly siliceous products of rock weathering. The particle is smaller than 2mm but is large enough to be visible to the naked eye, the smallest size being 0·06mm to pass a No. 7 but to be retained on a No. 200 B.S. sieve.

256

A sand is definitely gritty and has no real plasticity. Dry lumps may
have some slight cohesion but clean sand can be very easily powdered
between the fingers. Fine grained sands exhibit some dilatancy. A
well graded sand is one containing a proportion of all sizes of sand
particles but with a predominance of the coarser grades. A poorly
graded or uniform sand is one in which the majority of the particles
are within a fairly restricted size range.

As for gravel, loose sand is readily removable by hand shovelling
and a 2 inch (51mm) wooden peg can easily be driven in but when
compact a pick is required and a peg is difficult to drive more than
a short distance.

In regard to both gravel and sand there is a danger of water
removing the finer particles leaving the coarser material in a less
stable condition. Water can move much faster through gravels and
sands than the much finer grained soils such as clay. This can happen
when fine sands are affected by water flowing underground from
high ground nearby and as a result a "quick-sand" condition arises.
For this reason the need for lowering the water table on sites of new
buildings is obvious and underground streams should be diverted
permanently before building operations are begun. With old
buildings the danger arises with changes in ground water movement
which may take place many years after buildings have been completed. For example it has often been thought that the construction
of new tube railways with lift and escalator shafts in London has
caused ground water to follow new paths alongside the tunnels
resulting in a washing away of sand and settlement in buildings
nearby founded on clay, overlying beds of sand.

Gravel is practically incompressible but over other sub-soils
lateral movement may occur and again drainage of subterranean
water may give rise to settlement, particularly if the gravel is over
wet clay. In such circumstances it may be possible to take steps to
confine movement of both gravel and sand by sheet piling. The Code
of Practice takes into account the susceptibility of sand and gravel to
disturbance by water movement by setting out values for bearing
capacity in both "Dry" and "Submerged" conditions. By submerged the Code means that the ground water level in the sand
or gravel is likely to be at a depth of less than the foundation
width below the base of the foundation. It is assumed for all
values that the width of the foundation is not less than 3 feet
(0·91m).

For foundations narrower than 3 feet (0·91m) on sand and gravel
the permissible bearing capacity decreases as the width decreases. In
such cases the permissible bearing capacity should be one-third the
value given overleaf multiplied by the width of the foundation in

Non-cohesive soils

Type of Soil	Bearing Capacity tonf/ft.^{2} (tf/m^2)	
	Dry	Submerged
Compact well graded sands and gravel-sand mixtures	4 to 6 (44 to 66)	2 to 3 (22 to 33)
Loose well graded sands and gravel-sand mixtures	2 to 4 (22 to 44)	1 to 2 (11 to 22)
Compact uniform sands	2 to 4 (22 to 44)	1 to 2 (11 to 22)
Loose uniform sands	1 to 2 (11 to 22)	$\frac{1}{2}$ to 1 (5·5 to 11)

feet. However in these soils the permissible bearing capacity can be increased by $\frac{1}{8}$ tonf/ft.^{2} (1·37tf/m^2) for each foot of depth of the loaded area below the lowest ground surface immediately adjacent.

Cohesive soils

Cohesive soils are defined as those such as clay consisting of the finer and altered products of rock weathering, possessing in their natural state cohesion and plasticity, the former even when dry.

Boulder Clay
A deposit of unstratified clay or sandy clay containing stones of various sizes.

Clay
A natural deposit containing a predominant amount of the finest siliceous and aluminous products of rock weathering. It is smooth plastic and greasy to the touch. It is sticky when moist, clinging to the fingers and dries slowly, the lumps holding together when dry. Wet lumps when immersed in water soften without breaking up. Clay shrinks appreciably on drying usually showing cracks. Dry lumps show appreciable strength and while they can be broken in the fingers they cannot be powdered. The harder clays are frequently fissured, the fissures opening slightly when the top soil is removed or a vertical surface is revealed by a trial pit.

258

Clay can of course, occur in mixtures of various proportions with sand and with gravel as Boulder Clay but whereas gravel and sand are usually described objectively as "compact" or "loose" the terms applied to clay are properly concerned with its moulding properties from "stiff" through "firm" to "soft" and "very soft".

Stiff Clay. A clay which at its natural moisture content cannot be moulded with the fingers and requires a pick or pneumatic spade for its removal.

Firm Clay. A clay which at its natural moisture content can be moulded by substantial pressure with the fingers and can be excavated with a spade.

Soft Clay. A clay which at its natural moisture content can be easily moulded with the fingers and can be readily excavated.

Very Soft Clay. A clay which at its natural moisture content is extruded between the fingers when squeezed in the fist.

Clay has the reputation of being never still due to continual changes in volume according to its moisture content. Although clays swell when wet they lose strength in this state as far as bearing capacity is concerned and are at their weakest. As such proper drainage is important on a clay site and adequate depth for foundations necessary to avoid seasonal changes in the volume of the clay, having particular regard to the effects of vegetation. If clay is examined in dry summer conditions consideration should be given to its probable deterioration under winter conditions. Mud, stones and clay shales may deteriorate very rapidly if exposed to the weather or to ground water. Generally, however, clay when found mixed thoroughly and equally with sand and gravel is at its strongest for the purposes of bearing capacity.

In addition to the shrinking and swelling effects arising from atmospheric changes, poor drainage and vegetation, clay is subject to long-term consolidation under loading and movement down slopes in excess of 1 in 10. Clay is also more prone to contain sulphates which can attack the concrete of foundations and floor slabs and corrode pipes.

Silt

Silt is a natural sediment of material of finer grades than sands. Most of the grains will pass a No. 200 B.S. sieve and the particles are not normally distinguishable with the naked eye. Silt is slightly gritty and moist lumps can be moulded with the fingers but not rolled into threads. It dries moderately quickly and can be dusted off the fingers, leaving only a stain. Dry lumps have appreciable cohesion but can be powdered between the fingers. Dilatancy is a characteristic of silt and to test this properly a small pat of moist

259

soil is shaken in the hand; in a silt some of the moisture appears on the surface but on pressing the pat between the fingers the water is drawn back and the surface becomes dry.

The categories for field assessment of structure and strength are again, as for clay, the moulding characteristics. Firm silt can only be moulded with strong finger pressure whereas soft silt can easily be moulded with the fingers.

The character of silt is such that for foundations the same considerations apply as for sand. Difficulties can arise from movement in water bearing ground and frost heave near the surface. As bearing soil it is poor as the particles have not the weight and ability to compact as for sand nor the characteristics when mixed with water to provide firm cohesion.

Cohesive soils

Type of Soil	Bearing Capacity tonf/ft.^{2} (tf/m^2)
Very stiff boulder clays and hard clays with shaly structure	4 to 6 (44 to 66)
Stiff clays and sandy clays	2 to 4 (22 to 44)
Firm clays and sandy clays	1 to 2 (11 to 22)
Soft clays and silts	½ to 1 (5·5 to 11)
Very soft clays and silts	nil to ½ (0 to 5·5)

Although the Code of Practice gives values for soft clay and very soft clays and silts it suggests that the bearing capacity should be determined after due investigation. The Code makes the same comment in regard to two other categories of ground, namely peat and made-up ground and gives no figures for possible bearing capacities.

Peat can be readily recognised by its fibrous black or brown appearance and smell. It is very compressible and varies greatly in volume according to its water content. Foundations on thick beds of peat when near the surface should be avoided, even when in the form of a raft, and should be taken down to a firm stratum below. In cases where the peat is of uniform thickness and is overlain by a substantial thickness of firm ground, ordinary foundations may be adopted for light domestic construction but in all cases a proper investigation should first be carried out.

Made-up ground or fill, identified by the presence of rubble, mineral waste, decaying wood or household refuse, should be avoided and foundations taken down to a firm bed. If the fill is found to contain injurious chemical wastes or be liable to spontaneous internal combustion they should be avoided entirely for obvious reasons. The support afforded by other types of fill depends on the composition of the material, on the manner in which it was placed and on the degree of consolidation it has reached. Fills of well compacted sand, gravel, chalk or slag are satisfactory for lightly loaded domestic building, while fills of clay or sandy clay are also satisfactory provided they have been properly compacted during placing. Movement may be expected however in a filling containing clay which has not been properly placed and compacted and which has not had time to consolidate in itself. Depending on the type of fill its thickness and method of placing, the time taken for consolidation may extend from a few months to many years. The difficulty with foundations on made-up ground is the variation which occurs over the area of the site, hence the obvious necessity for reinforced raft type foundations, piles or the construction of flexible types of buildings such as those that have been developed for use in areas liable to mining subsidence.

There remain in the Code of Practice various classifications of rocks and typical bearing capacities. Rock obviously forms the strongest support for buildings but this fact sometimes leads to carelessness in overlooking cleavages in the rock or patches where it is soft and crumbling. Included in the classification is chalk which when dry makes an excellent base but when damp is softened. Sites on chalk therefore require adequate drainage prior to building and protection from ground water subsequently. Chalk also occurs in a shattered state being slightly compressible or crumbly in this condition. For rock to be considered solid and suitable for foundation work it should be necessary to employ a pneumatic or other mechanically operated pick for excavation.

The danger of swallow holes arising in chalk and limestone areas is considerable due to the action of underground streams, if not diverted, or of soakaways being placed too near a building. In addition frost heave is a factor to be taken into account for buildings on chalk, particularly if foundations are less than 18 inches (0·46m) below ground level in fairly sheltered positions. In mountainous areas or those subject to prolonged periods of frost it may be suspected if foundations are at a depth of 2 to 3 feet (0·61 to 0·91m).

Rocks

Type of Rocks	Bearing Capacity tonf/ft.^{2} (tf/m^2)
Igneous and gneissic rocks in sound condition	100 (1090)
Massively bedded limestones and hard sandstones	40 (440)
Schists and slates	30 (330)
Hard shales, mudstone and soft sandstones	20 (220)
Clay shales	10 (110)
Hard solid chalk	6 (66)
Thinly bedded limestones and sandstones	To be assessed after inspection
Heavily shattered rocks and the softer chalks	

It will be noted that for thinly bedded limestones and sandstones and heavily shattered rocks and the softer chalks the bearing capacity is to be assessed after further investigation. It has been suggested elsewhere that sandstones that may be crumbled by hand have a bearing capacity of about 1·5 tonf/ft.^{2} (16·5 tf/m^2) but it would be advisable to follow the advice in the Code of Practice and carry out a proper investigation.

It will also be observed that the applicable field tests set out in Column 3 of the Table to Regulation D7 of the Building Regulations follow very closely those described in the Code of Practice C.P.101:1963 and it is presumed that the Regulations are based to a great extent on the recommendations of the Code but providing a further margin of safety.

Finally in regard to soil bearing capacity the Code of Practice makes particular point of stressing that due care should be paid to ensuring an adequate depth of the given soil and, in certain cases, in order to limit the amount of settlement consideration may have to be given to restricting the bearing pressure to a lower value than the bearing capacity.

The Code of Practice continues with statements on the general design of foundations, sub-soil drainage and the selection of suitable foundations for various types of ground related to new buildings of the type covered by the Code.

As to sizes, beyond the basic rule that the angle of spread of load from the wall base to the outer edge of the ground bearing for strip foundations is not to be more than a quarter of a brick per course ($2\frac{1}{4}$ to 3 inches$=57$ to 76mm) for brickwork, or 1 to 1 for concrete with a minimum thickness for the foundation of 6 inches (152mm), there are no set rules. Most of the recommendations are in the form of advice to engineers designing wide strip foundations (which are defined as strip foundations of such width that transverse reinforcement is necessary), ground beams, rafts, pile foundations and retaining walls. Readers interested in the engineering aspects of foundation design are referred to the Code C.P.101:1963 itself and the principal publications on the subject, Civil Engineering Code of Practice No. 4 "Foundations" (issued by the Institution of Civil Engineers) and Civil Engineering Code of Practice No. 2 "Earth Retaining Structures" (issued by the Institution of Structural Engineers).

While therefore the Code of Practice C.P.101:1963 contains much valuable information in regard to general foundation design in relation to site conditions and as such should form part of the library of every surveyor dealing with repairs to buildings, some of the recommendations are directed more to the engineer rather than the surveyor for types of foundations other than strip foundations or unreinforced pad foundations. This is not to suggest that the surveyor should ignore the recommendations directed to the engineer for it is only by being familiar with current practice in this field that he will be able to advise his client correctly when the time may come to consult an engineer and the need arise to discuss the engineer's proposals.

Where damage to a building is due to factors below ground level the possible causes have been set out in detail in Chapter 2 and the steps necessary to establish the fact have been described in the section of that Chapter dealing with the investigation. Mention was made of a trial excavation to expose the foundations at some point and the possible need for a study of the sub-soil. A great deal of information will already have been assembled in regard to the building, the site, adjacent buildings and the topography of the surrounding area so that an investigation of the foundations and the sub-soil may well be no more than a confirmatory exercise to prove the deductions already made. It is nonetheless necessary, however, and some consideration must be given to its scope.

The age of the building should be considered first in relation to the type of investigation. It has been mentioned before that all new buildings undergo an initial settlement but if, with a relatively new building, settlement shows signs of continuing in a differential manner then the possibility of overloading the foundations at a particular point arises. Confirmation of this might be provided by driving with a sledge hammer a pointed metal rod say of about $\frac{3}{4}$ of an inch (19mm) in diameter and about 6 feet (1·82m) long into the ground at various points alongside the outer edge of the foundations to the external wall. The penetration should be noted at each position, uniform soil being indicated if the penetration decreases with depth. Should, however, the penetration per blow suddenly increase the indication is that the lower stratum at that point is weaker. The depth of the weaker stratum can be approximately determined by replacing the 6-foot (1·82m) rod with a longer one and driving this down until a soil offering greater resistance is encountered. Useful confirmatory evidence might well be obtained in this manner of a suspicion derived from above ground inspection.

General overall differential settlement continuing in a fairly new building might well indicate an error in the design of foundations in relation to the bearing capacity of the soil. In these circumstances the soil could be exposed at the level of the underside of the foundations and a loading test applied to ascertain the yield point or samples removed for laboratory tests.

It is also a straightforward matter to calculate the loads on the ground per square foot or metre by taking the total of the combined dead and imposed loads per lineal foot or metre of foundation and dividing this by the total width of the foundation. Weights of materials should be taken from B.S.648:1964 "Schedule of Weights of Building Materials", if the Appendix is inadequate.

The above investigations might produce a provisional indication of the cause of the trouble but it is not suggested that it should form a reliable guide for prescribing an expensive scheme of spreading the weight of the structure over a greater area of the sub-soil. Before that stage is reached further investigation is highly advisable, but prior to discussing this investigation the case of an older property might first be considered.

The fact that a house has stood for years without substantial movement is of some importance when considering the cause of troubles which may suddenly affect it. Immediately it suggests that it is at least unlikely that the original construction is at fault although this of course cannot entirely be eliminated. Assuming that all causes above ground can be discounted, overloading of foundations and differential settlement in foundations also seem unlikely in view of past history providing no recent alterations have been made to the structure. Much more likely a cause would be an undermining of the foundations or a movement of soil below the level of the underside of the foundations. In the circumstances exposure beside the existing foundations whatever they might consist of, would be unlikely to provide information of any value. The soil would probably look the same as it would have done before the movement occurred and all that would be likely to be seen would perhaps be a crack in the foundations themselves. The need for a much closer investigation into the causes of undermining should be apparent be it along the lines of leaking drains or water mains, nearby excavations, the effects of tree roots or the like. That the investigation may have to be extended into deeper ground should also be apparent when it is realised that strip footings and pad foundations increase the pressure in a uniform soil significantly to a depth and breadth roughly equal to $1\frac{1}{2}$ times the width of the foundation. When it is considered also that soil is seldom uniform and within this area of pressure firmer or weaker strata may occur, as for example when sand overlies a soft clay, and disturbance of soil within or even below this stress envelope can cause movement, the need for a full sub-soil investigation should be obvious. For example a strip foundation 3 feet wide (0·91m) positioned with its underside 3 feet 6 inches (1·07m) below the surface will require an investigation to a depth of at least 9 feet (2·74m).

Foundation work to an existing building is likely to be extremely costly and clearly the absolute need for it must be thoroughly established. The fact that a building subject to movement might take up a new position of repose before any danger to its stability arises, must not be lost sight of and, if circumstances permit, the execution of foundation work should be delayed for as long as possible. If, eventually, foundation work should prove necessary, then there is all the more reason that a thorough sub-soil investigation should provide the prelude to the design of the new work. With the likely expense involved all risks of failure after the work has been completed should be reduced to a minimum and it ought to be concluded therefore that no foundation work to an existing building should be commenced unless and until a full sub-soil investigation has been carried out and the results of the investigation fully assessed.

Chapter 2 dealt fully with the site investigation above ground level from the point of view of ascertaining the possible cause of defects and much information from local sources, old maps and records, the physical inspection of the site and surrounding area will have been assembled by the time the stage of sub-soil investigation has been reached. The notes would also include information on the topography of the area, its vegetation, its liability to flooding and the possible levels of ground water. The object of the soil investigation will be to determine the strength and deformation characteristics of the soil under load and to identify the conditions in which the soil is otherwise susceptible to movement. From the information obtained a scheme for the solution to the problem will be prepared and therefore it is important that the sub-soil investigation is carried out with this eventual end in view. Many of the firms who undertake site investigations are branches of specialised contracting concerns and while it is not suggested that the results of investigations produced by such concerns would be other than completely factual, it is considered that the client's best interests might well be served if an entirely independent organisation specialising in this field were instructed by the surveyor at this stage. Alternatively if the problem by this time had reached the position where the employment of skilled engineering assistance seemed likely, then the interests of the client might best be served if an engineer was appointed at this stage. In view of the number of firms with patented foundation systems and the possibility arising of conflicting advice of a highly technical nature based on the sub-soil investigation being obtained, the appointment of an independent consultant has much to commend it. Only an engineer in this capacity will be able to weigh the merits of the various systems in an unbiased manner and it may well be that he will prefer the site investigation department of a specialised contractor which might possess more suitable equipment and have greater laboratory facilities than an independent firm that relied solely on obtaining this type of work. In such circumstances, however, the consultant will be able to ensure that the information obtained on the sub-soil survey is interpreted in a factual way sufficient for him to advise the client whether any of the patent methods available, and not just those of the particular firm instructed, are appropriate to the circumstances.

The sub-soil investigation would probably follow fairly routine lines and involve the excavation of two or more trial pits to establish the soil profile. These pits of suitable size to accommodate a man, timbered if necessary, would have to be sufficiently deep to establish the nature of the soil to the depth of stress previously mentioned but care would have to be taken to ensure that they were not within the stress envelope of the existing foundations otherwise further disturbance might be induced. One pit at the front and one at the back of the building might well be sufficient but on sloping sites others may have to be dug so that any variations in the profile can be noted. Trial pits represent the best method of examining soil as they are easily accessible, can be inspected at all levels and samples can be removed with a spade or knife in an undisturbed state as soon as possible after excavation for further closer inspection and testing. In examining the soil in a trial pit it is of course necessary to determine whether it is natural or made-up ground, whether underground water is present and whether a less resistant soil exists a few feet below the bottom of the pit. Made ground may be distinguished from naturally deposited soils by the presence of cavities and often by foreign substances such as pieces of brick, wood, clinker, rubble or refuse. If made ground is exposed then the pit should be extended through the full depth of the fill, if practicable, so that the level and character of the natural ground below can be ascertained.

Trial pits are relatively expensive to form but as the investigation being considered is necessary due to suspected ground movement the extra cost is usually justified as they provide more information than bore holes. Their siting can be intelligently considered in relation to the movements in the existing building to provide much useful data. This data can of course be supplemented by the use of bore holes on other parts of the site to obtain confirmatory evidence. In soft or firm clay soils the post-hole auger can be used by two men to extract samples up to a depth of 20 to 25 feet (6·1 to 7·6m). Therefore if the site should prove to be entirely of clay it can be seen that with the use of the notes on field assessment of structure from the British Standard Code of Practice C.P.101:1963, trial pits and bore holes, the need for specialist equipment and specialist advice might not be necessary. However the situation is unlikely to be as simple as this and specialists are likely to be required to provide casing tubes to prevent the collapse of bore holes in sand and gravel, to carry out standard penetration tests with percussive tools on these soils, to take samples to the laboratory for the relative density tests on non-cohesive soils and for undrained triaxial compression tests on cohesive soils.

Generally the information required on the sub-soil are the following characteristics and the depths at which they are observed:

Soil type.
Soil uniformity.
Whether the soil is breakable in the fingers.
Whether the soil is gritty, smooth, plastic or sticky.

267

Whether the soil is homogeneous, fissured or shattered.
Whether organic or foreign matter is present.
Soil colour and smell.
The depth of the water table.
The analysis of soil and ground water for sulphate content.

The comprehensive quantitative field and laboratory tests which can be carried out are described in British Standard Code of Practice C.P.2001 (1957) "Site Investigations" and British Standard B.S.1377:1961 "Methods of Testing Soils for Civil Engineering Purposes" and should be referred to by those interested in closer study.

Where the sub-soil investigation in trial pits or information from other sources suggests that piling may be necessary as part of the reconstruction of foundations the information on soil characteristics at the lower depths required can only be economically obtained by means of bore holes. Such may be the case too where large trees are growing on clay soils, the effect of the roots on which may extend to 15 to 20 feet (4·57 to 6·1m).

From the information assembled to date which as may be imagined can amount to a substantial volume, a critical decision now has to be taken on the correct prescription for a remedy to the diagnosed cause of the defect. In a manner similar to the way that cracks in brickwork represent the common symptoms of different causes, so the remedies for foundation failures and soil movements are limited to a few which are satisfactory for a number of causes. The important thing is to establish the cause so that the appropriate remedy can be selected. As the number of remedies is limited, it is considered appropriate that these are described in detail in the first instance and their application related if necessary to the five sub-divisions of Part 2C of Chapter 2 "Defects Arising from Foundation Troubles or Ground Movements". The remedies and the causes set out in the five sub-divisions will be discussed by way of summary at the end of the Chapter.

TYPES AND METHODS OF UNDERPINNING

The technique of underpinning whereby a new foundation is constructed beneath an old foundation or a new foundation is formed at a lower level to take the place of an old one which is to be removed has for long been an established method of dealing with foundation problems, besides being necessary in cases where new buildings with foundations at a lower level are to be erected adjacent to old buildings. Underpinning can serve two purposes, either to spread the load over a greater area of the sub-soil or, alternatively, to carry the foundation down to the level of a sub-soil which has a greater bearing capacity. In either case it is necessary to give consideration to two factors before the work is carried out. It is necessary to ensure in the first instance that the work formerly supported by the old foundation is given adequate temporary support during the operation. Secondly, in completing the new work, that it can be finished in such a way that the final "pinning-up" not only carries the whole load that was formerly carried, but that it will do so without appreciable settlement in itself.

High labour costs at the present time mean that underpinning is very expensive indeed and there is little doubt that these costs will continue to rise in the forseeable future, the materials part of the total cost of such work being relatively low. It is possible that this factor more than any other has led to the development of a number of systems of underpinning designed to reduce the amount of physical labour involved and even some systems designed to obviate underpinning in the traditional sense altogether. Against this however at the present time is the fact that the traditional methods are reasonably well known and familiar to contractors and operatives alike so that for a small job involving not too much depth it may still be competitive to design a scheme on traditional lines.

The need for a relatively simple scheme of underpinning might well arise in the case of an old building where a lack of a concrete foundation and decay or failure in the old brick footings has caused some settlement to occur perhaps after two hundred years or so. Another suitable instance might be where overloading occurs which cannot be relieved by any other practical and more economical means, possibly where the old brick footings cannot take the overload or where the load has come upon a pier. If the case concerns a pier then the load on the pier would have to be temporarily carried on dead and needle shoring but in the case of a long foundation however, shoring would only be necessary at the ends of the wall if the work was carried out in short lengths leaving enough of the old work between simultaneous excavations to carry both its own share of the load together with that of the portions removed. Existing conditions at "A", this simple type of underpinning, at "B", and the order of work on a 24-foot (7·3m) length of wall on the elevation at "E" with the shoring at one end are shown on Figure 49. The principle is that short lengths of between 3 to 5 feet (0·9 to 1·5m) should be excavated at a time and no length should be tackled until the adjoining length has set. Two lengths however can be carried out at the same time provided these are well separated, hence it is as well to prepare the scheme in advance so as to utilise time and labour to the best advantage. For this reason it is sometimes more suitable to divide a wall into a greater number of shorter lengths under 5 feet (1·5m).

The final pinning up can be carried out as shown at "B" with two courses of slates tightly driven into the last mortar joint in a similar manner as adopted when a slate damp course is inserted to an existing wall. Slates however are difficult to drive in without breaking and cannot be driven for any distance satisfactorily. For this reason if the underpinning is completed below ground level, for example up to the bottom of an existing foundation, the final three inches of pinning up can best be carried out with a damp mix of concrete well rammed into the gap. In the case of pinning up to brickwork a similar tight joint could be obtained with a narrower joint well filled and rammed with a cement mortar 1:3.

It must be made clear that the first type of underpinning illustrated can be used only where the cause has been definitely established as decayed foundations or an overload at a specific point, for example on a narrow pier. Its use pre-supposes that the ground at the original base of the old foundations is satisfactory for the loads involved when only a normal strip foundation is provided in accordance with the Building Regulations. It amounts in effect to providing the foundations which would have been necessary if the house had been constructed now.

The second method shown at "D" for existing conditions at "C" on Figure 49 is a suitable alternative method for underpinning a pier which is overloaded. This can often arise following an alteration to a building which is carried out without due regard to its effects. The method enables a pier or a whole length of wall if necessary to be underpinned and the load spread over a greater area of the sub-soil at the same depth and without causing any disturbance to the support of existing foundations in the same building. It may also be resorted to in circumstances where the sub-soil can be established as being no better at a lower level than nearer the surface or where ground water nearer the surface prevents the suitable formation of new foundations at a lower level. It has the disadvantage however of involving disturbance to the interior since obviously the load must be spread evenly on both sides of the wall. If it were necessary to consider this method for a whole building it is possible that although it may be more costly to adopt patented methods developed recently, the convenience of these may prove more satisfactory for the occupants. No temporary support is required, the steel needles, at 5 to 6 feet (1·5 to 1·8m) centres, or closer as required, fulfilling this function in a permanent form.

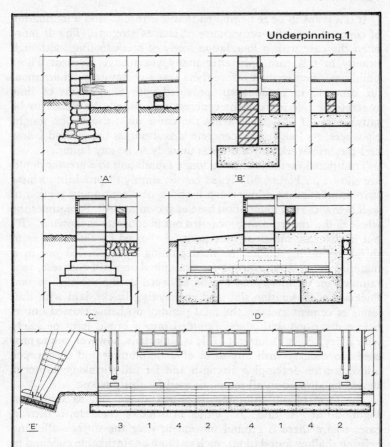

Underpinning 1

'A' 'B' 'C' 'D'

'E' 3 1 4 2 4 1 4 2

Poor bricks used below ground will crush in time when the ground is of good bearing capacity as at 'A'. New foundations can be provided by underpinning as at 'B', utilising the slate pinning up as a d.p.c. and reconstructing the poor wood floor, although the provision of a solid floor would be cheaper. The work can be carried out in one length if the wall is needled and shored but it is safer to work in short lengths when only the ends need be shored as on the elevation at 'E', where the order of working is numbered. As the ground is assumed to be good foundations are shown taken down to the frost line only.
Overloading can force otherwise sound foundations, 'C', downwards. A solution is to spread the load over a greater area of sub-soil by concreting to the appropriate width, incorporating the existing found-ation and building in either one or more permanent R.S.J. needles. The needles must be solidly built into the wall and supported on steel bear-ing plates and folding wedges and finally encased in concrete. Care must be taken that safe bearing limits are not exceeded on building in and wedging. No temporary support is normally required and a whole length of wall can be dealt with in this manner if the original found-ation width is inadequate and the sub-soil at a greater depth is found to be of the same bearing capacity as at the higher level.

Scales: details 1:40, elevation 1:100

49

271

It is a point to be remembered that it is rare to find a foundation of concrete defective on grounds of lack of strength. This is more often the case with a foundation solely of brick footings, although usually in this case only after many years have elapsed. Those buildings, often erected before there was any statutory requirement for concrete in foundations, provided with foundations of lime concrete or inferior cement concrete will usually be found to be satisfactory. If settlement arises the cause must usually be sought elsewhere. As long as the concrete is as strong as the ground below and the brickwork above there is unlikely to be any failure.

Traditional methods of extending a foundation to a greater depth are shown on Figure 50. These consist simply of providing a new strip foundation at a lower depth and a new continuous section of wall below the old foundation base as shown at "A". Sometimes the whole of the underpinning is carried out in concrete as shown at "B" but in this case sufficient time must be allowed for the concrete to shrink on drying before the final pinning up is carried out in a material that will not shrink, for example damp stiff concrete, well rammed in. Greater speed can be achieved by the use of a normal thickness of foundation slab and engineering bricks, laid with thin joints of cement mortar, the final pinning up being carried out as before described with slates rammed into a broad joint or solely with a dry cement mortar 1:3. It is important, however, not to proceed too quickly with any form of underpinning and the proper allowance for developing strength and for full shrinkage to occur should be allowed in all materials used for this purpose.

The form of underpinning described above and as shown on Figure 50 at "A" and "B", either in brick or concrete, is used in cases where there is ground movement near the surface affecting existing shallow foundations, such as those on shrinkable clay and in any circumstances within a reasonable depth where there is disturbance to the soil immediately below the existing foundations. It is also among the measures usually adopted to extend existing foundations to a lower depth when new construction to a lower level is to be carried out adjacent, for example the formation of a new basement adjoining.

If the bottom of an underpinning excavation should prove to be of moist clay, which is compressible, there is a danger that the final pinning up may not be sufficient to prevent appreciable settlement after the work is completed. In such cases the wall could still be underpinned in short sections by providing a new concrete base at the lower level and inserting jacks between the top of this and the underside of the old foundation above. These could be left in position, being tightened up as required until all appreciable move-

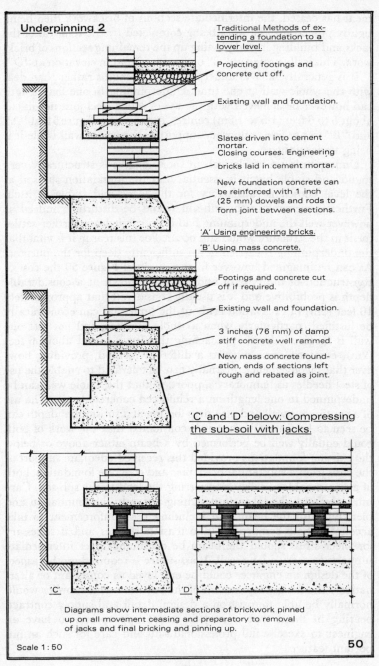

Underpinning 2

Traditional Methods of extending a foundation to a lower level.

Projecting footings and concrete cut off.

Existing wall and foundation.

Slates driven into cement mortar.
Closing courses. Engineering bricks laid in cement mortar.

New foundation concrete can be reinforced with 1 inch (25 mm) dowels and rods to form joint between sections.

'A' Using engineering bricks.

'B' Using mass concrete.

Footings and concrete cut off if required.

Existing wall and foundation.

3 inches (76 mm) of damp stiff concrete well rammed.

New mass concrete foundation, ends of sections left rough and rebated as joint.

'C' and 'D' below: Compressing the sub-soil with jacks.

'C'   'D'

Diagrams show intermediate sections of brickwork pinned up on all movement ceasing and preparatory to removal of jacks and final bricking and pinning up.

Scale 1 : 50

50

273

ment has ceased, the intermediate sections of brickwork then being tightly pinned up, the work being completed by the removal of the jacks and building in and pinning up the remaining sections of brickwork. This is illustrated at "C" on Figure 50 and in elevation at "D".

It is generally safer to underpin in short lengths rather than deal with the whole wall at one time. Underpinning in one long length can however be achieved with the use of rolled steel joist needles at about 5 to 6 feet (1·5 to 1·8m) centres, as shown on Figure 51, at "A" and "B" to provide temporary support to the whole wall while it is being underpinned.

Underpinning a whole wall in short lengths is structurally very sound and stable but it is essential that the foundation sub-soil at the level chosen is satisfactory for the loads and stable in itself. Further movement in the sub-soil would be disturbing indeed as however well the underpinning had been carried out further settlement in the structure would still occur. For this reason it is vital that the underpinning is carried down sufficiently deep for the purpose. As can be imagined however from a study of Figure 50 the cost of construction of the type of underpinning shown at a considerable depth is prohibitive and it is usually considered that approximately 10 feet (3m) of excavation is about the limit that can economically be justified, particularly when a whole building and not just one wall is involved. Even approaching this level, say at about 6 feet (2m), common sense suggests a different method, providing however that inconvenience internally can be tolerated to enable the use of steel needles as temporary support, so that the whole wall can be underpinned in one length on a reinforced concrete beam. The use of a continuous wall and new strip footing at a substantial depth can be seen to be wasteful when it is considered that the work of both could equally well be performed by a beam either above or below the existing foundations provided this received adequate support at the ends from a substantial brick pier and concrete foundation, both of a size capable of safely transferring the load to the sub-soil. Care must obviously be taken in designing not only the foundation and pier, but also the beam and including the reinforcement to take account of both compression and tension stresses and if necessary for sheer stress should the beam be continuous over intermediate supports to carry a long wall. If assistance is required on this aspect of the design an engineer could be employed as consultant or alternatively the design department of the reinforcement supplier would normally be able to assist on a design, detail and supply contract, bearing in mind that it may be more appropriate to have an engineer to exercise full professional skill and care for such an important feature.

The system of underpinning utilising pier supports and a reinforced concrete beam is shown on Figure 51 at "A" and "B".
Traditional underpinning using a ground beam of this type always
involves the use of temporary needles so that its adoption is sometimes ruled out if the inconvenience and disturbance involved with
the use of these is not permissible. In such cases resort to the strip
foundation and continuous wall might well be prohibitive on the
grounds of economics. An ingenious patent method of overcoming
this problem has been developed by one firm specialising in foundation work and the correction of defects owing their origin to below
ground level movements. This firm has developed "stools" to take
the place of needles, which are short struts either in concrete or
steel about 9 inches (229mm) square and 18 inches (457mm) high
which are inserted into holes cut at about 3-foot (911mm) centres in
a good brick wall (or less if the brickwork is poor) and pinned up with
top and bottom plates. The stools when made of perforated concrete
"U" sections, and set at the correct level, usually with their tops
about 6 inches below the damp proof course, become part of the
reinforced concrete beam. The reinforcement can be threaded
through the perforations in the stool, the intervening brickwork
being cut away as the wall above will be carried entirely on the
stools. Once the reinforcement is in position the beam can be
shuttered and the concrete poured leaving a gap at the top to be
filled on the final pinning up. This procedure has the merit of simplicity and economy in the amount of work involved and following
the completion of the beam the brick piers and concrete foundations
can be constructed and pinned up in the normal way. This method
of cutting away and forming the beam is shown on Figure 51 at
"C", "D", "E" and "F", and it will be seen that in the circumstances
shown no disturbance to the interior is involved.

When it is not possible to find a suitable sub-soil level within about
10 to 15 feet (3 to 4·6m) of the surface and it is necessary to provide
foundations at a lower level even underpinning by brick piers is
uneconomic and it is necessary to consider the use of piles. Pressure
piles require a minimum of headroom for boring and casting,
obviate vibration and are generally considered the most suitable for
the purpose. There are a number of variations which can be adopted
depending on circumstances and the traditional methods without
involving the use of patent stools are shown on Figure 52 "A" to "E"
inclusive. The most economical way is shown at "A" in section and
at "B" in elevation where a beam is formed above the level of the
existing foundations together with reinforced concrete needles and
piles on either side of the wall. Less piles are involved with this
method than with the scheme shown at "C", which omits the beam

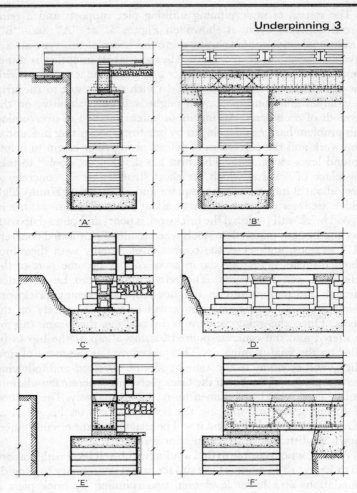

Underpinning the whole length of a foundation to a depth beyond
about 6 feet (2 m) is uneconomic and in these circumstances
the support can be provided by brick piers to the appropriate
depth and an R.C. beam as at 'A' and 'B'. To do this by traditional
means involves temporary support to the whole wall by needles
and the consequent disturbance internally. The use of patent "stools"
as permanent needles which become part of the beam overcomes
this problem. 'C' and 'D' show the wall cut away and the stools
inserted. 'E' and F'' show the completed beam, the pinning up
between the stools and the top of a brick pier on a corner
with fine concrete cap and pinning up to the underside of
the beam. Temporary support to the excavations is omitted for
clarity but use can be made of precast concrete or brick shuttering
and precast concrete in the back of excavation which can be left
in position.

Scales: 'A' and 'B', 1:100: remainder 1:50

51

and relies on reinforced concrete needles and piles at closer centres as shown also on the elevation at "E", but still on either side of the wall. If it is not possible to pile from both sides of the wall then a cantilevered system shown at "D" could be designed. For some smaller properties it is convenient to extend the reinforced concrete beam forming the new lower section of the wall in "A" to beyond the corners of the building and position single piles at these points to support the beam, with possibly piles in doorways elsewhere as intermediate support. It is this type of scheme which is favoured by the firm that utilises stools to form the reinforced concrete beam at about ground level and the advantages involved by the saving on piles and, in the case of the patent method of forming the beam, lack of disturbance internally will be evident from the drawing. This method is shown on Figure 52 at "F" as a section through a door opening and in elevation at "G" the non-patent method being identical but requiring the use of the steel needles as at "A" and "B" for temporary support. With this patent method a house built perhaps before or just after the Second World War with shallow foundations on a shrinkable clay soil and now affected by the action of tree roots can be provided with a foundation scheme very similar to that which it would have had if built later with the benefit of the advice given by the Building Research Establishment. The B.R.E. was instrumental in evolving the foundation system of short bored piles with reinforced concrete ground beams for two-storey dwelling houses shortly after the Second World War, but reference will be made later in this Chapter to the advice on remedial measures for older houses affected by settlement in these circumstances. Underpinning is not necessarily the best solution as other factors, particularly the age of trees whose roots may be causing the trouble, have to be taken into account.

Even apart from the variations available for the use of piles in underpinning discussed above and shown on Figure 52 at "A" to "G" inclusive, it is still possible with special equipment to drive piles directly below existing foundations. Sectional precast concrete piles are used, the first section with a steel tip and with steel dowelled joints between sections. The sections are forced into the ground by means of a hydraulic jack placed between the pile and either the underside of the old foundation or the underside of a new R.C. ground beam. The jack is operated from a pump outside the excavation. This is illustrated in outline at "H" on Figure 52. The distance between piles will depend on whether an existing foundation is retained in which case they will be fairly close together or whether an R.C. beam is installed. In the former case care is required on the exercise of pressure against the base of the old foundation having

277

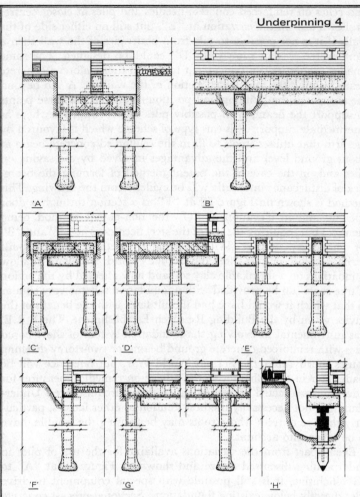

'A'   'B'

'C'   'D'   'E'

'F'   'G'   'H'

For very deep underpinning resort must be had to piles. There are
many variations which can be adapted to particular cases, some
of which only are shown here in outline. In section 'A' and elevation
'B' an R.C. ground beam is shown supported by needles with piles
on either side. Many more piles are required for sections 'C' and
'D' and elevation 'E' omitting the beam and relying on needles at
closer centres. Piling can be on both sides, as at 'C', or on one
side only and the needles cantilevered as at 'D'. For small buildings an R.C. beam, shown here on section 'F' and in elevation
at 'G' formed with patent stools, can be extended to be supported
on single piles beyond the corners and perhaps with intermediate piles in doorways. In some circumstances sectional
precast concrete piles can be driven by hydraulic pressure below
and against existing foundations or new ground beams as at 'H'.

Scale 1:100   52

regard to its condition, the state of the wall above and the positioning of the piles in relation to window and door openings. As with all
piling the advice of a consulting engineer is essential.

For many years now cement grout, pumped into the sub-soil
under pressure, or chemicals have been used to stabilise the sub-soil
when it has been necessary to carry out underpinning in soft permeable ground. Although these methods are of more value in the
field of civil engineering, for example in the construction of dams
and tunnels, further developments along these lines have provided
a satisfactory means of forming underpinning to older buildings
adjacent to the construction of deep basements included as part of
the re-development of sites in central areas. For example cement
clay grouts have been used to fill voids in made ground and open
waterlogged gravel and to enclose a chemical grout which sets below
the foundations. This forms the underpinning down to the level of
the proposed new foundations which are to be constructed adjoining,
all this work being carried out before the excavation necessary to
form the new basement. The injection process carried out at low
pressure assists not only the new construction, by helping to keep
the deep site dry, but also helps to prevent the run-off of water from
surrounding sites thereby avoiding disturbance of the bearing
capacity of loose and waterlogged soils. Most of the adjoining old
buildings in a particular recent example of such work dated from the
18th century and it was considered that the vibration from sheet
piling which would have been necessary by adopting traditional
constructional methods would probably have caused damage to the
old brickwork and disturb the stability, rather than restrain any
tendency to movement. The application of this method is shown on
Figure 53 at "A" as an example to show what can be done in
difficult conditions.

The work involved in grouting sub-soils with cement, clay-
chemical mixtures, and chemicals alone is highly specialised and can
be entrusted only to engineers and contractors experienced in this
work. In particular the question of pressure is vital. Certain soils
will suit the treatment at a certain pressure which has to be determined by site investigation and laboratory study by the specialist
in conjunction with the engineer. However, the system may be
extremely advantageous over traditional methods of underpinning in
certain circumstances where site conditions due to water and poor
sub-soil warrant. Here again, however, many of the working
methods, equipment and techniques are the patents of specialised
contracting firms and the question of the consulting engineer in relation to their employment by the building owner should be borne in
mind. The same might be said for the surveyor acting for owners of

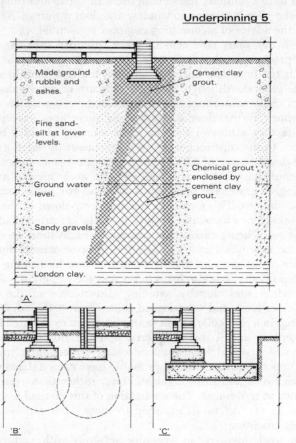

Made ground rubble and ashes.

Cement clay grout.

Fine sand-silt at lower levels.

Chemical grout enclosed by cement clay grout.

Ground water level.

Sandy gravels.

London clay.

'A'

'B'   'C'

'A' above shows underpinning carried out by injection to enable the
level of the ground on the right to be lowered by approximately
16 feet (4·9 m) for the formation of a deep basement next to six
storey 18th century houses. The work, carried out before excavation by drilling and the insertion of injection tubes, consists
of a cement clay grout to encase the existing foundations in
made ground and further underpinning down to good ground
of a chemical grout enclosed by cement clay. On gelling the
new underpinning retained the ground water below the
existing buildings and reduced seepage into the excavation
necessary for the formation of the new R.C. raft and
retaining walls.
'B' shows what might happen if the new wall on the right is
built close to an existing wall even with foundations at the
same level. In uniform soil the stress envelopes would overlap
and settlement in both walls may result. It is safer to
underpin and provide a wide foundation, reinforced as necessary, for both walls as at 'C'.

Scale: 1 :100   53

280

buildings on adjoining sites where work of this nature is proposed. There is little doubt that in such circumstances the adjoining owners should be advised by the surveyor to appoint a consulting engineer known to specialise in this work and it is considered reasonable in the circumstances that the instigators of the scheme should meet his fees in the usual way as between building and adjoining owner either under Part VI of the London Building Acts (Amendment) Act 1939 or if outside London, under Common Law.

It is perhaps a symptom of the present age that increasing speci- alisation has led to investment and research in the development of various methods of foundation construction appropriate for use on soils formerly not considered suitable for supporting buildings. This tendency, coupled with advances in the scientific study of soil, should be of great assistance in securing a reduction in the incidence of foundation difficulties. Whether this reduction will extend to domestic construction of the kind envisaged in this book is debatable, but there are signs of a greater understanding of the problems likely to be encountered by developers and contractors, certainly of the larger groups. The difficulty is that in many instances where the research and development results in a successful new technique being evolved the system is, quite properly, patented. For this reason some of the possibilities discussed in this Chapter can only be dealt with by way of general principles and may or may not be suitable for the smaller type of job. Highly specialised techniques involving much investigation and perhaps laboratory study would seem inappropri- ate where traditional methods may well be quite feasible. Probably the investigation would cost as much as the physical work by tradi- tional means. On the other hand, surveyors dealing with large estates may well find the methods appropriate where the cost of investigation can be spread over a number of properties.

We have already described chemical injection as a possible means of stabilising soil and preventing water movement and similar remarks apply to a number of patent methods to make excavation easier in waterlogged and loose ground. Traditional methods of driving sheet piles are not always appropriate when existing build- ings adjacent are old and fragile but patent excavation shields have been developed which permit deep excavation in difficult soils, such as running sand, without vibration. The use of these shields can avoid the need for lowering the level of ground water on a site which is usually necessary with the traditional method of sheet piling, but which can be dangerous to adjoining buildings by causing water to run towards the excavation and disturbing the sub-soil support to the foundations as a result. Another method involves freezing the sub-soil which is very useful for dealing with very soft wet clay encountered in deep excavations near existing buildings. Yet another method useful for stabilising certain clays involves the use of special electrodes and the principle of electro-osmosis to establish a barrier of stable soil.

Finally before summarising the methods of dealing with defects originating from below ground level and relating these to the various causes, mention must be made of a very interesting and practical means of re-levelling buildings and restoring, at least to a great extent, the conditions which existed before the settlement took place. Previously we have discussed the use of patent "stools" in place of needling which can then form part of the beam in a beam and pier or beam and pile scheme of underpinning. The same firm has continued the development of stools in the form of screw and hydraulic jacks, in other words movable stools, which can be inserted into the walls in the same way as the stools. By careful consideration of the original settlement and control of the jacking operation which can be manual, semi-automatic or automatic by electrical devices working in conjunction with water levels, the settlement can be reproduced in reverse. Combined with a beam and pier or beam and pile scheme of underpinning, the company using this method claim to have re-levelled buildings 18 inches (457mm) out of level in mining areas, which must be accounted a considerable achievement. The company claims that almost any distorted building can be jacked back into shape and that the cost can be under half the cost of re-building which would probably have been necessary before this method of jacking had been evolved.

An extension of the system of jacking has also been developed for providing a system of foundations for areas particularly prone to settlement, for example coal mining areas and areas where brine pumping takes place. The system is based on providing jacking positions in the foundations so that the building can be re-levelled on more than one occasion should settlement be repeated. Primarily intended for new buildings the system might also have its use, in particular cases, for repair operations.

Chapter 2 set out the symptoms of defects arising from "Foundation Troubles and Ground Movements" and sub-divided these into five sections. The methods of repair which have been set out in this Chapter are available for the correction of these defects, but it is as important to select the correct remedy as it is to diagnose the cause of the defect. At this point, therefore, some consideration will be given to which remedy is applicable to each case or to discuss the alternatives if more than one method is available. At the same time certain practical remedies available which have been hinted at but not involving excavation, will also be discussed.

REMEDIES FOR THE FIVE CATEGORIES OF CAUSES GIVING RISE TO FOUNDATION TROUBLES OR GROUND MOVEMENTS

(1) *Overloading of Foundations*

Very often the immediate reaction to a diagnosis of overloading is to underpin. However before any consideration is given to this it is always advisable to consider any possible methods of relieving the overloaded section, either by redistributing the weight more evenly or by transferring it elsewhere entirely. As often as not this can be done at a far cheaper cost. If it is impossible however, then underpinning to spread the load over a greater area of the sub-soil must be resorted to as shown on Figure 49 at "D", remembering that the underside of the foundation should be at the same level as existing foundations.

(2) *Differential Settlement in Foundations*

Where differential settlement in foundations arises due to foundations of bay windows, back additions, or other extensions to the main body of the building being at a different level, it is sometimes possible to tie smaller features back to the main building if the differential settlement is not too great. If it is serious however, it will be necessary to follow current practice and provide a foundation at the same level as that elsewhere by underpinning with concrete as shown on Figure 49 or with concrete and brickwork, although probably to a much more limited scale, as shown on Figure 50.

Along a length of wall where a differential settlement has arisen owing to the presence of a pocket of weak soil, the movement might well be dealt with by the provision of a ground beam of reinforced concrete, so as to distribute the load on to adjoining sections of foundations bearing on firmer ground.

(3) *Undermining of Foundations*

The undermining of soil supporting foundations may be by natural means or due to man-made operations. If due to leaking drains, then it is conceivable that if the effect is not too advanced a simple repair of the drains by relining might suffice. On the other hand, as with buildings, drains do not usually just develop faults without some cause and although simple lining may be both effective and cheap, it would be essential to check the drains again say every three months for a year to ensure that they do not continue to develop leaks. If they do, the investigations described in Chapter 10 should be undertaken to establish and remedy the cause. The effect on the building may be in the form of differential settlement in the case of a drain passing under a building or a leaking gulley, or even whole wall movement if the drain is parallel to a wall of the building. The remedy of a reinforced concrete ground beam would cope with differential settlement just as it would with the effect of a swallow hole while for whole wall movement a beam plus underpinning by brick piers may be necessary, coupled perhaps with jacking the wall partially back into position.

If a building which has been stable for years and which is founded on a sandy soil or gravel suddenly starts to move then it is almost certain to be due to some change in water movement below ground, more than likely originating some distance away. Steps must be taken to ascertain the direction of the flow and to divert it past the site of the building or alternatively it may be necessary to sheet pile around the building to prevent the soil movement. If the sand or gravel overlies a bed of firm clay then it may be simpler to underpin with reinforced concrete beams and piles down to the level of the clay.

In regard to man-made operations such as excavations for new drains near a house, or for a basement or new foundations adjacent to an existing building, then it is to be hoped that notice of these will be given in advance so as to ensure that proper precautions are taken to adequately support the sub-soil from which the existing building derives its support. In this respect, as mentioned before, it should be borne in mind that the stress envelope extends to approximately $1\frac{1}{2}$ times the breadth and depth of the existing foundation so that an excavation within an angle of 45° from the bottom of an existing foundation can cause disturbance, particularly in sands and gravels which derive their strength from lateral restraint. Any excavation below the level of the bottom of the foundations warrants consideration in this respect. If excavations are for drains then these should be back-filled with weak concrete.

If new foundations are placed close to existing foundations the stress envelopes mentioned above will overlap and the load on the soil will increase. If the soil is of clay, consolidation may occur and accordingly it is therefore necessary to underpin the existing foundations down to a point where the bearing capacity is satisfactory for the combined load to be spread over a large reinforced concrete footing. This footing must be sufficient to take the load from both walls, even if this means founding the new building at a slightly lower level than had originally been considered. See Figure 53 at "B" and "C".

If the foundations of a new building are intended to be at a lower level than the existing building, then underpinning to the new level is necessary either by traditional means, by reinforced concrete beams and piers or one of the patent processes that have been discussed.

If the undermining occurs due to extraction of coal or ores or brine pumping to extract salt, then buildings must be shored until there is evidence that the movement has ceased in the ground. This may have to be for some time but it is unwise to contemplate jacking to re-level a building until the subsidence has ceased and only then can the building be pinned up from either its existing foundations if these are still satisfactory or be underpinned on new foundations.

(4) *Consolidation of Soil Below Foundations*

The remedy for consolidation of soil below the foundations causing differential settlement depends on the degree of the damage. If it is slight over the whole building, a reinforced concrete ground beam would help to distribute the load along the whole length of the walls, evening out the greater loads which arise between window and door openings; this may be sufficient in itself.

If the settlement is confined to one corner, for example if a corner of a house has been founded on the edge of a filled in pond or ditch and the remainder of the sub-soil over the site is satisfactory, then a single pile or pier could be sunk and the corner of the building supported on reinforced ground beams extending along the walls on either side of the corner in the form of cantilevers.

On the other hand buildings with foundations entirely on unstable ground such as silt, peat or poorly made ground usually have to be wholly underpinned, on reinforced concrete beams and piers if the depth to stable ground does not exceed 10 to 15 feet (3 to 4·6m), or on piles if in excess of this amount.

(5) *Movement of Soil Below Foundations*

Certainly in Eastern England the most likely form of trouble due to movement of soil below foundations arises with shrinkable clay soils.

Mention of the work of the Building Research Establishment in relation to short bored pile foundations on shrinkable clays after the Second World War has already been made and at about the same time some consideration of remedial measures on existing buildings affected by shrinkage of clay soil was also given. The investigation work arose after reference to the Establishment of extensive damage

285

to buildings following a particularly dry summer, that of 1947 in the south-east of England. Although there have been some dry summers since then none have been quite so troublesome to buildings, but there is always a possibility of a similar period of virtual drought. Having regard to the fact that each passing year involves growth in the vegetation around existing buildings, and that new planting takes place, damage to buildings not previously affected could take place. Buildings affected are likely, in the south-east at any rate, to be houses constructed since 1947 or alternatively houses in suburban areas where new planting both of shrubs and trees has taken place, not necessarily in gardens only but possibly along roads and footpaths as well. The prospect of damage is less likely in the inner suburbs of towns where existing trees tend to be mature but it is noted that even now some local authorities plant fast-growing trees in footpaths which may well cause trouble in the future.

With buildings on shrinkable clays the scope of remedial measures is governed by presence or lack of vegetation other than grass and if such vegetation is present by its characteristics, particularly the age of trees.

In open ground in the absence of drying by the roots of trees or shrubs where, after a particularly dry summer, a house develops cracks, it is probable that these would partially close up again during the following winter. However a further dry season is almost certainly liable to make the old cracks open even further and continuing dry seasons would present a progressive deterioration. Accordingly it is necessary to take steps to prevent the clay drying out around the external walls of the house. It may be sufficient in these circumstances, particularly if the damage is relatively slight, to surround the house with precast concrete or stone paving laid on a bed of 3 inches (76mm) of fine gravel or sand and extend this paving for a width of about 5 feet (1·5m).

If the house has particularly shallow foundations, for example a mere 12 inches (0·3m) deep and has been subjected to seasonal movement for a number of years before any action has been contemplated, it may well be necessary to underpin the whole of the external walls down to a level of about 3 feet (0·9m). This could be carried out either by the provision of a continuous strip footing at the lower level and a continuous wall to the full thickness of the existing foundation in engineering bricks, or, alternatively, by bricks, piers and concrete bases and a reinforced concrete ground beam. If the old foundations are at, say, 2 feet (0·6m) below ground level it is possible that the provision of a ground beam alone, utilising the patent method of construction with concrete stools might serve to provide a monolithic frame to spread the load and tie the building

286

together at ground level. Coupled with paving this might well prevent further movement, but if the paving did not commend itself to the owner then it would be much safer to proceed and underpin as before described, the difference in cost probably not proving very great.

If the movements are associated primarily with the action of roots, for example on foundations something to the order of 2 to 3 feet (0·6 to 0·9m) deep, then the problem is more serious and the provision of paving will do nothing to improve and, indeed, probably aggravate the position. If the trees or shrubs causing the damage have not reached maturity then it is sensible to cut them down and to poison the roots by drilling holes in the stump and filling these with a solution of sodium chlorate. During wet weather following this operation the ground will slowly swell up and the cracks in the house will partially close. As for the case with seasonal movements, it is a wise precaution to defer filling the cracks until after at least one wet season has elapsed, otherwise if the horizontal cracks are tightly wedged, as they should be, with slates, other cracks could appear as a result of the upward movement as the soil recovers. If the owner will agree to leave the cracks for two wet seasons so much the better.

If opposition is raised to the cutting down of trees and shrubs, then the only alternative is to underpin to a depth below the level of the roots which may be anything between 7 to 12 feet (2·1 to 3·6m) with the aid of ground beams and short bored piles. The opposition to the destruction of trees and shrubs may be very real and genuine and there must be many instances where those who can afford it would rather pay for underpinning and keep their trees. It would be as well however for the surveyor, before providing his client with the necessary information to enable this sort of decision to be taken, to consider the possible effect on any other properties nearby of leaving the trees in position. A client would be entitled to expect a surveyor to consider this aspect before a decision is taken in view of the possibility of an action against the owner of the trees for the spread of roots in the future.

If on the other hand the trees have reached maturity and the house is fairly old it seems highly unlikely that further movement will continue except perhaps in the most exceptional of dry seasons. Underpinning to an appropriate depth could be carried out as an absolute safety measure for clients with the appropriate finance and a house to match but others less fortunate may be prepared to take the chance, leave the trees as they are and make good the cracks. It should be noted that in the case of mature trees in clay, it is more dangerous to cut down the trees, as the clay will be in a dried state

287

and very likely to swell considerably over a number of years, causing far more damage.

Remedial works in connection with tree root damage are often complicated by the fact that the roots belong to trees on adjoining land, so that even though litigation may be avoided there is a possibility of a claim for damages. It is therefore prudent for the surveyor acting for both the owner of the house damaged and the owner of the trees to find out about the investigations carried out by the Building Research Establishment on this subject and study the advice which it has provided. There is a tendency sometimes to immediately assume that underpinning is necessary without taking into account other factors which may suggest that this is not the best remedy. An owner who carries out underpinning works and then seeks to recover the cost from a neighbouring owner will rightly be disgruntled if it is shown that the underpinning was not really necessary and his claim fails on that account.[1]

A further factor with clay soils is their tendency to slip when the site exceeds 1 in 10. The movement may be differential if the building has a rigid damp proof course of, for example, slates. On the other hand if the building has a damp proof course of a material such as asphalt or bituminous felt the movement may be in the form of a side slip of the structure below damp course level leaving the structure above quite stable. In either case, however, if the movement is progressive it would be necessary to underpin and anchor the building to a firm immovable strata by means of reinforced concrete piles. If the movement is initial only and not progressive, in the case of differential settlement, repair of the cracks and reinstatement of the damp proof course would be all that was necessary. If the damp proof course is of asphalt or some other material providing a slip joint, then the method of bonding new brickwork as shown on Figure 39 and described in Chapter 2 should be adopted.

Damage by frost heave as discussed in Chapter 2 is usually confined to new buildings before they are occupied or in outbuildings with very shallow foundations, less than 18 inches (457mm) deep on fine sand, silts and chalk. In severe cases underpinning to a lower level may be necessary to avoid a repetition, but in particular the concrete floor slabs are generally affected and these may need breaking up so that a replacement of the filling below the floor can be carried out with a material which will not be affected by frost to a suitable depth. If main walls are severely affected by arching of the slab forcing the walls out of upright it is almost certain that these would require rebuilding. Since frost damage in the main structure

[1] *Pettifer v. Cheshunt Urban District Council.* Estates Gazette 19th December 1970, page 1507.

288

itself is confined to new buildings, the damage is more likely to be the responsibility of the contractor to put right.

Similarly, in the case of sulphate attack on the foundations and solid concrete floor slabs, the replacement of the material causing the trouble if this is the hardcore, or the slabs and foundations by sulphate-resisting concrete, shielded if necessary by asphalt, would normally be the responsibility of the original builder under the contract provided any action to this effect is taken within seven years of the defective condition being ascertained.[1] On the other hand if the damage is caused by a sudden change of direction in the ground water bringing soluble sulphates with it, then it is unlikely that there could be any claim and in addition to the other works necessary, steps would have to be taken to divert the water.

[1] *Devereux v. Benbow*, Estates Gazette 25th January 1964, page 249 and *Hancock and others v. B. W. Brazier (Anerley) Ltd.* Estates Gazette 26 February 1966, page 773.

Chapter 5
Timber

Contents

INTRODUCTION

TIMBER has formed part of the structure of practically every building that has ever been erected in this country. Even today when the principal structural elements of modern industrial or commercial buildings are of steel and reinforced concrete, items such as doors and fittings of various kinds will still be found to be of timber. Up to eighty years or so ago before the advent of steel and concrete, even the floors and roof structure of many such buildings would be of timber. In the domestic field timber formed almost the sole structural material in the vast majority of houses up to about 1600 providing a complete frame of wall, floors and roof, much in the way that steel and concrete are used in larger buildings today. Although abandoned in the towns because of the danger of fire, timber framed houses continued to be built in country districts up to the 19th century. Even after legislation had been passed to prohibit timber framed houses in towns timber continued to be built into the external walls of the new brick or stone buildings, which although not visible often played an important part in stiffening the structure, particularly when such timbers formed part of a rigid framed floor. As there are some 17,000,000 houses in the country practically every one containing timber in the framing to the floors, roof and probably the staircase, even apart from the joinery items of windows and doors etc., it is probably true to say that in any work of substantial repair timber will form some part of the scheme in almost every case. Timber being an organic material has characteristics which, while making it an admirable and versatile material for building purposes, can also bring about its own decay and renders it susceptible to attacks from fungus and insects. It is important to bear these characteristics in mind in repair work as renewal or repair of timber may have to be coupled with other work to ensure immunity as far as possible from these destructive agencies. This is true whether the timber is employed in the roof, floors or the walls. In addition in all cases of timber used in buildings other than where it is used purely for decorative features, the particular function of the member under review must be considered and its inter-relation to other members. This is a cardinal point to remember when considering the type of repair to be adopted. Timbers are placed in certain positions in a way to withstand particular stresses and a failure to appreciate their proper function may well result in an incorrect diagnosis of the cause

295

of failure and almost certainly to an incorrect specification for repair. In these circumstances sometimes a costly renewal operation is carried out which is quite likely to repeat past design faults and may give rise to a repetition of the failure a few years later. A simple repair based on full knowledge of the failed member might well have cured the defect for all time at far less cost.

Unlike the materials which have been dealt with so far in this book, brick, stone and plain concrete, which are used principally in domestic construction to resist compressive stresses only, timber has the extremely useful property of resisting both compressional and tensional stresses. As such it is a more adaptable material than any of those previously mentioned and can be used to fulfil more functions. Thus we find timber used in floors and roofs to resist both compressional and tensional stresses where it can serve a purpose which until 90–100 years ago no other material could approach for efficiency and economy. At the same time however timber can be used purely as a compression member and thus it is found also as a walling material usually in the form of a strut as part of a rigid frame. There is furthermore a long tradition of timber used as a piling material, particularly in marshy or waterlogged ground stretching back to, and including, mediaeval times. Whereas the use of brick, stone and concrete is confined to walls and foundations in domestic construction, timber on the other hand will be found as a structural walling, roofing and flooring material, amongst its many other uses. Though there are some examples from the past of scamped timber construction in evidence there is also a very long tradition of the sound use of timber for structural purposes. With the benefit of a good apprenticeship the carpenter exercised much influence in the past and was usually sufficiently proud of his craft not to permit the worst excesses of skimping found in other trades. With his knowledge of timber, framing, joints and setting out he was not a person with whom to argue. As such, in general, the need to legislate on the structural use of timber did not arise until relatively recently and most legislation was confined to preventing its use where there was a danger to buildings from the spread of fire. These factors combine to suggest that a somewhat different approach from that adopted in previous Chapters is necessary to deal with the multitude of uses found for timber in buildings. Much of the repair work to the timber itself and the joints of a frame together with the work necessary to eradicate fungal or insect attack is the same whether a roof, floor or wall are under consideration, and accordingly these items can be conveniently grouped together at particular points in the Chapter as being of general application. This permits the remainder of the Chapter to be devoted to the problems which arise in the use of timber as a structural element in particular positions such as roofs, external walls, partitions and floors.

The long tradition of carpentry and the relative absence of legislation does not mean that timber has been used in an unchanged manner over the time span covered by the range of buildings described in this book. Indeed its use has changed considerably and a few examples might well serve to illustrate the various factors which have caused these changes. Up to the reign of Elizabeth I oak was generally, except for one or two periods when economic situations forced the price up, cheap and plentiful. As such it could be used with a degree of prodigality which was never to arise again at any later period. In emulating the brick and stone buildings of the nobility quite massive structures were built for the wealthier merchants involving a number of storeys with the cantilevered floors that enabled this to be done with no risk of collapse. The enormous factor of safety resulting from the lavish use of timber has helped to preserve many of these structures to the present time and if it had not been for this they would probably long since have disappeared. These conditions were not to last and the many competing demands for oak such as for shipbuilding, for smelting iron, for tanning and for charcoal making all resulted in a denudation of the indigenous forests. Even so by the time timber framing was banned in London the increasing shortage and expense of oak and a growth in technical knowledge had forced carpenters to many economies and to design their structures utilising far less timber than hitherto. One result of this was that rafters and floor joists were set out as they are today with the narrow side uppermost instead of the flat side as they had been previously. As such the joists and rafters were better able to resist the loads placed on them and a saving in timber resulted.

The timber which began to be imported in the latter part of the 16th century was not the hardwood with which carpenters had been familiar in the past but the softwood from Northern Europe brought through the Hanseatic ports. The material was different, not quite so strong as the heartwood of oak and not available in the same large scantlings. On the other hand the Renaissance had arrived and it was no longer necessary to span large areas with open roofs. The owner might still desire the luxury of large rooms but required a decorated plaster ceiling instead. This could be achieved with a softwood timber truss of comparatively coarse utilitarian design compared with the complicated design of the finely carved open timber roofs in oak. Imported softwood lacking the fine appearance and colour of oak, lent itself more to a form of carcassing construction hidden by other features, thus in many ways a virtue was made of necessity. Great feats of carpentry in consequence became a thing of the past and although complicated work was carried out, for example the trussed beams and partitions of Georgian and Victorian times, undoubtedly the peak in carpentry achieved in the early part of the 16th century has never been matched. On the other hand good quality imported softwood from the natural forests of Northern Europe and North America carried the builders of the Industrial Revolution through to Victorian times and served them well for immensely strong floors and large span roofs until the advent of steel provided an alternative which had the cardinal advantage of greater fire resistance.

Until the middle of the 19th century tradition rather than science determined the sizes for structural timber members. This was true however of all materials at the time, even cast iron which was increasingly used for structural work in the early part of the 19th century. Most engineers relied on load tests to verify their designs, a method somewhat time consuming, wasteful and expensive as can be imagined. The need for a vast number of large new bridges in a short space of time brought about by the rapidly expanding railways concentrated research on the solution of the rigid framed truss. The cost of iron was such that a reliable method of design became an urgent necessity. Most of the problems were solved by the middle of the century but the solutions demanded, as did Navier's Theory of Bending used in the design of beams and developed in the 1820s, that the limit up to which a material behaves in an elastic manner without suffering permanent deformation be known. Both cast and wrought iron and later steel could be manufactured and tested to determine this limit. As the variable strength of timber had always been a problem, once steel was produced with pre-determined strength characteristics there seemed no reason why the strength of timber should not be ascertainable. The development of mechanical stress grading machines which classify timber pieces by measuring their stiffness enabled this to be done. The problems solved and the principles developed in the 19th century for the design of steel trusses and other framed structures could now, as a result, be utilised in timber construction so that there is a new completely scientific basis for calculating timber sizes and a range of basic stresses for timbers of known quality. Design as a result becomes simpler.

The demand for timber has continued to increase enormously and over the last fifty years even the natural coniferous forests of the north have become near exhausted. As a result a new industry has grown up, that of forestry, to supply the need. Techniques have been developed so that coniferous trees grow faster but this has its effect on the quality of the timber produced. Large sizes of sound heartwood are difficult to come by and expensive when found. The

bulk of the supply is now of lower strength and commercial requirements demand that much sapwood is included. This has a direct
bearing on the incidence of fungal and insect attack and will be
referred to again later in this Chapter, but at the same time sizes
of timbers in the interests of economy are enabled by science to be
cut to the bare minimum. There are obvious dangers inherent in
this so that probably the future of timber for structural work of real
significance lies in the techniques of laminated construction based on
the use of the immensely powerful synthetic adhesives now available.
On the other hand the small house seems likely to continue with its
simple framed timber roof and timber floors for some time to come
utilising for the roof relatively small section members fixed together
with bolts and connectors in the manner which has become familiar
with, for example, the timber roof trusses designed and developed
by the Timber Research and Development Association and much
used since the end of the Second World War. These trusses make the
best use of timber available at the present time and eliminate the
need for timber joints of the traditional type which have now
become costly because of the time needed by the carpenter to cut and
fit them properly. For reliability timber is limited to small sizes.
They are in themselves surely sufficient comment on the changed
circumstances reflected in the use of the material over a short period
of thirty years. The pace of change seems to increase as the world
gobbles up its natural resources! As far as building is concerned there
are many who would be glad to see the end of timber as a structural
material, considering that its organic origins are much too much of a
liability. Certainly in the domestic field however an intensive search
for a suitable substitute has failed so far to produce anything to
match timber's varied properties and adaptability.

PITCHED ROOFS

Generally it can be said that the use of timber has become not only
more scientific over the years but also more simplified. Nowhere is
this more in evidence than in the structure of pitched roofs. Admittedly the work of design will often be carried out by a structural
engineer, qualified in the design of timber structures, but when the
design is produced it will often be astonishingly simple to assemble
the material and cut and fit it together. A certain amount of skill
obviously is required but the designer will not necessarily be relying
on the skill of the carpenter but rather on the known strength of the
members and the type of connectors to be used, themselves responsible in no small way for the revolutionary changes in design methods.

The designs may well be made generally available so that the architect, surveyor and builder without the necessary structural knowledge can choose from a wide range of layouts for various spans and various types of roof covering and be sure of obtaining a satisfactory truss, subject to reasonable workmanship. We have already traced some of the economic and scientific factors that have enabled matters to reach this stage in the introduction to the Chapter, but there are other factors involved. When the words "pitched roof" are mentioned one thinks at once of an inverted "V" and of course it is true that many roofs are this and little else. What goes on inside will vary with the span, the support available from below inside the building and, as we shall see later in this Chapter, on the period of construction. However there are other shapes to roofs apart from the simple inverted "V" shape and, although this shape occurs throughout all periods, other influences were at work which determined that the typical house at some particular period had a roof of a different outline. Apart from the differing types of construction, we can therefore consider roofs from the aspect of shape to suit particular types of houses at various times. Construction and shape do, of course, go hand in hand but the shape at various times in history has undoubtedly been the prime consideration in the mind of the builder rather than a suitable design according to the layout of the building below, which is the way which a designer with an eye to structure would follow. Coupled with this, however, there has always been the aspect of economy reflected in the principle of covering the area of the building in question at the least cost of the combined labour and materials. In this respect, of course, it must also be remembered that labour costs in relation to materials were much more favourable in the past than they are today, so that it was often more economical to form an elaborate timber structure to support a slate roof than to form a flat roof and cover it in lead.

It is therefore necessary to devote some attention to the different shapes adopted for use on houses over the last few hundred years. The temptation to use such a phrase as "the development of roofs through the ages" is to be avoided, since this is just not true. Although, as has been said, changes have occurred these are by no means by way of development in the domestic field. In considering roofs it might seem logical to follow the sequence adopted in most books on building construction and progress through the series of close-coupled roofs in their single, double and triple forms to the roofs based on trusses. Even this, however, implies a progression, either from the garden shed to the mansion or at least by way of an increase in span. In older buildings however it will be found that all the various types of construction will occur over a wide range of quite similar buildings, both in size and character. An exception must be made in respect of houses built in the last fifty years or so but before this, however, in the days of a plentiful supply of cheap labour, if often proved economical to employ a trussed roof for quite small-scale buildings. Rather than foliow the normal sequence adopted in the textbooks therefore, it would seem better to follow through from the outskirts of the average town and consider the shapes and types of roof structure adopted for houses over the years ending with the oldest in the centre. This will be found to cover a high percentage of the types of roof normally encountered, leaving but a few unusual types to be considered separately. Working from the outskirts towards the centre might be thought to be a reverse of the logical procedure but on the other hand the houses on the out-skirts of the towns are usually smaller, the roofs less complicated and the building types more readily identifiable. The reasons why this should be so are fairly simply stated.

Roof Structures of the Smaller House where the roof intended as a Feature

Although opportunities for employment had been increasing since the early 1900s, resulting in a general shortage of domestic staff for the middle classes, the shortage became very much more pronounced following the First World War and has remained so ever since. Coupled with this factor the great growth and relative cheapness of the public transport systems, the greater range and speed of the motor buses and electric trams, as against the old horse buses, and the spread of the suburban railway systems, particularly when electrified, all combined to produce a demand for a small family house to be run by the housewife on her own with a nice garden for the husband to cultivate well away from the factory chimneys and the soot and dirt which existed nearer the centre of the towns, coal still being the principal form of fuel between the wars. This demand was fulfilled by the vast numbers of small semi-detached and detached houses which tend to have quite a remarkable likeness in whatever part of the country they happen to be situated. Land was relatively cheap and beyond one or two ineffective Town Planning Acts, there were few restrictions of any sort to cramp the builder or developer's style (or one might say lack of it!). Even the by-laws in many areas were of a rudimentary kind, incorporating few of the really meaty sections of the old model by-laws.

The roofs of the inter-war period semi-detached and detached house of the speculative kind have their distinctive features, but these were governed by fashion rather than anything else. Slates were thought grey and drab, too reminiscent of the smoke and grime of the central areas and also a little too like the council house of the period. Hence tiles were the vogue, resulting in a fairly steep pitch. Another feature that tended to set the speculative house apart from its council neighbour round the corner was the use of a hipped slope rather than a gable end. Irrespective of these fashionable imprints, which even so are perhaps not so noticeable to the average eye as the all pervading bay window, porch and rough-cast or pebble-dash rendering, the roofs are relatively simple, traditional and in fact little different from those on the smaller Edwardian terrace house of the immediately preceding period from 1900 to the outbreak of the First World War. These houses were provided with plain simple pitched roofs, covered with slates on the cheaper buildings and tiles on the more expensive, with the ridge running parallel to the frontage and the slopes draining to the front and rear. Spans were generally fairly small and although most of the roofs found are double, that is the rafters are supported on a system of purlins and struts, it was seldom found necessary to be unduly elaborate. This type of roof however is of course not confined to the smaller estate developments in the two outer concentric rings which we have discussed so far. They are also typical of the smaller houses built in country areas of practically any period, to the country cottage and to the small "worker's" cottages often built in terrace form, which surround the inner areas of the smaller industrial mill or mining towns of the Midlands and the North, Wales and Scotland.

Up to now we have noted only the smaller houses in the periods discussed and their respective positions around the towns. Clearly however the simple triangular shape, not too complicated in structure by an excessive span can be repeated, doubled or trebled so that quite large houses can be covered. This is really how roofs developed in a way from the simple couple, that is two inclined rafters leaning together at the top. While it is possible to form a house with all the rooms lengthwise below such a roof, it is a stage better to form a squarish shape in plan by putting two such couples side by side with a gutter in the middle over the structural wall. This form of roof will be found on many houses up to the beginning of the 18th century and was revived again in the latter half of the 19th century in the period of Gothic revival. At this time however the ridges and gutters would more often be at right-angles to the front elevation and the roof gables would be finished with elaborately carved barge boards and sometimes finials.

Figure 54 shows the types of roof used to cover the small house of the various periods discussed to date, together with the few less familiar from other periods which fall into the same category. One

302

cardinal feature of them all is that to the building itself the roof is of importance by way of appearance. It stands out as a feature and it is treated as such. There is no attempt to hide it, as there was in the 18th and 19th centuries on terraced houses. The reason for this is pretty obvious. Most of the buildings considered are of small scale and two storey, but hide the roof of such a building behind a parapet and it looks pretty mean and box-like. The tendency in the periods discussed is that the house should be thought of individually even though it might in fact be one of many and, to coin a phrase, to hell with architectural unity!

The text on the pages next to Figure 54 describes the principles of construction of these simple roofs and indicates typical defects. It should be noted in particular the indication on the drawings of those members in tension (arrows pointing towards the centre) and those in compression (arrows pointing towards the ends). These are important points to bear in mind since the type of repair to any failed members will be governed by this consideration, provided it is only a question of repair to individual members, for example a split due to overloading, the inclusion of knots in the timber or to unequal stresses; perhaps in a purlin where it passes over a strut. Repairs, however, to individual members will be dealt with as a group at the end of the roof section of this Chapter, since there is no difference in the repair according to the type of roof but only in so far as the timber is employed to perform a particular function.

The normal breadth of timber rafters considered to be economical for roofing work was for long considered as 2 inches (51mm) and for many years rafters were nearly always specified as 4 by 2 inches (102 by 51mm). By the normal rule of thumb of span over two giving the depth of 2 inch (51mm) timbers at 15-inch centres (381mm) it follows that rafters over 8 feet (2·44m) in length on the slope should be supported. Most books on building construction illustrated roofs utilising 4 by 2 inch (102 by 51mm) timbers and showed roofs for various spans on this basis. On these drawings the angle of pitch is also marked and this angle of course forms an important variable in the design of the roof structure, governed in its turn by the type of covering selected. Here, as pointed out before, we are presented with ideals but in examining an old roof we have to start from what is found before ascertaining whether it is adequate or not in itself. To pursue the example of rafters, we may find that in an old roof they are 3 by 2 inches at 15-inch centres (76 by 51mm at 381mm) not 4 by 2 inches (102 by 51 mm). Following the rule of thumb, these should not be unsupported above 6 feet (1·83m) in length on the slope. Clearly however even if this is not the case and there is nothing wrong with the roof, nothing need be done. Many non-ideal roofs will be found which are perfectly satisfactory. It is when the roof is showing signs of weakness combined with the presence of non-conforming members that a full investigation of sizes in relation to lengths, pitch, span and weights of covering must be made. It is always possible with an old building that the original covering has been replaced at some time in its history by something heavier, for example heavier slates were used to replace the clay pantiles of many of the smaller buildings in the 19th century. The preparation of a scale drawing is almost essential for any existing roof showing weakness before the true reason for failure can be established. The detailed measurements required to prepare this drawing and the time taken may prevent any hasty and wrong assumptions being made in regard to the failure and it will certainly ensure that a full knowledge will exist of what is present in the existing structure. Armed with this information, it is an easy matter to check whether the reason for failure lies in inadequate timbers using the ordinary rule of thumb methods for rafters and ceiling joists, if they are of 2-inch (51mm) timber, or the very helpful tables provided in the Building Regulations 1965 and 1972 for alternative sizes and spacings, loads and pitches of timbers in roof construction. In the Appendix will be found a number of weights of materials used in roofing work which will enable the dead weight of most existing coverings to be calculated so that these can be used in conjunction with the tables.

Failure in a roof, due to inadequately sized timbers, can be arrested provided the efficiency of the roof covering is not impaired and the question of appearance is not paramount. This can be done by the provision of support if none exists or the addition of further support if that present is proved inadequate. It is seldom necessary to take off the roof and reconstruct it entirely but this may be essential if the pitch is so reduced in places as to make it impossible for the covering to function efficiently. For example, an already shallow pitched roof carrying large slates may sag to a point where the existing slates will not prevent water being drawn in by capillary action. Larger slates may be unobtainable, in which case reconstruction would be the only remedy. As for reconstruction this need not be covered by this book as ample guidance exists in the many volumes for new building construction available and the ideals expounded therein can be followed.

Measures to strengthen a roof in weak state due to inadequate timbers for the loading are shown in Figure 55. These methods are of course partly in the nature of forming a double roof out of a single roof. Later alterations to roof structures can be a source of weakness, defects arising, for example, by cutting for the insertion of a dormer window. Cases have arisen where quite large dormer windows have been formed in roof slopes merely by cutting short three or so rafters and introducing a trimmer rafter, which in itself is often of the right size, but without any doubling of the ordinary common rafters on either side to make them into trimming rafters. As a result the common rafters sag, pulling down the rafters which have been cut short and frequently introducing defects in the roof portion of the dormer. If the settlement has not gone too far it may not be too late to strengthen what have become the trimming rafters by adding further rafters alongside the existing so as to prevent further movement. More often, however, it will be necessary to strip the covering and dismantle the structure in the area of the dormer and reform it in the correct manner. Making some form of opening of this type in an old roof always throws an undue strain on surrounding members not intended to take additional loads and it is always necessary to give due consideration to this factor when such alterations are made.

Sagging and other signs of weakness occur also in double roofs where the rafters are supported on purlins. Irrespective of the adequacy of the purlins, it is always possible that the roof is generally of too light construction in which case general strengthening will be required, much in the same way as before but this time the double roof is converted into a triple roof by forming trusses. An example is shown in Figure 55 at "C". Generally, however, with the type of double roofs shown on Figure 54 it is some failing in the support which has caused the roof to sag as outlined in the text on the adjacent pages. Methods of dealing with these problems are precisely the same as shown on Figure 55 at "C" including the cases of the purlin inadequately strutted and the strut deprived of its proper support, since the method provides complete and entirely new support in substitution of the original.

In dealing with the repair of a roof which has spread, regard must be had to the condition of the walls supporting the roof. There are two distinct cases here. One is where the roof thrust has been so severe that the walls are so far out of plumb, and probably cracked at the top, as to be unsafe and the other case arises where this condition has yet to be reached. In the former case, rebuilding the top of the walls will be necessary and therefore this must be done before the roof is strengthened. To do this it is necessary to shore the roof completely by a system of dead shoring internally down to solid ground. When the load of the roof has thus been taken off the walls in question, the tops can then be rebuilt. Only then can the roof be dealt with, either being picked up in its existing position on a new wallplate and subsequently tied in securely or, alternatively, by

305

TIMBER

Figure 54

Untrussed Couple Roofs

Although not very many houses are built a single room in depth nowadays, there are plenty still in existence from earlier times with a simple close coupled roof as at 'A', shown in cross and longitudinal sections, while the form has always been popular for back additions. Designed to produce a rigid triangulated framework so that the weight is transmitted vertically to the walls, it relies on adequate nailing at the joints between the feet of the rafters and the wallplate, the rafters and the ceiling joists forming the tie (1) and the tops of the rafters and the ridge piece (2). A version shown at 'B' and known as a "collar" roof permits a substantial saving in brickwork for the external walls by forming rooms partially in the roof space. It is frequently found in cheap work but relies for equilibrium on the correct positioning and secure fixing of the collar to the rafters (3). A substantial increase in the length of rafter usually requires the introduction of a purlin (4) in the design to keep the size of rafters to a reasonable minimum. With a house two rooms deep as at 'C', intermediate support for the purlins can be obtained from a structural partition (5) parallel to the frontage. If there are to be large through rooms then it may be necessary to introduce binders as at (6) on 'D', if a hipped slope is proposed, and these might be carried on a structural partition at right-angles to the frontage (7). In narrow fronted terrace housing larger purlins can sometimes be used spanning from party wall to party wall and eliminating struts. In cheaper work the collar shown on 'C' and 'D' is often omitted.

Except in cases where a property is built with the gable as the front elevation, it will be noted that in most examples the weight of the roof is carried by walls broken up by window and door openings. In all examples roof thrust is common forcing the tops of the supporting walls outwards due to inadequate nailing particularly at (1) in 'A' and at (8) in 'C' and 'D' where lengths of ceiling joists must be properly fixed together to act as effective ties. With the roof at 'B', in better class work the joint of the rafter with the collar (3) is formed by a dovetail halved joint but in cheaper work nailing is relied upon, with the consequential thrust if the number of nails used is insufficient or the work ineffectively carried out. Little resistance to thrust is provided by the collar if this should be positioned above the half-way mark. Often with a hipped slope there is a tie for the front and rear slopes by ceiling joists but none for the feet of the rafters on the hip with consequent thrust arising. Sagging in the rafters and purlins can occur if there is settlement in the load bearing partition of 'C' and 'D'. Bearing in mind, for example, in 'C' that such a partition is taking a load equal to twice that of the front and rear external walls, such settlement is not unusual. Frequently sagging arises when the ends of purlins

306

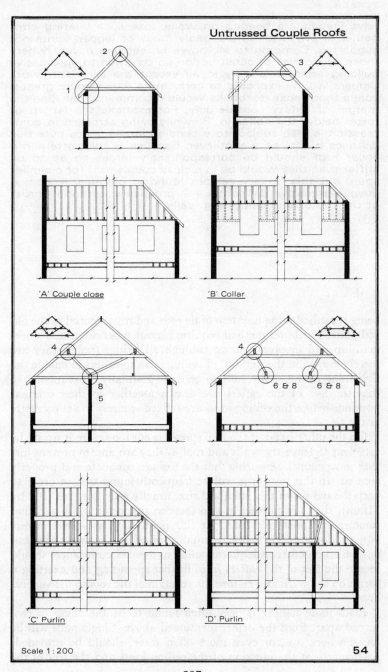

Untrussed Couple Roofs

'A' Couple close

'B' Collar

'C' Purlin

'D' Purlin

Scale 1:200

54

TIMBER

have inadequate bearing on walls, lose such bearing altogether or when joints are badly made or lapped joints not
supported. Common to all, however, sagging occurs where
those economies in construction so common to speculative
building arise. Invariably in all except the very best work
timbers will be expected to carry more weight over greater
spans than most textbooks would recommend, reducing the
margin of safety considerably. For example the length of
rafter below the collar in 'B' while being stressed in compression is also subject to a bending stress, since over this
distance it acts as a cantilever. Because of this rafters in a
collar roof should be correspondingly larger so as to be
stiffer than they would be in a close couple roof for a similar
span, but this is very seldom found in practice. In consequence excessive deflection will produce substantial thrust
at the top of the supporting walls.

---

being remedied using a system of tie rods and nuts secured to the old
wallplate. The latter method requires careful supervision and workmanship and involves cutting through all fixings (unless they are
merely lapped in the middle) of ceiling joists to rafters to enable the
tightening of the centre nuts to be done gradually, in sequence, so
that the feet of the rafters are drawn together to their original
positions before the ceiling joists are refixed securely to act correctly
as the tie.

On the other hand, if the roof spread is not too severe it would be
sufficient to leave the walls and roof as they are and to prevent further movement by ensuring that the ties are adequate and properly
secured. In this respect it will be frequently found that in order to
keep the ties down to a standard size, usually 4 by 2 inches (102 by
51mm), they are formed in two sections supported on a partition
somewhere about mid-span. At this point they are often merely
lapped alongside each other, usually spiked to the wallplate, but
not nailed together. Adequate nailing in these circumstances should
secure the feet of the rafters from further spreading and exerting a
thrust on the walls and restore the reaction of the roof to the vertical
line.

Inadequate nailing is very often found to be the cause of roof
spread apart from the defect mentioned above. Single nails will be
found where two, or even more often three, should be provided,
particularly at the junction of the ceiling joists and the feet of the

308

rafters. These single nails are quite inadequate to resist the pulling force exerted by the weight of the roof on this joint, with the result that the nails are pulled or distorted. This is particularly serious in a collar type roof if nailing is employed in lieu of the dovetailed halved joint correctly adopted in better class work. Extra collars with stronger joints to the existing rafters may be the answer in these circumstances, provided matters have not progressed so far as to necessitate reconstruction.

Hipped roof slopes are often prone to spreading at the feet of the rafters since these are seldom tied, the tie being limited to the two main slopes. In better class work, the tie is provided by an angle brace fixed to the wallplate across the corners. If this is not present and roof spread is found but is not too serious then the provision of an angle tie, coach screwed securely through packing pieces to the wallplates should suffice. Lack of space in shallow pitched roofs may necessitate the use of a metal tie in lieu of timber. An alternative would be to bolt a twisted metal strap to the feet of the rafters and secure this to each of say five or six of the existing joists spanning at right-angles, placing also some strutting between the joists to prevent them from winding and twisting. Yet another alternative would be to provide a series of ties above the existing joists these to be spiked on to a bearer securely fixed to the top of a convenient partition. These alternatives are illustrated on Figure 55 at "D", "E" and "F".

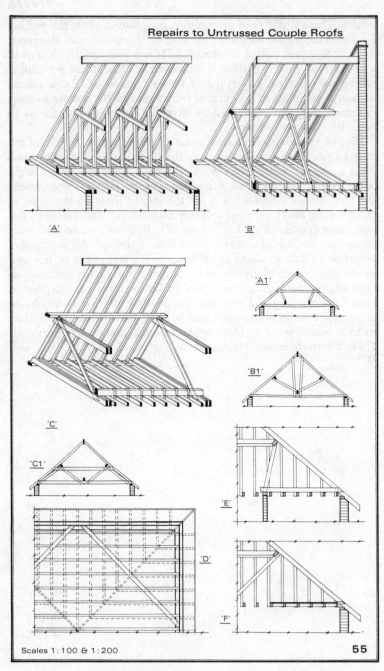

Repairs to Untrussed Couple Roofs

'A'   'B'

'A1'

'B1'

'C'

'C1'

'D'

'E'

'F'

Scales 1:100 & 1:200

55

310

Figure 55

Repairs to Untrussed Couple Roofs

Existing weak roofs due to inadequacy in the timbers can be strengthened by the introduction of stout binders spanning between load bearing partitions as in 'A' and 'A1'. Ceiling joists can be suspended from galvanised twisted metal straps or sheradised framing anchors, as available now. The rafters can be strutted from the binders and collars, provided for every third couple, add to the rigidity. If no cross partitions are available a beam can often be inserted between existing ceiling joists. Another useful method of strengthening an existing roof is to form a kind of truss out of every fourth couple as in 'B' and 'B1'. A rigid framework is formed with long ties from the apex to the centre of the ceiling joists to carry a binder as before and struts are taken from this binder to support newly inserted purlins. This is one method of forming a double roof out of a single roof but there are, of course, many others; the most suitable for any particular roof depending on the circumstances.

Existing double roofs deprived of their proper support from below, e.g. by the removal of, or settlement in, a partition or where the roof is generally feeble may need additional support from trusses inserted every sixth or eighth couple between the existing rafters. Nowadays these may well take a form similar to modified T.R.D.A. trusses being framed up of small sections and bolted together with connectors as at 'C' and 'C1'. These can be used to support existing purlins and a new binder if this is necessary. Again many forms of truss will be suitable depending on the circumstances.

'D' 'E' and 'F' show three alternative methods of strengthening an untied hip slope to prevent thrust on the top of the wall. 'D' utilises angle ties, either in timber or metal, coach screwed to the existing wallplates, 'E' a timber tie bolted to the foot of each rafter and well spiked to the top of an existing partition conveniently found parallel to the outer wall. If no partition is available an alternative is provided at 'F' with a metal tie screwed to five or six ceiling joists with solid strutting between. Only the centre half of the total of hip rafters need tieing in this way since the shorter rafters nearer the corners are stiffer and the wall below will be more capable of resisting thrust closer to the corners where the strength derived from the bond to return walls is more effective.

Roof Structure of Houses where the roof intended to be hidden

We have dealt so far with single and double triangulated roofs on the typical mass-produced houses from 1900 onwards in the outer two concentric rings of the larger towns and cities, giving also rather more than a passing mention to those buildings from other eras which were provided with roofs of a similar type and which are, of course, by far the most frequently found. Moving in towards the centre of the larger towns and cities we come across quite a distinct change in the character of many of the houses, one which did not alter in its basic principles for two hundred years or so. The social conditions which give rise to this type of house did not alter very much over this period and therefore the basic type remained the same albeit for slight changes in fenestration and ornament brought about by changes in fashion. The town house of the middle classes of this period is distinguished by its height, usually four or more floors with a basement and relatively narrow frontage and the all important fact that it formed part of an architectural unity by way of an identical façade with those of its neighbours. These long lines of terrace houses were topped on their front elevation by an elaborate cornice and a parapet wall. There was no necessity to make a feature of the roof and indeed the designers, be they architects or builders, did their best to conceal the roofs, or if it was essential to form rooms therein, to make them as unobtrusive as possible. The whole emphasis was concentrated on the front elevation and although there were many variations internally, as discussed in Chapter 1, the general basic shape is remarkably similar throughout the country and from one terrace to another.

As to the roofs of these tall terrace houses it is conceivable to find those types which we have already discussed. Indeed some of the earlier types have two simple coupled roofs with the ridges parallel to the front elevation with a gutter in between, the support to the two inner slopes being derived from a load bearing partition separating the front and rear rooms. Such roofs, covered with clay tiles or pantiles are usually, of course, prone to the defects discussed previously and these defects should be dealt with in a similar manner. Furthermore some properties of this type are covered with roofs of the mansard shape. There are however many more which utilise a type of roof not mentioned previously but which is particularly suitable in the circumstances. Utilising slates, which came greatly into use in the 18th century, and a fairly shallow pitch, the double lean-to roof provided the ideal solution, since its total rise for the average house needed to be only 4 to 5 feet (1·22 to 1·52m), depending on the frontage distance and, as a result, it could be

312

totally hidden behind the parapet without this being unnecessarily high. Furthermore chimney stacks could be limited in height utilising this type of roof so that they were totally invisible from the street. This type of roof with the principles which govern its construction together with the typical defects for which to look is shown on Figure 56.

The principal defect found with the double lean-to roof arises most often from deflection in the gutter beam, due either to its being undersized or through settlement in the central partition. Generally if this results merely in water lying in the gutter and a danger of flooding it is sufficient to fir up the gutter to a proper fall. Occasionally, however, persistent flooding will cause an outbreak of dry rot in the confined space below the gutter which will affect the beam and the lower end of the rafters necessitating the renewal of the former and the repair of the latter. The opportunity can then be taken to provide support for the gutter beam on a new cross beam so that the weight of half the roof is taken off the central partition, which is probably excessively overloaded already from the floors below.

Deflection in the gutter beam from whatever cause is usually accompanied by an uneven appearance in the covering brought about by the consequential movement in the rafters. Since appearance does not matter with this type of roof, hidden as it is by the parapet, it is not necessary to correct this but it may be essential to provide new support to the top end of rafters which may well have slipped off the wallplate at the top. This can be provided by the provision of an enlarged wallplate supported on wrought iron corbels built into the party wall. This type of repair may be found to be necessary even if there is no settlement in the gutter beam should the plate be carried on brick corbels, as these are often found to be broken.

In a terrace with roofs of the double lean-to type, the party walls take an equal amount of thrust from both sides which of course balances and maintains stability. However at the ends of the terrace there is a flank wall which merely takes thrust from the one side. As there is seldom very little lateral restraint provided to such a wall from the floors below, movement will cause complications to arise by eventually threatening to deprive the top end of the rafters of their support. Provided that the movement is not so serious as to require rebuilding in the wall below, an enlarged wallplate will usually suffice to pick up the ends of the rafters, although of course additional work will be required to tie in the wall to prevent further movement as described in Chapter 2.

Settlement in the central partition in the larger terrace houses of this period may also deprive the purlin of its support if this is strutted from the partition. If a new cross beam is being provided, then the problem of supplying the purlin with additional support is simple but should no action of this sort be contemplated it may still be necessary to strut the purlin securely in a different manner, such as from a plate secured to the party wall.

Problems of light construction and overloading in double lean-to roofs are met in the same manner as for the types of roof previously described, that is by making a double roof out of a single roof, or alternatively, if the roof is already a double roof, by strengthening the existing features since forming a truss is not feasible with this type of roof. Strengthening normally consists of introducing larger members alongside the original, particularly by way of larger purlins and struts, and wedging these securely but without straining the existing features by over-tightening. If there is sagging in the rafters on either side of a central purlin then the introduction of two additional purlins would be a solution.

Lean-To Roofs for the Back Addition

While the double lean-to roof is found as the main roof type in the inner suburban areas on houses built over the 200-year period up to 1900 there are very few, or more likely none, which have as a main roof the ordinary lean-to structure. Yet over this period and since, many buildings provided with a back addition present such a feature on inspection. This simple form of roof was considered ideal for covering the single room additions so often provided in the terrace schemes. They enabled each tall narrow house to be provided with an additional room per floor usually at the half landing level.

The single lean-to as illustrated at the bottom of Figure 56, however, has its problems, usually associated with thrust which if too severe generally means that it is cheaper to take it down altogether and substitute a flat roof instead. However there are many occasions when a relatively simple repair to render the tie effective would be much cheaper and perfectly adequate to obviate further trouble. In this respect the tie must be securely nailed to the feet of the rafters and securely fixed to the wall at the other end. This is usually achieved by spiking the tie to a plate in turn securely attached in a rigid manner to the brickwork as shown bottom right on Figure 56.

Timbers which are inadequate or overloaded can be dealt with in the same manner as those in a double lean-to roof by the addition of binders and a purlin as shown again, bottom right, on Figure 56.

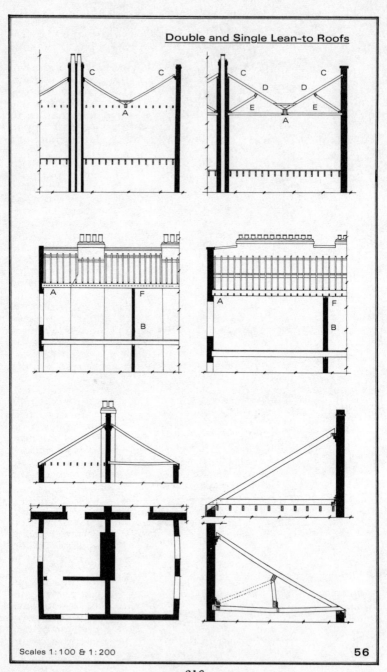

Double and Single Lean-to Roofs

Figure 56

Double and Single Lean-To Roofs

Double lean-to roofs, two examples of which are shown, are found principally on 18th- and 19th-century terrace. houses of three or more storeys built with fairly narrow frontages. Coupled with cornices and parapets and the use of slates, the low rise of such roofs enabled this feature to be totally hidden from the street. Occasionally small hipped slopes at the front enabled a further saving to be made on the height of the parapet.

Support is provided from a gutter beam 'A' carried on front and rear walls and usually an intermediate central partition 'B'. The gutter beam carries the feet of the rafters, the tops being carried on a wallplate 'C' or built in. If the frontage was increased purlins were sometimes introduced, 'D', supported on front and rear walls and strutted, 'E', either from party or flank walls or the intermediate partition.

Typical defects arise from sagging in the gutter beam due to inadequate sizing or even more frequently settlement in an overloaded central partition. Another frequent cause is rot in the beam and feet of the rafters due to neglect. Rafters as a result may slip off the wallplates or the supporting brick corbels may break. Movement in an exposed flank wall may arise through thrust, although such movement is usually confined to the end house only. Other movements and settlements in the roof structure may be caused by rot in the ends of purlins, where built in to external walls, bad joints or a failure of struts particularly if these are supported off the central partition.

Repairs, if not purely involving straightforward renewal, may consist of providing a new beam spanning the width of the property to support the gutter at 'F'. If the tops of rafters are in danger of slipping off their support, then splicing on new lengths should suffice or alternatively a larger support can be provided. Often the repair of the cheap type of roof shown on the left necessitates improving the standard so that it begins to take on the appearance of the roof on the right with purlins and struts.

The single lean-to roof found on so many back-additions may be arranged, as on the bottom left drawing, with ceiling joists providing no tie at all and resulting in thrust at the top of the flank wall. This could be restrained from moving further by the addition of a tie above the existing ceiling joists, as shown on the right, provided the end of the tie is securely anchored to the party wall. It is the absence of this secure anchoring that causes many ceiling joists/ties to pull out of the pockets in which they are set in the party wall. The drawing at bottom right presupposes inadequate original timbers and accordingly the addition of a purlin and a binder with struts between the two forming a type of box beam to support sagging rafters from below and sagging ceiling joists from above. If no binder was required the purlin

317

could be strutted if necessary from the party wall as shown
by a dotted line, where a steel angle bolted thereto serves
also to provide a secure fixing for the ends of the ties, one
of many variations possible to prevent movement at this
point. It should not be overlooked in repair work that the
Building Regulations prohibit combustible material being
carried on to (or over) a separating wall and that the London
By-laws prohibit the building in of timber into the required
thickness of a party wall. Repairs are therefore sometimes
restricted to the use of metal corbels and ties.

Roof Structure for the Larger House or those involving Framed Construction

The types of roof described so far in this chapter probably cover about 90 per cent of the buildings throughout the country and will certainly be found most frequently by those concerned with maintenance and repair. There remain, however, the buildings in the centre of the larger towns and cities some of which may well have been changed from their original residential purpose. These if they are small probably have roofs of the type already described or of the simple mansard type. If they are large however it is much more likely that they are provided with triple roofs, the purlins being supported on timber trusses. Triple types of roof in timber are to be found on most of the larger domestic buildings built before 1900, as well as some since, but in particular in houses where it was desired to provide very large rooms on the main floors. As such they might also be found in smaller mews premises where the original purpose of stabling etc., required a large clear uninterrupted space at ground level. If only because of the additional thought that went into the design of such a roof, it is usually found that the troubles which beset the roofs previously described in so far as the design is concerned such as inadequate timbers, overloading, roof thrust and inadequate bracing are rare. What is found, however, are defective joints, causing weakness, deterioration in the timber brought about by neglect of the covering, causing rot, and also but very occasionally, lack of strength in the timber due to the attacks of wood boring beetle. The latter may however be more serious in the older buildings of an individual type where the trusses, and for that matter the other timbers comprising the roof structure, are of oak. Movement in the supporting walls from settlement or lack of restraint may however throw an additional load on a truss which while perfectly able to sustain the design load, fractures, splits or becomes distorted under the additional load to which it is subjected.

The types of truss found vary widely, their adoption being principally governed by the span to be covered but also, in regard to the design, depending on the original year of construction. The 19th-century wood trusses followed a fairly set pattern which will be familiar to most practitioners from their textbooks, although in the more recent editions of the standard works it has been noticed that they are now rarely mentioned and then only to say that this or that type are obsolete. Prior to the 19th century, however, the trusses took more individual forms dependent upon the designer or craftsmen constructing them. While there are many ways of achieving the same result which are perfectly satisfactory there are some, of course,

319

which are not quite so sound and may by now be showing evidence of defects, particularly at the joints. A few of the typical types of truss encountered are illustrated in outline on Figure 57, together with some of the early types of roof construction. It should be borne in mind that some of the earlier examples shown, those prior to about 1700, will be found to be made up of oak in most cases (particularly in the Midlands and the South) since this was the principal indigenous timber used in building construction. The importation of softwood for building construction from Northern Europe did not begin to be profitable until about this time. It should also be noted that the trusses were not always used in the same manner as those shown in books on building construction. Early trusses were often spaced quite close together and supported a series of purlins which in turn carried boarding, the common rafters being omitted entirely. This type of construction continued to be adopted in certain instances where the spans were large and the pitch relatively shallow. Early roof trusses again are not necessarily always what they appear to be and it should be noted that the centre post in the mediaeval Tie-Beam or Crown Post roof is not a tension member, as in the later King Post roof truss, but a compression member. In the later King Post roof truss the tie-beam is hung from the post but in mediaeval times the tie-beams always support the posts whether in the centre or not. The absence of a ridge should also be noted on the early forms of roofing.

It is more important than ever with early forms of roofs to prepare a drawing before embarking on repairs and to analyse the structural significance of each of the members. If doubt should exist in the mind of the surveyor as to the precise function of any particular timber then there should be no hesitation in obtaining the advice of a qualified timber engineer on the subject, preferably one with an interest in old buildings. It is essential to appreciate the function of each of the individual members in order to understand the working of the frame as a whole. As has been said before, it is also vital to know why a particular truss or an individual member in a truss has failed before considering the repair. This is particularly so in relation to the trusses of a wholly timber framed building, but is no less important in regard to trusses supported on brick or stone walls. In the former case, the framing of the whole building must be thought of as one and sometimes the troubles in the roof can be traced to the cutting or deterioration of a structural member some distance away. If this is so, then the correction of the defect elsewhere would arrest movement leaving the split timber or burst joint to be repaired only. The same applies to trusses supported on brick or stone walls. If the walls have moved, then restraint applied to these would leave probably no more than repairs to the individual members of the truss. Many of the mediaeval framed buildings which remain to us have been subjected to considerable alteration through their history, mainly to effect the desirable improvements which have been felt to have been necessary to keep them up to date. To effect the provision of a staircase and new doors and windows has often meant the cutting of principal structural members in the framework of the floors and walls. Where rooms are originally provided in the roof the formation of new door openings very often involves cutting a structural member normally hidden within a partition. Even where no such rooms are provided, the cutting of truss members can occur when a chimney stack is built through the roof. Such cutting invariably has a considerable effect on the whole building. If the cutting was carried out a long time ago and the building still stands then, even though it may be warped and distorted, it has probably taken up a new position of repose and become perhaps to some eyes more attractive as a result. Where the cutting is more recent and there is evidence of continued movement then steps must be taken to arrest this. Similarly, if there are to be more alterations made then the implications of these must be considered even on a structure which is evidently stable at that time.

Generally with framed timber structures it is a sound assumption that sizes of the timbers used are adequate in all except the most extreme conditions of overloading. Indeed the oak framing of mediaeval buildings is far stronger and has a far greater margin of safety than would be thought to be necessary today. Early timber trusses of the 17th and 18th centuries likewise are provided with timbers of ample scantling. Generally, therefore, total renewal of trusses and members can be avoided on the grounds of inadequacy and should features be overloaded beyond a reasonable limit, steps should be taken to transfer some of the load elsewhere, if possible back to where it was before. We are left therefore with a consideration mainly of the repair or partial renewal of individual members and the repair of joints howsoever these may have become defective.

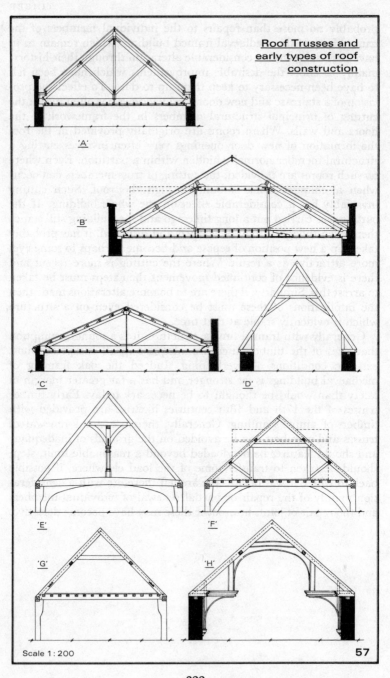

Roof Trusses and
early types of roof
construction

'A'

'B'

'C'

'D'

'E'

'F'

'G'

'H'

Scale 1:200   **57**

TIMBER

Figure 57

Roof Trusses and early types of roof construction

Larger spans for roofs during the period from the middle of the 17th century to about the middle of the 20th century followed the pattern shown here at 'A' 'B' and 'C' for the majority of domestic buildings. Appearance had ceased to count, so that the softwood now beginning to be imported at the commencement of the period could be framed into the rather inelegant, but efficient, King and Queen Post trusses, the joints being strengthened with metal straps and bolts. Such trusses reached their ultimate in design during Victorian times and comprised other variations and examples not shown here, although similar trusses to 'A' shown here with its slope suitable for tiling might well be found in 18th-century structures. The Queen Post was useful not only for the larger spans but also for occasions when rooms were required in the roof space, since the King Post was unsuitable in these circumstances. Another form of truss, known as the Mansard, was something of a combination of the two types 'A' and 'B' shown, a King Post truss on top of a Queen Post but with the lower roof slopes at about 60–70°. The version at 'C', known as a King Rod truss, replaces the central timber post with a long metal bolt, which is more efficient in tension. The example shown with a shallow pitch has boarding carried on purlins, the common rafters being omitted, and is suitable for large slates or for lead, copper or zinc as a covering. The Queen Post at 'B' with a pitch for ordinary slates is typically found in the largest of Victorian houses. Houses of an earlier date with this approximate span are more likely to have variants of the Queen Post Truss shown at 'F'. The trusses shown are usually positioned at about 10-foot (3.05m) centres unlike modern TRDA trusses (not shown) which, being of much lighter construction, require closer spacing.

The roofs of mediaeval buildings developed in two ways depending on whether the building was wholly timber framed or not. For structures with strong mass walling and gable ends the trussed rafter type of roof was satisfactory. Each couple was strengthened as shown at 'D' and the gable ends protected the structure from wind pressure which, owing to the absence of longitudinal bracing, tended to cause undue racking effects when this type of roof was used on wholly timber-framed buildings. Initially wholly timber-framed buildings were based on cruck construction or a little later on the arcade principle and were successfully roofed on these designs since there were many points of support for the transmission of loads and much bracing inherent in the construction. From the arcade principle can be traced the evolution of the successful roof type shown at 'E', once known as the mediaeval King Post roof but now known as the Crown Post type to distinguish it from the later version which is based on a distinctly different structural design.

323

The Crown Post is a compression member and rises from the tie-beam to support a "medial", or longitudinal, purlin below the collar attached to each couple. It is not a truss as such since there are no principal rafters but it is the most frequently encountered of all mediaeval roofs on domestic property. Many differing arrangements will be found for the bracing. Sometimes bracings are taken from the tie-beam to the post, sometimes only to the purlin or alternatively to the collar but more often to both as shown here. Often the Crown Post will be elaborately carved as being originally part of an open roof. Trussing became much more common towards the end of the mediaeval period and three types are shown at 'F' 'G' and 'H'. The Queen Post and simple collar type with wind bracing at 'F' and 'G' respectively both provide room in the roof space and like the Crown Post are both based on the main framing with tie-beam. Common rafters are shown dotted and it will be noted that the purlins are framed into the principal rafters (not carried on top as later), the usual mediaeval practice, along with the use of timbers broad side uppermost (as shown) instead of the reverse which is more sound structurally. Sometimes the purlins were held to the same depth as the principal rafters and the common rafters framed into the purlins.

Finally at 'G' an example of a small single Hammer-Beam roof developed from the earlier Tie-Beam and Queen Post roofs where open construction was required with a feeling of height. At Westminster Hall in 1395 a double form of this roof in combination with collar braces was used over a clear span of 68 feet (20.7m), one of the crowning glories of mediaeval carpentry.

Repair of Defective Members and Joints

The carpenters of the timber framed buildings and of the open roofs of stone or brick buildings up to around 1600 seldom used anything but wood pins or pegs to secure the joints and these were made from the heart of oak. Wrought iron used in the production of bolts, nails or clamps was far too expensive for ordinary building purposes and, in any event, used untreated would have soon succumbed to the acid in the unseasoned oak. Galvanising was unknown and although wrought iron was sometimes tinned against rust, the use of bolts treated in this way was restricted to very special cases where joints were liable to extra strain. The occasional clamps seen in old buildings are usually a much later addition, added when joints have shown a tendency to burst perhaps because of unequal settlement or undue shrinkage.

The very high strength of the heart of oak pins rendered the use of anything else unnecessary and the carpenters of the Middle Ages developed to a high degree joints for all purposes, many of which are still sound and almost undetectable to this day. The joints varied substantially in character, but there seems to be little doubt (as verified recently by radiocarbon analysis) that by 1250 a full range of mortice and tenon, lap dovetail and scarf joints were in use to solve all the likely problems that would arise in tying together, for example, the four-way joint at the junction of the principal rafter, top plate, tie-beam and principal post in a wholly framed building. The mediaeval ethic that the carpenter should solve all his problems using timber alone did not however survive the shortage of oak, the introduction of softwood and the greater availability of iron. As a result most people hold to the view that from 1600 or so the art of carpentry went into a severe decline. Certainly in support of this viewpoint 18th-century textbooks began to show joints made with iron bolts and plates. It must be acknowledged, however, that circumstances had radically changed and, in his adaptation to these altered conditions, the carpenter showed considerable ability in making efficient structures with a material inferior to that in use before and also in using metal to give just that additional strength in tension at vital points that the softwood timber available required to prove its worth and to enable its use to be continued well into the 20th century. However, when it comes to dealing with old timber framed structures there is much to be said for repairing timber with timber and admirers of the skill of the early carpenters are keen to show that all repairs can be carried out with this material alone. In propagating this belief they point out that they are following the old practice, although it is a viewpoint which is somewhat open to challenge. Nowadays we are concerned with preserving as much of the original work as possible but this idea would never have occurred to mediaeval builders. They were as much concerned with fashion as anyone since. If a building was much out of repair, it would have been pulled down and rebuilt in the latest style. If individual members were defective, they are more likely to have been renewed in their entirety rather than patch repaired as we would do today. To take the trouble to preserve the crumbly worm-eaten timbers that are often all that now remain would have been considered laughable. Patch repairing, confined to timber alone, can necessitate the removal of more timber than would be strictly necessary on structural grounds if a repair utilising metal as well as timber was to be adopted. The latter type of repair, while being not only more efficient structurally, often represents a more appropriate use of currently available materials and an acknowledgment of developments since earlier times without in any way detracting from the validity of the original design. The view to which everyone certainly subscribes, however, is that repairs to a wholly framed structure or open roof should be as unobtrusive as possible. For this reason the addition of exposed metal plates, metal angles and straps or even plywood gussets, useful though these undoubtedly are in other circumstances, is to be deplored and repairs should appear on completion, so far as is possible, to be part of the original.

A common need with a wholly framed structure is to renew the base of a principal or subsidiary post. Although framed walls are not dealt with until the next section of this Chapter, an illustration of such a repair to a defective member appears first at "A" on Figure 58, since it represents the simplest stepped joint used for lengthening members wholly in compression. This work is often carried out in conjunction with the renewal of a section of the ground sill and the opportunity is taken of showing the joint between new and old sections of this member. This is in the form of a longitudinal bevelled dovetail halving, the joint traditionally used for this purpose and which is also used for joining sections of a wallplate at the top of a masonry wall taking the feet of principal and common rafters as well as the ends of tie beams. Such wallplates as in the case of ground sills are rigid members of a frame and should not be cut and weakened by feeble jointing when new sections are inserted. Another common form of joint suitable for connecting new to old lengths of ground sills is shown at "F" on Figure 60.

When renewing the lower end of a common rafter and it is possible to make the join of new to old above a purlin, then it can take the form of a simple scarf as shown at "B". Other compression members such as principal rafters and struts in a truss, together with the ends of members subjected to a bending stress, for example beams and purlins, can be repaired by scarfing on a new section as shown at "C" on Figure 58. That such repairs should be satisfactory must be fairly obvious since it amounts to a replacement of a defective section of timber by new wood of the same sectional area. Provided the timber is similar in character to the original, the grain lies in the same manner as the timber replaced and the faces of the new timber to the old are accurately fitted together, the replacement timber will function as the old in transferring the load along the member. In forming the joint between new and old it is important that the cuts are made as near as possible in a direction 'normal', i.e. at right-angles, to the grain to avoid splitting the timber. It is for this reason and to ensure an accurate fit, that a stepped joint is usually made and which should be filled with a waterproof glue. The Department of the Environment recommends that while pins may be used to locate the inserted section they should not be relied upon to transmit any load. The hardwood wedges are so arranged as to draw the scarf joint together.

With defective members in tension, for example the King Post in a later truss, tie-beams, collars and braces and other members often substantially in tension, such as bresummers in a framed structure, different methods are necessary. A plated scarf joint would be satisfactory from a technical point of view, but as the plating would have to be carried out on the top and underside of the member it would not necessarily be practical or pleasing in appearance if the timber was exposed to view. In this connection it should be remembered that it is a knot, a cut notch or a hole subsequently drilled in tension members or members subjected to a bending stress that cause the main damage, whereas a wide shake or a split along the line of the grain will have little effect. The important point is that the strength of timber in tension depends on the continuity of the grain. In this respect the rules for safe notching in beams set out in the British Standard Code of Practice C.P.112, 1967 edition, "The Structural Use of Timber in Buildings" might form a useful guide when old timbers are being inspected. The Code gives a rule such that the effect of notching can be ignored in the following circumstances provided loads are uniformly distributed:

(1) Where a notch is cut not exceeding $\frac{1}{8}$ of the depth of the timber not nearer than $\frac{1}{8}$ nor further than $\frac{1}{4}$ of the span from the end of the member in joists not exceeding 10 inches (254mm) in depth.

The 1952 edition of the Code gave a further recommendation which is also useful:

(2) Where a notch is cut not exceeding $\frac{1}{8}$ of the depth of the timber not nearer than $\frac{7}{48}$ nor further than $\frac{11}{48}$ of the span from the end of the member

and the advice that in no circumstances should the depth of any notch exceed $\frac{1}{3}$ the depth of the timber. The Code also indicates that compression members should not be notched at all and if it is necessary to drill them, the hole formed should be in the centre half of the face of the member.

Where loads are relatively light on tensioned members for example on most collars and braces it may be possible to cut out the damaged portion completely and to insert a new matched portion of timber making the joint at each end with a mortice and tenon, fixed by pinning and the use of waterproof adhesive as shown for a repair to a collar at "D" on Figure 58. More often, however, it will be necessary to introduce a steel flitch plate cutting a slot instead of a mortice in the old sound timber on either side to accommodate the steel. The steel plate must be carried back at least three times its own depth on

327

either side of the joint of new wood to old. In these circumstances as the new timber has no structural significance and merely serves to mask the steel the faces of new and old wood may be butt jointed and the assembly is completed by a series of staggered bolts. If the timber is exposed the heads of the bolts can be recessed and pelleted and similarly the underside of the steel plate can be covered by a wood slip or the replacement of a moulding previously removed from the old beam for the purpose. A more elaborate repair of a somewhat similar nature to replace a defective section of a heavy exposed tie-beam is shown at "E" on Figure 58, but here the plating in timber forms an important structural element. This type of arrangement shown, however, permits the use of shear plates in the assembly, thereby ensuring that stresses are evenly distributed. For obvious reasons these cannot be incorporated in an arrangement whereby the steel is merely let into a slot in the old timber. The sections show recessed and pelleted bolt heads and nuts and the underside of the steel concealed with a wood slip.

On Figure 58 examples "A" to "D" show the repairs to defective members carried out with oak pegs, preferable in most respects for work to wholly timber framed mediaeval buildings or trusses in oak. When pegs are used the practice of draw boring should always be adopted as well as tapered pegs utilised, so that when the pegs are driven the joint is tightened. Leaving the pegs projecting slightly enables further driving at a later date, if there is any shrinkage.

A beam which is fractured, i.e. a member subjected to a bending stress, as distinct from decayed along its length, might well be simply repaired by the introduction of a steel plate in a narrow slot along its bottom edge to reinstate the member's tensile strength in a similar manner as described above. This method, as shown at "F" on Figure 58, would be satisfactory to deal with a split extending to about mid depth from the bottom of the beam, the timber above being sound and satisfactory to resist the compressive stresses. A fracture to a lesser degree could probably be satisfactorily repaired by the provision of a steel tension strap or rod anchored by bolting to sound timber near the ends of the beam or stressed by bolts passing at an oblique angle into sound timber on either side of the fracture, as illustrated at "A" on Figure 58. These forms of repair are ideally suited to beams in early roof trusses which have failed under the pressure from the Crown Post. In all cases however where steel is employed it is important that it should be of the stainless variety or at least be clean and treated with rust resisting paint before use. Alternatively phosphor bronze, delta metal, or gun-metal can be used in conjunction with oak.

In considering repairs to members of a framed structure the importance of the ground sill and top plate must not be overlooked and this consideration applies equally to the wallplate on which many roof trusses rest at the top of mass load bearing walls. In order to maintain continuity in the frame at eaves level in many old buildings complicated halved, bevelled and dovetailed lengthening joints, as shown at "A" on Figure 58 for a ground sill, were resorted to in the past and the essential function with similar joints must be maintained in any repair work. The same attention to detail is required in order to ensure that they do not buckle outward in a horizontal plane and are capable of resisting thrust from inadequately tied rafters between trusses. The top plate in a wholly framed building is usually a substantial member for this very reason.

Up to now we have considered the repair of the individual members of a framed structure but a failure at the joints is an equally serious matter. It is joints, particularly those at the eaves and apex which are particularly prone to damage by fungal and insect attack. Elsewhere joints may be disrupted more by pressure and movement in the frame itself. More often than not the repair of the individual member will also involve the renewal of a joint, as for example at "A" and "C" on Figure 58, and again in this respect function is all important. The repair must be carried out in such a manner that enables the joint to carry out the function for which it was originally designed. This usually involves the removal of the damaged timber and its reinstatement in the same form, if the decay extends through the whole of the joint, pinning in the same manner as before but not glueing. If part only of the joint is damaged it may be repaired. For example a decayed tenon may be cut off an otherwise sound member, a mortice in the old wood formed and a false tenon inserted to be pinned at both ends or alternatively to form part of a renewed section of timber at one end. It will sometimes be necessary to form a deep mortice in the old timber in order to allow the false tenon to slide into position and then be wedged tightly when located. If the insertion is merely the tenon, one end only should be glued in the false mortice to make up any gaps, but the joint itself should be pinned only, so as to allow for structural movement in the frame itself. In a similar manner reinstatement section by section of the walls of a mortice can be carried out by insertion of new wood as shown at "H" on Figure 58. In such ways joints between collars and rafters, purlins to principal rafters and tie beams to wallplates, can be restored. It must be stressed however that the method and extent of the repair will depend entirely on the amount of defective timber which has to be cut away and general principles only can be suggested as to means. The judicious use of metal flitch plates and straps can be of considerable advantage in strengthening sections adjacent to joints as for example at "F", "G" and "J" on Figure 58.

It will be noted that there is a substantial difference between the methods of dealing with defective members and defective joints. In the case of the former the intention is to restore the member to its previous strength and effectiveness and to achieve this it is necessary to fit the new sections very accurately and to make rigid fixings between new and old. The pegging or bolting must be carried over a wide area to minimise the risk of splitting along the grain and pegs and bolts should be staggered. Bulldog washers should also be employed when bolts are used beneath bolt and nut heads and all spaces should be sealed and filled with glue. All the connections are, as a result, very rigid. On the other hand, with the repair of joints it is essential that the connections between members of a frame have a certain amount of flexibility to allow for seasonal and other movements, as in the original construction. This is invariably achieved by the use of slotted joints such as the mortice and tenon in various forms, the correct positioning being obtained by the use of hardwood pins, but few in number. The bolting of beams to padstones or wall-plates and rigid inflexible connections between members are generally to be avoided, except where such features are specifically designed to act as ties, as much damage can be caused by such connections. Mediaeval buildings were often built of green oak which can warp and twist to a quite considerable extent and this is often the reason for much of the distortion visible in wholly framed buildings. The use of flexible joints by the original builders permitted this distortion to occur without harm and there is no cause for undue alarm when such distortion is present, provided the joints have not been pulled apart. On the other hand, distortion may indicate a failure in some part of the frame and it would be advisable to suspect this until it is proved otherwise by close examination. The typical causes of such failure have already been mentioned previously and arise principally from the cutting of framed members to insert chimney stacks, staircases, windows and doors but may also of course arise from failure in a member or joint due to fungal decay or insect attack. Often in a wholly timber framed building there are hidden braces halved over the back of studs and concealed externally by the panel filling and internally by wall plaster. Clearly if defects exist the reason should be sought out and steps taken to effect the necessary repairs. The cause of such failures may be easy or difficult to trace depending on their nature but progressive movement would certainly indicate their seriousness and measurement of movement in the same sort of way as with load bearing walls over a period may be necessary. If progressive movement does not exist, or if it has been arrested, it is not usually necessary to do anything further to a distorted frame, but occasions may arise when action does become necessary and provided the frame can be loosened from fixed or rigid structures, this might take the form of jacking with extreme care back into the original position. The framed method of original construction does of course lend itself also to the collapsing of the timber frame and its re-erection in true shape. Such a drastic step however is hardly in the purview of the present volume, which might well be likened to the entire moving of old buildings on jacks and rollers to a new site, equally possible with a framed structure and occasionally carried out in special circumstances.

It must be remembered that a number of early roof types were specifically designed to exert a side thrust at the top of the walls, the tie-beam being omitted to make an open roof, for example those shown at "D" and "H" on Figure 57. Probably not many of these are encountered in domestic construction but it should not be overlooked, if they are to be investigated, that over the years it may be the walls, originally of sufficient strength to resist the thrust, which may have become weakened by age. The movement in the tops of the walls may so distort the roof structure as to disrupt the joints or fracture the timbers. The repair in these circumstances may therefore consist of a strengthening of the walls rather than the provision of ties. In this respect, the introduction of a reinforced concrete plate along the top of the wall, suitably tied at any cross walls, may be sufficient to arrest further movement. This may also be coupled with grouting to a masonry wall if the stonework is thick enough but weak. The repair of any fractured timbers or burst joints can then be carried out as previously described.

Framed timbers and joints which are hidden from view can of course be repaired if required in precisely the same way as previously described, but the task will be made easier by the fact that the timber used is likely to be softwood and that steel plates can be left exposed on the sides, together with bolt heads and nuts, without detracting from appearance. In addition, various forms of strapping in metal or the fixing of plywood gussets as shown at "H4" on Figure 58, can be resorted to so as to reinforce joints which are showing signs of weakness. Even so, care is necessary to prepare and smooth down the surfaces of the timber before fixing. Leaving voids not only reduces the efficiency of the repaired work, but also leaves spaces very suitable as a breeding ground for woodworm beetles. All metal should at least again be treated with rust resisting paint.

In the repair of timbers which do not form part of a truss or a framed wall, for example common rafters, ceiling joists and for that matter floor joists, much repair work where these are hidden can be carried out by the simple expedient of doubling the timber, up to the next support, by providing a new section alongside. If the defect in the existing timber is not due to rot, it may be possible to leave the old timber in position, bolting new and old together and in the case of a common rafter birdsmouthing the new over both the wallplate and the purlin. If a defective section of rafter has to be removed the section remaining and the new member should be well lapped at the purlin and each member well spiked both to the purlin as well as to each other.

More often than not it is the ends of rafters and ceiling joists which require repair due to rot. In these cases the use of timber connectors can be invaluable. For most work in normal domestic construction based on timbers of about 4 by 2 inches (102 by 51mm) scantling, cutting off the ends and lapping new sections to the old, with a series of bolts and timber connectors, is perfectly adequate. In this field the use of split ring connectors for timber to timber joints is to be preferred, as providing a greater load bearing capacity than the toothed plate type of connector.

Split timbers requiring repair where it is desired not to disturb other features, such as roof battens, slating and tiling or ceiling plaster, which would be necessary if replacement were adopted, require a different treatment. Fish plates or a duplicate member for part of the length will be needed. It is not normally possible to fix fish plates along the top and bottom edges of a member, where they would be most effective, so that it is usually necessary to use side plates. Fish plates on either side of the member can be bolted on and the use of shear plate connectors can provide additional strength to the joints. Alternatively a duplicate section of timber can be bolted, using split ring connectors, on one or both sides. In either case, the plate or duplicate member must be of sufficient length to make a stiff joint with the sound timber beyond the split and three bolts at least on either side of the defect are required.

A split in a substantial member such as a purlin may need repair as described above but, far more likely, a suitable remedy would lie in the provision of an additional strut at the point of failure, wedged just sufficiently tightly to prevent further movement but not over tightly to force the roof upward. Similarly there is usually no need to repair a split strut but, instead, it is sufficient to provide a new strut alongside to arrest any further movement.

As previously mentioned in the simpler roofs which rely on nailing for their stability, an insufficiency of nails is often found to be one of the principal reasons for failure. Often single nails are used when two or more are necessary, for example where rafters rest on a wallplate and, in particular too few nails to connect collars and ceiling joists acting as ties to pairs of rafters. Partly drawn nails can be driven home and additional nails or coach screws can be fixed where required. It has been found practicable, where nails have been bent as well as partly drawn, to cut through the bent nails with a hacksaw or with a portable electrically driven grinding wheel. Using portable wedges, it is possible to hold the timbers in their existing position and, if required, to force the displaced timbers back into their former position before making the joint secure again with fresh nails or coach screws.

In any work involving nailing it must be remembered that over nailing causing the wood to split is as bad as under nailing. For example, the normal joint between collar and rafter in roof construction, using 4 by 2 inch (102 by 51mm) timbers and No. 7 gauge 4 inch (102mm) nails, following the recommendation contained in Code of Practice C.P.112 for nailing to avoid splitting can only take two nails. By pre-boring the timber with holes between $\frac{2}{3}$ and $\frac{4}{5}$ the diameter of the shank, six nails can be used making a joint three times as strong without any risk of splitting the wood.

In considering the repair of pitched roofs a considerable part of the ground to be covered in this Chapter on timber has been dealt with. Simple framing in roofs on modern small houses has led back through the more complicated structures used to cover larger spans in the more substantial older buildings to those involving the use of trusses. The repair of individual members, both in simple frames and trusses, and the repair of joints, both complicated and where timbers are merely lapped and spiked or nailed, have also been considered. Much of what has been discussed before will be relevant to the subsequent sections of this chapter as the principles will be found to be the same whether the timber is used in wall framing, floors or flat roofs. Accordingly it will often be necessary to refer back to material previously dealt with in order to complete a consideration of the remaining elements of a building where timber is employed. Much repetition can be avoided by this method, but it is necessary for a thorough understanding of the previous sections to be grasped if the subsequent sections are to be of value.

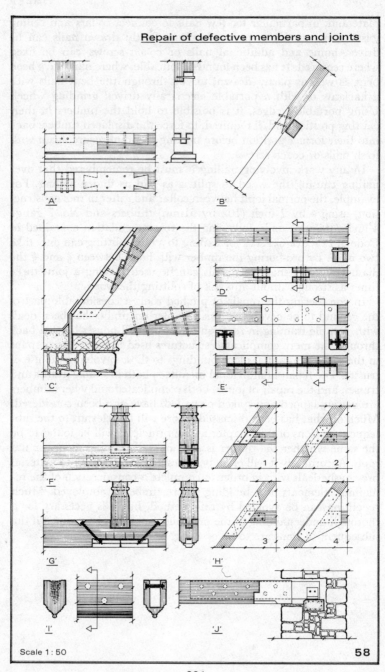

Repair of defective members and joints

'A'

'B'

'C'

'D'

'E'

'F'

'G'

'H'

1 2 3 4

'I'

'J'

Scale 1:50

58

Figure 58

Repair of Defective Members and Joints

Where timbers are hidden the repair of defective members and joints presents few problems and much can be done by the simple expedient of renewing sections, bolting new lengths alongside the old and strapping joints or fixing angle brackets. Where timbers are exposed however and it is essential to retain and preserve as much as possible of both the material and the character of the old, then suitable lengthening joints have to be used and new matching wood obtained and prepared for use in the manner of the original. 'A' shows the renewal of the lower section of a post with a stepped and pegged joint to the remaining part of original, accurately cut and fitted and secured with waterproof adhesive. The mortice and tenon joint at the base is to a renewed section of ground sill, jointed to the old with a pegged bevelled dovetail halving to maintain the original rigid nature of the ground frame. 'B' shows a simple scarf joint for a common rafter where a join of new to old can be made above a purlin.

Often the bearing ends are those affected by rot as for example the principals at 'C'. Scarfing new ends is the traditional method of dealing with the problem to both principal rafters and tie-beams. While many different types of scarf joint exist the stop-splayed scarf with under squinted square butts, transverse wedges and four face bolts or pegs (as shown here) is generally considered one of the most satisfactory. For a relatively lightly loaded member purely in tension, such as the collar at 'D', a section requiring renewal in the region of the centre could be replaced with new matching timber, the joint on either side of new to old being made with a mortice and tenon, pegged and glued as shown in elevation, plan and section. With a more heavily loaded tie-beam also in tension, as at 'E' shown again in elevation, plan and two sections, the introduction of a metal flitch plate may be necessary either in a slot on either side of the renewed section, or in the form with a timber plating as shown at 'E' which has the advantage that shear plates can be utilised in making the bolted connections between timber and metal. Bolt heads can be pelleted and the steel plate hidden by a wooden slip in the bottom edge.

Splits in a tie-beam below the Crown Post in a mediaeval roof might be dealt with in one of two ways. In the elevation and section at 'F' a metal plate has been introduced in a slot along the lower edge, while at 'G' a smaller split has been dealt with by the introduction of a tension strap screwed to the underside of the beam and secured by diagonal bolts and tapered washers. A slip of timber in 'F' or the refixing of a moulding previously removed as in 'G', obscures the metal when viewed from below.

Where there is decay, as in the side of a common rafter at 'H' affecting also the tenon of the collar, the defective timber

335

TIMBER

can be cut out and the joint restored by piecing in new wood. In 'H1' a new mortice has been formed in the collar, a false tenon inserted and glued and pegged. The other end of the false tenon awaits pegging on completion but the first section of wedge shaped timber has been driven in behind the false tenon (as the initial stage of piecing in the common rafter) and screwed to sound timber below. 'H2' and 'H3' show successive stages of the piecing in, as further wedge shaped sections are driven in and screwed both to the new layer below and the original sound timber. On completion the false tenon is pegged in the common rafter. Finally, by way of contrast in 'H4', a reinforcement of the same joint is shown by the screwing of external quality plywood on both sides of rafter and collar which would be perfectly satisfactory and very much cheaper if the joint were hidden as it might well be in the circumstances of a roof as at 'D' on Figure 57 where often a semicircular ceiling would be added subsequent to the original construction. Such typical strengthening lends itself to many of the joints of hidden structures.

Sometimes decay instead of requiring piecing in from the outer edges necessitates renewal of the interior of a heavy timber. 'I' shows a beam decayed in the centre which can be reinstated by hollowing out and filling, or more often by cutting up into sound portions and using these to build up a new beam of the same section as the original and as shown in the section.

At 'J', the renewal of the decayed end of a beam is shown utilising a metal flitch plate so as to avoid the undue building in of timber to the stone wall. All the new end appears to have a bearing when in fact it is the flitch plate, to which metal angles have been fixed, which provides the true bearing on a concrete plate.

336

TIMBER FRAMED WALLS

The interesting fact that the roofs of even some small buildings in the past are of complicated construction has already been mentioned. That this was because of the radically different nature of the method of construction for timber framed buildings compared with those of brick and masonry should now be rather obvious. Clearly when the strength of the walls lay purely in a series of posts set up at intervals, it was necessary for the bulk of the weight of roof framing and covering to be carried directly on these posts thereby necessitating the use of trusses and leaving a minimal weight from about a quarter span of common rafters and covering to be taken on a horizontal top plate, which might more properly be referred to as a beam rather than a plate, at the top of the vertical framing. Mention has been made in Chapter 1 of the initial developments in timber framed houses and how the system of framing arose out of the cruck construction, Figure 1(a), of the 13th and 14th centuries. The rectangular single-storey timber framed house developed slightly differently in the two principal forested parts of the country, the West Midlands and the south-east, including East Anglia, due to a number of reasons. In the West Midlands the timber framing tended to be more massive as the roof covering was often of thin slabs of the local stone and correspondingly very heavy. Even so there was a greater use of horizontal members between the studs which formed squarish panels and which were often decorated. The studs tended to be a little farther apart than those in the earlier houses of the south-east and more use was made of stout diagonal braces, see Figures 1(c) and 5(a). In the south-east the roof covering was mainly of thatch and later of tiles, so that the timbers could be somewhat lighter. There is a predominance in the south-east, however, of timber studs set close together to rise to the full height of the single-storey building and in consequence forming long narrow panels uninterrupted by horizontal members and, at least where visible, diagonal bracing. The general appearance of such framing is as shown at (b) and (c) on Figure 2 ignoring other factors on these drawings.

The introduction of the jettied storey enabled timber framing to be used satisfactorily for more than one floor and overcame the tendency of the framing to splay outwards by pressure from the first floor, which was also aggravated by the practice of laying floor joists on their flat sides causing undue springiness. By cantilevering the floor joists out over the wallplate and erecting an entirely separate frame on a sill placed on top of the ends of the extended joists, the whole weight of the upper storey and the roof was transferred vertically downwards through the ground floor frame. The tendency to springiness in the first floor joists was counteracted by the resistance of the wallplate at the top of the ground floor studs. By this means three or four storeys could be built quite safely. To begin with, the jettied first floor was only arranged on the two opposite long sides of the house corresponding to the line of the main framing and this, of course, was suitable for the houses lining streets and possessing party walls. Later, however, the use of the "dragon" beam enabled projecting storeys to be arranged on adjacent sides for detached buildings. The dragon beam consisted of a stout timber set diagonally to project outwards from the corner at first floor level and into which the cut joists on the corner were framed. Sometimes the end of the dragon beam would be provided with a separate free-standing corner post, but mostly it was supported by a bracket from the corner stud of the ground floor frame, see Figure 3(a).

Jettied construction, however, required an extremely lavish use of timber and not long after its real flourishing in the 16th century, the shortage of oak began to be felt in the south-east where there was a greater demand for other uses, more so than in the West Midlands. Commencing in the south-east, therefore, a gradual change took place in that jettied construction was abandoned as being too consuming of material and therefore too costly. The carpenters of the time had to make the best use of what was available and the result was framing where widely spaced, misshapen posts, rose the full height of two floors with considerable use of diagonal braces to give a degree of stiffness, similar to that shown on the left-hand cottage at the foot of Figure 6. Working to a pattern for appearance was virtually impossible. Supporting the first floors proved a problem and necessitated the introduction of transverse secondary beams into which the joists were framed. The system produced basically buildings which were from the start prone to movement, lacking the stiffness and sturdiness of what had been built before. These buildings needed the support which, at this time, was often provided by a massive central brick chimney stack.

The shortage of oak eventually affected construction in the West Midlands but by this time, about the middle to end of the 17th century, softwood was already being used as a framing material in East Anglia. Now, however, there was less need to attempt jettied construction in the new material as the supply was sufficient, coupled with the new idea of laying joists narrow side uppermost, to enable a reasonably sturdy frame to be constructed without it. This frame in East Anglia would be lathed over and covered with a thick plaster sometimes combed and pargetted as decoration. Soon in Surrey timber framing of this type was tile hung and in Kent weather boarded, see the middle and lower drawings on Figure 6, and these forms of construction continued in country areas well up into the 19th century.

Rather in the same way that it is impossible to be precise on the various forms of mediaeval roof trusses, so it is with the framing of the walls to which they are directly related. Too much space cannot be devoted to this type of building in view of the relatively small proportion remaining compared with the overall total of domestic buildings, but a surveyor faced with the task of repairing a timber framed building for the first time will find many fascinating problems and the need to approach the work in a somewhat different manner from repairs to other buildings of monolithic construction. It is hoped that Figures 59 and 60 showing details of a timber framed house will be fairly representative of the type of construction likely to be found. Many structures however will be greatly inferior in detailing.

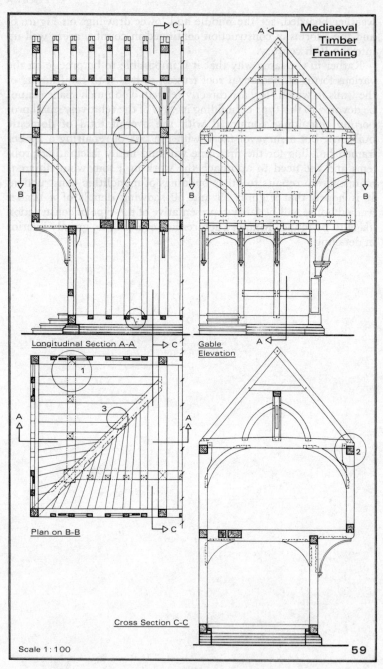

Mediaeval Timber Framing

Longitudinal Section A-A

Gable Elevation

Plan on B-B

Cross Section C-C

Scale 1 : 100

59

340

Figure 59

Mediaeval Timber Framing

The drawing shows part of a small mediaeval timber framed town building for a merchant or trader on the corner of two streets. The style and character suggest construction in the first half of the 16th century employing a lavish amount of timber to achieve the intended purpose of utilising a narrow restricted site to its utmost by overhanging the street on two adjacent sides. A slightly greater frontage would have made it worthwhile to bring the roof space into use by adopting the side purlin type of roof, increasingly being used once the need for open hall type houses had declined, but instead the familiar Crown Post type is retained. The longitudinal Section A–A and the cross section C–C enable the bracing to the collar or medial purlin to be seen, along with that to the Crown Post from the tie beam, and also the absence of a ridge piece.

The value of wind bracing was fully appreciated at this time. In the gable the studs are halved on face so that the brace is visible and is as much decorative as utilitarian. On the other hand in the first storey the studs are halved at the back to allow the braces to pass and accordingly these would be totally hidden from the exterior.

The gable elevation containing the entrance at ground floor level is treated differently from the remainder. Alternate studs are omitted, but the two remaining studs are of thicker scantling and the plate carrying the overhanging joists is supported by bracing in the form of three four-centred arches which form the head of the window and door openings. Additional stiffening to the overhang is provided by the curved brackets, mortice and tenoned to the studs and the underside of the appropriate joist and provided with support from small carved corbels. The large corbel and bracket on the corner to support the dragon beam could provide the opportunity for elaborate decoration.

Unlike softwood carcassing of later times which, being intended for subsequent covering, could be jointed together in an obtrusive manner, the craft of the mediaeval carpenter is by no means obvious from an examination of oak framed buildings of this period. One timber butts against another, the outline of both being preserved at the point of contact so that there is often no visible means of jointing at all. Much of the work is done by the simple mortice and tenon joint and the pattern of the oak pegs or pins used gives some indication as to the position, even if not to the often complicated shapes of tenon and mortice which remain obscured. Some examples of typical joints are shown on Figure 60 and references are made on that diagram to the numbered circles shown here.

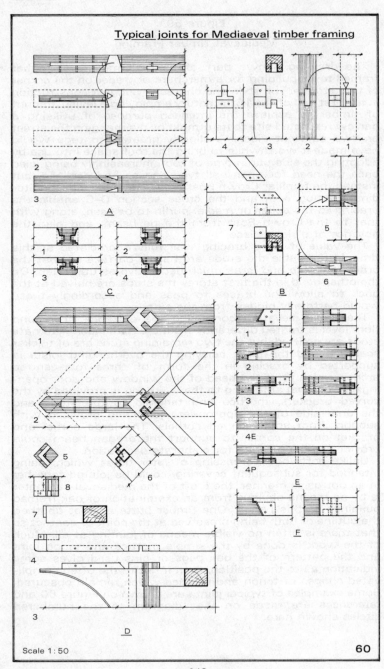

Typical joints for Mediaeval timber framing

Scale 1 : 50

60

Figure 60

Typical Joints for Mediaeval Timber Framing

This drawing shows typical joints used by carpenters in the mediaeval period for oak framed timber buildings, with particular reference to the house shown on Figure 59.

The details above 'A' correspond with the point circled 1 on Figure 59 and show the dovetailed joints usually adopted where the overhanging joists cross the top plate of the ground storey. Detail A2 shows the top of the plate and the end bracket while A1 and A3 show the cutting in the underside of the end joist/plate and the first joint in from the corner respectively.

Above 'B' are the details of the tying joint between main post, top plate, tie-beam and principal rafter circled at 2 on Figure 59. B1 and B2 show the top of the post and the underside of the plate, while B3 and B4 in side elevation and in elevation from the outside show how the connection is made with a mortice and tenon and two pegs. B5, viewed from above, illustrates the top of the post and top plate when connected ready to receive the tie-beam, the underside of which is shown at B6. Note how there is a mortice and tenon joint with one peg between the tie-beam and the top of the post and a shouldered dovetail joint to the top of the plate. The components of the assembled joint are shown at B7, the principal rafter being tenoned into a mortice in the end of tie-beam and secured with two pegs. Most problems of framing in the walls and roof had been solved with the use of effective joints by about 1250 as shown above and also at 'D' 'E' and 'F'. The joint which provided mediaeval carpenters with most difficulty was that between flooring joists and main beams and ideal solutions were not found until the latter half of the 16th century. Prior to that time all sorts of elaborate joints had been devised but most of these removed too much material from the main beam, often weakening it severely in the process and reducing the effective strength to a mere fraction of its total. Where ordinary joists are much less in depth than the main beam, the simple soffit tenon with diminished haunch and peg shown at C4 represents maximum efficiency since the amount cut away from the main beam represents waste material (from a structural point of view) and the full depth of the joist is used for bearing. C3 is not so efficient since the mortices in the main beam are taken from structurally important timber (i.e. the "web") and only about half the depth of the joist is employed in bearing. It is axiomatic that 100 per cent efficiency cannot be achieved where main beam and joists are of the same depth. At most only three-quarters to seven-eighths of the joist can be used for bearing and even to achieve this it was often necessary to cut unduly into the compression areas and the "web" of the main beams to form housings. C2 does this to some extent as well as cutting into the lower tension area of the main beam. In substance C1 is about the most efficient joint, in the circumstances, that can be achieved and the fact that it bears a striking resemblance to the tusk-tenon joint of later times is no mere coincidence. If we take it that such a joint was used for securing the ends of the overhanging joists into the dragon beam as circled 3 on Figure 59 we shall ascribe to the carpenter a high degree of skill indeed. More often greater reliance would be placed on an even more oversized dragon beam and a less efficient joint.

Above 'D' are details of the overhanging corner for the Figure 59 building. D1 and D2 show the underside of the dragon beam and the top of enlarged corner post with bracket already fixed. It will be noted that the top plates for the ground storey are housed and pegged near the top of the post but that the post, cut appropriately for the top plates, also provides a keyed joint for the underside of the dragon beam in addition to the pegged mortice and tenon to the bracket. This is shown also in true elevation at D3 and D4 from along the side of the dragon beam and bracket. The fixing of the corner post to the first storey is carried out by a mortice and tenon with pegs both to the dragon beam and also to the plate carried by the oversailing joists. The underside of the post is shown at D5 and the mortising at the foot of the post for the plate in plan at D6 and in elevation at D7. The elevation of the lower end of the post is at D8.

Besides the scarf joint illustrated on Figure 58 at 'C' many other scarf joints were developed during the mediaeval period, all with varying degrees of efficiency. The scarf shown circled at 4 on Figure 59 to the top plate (and also used in the collar purlin) is shown in more detail at E2 (in both elevation and plan). Both this scarf and that shown at E3, in varying degrees of length and with varying distribution and number of face pegs, were widely used in the 15th and 16th centuries and examples of E2 have been dated from the 14th century. This type of scarf remained common until a general advocacy of bladed scarfing, shown for example at 4E (in elevation) and 4P (in plan), arose towards the end of the 16th century continuing right through the 17th and 18th centuries and tending to displace the earlier form. The integration of the ends of the two timbers is not so satisfactory with the bladed type of scarf than with the other forms. A rarer type of scarf, dated from the 13th century, is shown at E1 but it is not very efficient at resisting the pulling and winding stresses necessarily encountered when used in a top plate.

The scarf at 'F' is commonly found used in the ground sills of nearly all mediaeval buildings, indeed even in preference to that shown at 'A' on Figure 58. The lipping at the top prevents the entry of water into the bridle and the joint is so designed that neither of the butted ends can subside without the other.

Repairs to Framed Walls

Reference has already been made on the need to consider a framed roof truss as a whole, but it is now necessary to consider how defects in the framed walls can also affect the wholly timber framed building.

In dealing with wholly timber framed buildings, or half-timbered as they are usually called if the framing is left exposed, it is almost certain that the building will be subject to some form of listing as of architectural or historical interest. Accordingly, great care must be taken in repair, as the interest will lie in and be dependent upon the extent and use of timber in its structure and possibly also for decorative features. If the building is to continue to be of value in this respect, it is essential to strive for the preservation of as much of the original work as possible and if it is necessary to replace members or parts of a member this should be carried out in timber of as near similar a type and character as previously existed and be used in the same manner as before. Timber repaired with timber, so as to perform the function for which it was originally designed, should be the aim. If it is not always possible to achieve this aim with timber alone, which should be in rare circumstances indeed, the use of steel may be resorted to, but only as a second best method and even then only when it can be totally hidden from view.

In a wholly framed building, the symptoms of defects are usually the distortion of the frame or the cracking and displacement of panels both internally and externally forming the infilling. The distortion may be of long standing resulting from the warping and twisting of green timber used in the original construction. Provided the joints remain sound and there is no evidence of movement there is no need for any repair. If however joints have opened, timbers are cracked or split or there is evidence of continuing movement, then a careful examination may reveal one or other of the typical causes resulting from the cutting of structural members. Examples of such cutting include that for the insertion of a door or window opening, a staircase, cutting a deep notch for pipes, the removal of a cross frame and braces to make two small rooms into one large room, the formation of a brick fireplace and chimney stack. Many alterations of this nature involve the removal of braces which are often an important feature of the framing, providing it with a resistance to wind pressure, distortion due to wind forces often being particularly pronounced in buildings with a paucity or total lack of such bracing. If too many of the braces, which are tension members, are removed or cut the structure can be dangerously weakened. Many of the wind-braces in the external walls are entirely hidden, being passed through slots in the intervening studs or halved over the studs and secured to the posts and sills or bresummers with pins. If dampness penetrates the joints between panels and studs these braces, being in an unventilated space, are prone to rot. Shrinkage and decay of the timber will allow the tenons to pull away. Partitions formed of cross frames can also contain concealed braces in a similar manner and decay where these are jointed to the posts, is not uncommon. Cracked internal plaster or cracks in panelling or distortion in the panelling may be an indication of this type of defect. Fungal decay and insect attack will, of course, also weaken main structural elements particularly at junctions of sills with posts, posts and bresummers and at the eaves, causing as much harm as removal or cutting of these members.

Since the stability of a frame relies on the satisfactory functioning of all the members of which it is comprised, it follows that a cutting or removal of one member, or decay at one particular point, may cause damage some distance away, which as a manifestation may be easy to spot. Once observed however it is not sufficient just to deal with that defect alone. The investigation must be pursued so that the real cause of the observed defect can be found and put right at the same time. For example, rot in a sill and the base of a post may lead to undue stress being thrown upon the members of a roof truss, causing possibly a fracture in a tie-beam. Obviously a careful repair with timber of the tie-beam will be of little value if the decay in the sill and post is not dealt with, together also with those defects which probably occur at the junction of post, wallplate and tie-beam and which may not have been very apparent on a superficial inspection. By successfully dealing with all three defects, the frame will again become a structural entity and be made sound without the need for additional struts, ties or posts as might have been thought at first necessary if the fracture in the tie-beam had been considered in isolation. Put in another way, the failed tie-beam might have suggested a failure in design whereas, in fact, the validity of the design will have been proved, when the defect has been traced to some other cause and the repair restores the design to its original shape, satisfactory for its function and providing the building with more justification for its retention.

With wholly timber framed buildings, the essential objective in the repair is to restore all members of the frame and the joints by which they are connected, to their original function. That this function was very well cared for in the minds of the original builders is all too evident from the amount of "damage" which a great number of mediaeval buildings have sustained, but which are still structurally sound and standing to this day, even though a little drunkenly! The reason is of course that certainly up to the middle of the 16th century there was seldom much reason to economise and oak members were used in far greater sizes than were structurally necessary. Such members can often take a substantial amount of cutting and sustain the ravages of the death watch beetle for some considerable time before being seriously weakened. It depends very often, however, on the function of the member and the position and extent of the damage. For example, in many historic buildings beams will be seen to have been sorely attacked by beetle yet, provided there is no active attack, the member retains sufficient depth of sound timber to maintain its function, only the sides being really affected. Similarly quite substantial cuts can have been made at the ends of beams with no loss of strength. On the other hand, a substantial notch on the underside of a beam near the centre can lead to serious deflection and probably a fracture, throwing undue stress on other members deriving support from the beam. Dry rot, of course, requires prompt and exhaustive attention on the rare occasions when it is found in oak framing, but wet rot in exposed timbers can continue for a long time without serious impairment of strength, although that does not mean to say that when ascertained it should be left. The structural effect of this and woodworm should not however be overestimated, as it may result in the removal of much timber which might well remain in position, always provided steps are taken to ensure that conditions giving rise to the wet rot are not allowed to continue and, in the case of beetle attack, suitable insecticide treatment is administered. It must not be forgotten also that what appears as wet rot on an exposed timber may give rise to suspicions that the same conditions are producing dry rot in timbers hidden from view and, accordingly, unventilated. Attacks of woodworm can also spread to hidden timbers and continual infestation in relatively confined areas can be a matter not to be ignored if conditions are favourable. For example, the frame may be deprived of the restraint from a brace from this cause and defects arising from this might be difficult to trace to their source, without some cutting away of internal plaster.

Function accordingly determines the type of repair, which will also be governed in extent by the degree of damage in precisely the same way as already described for the repair of compression and tension members and the repair of beams in the section of this Chapter devoted to trusses, to which reference should be made.

As the repair of a wholly timber framed building invariably involves the use of oak, since in this section the traditional half-timbered building is under consideration, it would be appropriate at this point to consider the timber itself to be used in repair work.

347

Ideally in the repair or partial renewal of oak timbers of a mediaeval building, one should seek to use second-hand timber which has aged and been exposed in a similar position to that which it is replacing. Provided that the second-hand timber is absolutely free of decay, minor defects, within reason, such as shakes, are of no consequence and even old mortices, provided they do not substantially affect the strength, can be tolerated. It is important however that the second-hand timber should be approximately the right size for the purpose, as even old wood will twist and warp on cutting down to size.

If second-hand timber is not available or if a whole section of renewals to members is necessary then new timber must be used, but the selection of new timber requires care. Apart from matching the original type, oak with oak, the quality should be as near to the original as possible and the Department of the Environment recommends that the moisture content should be limited to 15 per cent, equal to the usual level in an existing building. In regard to seasoning, the Department suggests, as a useful rule of thumb, that no timber should be used that has not been air seasoned, not kiln-dried, in its required size, with allowance for working, for at least one year for every inch of thickness. Greater care is necessary to match quality, grain and moisture content if the new timber is to form part of an existing member and is to be jointed to it with an adhesive. If the two sections are not well matched seasonal movements will cause distortion and twisting. On the other hand, generous allowance for such movement can be made in the joints between members as was done in the past, to overcome this problem.

It is not the purpose of this volume to enter into an argument on the finish to new oak where it forms part of a mediaeval building. All authorities however advise that the artificial ageing of new oak is to be deplored. Controversy still reigns, however, on the merits of using the adze. Some regard its use as an affectation, particularly since its skilled use by early craftsmen left a finish indistinguishable from planing. The Department of the Environment suggests that while the smooth finish produced by machine planing is undesirable, an adze should be used provided a good reasonably smooth surface is produced and totally avoiding the scalloped antique finish, so popular in the "Tudor" restaurant of the present time. It suggests that combing with a saw blade or a rasp file to exaggerate grain is permissible on the matching of a small insertion, but not on large areas. Although one distinguished restorer was happy to leave saw marks visible, the Department suggests that these should be removed by hand planing. Similarly their advice is that mouldings should be machined oversize and finished on the carpenter's bench to avoid the mechanical appearance which can always be detected. That this in itself rather smacks of artificial ageing does not seem to bother the Department.

In regard to the weathering of exposed oak, the main danger points for rot arise on the horizontal ledges formed by the ground sill and bresummers where these exist, the underside of the sill and the vertical joints formed between the panels and the studs. Where new horizontal members are being introduced, which have to project beyond the face of the panel, the upper surface can be given a slight weathering, provided the grain is very close but far better for protection is a 4 lb. (19·5 kg/m²) lead flashing, taken up under the panel filling if of wattle and daub, or tucked into the first brick joint if the panel is nogged. A renewed sill should always be bedded on lead as, of course, no form of damp proof course was provided originally in this type of construction. Reliance was placed on masonry or brickwork below the sill to keep rising dampness to a reasonable level, coupled with the thickness of the oak itself. The opportunity should always be taken of inserting lead below an old sill in a scheme of repair as it is clearly only a matter of time before the underside of the sill rots, however sound the timber may appear from the exterior. Although the practice of setting the panels back about ½ inch (12·5mm) from the face of the studs improves the joint between the two from the weatherproofing aspect, it is not usually desirable. The resulting projection beyond the panel face of the horizontal members provides a source of weakness which the method of protection described above does not entirely overcome. It has also a fatal result from the aesthetic point of view as the result is remarkably similar to sham half-timbering. It is far better to finish the panels flush with the face of the framing and in order to provide a water check within the thickness of the panel to bed in mastic and screw oak fillets to the sides of the main posts and studs ("C2" on Figure 61). It will sometimes be found that the original posts and studs are already grooved to provide a fixing for lathing in which case the fitting of the fillet bedded with mastic in this groove provides an even better waterproofing measure ("C1" on Figure 62). Any shrinkage in panels where they meet the posts can also be pointed up in a pliable waterproof mastic applied, if necessary, under pressure.

If rot or other defects necessitate the renewal of a panel, it is necessary to give some consideration to the type of filling previously used so that this can be faithfully reproduced. Panel fillings usually tend to be either of wattle and daub or brick, although the former greatly predominate. However, the wattle and daub method took different forms according to the nature of the framing. In times when timber was plentiful, houses tended to be built with studs set at close

349

intervals rising the full height of the storey. This produced a long narrow panel which was provided with split oak laths sprung, often in an irregular manner, into grooves in the sides of the studs, as shown at "A", left-hand panel, on Figure 61. Later when timber shortage necessitated a wider spacing of the studs it was necessary to introduce more horizontal members producing a squarer panel. Holes would be left in the horizontal surfaces of sills and the horizontal members and into these would be sprung staves of split oak usually about 2 inches (51mm) longer than the height of the panel. Hazel boughs would then be threaded between the staves forming a close basket work (or wattle) pattern, as shown in stages at "B" on Figure 61. Sometimes laths would be plaited through the staves instead of hazel boughs or alternatively these would be tied to the staves with leather thongs. Strictly speaking the term wattle and daub only applies when larger panels were involved as the longer narrow panels could be successfully dealt with by lathing only. The filling of the panels would normally be completed by the daub, comprising a mixture of wet clay with flax, straw, or cow hair well worked up with a spade until plastic and adhesive and thrown on in layers from both sides until the required thickness was built up. When this had dried and set quite hard, it was usually given a coating of smooth lime hair plaster, to fill up all the crevices, provide a more waterproof surface, not so subject to excessive shrinkage or cracking as would have been the case if the daub had been left exposed. Even so, shrinkage, particularly in the larger square panels, still took place coupled with the seasonal movements in the wood and at later times many half-timbered buildings have been altered by way of the removal of the wattle and daub panels and just occasionally their replacement by brick nogging, or, alternately and more likely, by the battening over of the whole frame and applying further coats of plaster or a cladding of tiles. Brick nogging used as a substitute in this fashion tends to introduce many further difficulties by overstraining the original frame and causing structural failure. On the other hand, brick nogging was often used in later mediaeval times as filling for the panels in the more expensive houses, in which case the frame would be designed to cope with the extra weight and often the studs would be grooved to receive the bricks. It does not follow, however, that nogging is superior for the purpose of filling the panels as the bricks can often prove to be more porous than a properly plastered daubed panel.

Other materials apart from wattle and daub and brick nogging were sometimes used to fill the panels, depending on the materials available in the locality of the building, clay lump in Suffolk, flint in Kent and Surrey, chalk in Sussex, sandstone in Hereford and in the region of Stamford slates, or other thin stones, were wedged tightly between the studs and plastered both sides.

While it is essential to match the exterior plaster finish for texture if only a few panels in an existing building are being replaced, it is not perhaps essential to slavishly copy the inner core if suitable alternatives are available, although this should not be entirely ruled out. The former principles should, however, always be adopted and whereas it may not be possible to use wood laths as a basis for the panel and indeed probably unwise to do so, it has been suggested that strips of slate wedged between close timber framing are suitable and for squarer panels a non-rusting form of metal lathing would be suitable instead. The art of daubing is not entirely forgotten and it must be remembered that where this has been used in the past, the source of the clay is almost certainly to be very close at hand, a garden pond or other local feature being the clue. A little determination by the surveyor and co-operation by the contractor is usually required to overcome a natural tendency to replace the filling with lightweight blocks and render them with cement and sand, something to be avoided at all costs. Cement in the mix will introduce a hardness to the finish entirely alien in the circumstances.

As to the exposed oak itself, it is not recommended that old timber be darkened and it is considered unnecessary for newly inserted wood to be stained as this will tone down on its own in due course. On no account should exposed surfaces be sealed and the use of bitumen or paint coverings prevent the wood from breathing, tending to direct water and allowing it to be drawn by capillary action into the joints, where decay most frequently commences. A clear liquid insecticide and preservative may however be applied, provided it has no sealing properties. Even the filling of shakes and splits with wood slips can be considered damaging, as water tends to be held in the grooves and in the space below the slip a space suitable for beetles to breed is provided. If a shake however is so formed as to lead water into the interior of the timber, it can be filled with mastic or a waterproof sawdust resin compound.

If it is desired to clean existing exposed timber, this can be done by scrubbing with soap and water, to which a small quantity of ordinary washing soda has been added. But on completion the timber must be thoroughly rinsed repeatedly with clean warm water. If the timber has been previously varnished this can be removed by the use of a solvent made from genuine turpentine and acetone, the correct proportion to be found by samples on selected areas. Once again however all traces must be washed off with clean water, also the case when removing old tar with strong caustic soda. The Department of the Environment do not recommend the use of

351

linseed oil, for the reason that being slow drying it collects dust and dirt but states that the application of a clear preservative is advisable. When the surface is quite dry, this can be followed by a thin protective coat of clarified beeswax dissolved in pure turpentine, with a final rubbing down using a soft cloth.

The advice extended by the Department that old wood should never be darkened artificially and that it is unnecessary to stain new insertions may run counter to local practice and possibly the client's own wishes and it must be recognised that this is really a question of personal taste and custom. While most authorities have come to accept that the appearance of naturally weathered, unstained, timber framing against a lightly colour-washed panel, as normally found in the Eastern Counties, is preferable, there is a long tradition of darkening the timber in the west and north-west. Although the stark appearance of black timbers against a brilliant white panel is perhaps overpowering, the treatment is still preferred by many, even although its use historically may be in question.

The wholly timber framed building is not, of course, always recognisable in the traditional half-timbered work with which it is usually associated. There are undoubtedly many more wholly timber framed buildings than would at first sight be apparent to anyone making a cursory inspection of the towns and villages. Many buildings which appear to be rendered and which one might at a glance assume to be of brick construction, will be found on closer examination to be timber framed, either built that way originally or perhaps in the 17th or 18th centuries given this appearance by plastering over the formerly exposed framework. To these must be added the many timber buildings put up during these centuries in country areas or in small towns and villages and then finished with weatherboarding, or hung with tiles. Even some houses which on the face of it appear to be of brick construction might prove to be of timber with a casing of brick, either for increased comfort or to keep up with fashion. Our forebears were very adept at altering the appearance of buildings and suppliers of materials equally inventive in devising products for the purpose. Perhaps the most famous of these is the type of tile made to imitate brickwork, often known as a "mathematical" tile and illustrated at "D" on Figure 61. When properly hung and pointed the appearance is almost indistinguishable to the eye and only readily apparent by tapping and by measurement. It must be clear how necessary it is to be satisfied by investigation of the true nature of the construction which is to be dealt with otherwise if this elementary, although by no means always easy, problem is not solved from the start all sorts of difficulties will arise. The impossibility of adapting a specification from one type of construction to another once the work has commenced is unlikely to elicit any sympathy from the client. Apart from this, however, the practical problems of dealing with a concealed frame can be considerable. It will not be possible normally to determine what has to be done until much of the covering, either internally or externally, has been removed and it is just the sort of job where costs can escalate to an alarming degree. Much co-operation and mutual trust must exist between all parties to the contract and, in particular, the client must be warned in advance of what might be expected to arise.

Notwithstanding the above factors the repair of the frame once exposed will follow precisely the same procedure as with an exposed frame. An advantage over the latter will lie in the fact that it will be possible to indulge in strapping with metal and fishing with both wood and metal to a degree which would not be permissible with an exposed frame. Cases must be treated on their merit in each instance, the overriding factor in each case being, as before, a full appreciation of the working of the frame as a whole and of each individual member of which it is comprised. It must be appreciated of course that concealment of the frame produces a higher incidence of dry rot which can be particularly prolific in the circumstances. As will be discussed later the investigation into the cause of such outbreaks must be rigorously pursued and measures taken to avoid a recurrence. Frequently the sealing off in the interest of obstructing draughts, of sections of the framing from ventilation adequate to prevent the spread of dry rot is the cause. Any scheme of reinstatement or improvement must bear this factor in mind and if, for example, steps are being taken to improve the insulating properties of the structure the correct positioning and differentiation of moisture and vapour barriers is vital. This point is illustrated on Figure 61 at "E".

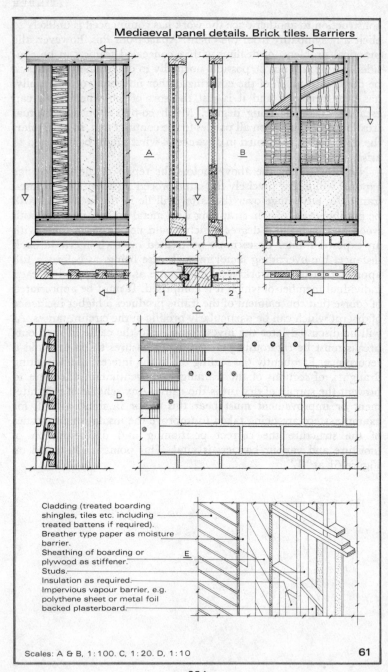

Mediaeval panel details. Brick tiles. Barriers

A

B

1   2

C

D

E

Cladding (treated boarding
shingles, tiles etc. including
treated battens if required).
Breather type paper as moisture
barrier.
Sheathing of boarding or
plywood as stiffener.
Studs.
Insulation as required.
Impervious vapour barrier, e.g.
polythene sheet or metal foil
backed plasterboard.

Scales: A & B, 1:100. C, 1:20. D, 1:10   61

Figure 61

Mediaeval panel details. Brick tiles. Barriers

The panels of early timber framed buildings, particularly in the south-east, tended to be long and narrow rising the full storey height as at A. The sides of the studs would be grooved and split oak laths sprung into the grooves and wedged as in the left-hand panel, at irregular intervals. A clay daub with added flax stems, straw or hair was then applied both sides and allowed to dry thoroughly so that any shrinkage cracks would appear. The panel was completed with a coating of lime plaster, both sides, filling up all cracks and spaces.

Later panels tended to be squarer in shape when studs were spaced further apart and it became necessary to introduce horizontal members and bracing, as at B. Holes would be left in horizontal members and oak staves sprung into position (top panels) to provide a framework for hazel boughs to be woven through and around (middle panels) to form a basket pattern. The daubing would then be built up as described above.

Further shrinkage and the inevitable movement in the frame would result in a very draughty house and invariably laths and counter laths would be applied to the internal face of the studs so that a nearly complete plaster face would be presented internally, leaving perhaps only the main posts showing. In replacement of panels, the addition of a throated oak fillet fixed into the existing grooves of the studs (C1), or screwed to the side of the studs or posts if they are not grooved (C2), is advantageous at keeping out driving rain and draughts if a simple reinstatement of daub and plaster on metal lathing is proposed as at C2. Another method of forming a new panel suggested, which would provide better insulating properties is shown at C1 and consists of plastered wood wool slabs with a cavity and an inner lining of plasterboard and plaster. It is necessary in these circumstances for the plasterboard to be either foil backed or alternatively for a vapour barrier of sheet material, polythene for example, to be positioned immediately behind the plasterboard to prevent condensation arising in the cavity.

The practice of updating buildings for appearance as well as for the sake of comfort at not too infrequent intervals is by now almost becoming a tradition in itself. Many old timber framed buildings now present a totally rendered face applied to lathing, others were tile hung, or weatherboarded in the past. When softwood was used for framing, one or other of these types of cladding had to be applied. Occasionally timber framed buildings would be cased in brickwork. Perhaps the most cunning of all the cladding materials available however were the so called "mathematical" or "brick" tiles. As shown at D in section and elevation given good fixing, preferably by screwing to stout battens, the effect could be indistinguishable from brickwork.

TIMBER

Even though softwood timber framed and clad buildings could eventually be made weatherproof and reasonably draught proof, their standards of insulation in the past were poor, at least in the form as mostly built in this country providing for accommodation at the lower end of the quality scale in small towns, villages and country areas. Repair involving substantial renewal of the cladding and internal lining provides opportunities to raise insulation standards, which if thoughtlessly taken can introduce new hazards. The correct positioning of moisture and vapour barriers is essential to avoid the dangers of dry rot. As mentioned in regard to C above, the vapour barrier must be placed immediately next to the internal lining on the warm side of the structure, so as to prevent water vapour from the rooms penetrating the construction with the risk of condensation. Such condensation could ultimately give rise to the possibility of rot even apart from the likely saturation of the insulation materials. Aluminium and copper foil backed plasterboards are suitable together with polythene sheet as well as certain specially prepared papers. As no vapour barrier is 100 per cent effective, provision must be made to allow any water vapour that does escape from rooms to pass on through the structure to the outer air before it condenses. This is achieved by ensuring that any sheathing material which prevents the ingress of moisture by driving rain or snow is of the breather type, i.e. it is a moisture barrier, but not a vapour barrier. The distinction between the two barriers and their correct positioning is vital. The section at E shows the proper arrangement of the barriers coupled with a sheathing over the studs of 1-inch nominal (25mm) tongued and grooved boarding laid diagonally over the studs. This provides an excellent stiffener for a feeble frame but in substitution of the boarding a $\frac{3}{8}$-inch (10mm) resin bonded sheathing grade (i.e. unsanded) plywood may be used and is equally effective. Over this is laid the moisture barrier of a breathing type building paper. The moisture barrier would be fixed direct to the studs if the boarding or plywood sheathing is omitted but the provision of the latter also raises the insulation value of the structure to a figure in excess of that provided by an 11-inch (280mm) brick cavity wall. The addition of insulation panels between the studs, for example polystyrene slabs, improves the insulation qualities even further.

TRUSSED TIMBER PARTITIONS AND BEAMS

A form of construction much used in the 18th and 19th centuries for the larger domestic buildings which both structurally and for the purposes of repair is related to ground already covered in this Chapter, is the trussed partition, or deep trussed beam as it is in effect. The formation of large reception rooms at ground and first floor levels often meant that the partitions forming rooms on floors above had no means of support from partitions in lower storeys. A beam across the ceiling of a larger room below would interfere with the elaborate decoration in plaster and its overall design and there would often be an insufficiency in the depth of the floor to accommodate a beam without it being visible. In these circumstances resort would be had to a form of partition independently supported from the walls at either end. Students of the earlier forms of building will be familiar with the general principles of how the construction, in many ways similar to King and Queen Post roof trusses, varies according to the requirements of door openings and whether the partition is parallel, or at right-angles, to the floor joists. These partitions serve not only to divide up a large area into smaller rooms without the need for individual support to the partition but may also be employed to carry the floor above and also the ceiling of the room below, if the partition is at right-angles to the joists and there is no objection to the beam being incorporated in the general design of the ceiling and being visible from the floor below. When upper floors are being dealt with in this Chapter it will be found that they can have a use in repair work to stiffen the ceiling and floor above a large room by attaching the joists to the tie-beam by the use of metal hangers, see Figure 63 at "J" and "M".

The design of trussed partitions and beams must always comply with the general principles of trussing. These are that the framework must be rigid, which implies the use of a system of triangulated shapes, secondly that all members must be subjected to a direct stress; in practice this means that loads must be applied at the apices of the triangles and thirdly that pressures must be applied only in a vertical direction at the points of support, see the three trussed partitions illustrated on Figure 62 at "A", "B" and "C". These principles were well understood in the 17th, 18th and 19th centuries so that in the same way as previously discussed with roof trusses, it can usually be assumed that the original design of the truss was adequate. Unfortunately such features usually occur in just those buildings which by their very size have tended to become a little obsolete for the purpose for which they were originally built. In subsequent alteration and adaption for different purposes a frequent necessity is the formation of new door openings and to many of those carrying out alterations in the past the cutting of a strut in a trussed partition has seemed to be of minor importance. Even the occupants of the original buildings were not averse to making holes in the tie-beams to suspend chandeliers thereby dangerously weakening the beams. The result of such cutting or piercing will be sagging ceilings and floors and cracks in the plasterwork or splits in the panelling of the partitions. Damage of this sort, where larger rooms occur below smaller rooms, might well give reason to suspect some tampering with a structural member in one of the many ways in which this can be done. A careful consideration of the floor plans of a building, coupled with the opening of the floor adjacent to the partition, should provide information as to whether the partition is likely to be trussed. There is seldom any need to strip its plastered or panelled faces to ascertain this point, but it may be necessary to do this to affect the proper repairs.

The repairs to the framework of a trussed partition are dependent on the degree of damage, but it will seldom be necessary to renew a whole partition, although the need for this cannot be ruled out in the case of a cut brace and the need to retain the door opening which has resulted in the cutting. More often than not, the procedure will follow that already described for the repair of roof trusses and much use can be made of plating and flitching to restore both members and joints to their proper function.

We have now completed consideration of timber in relation to its use in simple framed construction and its more complicated use in framed trusses for walls, pitched roofs and partitions. Although framing occurs in other items of building construction in timber, these are more to cope with special cases where a departure from the general circumstances occur, for example the trimming in floors around openings. There remains therefore the simple use of timber in traditional floors and flat roofs, where it is used pure and simply as a beam, subject to a bending stress, for which purpose it has proved eminently suitable for hundreds of years and continues to be so in domestic construction.

TIMBER FLOORS, FLAT ROOFS AND STAIRCASES

In considering repairs to timber floors it is appropriate to divide them into the two categories, hollow floors at approximately ground level and suspended floors above ground level, the latter category also including flat roofs, the basic construction being the same. For obvious reasons the types of defects arising are different and the techniques of repair require methods appropriate to the different conditions.

Suspended Timber Floors at Approximately Ground Level

Problems arising with hollow timber floors at approximately the level of the ground outside are inevitably bound up with those of dampness and ventilation. Students of building construction will be aware of the principles to be followed in new building to prevent the incidence of rot in hollow ground floors but may not be aware that these principles have really only been followed during this century by the majority of builders and even then site difficulties have sometimes meant that short cuts have been necessary, leaving the floor at risk. Much estate building before the turn of this century took little notice of the principles which although known to architects tended to be ignored by the estate developers and the builders of the time. The lack of requirements for site concrete below buildings and damp proof courses, coupled with ignorance, has meant that many wood floors, particularly in basements have been prone to trouble from the day they were constructed.

A lack of site concrete and damp proofing, inadequate ventilation and a defective floor at basement level usually leaves little alternative but the removal of the wood floor and its replacement with a solid floor, properly damp proofed. This is the most economical method of dealing with a basement and usually a suitable floor finish can be found from among the many available. These include wood boards on a system of battens and counter battens, well treated with preservative, always provided that adequate ventilation can be provided to the battens by grilles to the external air or skirting grilles and that the concrete below is thoroughly dry and itself properly damp-proofed. Very often the height of the rooms internally and the relative level of the ground outside prevent a basement from being dealt with in any other manner than that already described. If, however, circumstances are satisfactory, there is no reason why a hollow wood floor should not be replaced. Clearly, however, the removal of the old floor, the laying of hardcore, concrete, damp-proofing, sleeper walls and the laying of joists and boards will be much more expensive than a solid floor replacement and it is not thought that many clients would wish to incur this additional expense, except in abnormal circumstances, in respect of basement accommodation. In the case of ground floor principal rooms in the absence of a basement, it might well be different and the merits and disadvantages of a solid floor as against a hollow floor might well be weighed up carefully in respect of an older property before a decision is taken. Although much of the criticism against solid floors is based on poor forms of finish and construction used in the past, in particular those adopted without a thermal barrier, it is a fact that many occupants prefer a hollow timber floor. A client is not likely to be pleased with his surveyor if he dislikes his new solid floor and subsequently realises that he could have had a hollow floor as before at only a little extra cost. He might well have been prepared to pay that extra cost if the merits of both types had been discussed and he had been given the opportunity to decide.

If a hollow floor is not in such condition as to require total replacement, it is probable that such defects as exist are essentially due to timber being in contact with damp brickwork or masonry and a lack of proper ventilation. Much can be done to alleviate these conditions and thus extend the life of the floor and in maintenance work this may be necessary until such times as a proper damp-proofing and modernisation programme can be undertaken. One of the main troubles is that the ends of joists or wallplates are set on damp brickwork and eventually rot away, causing the floor to sag, as illustrated at "A" on Figure 49, in connection with defective foundations. Pockets of stagnant air very often occur in just such places as corners where timbers are built in and as a result an outbreak of dry rot develops. Often, in addition, there are sections of floor which are totally unventilated in cases where a portion of the ground floor in the house, for example a kitchen, already has a solid floor. In these circumstances, apart from the full treatment for any dry rot that may exist, defective timber has to be removed and reinstated with new treated timbers, but there is absolutely no use in putting them back without isolating them from damp brickwork by the use of damp-proof material, such as bitumen felt. This is satisfactory for wallplates which can rest upon the felt in fairly open ventilated positions on sleeper walls but is not very satisfactory for the ends of timbers built into walls. Far better is to cut the ends of timbers off and support them on newly built sleeper walls set back from the original wall face and constructed on the proper principles in honey-comb fashion, more or less as shown adjacent to the wall at "B" on Figure 49. This work must be carried out in conjunction with improvements in the sub-floor ventilation and various typical difficulties in this regard together with suggested improvements are shown on Figure 62 at "D", "E", "F" and "G".

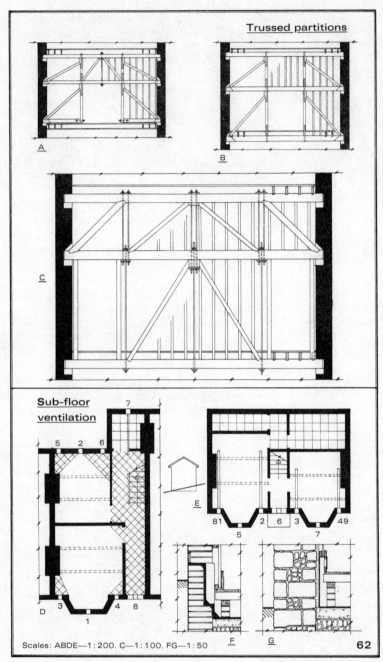

Trussed partitions

A

B

C

Sub-floor ventilation

D

E

F

G

Scales: ABDE—1:200. C—1:100. FG—1:50

62

Figure 62

Trussed Partitions

Partitions dividing up space above large ground or first floor reception rooms in many 18th- and 19th-century properties are very often in the form of deep beams relying only on structural walls at their ends for support. The design of such partitions varied widely according to the height, span and the need for door openings. Early versions relied solely on timber but in later designs some of the tensional members were sometimes in the form of iron or steel rods. Such partitions could also usefully be designed to carry floors above and below.

If the partition is parallel to floor joists above and below, it can be of relatively simple design, rather similar to that shown on Figure 63, but if at right-angles to the joists and requiring a central opening as at A then an intertie is necessary, the construction of the partition below the intertie being suspended therefrom. If a basically similar layout as to the door opening is required but in addition the partition is needed to support both the floor above and the one below, then the arrangement at B would be found suitable. Joints and straps similar to those required for the early forms of roof truss are used.

In a case where door openings are needed at both ends of the partition, the arrangement of the frame might be as shown on the drawing at C to larger scale, where it will be noted that much use is made of long bolts in lieu of timber vertical tension members. In both B and C it would be necessary for the lower sill member to show as a beam on the ceiling of the room below. If no door openings were required then, of course, the sill could be above floor level and the joists could be suspended from the sill by straps or hangers. The sill is then very vulnerable to subsequent cutting along with a brace as well if, later in the life of the building, it is found necessary to form a new door opening.

Sub Floor Ventilation

Most terrace houses built before 1920 were based on the idea of a main building with a subsidiary back addition at ground floor level, which usually contained a scullery with laundry facilities and consequently a solid floor. Such a house is shown in plan at D. Ground floor reception rooms with wood floors were ventilated in a rudimentary way with seldom more than one air brick in the front wall (in this example in the front of the bay marked 1) and one in the rear wall (2). Even with honeycomb construction for the sleeper walls (shown dotted) and the lower sections of the main partitions (shown solid), substantial areas of the floor would be at risk through lack of adequate ventilation (at least those areas shown cross hatched). Conditions can easily be improved below the main rooms by the addition of further air bricks at 3 and 4 in the front wall and 5 and 6 in the rear wall. The area of flooring in the entrance hall and by the foot

363

of the staircase, however, is more difficult to deal with and only two possibilities are available. The most commonly adopted remedy, since very often the original wooden floor is rotten, consists of the replacement of the existing hollow floor with one of solid construction. If, however, a new floor is to be laid in the back addition (not unusual as part of an improvement scheme) the opportunity will arise to lay a pipe within the depth of a new solid floor so as to bring ventilation to the rear of the staircase section from a new air brick in the rear wall of the back addition, marked 7 on the drawing. In combination with another new air brick below the main entrance step, 8, adequate through ventilation can now be provided to the whole of the ground floor section of the main building.

Through ventilation to the underside of the ground floor of a house built into the side of a hill can prove to be virtually impossible to achieve, particularly if the ground at the sides of the house is also well above floor level as envisaged at E. A solution might lie in providing pipes to duct air from new air bricks, marked 1 2 3 and 4, in the front wall to the rear section of the flooring. It should be remembered that it is the movement of air over the face of the air brick that sets up currents within the floor space, so that while air is being drawn out through the pipes in this example replacement air is being drawn in through the remaining air bricks on the front wall, marked 5 6 and 7. Close examination of the floor plan would suggest that additional air bricks alongside those connected to the pipes at points 8 and 9 would be advantageous to deal with any stagnant air in the corners.

When the sub-floor space is a little below the external ground level air can normally be ducted down, as shown at F in section, from an air brick set at the normal level. If cutting openings for air bricks through heavy thick masonry walls is too daunting, a palliative may lie in the provision of skirting ventilators around the perimeter of the room provided a suitable waterproof treatment is applied to the surface of the site concrete and to the interior face of external walls below floor level as shown at G. The same ventilator grilles might usefully ventilate a cavity behind the wall lining if the incidence of rising damp is not too severe; treated timber is used and the lining is fixed to battens on counter battens. As the method is a palliative only, there is a risk of failure and accordingly the building owner would be entitled to a full explanation of the implications.

On completion of any work to improve sub-floor ventilation, the simple test of holding a lighted match against the air vent will quickly demonstrate whether any air is being drawn in, always provided that the day chosen for the test is not entirely still.

Suspended Timber Upper Floors

With suspended upper floors, the principal defects are sagging and excessive vibration. Before anything can be done by way of repair it is necessary to ascertain the cause of the trouble. Sagging and settlement can take various forms in a floor. It can amount to a tilt in one direction or another and may be due to an unequal settlement in the supporting walls or partitions, there being nothing wrong with the floor itself. It can be produced by an overloading of the floor in excess of its original design limits, either by heavy furniture over a period or the addition of a partition without proper regard to its independent support. Sometimes an intermediate support which the floor had at one time has been removed, for example where two rooms are thrown into one. The original timbers may have been too light for the span in the first place. If the floor has been overloaded then settlement will result, but even if not the floor will probably vibrate excessively. Rot or decay at the ends of the joists will weaken their bearing and also induce vibration, leading possibly to ultimate collapse.

It follows that if the cause of the defect is other than in the floor itself, then steps must be taken to deal with the other matter first before consideration can be given to the floor. As for all investigations into structural matters, it is usually necessary to follow a process of elimination in order to correctly assess the precise cause of the failure. In regard to floors, it is usually a simple matter to take up a few boards and to check whether the joist size and spacing are adequate for the span involved. This can be done within certain limitations using the rule of thumb of span over two plus two giving the depth if the timbers are of 2-inch (51mm) scantling and at 15-inch (381mm) centres or by comparing the spacing and timber size with the table provided in the Building Regulations 1972, again within set limitations, or alternatively, if necessary, by calculation. Most floors can be checked by one or other of the two former methods quite simply, but there are occasions when resort to calculations is necessary. The limitations on the use of the rule of thumb and the tables are set out fully in the section of this Chapter dealing with calculations and reference should be made to this section for a consideration of all the factors that may be involved. Even so it is always possible to produce an answer one way or the other whichever method has to be adopted.

Once the floor construction has been checked by one or other of these available methods, a decision on further investigation can be taken. If the general construction is satisfactory then the cause of the defect must be sought elsewhere. For the next stage, it is usually necessary to open up at the ends of the joists so as to examine the bearing and ascertain conditions at that point. Decayed or displaced ends of joists will cause sagging in a floor, as will a reduction in the bearing of a joist on the wall which might be caused by the wall bulging outwards and partially depriving the joist of its support. Decay which extends only to the parts of the joists built into the wall can be cut off if only due to wet rot and the ends of the joists picked up on metal hangers or by some other method as shown on Figure 63 at "A" to "D". If due to dry rot, it will of course be necessary to cut back much further and bolt on new ends, as shown at "E" on Figure 63 or provide other forms of support for the shortened joists as shown at "F" and "G", corbels or metal hangers being used for support from walls. If the bearing has become inadequate, then it will be necessary to provide additional support parallel to the wall in the same way as if the ends had been cut off. There are various ways in which this can be done, as already indicated on Figure 63 at "A" to "D". Bearing in mind that the British Standard Code of Practice suggests that all joists should have a bearing of at least $1\frac{1}{2}$ inches (38mm) except on brickwork and masonry when it should be 3 inches (76mm) it is clear that the method shown at "D" of dovetail housing the joists to a plate fixed to the wall is not as sound as the remainder shown, but on the other hand it provides a secret fixing and helps to restrain a wall from further movement. The use of metal hangers would overcome this objection and would be cheaper, but it is not always practical to use hangers.

If the disturbance to support occurs at a partition and is due to the partition settling, the position may be complicated by the fact that the trouble is general throughout a number of floors and rooms on either side of the partition. This is a defect frequently arising in the tall narrow-fronted Georgian and Victorian terrace houses, where floors are carried on front and rear walls and a partition parallel to the frontage. Often the only way to prevent further movement is to substitute a substantial beam spanning from party wall to party wall at ground floor level. It may be possible to jack the partition above the beam, and correspondingly the floors, partially back to their original positions. This would probably only be possible if large-scale repairs were being carried out, because as a result of jacking there is almost a certainty of doing damage to the roof and possibly elsewhere in the building. More often the beam will be put in to prevent further movement, leaving the existing floors to be firred up level as required.

If a floor is sagging due to overloading from a new partition, the method of overcoming the trouble will depend on whether the partition is parallel or at right-angles to the joists of the floor and on the partition's weight. Usually, if heavy partitions are installed care is taken to arrange for support, but the temptation to put a timber framed and plasterboard partition on an existing floor without proper support is often great. A heavy partition, irrespective of whether parallel or at right-angles to the joists, would need a beam to support it. If a beam has not been provided for the reason that it was desired not to disturb the appearance from below, it might be possible to arrange for a steel beam to be formed within the depth of the floor as shown on Figure 62 at "H" or at "G" if a small steel joist was used, but in the case where this method is used to support a partition already built, the weight of the partition would have to be carried on needling and dead shoring while the work was carried out. Where the partition runs parallel to the joists, the beam can usually be inserted from below and might well consist only of doubling or trebling the existing joist.

If the floor construction was too light from the very first instance, or over the years the timber has lost some of its strength or has been weakened by cutting, often the case with older houses which have subsequently had gas and electrical installations added, there are three basic alternative strengthening measures which can be adopted depending on circumstances. In a general scheme of alteration and improvement, it might be possible to arrange for a new partition to provide additional support. Arranged from below this could be of either timber or of partition blocks depending on the circumstances, provided it was gently but firmly wedged to the underside of the joists. Working solely from above it is possible to support the floor from a trussed partition formed across the room itself where the floor is defective, as illustrated on Figure 63 from "J" to "M". There are probably few cases, however, where the formation of new partitions for this purpose is really convenient so resort must normally be had to one or other of the remaining two methods. The first of these, utilising new beams, involves the provision of a beam at mid-span again which can be gently wedged up to the floor and which can either be exposed below the ceiling of the room below or arranged secretly within the thickness of the floor itself as shown at "H" and "G" on Figure 63. Even this may not always be practical to arrange, as often a beam at right-angles to the joists at mid-span ends in the centre of a chimney breast where there would be no adequate support from thin brickwork. Still utilising beams, another solution might consist of two smaller beams at approximately $\frac{1}{3}$ and $\frac{2}{3}$ of the span. The final alternative consists of taking up the boards and laying new joists in the spaces between the old. By this method on relaying the boards a level floor can be obtained and if the sag in the ceiling below can be tolerated there is no need to disturb this. The extra strength can be obtained by using joists of thicker scantling than previously used so as to avoid increasing the overall thickness of the floor, all as shown at "I" on Figure 63.

Undue vibration in suspended timber upper floors is often associated with sagging to some degree and, of course, the methods previously suggested for dealing with the deflection will cure the vibration. However, undue vibration often occurs in houses of cheaper construction on account of the omission of strutting within the depth of the floor. Unrestrained joists tend to wind and buckle and to overcome this problem the 1952 edition of British Standard Code of Practice C.P.112 recommended that any joists having a depth exceeding three times the breadth and/or a length exceeding fifty times the breadth should be laterally restrained and that the distance between such restraints should not exceed fifty times the breadth. For example 8 by 2 inch (204 by 51mm) joists spanning 12 feet (3·66m) although satisfactory from the structural point of view and probably so for a somewhat greater span than this, depending on the loading and spacing, should have one line of strutting. This can consist of 2 by 1½ inch (51 by 38mm) timbers nailed through a saw cut at the end or, better still in new or replacement work, of solid strutting of 1 inch (25mm) boards with a 1 inch (25mm) wrought iron bolt alongside. In Scotland "dwangs" the same size as the joists are normally used. In adding herring bone strutting or solid strutting to existing floors the wedging at the ends to the walls must not be forgotten, otherwise the operation is valueless. The 1967 edition of Code of Practice C.P.112 also contains recommendations in regard to lateral support, but the emphasis is less on its provision than on the degree of resistance to winding and buckling to be expected if the ratio of depth to breadth of joists exceeds certain limits. The whole range of lateral support is considered besides strutting and this includes the type of fixing at the ends and whether additional rigidity is provided by boarding or sheathing secured to the upper compression edge. Since there is no mention of length or span, the recommendations are not so adaptable for use in the consideration of old floors and flat roofs and accordingly the advice contained in the earlier edition is to be preferred in this respect.

Sagging ceilings at top floor level are also not uncommon in cheaper construction due to inadequacy in the ceiling joists. Often very light timbers are expected to span substantial distances and support a ceiling, with little regard to whether they are large enough for the purpose. This is particularly so if there is no question of the ceiling joists forming a tie to the roof construction as is the case with the double lean-to roof of 18th- and 19th-century properties as shown on Figure 56. If the roof structure is sound and loading light, the ceiling joists can often be given additional support by the provision of hangers at mid-span fixed to a sturdy member of the roof, such as a purlin or the ridge or, alternatively, to a batten fixed to a number of rafters to distribute the load. Alternatively it is usually possible to introduce a bearer spanning from an external wall to a load bearing partition and to fix the ceiling joists to this.

Timber Flat Roofs

Defects in the timber of flat roofs are dealt with in the same way as described previously for floors but of course the ease of access for repairs will depend to a great extent on whether the covering is being renewed at the same time. If not then the work must be carried out from below which is somewhat restrictive to say the least on the methods which can be adopted.

Trimmed openings in Floors and Flat Roofs

Within floors there are usually various constructional features in older properties involving trimming for openings, both for stair-cases and to support hearths. These are very often not constructed ideally and many instances can be seen of cracked ceilings following the line of hearths in the rooms above, where timbers have proved to be inadequate to support the weight or joints have been badly formed and have burst apart. If the condition is not too serious, further movement can usually be arrested by strapping the joints. On the other hand joints can be reformed in new timber, the tim-bers being jacked back into position at the same time. It is highly unlikely however that this operation could be accomplished with-out the need for remaking the ceiling below. At the present time when much effort is expended in old houses removing fireplaces and surrounds, there is of course no reason to retain hearths, so that more often than not it would be as well to remove them if trouble is being experienced and to fill in the opening with new timber.

Staircases

With openings for staircases of course one can hardly dispense with them in the same way as with redundant hearths and fill in the opening. Notwithstanding this however, the same forms of repair for the trimming to the openings can be carried out, if the repair is concerned with a simple straight flight in a two-storey house. Jack-ing up will also restore the staircase to its former position, when repairs can then be carried out to ensure that it is sound. More often

Repairs to timber floors, flat roofs and staircases

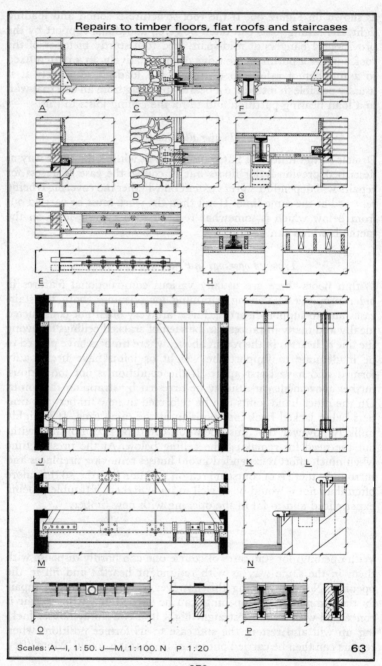

Scales: A—I, 1:50. J—M, 1:100. N P 1:20

63

Figure 63

Repairs to Suspended Timber Floors, Flat Roofs etc. and Staircases

Timber built into external walls at upper floor and flat roof levels is at risk in regard to dry or wet rot should pointing be totally defective, pipes or flat roofs leak or other defects allow water to penetrate to poorly ventilated spaces. The cutting off of the rotted ends of joists built into walls is therefore not an uncommon repair and means of suspending the joists clear of the wall may have to be devised. If it is merely those portions actually built in that have to be removed, for example because of wet rot, then in respect of brick walls a simple solution such as shown at A or B can be adopted. In building up the pockets a stout galvanised hanger can be built in and wedged into position as at A, or alternatively an iron corbel built in at intervals, as at B, to support a new wallplate to carry the notched ends of the joists. Nailing of joists to hangers and wallplate maintain the joists' function of restraining lateral movement in the brickwork. These methods are not so appropriate for masonry walls but support at intervals for a metal angle as at C, or a timber plate as at D, can be provided by casting rag-bolts into concrete blocks and building the blocks into the masonry. In C, the cut ends of the joists merely rest on the angle and it is necessary to provide lateral stiffeners wedged between the joists as shown. In D, the joists are housed into the plate but unless the housing is in dovetail form neither of the methods shown at C and D will provide any lateral restraint to the walling. This however may not be so important in regard to masonry walling in view of its greater thickness.

If more than the mere ends of joists have to be removed then support to the remainder in an entirely different form is required. New sections can be bolted on with either shear plate or split ring connectors as at E shown in plan as well as in section. The new ends may be either in single form or in a double form as shown dotted according to the loading and the need to make a rigid connection. Bolts should be staggered and the lap should be at least six times the depth of the joist. The new lengths at E are shown carried on hangers and the original pockets in the brickwork built up. Another method shown in two forms at F and G, employs a steel beam (although it could be of timber, or concrete, of course if required) to carry the sound ends of the old joists and one end of the new joists. At F, the beam is simply placed below joist level and adequate existing support assumed at each end of the beam. New and old sections of joists should be lapped and nailed together above the beam as shown. At G, the ends of the sections are cut and carried on bearers attached to the web of the beam so that this is less obtrusive from below. Assumed on this drawing is the need to form a pier to provide support to the steel beam, perhaps from a thin brick partition not strong enough in itself for the additional point load. To maintain the tie, each end of both existing and new joists require spiking to the bearers. While H is intended to show how an existing weak floor could be strengthened in an unsightly manner, always provided loads were sufficiently light, by the incorporation of a heavy T-bar or two angles (as shown) bolted together back to back, it could also if circumstances were suitable be a substitute detail for G. Parallel flange bars or angles should be used to provide an even bearing and as for detail C stiffeners are required for wedging tightly between the joists to hold them in position. If for strengthening an existing floor, a metal strap should be used to improve the joists for restraint purposes since the cutting to insert the new support will be a weakening factor in this respect.

One of the simplest ways to strengthen an existing floor available in some circumstances and one which does not involve disturbing the ceiling of the room below is shown at I. This consists merely of providing new joists in the spaces between the existing joists but of larger breadth than the original so that they can be of lesser depth but still be amply sufficient to carry the loading. The old ceiling, provided it is securely fixed, can remain attached to the old joists while the new joists carry the flooring and the imposed load at the same level as the original. The original joists at I are shown deflected at mid-span.

The trussed partition at J, in elevation and at K in cross section, in appropriate circumstances, could also provide support to a floor from above without the need to disturb the ceiling below. This particular partition could also support a floor above by wedging up (not shown), as necessary, to the underside of each joist, ceiling plaster being cut away as required on both sides of the partition. Joists of the sagging floor below are secured by metal hangers to the lower sill. The partition at J and K is of traditional construction with steel rods for tension members in place of the more usual posts (as shown in A on Figure 62). The partition could also be designed in the form of a TRDA truss by a timber engineer and typical details are shown, in cross section at L and in elevation at M, of the head and sill.

The small section at N through a few treads of a staircase show replacement nosings glued to the existing treads and risers and in addition screwed to new angle blocks. Additional stiffness is provided by a new central carriage and brackets to each tread.

Mention has been made in the text of a tendency for unsupervised workmen to cut notches in timber joists thereby reducing the effective section. This can sometimes be overcome by the provision of a steel plate screwed to the top of the joist as at O. A timber weakened by severe shakes can be strengthened by simple bolting. If the timber is exposed the work can be hidden by counter sinking and pelleting as at P.

than not, however, the settlement in landings and the staircase of multi-storey Georgian and Victorian houses is of a much more complicated nature, often involved with settlement in walls and partitions and settlement and decay in supporting lower floors and posts. To restore such a staircase to sound condition and appearance involves tackling each of the possible sources of trouble, correcting defects as necessary, easing the staircase back into position by propping and then overhauling each part. Generally it is probably cheaper to take out each flight, repair it in the workshop, deal with the supports and then re-erect it. It is unlikely to be necessary to renew flights entirely, unless these have been very badly worn and ill-treated over the years.

Staircases in houses do, of course, receive over long periods of time heavy usage, particularly in the multi-storey house which has been in the occupation of a number of families. Even apart from settlement in the supports to the flights causing unequal stress on the components and thereby loosening them, time and usage alone will cause such loosening in addition to wear. Shaky treads, excessive vibration in use, creaking, loose newel posts and balustrades are all symptoms of heavy usage. Many of the staircases on houses forming part of an estate were often skimped at the time of building, as this is one feature where the effects of such skimping would take some time to become apparent, even more so where soffits were plastered. In these cases it is necessary to strip plaster before much can be done, an operation which does unfortunately add to the cost. Much however can be done, fairly simply, by checking, driving home or renewing wedges which may have worked loose or become broken and where treads and risers are housed into the strings. Strengthening in most cases can be done by providing angle blocks, if none exist, or adding more if they have been sparsely provided. They should be employed both along the length of the treads and risers and also at the ends, to make a three-way connection between treads, risers and strings. In repair work they should be screwed, where possible, as well as glued. In extreme cases, where a staircase is very weak it would be advantageous to add a carriage and this would be an essential in any staircase flight over 3 feet (914mm) wide.

Worn nosings are dealt with by cutting out for a width of about 3 inches (76mm) over the whole length of the tread and piecing in new timber, as shown at "N" on Figure 63, well glued to the old wood and the riser and screwed to a substantial angle block below. Broken balusters can be repaired by dowelling and strengthened by the addition of metal brackets. Further comments of a general nature on staircases will be found in Chapter 9.

Calculations for Joists and Beams in Floors of Domestic Construction

Note to the Calculations in Metric Units

The change over to the metric system where it affects the calculations envisaged for timber floors introduces one or two complications which although familiar to engineers may not be so well known to surveyors, architects and builders. In Britain and on the continent until comparatively recently force was usually expressed in terms of the local gravitational pull on a known mass and even more commonly and loosely referred to by weight, for example pounds per square foot. Since gravity varied by about 0·5 per cent over the earth's surface the term "pound weight" and "kilogramme weight" when meant as a force could only be used for work not involving a high degree of accuracy, as for example that with which we are concerned here. To overcome this problem for work of a fine degree of accuracy both the pound force and the kilogramme force were defined in terms of the international standard gravity basis. Even so the confusion of units of mass with units of force continued, for example the Building Regulations 1965 and the London Building (Constructional) Amending By-Laws of 1964 continued to refer to "pounds per square foot" for floor loading when in fact it would have been more correct to refer to "pound force per square foot" and these documents thus continued a common practice. To overcome the confusion and to bring the metric system, evolved at the time of the French Revolution, up to modern requirements the Eleventh General Conference of Weights and Measures in 1960 evolved the Systeme International d'Unites (SI) (International System of Units) which was subsequently endorsed by the International Organisation for Standardisation. The symbol for this system of units is "SI" and it is to this system that the change over to metric is being made.

The SI units separate mass from force entirely and whereas the primary unit for mass is the kilogramme (kg) the supplementary unit for force is the newton (N), which is defined as that force which, applied to a mass of 1 kilogramme, gives it an acceleration of 1 metre per second per second (kg m/s^2). The SI system provides for standard symbols representing the primary units and their supplementary and derivative units, some examples of which already being indicated in brackets above, and also standard prefixes and symbols for multiples e.g. for force

1 meganewton (MN) = 1 000 kilonewtons (kN)
1 kilonewton (kN) = 1 000 newtons (N)

It is for the reason that the SI system has been adopted that the metric equivalents of the Building Regulations 1965 and the London

Building Constructional By-Laws for example show that for floor loading in residential buildings 30 pounds per square foot is to be taken as 1·436 kilonewtons per square metre (kN/m²) and not 146·5 kilogrammes per square metre as might have been expected. The irritating point in regard to this is that to change kilogrammes to newtons the conversion factor is not 10 as one might have hoped in the metric system but 9·807, thus 146·5 kg/m²×9·807=1436·72 N/m²=1·436 kN/m². Derived units based on the newton include moment of force expressed as newton metre (Nm) and for pressure and stress the newton per square metre (N/m²) but these are self-explanatory once the main point of the introduction of the newton is appreciated. They will be encountered in these calculations however and a short list of conversion factors is appended below.

If a satisfactory change over to the SI metric system is to be achieved, it is important that the calculations are worked through from the start and thought of in metric units and that British units are not merely converted by the use of factors, useful though these may be for checking in the interim stage of the change over. Accordingly while the British unit workings are expressed in the way familiar to most surveyors, architects and builders those in metric units will follow the SI system and it will be found therefore that they can be satisfactorily related to the metric equivalents of the Building Regulations 1965 and the London Building Constructional By-Laws, together with the values given in the Building Regulations 1972.

Conversion Factors

The SI System of Units

Quantity	Unit	Symbol
Length	metre	m
Mass	kilogramme	kg
Density	kilogramme per cubic metre	kg/m³
Force	newton	N (kgm/s²)
Moment of Force	newton metre	N m
Pressure, stress	newton per square metre	N/m²

The system is exclusively decimal thus:

1 millimetre =0·001 metres
1 000 millimetres=1 metre
1 000 metres =1 kilometre

It will be noted that the decimal point continues to be used but the comma to separate large units into groups of three is abandoned and the digits of large numbers are separated by small gaps into groups of three starting from the decimal point.

Conversion of Non-SI metric units to Equivalent Values in SI Units

Force

1 kilogramme (force) (kgf)=9·806 65 N

Pressure Stress

1 kilogramme (force) per square metre (kgf/m²)=9·806 65 N/m²

Conversion of Common British Units to Equivalent Values in SI Units

Length

1 yard (yd.) =0·914 4m
1 foot (ft.) =0·304 8m
1 inch (in.) =0·025 4m=25·4mm

Area

1 square yard (yd.²) =0·836 127m²
1 square foot (ft.²) =0·092 903m²
1 square inch (in.²) =645·16mm²

Volume

1 cubic yard (yd.³) =0·764 555m³
1 cubic foot (ft.³) =0·028 317m³
1 cubic inch (in.³) =1 638·71mm³

Mass

1 ton   =1 016·05kg
1 hundredweight (cwt.) =50·812 3kg
1 pound (lb.)   =0·453 592kg

Mass per unit length

1 lb. per yard (lb./yd.) = 0·496 055kg/m
1 lb. per foot (lb./ft.) = 1·488 16kg/m
1 lb. per inch (lb./in.) =17·858kg/m

Mass per unit area

1 pound per square foot (lb./ft.²) = 4·882 43kg/m²
1 pound per square inch (lb./in.²) =703·070kg/m²

Density

1 ton per yard cube (ton/yd.³) = 1 328·94kg/m³
1 pound per foot cube (lb./ft.³) = 16·018 5kg/m³
1 pound per inch cube (lb./in.³)=27 679·9kg/m³

Force
    1 ton (force) (tonf)   =9·964 02kN=9 964·02N
    1 pound (force) (lbf) =4·448 22N
    1 ounce (force) (ozf) =0·278 014N

Force (weight) per unit length
    1 ton (force) per foot (tonf/ft.)   = 32·690 3kN/m=
                                                           32 690·3N/m
    1 pound (force) per foot (lbf/ft.) =14·593 9N/m
    1 pound (force) per inch (lbf/in.)=175·127N/m=
                                                           0·175 127N/mm

Moment of Force (torque)
    1 ton (force) foot (tonf ft.)   =3·037 03kNm
    1 pound (force) foot (lbf ft.) =1·355 82Nm
    1 pound (force) inch (lbf in.) =0·112 985Nm

Pressure, stress
    1 ton (force) per square foot (tonf/ft.^{2})   =107·252kN/m^2
    1 ton (force) per square inch (tonf/in.^{2})   =15·444 3MN/m^2
    1 pound (force) per square foot (lbf/ft.^{2}) =47·880 3N/m^2
    1 pound (force) per square inch (lbf/in.^{2})=6 894·76N/m^2

The foregoing conversion factors are taken from "Changing to the Metric System—Conversion Factors. Symbols and Definitions" Third Edition, 1969, published for the Ministry of Technology by Her Majesty's Stationery Office, price 22½p. The booklet provides a useful introduction to the International System of Units (SI), numerous definitions and many more conversion factors apart from those set out above.

It will be noted that the metric equivalents of British units, particularly those equivalents of units in the Building Regulations 1965 and the London Building (Constructional) Amending By-Laws No. 1 (1964) produce awkward figures with many digits resulting in calculations somewhat less simple than those using the British units. There is of course a strong case for rounding off metric values and indeed this has already been done in some revised British Standard Codes of Practice and in the Building Regulations 1972. Eventually the London By-Laws will be revised with appropriate rounded off figures, but until this is done the strict metric equivalents apply in London as the B.S. Codes have no legal effect. The temptation to bring to the nearest whole number or tenth unit, be what it may, in the following calculations has been resisted, not only for the above reason, but also to enable a fairly strict comparison to be made between the two sets of figures. Even so a certain amount of rounding off in British units produces anomalies in the metric lines of working so that answers are not necessarily exact equivalents when the two are compared by utilising the conversion factors.

Calculations for Joists and Beams in Floors of Domestic Construction

In the design of new dwelling houses outside the Inner London area it is quite possible in normal circumstances to specify sizes of timber joists etc. by utilising the tables set out in the Building Regulations for houses in single family occupation not exceeding three storeys in height. These tables provide economical sizes for timbers in line with modern practice and allow for the use of timbers of slightly smaller scantling than would be the case if the old rules of thumb were adopted, which provided for a higher factor of safety and wider variations in the quality of timber. If the building in question does not come within the scope of the provisions of the Building Regulations enabling the tables to be used or is within the Inner London area then subject to the ruling of the District Surveyor or Building Inspector either rules of thumb or calculations have to be adopted to determine timber sizes. Both the Building Regulations of 1965 and 1972 and the London Building (Constructional) Amending By-Laws (No. 1) 1964 make reference to British Standard Code of Practice C.P.112:1952 "The Structural Use of Timber in Buildings". The Regulations in both their 1965 and 1972 versions permit construction in accordance with the Code to be "deemed to satisfy" construction, but the London By-Laws take precedence over the Code, reference to it being merely contained in the Explanatory Memorandum, to the effect that design should not be inferior to the standards of the Code. Unfortunately, this Code of Practice is essentially of a theoretical nature and is intended primarily for the use of chartered civil or structural engineers, qualified in timber engineering and responsible for the design of timber structures. As such, although there are snippets of useful information, the nature of the recommendations is far beyond the scope of the average surveyor, architect or small builder who has to deal with the smaller domestic building where the employment of an engineer is hardly warranted. A more recent Code of Practice C.P.112:1967 to which reference is made in the Building Regulations 1972 has now been issued which supersedes the 1952 edition and is considerably enlarged and extended. This new edition acknowledges the need for some simpler guidance in the realm of purely practical application, but there is no suggestion when this might be forthcoming. Accordingly one is left with either one of three methods for determining sizes of timbers for new or replacement work or for checking whether sizes in existing buildings are satisfactory for the loads which they are to support. The three methods are as follows:

(1) *By using the tables in the Building Regulations 1965 or 1972.* These provide for a varying number of nominal joist sizes ranging from 3 by 1½ inches (76 by 38mm) to 9 by 3 inches (225 by 76mm) at varying centres and for various dead loads, but are restricted for use to single family domestic construction not exceeding three floors in height and to timber with a bending stress of not less than 800 lbs. per square inch (5·516N/mm²). The imposed loading on a floor is accordingly limited to 30 lbs. per square foot (1·436kN/m²), so that for a building constructed as a dwelling house but used for any other purpose they are of no value and also would not be so if, for example, the timber was either of an inferior quality or if, for checking existing work, the sizes of timbers did not appear in the tables.

(2) *By using the rules of thumb.* These by their nature have similar but rather more serious disadvantages than the tables in the Building Regulations. Again they presume purely domestic loading and an average quality of timber but they have also always assumed a standard width of timber, namely 2 inches (51mm) and a standard spacing of floor joists at 15 inches (381mm). In checking whether floor construction is adequate or not there is usually one factor which does not comply thereby rendering the rules valueless. For new or replacement work similar circumstances often apply and in any event adoption of these old rules tends to be somewhat wasteful of timber nowadays.

(3) *By the use of Calculations.* The objections to the above two methods can be overcome by the use of simple calculations where any variation or unusual circumstances can be accommodated as will be seen from the following examples. On the other hand the use of calculations in regard to old work requires care, since conditions have to be accepted as they are found and not as they might be in new work. Generally, however, the bulk of repair work and the checking of the strength of old floors can be carried out without the use of calculations by the use of the tables and the empirical rules of thumb. These are perfectly satisfactory given commonly used sizes of timber provided the floor joists have not been unduly cut by notching, the bearing is satisfactory, and the timber is of reasonable quality. There is no reason to use calculations if the floor can be adequately checked by other means. On those occasions however where, as we have seen, this is not possible, it may be necessary to use them. However, calculations to a fine degree are inappropriate in dealing with older buildings when so many other factors have to

be taken into account, such as age, quality and ill-usage for example. A designer for new work will be thinking in terms of new material whose strength is known in advance and of workmanship which will be satisfactory. The surveyor dealing with old buildings will know that it is necessary to temper the arithmetical work with consideration of the practical conditions. This can best be illustrated by posing an often encountered problem and dealing with the steps necessary to solve it. By this example an existing floor will be checked for strength, timber sizes found for a new floor of adequate strength and as an alternative to entire renewal the size of a timber beam to support the existing floor calculated.

In the centres of our towns and cities there are many fine old dwelling houses which are now used for other purposes. Many of these form satisfactory offices for the smaller firm or organisation yet the buildings were never designed for this purpose. The surveyor may be asked if the floors are satisfactory for the new purpose, particularly nowadays when a fair amount of equipment is used even in the smaller office. Before giving an opinion the surveyor will need to inspect to ascertain the existing circumstances and condition. For example, by taking up some floorboards he will ascertain whether the bearing of the joists is satisfactory. If it is, the size can be noted which for this example will be 9 by 2 inches (229 by 51mm) softwood at 15-inch (381mm) centres, spanning 14 feet (4·271m) between the centres of the bearings and carrying nominal 1-inch (25mm) boarding and a lath and plaster ceiling, see "A" and "B" on Figure 64. The joists have been notched near the ends for a gas installation at some time in the past, but the work has been carried out within the limits laid down by the Code of Practice C.P.112: 1967 (see page 327) and the timber is of reasonable quality.

It will be noted that if the building is to continue in use for residential purposes, the floor could be checked quite easily once the dead load of flooring and ceiling had been calculated both by reference to the tables in the Building Regulations 1965 and 1972 and by rule of thumb. By either method the floor would be satisfactory but the factor preventing the adoption of either of these methods is the change of use from residential to office purposes involving an increase in the floor loading. It is interesting to see the effect of this change of use on the answer but a number of other factors necessitating calculations could have arisen and in explaining the stages of the calculations the possible alternative factors will be examined.

The calculations necessary to check whether an existing floor is strong enough for its purpose can be divided up into three separate stages. Stage 1 consists of estimating the actual load or weight of the floor together with the loads the floor itself is expected to carry. Stage 2 consists of determining the internal forces set up by the total expected load on the member concerned, i.e. a joist in the floor, while Stage 3 checks whether the member is strong enough to carry the load and the forces set up by the load.

Stage 1.

In regard to Stage 1 it will readily be appreciated that the floor is made up of a series of joists which are connected together by the floorboards and accordingly act as a unit. Notwithstanding this fact, the total strength is governed by the strength of the individual joists and it is to the load carried by a single joist that attention must be directed. Similarly it will be appreciated that there is no question of a heavy load acting at a specified distance from one end along the joist, the joists in the floors under consideration here are uniformly loaded, i.e. the total load is evenly distributed along the length of the joist, and initially it is necessary to ascertain the load per unit length, whether it be in pounds per foot run for British units (lb./ft.) or newtons per metre run (N/m) for metric units.

Now the loading on any timber joist or beam is made up of two parts, the live or imposed load and the dead load or permanent load. The live load comprises the allowance which must be made depending on the use to which the floor is to be put. These allowances are set out in the Building Regulations 1965 Schedule 5 page 110, in the Building Regulations 1972 on page 29 where reference is also made to British Standard Code of Practice C.P.3, Chapter V, Part 1, 1967 in which figures for various uses are rounded up in metric terms and in the London Building (Constructional) Amending By-Laws No. 1 1964, Table I, page 9. Although the wording is slightly different, the values are generally much the same and accordingly for more general use, the relevant figures which might conceivably by applicable to domestic type construction in its broadest sense are set out overleaf taken from the Building Regulations 1965. The higher figures used in C.P.3, Chapter V, Part 1, 1967, which would be applicable under the Building Regulations 1972 are shown in brackets.

Those practising in the Inner London area should consult the London By-Laws for the precise wording of the requirements for that area. It should be emphasised that the figures overleaf are only an extract from Table 2 to Schedule 5 of the Building Regulations 1965, but it is considered that the figures should be sufficient for those dealing with buildings of the dwelling house type, even when not still used for residential purposes. It should perhaps be pointed out, however, that office floors used for storage or filing purposes require a minimum imposed floor load of 100 lb./ft.² (4·79 or as now 5·0 kN/m²) and bookstores and stationery stores 200 lb./ft.² (9·58 kN/m² or as expressed in C.P.3, Chapter V, Part 1, 1967, 4·0kN/m² for each metre height of storage). It is not always appreciated that paper is so extraordinarily heavy.

Minimum Imposed Floor Loads

	Floor		Minimum Imposed Load	
Class	Description	Pounds per square foot of floor area (lb./ft.²)	Kilonewtons per square metre of floor area (kN/m²)	
1	Floors of houses having not more than three storeys and the upper floors of maisonettes, in either case designed for occupation by one family	30	1·44 (1·5)	
2	Floors (other than those described in Class 1) of buildings or parts of buildings used for residential purposes including tenements; floors of hospital wards, bedrooms and private sitting rooms in hotels and dormitories	40	1·92 (2·0)	
3	Floors of offices above the entrance floor; floors of light workrooms without storage; floors used for the parking of vehicles not exceeding 2½ tons (2540·1 kg) gross weight	50	2·39 (2·5)	
4	Floors of banking halls; office entrance floors and office floors below entrance floor and floors of classrooms in schools	60	2·87 (3·0)	

For the example we are dealing with, it will be seen that the allowance for the live load must be taken at 50 lb./ft.² or 2·39kN/m², as an office floor above the entrance floor. In British units, the area of floor being carried by a foot length of joist is 1¼ square feet (the joists being at 15 inch centres) so that the imposed load on the joist in this case is taken at 50 by $1\frac{1}{4}$ equalling $62\frac{1}{2}$ lbs. In metric units, the area of floor being carried by a metre length of joist is 0·381 square metres (the joists being at 381mm centres), so that the imposed load is 2·39 by 0·381 equalling 0·911 kilonewtons (911N).

The dead load comprises the weight of the floorboards and the ceiling below of lath and plaster, together with the weight of the joist itself. Considering that the proportion which the dead load bears to the live load is seldom high in the type of work which is being considered, it is not critical that this figure of dead load should be absolutely accurate. On the other hand, it should be sufficiently accurate to render the calculations valid and, accordingly, although rounding off to the nearest pound or ten newtons is permissible, reference must usually be made to tables of weights of materials for the necessary degree of accurate information. British Standard 648: 1964 "Schedule of Weights of Building Materials" gives some help in arriving at a figure for a dead load in certain cases, but it will often be found rather inadequate for many of the examples encountered in practice. It is hoped that for the purpose of the type of calculations envisaged here the schedules set out in the Appendix will be found of more practical value. Even the Appendix, however, cannot lay claim to being exhaustive. From the Appendix it will be seen that the basic figures for dead loading to be applied in this instance are:

In British units:
1 inch nominal softwood flooring weighs 2·3 lb./ft.²
say 3 lb./ft.²
$\frac{3}{4}$ inch lath and plaster weighs 8·8 lb./ft.²
say 9·0 lb./ft.²

In metric units:
25mm nominal softwood flooring weighs 11·2kg/m²
say 12·0kg/m²
19mm lath and plaster weighs 42·9kg/m²
say 43kg/m²

The figures for flooring can be checked quite easily, provided one remembers that most softwoods weigh between 25 and 40 lb./ft.³ Taking a fairly high mean at 36 lb./ft.³, it follows that a 1 inch layer would weigh about 3 lb./ft.² making no allowance for the reduction to finished thickness. Should the flooring be found to be $1\frac{1}{4}$ inch oak the weight could be calculated per square foot in a similar manner. Taking this hardwood at 48 lb./ft.³ the weight would be 5 lb./ft.² as compared with 4·3 lb./ft.² in the Appendix, which allows for the reduction from nominal size to finished thickness.

Similarly for metric units, softwoods weigh between 400 and 640kg/m³. Taking a mean at 575kg/m³ it would be sufficiently accurate for our purposes to take a 25mm layer at 14kg/m². If the flooring was of 31mm oak, the weight could be calculated taking this hardwood at 770kg/m³ at say 24kg/m². With the SI metric system of units kilogramme weight forces have to be converted into the newton unit before the next stage thus:

25mm softwood flooring $=12$kg/m² $\times 9 \cdot 807 = 117$N/m²
19mm lath and plaster $\ =43$kg/m² $\times 9 \cdot 807 = 422$N/m²

These basic figures are for the square foot or square metre and in order to arrive at the weight per unit length the values have to be adjusted since the joists are at 15 inch (381mm) centres as follows (see "C" on Figure 64):

In British units:
1 inch nominal softwood
flooring
$1 \times 1\frac{1}{4} \times 3 = 3\frac{3}{4}$ lbs.
$\frac{3}{4}$ inch lath and plaster
$1 \times 1\frac{1}{4} \times 9 = 11\frac{1}{4}$ lbs.

In metric units:
25mm nominal softwood
flooring
$1 \times 0 \cdot 381 \times 117 = 44$ newtons
19mm lath and plaster
$1 \times 0 \cdot 381 \times 422 = 161$ newtons

There remains the self weight of the joist to be taken into account before the total dead load can be ascertained:

In British units:
A 9 inch by 2 inch softwood
joist at 36 lb./ft.³ weighs
$1 \times \frac{9}{12} \times \frac{2}{12} \times 36 = 4\frac{1}{2}$ lb./ft.

In metric units:
A joist of 229mm by 51mm
in softwood at 575kg/m³
weighs $1 \times 0 \cdot 229 \times 0 \cdot 051 \times 575 = 6 \cdot 7$kg/m which converted to newtons equals
$6 \cdot 7 \times 9 \cdot 807 = 66$N/m

The total load per foot or per metre unit length of joist is therefore as follows:

		British units	Metric units
Imposed Load:		$62\frac{1}{2}$ lb./ft.	911N/m
Dead Load:			
Flooring	$3\frac{3}{4}$	44	
Ceiling	$11\frac{1}{4}$	161	
Joist	$4\frac{1}{2}$	66	
		$19\frac{1}{2}$ lb./ft.	271N/m
		82 lb./ft.	1 182N/m

and having established this figure it is now possible to move on to Stage 2 of the calculations.

Stage 2

The second stage consists of a calculation to determine the internal forces set up by the load on the member concerned, i.e. the joist in the floor, which is a beam subjected to bending. The effect of these uniformly distributed loads on the joist supported at the ends is to set up on the joist a "Bending moment" which is given by the following formula:

$$\text{Bending Moment (BM)} = \frac{wL^2}{8}$$

where w = the load, force per foot run in pounds or per metre run in newtons

L = the length of span in feet or metres

With the information already obtained the Bending Moment in this example is simply found as follows:

In British units

$$BM = \frac{82 \times 14 \times 14}{8} \text{lb. ft.}$$
$$= 2{,}009 \text{ lb. ft.}$$

In metric units

$$BM = \frac{1\ 182 \times 4 \cdot 27 \times 4 \cdot 27}{8} \text{Nm}$$
say 2 694Nm

As it is necessary subsequently to deal with "stresses" in materials and the size of the joist, it will be found convenient at this stage to convert the Bending Moment into smaller units. In Britain stresses in materials are usually given in pounds per square inch (lb./in.^{2}) and under the SI system of metric units in newtons per square millimetre (N/mm^2), so the aporopriate multipliers are 12 in British units to bring to inch units and 10^3 to bring to millimetre units thus:

In British units:
$$BM = 2{,}009 \times 12$$
$$= 24{,}108 \text{ lb. in.}$$
say 24,100 lb. in.

In metric units:
$$BM = 2\ 694 \times 10^3$$
$$= 2\ 694\ 000 \text{Nmm}$$

Stage 3

In Stage 2 we have calculated the Bending Moment produced by the loads carried on an individual joist in the floor. The purpose of the next Stage, (Stage 3), of the calculations is to make sure that the joist is capable of resisting the Bending Moment without exceeding the permissible "stresses" and "strains" for the material concerned, i.e. timber. The Bending Moment that the joist can safely resist is called the Moment of Resistance of the joist. For a simple beam of rectangular section this is given by the expression or formula:

$$MR = \frac{fbd^2}{6}$$

where f=the maximum permissible stress in the timber (lb./in.^{2} or
N/mm^2 as the case may be, as discussed in Stage 2)
b=the breadth of the joist in inches or millimetres
d=the depth of the joist in inches or millimetres

As to the maximum permissible stress in the material, this varies according to the quality of the timber under consideration, be it as found in an existing building or as may be selected from what is available for new or replacement work. British Standard Code of Practice C.P.112:1952 divides structural softwood timbers into two groups, the species in each group having similar strength characteristics even when containing the permissible gross features (knots, splits, shakes, checks, etc.) set out and to be measured, if present, in accordance with British Standard 1860: Part 1, 1959. Group 1 comprises Douglas Fir (coast) and Longleaf and Shortleaf Pitch Pine, which are permitted to be stressed to 1,000 lb./in.^{2} (6·895 N/mm^2) while Canadian Spruce, European Larch, Redwood, Whitewood and Western Hemlock are restricted to 800 lb./in.^{2} (5·516N/mm^2) for flexural and compressive stresses parallel to the grain. The 1967 edition of the Code abandons the division of timbers into two groups and instead sets out the basic stresses applicable to various structural timbers. These basic stresses are governed by the general characteristics of the species free from all visible defects. While all those timbers formerly categorised as Groups I and II in the 1952 edition are included, the range of timbers considered is extended to additional imported and home-grown softwoods not previously mentioned together with some hardwoods. Rules for the grading of timber according to the visible gross features are covered in detail in Appendix A of the Code and Tables 3 and 4 set out the various stresses relating to the grades for particular species in both seasoned and unseasoned states. Thus imported seasoned Douglas Fir 50 grade can be stressed to 950 lb./in.^{2} (6·55N/mm^2), 65 grade to 1,250 lb./in.^{2} (8·619N/mm^2) while 40 grade can only be stressed to 750 lb./in.^{2} (5·171N/mm^2). For new work the Code points out that as the cost of artificial drying of timbers over 2 inches thick (51mm) rises very sharply, the basic stresses for green unseasoned timber should always be used for solid timber members more than 4 inches (102mm) thick. In regard to imported Douglas Fir the corresponding figures for green unseasoned timber at 50 grade would be 800 lb./in.^{2} (5·516N/mm^2) and for 65 grade 1,000 lb./in.^{2} (6·895N/mm^2)

On this occasion it is possible to discern a certain measure of unanimity between the Codes of Practice and the two documents which comprise the statutory requirements governing the use of timber for structural purposes. The Building Regulations 1972 adopt the Code of Practice C.P.112 in toto, both as to the 1952 and 1967 editions and the tables for timber sizes for residential buildings not exceeding three storeys in height set out in Schedule 6 can be used provided the timber consists of one of the species set out in Group II of the 1952 edition of the Code, 50 grade, or 40 grade for those imported timbers of Group I. The London Building (Constructional) Amending By-Laws (No. 1) 1964 utilise the identical classification for softwood structural timbers as in the 1952 Code but refer to them as Grade A and B, corresponding with Groups I and II respectively in the Code. The permissible stresses are the same, but to utilise these stresses the London By-Laws require the provision of adequate lateral restraint in floors against winding or buckling. What is adequate is not defined, but the 1952 edition of the Code contains detailed recommendations to this effect (see page 368 of this Chapter) and compliance with these would probably satisfy the District Surveyor.

In checking the strength of floors in old buildings, it will be a matter purely of experience whether the surveyor will feel confident in using a figure of 1,000 lb./in.² (6·895N/mm²) for his calculations assuming that all other factors are satisfactory. Far more likely it will be necessary to adopt the lower figure of 800 lb./in.² (5·516 N/mm²) as the maximum stress for the existing softwood timbers and indeed there may well be occasions when there will be every reason for taking a figure somewhere below this. There will be times when the timber used appears to have been of particularly poor quality and to have gross features somewhat in excess of those laid down in Table 4 of the Code of Practice C.P.112:1952 (applicable to the Building Regulations 1972 and repeated in the London By-Laws as Schedule V). It has been suggested that in floors of buildings in excess of 150 years old a figure of 600 lb./in.² (4·137N/mm²) for softwood timbers is appropriate in many cases.

However in the example being considered here it will be assumed that the house was originally well built and that it is satisfactory to use a stress of 800 lb./in.² (5·516N/mm²) for the timber of the joists. Accordingly the calculation for the Moment of Resistance of the joist is as follows:

In British units:

$$MR = \frac{fbd^2}{6}$$

$$= \frac{800 \times 2 \times 9 \times 9}{6}$$

$$= 21{,}600 \text{ lb. in.}$$

In metric units:

$$MR = \frac{fbd^2}{6}$$

$$= \frac{5\cdot516 \times 51 \times 229 \times 229}{6}$$

$$= 2\ 458\ 000 \text{Nmm}$$

387

The three stages of the calculations are therefore completed and there are now available the two figures representing (a) the forces acting on an individual joist in the floor and (b) the strength of the joist itself. Comparing the two values:

In British units:
Bending Moment (BM)
24,000 lb. in. >Moment of
Resistance (MR) 21,600 lb. in.

In metric units:
Bending Moment (BM)
2 694 000Nmm >Moment
of Resistance (MR)
2 458 000Nmm

it is found that the Bending Moment is in excess of the Moment of Resistance so that while this particular floor would, in normal circumstances, be satisfactory for residential purposes it would not satisfy the statutory design criteria for office purposes.

It should be fairly obvious that for a floor to be satisfactory the value for the Moment of Resistance should at least equal and preferably exceed the Bending Moment and it is interesting to pursue this example in order to demonstrate how, in the formula for the Moment of Resistance, joists of an adequate size are selected once the quality of available timber has been ascertained. In figures what is required here is a joist with a breadth of 2 inches (51mm) stressed to 800 lb./in.^{2} (5·516N/mm^2), assuming that is the quality generally available, which will have a Moment of Resistance equal to a Bending Moment of 24,000 lb. in. (2 694 000Nmm).

In British units:

$$MR = BM$$

$$\frac{800 \times 2 \times d^2}{6} = 24,000$$

$$d^2 = \frac{24,000 \times 6}{800 \times 2}$$

$$d^2 = 90$$

$$d = \sqrt{90}$$

$$d = 9 \cdot 48 \text{ inches}$$

In metric units:

$$MR = BM$$

$$\frac{5 \cdot 516 \times 51 \times d^2}{6} = 2\ 694\ 000$$

$$d^2 = \frac{2\ 694\ 000 \times 6}{5 \cdot 516 \times 51}$$

$$d^2 = 57\ 458$$

$$d = \sqrt{57\ 458}$$

$$d = 240 \text{mm}$$

It will be seen therefore that joists of the next whole size available, 10-inch (254mm) depth would be required to produce a floor sufficiently strong for the likely loading arising from office use.

Probably the cheapest way of providing additional support to a floor which is inadequate for its purpose, is by way of the provision of a beam dividing the span of the joists into two. Before considering the factors involved and the calculations necessary to derive the size of such a beam it is of interest to note that should it have been necessary to renew the joists entirely, a re-calculation of the Moment of Resistance, utilising a breadth of joist at 2½ inches (64mm) would show that 9 by 2½ inch (229 by 64mm) joists would fulfill the same purpose as 10 by 2 inches (254 by 51mm) as far as strength is concerned. Joists of this size would be more expensive but this additional expense may be more than offset by the advantage of retaining the old ceiling of the room below, both undisturbed and certainly not marred by the appearance of a beam. In some circumstances with care the new joists could be put in the spaces between the old joists to take the imposed and dead load from above, without disturbing the ceiling at all, which could be left attached to the old floor joists. (See "I" on Figure 63.) The calculations for the thicker joists would be as follows:

In British units:

$$MR = \frac{800 \times 2\frac{1}{2} \times 9 \times 9}{6}$$
$$= 27,000 \text{ lb. in.}$$

In metric units:

$$MR = \frac{5 \cdot 516 \times 64 \times 229 \times 229}{6}$$
$$= 3\ 085\ 488 \text{Nmm}$$

as against a bending movement of 24,000 lb. in. or 2 694 000Nmm.

If the floor joists themselves are sound and no reasons for entire removal and replacement of the old floor exist, the method usually adopted of providing additional support is, as has been already suggested, by means of a mid-span beam. There are often aspects of appearance to consider in providing such a beam, even apart from problems of headroom and support to the ends with which we are not too concerned here. Sufficient to say that it may be far better instead to provide two beams at one-third and two-thirds of the span and this usually improves the appearance as well as solving the problem of end support in relation to chimney breasts (see "E" and the notes on Figure 64). With two beams, however, there is no difference in the principles of calculation, merely that the area of floor to be carried by each beam is less and correspondingly each of the two beams can normally be of smaller size than a single beam used in similar circumstances.

The calculations for a beam uniformly loaded follow very closely that outlined for an individual joist and for this example much information is already available for the purpose. Stage 1 as before consists of assembling the component parts of the total load on the beam per foot or per metre length according to the units being used. Clearly however, the beam is to carry a very much larger area of floor than the individual joist so that the basic information must commence with the load per square foot or per square metre of the

Suspended Floors

The floor considered in the section on calculations is shown on plan at 'A' and deflected under its office loading in section at 'B'. The trimming around the fireplace opening tends to make difficult a repair by adding broader joists between the existing and as a result the provision of a central beam in order to reduce the span of the joists by half has been decided upon. The beam is shown on the plan but from the section 'E' and elevation 'F' it will be seen that from the point of view of appearance, two smaller beams dividing the span into three would have been much better (as shown by dotted lines on section 'E').

The area of flooring and ceiling carried by each joist is shown at 'C' between the dotted lines as arrowed and depends on the spacing of the joists. The imposed load acts over the same area on a single joist.

Cross firring as shown in detail at 'D' is a useful method of levelling a floor if the old boards are badly worn. The general arrangement is shown at 'E' which also shows the single central beam in position. The area of flooring, joists, ceiling and imposed load carried by the beam is delineated by the dotted lines and arrowed. A side elevation of the beam is at 'F'.

Scales 1 : 20 and 1 : 100

64

floor as a whole. From the earlier information we know that for the dead load:

In British units:
1 inch nominal softwood flooring weighs 2·3 lb./ft.^{2} say 3 lb./ft.^{2}
$\frac{3}{4}$ inch lath and plaster ceiling weighs 8.8 lb./ft.^{2} say 9 lb./ft.^{2}

In metric units:
25mm nominal softwood flooring weighs 11·2kg/m^2 say 12kg/m^2 or 117N/m^2
19mm lath and plaster ceiling weighs 42·9kg/m^2 say 43kg/m^2 or 422N/m^2

We also know that the imposed load is to be 50 lb./ft.^{2} (2·39kN/m^2 or 2 390N/m^2) but previously it has only been necessary to take the load per foot or per metre length of joist. This latter item has now to be converted to the weight per square foot or per square metre of joists at 15-inch (381mm) centres. We know already however that a 9 by 2 inch (229 by 51mm) joist weighs 4$\frac{1}{2}$ lb./ft. (6·7kg/m) so that to find the figure which should be allowed per square foot or per square metre over all the floor, it is necessary to divide this figure by the area of floor supported by the joist, in this case 1$\frac{1}{4}$ by 1 foot (0·381 by 1m).

In British units:
$$\frac{4\frac{1}{2}}{1\frac{1}{4} \times 1} = \frac{9 \times 4}{2 \times 5}$$
$$= 3·6 \text{ lb./ft.}^2$$
say 4·0 lb./ft.^{2}

In metric units:
$$\frac{6·7}{0·381 \times 1·0} = 17·6\text{kg/m}^2$$
which converted to newtons equals 173N/m^2

At this stage any method adopted to level up the floor which added to the total load would have to be taken into account. There are various ways of doing this. One method consists of taking up the old boards, firring up the existing joints and either relaying the old boards or providing new. Yet another method which is useful if the old boards are badly worn, is to fix firring pieces at right-angles to the existing joists, direct to the old boards and provide and fix new boards thereto (see "D" and "E" on Figure 64). The addition of 4 lb./ft.^{2} (157N/m^2) to the loading would be ample in the circumstances since the heaviest of the firring pieces would be in the centre, at the point of maximum deflection, where the additional support is to be provided. Accordingly all components of the loading having been dealt with we can now add them together as follows:

		British units	Metric units
Imposed Load:		50 lb./ft.²	2 390N/m²
Dead Load:			
Flooring	3	117	
Ceiling	9	422	
Joists	4	173	
Firring	4	157	
	–	20 lb./ft.²	869N/m²
		70 lb./ft.²	3 259N/m²

It is assumed for this example the likely circumstances that the existing joists are spanning the shortest distance between supports and accordingly the length of the beam will be some figure greater than the 14-foot span (4·267m) of those joists, let us say 16 feet (4·877m) as on Figure 64. Once again however we must ascertain the load per lineal foot or per lineal metre on the beam. Now it should be obvious that if the existing joists span 14 feet (4·267m) a beam at mid-span will be carrying 3 feet 6 inches (1·067m) of flooring on either side and that the beam itself is carrying a total load from the existing flooring per foot or per metre length of:

In British units: *In metric units:*
  (1 ft. × 7 ft. × 70) lb./ft.   (1m × 2·134 × 3 259)N/m
  =490 lb./ft.   =6 955N/m

To this must be added the self weight of the beam together with any casing to be provided before Stage 1 can be said to be completed. Here for convenience a casing will be omitted but a reasonable size of beam must be assumed and if it should prove to be inadequate then this concluding part of Stage 1 and the calculations of the Bending Moment and Moment of Resistance in Stages 2 and 3 must be done again until the correct size of beam is obtained. For this example a 15 by 7 inch (381 by 179mm) beam will be taken in the first instance. The self weight of a unit length of softwood beam of these dimensions is as follows with timber at 36 lb./ft.³ (575kg/m³):

In British units: *In metric units:*
  $1 \times 1\frac{1}{4} \times \frac{7}{12} \times 36$ $1 \times 0·381 \times 0·179 \times 575$
  $=26\frac{1}{4}$ lb./ft.   =39·28kg/m which con-
  say 30 lb./ft.   verted to newtons on mul-
                                   tiplying by 9·807 equals
                                   385N/m

Adding together all the components of the loading per unit length of beam the totals are:

In British units:
  Loading from floor   490 lb./ft.

  Self weight of beam   30 lb./ft.
  _____
                520 lb./ft.

In metric units:
  Loading from floor
                     6 955N/m

  Self weight of beam
                       385N/m
  _____
                7 340N/m

Stage 2

The Bending Moment can now be calculated to indicate the forces acting on the beam and for which the beam has to be designed to resist. Applying the formula as previously discussed the values are as follows:

In British units:
$$BM = \frac{wL^2}{8}$$
$$= \frac{520 \times 16 \times 16}{8}$$
$$= 16{,}640 \text{ lb. ft.}$$
and converting to inch units
on multiplying by 12
$$= 199{,}680 \text{ lb. in.}$$

In metric units:
$$BM = \frac{wL^2}{8}$$
$$= \frac{7\,340 \times 4 \cdot 877 \times 4 \cdot 877}{8}$$
$$= 21\,799 \cdot 8 Nm$$
and on converting to millimetre units on multiplying by 10^3
$$= 21\,799\,800 Nmm$$

Stage 3

It has already been assumed that a 15 by 7 inch (381 by 179mm) beam will be used for the purposes of the calculation, so that immediately the Moment of Resistance of such a beam can be ascertained. The two Moments can then be compared to see whether the Moment of Resistance is greater than, or at least equal to, the Bending Moment as it must be if the beam is to be considered strong enough for its purpose.

Assuming in this instance that only timber of 800 lb./in^2 stress quality (5·516N/mm^2) is available (though for a purpose such as this every endeavour would be made to secure material of better quality) the values for the Moment of Resistance would be as follows:

In British units:
$$MR = \frac{fbd^2}{6}$$
$$= \frac{800 \times 7 \times 15 \times 15}{6}$$
$$= 210{,}000 \text{ lb. in.}$$

In metric units:
$$MR = \frac{fbd^2}{6}$$
$$= \frac{5 \cdot 516 \times 179 \times 381 \times 381}{6}$$
$$= 23\,867\,791 Nmm$$

As the Moment of Resistance exceeds the Bending Moment by a small amount the 15-inch deep by 7-inch (381 by 179mm) beam is satisfactory but if it had not been, then it would have been necessary to recalculate both Bending Moment and Moment of Resistance using a larger size of beam.

With experience a surveyor will have a shrewd idea of the approximate size of timber beam that would be necessary in various circumstances, so that very often the correct size will be selected at once or perhaps only one incorrect size will need to be rejected in the calculations. Should the first complete run through of the calculation prove unsatisfactory by a wide margin, however, then by substitution in the various formulae and the use of approximations, sizes can be obtained which stand a good chance of proving suitable on recalculation. For example, it will be evident that the self weight of the beam is really a very small proportion of the total load, so that rounding upward the figure obtained for the Bending Moment using a beam that is too small, will produce a reasonably satisfactory total for use in the following combination of formulae:

$$MR = BM$$
$$\frac{fbd^2}{6} = BM$$
$$bd^2 = \frac{BM \times 6}{f}$$

In the example used here, should the beam chosen have proved inadequate the Bending Moment could have been rounded up to 200,000 lb. in. or 22 000 000Nmm and could have been employed to obtain approximate sized beams as set out below which might prove suitable:

In British units:

$$bd^2 = \frac{200,000 \times 6}{800}$$
$$= 1,500$$
if b = 8 in. then:
$$d = \sqrt{\frac{1,500}{8}}$$
$$= 13 \cdot 7$$
say 14 in.
or if b = 9 in. then:
$$d = \sqrt{\frac{1,500}{9}}$$
$$= 12 \cdot 9$$
say 13 in.

In metric units:

$$bd^2 = \frac{22\ 000\ 000 \times 6}{5 \cdot 5}$$
$$= 24\ 000\ 000$$
if b = 200mm then:
$$d = \sqrt{\frac{24\ 000\ 000}{200}}$$
$$= 346$$
say 350mm
or if b = 225mm then:
$$d = \sqrt{\frac{24\ 000\ 000}{225}}$$
$$= 326$$
say 325mm

394

On returning to Stage 1 the self weight can be corrected for one or other of the two alternatives above and then Stages 2 and 3 can be recalculated to make sure that the actual Moment of Resistance exceeds the Bending Moment.

From the earlier sections of this Chapter it will be recalled that in mediaeval times it was the practice to use structural timbers broad side uppermost and consequently large scantlings were frequently employed when smaller sizes with the narrow sides uppermost would have done equally well. The strength of timber is utilised to its best advantage when timbers are placed narrow side uppermost and the relationship of breadth to depth is an important factor in the performance of a beam's functions. For example, although a beam might have a Moment of Resistance greater than the Bending Moment it is required to resist, it may be so thin that it is in danger of winding and buckling when placed in position if it is not provided with lateral restraint. Furthermore a very thick beam in relation to its depth, while exhibiting adequate strength characteristics, may deflect or sag unduly causing cracking to ceilings or other finishings and giving an appearance of insecurity.

Lateral restraint, within the depth of floors, by the provision of herringbone strutting in accordance with the provisions of the 1952 edition of Code of Practice C.P.112 has already been discussed, but here it is necessary to check whether the mid-span beam now proposed requires restraint within the requirements of the Code. It will be recalled that if a beam has a depth exceeding three times its breadth and/or a length in excess of fifty times its breadth restraint is required. The depth of the proposed 15 by 7 inch (381 by 179 mm) beam is in fact only just over twice its breadth and nowhere near fifty times the breadth in length, so that compliance with the Code requires no lateral support to be provided to this beam.

The 1967 edition of Code of Practice C.P.112 varies the requirements of the earlier edition by permitting greater ratios of depth to breadth in certain conditions. These are where the ends of the beam are held in position and also where the compression (top) edge of the beam is held in line in addition and, finally, when both compression and tension edges are held in line as well as the ends being held in position. In the example here it would not be desirable to hold the ends of the beam in position by building them solidly into the brickwork, particularly the brickwork of the external wall where, indeed, it would be more suitable to leave an air space all round the end of the beam. In fact this proposed beam would be considered as "simply supported" and accordingly under the 1967 Code be classed as having no lateral restraint and thus restricted to a maximum depth to breadth ratio of two. On this basis the depth of the

beam would be limited to 14 inches (356mm) despite the fact that
on installation to be effective it would have to be wedged gently into
position below the existing joists and that it would be an easy matter
to spike the existing joists to the new beam, thus providing a certain
measure of restraint to the top, compression, edge of the beam. Too
much, however, need not be made of this difference in the two
editions of the Code, since by complying with the earlier edition the
requirements of both the Building Regulations 1972 and the London
Building (Constructional) Amending By-Laws (No. 1) 1964 are
satisfied. In the rather unlikely event of the wood beam already
calculated and proposed not complying with the depth and length
ratios of the 1952 Code it would not really be possible to provide
restraint in the circumstances of this example and accordingly a
beam with a more appropriate depth to breadth ratio would have to
be selected, a situation which of course could be avoided by bearing
the point in mind from the commencement of the calculations.

As to deflection, both 1952 and 1967 editions of the Code of
Practice C.P.112 recommend that for floors any movement should
be limited to 0·003 or 1/333 of the span when the floor is fully loaded,
this being considered an appropriate amount having regard to the
type of structure envisaged. From before it has been seen that work
in accordance with both editions of the Code satisfies the Building
Regulations 1972 and in this case the requirements of the London
Building (Constructional) Amending By-Laws (No. 1) 1964 are also
satisfied if deflection does not exceed that amount on calculation.
Relating this standard to the example under consideration the
maximum deflection in a beam with a span of 16 feet (4·877m)
should not exceed 0·58 inches (14·6mm). The amount of deflection
in a beam should be investigated so as to ensure that it complies with
the requirements of both the Building Regulations 1972 and the
London By-Laws and the amount of deflection under conditions of
full load can be found by calculation. The maximum deflection for
a beam uniformly loaded for its full length is at the centre and the
value is found utilising the following formula:

$$\frac{5}{384} \frac{wL^4}{EI}$$

Where w=weight force or load per unit length in either lb./in.
or N/mm

L=total length or span of the beam in inches or millimetres

E=the modulus of elasticity in lb./in.² or N/mm²

I=the moment of inertia for the section, in.⁴ or mm⁴

The first two items are familiar from the earlier sections, apart from the difference in the units, but further comments are necessary in relation to the last two items. The modulus of elasticity, Young's modulus, is a measure of the stress needed to deform the material under consideration. There are values for the metals used in structural work and in British Standard Code of Practice C.P.112: 1952 the values for Group I and II timbers (corresponding to Groups A and B in the London By-Laws) are as follows:

Basic Stresses

Timber in accordance with C.P. 112:1952	Modulus of Elasticity			
	Mean		Minimum	
	lb./in.^{2}	N/mm^2	lb./in.^{2}	N/mm^2
Group I	1 600 000	11 031·616	1 000 000	6 894·760
Group II	1 200 000	8 273·712	750 000	5 171·070

The 1967 edition of the Code provides for a much wider range of timbers with stress values given for timbers in unseasoned as well as seasoned conditions. This edition may be used if required outside London. The mean values from the above table are to be used for the purposes of calculating deflection for rafters and floor joists, where it can be shown that transverse distribution of the load is achieved. For principal members, beams, binders etc., acting alone, however, the minimum values must be used. Accordingly the appropriate value to be adopted for these calculations where a Group II timber beam is to be used is 750,000 lb./in.^{2} (5 171·070N/mm^2).

The moment of inertia of a structural element is a factor directly related to its shape and size. For a rectangular section as used in this example the factor is found from the following formula:

$$I = \frac{bd^3}{12}$$

where b = the breadth of the beam in inches or millimetres
 d = the depth of the beam in inches or millimetres

In British units:

$$I = \frac{7 \times 15 \times 15 \times 15}{12}$$
$$= 1,969 \text{ in.}^4$$

In metric units:

$$I = \frac{179 \times 381 \times 381 \times 381}{12}$$
$$= 824\ 900\ 000 \text{mm}^4$$

397

It is now possible to make the figure substitutions for the letters in the formula $\dfrac{5}{384}\ \dfrac{wL^4}{EI}$ so that the maximum deflection can be calculated as follows. Note the care necessary to ensure that the units are kept the same throughout, i.e. pounds and inches or Newtons and millimetres as the case may be as otherwise wrong values will be obtained. For this reason the figures for the weight (load) per unit length used in the calculation to find the Bending Moment are reduced from lb./ft. (N/m) to lb./in. (N/mm) on dividing by 12 (10^3). It is simpler to do this than to adjust the figure for the modulus of elasticity which is usually given in lb./in.^{2} or N/mm^2, as the case may be, in the Codes of Practice and the London By-Laws.

In British units:

maximum deflection

$$= \frac{5}{384} \times \frac{43 \cdot 4 \times 192^4}{750,000 \times 1,969}$$

$$= 0 \cdot 52 \text{ inches}$$

In metric units:

maximum deflection

$$= \frac{5}{384} \times \frac{7 \cdot 340 \times 4\ 877^4}{5\ 171 \times 824\ 900\ 000}$$

$$= 12 \cdot 7 \text{mm}$$

It will be seen therefore that the maximum deflection does not exceed 0·58 inches (14·6mm) or 1/333 of the span as laid down in the Codes of Practice and the London By-Laws and therefore the 15 inches deep by 7 inches (381 by 179mm) timber beam selected will be satisfactory on all counts both in London and also outside London since the requirements of the Building Regulations 1972 are also satisfied.

However, obtaining a timber beam in one piece of the size envisaged in this example is difficult at the present time in good quality timber, a situation which is unlikely to improve in the forseeable future. As an alternative to a beam in one piece it may be possible to make up a suitable beam from smaller sections. For example a beam 14 inches (350mm) deep with a breadth of 8 inches (200mm) might well be made up of two sections each 14 by 4 inches (350 by 100mm) joined together with suitable bolts and connectors so that when in position the two sections behave as one. On the other hand the use of a steel beam would be far more common nowadays in normal repair work, the corresponding size being much smaller. As so much information has already been assembled in regard to this particular floor, it would be sensible to pursue the matter and to discuss the methods available for proceeding to ascertain the size of a steel beam to fulfil the same function as the timber beam already calculated. There are in fact three methods available for the surveyor, architect or small builder faced with this problem, all of which have their particular merits depending on the circumstances of each case. Here however the detailed calculations which can be made in a manner related to, but by no means as simple as, the methods used previously to ascertain the sizes of timber beams are not discussed. Whereas an engineer, or for that matter a surveyor, architect or builder with a particular skill in this field, would find no difficulty, others dabble in this aspect of design to their peril. Recent increases in permitted stresses for the various grades of steel are primarily due to improvements in the quality of the material and while enabling substantial economies to be made in new work have lesser relevance to the subject of repairs to old buildings. More factors have to be taken into account in the design of steel beams in order to comply with the relevant British Standard Code of Practice than is the case with timber and for these factors to be dealt with adequately requires a knowledge of structural design not normally available to the average surveyor, architect or builder. For example it depends on whether a beam can be said to have adequate lateral support as to what degree of stress can be permitted in the steel. Furthermore not only the degree or deflection requires investigation but also shear stress in the beam and web buckling and crushing. All these factors are of day to day routine to an engineer and a reference to such a person is one method of securing the required information and this is discussed first below.

(1) For extensive works of repair the calculations for steelwork can be entrusted to a suitable engineer, preferably in the form of a consultant responsible direct to the building owner or, alternatively, for a small job involving a few beams only, on direct instructions from the surveyor or architect. It is suggested that it is preferable to employ an engineer who is experienced in dealing with old buildings, since he will be aware of the type of difficulty likely to be encountered in the work. If the engineer is employed as a consultant it is also recommended that he is instructed to calculate the loads involved himself. He would no doubt wish to do this in such circumstances, but if he is employed direct there might well be a case for the surveyor or architect supplying detailed information on loading for the engineer to work from, provided they in turn are confident that they are capable of dealing with this aspect of the work in a suitably precise manner. Whether in the case of the particular problem under consideration in this section, an engineer would do any more than consult safe load tables as outlined in (3) below is debatable but he would at least have the requisite skill to know for certain which method of selection, in all the circumstances, it is best to adopt. However the employment of an engineer may work out slightly more expensive to the building owner than either (2) or (3) below and this point might need to be borne in mind.

399

(2) Most suppliers of steel sections also run a design department within their organisation so that, on the receipt of instructions, they will be able to estimate for the design and supply of the appropriate sections, the design fee being added to the cost of the material. Once again it is considered better for the contractor to take the necessary information as required from the site and not have this supplied by the surveyor, since this will of necessity ensure that the supplier is fully familiar with all the circumstances and conditions and does not rely merely on information supplied and in drawings. When it comes to the detailing of the steelwork, it is probable that the contractor will send the completed drawing to the surveyor or architect for "his approval". It is advisable in these cases (as it is in relation to all specialist sub-contractors or suppliers) to be hyper-cautious and to approve "the general arrangement insofar as it effects other work or details" and not to give an approval to the calculations and finer points of detailing which should remain the responsibility of the sub-contractor to ascertain and set out correctly.

(3) The third method available is to consult safe load tables and if a suitable beam having regard to all the factors involved can be found direct, for the surveyor to specify that beam for installation. Safe load tables save engineers a considerable amount of unnecessary work in the way of calculations by tabulating the safe loads which can be applied to beams, joists, channels, angles etc., when uniformly loaded over a range of spans. Their use by others not qualified as engineers requires care, since the tables are not for obvious reasons capable of use in solving problems involving point loads or eccentric loading. It is always necessary to call in a specialist in these circumstances as also whenever there are more involved structural problems, such as, for example, the provision of steel lintels over new openings in walls.

For specifying new work in steel, it is now necessary to use metric values as the industry has made the initial changeover to the metric system. In other words, all steel sections are now set out in the metric equivalents of the former quoted British units, although the complete change to internationally co-ordinated metric standard ranges of steel sections awaits agreement among the substantial number of bodies concerned, besides which a considerable time will be needed to effect the necessary production alterations. In this respect it should be noted that at present nominal sizes are not the same as actual sizes and that as before, when British units were used, it is still necessary to specify the weight of beam or joist to be used as there may be up to three different beams available within one nominal size in a particular grade of steel. For example a nominal 254 by 102mm Universal beam can be obtained in three weights 28, 25 and

22kg/m respectively varying in size from 260·4 by 102·1mm through 257·0 by 101·9mm to 254·0 by 101·6mm in Grades 50, 43 and 55 steel, all nine available beams having different strength characteristics.

At the time of writing the current publication of safeload tables is that available from the British Constructional Steelwork Association Ltd., Hancock House, 87 Vincent Square, London, S.W.1 entitled "Handbook on Structural Steelwork" 1971 (with a Revision Supplement also dated 1971) a substantial paper-back of 400 pages, price £1.50.

One of the immediate limiting factors in regard to the use of the safe load tables applied to a problem such as this, is that when a steel beam is supporting wood joists the joists cannot be considered as providing any lateral support. Accordingly there is a critical span in respect of each Universal beam or joist above which the allowable stress in the steel must be reduced in accordance with Clause 19a (ii) of B.S.449:1969. The critical span given in the tables for each section represents the maximum effective length of the compression flange which may be permitted without reduction of flexural stress. A glance at the tables for Grade 43 steel joists and Universal beams shows that none of the joists can be used under these conditions over a span in excess of 2·424m and the first Universal beam which can be used (as in the example) for a span of 4·877m without reduction of flexural stress is of a nominal size of 533 by 330mm, a steel beam substantially in excess of the wood beam calculated as being required in similar circumstances, a solution to the problem which is patently ridiculous! It will be immediately apparent therefore that the safe load tables are of somewhat limited value for the type of problem which has been discussed. Obviously there will be a steel beam suitable for the purpose but having regard to the span involved, it will have to be somewhat deeper than the strict strength factor alone would indicate. The problem here in regard to steelwork is that there is a relatively light load and a relatively large span involved and to satisfy the requirements of B.S.449:1969 (which is also the Code of Practice) calculations have to be made.

The safe distributed load in the tables is set out in kilonewtons for spans in metres and in order to use the tables it is of course necessary to extend the information which may have already been obtained so as to find this total load. To this must be added a reasonable allowance for any casing and for the weight of the beam. In the circumstances as a guide, a beam depth of about one-twentieth of the span is often suitable with a breadth to the order of a half to two-thirds of the depth.

As has been seen already however, it is necessary in this example for the beam size to be calculated in view of the span so that the matter must be dealt with under either methods (1) or (2), unless the surveyor or builder is skilled at the further stages of the calculations. This will often be the case in similar examples and merely serves to illustrate the limitations of safe load tables in hands other than those of an engineer. To summarise therefore on the use of the safe load tables where employed to determine a beam size supporting a wood floor not qualifying as suitable to provide lateral restraint:

(*a*) The critical span must first be checked and if the span is beyond the length at which point the allowable stress must be reduced, then beam calculations must be carried out and the tables are no help in that instance.

(*b*) Should the span be fairly small then on calculating the distributed load along the beam it may be possible to select a beam capable of carrying that load or, more appropriately, slightly more than the load in question. To be read off from the tables direct, the safe load figure must be in italics as figures either in bold type or ordinary type require checking for the load bearing capacity of the web or for deflection respectively. Though these calculations are relatively simple, it is not the purpose of this volume to venture further along this path which, as has already been stated, is best left to those skilled in weighing all the factors involved.

It must not be forgotten that calculations for structural works of the nature dealt with in this section require checking by the Building Inspector or District Surveyor as the case may be. It has been known for rather imprecise figures to be submitted by inexperienced surveyors, architects or builders in the hope that the Building Inspector or District Surveyor will make the necessary amendments and work out the right answer, but this is quite a wrong practice. The function of these officials is to check and approve calculations and detailing and not to do other people's work (for which they are probably getting paid) for them.

In concluding this section it seems appropriate to point out that at one time practically all the work covered by the calculations herein could have been avoided with the use of a pamphlet published by the former London County Council as an Explanatory Memorandum to the London Building (Constructional) By-Laws 1952, but not now available or applicable under the Amending By-Laws (No. 1) of 1964. The Explanatory Memorandum contained a range of tables which enabled the sizes, centres and spans of timber joists and binders (beams) to be determined when the total uniformly distributed load (i.e. the dead plus imposed load) on the floor or flat roof was known. A very wide range of loadings and timber sizes was covered utilising the two grades of timber still applicable. Further tables for joists, rafters, purlins and floor boards for two-storey domestic construction in one occupation were also included and it is regrettable that means were not found to continue this form of "deemed to satisfy" advice after 1964. The advice was so much more extensive than that provided currently in the 1972 Building Regulations.

There is however a pamphlet produced by the Timber Research and Development Association entitled "Design of Timber Members", which gives stresses and typical calculations for beams and columns in accordance with British Standard Code of Practice C.P.112:1967 together with beam span tables for a range of timbers. This pamphlet takes account of Forest Products Research Bulletin No. 47, "Working Stresses for Structural Timber", which collects the wider range of imported and home grown softwoods covered by C.P.112:1967 into two strength groups (S1 and S2), but even this exercise still leaves eight timbers, i.e. the four grades available in each strength group, to be tabulated for working stresses in both seasoned and unseasoned states.

The four beam span tables set out in the pamphlet have been prepared for two softwoods, S2–50 grade and S1–50 grade and two hardwoods, Keruing 65 grade and Greenheart 65 grade, in sizes up to 16 inches (406mm) in depth and for any width. There are limitations set out and circumstances arising out of loading factors which need careful study and which to a practitioner with limited engineering knowledge may prove a little difficult to follow. To those with the requisite skill, however, they will be invaluable for specifying new or replacement timbers and may, in certain circumstances, be of assistance in checking the strength of existing floors.

FUNGAL AND INSECT ATTACK

The General Scene and the Specialist Contractor

War damage and neglect of maintenance during the Second World War left behind a legacy of trouble brought about by fungal attack on timber in many houses. Since the immediate post-war period, although there is a greater awareness in members of the public of the dangers of such attacks, there are still many instances of costly outbreaks occurring.

There has, however, been a marked change in the way that most of these new outbreaks are being tackled, as against those of twenty years ago. The writers wonder how many surveyors at the present time write those long, carefully phrased specifications for dealing with an outbreak of dry rot which were the common product of most offices before the Second World War. Very few, it is imagined are called upon nowadays for the purpose and most clients now rush to a new breed of specialist contractor who has appeared on the scene. Even if the surveyor is called in he, in turn, very often calls in the specialist contractor. It is not that the specialist does anything different to deal with the outbreak than an ordinary building contractor would do, working to a prepared specification and under the supervision of a surveyor. What the specialist does offer, however, is a guarantee and it is this guarantee more than anything else that has changed the situation.

It is much the same with attacks on timber by wood boring insects. The public has become much more aware of "woodworm" in the last twenty-five years or so, partly due to publicity by government agencies and partly due to the requirements of mortgage institutions, such as Building Societies and local authorities, that a property should be free of attack. However, it is not only this increased awareness that makes "woodworm" seem more prevalent now than before the Second World War. There is evidence to suggest that attacks in the timbers of buildings by wood boring insects are on the increase. Before the war attempts to eradicate an infestation were often unsuccessful, as the insecticides available at the time were effective only on ingestion by the insect or larvae and were of limited persistence. The application of these insecticides was usually on a fairly limited scale and often, as a result, it was necessary to repeat inspections and treatment for a number of seasons, without even then being entirely sure that some insects would not escape to lay their eggs elsewhere. Furthermore there was no guarantee available.

It might be asked why, if surveyors are prepared to tackle this work, do they not offer a guarantee. After all they profess to have the knowledge to deal with fungal and insect attacks and have for many years in the past supervised contractors carrying out this work. What must be remembered however is that a contract to carry out such work subsists between the building owner and the contractor with the surveyor merely as the building owner's agent. The supervision which the surveyor exercises is periodical only and he cannot by the very nature of his work be on the job the whole time. While the surveyor owes a duty of care both in the contractual relationship with his client and in the law of negligence in respect of his instructions to the contractor and in the periodical supervision exercised, it is the contractor's duty under the terms of the contract to see that the day to day performance of the works is satisfactorily carried out. A number of old established building contracting firms who maintain that they had years of experience dealing with fungal attacks before the specialists appeared upon the scene are indeed prepared to give a guarantee for their work along the same lines as that now issued by the specialists. Clearly, however, before such firms will issue a guarantee they themselves have to be satisfied that the scope of the work is sufficient to cope with the possibility of a fresh outbreak. There should, of course, be no clash of opinion here between the contractor and the building owner's surveyor but this possibility cannot be ruled out. However, it is considered that an arrangement such as this might well be to the building owner's advantage in being somewhat cheaper than employing a specialist contractor, even allowing for the fact that fees in addition to the contractor's account have to be paid. The surveyor in whom the building owner has confidence will supervise a long established firm well known to owner and surveyor, both of whom will probably be familiar with the building in question and its past history and who will also, no doubt, be involved on its future maintenance. Continuity can thus be achieved and assurance gained that the area of the outbreak can be kept constantly under observation in the future.

The choice between an ordinary contractor with or without a guarantee (under a surveyor's supervision) and a specialist contractor may be a difficult one for the building owner to make. The surveyor may be asked to advise on the choice and in this connection the following points do perhaps need consideration. An important factor at the time of writing concerns the volume of work of this nature that continues to arise. There is ample evidence to suggest that outbreaks of fungal decay, as well as insect attack, continue at a high level. This has meant that the well known specialist firms are kept very busy, can to some extent pick and choose their contracts and can use busy order books to introduce delays before work can commence and can also quote surprisingly high prices, the high prices being due to some extent on the often need to return to carry out a second treatment in respect of insect attack. The field has therefore been left open for a number of new firms to mushroom offering, on the surface, the same type of service to building owners as the more well-known firms, sometimes apparently at a lower cost. There is little doubt that the newer firms are perfectly genuine and probably do their work well, within the limitations of a difficult labour market at the present time. To be competitive, however, these new firms have to offer the same free inspection, advice and estimating service as the bigger firms and also a twenty-year guarantee on the work carried out. Whether the volume of work will continue at the same high level in the future remains to be seen but if it does not, the possibility that the smaller firms will withdraw from the field should not be overlooked. If this should be the case then those building owners who need to rely on the original guarantee will find themselves waving it at thin air, with nobody to nail it on to. This rather suggests that if it is the supplying of a guarantee that is to influence the client's decision, then some regard to the position and standing of the firm supplying it should be taken.

What of the guarantee itself? It must be admitted that some building owners rather assume that if Messrs. So and So deal with an attack of dry rot or woodworm in their house, then the guarantee given will render them immune from the cost of dealing with any other attack of either within the guarantee period, irrespective of the cause. This is clearly ridiculous but it does not stop many owners from sharing this viewpoint. The guarantees vary in their form but in no circumstances can they be considered to extend in the case of fresh outbreaks of woodworm beyond the re-treatment of areas previously dealt with and in the case of fungal outbreaks, only to beyond the areas originally affected if it can be shown that the attack has spread from timbers treated earlier. In other words, the guarantee is rather limited to the sort of claim that could be made on the count of bad materials or poor workmanship not being in accordance with the implied terms of any building repairs contract. None that have been examined can be said to go any further than this and indeed it would be very surprising if they did. On the other hand none endeavour to reduce the building owner's rights under Common Law or the Sale of Goods Act 1893 and at least the setting out of part of these rights on a piece of paper provides a building owner with some visible form of assurance not requiring the services of a solicitor, which would be necessary if a remedy for defective workmanship was sought by any other means. The scope of some guarantees came in for criticism arising out of a case in the courts a few years ago concerning opening up and making good and whether these items could properly be said to be covered by one specialist contractor's guarantee. In the particular case, the specialist's liability was held to be limited to mere re-treatment of timbers free of charge, leaving the other much more expensive items to be paid for by the building owner. This highly unsatisfactory state of affairs led to the amendment of a number of guarantee forms so that now many specialists accept the full consequences of any failure to carry out their work properly. The trouble is that once one attack has been dealt with, owners can be lulled into a false sense of security and as a result blissfully neglect their maintenance. In consequence a further outbreak arises, very often from an entirely different source and spreads back into areas already dealt with by the specialist previously. An owner may then feel aggrieved when it is pointed out to him that no claim can be entertained under the guarantee and the arguments between the representatives of both sides can range very widely in these circumstances.

To be fair, however, the guarantees do provide two advantages over the normal legal remedy which might have to be resorted to if they did not exist. One is the period of guarantee normally provided which is twenty years and is considerably in excess of the statutory period of six years provided by the Limitation Act for the bringing of an action arising out of a contract. In this connection it must be noted that the period of six years runs from the time of completion of the contract and not from the discovery of the defect which gives rise to the claim. The second advantage is that the guarantee can be assigned to a new owner if the property is sold. The new owner is then entitled to the benefit of the unexpired portion of the guarantee. This can be advantageous to a building owner if there is evidence of work having been carried out which always tends to alarm a prospective purchaser and his surveyor. Since only the parties to a contract can sue on it, the guarantee does extend to another party the rights, such as they may be, given by the guarantee and provide a protection which would be completely absent at law in the circumstances. In the case of a sale which has gone off on the discovery, hitherto unknown, of an outbreak of dry rot or woodworm a very cogent argument would exist for work to be carried out by a specialist contractor giving a guarantee.

With the increased use of specialist contractors since the end of the Second World War, there has been a tendency to consider that many adopt highly sophisticated techniques in the work of eradication. This is just not so, although it must be admitted that many being geared to deal specifically with particular problems go about their work with an air of efficiency not always to be found in the general building contractor. On the other hand some of the specialists require attendance by general contractors and anything in the least bit out of the ordinary requires more than just attendance. The methods generally are eminently traditional, particularly so far as work in connection with dry rot is concerned but the development of more potent fungicides and insecticides has led to an improvement in the quality of chemical treatment for both dry rot and woodworm for which credit is due to a great extent to the specialists and this fact should be acknowledged. Now, however, that the necessary chemicals are generally available and are covered for testing by two British Standards there need be no difficulty in specifying and obtaining the appropriate fluids. With this information available and reliance placed on fungicides and insecticides tested in accordance with the British Standards and carefully selected for the purpose, there is every reason to believe that the surveyor should re-assert himself when the circumstances permit and take control of remedial works, particularly in regard to dry rot outbreaks. In regard to woodworm the use by skilled operatives of spray equipment and some of the more toxic solvent based insecticides with certain dangers to the operatives involved suggest that in respect of those cases where substantial renewals of timber are not involved the use of a specialist firm might well be more appropriate.

Fungal Attack

All surveyors in inspecting dwelling houses preparatory to pre-paring a specification for repairs look for dry rot. The difference between a relatively inexperienced surveyor and one with more ex-perience is that the former will look everywhere very closely indeed, whereas the latter will know where to look depending on the age and type of property. The former will probably be surprised if once the repairs are put in hand, dry rot is found when there was no visible sign on the exposed surfaces of timber, but the latter will not. All too often the older type of house when opened up for repair or alteration will reveal an attack of dry rot at some stage or other. On the other hand in dealing with the older properties the surveyor is sometimes surprised that rot is not more extensive than it is, when the condi-tions are so often seemingly favourable. There are two possible reasons why this should be so. One is undoubtedly that much of the wood used in buildings constructed fifty years or more ago was of better quality than that used since. Sapwood was much more rigorously excluded than it is now and the slow growing trees planted by nature produced a denser, closer ringed, heartwood for conver-sion. Such timber has greater powers of resistance to fungal attack and in some cases an old attack of dry rot will be found which has died out through lack of sustenance, always provided that the mois-ture source originating it has ceased. The other reason is that in older building, timbers built in many positions which appear to be unventilated do in fact have a current of air passing over them. One has only to put one's hand down the side of architraves or along the base of a window panel on a windy day to realise that an abundant amount of air does in fact penetrate around old window frames. This is of benefit to the woodwork if not to the occupants.

The reverse of the penny applies however to properties built in the last fifty years or so. Improved forestry techniques have resulted in a much more rapid growth in trees planted by man and the result is that there is less heartwood and a much greater proportion of sap-wood utilised. Although the dwelling houses of the period have, in the main, been built with the benefit of the legislation requiring adequate damp proofing, poor workmanship or a lack of mainten-ance involving bridged damp courses, blocked air bricks, choked gutters and downpipes and leaking roofs can give rise to rapid and dramatic outbreaks of dry rot since the sapwood is much more readily attacked. It is uneconomic in most circumstances of building today to exclude sapwood and this factor has come at a time when timbers, both for structural and joinery purposes have been pared down to the minimum. As a result in structural timbers there is a far smaller factor of safety in timbers incorporated in buildings put up in the last twenty years or so than formerly. The scientific use of timber has permitted much smaller sizes to be used and shortages and economy have ensured that this practice has been fairly rigor-ously followed. In consequence timbers weakened by outbreaks of dry rot (or attacks of woodworm for that matter as the same con-ditions apply) may fail at an early date. Newer buildings as long as they are well designed and constructed and subsequently kept warm, dry and well ventilated are unlikely to develop fungal attacks but, as we know, this is not always the case. Apart from the greater risk to structural timbers by the use of more sapwood from both dry rot outbreaks and attacks by wood boring insects, joinery items such as windows and doors have become highly susceptible to wet rot. There are many cases of failure after 5–6 years in newish houses built since the Second World War.

However, this is perhaps to digress from the original point which was that the prudent surveyor in dealing with the repair of old buildings will wisely provide for the eventuality of the discovery of an outbreak of rot. Such provision is particularly important where repair is coupled with improvement, budgeted to the client's maxi-mum resources. Many a scheme of this nature has almost come to grief for the lack of such provision, the client probably ending up at best with a much less improved house than he had hoped for and probably a grudge against his surveyor into the bargain. On the whole it is considered that this sort of situation arising is really rather inexcusable and reveals some cardinal lack of knowledge in the sur-veyor or at least a lack of adequate communication between sur-veyor and client. Owners of buildings do not always appreciate the fact that an outbreak of dry rot can exist with no visible evidence on the surface of timbers. This point needs to be brought to their attention. On the other hand, to a surveyor with a reasonable knowledge of his subject, the likely places for an outbreak should be ascertainable by an inspection coupled with reasonable assumptions based on his experience of types of construction from past periods, however this may have been acquired, be it by reading or practice over a period. Of course in many cases it will be possible to open up the structure in advance and be sure, but this may not be practicable in all circumstances. If on opening up, an attack is found, the only way to enable an estimate to be prepared is to continue the exposure works until all trace of the fungus has ceased, which is of course necessary in the same manner for an attack where there are visible indications. If it is not practical to open up but there are good grounds for suspicion then the amount of the provision can be a difficult matter to decide. It must obviously depend on the circumstances but the surveyor should undoubtedly err on the generous side and warn his client of the consequences, both by word of mouth explanation and in writing, should the provision prove to be inadequate.

Those places in a neglected house where dry rot is a likely possibility can be summarised as follows:

(a) In flat roof construction which is invariably unventilated.

(b) Below parapet gutters or valley gutters in pitched roofs which are poorly ventilated. It is often the better quality house with a boarded roof and closed eaves which is more prone to attack in these positions.

(c) Where timbers are built into brickwork and subsequently plastered or otherwise concealed, for example wood lintels, nearly always employed before 1900 and often used since and bonding timbers and fixing blocks in Stuart, Georgian and some Victorian houses.

(d) In panelling and matchboarding on walls and in particular around door and window openings with shutter boxes, panelled heads and aprons. In lath and plaster construction on outer walls.

(e) In basement or ground floor construction where there is no damp proof course and inadequate ventilation. In wood floors generally where there has been any form of plumbing leak.

In (a) and (b) fungal decay will depend, as always, on a level of moisture above that necessary to propagate an attack, but it should be remembered that this can arise not only through roof defects but also through penetration from parapets and copings. Similarly with (b) and (c) trouble usually arises only when water penetrates the brickwork enclosing the timber, which may be due to defective pointing or leaking pipes or gutters but may also be due to driving rain penetrating thin brickwork. The thicker the wall the less likely is this to happen. In basements and ground floors patches of rising damp are likely to draw attention to themselves, but occasionally quite remarkable effects can be achieved in disguising the appearance of rising damp sufficient to deceive on a cursory inspection.

We have considered some of the positions where dry rot is likely to arise in the ordinary course of events in old houses but what of the signs on the surface, if any, which might help to confirm the presence of an attack? These may be slight but before the stage which most surveyors find easy to identify, that is the breaking up of the surface of the wood both along and across the grain, there are often other signs. For example in plastered ceilings, particularly those on laths, cracks will appear below areas where dry rot exists due to the movement in the wood above. Similarly where plaster covers other timber features, cracks in the plaster and bulging of the surface will indicate movement and probably decay in the wood. With panelling that is painted on the exposed surface the splitting of the wood and its breaking up into cubical sections takes considerable time and by the time this is apparent an attack is very advanced indeed. However the shrinkage and drying out of the wood on the rear hidden face will introduce all types of stress on the exposed face and early signs might well take the form of opening at the joints, both of the panels to the stiles and rails and also at the angles and joints of these latter features. Later, the stresses may well cause the panel to warp slightly on the surface or to appear wavy or irregular in some manner and at this stage probing with a sharp pointed tool will probably indicate a soft area in the region of the movement. This warping or waviness is the prelude to the first longitudinal crack to appear on the surface of the timber.

A damp musty smell is a further indication of the presence of dry rot but the attack usually has to be fairly severe before this is particularly apparent. It is a useful guide however on opening the door for the first time in a house or basement which has been left closed up and unventilated for a period or in cupboards or other enclosed spaces not continuously ventilated. Opening up floors can present the same smell. A further useful indication of an attack of dry rot is the presence of a fine powder, rusty red in colour which in fact comprises fungus spores. These spores can be blown about in currents of air, often being blown up through cracks between floorboards if there is an outbreak in a floor or, alternatively, drop down below a feature subjected to attack. The spores are produced in great quantity by the fruiting body of the fungus and an early sign of attack is often the presence of a mushroom type pancake growing out of a crack in panelling or from around the edge of a window or door frame. In the presence of these bodies the spores may be widespread as a red dust throughout a room. They might well appear when timber features are subjected to blows from a hammer which in itself is a further useful test for the soundness of timber. If the timber is decayed, a dull and dead sound will be heard in contrast to the ringing note apparent when sound timber is struck.

Any of the indications described can give rise to suspicions that dry rot exists and if the circumstances of a high level of moisture in the area are also present then the suspicions are almost certain to be confirmed on opening up. It is on these occasions that a moisture meter can be very useful. Those providing a relative scale for moisture in buildings are usually marked in such a way as to indicate whether there is sufficient moisture present to support fungal growth. This can be invaluable on painted timber as there is seldom any indication either by touch or change in appearance whether there is a high or low moisture content.

A supply of moisture is one of the five conditions necessary for the growth of dry rot. It must be remembered however that it is dampness not saturation that is required for growth. Air seasoned timber when built into houses is normally at between 15–18 per cent moisture content of the oven dry weight and with normal heating this soon drops to 12 to 14 per cent and can be lower with central heating. As soon however as the moisture content rises, by whatever means, to 20–25 per cent the timber is susceptible to attack, with the optimum moisture content for growth being at around 40 per cent of the dry weight. At about this level there ceases to be sufficient oxygen (the second condition necessary in the cells of the timber to support growth and respiration) and by the time the wood is completely saturated it is completely immune from attack. Drying out of timber which has been saturated in a house does of course bring it down to a state suitable to support fungal growth, hence the space devoted to reinstatement of fire damage in a building at the end of Chapter 2 and the care necessary to ensure that an outbreak of rot does not arise after a fire has been quenched.

The three other conditions necessary for growth are a suitable temperature, a food supply and, of course, the spore of the fungus itself. In regard to a suitable temperature the range of temperatures found in the average domestic building are entirely satisfactory but the ideal temperature for vigorous growth is around 65°F (18·5°C). The food supply is clearly, in most cases, the timber itself but it should not be forgotten that books and papers stored in damp areas can also provide a suitable food supply. As to how the spores happen to be in the right position for an outbreak to develop is perhaps academic, since if the other conditions are right a fungal outbreak will start and far more often than not it will be the true dry rot fungus, if the situation of the timber is at all unventilated. A statement such that all timbers contain the seeds of their own destruction is probably very true as the spores can remain practically invisible and dormant in all situations of a house merely awaiting the right conditions to flourish. The use of timber treated thoroughly with a wood preservative is the only guarantee that the presence of spores, which cannot be precluded by any known precautions, will be of no consequence.

Opening up in the area where there is evidence or suspicions of an attack will enable the fungal growth to be examined. In unventilated positions, in the vast majority of cases it will be the true dry rot fungus, merulius lacrymans, that is causing the damage, but it must be remembered that there are other fungi which attack wood including the wet rot fungus, coniophora cerebella, and it is important to distinguish them as the processes for eradication differ. The following table reproduced with additional comments and italicizing from Forest Products Research Bulletin No. 1 "Dry Rot in Wood" sixth edition, setting out in the form of a summary the various characteristics of fungi attacking timber in buildings, should assist in identifying the organism, particularly when considered in conjunction with the situation of the outbreak.

As already stated in the vast majority of cases the fungal attack will be of either merulius lacrymans or coniophora cerebella but if there is any doubt samples of the infected timber should be taken together with specimens of the fungus and these submitted to an authority on mycology for identification. Merulius lacrymans and poria vaillantii are both distinguished from the remainder by their ability to form strands or strings which conduct moisture across or through inert material such as stone, brickwork, concrete or steel to attack dry timber possibly some considerable distance away from the original outbreak. This aspect is much greater developed in merulius lacrymans than in poria vaillantii, which requires more moisture in the wood for growth than does merulius and accounts for many of the instances where merulius commences, for example, at one floor level and is also found later at another floor level, the strands carrying the moisture behind plaster and through the intervening brickwork. It is also for this reason that an outbreak of true dry rot is of serious consequence as methods of eradication must be drastic to ensure that all such strands are destroyed otherwise there is a danger of the outbreak reappearing, either elsewhere or in the replacement timber, although all replaced timber should, of course, be preservative treated to avoid any danger of this.

With coniophora cerebella, the wet rot or cellar fungus, there are no conducting strands of this type and provided the source of the dampness giving rise to the original attack is removed replacement with treated timber or preferably some other material, is all that is required. The remaining types of fungus set out in the table can be dealt with in the same way as for coniophora cerebella.

Fungus	Effect on Wood	Strings on the surface of the Wood	Other Growths on the surface of the Wood	Fruit Bodies
Merulius lacrymans "Dry Rot"	Rotted wood shrinks & becomes split up into pieces by deep *cross cracking* Generally occurs in persistently *damp not wet* positions and in unventilated situations. The wood becomes lighter in weight, loses its resinous smell and darkens in colour. In appearance like charred wood apart from colour	Strings grey, sometimes as thick as a lead pencil, becoming brittle when dried	In damp dark places soft white cushions; in drier places thick silver grey sheets or skins usually showing patches of *lemon yellow and tinges of lilac*	Fleshy, soft, but rather tough, shaped like pancakes or brackets. Spore bearing surface yellow red brown, with wide pores or labrynthine ridges and furrows. Margin white
Coniophora cerebella "Wet Rot" also known as "Cellar Fungus"	Causes considerable darkening of the wood and *longitudinal cracking.* Cross cracking not usually visible on the surface. Usually found in damp situations where	Strings slender, usually thread-like, at first yellowish soon becoming deep brown or nearly black	Occasionally very thin skin-like growths	Sheet-like in shape. Fertile surface greenish to olive brown, bearing spores on many minute pimples

Fungus	Effect on Wood	Strings on the surface of the Wood	Other Growths on the surface of the Wood	Fruit Bodies
	there has been leakage of water and in vaults and cellars. In floorboards etc. there is often a "shell" of sound timber			
Poria vaillantii "White Pore fungus"	Rot similar but less widespread than that produced by Merulius. Several species of Poria occur in houses *all requireing more moisture than* Merulius	Strings *white* seldom thicker than stout twine, remaining flexible when dried.	*White or Cream* coloured sheets and growths *never showing* colouration.	Shaped like sheets or plates, white in colour. Spore bearing surface white, showing numerous minute pores
Paxillus pan- uoides	Causes a characteristic *yellow discoloration* in the attacked wood, which finally becomes red brown. Similar in action to Coniophora cerebella	Very slender, yellow but eventually brownish yellow	Rather hairy or woolly, dull yellow, sometimes pale violet in colour	Fleshy, fan- or shell- shaped stalkless. Spore bear- ing surface with radi- ating ridges (gills) at first yellow then ochre

Fungus	Effect on Wood	Strings on the surface of the Wood	Other Growths on the surface of the Wood	Fruit Bodies
Lentinus lepideus	Causes an internal brown cubical rot. This fungus and the attacked wood have a characteristic strong aromatic smell	None	Only present occasionally. Purplish brown felted woolly sheet	Normal form shaped like a mushroom with radiating gills beneath, tough and woody. Frequently abortive forms occur without a cap and consisting only of cylindrical branching out growths
Trametes serialis (Poria monticola)	Causes "dote" in the form of isolated small pockets of brown rot. Eventually may cause general brown cubical rot. Usually found only on timber imported from America	Slender, white much branched	Only developed under very damp conditions, soft white cotton, woolly, sometimes with dark brown patches	Seldom seen in houses: consisting of thin plates or broad thin teeth forming wide pores

True Dry Rot

The places where true dry rot is likely to be found, the signs, both obvious and rather less obvious, of decay and tests for the soundness of timber have already been discussed. In opening up it is necessary to pursue the investigation until the limit as well as the origin of the attack are established. All hidden timbers in the area of attack must be exposed and plaster removed from walls to at least 12 inches (305mm) beyond all signs of fungal growth. Where timbers of large size are involved, it must be remembered that although the outer sections may appear completely free the interior may be affected. A useful method of establishing whether this is so is to drill small holes with an auger and to withdraw shavings separately from each inch of depth and examine these for evidence of fungus. By this means fungal growth, decay or cavities in the centre of the timber can be ascertained, but great care must be taken so as not to unduly weaken structural timbers when using this method.

Once the cause, i.e. the excessive moisture and extent of the outbreak have been established, the source of the moisture giving rise to it must be stopped. This in itself may be a relatively simple matter and obvious insofar as it arises from a neglect of maintenance as already mentioned, but alternatively in older properties it may be the result of a complicated inherent defect in the property, for example a lack of damp-proofing in a basement. Whatever the source it must have prior consideration to remedial measures against the fungus, since it may well be that radical structural improvements must be carried out which will tend to over-ride factors of simple reinstatement of timber. The point being that reinstatement, even with treated timber, is useless if a basic defect in design or construction will continue to allow a high incidence of dampness, unless in the exceptional circumstances where such damp conditions can be tolerated.

Although it has been said that the actual source of the infection, as distinct from the moisture, is probably impossible to determine and in view of the way spores can be blown about more of academic interest, a few pointers can be given which might be of assistance in helping to prevent the spread of spores. In the past it is often thought that spores were brought in with the coal, since much of the pit-wood in coal mines is affected by fungus. The practice of storing coal in an unventilated cupboard below the staircase gave rise to many outbreaks in the floor and staircase construction of old houses. Firewood taken from timber affected by rot and stored in the coal cellar could be another cause. Spores carried by vermin and on clothes are often thought to be the cause of infection and it is usually

417

considered that spores may be present on timber when originally
built into the house and lie dormant for many years. Similarly,
timber introduced for repairs could be infected without it being
realised. Many houses built without site concrete or hardcore are
often left with quantities of scrap pieces of timber, wood shavings
and sawdust below the lowest floor construction and some such
timbers even become buried in the soil. Subsequent lifting of floors
and cutting by electricians, gas fitters and plumbers can give rise to
the same effect. In upper floors, sawdust has even been used in the
past as a pugging and although perhaps not infected at the time can
encourage an outbreak. In dealing with an outbreak of dry rot the
surveyor and contractor should see that a suitable sense of responsibility is adopted so as not to add to the spread of spores in the surrounding area. All too often one sees dry rot infected timber thrown
around, eventually to land on a skip parked in the roadway to be
removed at a later date. By this means spores become scattered far
and wide and instead, where possible, the infected wood should be
carefully removed and burnt, being cut off at least 1 to 2 feet (305
to 610mm) beyond any trace of infection. Similarly fungoid growths
should be carefully scraped off into bags and burnt together with all
dust and dirt from the area which may also contain spores. Tools
used for cutting out affected wood should be wiped over with an
antiseptic.

Once all decayed timber has been removed, it is necessary to
consider the removal of all traces of fungus from brickwork or stonework adjacent. If strands are present on the surface it will almost
invariably be found that they have penetrated into joints and sometimes through cracks and fissures in the bricks themselves. The
degree of penetration is of course impossible to determine unless
some bricks are pulled out, but provided the source of dampness can
be removed and the wall dried out and kept dry in the future it was
considered, until fairly recently, that the application of a flame from
a blow lamp or flame gun over the surface of the brickwork slowly
and repeatedly until it became uncomfortably hot to touch provided
a suitable initial treatment. This, followed by brushing and spraying
with a fungicide applied freely to the surface and worked well
into the joints from which loose mortar should have previously been
raked out, was considered to be effective in rendering any strands
harmless. On the other hand, carelessness in the use of this method
has led to a number of fires in the past and as a result the method
has tended to lose favour. There has also always been considerable
doubt that the process, even apart from being skimped, might not
be entirely effective in dealing with strands buried deep in very
thick walls, particularly where dampness is likely to persist.

Heat treatment has accordingly been increasingly replaced by the method of impregnating the wall with fungicide. Before this is carried out however it is necessary to deal with the surface strands and this is usually done by spraying the brickwork with fungicide, thoroughly wire brushing and then spraying again. Impregnation is then carried out by drilling ½-inch (12·5mm) holes, 6 to 9 inches (152 to 229mm) deep at the top limit of the infected area. The holes should be about 2 feet (610mm) apart horizontally and vertically in staggered rows and should slope down into the wall. Fungicide can be introduced through funnels at the top and the process should be continued until the solution appears from holes cut at the bottom of the infected area. After the irrigation of the wall in this manner it must be left to dry out before replastering and redecoration is attempted, otherwise an efflorescence of soluble salts from the brickwork is likely to develop. If salts do appear on drying out these should be brushed and not washed off. If there is a danger of the wall remaining or becoming damp again which cannot be prevented by orthodox means or the cure of which would be too uneconomical, it is possible now to obtain fungicidal plugs which are in the form of sticks of concentrated fungicide for insertion into brickwork adjacent to timber. These plugs are water soluble and when moisture comes into contact with them the water becomes a fungicidal solution, thus forming a barrier. If the moisture reaches timbers adjacent to brick or stonework it will be in the form of a fungicide preventing an outbreak of rot, instead of encouraging it. It is far better, of course, to ensure that the brickwork is dried out and to prevent dampness occurring again but it must be recognised that this is not always possible and in such circumstances plugs of this type are very useful. The plugs are usually inserted at 3-inch (76mm) centres in holes formed in the mortar joints about 3½ inches (90mm approx.) deep.

At one time sodium fluoride was extensively used as a fungicide for the eradication of dry rot strands in brickwork but both this chemical and magnesium silico-fluoride, which was also widely used, are neutralised by lime mortar and accordingly as attacks are often in the older type of building constructed in lime mortar their use is not now recommended. One of the most effective fungicides is a solution in water of sodium pentachlorophenate at 8 ounces to a gallon of water (50 grammes per litre), but care must be taken in use to avoid splashing on the eyes or face. Another is a solution in water of sodium orthophenylphenate. There are of course a number of proprietary fungicidal solutions on the market, for this purpose, some of them based on pentachlorophenol, one in particular which is both fungicidal and insecticidal as well as being non-inflammable.

419

Whatever proprietary solution is used, however, it is important that it should be suitable for wall sterilisation, i.e. water based and that it should comply with British Standard 838:1961. In addition the maker's instructions should be implicity followed in application, including any safety precautions for its use.

The removal of the infected timber and the sterilisation of brick or other wall construction where the fungus is present being completed, attention must be given to the treatment of sound timber remaining in the area with preservatives and the type of treated timber to be used in replacement work. It is recommended that all timber within 8 to 10 feet (about 3m) of the extent of the attack should be treated with preservative and it is obvious that this can usually only be done by brush application or coarse spraying. The type of fungicide to use will depend on the circumstances and the position of the timber. Since tar oil preservatives are of limited application and should not be used internally within a building, it is preferable to use the water-borne type. These are often proprietary of the copper/chrome and copper/chrome/arsenate types but among the non-proprietary ones suitable are a solution of 6 ounces of sodium fluoride to a gallon of water (37 grammes per litre). This gives a 4 per cent solution and should be applied in two coats by brush, care being taken to ensure penetration into cracks and cavities. If it is considered that a non-poisonous solution should be used this may be obtained by dissolving 8 ounces of borax in a gallon of warm water (50 grammes per litre). The use of water-borne fungicidal preservatives is advantageous in that they are odourless, they do not creep and cause staining in plasterwork, they are usually, or can be obtained, colourless and when dry the timber can be painted. Other forms of solvent type preservatives may be used which consist of a toxic substance such as pentachlorophenol or copper napthenate dissolved in an organic solvent such as white spirit or solvent naptha, so that when the solvent evaporates the toxic substances remain in the wood. As long as the active constituent is present in sufficient quantity this type of preservative is very effective. Reliable proprietary types are generally available from firms specialising in wood preservation.

It is important to remember, however, in the application of preservatives to in-situ timbers that the timber should be clean and free of dust and dirt and should also be air-dry at the time of application. Timber which is damp though not infected should be allowed to dry out thoroughly before any application is made.

Although it has been mentioned that it is necessary to cut out all infected timber there are rare and special occasions where timber known to be infected might well have to be retained if at all possible.

For example a heavy beam slightly affected at one end only, and which would be very costly to replace or which it is desired to retain for architectural or historical reasons could be treated by boring into it a number of holes at an angle to the grain and filling these repeatedly with preservative or with a paste made up of preservative salts. Again great care must be taken not to weaken structural members on this operation. Pastes will slowly diffuse out and form a barrier against the further spread of the fungus. A proprietary paste emulsion based on pentachlorophenol is also available for use on large timbers particularly where the ends of these are built into brickwork or masonry. This paste, when applied, slowly dissolves into the timber and is equivalent to steeping in a solution. It has the advantage of being both fungicidal and insecticidal. There is always risk however in leaving infected timber within a building and the decision to do so should not be taken lightly. On the other hand, carved and valuable joinery which can be removed may be sterilised by heating it in a drying kiln; six hours at a temperature of 130°F (55°C) in a humid atmosphere should be sufficient to sterilise even thick timbers.

Timber used for reinstatement should be pressure impregnated with preservative if the outbreak of dry rot has been severe, where it has been necessary to sterilise brickwork or where walls are so thick as to make sterilisation difficult and, in particular, where walls are likely to remain damp. Water-borne preservatives are used in this process and there is now a network of merchants and suppliers who deal in timber so treated. Accordingly no difficulty should be experienced in obtaining supplies.

It is not possible to generalise on the reinstatement of timber from the structural point of view, since this will depend upon particular circumstances and the position of the outbreak. Much advantage can be gained by avoiding the use of timber if at all possible as this obviates possibility of re-infection. This, however, is not usually possible so that the following brief comments on the main principles to follow will have to suffice at this point, although reference may be made to other sections of this chapter for details and to other appropriate chapters for work in connection with damp-proofing, porous brickwork, etc.:

(1) As far as possible new timber should not be allowed to come into contact with brickwork which has been infected by fungus. Alternative supports should be provided wherever appropriate, but if it is unavoidable that new wallplates or joist ends should be bedded on exterior walls they should rest on bituminous felt which should also be brought up round the sides and ends so that nowhere do the brick and timber actually make contact.

(2) Unnecessary woodwork should be eliminated from replacements for example cornices, picture rails, panels and linings to windows if not essential to appearance.

(3) Built in timbers such as lintels and bond timbers should be replaced with reinforced concrete or possibly steel. Defective skirtings in basement rooms should be replaced by cement skirtings. Also in basements where walls are damp and have been infected with fungus, it is preferable to renew wood windows in steel or aluminium, particularly if any damp-proofing to satisfy Basement Room Regulations is to be achieved by a lining rather than the insertion of a damp proof course.

(4) If the ends only of joists or a beam are affected and the remainder is sound, it is possible to effect a repair by splicing a new end or ends in treated timber as previously described in this chapter.

(5) A thorough check on ventilation to the underside of floors and the backs of panelling should be carried out and improvements made where necessary following the recognised principles, for example with air bricks for underfloor ventilation there should be $1\frac{1}{2}$ square inches (about 970mm^2) for every foot run (305mm) of wall, suitably disposed.

The final stage of the reinstatement work will comprise the replastering and decoration and it is at this point that a further barrier to re-infection from brickwork can be applied. This comprises the use of a fungicidal plaster or paint based on zinc oxychloride cement. This can substantially prevent the emergence of merulius growths from infected brickwork and when skilfully applied can be entirely effective in this respect. In regard to moderate or severe outbreaks most surveyors would specify its use as an added insurance, but in very light outbreaks, caught at an early stage where there is little or no evidence of fungal growth in the brickwork, it is likely to prove effective on its own and to avoid the need for irrigation of the walls. It can also be usefully employed on occasion when the risk of efflorescence from irrigation may not be acceptable. The paint is intended for application direct to brick walls or cement rendering that is sound, while the plaster can be used as an undercoat below a setting coat of retarded hemihydrate plaster. If walls are damp, however, the zinc oxychloride should be used as the middle coat of a three coat rendering, the first coat being of cement, lime and sand of 1:1:6 mix. The barrier should be continued at least 12 inches (305mm) on either side of the timber to be protected.

Much can be done by owners and their surveyors to prevent costly outbreaks of dry rot, wasteful in resources of money, labour and materials, by attention to the proper maintenance of buildings to prevent those incursions of dampness which so often give rise to outbreaks. So often the damp penetration is allowed to continue until the outbreak of dry rot is all too obvious. There is always a danger in neglect of this order of the spread of an outbreak of dry rot from one house to another, particularly in terrace properties of cheap construction where party wall separation at roof level is not always ideal. This can have serious consequences for an owner, in that he may well be faced with the cost of eradication and repair in the adjoining house as well as his own. On the other hand damp penetration quickly cured often leaves timbers in a saturated condition which later produces an outbreak when the moisture content reaches the appropriate level. Although it is persistent dampness which usually causes dry rot, following any damp penetration the possibility of dry rot should not be overlooked, prevention being better than cure. For example if wood floors become saturated by a plumbing or substantial roof leak the floor coverings should be removed and floorboards alongside walls taken up until timbers return to the moisture content level normal to the building. As an aid to this windows should be left slightly open and this should always be done in basement and top floors when a building is left for any length of time unoccupied. When a building is left empty over winter months the water system should always be drained down as well as being shut off from the main. Owners who leave property empty should be advised to arrange for regular inspections as, apart from blocked gutters and the like, leadwork can easily be removed from roofs without anyone being the wiser. With properties adjacent to trees it is sensible to assume that gutters will become blocked in the autumn and to fit wire balloons to outlets and arrange for periodic clearing. In some instances, for example damp penetration through a flat roof or below an eaves gutter, it may even be necessary to remove sections of plaster to ensure that hidden timbers dry out thoroughly and remain ventilated during the process.

An attack by fungus on the timbers of a house is often the prelude to an infestation by wood-boring insects. The action of the fungi in breaking up the wood makes it more susceptible to attack by insects. Cracks in the surface of painted wood provide suitable positions for mature insects to lay their eggs and the composition of the timber during and after a fungal attack makes it easier for the larvae of the insect to eat and digest. Accordingly it may be necessary to use both a fungicidal and insecticidal solution for the treatment of existing and replacement wood. In this case it is not recommended that solutions be made up from purchased chemicals but that proprietary solutions be obtained from recognised manufacturers and suppliers of which there are a number and which are warranted to be effective for both purposes and tested in accordance with the appropriate British Standards.

Attack by Wood-Boring Insect

Attacks on the timbers of a building by wood-boring insects in the absence of an infestation by fungi require a different treatment, but not one so drastic as that required for an outbreak of true dry rot. In the first instance, however, it is necessary to identify the type of insect causing the attack as well as establishing its extent before the need for remedial measures is considered.

In this country there are four types of wood-boring insect which can cause structural damage to timbers. These are:

(1) The common furniture beetle (anobium punctatum), which is widespread, causing damage not only to structural timbers and joinery but to plywood and furniture as well. Infestations by this beetle are far more commonly found than by any other.

(2) The house longhorn beetle (hylotrupes bajulus) which is confined at present to northern parts of the county of Surrey and parts of Hampshire and Berkshire. It is against attacks from this beetle that Regulation B4 of the Building Regulations 1972 requires softwood roof timbers to be pre-treated with preservative in the areas set out in Schedule 5. The Forest Products Research Laboratory of the Building Research Establishment at Princes Risborough, Aylesbury, Bucks., wish to be notified of outbreaks elsewhere as there is evidence to suggest that the area of attack is spreading.

(3) The death watch beetle (xestobium ruforillosum) which is widespread in England and Wales but rarer in the north of England and not found at all in Scotland and which confines its attention to the sapwood and heartwood of hardwoods, principally oak, usually commencing where some decay already exists. It is of more importance in timber framed houses and is rarely found in brick or stone buildings except where the roof or floor structure are of oak.

(4) The Lyctus powder post beetle (various species), so called because of the manner in which its larvae reduce the timber attacked to a flour-like powder. The larvae attack the sapwood of hardwood, preferring the open pore type such as oak, ash and walnut. Softwoods are never attacked so that in domestic construction infestations are comparatively rare. They may however occur in the sapwood of oak used in framing or in decorative hardwood joinery items and flooring.

In the absence of some failure, such as the collapse of a floorboard, signs of an attack only materialise in the form of the exit hole produced when the fully grown beetle emerges from the wood. Quite a number of wood-boring insects however produce exit holes and it is important to distinguish those attacks involving the four beetles set out above and which usually require treatment from those of other beetles which do not. To do this requires a knowledge of the shape and size of the exit hole produced by each beetle, the type of timber which it attacks and the characteristics of the bore dust produced by the larvae tunnelling in the wood. These differences can best be set out in a short table commencing with those species which when found will usually cause further damage unless eradicated.

Type of Insect	Type of timber attacked and situation	Exit Holes	Bore Dust
Common furniture beetle	Mainly sapwoods of both softwoods and hardwoods. Wicker-work and cheap ply-wood particularly favoured as are floor-boards where sapwood often forms a high proportion. Primary and subsequent infesta-tions can produce persistent attacks over a long period eventu-ally weakening struc-tural members	Circular $\frac{1}{16}$th inch (1·5 mm)	Finely granular consisting of lemon shaped pellets. Piles of this below affected timbers are a useful indication of attack. Gritty to the touch
House longhorn beetle	Generally the sap-woods of softwoods are affected, not hard-woods. Attacks com-mence in roof struc-ture and work down-wards and will persist until the sapwood is disintegrated within a thin light shell casing of intact wood. Warmth favoured hence attacks often commence around chimney stacks, within roof space. Slight blisters on wood may indicate presence of	Oval, $\frac{3}{8}$th by $\frac{3}{16}$th inch (10 by 5 mm)	Mixture of finely divided wood dust and particles with excrement con-sisting of short compact cylin-ders almost as broad as they are long. Bore dust is not ex-pelled from galleries

Type of Insect	Type of timber attacked and situation	Exit Holes	Bore Dust
	larvae but usually a probe needed. Larvae may tunnel for years		
Death watch beetle	Old timber only is attacked and then only hardwoods usually oak (both sapwood and heartwood). Most damage usually occurs in built in parts such as ends of tie-beams, wallplates and other woodwork in poorly ventilated places where, in presence of moisture, conditions would be suitable for fungal attack	Circular ⅛th inch (3mm)	Distinguished by the presence of small oval or bun shaped pellets in the dust
Lyctus powder post beetle	All hardwoods but usually only the sap-wood. Softwoods are never affected. Hard-woods such as oak, ash, walnut and elm with open pores are more liable to attack	Circular 1/16th inch (1·5mm)	Floury, talc-like powder

The following wood-boring insects can also be found in buildings, but to a much lesser extent. On the other hand they can be confused with the more serious pests by those unfamiliar with their various characteristics. No treatment of timber is usually required as all die out within a few years and sometimes within a year of construction work being completed. Accordingly when signs of their presence is found in buildings more than a few years old activity can be entirely discounted.

426

Type of Insect	Type of timber attacked and situation	Exit Holes	Bore Dust
Ambrosia beetle (pinhole borer beetle)	All timber both sapwood and heartwood but originates in the forest and dies out when timber converted and seasoned	Circular $\frac{1}{50}$th to $\frac{1}{8}$th inch in diameter (0·5mm to 3mm) according to species	None
Waney-edge borer beetle	Occurs only between the bark and sapwood of softwoods. Originates in logs and newly converted timber and occasionally found in roof timbers with waney edges	Circular, $\frac{1}{16}$th inch (1·5mm)	Brown and white oval or bun-shaped pellets according to whether larvae feeding on bark or sapwood
Forest longhorn and jewel beetles	Sapwood of softwoods and hardwoods only and originates in the trees and logs. It is possible to confuse these with the House Longhorn beetle but if there is any doubt the Forest Products Research Laboratory should be consulted by sending a sample of affected wood	Oval, of various sizes according to species	Mixture of pellets and wood splinters
Wood-wasps	Sapwood and heartwood of softwoods. Dies out within a year, originating in trees and logs	Circular, $\frac{1}{8}$th to $\frac{1}{4}$ inch (4 to 6mm)	Tightly packed chips of wood
Ship-worm	All timbers but only arises in those floated in salt water and dies out on removal from water	None	None

427

Type of Insect	Type of timber attacked and situation	Exit Holes	Bore Dust
Powder post beetles (Bostrychidae)	Sapwood of imported hardwoods only. Originate from overseas and die out within a year	Circular up to $\frac{3}{16}$th inch (5mm)	Flour-like powder
Wood-boring weevils	Softwoods, hardwoods and plywood may be affected but infests only damp and decaying wood. Both larvae and the adult weevils will probably be present in the timber all the year round. Measures taken to deal with the damp and the decay in the timber will also deal with the weevil	Ragged in outline up to about $\frac{1}{16}$th inch (1·5mm)	Both weevils and the larvae tunnel into the wood leaving pellets of similar appearance but smaller than that of the common furniture larvae

Another member of the anobidae family which does not attack timber and is commonly known as the bread beetle (stegobium paniceum) might be mistaken for a common furniture beetle if seen at the appropriate time of the year. The two insects are somewhat similar in appearance but there will be no evidence of exit holes in timbers, food being the main source of nourishment, particularly that made of flour or meal, although there are cases of books being affected. There are only a few entomologists available for consultation if the surveyor is in doubt on the identity of larvae or insects but the Forest Products Research Laboratory at Princes Riseborough, Aylesbury, Bucks., will identify any specimen sent to them free of charge.

The evidence of attack being identified as due to one of the four types of beetle normally likely to cause serious damage, a full inspection of the building should be made to establish the extent of the infestation, to assess whether it is active or not and the damage that has been caused. This involves the rather laborious close inspection of all visible timbers in some detail with torch and bradawl, because it is more often that the attack will be concentrated on one or two members in particular areas, for example a few rafters in a roof space. With upper floors, it is often possible only to take up occasional floorboards for checking the undersides, where exit holes are more frequently found, and the joists. Signs of activity include new clearly formed exit holes, piles of dust around holes in horizontal and undisturbed surfaces or diffuse bore dust below members attacked, live larvae within the timbers or even the beetles themselves, from June to August in the case of the common furniture and house longhorn beetles, from April to June in the case of the death watch beetle and from spring to autumn for the powder post beetle.

Signs of activitiy indicate the need for treatment, but it must be remembered that attacks by wood-boring beetles do die out of their own accord, presumably because in some way or other conditions cease to be favourable. In view of the nature of the larvae to tunnel in the wood, the absence of the signs of activity set out in the previous paragraph is not always an indication that the attack is extinct. It is necessary in these circumstances either to remove sections of timber for close examination in order to detect living larvae or to wait and reinspect at around the time the adult beetles leave the wood for evidence of fresh exit holes, bore dust and possibly the insects themselves.

The first stage of remedial measures is to remove dust and grime from affected timbers with a powerful vacuum cleaner. Once this has been done, structural timbers that have not already failed under intensive attack should be scraped to remove all powdered wood, in order to assess whether sufficient strength remains or whether it will be necessary to renew the member or supplement it with another alongside, in the manner already described previously in this Chapter. Obviously timbers which have failed must be renewed or repaired, and perhaps supplemented as well.

If an active attack is found in a roof space or in a floor, it is always advisable to treat the whole of the roof space and the whole of that particular floor rather than just the areas immediately affected. Application of the insecticide can be made either by brush or spray, although for large areas or spots difficult of access, a low pressure coarse spray is clearly preferable. What is desirable with both methods is to flood the surface of the wood but without causing an excessive run-off which might cause staining. One application is usually sufficient on rough sawn surfaces which absorb about a gallon per 200 square feet of surface (equivalent to about 4 square metres per litre), but with smooth planed surfaces it may be necessary to repeat the treatment after about two days in order to achieve the desired rate of absorption. It is useless to spray painted surfaces and only the backs of such surfaces should be treated, although there is considerable advantage in injecting any flight holes on the painted surface with insecticide under pressure as eggs are often laid in old flight holes. Most insecticides will kill any larvae which are reached by penetration into the wood both by respiration and ingestion and some by contact, but in any treatment of an active attack there are bound to be larvae at a greater depth than that reached by the insecticide. These larvae will continue to tunnel at safe depths and eventually come near to the surface to change into an adult beetle and endeavour to emerge. Unfortunately the adult beetle does not eat wood at this stage so that a simple poison to beetles and larvae is not really sufficient to cope with this problem entirely and an insecticide which kills both on ingestion and contact is required. The use of such an insecticide will generally ensure that on contact with treated timber the adult beetle will either die in process of emerging or subsequently when crawling around on the timber. If it should survive to lay more eggs then these too should be affected by contact or later as larvae by ingestion. Even so it is always possible for some parts of a roof or floor to be missed or the application to be so slight as to be ineffective so that the presence of fresh exit holes, bore dust or live beetles in the summer months indicates that the original treatment was not entirely effective and that a further application is necessary.

At the present time insecticides which are effectively toxic both by contact and ingestion are based on the chlorinated hydrocarbon types dieldrin and lindane (gamma B.H.C.), the latter to be preferred as being less harmful to other organisms. These are very potent even in small quantities but in order to provide a protection to the timbers against subsequent attack for a number of years it is necessary to use a fairly high concentration, 0·5 per cent of lindane in a penetrating organic solvent. The cost of insecticides depend on the degree of refinement of the solvent and if the work is being carried out by a building contractor rather than a specialist, economy can be achieved by purchasing different grades. The less refined grades are suitable for roof spaces and under floors and the more refined clear odourless grades for joinery, built-in cupboards and the like.

As will be apparent the type of insecticide needed to eradicate an infestation of wood-boring insects needs to be of a different type to that merely required for the preservation of sound timber against the possibility of attack. Since an attack must originate with the laying of eggs on the surface or in cracks in the wood from which the larvae develop and start tunnelling into the timber it follows that an insecticide which kills only by ingestion is suitable. There are many more types, apart from the chlorinated hydrocarbon types referred to above, available which perform this function hence the Building Regulations 1972 state that the requirements of Regulation B4(2) (requiring treatment to roof timbers in certain areas against the house longhorn beetle) shall be deemed to be satisfied if:

(a) the timber is treated in accordance with the provisions of B.S.4072:1966, or

(b) the timber when freshly felled and milled and having an average moisture content of not less than 50 per cent of its oven dry mass, is treated by diffusion with sodium borate to produce a net dry salt retention of not less than $5 \cdot 3 \text{kg/m}^3$ of boric acid equivalent; or

(c) the timber is completely immersed for not less than ten minutes in an organic solvent type wood preservative solution containing not less than 0·5 per cent gamma B.H.C., dieldrin or other persistent organochlorine contact insecticide and any surfaces subsequently exposed by cutting the timber for fitting into the building are thoroughly treated by dipping, spraying or brushing these surfaces with the same type of preservative.

The full title of B.S.4072:1966 referred to above is "Wood preservation by means of water-borne copper/chrome/arsenic compositions".

Considering the amount of damage done by wood-boring insects and the amount of money spent annually on eradication it seems odd that courage could not have been found for the Building Regulations to require preservative treatment to all timbers in new buildings irrespective of their position. By this means all future buildings could be freed from the risk of insect or fungal attack and this in itself in due course would contribute to a lessening of the number of insects to cause attacks to existing buildings since breeding would eventually be curtailed. The increase in the demand for pre-treated timber would in due course bring down the cost of such treatment, there being very limited demand for it, in the domestic field, at the present time. Legislation of this nature might well be combined with the form of compulsory insurance against infestation, as is required on some parts of the continent, unless full treatment is carried out.

A list of the manufacturers of liquid insecticides and of suppliers of preservative treated timber can be obtained from the British Wood Preserving Association, 62 Oxford Street, London, W.1. The Association also publishes a guide to safety precautions, including fire and electrical precautions, to be taken when chemical treatment is carried out. These are essential, since the relevant solvent substances in insecticides include white spirit and petroleum with their attendant fire risks and the toxic substances combined with the solvents are harmful when inhaled or absorbed through the skin. The fire risk may persist for a week while the solvents are evaporating and operatives must wear overalls and rubber gloves and face masks in addition, when sprays are used. Furthermore it is always necessary to cover water cisterns in the roof space when chemical treatment is being carried out.

The treatment of death watch beetle in old timber framed houses can perhaps be looked upon in a slightly different light to the treatment of softwood comprising the carcass of the ordinary brick or stone built house. The object will be to preserve as much as possible of the old timber so that to do this it may be necessary to limit the amount of wood cut away to the sapwood only or to that which is structurally dangerous although preferably even this can be left by transferring the load elsewhere. In addition frequent inspections should be arranged and perhaps a number of treatments to ensure that the infestation has ceased. Much more important however is to ensure that all wood that is obviously decayed by fungal attack be removed and that sound wood is kept dry and ventilated as it is decayed wood and dark unventilated places that provide the breeding ground for death watch beetle.

MAINTENANCE

Timber used in dwelling houses falls roughly into three categories for maintenance purposes. Internally there is the timber left rough from the saw forming floors, roof structure and sometimes, but not so often nowadays, the interior of partitions. This timber forms the "carcassing" and no maintenance as such, is normally required to it. As we have seen, however, carcassing timber must be kept dry, at the normal moisture content of timber in the building, otherwise there is a danger of fungal attack. In addition, there is always the possibility of attack from wood-boring insects. Both of these can be avoided by the use of pre-treated timber in new buildings, but there is no legislative requirement for this to be used in general at the present time, despite the obvious sense of such a requirement. Existing timbers in a building could be protected in such a way, but the cost of this, as merely a matter of prevention rather than cure, is clearly so much greater than would be the case if pre-treated timber was used originally that it is seldom considered. The disturbance, the raising of floorboards, the need to remove dust and dirt before treatment and the limitation on use of the building for a week or so afterwards, hardly warrants the expenditure and even then there would remain a proportion of timber untreated, as some would remain totally inaccessible.

The remaining timber internally comprises the joinery and the floors. The latter may be provided with a variety of finishes, ranging from paint to polish which require periodical attention.

432

Externally, timber as we have already seen can be used as an exposed frame, as in the mediaeval house, but the maintenance of exposed oak in these circumstances has already been dealt with as being a special case not so often encountered. In most cases, timber exposed to the weather will be in the form of cladding, windows or doors. Exposure to sun and rain will affect timber in a number of ways if left untreated. There is swelling in wet weather and shrinkage in dry conditions. These continual movements can cause slight cracks to appear in most timbers and eventually the surface of the timber takes on a spongy characteristic, which not only holds dirt but can also encourage mould and fungal growths. In addition, the colour characteristics of the wood will change and these might also be affected by pollution in the atmosphere. Design plays an important part in the durability of wood exposed to the weather, even when it has a protective coating. Many instances will be found in domestic buildings of poor detailing which allows water to collect and even some positions where it can become entrapped, particularly in window design. The protective coating will fail first at these points, allowing moisture to penetrate into the wood. Other cases arise where end grain is left exposed in cheaper domestic construction. The use of sapwood, which cannot be economically excluded for ordinary grade softwood joinery timbers presents problems in modern construction, as this is more subject to moisture absorption, with the result that any sapwood near an open joint will decay far more rapidly than heartwood in similar circumstances. In modern construction, condensation plays an increasing part in the decay of window joinery due to light construction and a failure to provide condensation and drainage channels. In maintenance work, much renewal will often be necessary in window and door joinery and the opportunity should always be taken to consider faults in the design of the item to be renewed, so as to avoid a repetition of past mistakes.

Most external joinery and often cladding as well, receives a coating of paint in domestic construction. This practice is of long standing and certainly extends back for a period of at least 400 years since the time imported softwood began to replace home grown oak. Although painting has a long tradition, it is still a practice that requires certain conditions to produce a satisfactory result. Those conditions are just those which, at the present time lend themselves to short cuts and economies. For example, a good quality paint should be used and there are plenty of cheap brands of paint on the market. Another condition to produce a good result is adequate preparation, but this work is laborious and costly and there is very little to show for it initially. The important factor in maintenance repainting is to carry out the work at the appropriate time, before

433

the old film has started to flake and crack. If properly applied a paint film should last five to six years, despite the insistence of many lease documents on repainting every three years externally. The situation is often compromised however by the fact that sills and the lower parts of frames and sashes, indeed all those parts more exposed to the weather, start to flake before other sections and, as a result, the periods between maintenance often have to be less than the ideal, otherwise damage to the woodwork will arise. There might be a case for repainting some sections before the remainder, but in view of the difficulty of matching both colour and degree of gloss, this would prove unacceptable to most owners.

Accordingly, on the assumption that a previous painting procedure has produced a satisfactory result, in maintenance it is necessary to keep an eye on the paint film in subsequent years, particularly on sills and the more exposed parts. An inspection once a year after two years have elapsed would be ideal. If these parts are sound after five years, so much the better as then a reasonably economical repainting can be carried out following thorough cleaning of the surface with a detergent or mild soap powder, thoroughly rinsed off subsequently; then slight abrasion to remove any gloss and provide a better key, a most essential part of the operation, followed by an undercoat and a top coat, if possible of the same make as the original. If the paint film shows slight signs of breaking down before five years have elapsed, then repainting must be carried out before this period is up. Most surfaces will probably be satisfactory for the normal two coat work already described, except that it may be necessary to rub down more to remove gloss from these surfaces which will not have undergone their full period of weathering. Surfaces which are slightly flaking or cracking need much more careful attention to remove all loose paint and it is often preferable to strip these sections entirely by scraping or burning off, avoiding the use of water altogether. Surfaces must then be clean and dry, the latter being particularly important and often difficult to achieve in our climate when bare areas have allowed rainwater to soak in for a period. Notwithstanding much can be done by covering up at this crucial moment. Knots or resinous areas should be treated with a shellac knotting and the whole section of bare wood primed with a white lead, oil based, primer, or a suitable proprietary primer recommended by the manufacturers of the paint being used. Two undercoats and a top coat should complete the painting. Aluminium primers should be avoided, as if used on external surfaces only they promote blistering. They are satisfactory only when used on all surfaces of new or replacement wood, in view of their nature as a vapour barrier.

If the existing paintwork is substantially missing or the paint surface is blistered, cracked, peeling, soft, very chalky or shows any signs of adhesion weakness, it should be stripped completely. Complete removal is also desirable if the paint film has been affected by mould growth or by bleeding through of bituminous paints previously applied, stains or preservatives or, alternatively, if there are already an excessive number of coats present clogging and spoiling the outline of mouldings. Burning off remains the best method of removing paint from woodwork, not too hot a flame being used and commencing with mouldings and narrow members before proceeding to general surfaces. Wood left exposed for any length of time is likely to be affected by mould growths and permitting the blow lamp to play gently on the bare areas is sufficient to sterilise these affected parts and destroy the growths. Carved undercut mouldings and areas near glass do not lend themselves to blow lamp stripping and a paint remover should be used of the organic solvent type to B.S.3761 not the alkaline type (see Chapter 9) and care should be taken to see that all residue is thoroughly washed away either with white spirit or water according to the maker's directions.

Where wood has been extensively softened by exposure to the weather or has become friable, it should be cut out and replaced with sound wood or alternatively planed or sanded down if this is practical. Where either of these methods is not feasible on the grounds of expense or because of a desire not to disturb the original more than necessary, a treatment as follows is recommended. The wood should be burnt off in the usual way and then treated with linseed or boiled linseed oil, sufficient to satisfy the porosity but not to give an oily film on the surface. After at least drying for 24 hours, the surface should be primed preferably with a lead based primer if there is no danger from its toxic nature but as second best with a leadless primer, but in either case paying special attention to end grain. With the priming completed, any cracks or holes should be filled with white lead based stopping or other similar non-shrinking filler. Undercoating and finishing can then be applied as for new work in accordance with British Standard Code of Practice C.P.231: 1966.

Where decayed wood is cut out and replaced, it is important that both new and old timber surfaces are well coated with a brush application of preservative, all end grain being liberally treated before any new piece is inserted.

Sometimes when paintwork requires renewal it is found to be generally sound apart from blistering on knots. The blisters should be removed by burning off, allowing the blow lamp to play on the knots for a further period so as to extract some of the resin. Following this heat treatment, two coats of shellac knotting can be applied, but preferably nowadays two coats of an aluminium primer, since it has always been difficult to get subsequent coats of paint to adhere to shellac knotting. Before undercoating, cracks and small holes should be filled with an oil filler. Very large heavily resinous or loose knots should be drilled out and the holes plugged with sound wood finished flush with the surrounding surface, any scars being filled as described above.

Paints suitable at the present time for external use on timber are those based on linseed oil and those employing an alkyd medium. Both are satisfactory, but the oil paints are softer and tend to permit dirt to be retained on surfaces while the alkyd based are not quite so elastic when hardened. In using both types it is important to avoid the application of too thick a paint film, as this causes flaking, to follow the manufacturer's recommendations on application implicitly and, in all circumstances, to avoid outside painting in wet and cold weather.

The labour cost in repainting work is exceptionally high compared with the cost of the materials. It pays therefore in obtaining competitive estimates, to choose reliable contractors and to advise clients not to accept an estimate that is clearly too low. Savings on external painting can only be achieved by skimping on the preparation and, although there may be little or no difference when the work is finished in the appearance, the effects of poor preparation will soon become apparent. One skimped repaint can be costly in the long run and the effects can last for years.

Well maintained painted external timber will last indefinitely and as a foil to brick or stonework is unrivalled. Undoubtedly, however, on modern houses where there is an increasing use of timber cladding a clear glossy finish can provide an attractive appearance, bringing out the colour and grain of the wood. It has the disadvantage of requiring even more frequent maintenance than a paint film and, initially, it is necessary to apply four or five coats at least of a good quality finish such as an alkyd or tungoil/phenolic varnish and to avoid sharp arrises where breakdown often occurs first. Durability under the action of the weather is not very good and two to three years at most will be the maximum before breakdown begins to occur. Even before then there may be a loss of colour or colour change in the wood. As soon as signs of this appear, the surface should be cleaned down with water, lightly rubbed down, bleached areas touched up and two more coats of varnish applied otherwise it may be necessary to strip the whole surface, a costly and difficult matter. Varnish is probably best used on surfaces which are sheltered as much as possible from the effects of sun and rain. As in the case of paint it is important to obtain a good quality exterior finish from a reputable firm. Good quality varnishes consist of a high proportion of drying oils treated with natural, alkyd, phenolic or other resins to give quicker drying properties. Other types of resinous finishes (epoxy, urea, vinyl, acrylic, polyurethane) have proved in the main unsuitable as treatments on external timber, although they may be perfectly satisfactory when used internally. Polyurethane, in particular, has shown that although it possesses fair durability, once it has weathered it is impossible to ensure that a fresh coat will adhere.

In many ways a more superior and economical finish for external cladding is provided by the penetrating "Madison" type of preservative. This consists of linseed oil, resins, wax and a preservative, a suitable formula appearing at the end of the Building Research Establishment Digest No. 21 (second series). The original type produces a matt finish but proprietary equivalents now incorporate semi-transparent pigments and produce a semi-gloss finish. These treatments are relatively low in cost, remain effective for about three years and allow the timber to breathe. They are readily recoated after weathering as they produce no surface film to crack and, therefore, need no stripping. They offer a water repellent treatment which prevents whitening of the timber or any darkening due to mould growth and are particularly suitable for use on western red cedar claddings. A recent development by the Forest Products Research Laboratory consists of "Timberlab" varnish, which it is considered will have a life comparable to an opaque paint.

On hardwoods no specific treatment can be recommended for exterior surfaces, "teak oils" being unsuitable and oiling with linseed oil usually causing heavy dirt retention. Madison type preservatives will not penetrate hardwood normally unless weathering has made the surface somewhat more absorbent.

For fences and outbuildings and sometimes for cladding if softwood is used, a tar oil preservative, such as creosote, is suitable but requires periodic applications to renew the colour and, in particular, if it has only been brush applied. Lighter or refined grades are available, or blends with other materials and are more suited for cladding, in view of the smell and stickiness of ordinary creosote. Organic solvent preservatives can be applied by brush and are available in a range of colours, but regular applications are necessary every two to three years for maintenance purposes. Whereas creosote cannot be overpainted organic solvent preservatives can.

Water repellents can also be applied by brush and will retain the colour of exposed timber cladding for three to five years in situations where it would normally bleach out in six months if left untreated. They can be renewed again by brush application, but it is unwise to overpaint unless a special paintable material has been used originally.

Stains can also be used on external timber, but they must possess external durability so that they are normally incorporated in water repellent preservatives or resinous solutions in an organic solvent. Those available either fade or wash off or darken in colour. Those which fade can be used initially and then be renewed every four to five years. The second type should be used only for touching up timber previously treated with a clear water repellent preservative and when the colour has bleached out.

Internal joinery is usually given some form of treatment to protect it from dirt and grease introduced by handling, but obviously the more stringent requirements of durability against the weather do not apply. Accordingly a wider variety of finishes is available. For painted work cleanliness, preparation and applications to well rubbed down surfaces and to a proper specification in accordance with the manufacturer's recommendations are equally essential. The usual lease term to repaint every seven years internally is often excessive, as well applied painted work, looked after and occasionally washed down with warm water and soap, followed by leathering, will last for many more years.

Chapter 6
Shoring

Contents

439

FEW surveyors or architects would claim that the subject of shoring provided them with a vital aspect of interest in their work. Generally the feeling is that it is one of those necessities which irritatingly add to the cost of most contracts but for which there is nothing to show. The consequence of this lack of interest is that all too often the matter is left to the contractor to sort out and to provide at the least possible expense. This is a mistaken policy even more so in works of repair than in new work for the following reasons:

(1) It is the duty of the surveyor to instruct the contractor to arrange for shoring when it is necessary and to specify what is required.

(2) Neglect to arrange for shoring when it is necessary puts at risk the lives of workmen, possible members of the public and occupants of adjoining buildings.

(3) The building owner will be put to additional expense if the collapse or further movement of features arises due to the neglect of the surveyor to specify shoring or if the shoring specified is inadequate.

(4) An intelligently arranged system of shoring designed with a view to facilitating all the works on the contract and thought out in advance can save the client money, particularly if shoring is so designed that it can be moved around on a large contract and reused without being dismantled.

There is a long tradition of methods of shoring in timber and most textbooks on building construction devote some attention to it. Notwithstanding this fact, the importance of shoring necessitates a section of this book being devoted to the subject but having particular regard to its need in repair work and to reiterate the general principles to be adopted in the design of shoring.

The temporary support of structures while building repair operations are in progress is one of those fields where there have been few changes over recent years in methods or the materials used so far as construction in the domestic field is concerned.

Timber has always been and remains the most adaptable material for the purpose and although adjustable steel props have tended to replace timber for light dead shoring for floors since the Second World War and rolled steel joists are occasionally used often in place of timber for needles, the general contractor nearly always has his store of timber ready for shoring purposes and his men are usually familiar with the operation of erecting it. Just occasionally one sees large raking shores on building sites formed from a vast number of steel scaffolding poles, but these will always be designed by an engineer in collaboration with a specialist firm of scaffolding contractors and even now the incidence of shores of this nature is surprisingly rare even on central sites being redeveloped adjacent to the largest buildings of monolithic construction.

General Principles of Shoring

Shoring should be carefully designed so that when the time comes to transfer the weight of the structure to be supported to it, this can be done without any jarring whatever. This means that the shoring must be wedged just sufficiently tight before any other work is carried out. The weight of the structure supported must be transferred through the shoring to suitable reaction points forming a rigid base. Since most shoring is taken to ground level it is important that suitable consideration is given to spreading the load according to the capacity of the soil to sustain it. During the time the shoring is in use there must be no danger from movement within the shoring or its foundation which might cause any appreciable movement or in an extreme case, disaster from collapse. In addition shoring must be designed to allow clear space for working both in regard to demolition, repair or rebuilding, the bringing in of materials and members fabricated elsewhere and particularly, in the case of needle shoring, be sufficiently strong to provide for the attachment of hoisting gear for the insertion of beams etc.

Timber is well known to expand and shrink in accordance with weather conditions and this factor must be taken into account in the design. Means of adjustment in the form of folding wedges must be provided so that these can be tightened in the event of shrinkage. In order to prevent these wedges from working loose if shrinkage does occur, they should be secured in position but in such a manner that does not prevent their subsequent adjustment. Frequent inspections should be made by the surveyor with the contractor and the necessary adjustments made as required.

The shoring should be designed to facilitate the transfer of the weight supported back to the main structure on the completion of the repairs in easy gentle stages so as to enable a check to be made on the completed work, retaining the opportunity of relieving the new work of all load in the unlikely event of this being necessary. If by a gentle transfer of the load all is well it must be possible to remove the temporary support without jar or disturbance to the permanent work.

Shoring can be divided into two main types. The first type is that erected to provide a wall with lateral support and to prevent movement in a lateral direction which would cause it to collapse. Raking and flying shores fall into this type and for that matter other means of tieing-in a wall such as tie-rods and plates also fall within this category. These other methods however are more of a semi-permanent nature as a means of restraint and have been dealt with elsewhere in this book. The second type is that erected to carry the weight of walls and floors while repair works are being carried out. Loads which act vertically are known as dead loads and this type of shoring is usually called dead shoring. When dead shoring is used to support the upper part of a wall it employs horizontal supports known as needles as previously described in Chapter 4, where needles were sometimes employed for the support of walls during underpinning works.

Raking Shores

An early requirement in many schemes of repair is the provision of lateral support to a wall which has assumed a lean outwards, is extensively cracked or bulged or has settled so badly as to give a suspicion that collapse is by no means a remote possibility. The most common, but by no means the only, way of providing this lateral support is by the use of raking shores. Another instance where this form of support is required arises when an adjacent building is demolished, depriving a neighbour of its support and yet another often occurs where underpinning is necessary to the foundations of a wall for one reason or another.

Standard practice is that raking shores should be erected at each end and at 12 to 15 feet intervals (3·6 to 4·5m) along the length of a wall at right-angles to it. In the case of underpinning, demolition of adjoining property or repair work along the length of a wall shores should also be erected at each corner in line with the wall.

For normal domestic buildings not exceeding four or five storeys in height built of brick load bearing walls the size of rakers should be as follows for the appropriate height of wall:

20 to 30 feet (6 to 9·1m) 6 by 6 inches (152 by 152mm).
30 to 40 feet (9·1 to 12·2m) 7 by 7 inch (178 by 178mm).
40 to 50 feet (12·2 to 15·2m) 9 by 9 inches (229 by 229mm).

In the unlikely event of the domestic building being outside this category it would be advisable to obtain the services of an engineer or a specialist shoring contractor to design a suitable system either using larger timbers or steel sections. Raking shores should if possible be in single timbers but if single lengths are not available it is permissible to use a splice as shown on Figure 65. If it is necessary

443

to splice more than one raker in a system of shores it is important that the splices are not opposite each other and that each splice is provided with lacings. The size of raking shore determines the width of wall piece and sole piece so that the shores can be secured to the sole piece by dogs and to the wall piece by the lacings.

In designing a system of rakers and arranging for their positioning it must be remembered that the thrust from the rakers must be counterbalanced. Where the raker meets the wall piece, the thrust on the raker is resolved into a horizontal component which provides the stabilising thrust against the wall and a vertical component which is transmitted through the needle and balanced by the weight of the wall above. A needle accordingly must not be placed where the weight or rigidity of the structure above is insufficient to resist this vertical component without lifting. If the wall to be shored supports floors and roof structure the centre line of the raking shores should intersect the middle point of the underside of the wallplates providing the bearing to each floor and the roof on the wall. The position of the centre line of the needles is found from the point of intersection of the wall piece and the centre line of the shore. There should be a needle and raker for each bearing point on the wall. Extreme care is necessary in shoring a wall on which bearing points are few. Where possible shores should be arranged in these circumstances where cross walls occur and at lower levels below the line of floors in corresponding positions but only where there is sufficient weight of wall above to resist the upward thrust. Alternatively it may be necessary to provide internal strutting from wall to wall if there is a danger of the wall being pushed in. Similarly where a shore is erected to provide horizontal support to a bulging wall, the needle should be positioned at the most prominent point of the bulge. Great care however is necessary in these circumstances so as not to overtighten the wedges.

It must not be forgotten that there is a certain amount of disruption in erecting shoring and if extreme care is not taken, the disturbance can bring about just that calamity which the provision of the shoring is intended to guard against. In shoring a wall which it has been established is "alive", i.e. on the move, it may be necessary to erect temporary "rigs", each consisting of an upright against the wall with a raker notched in. These rigs can be put up off the line of the shoring while the holes for the needles are being cut and other work prepared for the "permanent" shores.

The angle at which raking shores are positioned with the horizontal is governed normally by the space available but ideally the outer raker should be between 60° to 70°. A raking shore at an angle steeper than 70° will offer little lateral support to a wall, while an outer raker in a set of shores at less than 60° will occupy not only too much space but will also have a tendency to sag under its own weight. In a multiple system of shores the raker to the top floor or roof structure can usually be arranged as a rider to save space and this is provided with folding wedges at the butt joint, as shown on Figure 65.

Once the centre line of the outer shore has been drawn in on the design the position and angle of the sole plate can be determined. The sole plate must slope down towards the wall and be at an angle of slightly less than 90° with the outer shore. The angle should be between 85° and 87° to enable the rakers to be levered up tightly against the needles with a crow-bar. The sole plate of 4 or 6 inch (102 or 152mm) timber and of the width of the rakers must be soundly supported and must spread the load borne by the rakers over an area sufficient to keep movement to a negligible amount. If necessary the sole plate must be carried on a grillage and the ground must be well rammed and concreted if not of adequate bearing capacity.

In order to distribute the thrust from the rakers over a greater area of the wall a 3-inch (76mm) wall piece is used of a width equal or greater than the rakers and fixed with pairs of metal wall hooks driven into the joints of the brickwork at about 9 foot (2·7m) intervals or more frequent intervals if necessary. The wall piece should extend at least 2 feet (610mm) beyond the top and bottom rakers and should be packed out to fit the wall above and below any bulge or tilt which makes a change in the inclination of the wall face.

A square hole is cut in the wall, as neatly as possible, one brick course high and about 4½ inches (115mm) wide to accommodate the needles. A hole the same size is cut in the wall piece and a cleat is bevel housed 1 inch (25mm) and spiked to the wall piece to keep the needle in position and to take a bearing on its upper face. Needles are cut from pieces of hardwood, about 4½ by 4 inches (115 by 102mm) to fit tightly into the holes in the wall and the wall piece. The needle is rebated at the top to leave a nib which will check it at the face of the wall piece when it is driven into the hole. Accurate fitting of the needle is important as on this depends the efficiency of the shore. The top of the rakers are notched for the needles so that when the rakers are levered into position lateral movement in the rakers is prevented. The needles project 6 inches (152mm) beyond the wall piece and 4½ or 9 inches (115 or 229mm) into the wall.

Where more than one raker is used they are set in position, the one nearest the wall first, and levered along the sole plate until they each take a solid bearing on the underside of the appropriate needle. For this purpose it is convenient to cut a slot in the foot of the raker

445

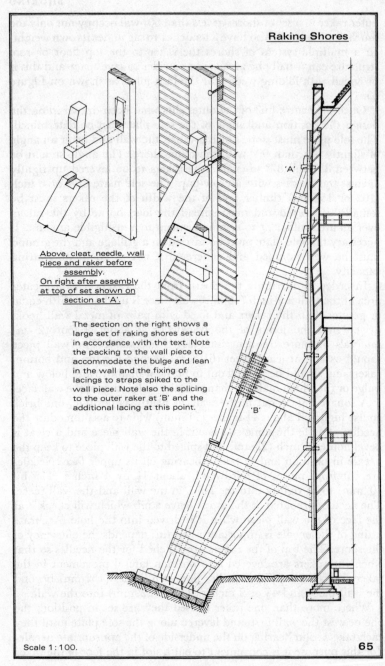

Raking Shores

Above, cleat, needle, wall piece and raker before assembly.
On right after assembly at top of set shown on section at 'A'.

The section on the right shows a large set of raking shores set out in accordance with the text. Note the packing to the wall piece to accommodate the bulge and lean in the wall and the fixing of lacings to straps spiked to the wall piece. Note also the splicing to the outer raker at 'B' and the additional lacing at this point.

'A'

'B'

Scale 1 : 100.

65

to enable a crow-bar to be inserted for the levering operation. The lower end of the outside raker is held firmly in position by a cleat spiked securely to the sole plate with three or four large nails or spikes penetrating at least 3 inches (76mm). Shaped blocks are driven between the feet of the rakers, working from the outside raker inwards until they are all secured. To conclude the operation on each set of rakers the lower ends of the rakers are secured to the sole plate with cast iron dogs and lacings, consisting usually of floor boards, are nailed across outside the rakers at higher levels to steady the longer outer rakers by connecting them to the shorter, stiffer inner rakers. The lacing should be about half as wide as it is long and should be fixed so that it is at right-angles to the outer raker. If the wall piece is of greater width than the rakers, a strap of the same width as the rakers is spiked to the wall piece and to this can be fixed the lacings, as shown on Figure 65, where a large set of raking shores is illustrated.

Flying Shores

Another and more efficient method of providing support in similar circumstances to that where raking shores are required and which should always be adopted in preference to raking shores if at all possible, is by the use of horizontal flying shores. Flying shores giving support from a sound wall to a defective wall running parallel provide a thrust that is immediately opposite to the disturbing force, do not rely on ground support, leave ground space clear and are more economical. On the other hand they do not have the near universal application of raking shores. It is necessary to have a wall parallel and at not too great a distance, no more than about 30 feet (9·1m), away and complications arise if the floors in the respective buildings are not level. If they are not level then considerable care must be taken to apply the shores as fairly between them as possible and exceedingly stiff wall pieces must be used to act as beams spanning from floor to floor. On no account must a horizontal shore bear on a wall between floor levels with a wall piece which is not stiff enough to resist bending.

Systems of flying shores are erected near the ends of the walls and at intervals of 8 to 12 feet (2·4 to 3·6m) depending on the construction of buildings against which they thrust and on the degree of damage. The size of timbers to be used varies according to the span but typical suitable sizes are as follows:

Span	Size of Flying Shore	Size of Struts
Up to 15 feet (4·5m)	6 by 4 inches (152 by 102mm)	4 by 4 inches (102 by 102mm)

447

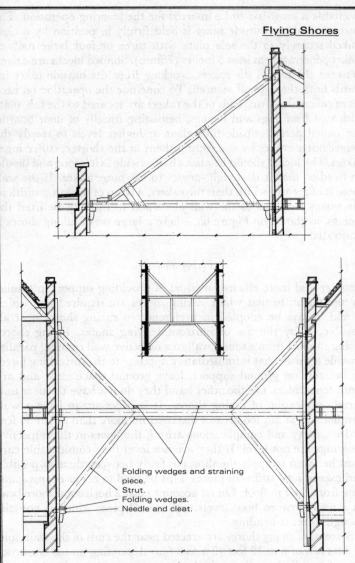

Flying Shores

Folding wedges and straining piece.
Strut.
Folding wedges.
Needle and cleat.

The arrangement shown at the top is suitable where building heights differ. The lower diagram shows the same problem as on the previous figure solved more efficiently by a flying shore spanning to a similar unaltered building still retaining its roof tie, ill advisedly removed in the building on the right to increase the top floor ceiling height. The small centre diagram shows the typical layout adopted when two flying shores are involved.

Scale 1:100

Span	Size of Flying Shore	Size of Struts
15 to 30 feet	6 by 6 inches to	6 by 4 inches to
(4·5 to 9·1m)	9 by 9 inches	9 by 4 inches
	(152 by 152mm to	(152 by 102mm to
	229 by 229mm)	229 by 102mm)

The principal parts of a flying shore are the wall pieces, the needles, the horizontal flying shore and the inclined struts. The wall pieces, except where they must be stiff members where floor levels differ, fulfil the same function and are of similar form to those adopted with raking shores and are cut to take needles and cleats in the same manner except that the lower cleats are inverted. The needles for the horizontal flying shore act as corbels and this member is provided with a pair of folding wedges at one end so that it can be tightened carefully without vibration to bear against the wall pieces. The inclined struts are fixed to bear at floor levels in the same way as raking shores, but at an angle of about 45°, the lower ends of the upper struts being held firmly against their needles by a straining piece lying along the top of the beam and by folding wedges.

The first stages in the erection of a system of flying shores follows very closely that for raking shores. Holes are formed in both the wall and the wall pieces which are then fixed to the wall, the needles are then cut, inserted and cleated. The horizontal flying shore is raised and placed on the cleats and end wedged, the lower struts being then fixed in position followed by the top struts. In fixing struts the top members are wedged at the straining piece but the lower struts are wedged at the needle. Three arrangements of flying shores are shown on Figure 66.

Dead Shoring

When a wall is entirely defective and has to be demolished completely and rebuilt it is necessary before demolition to relieve the wall of all the loads which it supports. If the wall is merely carrying a relatively few point loads this may be done by providing a dead shore directly under each member. If the wall is supporting distributed loads, as for example a wallplate carrying the feet of rafters and the ends of ceiling joists or floor joists then it is usually more convenient to erect a "head tree", a horizontal beam parallel to the wall and support the various members on this, supporting the head tree in turn on a system of dead shores taken down to a firm base, if necessary with a sill as well to spread the load.

The dead shores, often nowadays in the form of adjustable steel props, can be carried down with head trees and sills at each level floor by floor, and wedged or tightened successively upwards from below. If the intermediate floors do not bear on the wall being rebuilt, the shores can be taken through holes in the floor cut for the purpose as the floor itself would be unsuitable for intermediate support. This system of dead shoring to take the load off a wall, provides an ideal framework for the screen which would have to be provided if the work was being carried out to occupied premises.

If only the lower part of a wall is to be rebuilt, with or without new foundations, or a long beam is to be inserted or renewed in a wall then a combination of dead and needle shoring must be adopted. In this case loads may have to be taken off the lower section of the wall and supported on dead shoring as described above, but the loads on the top section of the wall can be left if required and the whole upper part supported on needles provided these are calculated to a suitable size. If the purpose of the needles is to support a wall while a beam is being inserted the needles must be placed above the proposed position of the beam and must be so calculated as to be of use in hoisting the beam into position.

The principle of needle support during such operations is based on the fact that reasonably sound brickwork will support itself by a corbelling action over a distance of about 5 to 6 feet (1·5 to 1·8m). The distance apart for needles to support brickwork will therefore depend on the state of the wall and needles may have to be placed closer together than 5 feet (1·5m) if the condition of the brickwork warrants it. Needles must always be positioned under piers and never below windows and doors and care must be taken in cutting the openings for them. In old stone walls it may be necessary to position the needles much closer, possibly as close as 3 feet (1m) and great care must also be taken to ensure that a loose and friable core does not run out as so much dust. In some cases it has been found more advisable to shutter and grout stone walls before any needling is carried out. In other cases boards have been successfully slid into position to prevent the core escaping.

Needles must be designed as beams, strong enough for the load they are to carry and stiff enough to do so without appreciable deflection. Except for very light loads it is considered that the general run of short grained softwood timber is not satisfactory for the purpose as short beams under heavy load tend to split along the grain. For heavy loads, needles should be of pitch pine or preferably of rolled steel joists or rolled steel channels bolted together in pairs. The needles are supported either on dead shores, or on head trees and dead shores and with, in either case, a sill. The dead shores should be placed as close together as possible in order to reduce the span of the needles. On the other hand an allowance of about 2 feet

6 inches (762mm) is necessary on each side of the wall as working space, so that inevitably they cannot be much less than about 6 feet (2m) long.

A uniform bearing of the load upon the needle should be provided either by packing, grouting or laying a bed of gauged cement mortar of say 1:1:6 proportion. Steel needles are sometines, as a temporary measure, built solidly into the brickwork or masonry. If this is not considered practicable or necessary they should be stayed laterally by timber blocking pieces.

Folding wedges will be required to ensure that the load is transferred in a controlled manner and to facilitate the removal of the shoring when the works are complete. If the needles are carried on head trees, the best position for the wedges is between the needles and the head trees. If each needle is carried on its own dead shore the wedges should be driven between the feet of the dead shores and the sill on which they rest. Timber wedges should always be in hardwood and should taper between 1 in 12 and 1 in 15. On occasions when steel needles and steel head trees are used the wedges should be of steel with machined faces to a taper of 1 in 24. Occasionally steel screw jacks are used which provide a gentler and smoother control to the wedging operation. The needles must be perfectly horizontal but need not be set at right-angles to the wall which they have to carry, allowing considerable latitude in their arrangement which can be very convenient at times (see Figure 67).

The ends of timber posts used as dead shores should be cut clean and square to butt evenly on the sill, wedges, needle or head tree as the case may be. The size of timbers must be adequate to take, as columns, the weight of the structure to be supported and the wedges must be driven just to take the load and no more. Wedging to relieve damaged walls of load must not be done by hard driving or violent jarring. Hard driving might disturb the stability of the super-structure, aggravate the damage already existing and may cause a serious accident. Shoring of the type described in this Chapter is not intended to push back into place brickwork which has bulged or become out of upright but to prevent further movement until repairs are carried out.

The loads that may be taken on baulk timber posts, of the heights and sections stated are set out in the table overleaf based on timber satisfactory for a compressive strength of 800 lbs. per square inch (5·516 newtons per square millimetre) on a short post. However, if the post butts directly against a sill, needle or head tree, so as to produce compression across the grain, the pressure must not exceed 400 lbs. per square inch (2·758 newtons per square millimetre). The

SAFE LOAD ON TIMBER POSTS IN TONS AND METRIC TONNES (i.e. 1000kg)

Unsupported height of Post in feet and metres	Section of Post in inches and millimetres				
	4" × 4" (102mm × 102mm)	6" × 6" (152mm × 152mm)	9" × 9" (229mm × 292mm)	2 (3" × 6") 2 (76mm × 152mm)	3 (3" × 9") 3 (76mm × 229mm)
10 (3)	1·8 (1·83)	8·0 (6·4) (8·13(6·5))	25 (14·5) (25·4(14·7))	3·6 (3·65)	8·0 (8·13)
12 (3·6)	—	6·0 (6·1)	22 (14·5) (22·3(14·7))	2·3 (2·34)	5·7 (5·8)
14 (4·3)	—	3·7 (3·75)	16 (14·5) (16·2(14·7))	—	3·2 (3·25)
16 (4·9)	—	—	11 (11·2)	—	2·2 (2·23)

maximum permissible loads in these circumstances are shown in brackets in the table.

It is advisable wherever possible to use single timbers of the size required. If these are not available it is possible to do the work using combinations such as two 3 by 6 inch (76 by 152mm) or three 3 by 9 inch (76 by 229mm) timbers bolted or securely spiked together provided the loads do not exceed those given in the table for these combinations.

Diagonal bracing should be fixed between dead shores in order to prevent any sway.

The sills which carry the dead shores should be as long as can be conveniently used of appropriate thickness and breadth to act as bearer beams to distribute the load to the ground. If the area of the sill in contact with the ground is not large enough to keep the pressure within the safe bearing capacity of the ground, a grillage should be formed of cross beams to spread the load appropriately.

In combination with needles and dead shores for relieving load it is always necessary to strut windows and any door openings and as a precautionary measure raking shores are positioned on piers and at the end of the upper part of the superstructure being supported.

Dead shoring with needles is clearly an expensive operation but is unavoidable in many circumstances. On the other hand much work of repair can be carried out in short lengths, underpinning for example, quite safely and this principle can be adopted for the renewal of lengths of brickwork in an old wall without the necessity for needling. Sufficient care is still necessary, however, to keep the work shored and strutted and to work in lengths sufficiently short and related to the condition of the wall. Furthermore, for the insertion of new beams in an old wall the patent method of using concrete stools as a substitute for needles has much to commend it and will facilitate the work provided a reinforced concrete beam is satisfactory and can be suitably designed, and is considered reasonable for the purpose. This method is considered preferable to that sometimes adopted of cutting away, from one side, half the thickness of the wall inserting a beam to support the half thickness cut away, pinning up and when this is set dealing with the other half of the wall in the same way. The renewal of an old beam, however, in the same way as will be seen for the renewal or repair of an arch, always involves the use of traditional needling and dead shores. An example of the temporary support needed before a beam can be renewed is shown on Figure 67.

In cases where a damaged pier or column or its foundation has to be replaced, it is advisable to remove all loads that can be relieved from the floors carried on the column, calculate all the remaining

453

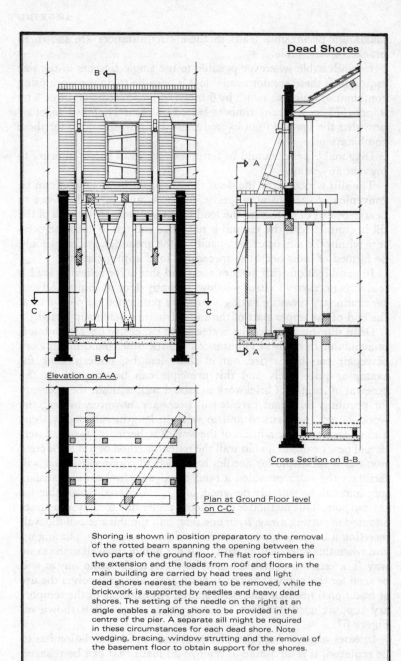

Dead Shores

Elevation on A-A.

Cross Section on B-B.

Plan at Ground Floor level on C-C.

Shoring is shown in position preparatory to the removal of the rotted beam spanning the opening between the two parts of the ground floor. The flat roof timbers in the extension and the loads from roof and floors in the main building are carried by head trees and light dead shores nearest the beam to be removed, while the brickwork is supported by needles and heavy dead shores. The setting of the needle on the right at an angle enables a raking shore to be provided in the centre of the pier. A separate sill might be required in these circumstances for each dead shore. Note wedging, bracing, window strutting and the removal of the basement floor to obtain support for the shores.

Scale 1:100

67

loads and to design a system of dead shoring to support them. This often turns out to be in the form of a braced hollow tower, due consideration being given to access for removing the defective work and the provision of working space and access for the new materials.

Shoring for Arch Repairs

Damaged arches often require a combination of both the types of temporary support already described according to the category and degree of damage to which they have been subjected. Some of the causes of damage to arches are as follows:

(1) Cracking, crushing or distortion of the arch ring by overloading or uneven loading.

(2) Damage by fire.

(3) Partial collapse of the arch ring through displacement of piers or abutments or through the removal of a stabilising load.

(4) Subsidence, or spread of an abutment, through damage to foundations.

The forms of temporary support usually required for each category of damage may be summarised as follows.

(1) Damage by Overloading

Usually an arch which has been damaged by overloading will require a certain amount of rebuilding. To do this, it is necessary to relieve the arch of its load by needles and dead shores as already described in this chapter. The undamaged portions of the arch also need support while the defective sections are cut out and replaced. This is achieved by erecting centering of the same form as used in the construction of a new arch, wedged up into position as shown on Figure 68 at "A".

Once the arch has been put in order any defects in the brickwork or masonry above the arch should also be repaired, but the needles should be left in position until the mortar has had a reasonable time to set and to harden. The load on the needles should then be relieved gradually and without shock by the cautious withdrawal of wedges. The centering should then be lowered fractionally by the loosening of the wedges until the arch just takes the load. As the final operation the centering should not be entirely removed until it is absolutely certain that downward movement of the arch has ceased.

(2) Damage by Fire

Where an arch has been subjected to intense heat, the damage usually takes the form of discoloration, cracking and spalling on the arrises. As discussed in the Chapter on repairs to stone walls discolouration of the stonework or mortar in masonry construction

455

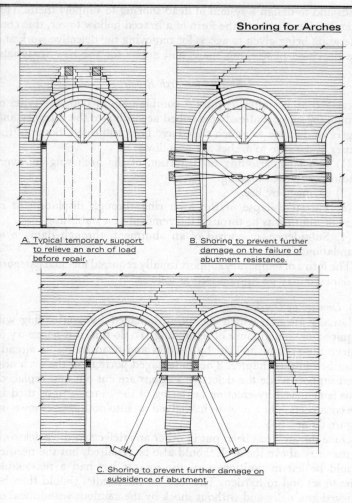

Shoring for Arches

A. Typical temporary support to relieve an arch of load before repair.

B. Shoring to prevent further damage on the failure of abutment resistance.

C. Shoring to prevent further damage on subsidence of abutment.

'A' above shows the typical support required when an arch has to be substantially rebuilt, in this case due to overloading. The needles necessary to take the load above the arch are shown but the dead shores are shown in outline only for clarity without bracing, etc. The serious failure of abutment resistance at 'B', due to inadequacy in size of the abutment, could be restrained temporarily in an emergency by wire rope and straining screws as shown but preferably by raking shores. The temporary support at 'C' would enable the foundations of the pier to be excavated for diagnosis. Note: The needles and dead shores in 'B' and 'C' necessary to take the load above the arches before repairs are commenced have been omitted for clarity.

Scale 1:100   68

456

without cracking or spalling can be counted as superficial and can be ignored. If cracking is extensive, the arch should be relieved of its load as before described and centred in the usual way before cutting away defective sections.

(3) *Damage to Abutments by Displacement*

Where the stability of an arch is endangered by damage to the piers or abutments on which it depends for support, the first step is to arrest further spread of the arch by tieing the abutments together as near as possible to the springing level of the arch. As an emergency measure wire rope and straining screws will usually provide the necessary check as shown at "B" on Figure 68. The arch should then be centered and if the abutment support on one side only has been damaged, a raking shore should be erected on that side to resist any tendency to spread further. Following the erection of temporary support, including needles and dead shores if necessary, the work of repair can then proceed once the cause of failure has been established and steps taken to cure it.

(4) *Damage by Subsidence of Abutments*

Where an arch is in danger through damage to one or both abutments by foundation failure, the steps to be taken will follow those described in the previous section except that it will be necessary to carry all temporary supports some distance away so as to leave the foundations accessible for examination and repair. A suitable arrangement for supporting centering to leave the foundations of a central pier accessible is shown at "C" on Figure 68.

General Precautions

Finally it has been mentioned before in regard to shoring of the need to ensure that wedges are not jarred or overtightened since the purpose is merely to restrain movement not to correct it. Just sufficient wedging to take the load and no more is required. There is furthermore simply no use erecting shoring and leaving it without further attention. A careful watch must be kept on all tell-tales and the distances from plumb lines to wall faces must be measured at intervals and checked against those taken originally, as it is only by these means that one can be sure that temporary supports are fulfilling the function for which they are intended. On the completion of the repairs shoring should not just be removed, even after due time has been given for new work to harden. Wedges should be gently loosened over a period so that loads are transferred gently on to the new work. It is not until it can be seen that new work is taking the load satisfactorily that shoring can be safely removed.

Chapter 7
Roof Coverings

CONTENTS

FROM very early times the roofs of houses in Britain have been built of pitched construction the only common feature being that the structure has been of timber. The roof coverings, however, have ranged through an extremely wide choice of materials varying from the plain tile or slates used almost universally throughout the length and breadth of the land to those coverings peculiar to certain districts such as stone or thatch. Latterly, however, as we have seen in Chapter 1, the growth of industry and transport in the Victorian age added to the wealth of new materials available on the market which not only included cheap mass-produced slates and tiles for house building, but provided, in addition, a range of metals suitable for the purpose. Of these metals, of course, lead and zinc are most commonly seen, but others such as copper are encountered in larger houses. More recently, however, still newer materials have grown in favour and asphalt is more widely used now as a roof covering than ever before while the various forms of bituminised felt with dressings are seen everywhere. It has accordingly been considered that the subject of roof coverings could best be dealt with in a separate Chapter. Timber roof structures have already been discussed in the Chapter devoted to Timber and the question of damp penetration through any part of the structure other than the roof covering will be dealt with separately in the Chapter devoted exclusively to this problem. In discussing the question of the repair and maintenance of the wide variety of roof coverings found in domestic use each material will be discussed in turn commencing with the coverings for pitched roofs. Subsequently the metals will be discussed and although these are normally associated with coverings for flat roofs the reader will bear in mind that this is not invariably the case and occasions will be found particularly with some larger houses where metal has been used on sloping roof surfaces with varying degrees of success. Due to the fact, however, that metal surfaces for pitched roofs are fairly rare and when encountered are used for comparatively small roof slopes, the sections dealing with a particular metal will embrace its use in all forms as a roof covering. The remaining coverings which are associated mainly with flat roofs will then be dealt with and finally reference will be made to the coverings for solid roofs.

Perhaps the most common covering for pitched roofs from very early times has been the plain tile and it is with a discussion of tiled roofs that the Chapter commences.

COVERINGS FOR TIMBER ROOFS

A. Pitched Roof Coverings

(1) *Clay Plain Tiles*

Plain tiles in this country, hand-made from clay, date back to Roman times. The Romans used baked clay tiles for roofing purposes and having regard to the thin nature of Roman "bricks" built into old walls it is probable that in the moulding and baking process little differentiation, if any, was made in the slabs used for both purposes, as well as for those intended for pavings. The skill departed with the Romans and in the non-stone areas the traditional roofing materials by the time of the early Middle Ages were thatch and shingles. What is certain however is that the making of tiles began again much earlier than the making of bricks, probably as a copy, in clay, of wooden shingles. The Ordinance of 1212 requiring new roofs in London to be of other than thatch gave baked tiles as a suitable alternative and by 1300 small manor houses in country areas of the south and east had tiled roofs. Wide variations in size and quality no doubt prompted the statute of 1477, in Edward IV's reign, which laid down the method of preparation and a standard dimension of $10\frac{1}{2}$ by $6\frac{1}{4}$ by $\frac{5}{8}$ inches (267 by 159 by 16mm). Not that such a statute had much effect as the indifferent control of temperature in the wood fired kilns of the time meant that some tiles came out larger and some smaller. Furthermore local variations persisted and by the time a statute of George I, in 1725, re-affirmed the size laid down in the earlier statute, the average size of a hand-made plain tile had diminished slightly to about $9\frac{1}{2}$ by $5\frac{3}{4}$ by $\frac{1}{2}$ inches (242 by 146 by 13mm).

With early hand-made tiles no metal detailing was employed. Soakers and flashings were relatively unknown and mortar fillets sufficed for cheaper work while tile listings were employed for larger houses at the junction with parapet walls or alternatively beautifully built projecting courses were formed in brick or tile under which the tiles could be tucked and the joint pointed up.

As the Georgian period drew to a close, the use of slates tended to supersede the use of tiles in most parts of the country. Excellent slates of varied colouring were quarried and produced for the roofs of mansions while other more cheaply quarried slates could be used for cottages and urban houses. Slates, indeed, became so universally used that up until about 1900 practically every new estate development over a long period of time, nearly a hundred years, used slate as the universally accepted roof material for houses in Britain.

With the industrial methods brought into being at the end of the 19th century tiles again emerged as a roofing material. The tiles however were produced unashamedly for cheap houses as houses of quality were still covered with slates. It was accordingly to the enormous numbers of new estates being planned for the outer concentric rings of existing cities and in country districts that batches of the mass-produced tiles were sent. In addition to this cheap tiles were also imported being produced abroad under the new mass production processes. After the end of the First World War the production and output of such tiles was enormous and vast estates throughout the country are provided with tiles produced at this time.

Early mass-produced tiles were unhappily not generally a success. The method of manufacture was not fully efficient, particularly in the grinding process of the clay so that air between the particles made such tiles very vulnerable to frost and lamination. The kiln burning method after drying was also not perfect so that enormous batches of the tiles emerged underburned. Once laid, the water absorbed by the exposed surface passed up the tiles to evaporate in the roof space and soluble salts were deposited as a result of this in the region of the nibs, these becoming eroded, leaving behind a white crystalline deposit.

Since economy was one of the main considerations for mass-produced housing, it was found during this period that cheap valleys could be formed by providing timber boarding at the angles in roofs which, when covered with zinc sheeting formed a watertight joint. This avoided the use of the expensive and complicated, swept, laced, and purpose-made valleys of previous centuries and although the appearance was rather pedestrian this was a cheap and, for a time at least, effective detail that saved a good deal of money over a large scheme. As new savings in cost to tiled roofs were sought so the detailing grew more stark and utilitarian. Ridge tiles became severely "V" shaped with or without a top roll moulded on and the angular forbidding appearance of mitred hips became commonplace. Such tiles to hips and ridges were of course produced by the same methods as the plain tiles so that they were subject to the same flaws but the fact that they were placed in exposed positions where they were not likely to be subject to the same creep of water underneath and also due to the fact that they were bedded in place rather than relying on nibs, result in them showing less apparent sign of defects than the plain tiles surrounding them on either side.

Tiled roofs just before the First World War and between the two World Wars in the new estates of houses almost universally employed sheet zinc for use as soakers with either cement fillets or zinc flashings used to cover the joint between the tiled roof slopes and the vertical brickwork of party walls and chimney stacks externally. Many years of wear have caused the metal work to have become badly corroded and thinned in urban areas and no scheme of repair work involving the renewal of tiles that are defective can be contemplated without considering the question of renewal of soakers and flashings as well.

Between the two World Wars, however, tiles were also revived as a roof covering for some of the larger houses and some of the more expensive estates of new houses. Such houses, however, employed hand-made tiles of good quality laid on felt and boarding with or without counter battens and the tiles have withstood the weather during the intervening years in general extremely well. Flashings and soakers to such roofs were normally formed in lead sheeting and in spite of the rather preponderant use of this material, the resulting quality has generally been good. Valley gutters are generally formed with purpose-made valley tiles and where the surveyor is asked to inspect such roofs he is often struck by the fact that they require very little maintenance in order to keep them in order.

The surveyor will, however, often be asked to examine, repair and maintain very early tiled roofs built between approximately 1600 and 1800 which, having survived intact for a very long period of time, have at last yielded to the ravages of time and decay. We will accordingly first consider the problems that such roofs present.

The Inspection

Even apart from the inevitable failures in achieving an even consistency of clay and the defects in the kiln burning processes, a high proportion of early hand-made tiles were astonishingly tough and durable. The tiles that survive and many have indeed survived, are admired for their rough textured surfaces and their slight irregularities which provide a pleasing appearance on the whole span of a roof particularly when mellowed by harmless lichens which tend to adhere to such surfaces. The marked camber from the top to the bottom of each tile is effective in the preventing of seepage of water underneath, but the cross camber also found is a less desirable feature since water is apt to creep between the edges and heads of the tiles. This, combined with an insufficient lap between one course of tiles and the next, often led to the practice of torching the heads of the tiles with lime and hair mortar from within the roof space.

Tiles of the period up to about 1650 were always hung in position with two oak pegs to each tile placed over the edge of rent oak laths. Fir or pine rent laths were introduced at a later date. No nails were employed and the tiles merely sat on the roof slopes depending on their weight for their stability and on what strength existed in the torching mortar below. The occasional tile slipped down the roof slope but the rough texture of the tiles one against another and the growth of moss or lichen helped to keep them in place. The tiles of such roofs and the laths were merely laid across the squared rafters typical of the period which met at the top; jointed in pairs without a horizontal ridge piece. This means that the undersides of the tiles are open to inspection since in the majority of cases there will be no intervening layer of any other material underneath the tiles.

Having inspected a comparatively intact roof covering from the exterior the surveyor may well be taken aback to find on climbing into the interior of the roof space that the wooden pegs have generally decayed badly. These may be rotted from moisture introduced through the torching mortar, which has become damp, or may be so affected with woodworm that they have no strength left at all. Other pegs may be shrunken and loose so that they may be pulled away with the finger, while thin pegs may have broken. The surveyor may marvel at the fact that although the fixings may be almost non-existent or completely inefficient, the tiled covering is nevertheless intact, particularly as the pitch of the roof of such houses is often rather steeper than the 40° or 45° common with modern tiled roofs, since in earlier roof structures, a pitch of 52° was relatively commonplace. Notwithstanding this, however, the surveyor should ascertain if a minimum lap of $2\frac{1}{2}$ inches (64mm) is provided to the tiles.

It is owing to such defects that the surveyor must always try to examine the underside of early tiled slopes. Often a roof trap will be provided but where no such trap is available an opening must be cut so that access to the roof space can be obtained if a proper investigation is to be made preparatory to repairs. With twin pitched roofs or roofs of "L" shape or even more complicated patterns, access may only be available to part of the roof space, and the surveyor is advised to try to ascertain from ladders if all the roof slopes are similar, or if piecemeal repairs have been carried out so that each slope has different characteristics. It is not uncommon to find that more accessible outer slopes may appear to be in good order while inner slopes due to the wear and tear from constant repairs to flashings and chimney stacks by many workmen over a number of years may be subject to a massive disintegration. This is particularly so in the case of buildings with a square plan with inner slopes leading to a square flat roof with secret gutters passing through the main roof pitches.

Another defect to tiled roof coverings of this period is that the tiling laths may have sagged away from their fixings to the rafters either by the nails having become rusted and snapped or by some movement in the structure that has caused stress resulting in the

465

same trouble. Again the external roof slopes may be relatively intact although graceful curves will have been imparted to the roof slopes to the delight of the passer-by but to the mortification to the surveyor who has to consider the question of repair.

In other cases inspection will be made more difficult by the fact that the tiles may be laid on boarding, perhaps as a later addition to the original structure. On other occasions, particularly in country districts, the surveyor may find that the tiles have been embedded in lime and hair mortar as a natural process in the building operation or alternatively that the tiles have been laid on a layer of second crop hay to prevent the penetration of wind and snow. The fixings for the tiles are particularly suspect under such circumstances and the surveyor is advised to procure the assistance of a skilled local craftsman in order to raise a small section of the roof covering so that the fixings can be examined. The importance of obtaining a good local craftsman is not only that he will raise part of the roof covering with a minimum disturbance but also that the surveyor will learn much from him regarding local building methods.

Once the surveyor has satisfied himself that he has full notes regarding the nature and condition of the tiled roof coverings he can turn his attention to details. The eaves in particular in early tiled roofs are often ragged and the undercloak will often become loose, and sections may be missing while verges may show less pronounced, but similar, defects. Valleys require inspection, since often these are badly laid or have been disrupted by well-meaning attempts to repair them. Ridges are particularly suspect since settlement in the structure may have caused cracking and dislocation of the tiles and often ill-fitting tiles of a later period may be observed replacing the ridge tiles of an earlier period which may have blown loose in a gale.

Before finishing his inspection the surveyor is advised to spend some time prodding and poking the various timber that he encounters for signs of wet, wood-boring beetle or wet or dry rot. Early tiled roofs with no underlay at least have the merit of providing good ventilation to the timbers so that there is a good chance that although the woodwork is generally damp stained it may not have rotted. Where, however, there is a considerable amount of torching or some other underlay not only will damp have built up below the tiles but also the ventilation will have been so severely reduced that dry rot is a much more likely possibility.

Repairs to clay plain tiled roofs

Where the surveyor finds that the pegs holding the tiles to old roof slopes have become so badly decayed and so defective that they are quite unable to provide support he will decide that there is little alternative but to strip and recover the roof slopes. This decision may be made with some reluctance if the tiles appear to adhere to the roof slopes externally, but the fact remains that repairs must be carried out. The mere fact that the tiled slopes have survived well into the 20th century does not in itself mean that they are likely to continue in this happy state. In an era of sonic booms and jet aircraft, let alone the natural hazards of nature, the surveyor is not likely to suggest to his client that matters be left as they are.

Accordingly, the surveyor will direct that the tiles be carefully taken up from the roof slopes and cleaned, sorted in sizes and stored carefully. Whether he carries out the whole operation at once or decides that it is best dealt with in sections is a matter for the individual circumstances concerned. If he has an empty house to deal with throughout the whole of one summer it is clear that the whole operation is best dealt with at once, but if he has to deal with the problem with a family living in the house at the same time he may decide that the roof could be recovered in sections so as to cause the least inconvenience possible.

When carrying out work of this sort the question of temporary covering assumes a considerable importance. The careful repair of old tiled roof slopes is not a speedy process since the structural timbers are probably uneven and careful preparatory work is necessary in order to achieve a satisfactory ground work for replacing the tiles. Cases have been known where the provision of extra tiles considered sufficiently satisfactory to match the existing ones have proved difficult to find and although of course the surveyor is unlikely to start stripping the roof slopes before the tiles are available, inexplicable last minute hitches may mean that he has a roof that is uncovered but which he cannot re-tile since the expected consignment has proved unsuitable. Another peculiarity of early roofs is that the absence of any underlay leaves the rafters exposed to the elements and more particularly there is no protection, however slight, to prevent the penetration of rain and wind. If the first floor ceilings of the dwelling house are of some historic interest, the last thing the surveyor wants to see is pools of water forming above them due to the absence of an efficient protective cover.

Accordingly it is for this reason that the provision of a complete temporary covered scaffold over the whole of the roof surface with protective sheeting down the sides is considered desirable. Such a cover is quite easy to arrange in most districts with large scaffolding firms and the employment of heavy duty polythene sheet has the advantage that being semi-transparent it allows the penetration of light so that work can continue at most times. It may be difficult to accomplish this in remote country districts but the surveyor is advised to save himself endless worry by taking pains to ensure that the temporary covering is as good as he can arrange. Hit and miss methods of repair carried out piecemeal with the use of tarpaulins should no longer be necessary and the surveyor is well advised to save his client and himself from the risk of flood damage which is all too likely to occur if the temporary coverings are not fully satisfactory. In some cases particularly in windy districts the use of heavy duty polythene sheet will not in itself be adequate so that the top decking of the temporary scaffolds should normally be covered with something more substantial, for example perspex or corrugated iron sheets fixed down by means of hooks to the scaffold.

Once the tiles have been stripped from the roof a thorough investigation can be carried out of the rafters and battens. In some cases the surveyor will be fortunate enough to find that there is little distortion in the roof slopes and the battens consist of rent oak laths or fir or pine rent laths which are in relatively good condition. Rent oak laths, however, present a particular difficulty. In order to be efficient these should be $1\frac{1}{4}$ by $\frac{3}{8}$ inches (32 by 10mm) but they can prove awkward to deal with since they are easy to split and if any length of such laths require securely refixing it is desirable for the nails to be offset below the centre so that if the lath should split the bigger proportion is above rather than below the crack. By this method a weakness is not presented when the tiles are hung. If the surveyor decides to retain rent oak laths he should remember that it is not possible to nail tiles into them and he must therefore employ tiling pins of square oak or composition or copper pins. It is of course assumed in this connection that the surveyor is re-using a large proportion of the old hand-made tiles without nibs otherwise, of course, there would be little point in retaining the oak laths at all. It also must be remembered that the tiles will depend on their own weight for their stability since they cannot be nailed and the surveyor must decide whether the particular circumstances of the case justify this. If the house is in a very exposed position this may not be desirable but if it is in a sheltered position there is no reason why the work should not be carried out in this way provided that special precautions are taken at the eaves, ridges and verges so that the wind is not allowed to penetrate under the tiling and blow sections away. The big benefit of carrying out work in this traditional way is that the tiled slopes are able to conform to slight movement in the roof slopes and yield slightly so that they bed down into a tightly linked mass over the years.

As we have said earlier the surveyor is not likely to find that the pitch of such roofs presents problems since this probably exceeds the present day minimum standard for tiled roofs. The slope may well be in excess of 50° as against the recommended standard of 45° with a minimum of 40° but if the surveyor should find that the pitch of the roof is less than 40° he should pay particular attention to the question of the lap of the tiles.

When the surveyor comes to examine the tiles taken from the old roof slopes he is likely to find that they are not of the standard size produced at the present time which is $10\frac{1}{2}$ by $6\frac{1}{2}$ inches (267 by 165mm). Old tiles may be found of varying sizes, 11 by 7 inches (280 by 180mm) being fairly common particularly in Leicestershire and occasions will be found where the tiles will measure only 9 by 6 inches (229 by 152mm) as in Kent. Much will depend for the method of repair how many tiles are fit for re-use. If the majority of the tiles are acceptable after cleaning the surveyor will be in luck and if the pitch of the roof slopes is steep he may possibly be able to make the tiles go slightly further by specifying a $2\frac{1}{2}$-inch (64mm) lap as against a lap found of 3 inches (76mm). In order to do this, however, he will have to be sure that the house is in a sheltered position and it is perhaps not worth risking this unless the conditions are completely favourable since the increased lap may have been provided for a special reason. On other occasions he may find that the lap already employed was insufficient since the roof slope might barely comply with the minimum standard so that the lap has to be increased to make up for this deficiency or the lap was probably some 2 inches (50mm) in the first place. Under such circumstances an allowance for a further percentage of tiles must be made. For work of good quality it should be possible to order new tiles to be made so as to match the existing ones. These are not usually incorporated in a block on the roof slopes but are mixed with the rest of the tiles so that after a time they weather in to the whole slopes and three to five years should be quite sufficient for the tiles to become indistinguishable from the remainder. This, however, is not a cheap solution, and the surveyor is advised to have regard to the circumstances of each individual case. The owner of a country house may be somewhat taken aback to learn, for example, that the surveyor has ordered tiles to be specially made for an inoffensive barn or stable block where the original tiles, although attractive, could be augmented by some other means in view of the comparatively humble purpose of the building. A peculiar and irritating difficulty occurs when the tiles are all of odd shapes and sizes. This can happen quite easily to old roofs which have been subject to repairs over a long period of time and under such circumstances the surveyor is advised to have all the different sizes stacked so that he may assess which, if any, of the various batches he wishes to retain and use as a basis for the new roof covering.

There will be other occasions where the purist approach of replacing the tiled roof exactly as it was will not be practicable. This may be so where the position is a very exposed one so that the surveyor does not think that this method of repair is desirable or alternatively there may be so few tiles capable of being re-used that it is not worth attempting this method.

Where, accordingly, the old rent oak laths or battens have to be removed as well as the tiles the surveyor will take the opportunity of considering the provision of an underlay material which will be a definite improvement by way of draught proofing on the roof covering that was provided before. He may consider, for example, waterproof fibre board, or boarding or bituminous felt or a combination of the last two, but in one respect it must be made clear that there will be a disadvantage as compared to the old roof covering. This is due to the fact that it will not be possible to carry out piecemeal repairs nearly so easily and no access at all to the tiles will be obtained from the roof space. Under such circumstances therefore it is very necessary to see that the new tiled covering is left in a completely secure and water-tight condition and it is for this reason that counterbattens are employed. These run from top to bottom of the roof slope, the ordinary tiling battens being laid at right-angles to them, so that in the event of any snow, rain or moisture penetrating under the tiles this can be allowed to run clear of the undersides of the tiles instead of building up moisture at the heads. The difficulty with counterbattens, however, as well as the layer of material underneath them, is that the level of the tiled covering is raised so that difficulty can be experienced with certain types of building at stacks, parapets and gable ends. A number of buildings are provided with beautifully built oversailing courses in masonry or brick designed to take the butt ends of the tiled roof slopes underneath, the resulting joint then being neatly pointed up in mortar. The increased height of the tiled coverings will entail cutting away these oversailing courses which may be a difficult and expensive matter but the added advantage of the improved roof covering may well offset this. Where new underlay or boarding is to be laid to old rafters it is most important that surfaces of the rafters are firred up so as to present a square surface for the new decking. An uneven or flexible decking provided as a base for a new tiled covering is not likely to enable the roof slopes to provide an indefinite life and the comments of the tiler if he starts work will make it clear what he thinks of the matter. If he is a good tiler he will probably leave the site saying he will be back when the roof is properly prepared.

In some early roofs, boarding over the rafters will be present already, and this may be so tough if it is of oak, that if the rafters are uneven or slim, it may be a highly risky business to contemplate trying to separate the two. Under such circumstances one can often say that the rafters are attached to the roof boards rather than the other way about, and instead of embarking on complicated repair work to little advantage provided the roof pitch is satisfactory, the surveyor is best to leave matters as they are and re-tile the slope using an underlay with counter-battens and battens under the tiles.

When the eaves of early tiled roofs are examined it can often be found that three layers of tile can be observed instead of the two layers that is more customary with later plain tiled roofs. The third course or "stretching" course might be bedded on a tilting fillet and the course above would be nailed down and bedded on mortar. The lowest course, known as the undercloak, has often, as an alternative, been laid with the concave side of the tile upwards. It is often not desirable to replace eaves details with old tiled roofs precisely as they were before. Often sprockets attached to the feet of the rafters extended the eaves at too shallow an angle so that water tended to lay on the tiles and force its way between them and cause decay. Sprockets ideally should be at an angle of no less than 40° and any great variation from this minimum standard is not desirable. When counter-battens are employed in re-laying the new roof slopes there may in any event be some difficulty in forming the eaves precisely as they were before. It is therefore suggested that in lieu of the three courses at the eaves, the roof boarding, felt and counter-battens be stopped short 4 inches (102mm) from the end of the sprocket pieces to allow room for a 4 by 2 inch (102 by 51mm) tilting fillet to be provided on which the undertile at eaves can be laid. The layer of felt under the counterbattens can be carried over the edge of the tilting fillet and there will, therefore, be two courses of tiles visible at the eaves instead of the three. This will form a perfectly acceptable detail which can be ended with a shaped fascia board and a 1½-inch (38mm) overlap can be allowed for a projection of the eaves into the gutter.

Where there are no sprockets, and the rafters form a simple straight slope to the eaves an improvement over the previous detailing would be to provide a neatly shaped tilting fillet formed to take the eaves undertile laid in its traditional manner with the concave side upwards. Two tiles again would be exposed at the end of the eaves and the overlap into the gutter would be similar. In the case of the eaves either with or without sprockets, the undertile would, of course, be the same, measuring 7 by 6½ inches (178 by 165mm), the difference being in the method of laying. It should be emphasised, however, that care in selecting the undertiles is a worthwhile

471

precaution, since the long-wearing qualities of the detail at this point depends upon the quality of tile used to a large extent.

Where sprockets are provided at the eaves it should normally be possible to redesign this detail in most cases but where this is not desirable, for example in the case of a cottage which forms one of a terrace, it may be that a shallow pitch to the sprockets has to be retained. Under such circumstances it is desirable to increase the lap of the tiles to $3\frac{1}{2}$ inches (90mm) or thereabouts over this section of the roof.

As in the case of the eaves the surveyor will often find that three courses of tiles are evident at the verges of the roof. The edges of the outer tiles overhanging the roof by some 3 to 4 inches (76 to 102mm), the two lower courses being nailed and all three courses being bedded solid with the edges flush and pointed up. The third course gives the outer tiles a slight tilt and in redesigning this detail to allow for counter-battens, the surveyor should be wary of feeling impelled to make too great a tilt which might look grotesque. If the surveyor is concerned as to the detailing at verges he might consider the question of incorporating mitred tiles under the verge. This is often worthwhile if the gable end presented is in an exposed position to wind and driving rain but the quality of such tiles with an old roof is all important and there will be circumstances where, if the original covering is being replaced with care, that mitred tiles would not be acceptable.

Ridges warrant particular care with old tiled roofs. In roofs of early construction the ridge was always the most vulnerable part and it is quite probable that the tiles or capping which the surveyor can see may not be the original covering provided. The ridge may be capped with ornamental 19th-century ridge tiles which conflict violently with the character of the roof and in such circumstances the surveyor does well to replace these ridge tiles with half round tiles of good quality. It may alternatively be possible to find hog-back ridge tiles as these form an excellent and more unobtrusive ridge-capping than half round tiles. In early tiled roofs there will probably be no timber ridge piece since the pairs of rafters will merely be joined together at the top ends. Under such circumstances the top tiling batten provided to take the ridge under tiles, which are 9 inches (229mm) long and $6\frac{1}{2}$ inches (165mm) wide and are used to maintain the normal gauge at the ridge, should stand slightly proud in order to allow the ridge under tiles to secure a good anchorage. If the ridge undertiles are heavily cambered however, this should not be so necessary.

Hips present something of a problem with early tiled roofs. The choice open to the surveyor will be either to use bonnet hip tiles or half round tiles since he is unlikely to be so insensitive as to employ "V" shaped ridge tiles for this purpose. It may be possible to collect some weathered hip tiles from local sources and as these present some irregularities it is desirable to make sure that the adjacent side tiles to the hip are cut and mitred, tile and a half tiles being employed for this purpose. The junction of a hipped end with the ridge necessitates the top pair of hip tiles being mitred under the end ridge which itself should be slightly tilted upwards so as to throw water clear of the detail. The exposed end of the ridge tile is then best filled with pieces of plain tile pointed up in mortar. The tilt to the end ridge tile is also desirable at chimney stack intersections and, as we have seen, at verges. So far as the lower end of a bonnet hip is concerned the eaves under tiles are mitred at the intersection and partly covered with a 2 to 3-inch (51 to 76mm) piece of plain tile called a "tongue" which is tailed into the mortar. The bonnet tile is then pointed up as in the case of the ridge intersection pieces with tile and mortar. If the original roof had a shaped wrought iron stay bar at the base of each hip, these, if in reasonable condition, could be replaced.

It should be emphasised at this point that with early tiled roofs it is desirable from the point of view of appearance to have as few details as possible that involve the visible use of an expanse of lead sheeting. Such roofs consisted only of plain tiles and mortar fillets were formed at the junctions of parapet walls and chimney stacks. The writers accordingly advocate a certain restraint in the use of lead sheeting and suggest that while soakers duly coated with bitumen be provided in the new roof structure that the use of heavy lead flashings are avoided unless technical considerations make their use imperative. The use of lead sheeting for ridge and hip details should also be avoided. There will, however, be occasions where it is difficult to exclude the use of lead sheeting completely. An example of this would be where the horizontal ridge of a minor roof meets the main tiled roof slope half-way up its span so that a rather awkward joint has to be formed at the junction of the ridge to the minor roof with the main roof slope and the two valleys on either side Under such circumstances it is difficult to avoid the use of a 6-lb. (2·7kg) lead saddle at the intersection which can be tucked under the tiles to the main roof slope and carried out externally over the end hip tile to the minor roof, forming a watertight joint. This of course only applies to swept or laced valleys since, if purpose-made valley tiles are to be employed, the lead saddle can be entirely hidden.

The detail at valleys is one of the most important aspects of an old tiled roof. These are likely to be swept or laced. The swept valley is the most delightful but is rarer since it involves the work of really skilled craftsmen. Each tile employed has to be specially cut from

one and half tile pieces and the effective reduction of the radius of
the curve near the eaves is the testing detail of such a valley. The
laced valley which, like the swept valley, employs a valley board to
pack out the angle of the roof, differs in that none of the tiles is cut
since these meet at their angled intersections. It should be emphasised, however, that in order to give the detailing of a laced valley its
necessary aesthetic appearance and full efficiency, the battens are
given a slight sweep up to where they join each other at the valley
intersection. Purpose-made valley tiles and valleys covered with lead
sheeting should be avoided for early tiled roofs as they spoil the
appearance.

Tiled roofs of the 20th century which have been provided to good
quality houses generally tend to have been laid to good principles
employing all that has been learned of the tiler's art since early times.
Such roofs will be found to have boarding with possibly an underlay
of felt as well and the tiles will probably be provided with counter-
battens. Almost certainly the details at chimney stacks and parapet
walls will incorporate lead and the quality of the hand-made or
machine-made sand-faced tiles will probably be satisfactory.

It is, however, with the cheaper roofs of the 20th century that we
must now concern ourselves. The tiles, for the reasons set out under
the heading of the inspection will often be in a sorry state and not
worth saving. Since roofs for mass housing in the late 19th and early
20th centuries commonly consisted of machine-made tiles laid on
feather edge boarding nailed directly to common rafters, it will be
appreciated that it is not enough merely to replace the tiles. One of
the reasons although by no means the only one for the failure of the
tiles is that water penetration will have tended to have been retained
in the lodgements formed by the tops of the feather edged boarding
and the fact that this boarding is salt stained or saturated or both
shows that some modification is required. The other big disadvantage of roofs of this type is that it is extremely difficult to effect
piecemeal repair work, since it is not possible to have access to the
tiles from the roof space and it is of course difficult to carry out such
work externally. Accordingly, the feather edge boarding should be
stripped and plain edge boarding be provided with a layer of underfelt and then counter-battens as well as battens should be set up as a
framework for the new tiles. Now that there are varieties of tried and
tested machine-made sand-faced clay tiles made in accordance with
British Standards on the market these should be employed for the
new roof covering. It should be emphasised, however, that if the
surveyor wished to modify the scheme suggested it is not desirable
for him to employ roof boarding and underfelt and save money by
dispensing with counter-battens due to the difficulty of keeping the

space under the tiles drained and ventilated. If a saving in cost has to be effected it will be preferable to dispense with roof boarding altogether and to provide an underlay of good quality reinforced roofing felt fixed in such a way that it drapes slightly loose between the rafters. This will enable water to be drained from below the tiles and for the top edges of the battens to be ventilated. Often on roofs of this period the battens will be found to be affected with wet rot where roofing felt is tightly stretched over the rafters.

Should it be necessary to replace one or two isolated affected tiles to an otherwise sound roof due to the fact that the tiles have either become broken or have cracked, it is very easy for an unskilled workman to cause a good deal of damage to other tiles in endeavouring to move a single tile. Under such circumstances the two tiles each side of the cracked tile should be carefully wedged up with small wooden wedges to enable the long handled ripper to be employed which if used with care should then cut the nails enabling the defective tile to be withdrawn.

Where a whole roof slope or roof slopes have to be re-tiled, new plain tiles with nibs should be nailed with two 1½-inch (38mm) long nails to each tile at least every fourth course. Where exposed conditions are encountered the tiles may need more frequent nailing and there are circumstances where it may be desirable for every course of tiles to be nailed. The two end tiles in every course should be nailed at verges and abutments and at each side of valleys and hips, the two courses of tiles at the top of ridges and at the bottom of eaves should also be nailed. Where the overhang of a verge exceeds 4 inches (102mm) the roof structure should project beyond the wall to carry the tiles. A good many examples of such detailing will be observed in the wide overhanging verges of late 19th-century Victorian houses where the usual detail is for the purlins to be carried through the gable wall with a soffit lining of boarding under the rafters.

The replacement of soakers and cover flashings should be carried out with care. The lengths of soakers should not ideally be less than the sum of the gauge and the lap and should in fact be made a little longer to enable them to be turned over the head of the tile. The width should be sufficient to allow not less than 4 inches (102mm) under the tiles with a turnup sufficient to give a maximum rise of 1½ inches (38mm) above and at right-angles to a line joining the lower edges of the tiles. The soakers should be coated with bitumen to preserve their life. If the use of metal flashings is unavoidable owing to the circumstances these should be well tucked into either joints of brickwork or grooves in masonry and should be wedged and pointed up in cement lime mortar. The use of tile projections in the brickwork as a substitute for flashings in order to provide a covering to soakers while often preferable on aesthetic grounds is somewhat risky as particular care is required. First of all the projecting pieces should be bedded in cement mortar into a chase cut into the brick-work and the upper surfaces of the tile sections covered with mortar which can be finished with an angled joint. So far as the lower sur-face of the tile sections are concerned the mortar bedding should on no account be allowed to ooze out and adhere to the roof surface. It should perhaps be added that the use of cement fillets is not recom-mended and pieces of broken tile set in mortar are little better.

So far as felt underlay is concerned it is perhaps worth mentioning that felt laid on roof boarding should overlap at horizontal joints by not less than 3 inches (76mm) and at other joints by not less than 6 inches (152mm). At hips and valleys a strip of 2-foot (610mm) wide felt should be laid from top to bottom overlapping the main under-lay. Where felt is not supported by boards the horizontal overlap should be not less than 6 inches (152mm).

(2) *Clay Pantiles*

Unlike double lap plain tiles, single lap interlocking pantiles were not manufactured in this country until comparatively late. It is probable that the first home produced pantiles were not made until around 1700 although Charles I granted a patent for the "makeing of Pantiles or Flanders Tyles" as early as 1636. Pantiles owe their use in this country to the trade with Holland and from where they were imported in considerable quantities during the 17th century. During the first sixty years or so of the following century however the imported tile was gradually superseded by the home product. Many of the old pantiles which still exist, however, are of Dutch origin and it is this factor which has influenced their use as although there was a vogue for this type of tile in the Georgian period it was essentially confined to those parts of the country having trade connections with the Netherlands. Thus for example although pantiles are rare in the south-east where local kilns supplied all needs by way of good plain tiles, quantities of pantiles were imported into London, to nearly all towns up the east coast and on into Scotland. It is rare to find pan-tiles in the Midlands or the western parts of the country with the exception of Somerset where the town of Bridgwater had trading connections with Holland and where eventually tiles were made locally.

Both hand- and machine-made pantiles went out of fashion at the end of the 19th century and very few hand-made pantiles have been made since. Machine-made pantiles, sometimes glazed in vivid hues, were popular with some estate developers in the 1930s and since the end of the Second World War there has been a revival of their popularity for use on small houses, more often now, however, made in concrete.

Pantiles form a good covering to roofs of simple shape and provide two cardinal advantages over plain tiles. Being laid to a single lap only, the weight of pantiling is substantially less than plain tiling and the design enables pantiles to be laid at a much shallower pitch than plain tiles. These two factors allow for a considerable saving in the timberwork necessary to support the roof covering. On the other hand pantiles are rather vulnerable to driving snow or rain and accordingly in certain exposed areas, for example in Norfolk, the practice grew of laying pantiles over a layer of reed and hair mortar as an integral part of the constructional process. Extensive torching was also adopted in lieu of this type of sub-roofing in less exposed areas and in Scotland pantile roofs were generally boarded. The main difficulty with pantiles is that while they fit snugly together they provide quite a good roof covering but even when originally laid some did not always fit very well owing to irregularities in their manufacture, and subsequent movement in the structure, or re-placement by a jobbing builder can effect disturbances that are hard to put right. It is for this reason that many old pantiled roofs will be found to be torched from both the exterior and from the interior as well, when access is available.

Where pantiles are employed the surveyor will therefore, for the reasons discussed, generally find that a lower roof pitch is common. This will probably not be lower than the recommended minimum of 30° but may well be less than the suggested maximum of 47½° for a normal pitch. Pitches in excess of this maximum are probably the result of an old thatched roof being recovered in pantiles. For pan-tiles the recommended lap is from 3 to 4 inches (76 to 102mm) depending on the degree of exposure.

Pantiles in exposed positions have always been rather suspect at the eaves and an interesting variation is often seen in Scotland where slates are used as an undercloak for the eaves of a pantiled roof. The lower few courses of exposed roof covering at the eaves is formed of slates with the pantiling commencing some distance above. This looks odd to English eyes but is nevertheless satisfactory in use. It certainly overcomes the universal difficulty in early pantiled roofs where the lowest double course of tiles at the eaves works loose and can often be lifted when leverage is applied with the hand. Modern practice with pantiles recommends that a course of plain tiles is laid at the eaves under the lowest pantile either on boarding laid on small sprocket pieces or alternatively arranged to project over the fascia to discharge into a half-round eaves gutter. The bottom course of pantiles is bedded in mortar on the plain tiles.

The ancient practice of galleting is still employed in modern building practice with pantiles. This is where two small pieces of plain tile are bedded in the channel of each pantile and packed up under the half-round ridge tiles partly in order to provide a secure bed for the ridge tiles but is also partly in order to save bedding mortar.

The detailing at verges has always presented problems with pantiled roofs. Due to this, gable walls, particularly to cottages and houses where pantiles are traditional, are commonly found formed above the roof slopes and are surmounted by copings. In Scotland where masonry is traditional, copings are of stone, while in England it is common to find a brick on edge coping with tile creasing at the top of a 9-inch (229mm) brick gable wall.

The repair of pantiled roofs

Most old pantiled roofs have suffered from neglect and careless maintenance and few are found that are in first-class condition. In some cases sagging roof timbers will have upset the side lap and head lap of the pantiles while in other cases the tiles themselves will either have been badly made or replacements carelessly fitted.

Early clay pantiles are extremely heavy as units and the surveyor is advised if the roof pitch is over 30° to ensure that the nails are sound. If the roof pitch is exceptionally steep heavy pantiles may have to be retained on hooks.

The chief difficulty with pantiles is, of course, finding others to replace those that may have become defective on a particular roof. Sometimes the search is hopeless and so few pantiles remain that some other covering has to be employed, but on the assumption that enough similar tiles can be gathered together to replace any defective tiles, the roof can be stripped and the pantiles stacked ready for re-use. When the roof slopes are re-laid the opportunity will be taken once the timber has been overhauled and the roof pitch itself has been diagnosed as satisfactory, of providing an underlay of bituminous felt or boarding. As in the case of a plain tiled roof it is never desirable to use battens laid on roofing felt placed on a rigid insulation material for the same reason as was set out earlier. Counter-battens are necessary in a case such as this and if counter-battens are not to be employed it would be preferable to dispense with the boarding and allow the roofing felt to sag slightly between the pairs of rafters.

Much of the trouble which the surveyor will encounter in dealing with pantiled roofs is that the variety in the types of tile provided from early times is so wide. 13½ by 9½ inch (343 by 241mm) tiles, the standard size laid down in a statute of George I, with battens gauged at 10½ inches (267mm) are reasonably commonplace but whereas modern pantiles have only one nib and one nail hole old pantiles usually have no nibs whatsoever. Some old pantiles are extremely heavy and the camber is not entirely effective. If a sufficiency of such tiles can be found however, a perfectly sound roof slope can be formed provided that the pitch is satisfactory but great care is required in dealing with details.

A further difficulty with pantiled roofs lies in the question of the verges. Whereas eaves can have a plain tile undercloaking which, due to the roof pitch, is in a fairly sheltered position, verges are exposed at gable ends and although an undercloaking of tiles is commonly provided with an overhang of 2 inches (50mm) with a maximum of 4 inches (102mm), an awkward joint is nevertheless formed between the pantiles and the plain tiling. The difficulty with right-handed verges is that whereas the full pantile can commence from the verge overhang, the upper course of plain tiling has to be extremely narrow so as to allow the edge pantiles to be nailed. With a left-hand verge, however, the position is complicated by the fact that the sweep of the pantile in this position cannot possibly provide a weathertight joint on its own so that half-round purpose-made verge tiles have to be incorporated, overlapping the end pantile and bedded down to the upper course of the plain tile undercloak. It will be seen therefore that it is impossible to avoid the use of torching mortar at verges to ensure a weathertight joint. A mortar consisting of one part of cement to one part of lime to four parts of sand has been commonly used but latterly a practice has grown of using a composition material which can allow for a certain amount of expansion and contraction. In either event, however, the detail is an unsatisfactory one and some maintenance must be expected from time to time in ensuring that verges are correctly pointed up.

The surveyor will commonly find, however, that in parts of the country where pantiles have been used for very many years, the tendency has been to avoid the rather awkward verge detailing so that gable walls are provided finished with low parapets. These can either be of masonry as in the case of Scotland where granite is extensively used, or alternatively of brick with a flint knapping as is commonplace in Norfolk or elsewhere, of course, they can be of brick. Newer houses in England being constructed with pantile roofs often have end parapet walls above gables formed with cavity construction. Like early plain tiled roofs early pantile roofs are sometimes constructed so that an overhang is provided at the parapet detailing which allows for the pantiles to be tucked underneath and the edge neatly pointed up in cement mortar. Due to the camber presented by pantiles, however, this does not form quite such a satisfactory joint as with plain tiles. It is, however, probably more common to find that parapets above gables are not formed with such overhangs, the internal brick faces being flush with the wall face below. Very often cement fillets are provided but more commonly perhaps, it has been the custom for the interior face of the gable parapet to be rendered, the rendering extending from the top of the tiles to the underside of the stone coping or the tile creasing of a brick on edge coping. Rather than this arrangement a sounder joint can be formed with a 6-lb. lead flashing tucked into the brickwork and wedged and pointed up and carried over the edge of the pantiles with a substantial overlap. This departs to some extent from the purist doctrine that lead should not be evident to any large extent when used in conjunction with tiled roofs but the detailing in this particular case is awkward and the advantages of a lead flashing are self-evident.

So far as the junctions of pantiled roofs with chimney stacks are concerned these will be more open to view than parapet walls above gable ends and it is best probably to form the detailing with a layer of cut plain tiles with galleting under, the whole joint being pointed up in mortar.

Valleys are also awkward to form with the use of pantiles and for this reason are usually avoided. Lead sheeting is commonly dressed over the valley board and carried up each side slope where it is taken over a tilting fillet in the usual way. A course of flat plain tiles is then formed at either side of the slope so that the cut pantiles can be bedded on the plain tiles in mortar. This detail has the disadvantage that the mortar is apt to become loose and rattle down the valley causing leakage at some time in the life span of the roof, but although purpose-made valley tiles of "V" cross-section or slightly curved are now available these will not fit in with the pantiles employed on earlier roofs.

The main point to be remembered in the repair of a pantiled roof is that pantiles are only fully efficient where they cover simple spans of as large a size as possible. Under these circumstances and when well laid, pantiles will provide excellent service, but they are at their worst when they have to be cut and fitted to awkward angles and intersections. Openings in pantiled roofs for dormer windows or other details are extremely difficult to make completely satisfactorily and where a small pantiled roof is encountered which is subject to a number of such features it will often be best for the surveyor to seriously consider whether another form of covering might not be better suited.

(3) *Italian and Spanish Tiling*

The surveyor will occasionally be asked to embark on the repair and maintenance of houses built between 1920 and 1939 and on some estates he may find that the builder or developer has been moved to apply an Italiate or Spanish style to the façade of the house as a whole and that nowhere is this more apparent than to the roof coverings which may be highly glazed and known as either Italian or Roman tiling on the one hand or Spanish or Sicilian tiling on the other. The tiles will be found in a wide range of bright colours. Blues and greens are perhaps the most popular, the greens ranging from a dark leaf colour to a vivid emerald, while the blues range from a deep navy colour to a very light cobalt.

The writers have found that roofs of glazed Italian or Spanish tiling provided to houses of reasonably good quality at this particular period have stood up to the wear of the intervening years on the whole pretty well. This is mainly because the glazing process adds strength to the tile and the glaze itself increases the resistance to the effects of frost. These advantages are perhaps fortunate and the writers do not envy the surveyors of future years who have to cope with the problem of the repair of roofs of this type since Italian and Spanish tiles are of a complex pattern and unless replacements can be found the question of repair could present a really serious problem.

Italian tiling falls into the categories of: (*a*) Old Roman, (*b*) Single Roman and (*c*) Double Roman. Old Roman tiling is a type of single-lap tiling consisting of flat undertiles which alternate with curved tiles, used here, as elsewhere throughout Europe by the Romans but original examples now surviving in this country only in museums. Single Roman tiling consists of the tiles being similar but wider, each consisting of a flat portion with an upturned edge and with a roll formed on the opposite side of the tile. Double Roman tiling is similar to single Roman tiling except that each tile has two rolls and two flat surfaces instead of one, hence the name. Tiles of these types have been produced in the West Country since the latter part of the 19th century and many have since been imported from abroad. Spanish or Sicilian tiling is very similar to old Roman tiling. Practically the only difference is that while the overtile is almost identical the under-tile is not flat like the Italian type but is concave shaped. This type of tile although common in the rest of Europe has only been used in this country since towards the end of the last century.

The great difference, however, between Italian and Spanish tiling compared with all other ornamental tiles, for example pantiles, is that the rolls to the tiles are tapered. This of course also entails the flanges being tapered so that all the sections fit together in a way that it is impossible to reproduce with any other type of tile. In addition to this the tiles are sophisticated in their manufacture. Some undertiles to old Roman tiling are provided with two transverse grooves near the head to minimise updrift. The overtiles are also often slightly shouldered at the rear to allow them to clear the undertiles in the course above at the headlap.

With all Italian and Spanish tiling the headlap varies from $2\frac{1}{2}$ to 3 inches (64 to 76mm) depending upon the pitch which should be a minimum of 35°. The side lap varies according to the type of tiling employed. It is probable that the surveyor will not encounter roof coverings of this type that depart to any great degree from these standards. Indeed the pitch often encountered is steeper than the minimum suggested. The tiles are generally found laid on battens fixed to either a layer of boarding or direct to the rafters with an intervening layer of bituminous felt. As in the case of pantiles a course of plain undertiles is employed at the eaves and the finish at the ridge is also similar to that for pantiles since half-round tiles and galleting are usually employed. The hip, valley and verge details are also the same as for pantiles. In the case of single Roman tiling, purpose-made single Roman tiles are available each having a double roll for the left-hand verges and purpose-made left-hand verge tiles provided with three rolls are available in the case of double Roman tiling.

The main peculiarity in the laying of Italian or Spanish tiles is that due to the height of the rolls it is difficult to secure them to the ground work even with the use of long nails. Thus it is common to provide 3 by $\frac{7}{8}$-inch (76 by 22mm) vertical battens between the undertiles for Italian tiling or 3 by 2-inch (76 by 51mm) vertical battens between the undertiles for Spanish tiling. Nails form no effective substitute for such battens.

A number of differing types of Italian and Spanish tiles will be encountered. Where the tiles are loose but can be re-fixed the surveyor will heave a sigh of relief for this is a comparatively simple matter as contrasted with the problem of trying to deal with the case where a number of tiles are broken and defective. One of the main defects encountered with tiles of this type is that very often a run-off from a poorly designed detail at an overhang or the junction with a minor roof will have caused black smears to be all too visible on the roof slopes which detract considerably from the appearance, particularly if the tiles are of a light colouring and highly glazed. The owner of the house may think it worthwhile for the surveyor to instruct the builder to clean these tiles so far as practicable and to redesign the troublesome detail but often the owner will prefer to leave matters as they are. Where, however, some of the tiles are defective or the detailing is poor, so that moisture penetrates the interior, something clearly must be done even although replacement tiles are not available. Perhaps the best method of dealing with the matter is to remove some sound tiles discreetly from a part of the roof that is not open to view from the ground such as the hidden slope of a minor roof behind a gable and to replace this slope with tiles that approximate as near as possible to those taken away. The tiles salvaged can then be used for individual replacements of broken tiles to the main roof slopes where these are in the more exposed positions both as regards weather and the inspection of passers-by.

(4) *Interlocking Tiles*

Very many houses built between the two World Wars have been provided with machine-made interlocking tiles. Large batches were imported from the continent where they were cheaply produced and often a stamped name on the underside of the tiles will give a clue to the place of origin. Machine-made interlocking tiles have, to a generous degree, the same faults as the machine-made plain tile of the same period. Inspection often shows that the same process of disintegration is under way due to initial faults in the manufacture of the tile and there is, accordingly, little prospect of the surveyor being able to suggest that piecemeal repairs are carried out under such circumstances.

It is also perhaps worth mentioning that the methods of fixing which the surveyor may encounter with interlocking tiles may show some variations on what might be expected. Some types for example provide holes in the nibs to enable a piece of wire to be passed through and curled round the batten to form an anchorage.

It is, however, likely that the gauge of the interlocking tiles found may not conform to the requirements of the tiles that the surveyor may select to recover the roof and if so it is not likely that the battens can be saved since the gauge will have to be re-calculated bearing in mind the length of the tiles that the surveyor wishes to employ, together with lap that is proposed, having regard to the pitch of the roof. In any event the opportunity will no doubt be taken for a layer of underfelt to be incorporated under the new tiled slopes and left to sag between the rafters.

(5) *Concrete Tiles*

Concrete tiles first made in England about the turn of the century and now made of normal Portland cement and clean well graded sand are now fairly common, amounting to about three-quarters of the current total production of roof tiles. Originally such tiles were coloured throughout since a colouring pigment, roughly of the same shade as weak tomato sauce, was added to the mixture during manufacture. More recently, however, it has become customary for the surface to be treated with mineral granules which have been coated with colouring by a process of vitrification. All the various sizes and shapes for clay tiles can now be produced in concrete.

Early concrete tiles were subject to the same process of disintegration as machine-made clay tiles but latterly, owing to their cheapness, the use of concrete tiles has become so common that production methods have improved, and it is hoped that most of the defects have been ironed out although only the exposure of these tiles to the elements over the next twenty years will prove if this is really so. The average size of concrete tiles is the same as that of clay plain tiles and they are very similar in shape since the camber and nibs are similar and each tile is twice holed. Like plain tiles the usual lap of concrete tiles is $2\frac{1}{2}$ inches (64mm) and the minimum pitch of the roof is recommended to be 35°; 45° or 40° if the lap is increased to 3 inches (76mm). The great difference in concrete tiles, however, is the variety of the colouring provided by the granules to the upper surface. These consist of stone chippings crushed and graded which are covered with pigment and gas fired in a kiln.

Where the surveyor finds plain tiles of concrete employed on a roof he may find that the pitch is less than the recommended standard of 45°. This may be particularly so at sprocketed eaves and under such circumstances it is worth his while to try and ascertain if the British Standard kite mark is visible on the underside of the tiles since concrete tiles conforming with B.S.473 and B.S.550 are not susceptible to frost. Single lap concrete tiles should not be used below a 30° pitch. The British Standard Code of Practice C.P.142 (1958) suggests that it might be possible to employ close fitting concrete interlocking tiles below this pitch if they have a satisfactory locking arrangement at the side and effective anti-capillary devices at the horizontal lap, but the use of any tile below a pitch of 30° is risky and the subsequent weathering and waterproofing qualities of the covering are doubtful.

(6) *True slates and stone slates*

True Slates

In certain parts of the country, clay deposits underground are concentrated to form shale, and where special conditions have occurred of enormous lateral pressure and heat, the resulting material produced was slate. Although, therefore, slate can be defined as a hard fine grained clay stone, it is not only completely different in texture from other stones but has, owing to the nature of its formation, a laminated structure giving parallel planes of cleavage, so that blocks can be separated into thin sheets known as slates. Their use as a roofing material in those parts of the country where the appropriate rock formations occur is of very long standing indeed and it is to the consideration of slates as a roof covering that we will now turn. Within the terms of this definition, it should be made clear that the material is quite different to that of stone slates, the parallel use of which has been traditional in many other parts of the country for centuries. Stone slates are formed of much thicker blocks of sandstone or limestone and stone slating will be discussed later under that heading, a term of description which, although strictly speaking incorrect, is now firmly established by long usage.

Slate is either quarried or mined underground and in districts where slate quarries or mines have operated for very many years, the majority of houses have been roofed with the local slate. For example there is evidence of quarries, closed when the Romans left, being re-opened in the 13th century and even of slates quarried in Devonshire being taken by sea to Winchester in 1170. The quarries in Westmorland are particularly well known since the slates produced, although expensive, are of excellent quality and a distinctive greenish colour but the term "Westmorland slates" includes those from a number of quarries such as those of Cumberland and North Lancashire. With the advent of the Industrial Revolution the enormous demand for cheap slates was met largely from Wales and although slate is produced in other areas such as parts of Cornwall and Scotland the main output of slates for the vast majority of estate houses is still from Wales. Although Welsh slates are generally bluish in colour, variations in colouring can be obtained according to the particular quarry providing the slates, which can range in colouring from purple to grey with other variations which have a characteristic mottling.

Slates differ from any of the roof coverings previously discussed in that the range of sizes available has always been and still is so enormous. Not only can a vast number of different sizes be procured, Bangor slates, for example, being obtained in no less than 32 standard sizes, but slates are also available in graded thickness. Slates are available in categories that are either uniform in length and width or alternatively are of uniform length but of random width. Slates can also be obtained in a third category of random sizes. It has long been the practice in good quality work for slates to be laid in graded courses. Westmorland slates are often chosen for this type of work since they are produced in random sizes, that is to say in varying lengths, but of similar proportions in width so that the average slate has a width of approximately half its length. These are delivered in assorted sizes and are laid so that the slates to each course are of the same length, but the small slates are laid nearest to the ridge, the graded courses increasing in size near the eaves. With this type of slating the margin and gauge varies with each course but the lap of the slates is uniform throughout.

There is a certain historical similarity between slates and tiles produced for housing purposes. Early slates produced without any of the mechanical aids that were subsequently introduced still retain their robust qualities and often last indefinitely while the techniques of laying, although at times achieving an undoubted excellence in the use of the swept and laced valleys, for example, nevertheless suffered from deficiences and the slates themselves have often outlasted the fixings. With mass-produced Welsh slates, however, produced in vast quantities for mass housing needs after 1850, it was the slates themselves that more often proved to be deficient in lasting quality. Since the techniques of laying were pretty well established and well known by this time it was often not the method of laying the slates which failed first but the quality of the slates themselves.

The Inspection

It is first assumed that the surveyor is asked to deal with the question of the repair of a roof to a Georgian house in an urban or country district. Such an instruction often comes about where an owner has become weary of the need for calling in a builder every few months to attend to yet another leak. The preliminary inspection may reveal, for example, that the roof covering is of attractive green Westmorland slates, laid in graded courses from top to bottom, the ridge, hips and valley details being of lead sheeting. It is possible that the surveyor will find that the condition of the Westmorland slates themselves is relatively satisfactory subject only to a few replacements being required. It is likely, however, that the method of fixing will not be at all satisfactory. Green Westmorland slates are heavy, and if hung with steel or zinc nails some considerable time ago, it is possible that the nails may be rusted and cause the slates to slip down the roof slopes. Under such circumstances the surveyor will doubtless wish to consider the practicability of stripping and re-covering the roof slopes using the existing Westmorland slates but before he embarks on this course it would be as well for other points to be investigated first. The most obvious matter to be considered is the question of the pitch of the roof slopes taken in conjunction with the lap of the slates. For roofs of 35° pitch the lap should not be less than 3 inches (76mm) and this should be increased by not less than ¼ inch (6mm) for each 5° reduction of pitch.

With certain types of slates, and green Westmorland slates are an example since the edges are worked and are thus uneven, the surveyor will often wonder if the gaps that he sees between the sides of the slates indicate any inefficiency in the covering. The answer to this is that it is not necessarily the gap between the slates of individual courses that matters since this in fact facilitates drainage instead of hindering it. The determining factor is the side lap which is the distance by which the side of one slate overlaps the slate of the course below. This provides lateral protection against water creeping sideways between the slates and penetrating the roof through the side joints. It is for this reason that slates with a minimum width equal to half their length may provide an adequate side lap for roofs of not less than a 30° pitch. The British Standard Code of Practice C.P.142 of 1958 recommends, however, that for roof pitches below 30° slates should be wider than half their length, and the proportion of width to length should be increased as the pitch is reduced. This is an important aspect of the weatherproofing qualities of a slated roof since snow, when dry and powdery, may penetrate slates and enter the roof space, or it may, on roofs of low pitch, cause water to be dammed up during a thaw in such a way that it can run over the heads of the slates or tiles.

In addition to the question of pitch and lap another aspect of the matter requires consideration. This concerns the condition of the holes to the slates which the surveyor wishes to re-use for the roof covering. The holes to early slates were made by hand, and often these were provided near the head of the slate and punched rather carelessly so that spalling has occurred and the top edge of the slate has broken away allowing the slate to be released from its fixing nails. It is suggested, therefore, that the surveyor makes an investigation of the slates by asking the owner's permission to move one or two sample slates from the roof from various parts so that he may examine them. From this inspection of a random sample of slates the surveyor can determine if the holes are at least 1 inch (25mm) from the top edge if head nailed or cleanly punched if centre nailed. The technique of hand punching is to tap the surface of the slate with a spike so as to form a neat hole, a larger hole being formed on the underside by pieces of slate breaking away on impact. The slater then turned the slate over and laid it with the larger sinking uppermost as this formed a convenient recess into which the nail head could be countersunk flush with the top surface of the slate. From his inspection of this small detail the surveyor will be able to tell if the original slater was a good craftsman. As a further example slates of this period were usually of uneven thickness and although Westmorland slates were often provided up to five to an inch thus having an average thickness of one-fifth of an inch (5mm) the slater should have compensated for any uneven thickness by hanging the slate in such a way that the lower exposed end was the thicker. Moreover the surveyor will also be able to determine from the size of the slates if these have been well hung in the first instance. It is common for small slates to be headnailed but the larger grade of Westmorland slates which, by their very size are liable to be lifted by the wind, should be centre nailed, as headnailing is not sufficient. Often the surveyor will find that slates to intermediate courses are fixed with a single nail and the practice of check nailing is sometimes employed to keep the slates in line. This consists of fixing a nail in a notch high up from the side of each slate about 3 inches (76mm) from the head and approximately 1 inch (25mm) from the side. This method does not have much to commend it as the notch is vulnerable to seepage from the joints in the course above and two nails either at the head or at the centre are preferable to this practice. Sometimes the surveyor will find that nails of insufficient size have been used and in order to obtain the maximum penetration these have been driven home hard with the result that the slates have been nailed so tightly together that the holes and edges have been damaged.

In the case of the Georgian house under consideration the surveyor will either find that the slates are centre nailed or head nailed to battens fixed direct to the rafters or that there is a layer of boarding under the slates, which in Scotland is known as sarking. If there have been appreciable deficiencies in the slated roof slopes the surveyor will undoubtedly find that the battens or the roof boarding, whichever he encounters, will be very badly dampstained. It is often possible to judge the extent of such damp penetration to battens but in an early slated roof it will probably be found that these have been saturated over so long a period and pierced with the shanks of so many nails that they are extremely fragile, and if there is any doubt about their condition they should, of course, be renewed. Boarding is less easy to investigate and it will almost certainly be necessary for part of the slating to be removed temporarily at a point where the condition is clearly suspect so that the state of the timber can be ascertained. Where the roof has been repaired so often that the battens or the boarding is no longer able to hold the nails the roof is said to be "nail-sick". The boarding as for the battens under such circumstances will therefore have to be removed.

The eaves detailing repays particular investigation with any slated roof. The Georgian mansion will no doubt have a double course of slates at the eaves, a course of short slates being first bedded down over which the first course of full length slate is laid. It may be found however that short slates are not employed for this under-cloak but that full length slates are used for this purpose laid side-ways. This is not a particularly good practice as sooner or later the joints in the undercloak will marry up with the joints to the course of slates above so that there is an ineffective bond. It is worthwhile, however, for the surveyor to ascertain if the eaves slates are properly nailed and if there is a tilting fillet or fascia board to support them. In Scotland the common practice, no doubt due to greater exposure to the northern winds, is to double nail the courses of slates nearest to the eaves. The surveyor might also ascertain if the slates have a 2-inch (50mm) overhang to ensure that water is discharged clear of the roof slope into an eaves gutter. It is not usual to find sprocketed eaves with early slated roofs but where sprockets are encountered at the eaves the pitch should not be less than 30°. If the pitch is less than this minimum standard, particular pains are needed to ensure that the slates are of good quality and are laid so as to be watertight.

The verges to an early slated roof are also worthy of particular attention. The overhang should not exceed 3 inches (76mm) with-out support from the roof structure and a slight inward tilt is desirable to make sure that water does not trickle off the edge of the verge and penetrate under the slates. Investigation should also be carried out to see if the proper detailing at the verge of slate and slate and a half widths are used or alternatively if wide slates are laid to form an undercloak. These slates should be closely butted together and the joints staggered so that they do not coincide with the joints in the slates above. The bedding of the undercloak should be investigated since when this is laid on brickwork the mortar should be intact or alternatively if laid on boards or battens the nailing to the under-cloak slates should be in good condition.

As mentioned earlier our Georgian house may have ridges and hips of lead sheeting which will probably have weathered to a whitish grey with long exposure. Stone ridges and hips are less common. The condition of the lead should be examined with care since splits and tears are likely and possibly indentations may have been formed on the top edge. Part of the lead can often be rolled back so that the top detailing of the slates can be observed, together with the condition of the wood roll, and the surveyor might ascer-tain if the slates to the top course are of such a length as to ensure that the lap is maintained in the courses below and also if the top course of slates is head nailed to a thicker batten than the remainder to provide a snug fit to the next course of slates lower down. The lead should be secured to the wooden roll by screws being sealed with a lead dot under the overlap and lead tacks fixed at 2 ft. 6 in. (762mm) intervals under the roll and over the ridge or hip board, the ends of the tacks being turned back to clip over the edges of the leadwork. Often the overlap of the lead on wood rolls is all too visible externally and ideally the wood roll should be cut away to take the extra thickness of the lead where the overlap occurs with a groove cut to prevent water penetrating the joint through capillary attraction.

The valley gutters to the roof slopes will either be swept or laced or of lead sheeting on wood boarding. These portions of the roof are particularly vulnerable since the pitch in the valley is several degrees less than that of the main roof slopes and the valley gutter provides a channel which takes a considerable amount of rainwater. Accordingly, metal valley gutters should be inspected to ascertain if the metal is correctly dressed over a tilting fillet on either side, extending for at least 1½ inches (38mm) beyond it, and detailed correctly near ridges.

Inspection of the main roof slopes at abutments to brick parapet walls, gable walls and chimney stacks, will possibly reveal that cement fillets are provided to the exterior angles in place of metal flashings, but the surveyor will not be certain until he investigates from inside the roof structure whether soakers are employed or not. The surveyor may find alternatively that slate fillets are employed, but these, to be efficient, should be bedded with cement mortar into a chase cut into the brickwork or masonry so that the upper edge of the slate fillet is completely covered. The mortar bedding under the fillet should not be allowed to adhere to the roof surface.

In concluding our inspection of our Georgian house the surveyor should look particularly at the detailing of dormer windows and mansard slopes. The joints between dormer windows and roof slopes are not often fully satisfactory and mansard slopes in particular, due to their greater pitch, show up any deficiencies in the hanging method employed for the slates.

Our second example will be of a later roof to a dwelling house built since the advent of the Industrial Revolution. As mentioned earlier it is not so much the fixings and technique of the laying of the slates which is likely to be at fault in this instance, but the composition and thinness of the slates themselves. Inspection of the undersides of the thin mass-produced slates of this period will reveal that these are probably of poor quality and particularly in urban areas the carbonate content will have reacted with the sulphur acids in the atmosphere and the rainwater of the urban areas, to form calcium sulphate which can reduce the slate to a condition that is far from satisfactory to say the least. The particular trouble is that owing to capillary action acidic rainwater remains under and between slates so that the decay commences from the underside where it is least open to view. The irritation of this particular tendency is that the decay destroys the area of slate surrounding the nail hole so that on certain roofs a number of slipped slates may be due to this cause rather than to the nails employed in the covering becoming rusted. It should be emphasised that this particular defect in slates is generally only visible from underneath. Often the exterior surfaces will appear to be reasonably satisfactory since the continual rainfall and deposits will apply a polished veneer whereas so far as the undersides are concerned, which are dry, flaking and disintegration occurs in a more recognisable form. Slated urban roofs of about 1850 or 1860 will almost certainly provide some indication of a general defect to the top surfaces owing to the presence of some lamination and the large number of tacks or tingles already employed, but the urban roofs of 1890 or 1900 may appear reasonably satisfactory at a casual glance, although this may by no means be the case when they are subjected to detailed investigation from below.

It is not only in urban areas where slates are liable to decay due to the effect of the impurities of the atmosphere on the carbonate content of the slates since pollution of the atmosphere is widespread. The amount of iron sulphide present also has an effect on the weathering properties. The sulphide oxidises to form hydrated iron oxide and sulphuric acid and should the slate also contain carbonates then the effect will be to decompose the slate entirely. Even since the Second World War many slates have been imported from abroad which are of poor quality and these have not proved capable of withstanding the acid attack experienced in the urban areas of this country. Such slates fade quickly and signs of blistering on the surface or an excessive number of breakages may indicate to the surveyor that they are due for renewal.

As we have mentioned earlier, it is likely that the surveyor will find that the pitches of slated roofs to Victorian and Edwardian houses are generally adequate. This is particularly so in terraced houses built just before the First World War where roof pitches were calculated and laid out adequately to the terrace as a whole. This statement, however, requires some modification in the case of some early Victorian houses. In the case of two-, three- or four-storey semi-detached houses of, say, 1840, sagging is evident to the roof slopes which will have accelerated the defects in the slates previously mentioned. This factor, taken in conjunction with the fact that slates of too small a size might have been used in the first instance, may have caused a complete disintegration so that the surveyor will probably find an impressive array of zinc tacks bristling on the roof slopes, together with other attempts at temporary repair such as applications of bituminous solution. The trouble with houses of this age and type is not so much that the roof pitch is greatly inadequate, although it may be near the critical minimum for slates, as a shallow pitch was fashionable, but that the rafters and purlins are usually too slender for the size and span of the roof so that they have sagged in consequence. With houses of this period the overhang at eaves and gable walls may be impressive, but in general the detailing at verges and eaves is probably of fairly conventional construction.

With Edwardian and Victorian properties the ridges and hips will probably be of slate sections. The mortar bedding may have perished so that the slated sections have become loose in consequence, and sometimes the surveyor will find that piecemeal repairs have been carried out either by the use of slate sections that do not match the remainder or alternatively that ridge tiles have been employed for the purpose.

One of the particular features of slated roof coverings of this period was the widespread use of zinc sheeting. This material was employed for zinc soakers at the abutments with parapet walls and chimney stacks and is also used for valley gutters on a base of timber boarding. Unless the zinc has been renewed in recent years the surveyor will almost certainly find that it is badly worn and has reached the end of its useful life. This is particularly so in the case of soakers since, as the usual practice at the time was to employ cement fillets as the outer covering for the joint at abutments, the soakers are likely to be perished at the right-angled joint between the slates and the brickwork. The minor slated roofs to additions, projections and bay windows to houses of this period also present problems. In most cases the joint between such roofs and the main structure will be ineffective since these are merely finished externally with cement fillets. In addition to this the hips of minor roofs, particularly to bay windows, whether these be of lean-to construction or pitched, were originally built using slate rolls and these need particular scrutiny since the rolls may have disintegrated or slipped from their fixings.

The Repair of Slated Roof Slopes

It is now necessary for us to look back to the first example discussed under the heading of the inspection, that of the Georgian mansion, the roof slopes of which were covered with green Westmorland slates. The surveyor was last left examining the detailing of the roof prior to climbing down a ladder, dusting himself down and proceeding to examine a motley collection of slates that have been collected for his inspection as samples. It is now that the surveyor has to decide, in the light of his inspection, as to the nature and extent of the repair work that he feels to be necessary having regard to the circumstances. If, as he suspected, the fixing nails to the slates have proved to be rusted and unsound, the surveyor must now decide if the slates themselves are worth saving and, if so, roughly what proportion must be rejected. Although he clearly cannot make a very accurate assessment of how many slates are likely to be defective since this can only be done when the roof coverings are stripped, nevertheless a decision at this stage as to whether the majority of slates can be saved or not will save money. If all the slates are badly spalled due to being inefficiently nailed in the first place the surveyor will obviously specify new slates for all the roof slopes. If, however, as we have mentioned, the tough qualities of the Westmorland slates enable more than a 50 per cent portion to be used again, the surveyor will obviously try to make use of them not only from the point of view of expense but also due to the fact that the slates will have weathered to an attractive texture so that it is equally desirable from the aesthetic point of view that they be used again. The risk element, however, in making a correct assessment as to whether 50 per cent or more of the slates are capable of being re-used is that if the surveyor specifies careful taking down, sorting and storing slates that subsequently turn out not to be fit for re-use, he will have cost his client some money which could have been better spent in another direction.

The surveyor must also decide from his inspection if he is going to leave the pitch of the roof as it is, or if he feels that some steps should be taken to improve it. The position of the house plays a part in this decision since if the site is an exposed one and the pitch is near the critical minimum, the surveyor will seriously debate whether he should fir the existing rafters to provide a slightly steeper pitch. Perhaps the only disadvantage of Westmorland slates laid to diminishing courses is that the Peggies or small size random slates are laid nearest to the ridge of the dwelling house which is the most exposed position of all. The reader must remember that in using the term diminishing courses the slater works from the eaves towards the ridge. Peggies are usually 9 to 12 inches (229 to 304mm) long when of good quality but inferior Peggies only 6 inches (152mm) long can be obtained and if the pitch is near the recommended minimum and the position is an exposed one the likelihood of penetration from rain or snow is the greater at this point than at the eaves. Accordingly, in having regard to the question of pitch the surveyor should think of the efficiency of the roof slope as a whole being ruled by the smallest slates used and, in particular, have regard to conditions at the apex of the roof.

If the pitch of the roof has to be slightly increased this will, of course, entail stripping the battens and boarding in any event, but if, as is more likely in the majority of cases, the pitch is adequate, the surveyor must next consider what combination of underlay or sarking he is going to adopt for the roof covering. As in the case of plain tiles, an underlay of reinforced bituminous roofing felt draped loosely between the rafters under the new battens will form a satisfactory improvement in itself if no underlay at all was previously provided. If, however, roof boarding is either to be provided, or the old boarding retained, it is desirable for counter-battens as well as battens to be provided as an underlay to the slates along with the felt for the same reasons as were given under the heading of plain tiles.

Once the surveyor has decided on the type and nature of the new underlay to the roof covering he must, as in the case of plain tiles, give some thought to detailing. If he is dealing with a simple pitched roof with hips at either end and plain eaves, there is not likely to be a great deal of difficulty either in firring the common rafters to a new pitch or in the provision of counter-battens where the surveyor considers that these are necessary. In the first instance some modification of the ridge piece and hips is necessary but this is not likely to lead to insuperable difficulties. Where the matter is often complicated, however, is where such work has to be carried out at vertical abutments with parapet walls and chimney stacks and in particular at the detailing with flat gutters behind parapet walls. A specially shaped tilting fillet of deeper section is required at such a junction and since it is not likely that the existing lead covering to the gutter is adequate to extend over the new fillet and have a sufficient lap under the slates, the provision of a new lead covering to the gutter may be necessary on account of this factor alone, since bad detailing at a point such as this cannot be risked. If, on the other hand, the roof structure consists of tie-beam and principal rafters, the common rafters being carried at the junction with the gutter on a pole plate, a facing board can be fitted plugged to the ends of the common rafters behind which the new tilting fillet can sit snugly. So far as the function with parapet walls and abutments with chimney stacks and other vertical brick surfaces are concerned the same difficulties can be encountered as were discussed under plain tiled roofs. Almost certainly the existing cover flashings will have to be stripped and in certain cases the brick masonry or projecting slate courses under which the previous roof covering fitted will have to be cut away. The surveyor must decide for himself according to the age, nature and character of the house whether he will re-make the detailing as it previously existed or whether he proposes on the other hand to set up lead flashings and soakers in place of the previous jointing. Much will depend on the quality of the roof, since, if swept or laced valleys were previously incorporated in the roof structure, and these are to be re-made, it will be best for the detailing at parapets and chimney stacks to be formed as it was before with perhaps the discreet addition of lead soakers where they cannot be seen, but if on the other hand the valleys are to be formed of wood with lead sheeting, it might be best for the detailing at parapets to be formed with lead flashings and soakers.

Once the underlay and detailing to the new roof covering has been decided, the surveyor will concern himself with the method of fixing the slates themselves. It will be the surveyor's decision, not that of the slating contractor, to decide if the slates are to be head nailed or centre nailed and this is worth some thought. If head nailed slates were provided previously and more than 50 per cent are to be retained, the surveyor is not likely to specify centre nailing since merely to inflict more holes in a slate that has already been perforated twice is hardly a practicable proposition. In any event head nailed slates offer a better protection for the holes as two thicknesses of slates are provided over each hole. The only probable exception to this however, will be where head nailed slates were provided previously but the position was so exposed that the surveyor has suspected from his inspection that the wind had tended to lift and fracture the slates near the nails. Under such circumstances, therefore, the surveyor will probably decide to specify that the slates be centre nailed to the new supports. Centre nailing is often more common to slate roofs than head nailing since it is not only more economical in practice, but it makes for ease of maintenance in the future as defective slates can be removed more readily. There is, however, only one thickness of slate over the centre nails which means that the risk of seepage from a cracked slate into the space below the roof covering is more likely than in the case of head nailed slates. The surveyor's decisions, however, must be governed by the individual circumstances of each case. If he should decide that centre nailed slates are desirable he should remember to specify the provision of an additional top batten to the ridge so as to tilt the ridge course, otherwise the tails of the short slates comprising this will ride on the course of the slates below.

In roofs of the type under discussion it is fortunately not often that sprockets are provided at the eaves. In the case of Westmorland slates laid to diminishing courses, the slates employed at the junction between the sprocket pieces and the rafters, if sprockets are provided, would be of a large size due to the near proximity of the eaves of the roof. This leads to an awkward detail that had to be overcome between the intersection of the sprocket pieces and the common rafters since it is difficult to lay long slates over an angled intersection such as this. The top course of slates will ride clear of the point of intersection by 2 inches (50mm) and this is undesirable both from the point of view of the fixing of the slates and also from the point of view of future maintenance since a workman clambering over the sprockets will break the slates due to the lack of support below. From the point of view of laying, centre nailed slates are extremely awkward to lay over an angle such as this since the slate is likely to ride clear of the batten and if the nail is driven home, the slate may well fracture. It is possible to lay head nailed slates with a rather better prospect of success but even so there is the risk of fracturing the slates adjacent to the fixing nails near the heads. Accordingly, it may be well worth the surveyor's time and the building owner's money to incur the extra expense of forming the junction between the sprockets and the rafters at a compound curve rather than at an angled intersection by means of firring. This will be particularly worthwhile in a roof of quality where swept or laced valleys are provided at other points.

If swept or laced valleys are present in the existing layout the surveyor will no doubt wish to retain these features if at all possible. If such valleys are not provided however, or if it is desirable for the swept or laced valleys to be modified, it is suggested that an open valley gutter is really the next best choice. Secret valley gutters where the slates are only about 1 inch (25mm) apart at the valley with two tilting fillets near each other below and a narrow strip of lead about 10 inches (254mm) wide are most undesirable and form a continual menace due to the fact that they cannot be cleaned out and are perpetually becoming choked and allow water to penetrate the roof covering. Another alternative is that of cut and mitred slates at the valley using soakers below, and although this is quite sound from the point of view of constructional detailing the writers find that jobbing repairs and maintenance in unskilled hands can disfigure and render inefficient valley detailing of this sort over a life span of many years. The advantage of the open valley gutters of traditional pattern where lead sheeting is laid on wood boarding is that the clear width between the edges of the slates, which is normally not less than 8 inches (203mm) provides a suitable self-cleansing channel and is accessible for maintenance. Furthermore, the boots of workmen climbing up the roof are less likely to do damage to the lead than they would to a mitred slate valley in a similar situation.

Cut and mitred slate hips with lead soakers underneath provide a neat finish and are not subject to the disadvantage of mitred valleys that they are subject to wear from workmen clambering over them. The reasons for and against the use of mitred hips are largely aesthetic. Although mitred hips look trim they also have a severe mechanical quality about them and it depends entirely on the type and period of the dwelling house as to whether the surveyor employs this type of finish or not. If the ridge detailing is finished as a wood roll with lead capping and the hip details previously consisted of the same construction the surveyor may prefer to employ this once again making sure that the lead is sound and that it is secured with a sufficient number of tacks and also that it has a sufficient overlap on each side of the hip.

In deciding what type of ridge covering to provide, the surveyor will doubtless have regard to the ridge capping that previously existed. This may have been of lead sheeting on a wood roll but if a stone ridge was provided, as it may well have been in some parts of the country, it might be possible to remove, store and set up the stone sections again once the slates are laid. In the Cotswolds such ridges can be seen and very attractive they are too. In most cases however, if the surveyor discards the idea of using lead because there is some slight risk of staining with the use of lead in conjunction with certain types of slates, he will find the choice of a suitable finish limited. The other alternatives are half-round tiles or specially-produced angular tiles of inverted "V" shape with flanged joints. It is, however, unlikely that the surveyor would employ either of the last alternatives with the sort of roof that we have under consideration. Half-round tiles would not be an acceptable choice for a roof of this type and the dark unyielding machined quality of the "V" shaped ridge tiles is more suitable for urban property built since 1850. An attempt should of course be made to have some relationship between the hip and ridge cappings. These will commonly be formed of one material such as lead sheeting unless mitred tiles are used at the hip when the ridge can be covered with an independent capping of its own. It should be remembered, however, that if the ridge is to be covered with heavy stone sections and the same sections are to be used for the hips, that hip hooks are necessary at the foot of the hip rafter to prevent any accidents from falling sections of stone. This is particularly so where old stone sections are replaced.

Elsewhere the surveyor will no doubt ensure that correct detailing is formed as a matter of course in accordance with current good practice. Slate undercloak at verges with slate and a half at alternate courses over, to give the correct bond, should be provided, and it is necessary to ensure that the detailing is correct. For example the butt joints of the undercloak slates should not coincide with the joints of the slates above and if possible a slight tilt should be provided so that water is thrown clear of the top slated surface. Slates of the appropriate size should automatically be provided at eaves and adjacent to the top ridge course and at hips and valleys. Short slates are really necessary at the eaves for example, since adapting normal size slates for this purpose is a bad practice for the same reasons as given under the section dealing with plain tiled roofs.

Having taken all this trouble to ensure that the slates to the repaired roof slopes are sound it would amount to serious neglect if the surveyor omitted to consider the question of the nails. Steel nails or zinc nails are not likely to be used again if these caused trouble in the past and perhaps the best type of nails for use with Westmorland or other slates of good quality are copper nails. Composition nails can also be employed but copper nails are in all respects to be preferred. Although galvanised iron nails can be used for battens, these are not desirable for use with slates. Nailing of the battens should be carried out with care as the whole of the roof covering obviously depends on this, and it is hardly necessary to point out that the battens must be sufficiently stout so as to take the roof slates on the one hand and to be capable of being nailed without splitting on the other. Battens are normally of sawn redwood being 1½ by ¾ inches (38 by 19mm) for small slates and 2 by ¾ inches (50 by 19mm) for large slates. In the case of slates that are over 1 ft. 6 in. (457mm) long even stouter battens are required measuring 2 by 1 inch (50 by 25mm).

Lead detailing to the roof slopes is worth care both in specifying beforehand and in supervising once the work is in hand. Stepped flashings and soakers at the junctions of slated roofs with vertical abutments such as parapet walls and chimney stacks need to be carefully made and fitted. The arrival of a batch of soakers of the wrong size, which are then hastily adapted on the spot to suit the true sizes of the slates will probably be missed by the surveyor at the time and it is accordingly a good idea for the surveyor to instruct that no cover flashings are fitted before he carries out a brief inspection. Care is also necessary in the making of the apron flashings and gutters at the rear of individual chimney stacks. The upstands and laps should be adequate and the gutter at the rear, in particular, should be dressed over a tilting fillet and shaped so as to allow water to run to each side of it instead of forming a water trap. Cover flashings when fitted should be well wedged in to brickwork and pointed up. There is a tendency to avoid making troublesome permanent joints at the tops of cover flashings on the part of some builders and an omission of this sort is difficult for the surveyor to detect subsequently, as a good thick mortar joint conceals a lot.

Metal detailing is also worthy of care at the junction of ridges with hips, valleys or abutments, since for example an 18 inch (457mm) square metal saddle under the slates will form a waterproof protection. Perforations in the roof surfaces for pipes, chimney stays and

498

ladder supports should be made weathertight by dressing over and under the slating a lead "slate" to which a sleeve is burned or soldered also made in lead. The sleeve should be bossed up round the pipe or stay and sealed at the top by a wrought iron collar or other means.

Care in detailing should also extend to dormer windows and mansard roofs. In the case of dormer windows it is necessary to ensure that the vertical slating is cut at an angle close to the main roof slating at the intersection and made weathertight with the use of soakers. Any unevenness or raggedness in the slates at the inter-section will form a weakness. So far as mansard roofs are concerned, care in ascertaining that the slates are being securely fixed is worth-while and the detailing at the upper end of the mansard slope itself is worthy of thought.

Finally, in considering the repair of our slated roof, we must, as in the case of our tiled roof, make provision for an effective temporary covering while the work is being carried out. Such a covering is fortunately likely to be slightly less expensive in the case of a slated roof since the lower roof pitch means that less vertical scaffolding is entailed and a lesser area of covering to the vertical sides.

In the consideration of the second main example set out in this Chapter, that is the urban roof constructed at any time since about 1860, a rather different approach to the problem might be required since it may be economically necessary to consider another type of roof covering. The type of house envisaged as we have seen is almost certain to have been provided with thin Welsh or imported slates originally and while replacement Welsh slates to British Standard Specifications can be obtained and all the factors already set out in the previous example considered and taken into account in the re-covering, it must be admitted that such work is at the present time comparatively expensive. The expense can be justified in many cases where the character of the locality and the house suggest that the life of the structure is still substantial. A hasty change in the type of covering to something much cheaper might well be regretted by an owner occupier when the work is completed, not because of the work-manship but because the appearance of his house has altered. Al-though few people can be found who have much good to say of Welsh slating in its commonly seen "estate builders" form it is sur-prisingly how even in the most routine two-storey terrace construc-tion the form of roof originally adopted is peculiarly apt to the general design, fussy and over-ornate though it may be.

The decision to change from one form to another form of roof covering is not one to be taken lightly. There are many alternatives and permutations, for example many old pantiled roofs were once changed to slates and more recently concrete interlocking tiles have been used to replace an old covering of slates. There are indeed so many different possibilities that it is beyond the realm of this volume to consider all the factors which have to be taken into account in every conceivable case. The surveyor must take what he finds in the old roof and consider in turn what adaption is required for each of the alternative coverings he has in mind according to the recommendations laid down for current good practice. It must be sufficient here to consider just a few of the factors to be considered in the change from thin, old and defective Welsh slates to something much cheaper on, say, a house with perhaps another thirty years or so of life only.

Before proceeding with a detailed investigation into the technical aspects the surveyor should satisfy himself on three general considerations. In the first place the basic economic necessity for the change should be established by discussion with the owner and a consideration of the future life of the building. In the second place the change in appearance should be considered in conjunction with the owner's opinions, perhaps by viewing another house in the locality where such a change has already been effected. Thirdly, assuming the surveyor is then instructed to re-cover using the cheapest suitable alternative a check would have to be made with the local planning authority to ensure that the proposals are not likely to be opposed under planning legislation. Obviously if roof slopes are mainly hidden by parapets the appearance aspect is unlikely to be of great account either from the owner's point of view or that of the planning authority but with exposed roofs and ornamental features this factor may be vital. One of the difficulties in a change-over from slates is that of the alternatives available plain tiles usually have to be ruled out on account of the shallowness of the pitch. Pantiles or interlocking tiles which are often selected because they are suitable for use at the same pitch as slates do not lend themselves to cutting and fixing to the ornamental features, such as the conical or pyramid shaped tops of bay windows, so commonly found on the type of property envisaged. In many examples seen of recovering with interlocking tiles in lieu of slates, it has been found necessary to remove such features and substitute a flat roof over the projection concerned with disastrous results to the appearance.

Assuming that the foregoing problems can be satisfactorily resolved a further important technical consideration concerns the comparative weights of the old and new roof coverings. Concrete interlocking tiles can weigh well over twice that of thin Welsh slating and even machine-made pantiles can weigh half as much again. An increase of weight on a roof structure barely adequate to carry the old covering could lead to serious troubles later and accordingly some strengthening of the structure may be a necessary preliminary operation before recovering takes place.

There are so many varieties of tiles available at the present time, some of concrete with slate aggregate, incidentally toning in with the colour of slates remarkably well, that it is always necessary to obtain information from the manufacturers or suppliers as to the correct weight when laid at various gauges, besides obtaining the assurance that the manufacture is in accordance with the appropriate British Standard for clay or concrete tiles so as to ensure a suitable degree of frost resistance.

As to the remaining factors all those requirements as previously set out for the appropriate roof covering must be followed in accordance both with the maker's recommendations and the suggestions of the British Standard Codes of Practice otherwise the whole operation will be pointless.

Stone Slates

The urban surveyor with his experience obtained in the big industrial cities may stand in front of a cottage in the Cotswolds and stare aghast at what he considers to be a picture of complete disintegration of the roof covering. Before he arrives at any snap judgments, however, it is as well for him to consider the whole point and purpose of stone slating. As we mentioned early in the Chapter dealing with slates, the term "slate" is used with a particular meaning in that connection, whereas stone slating implies a quite different type of roofing material. The sandstone and limestones from which stone slates are formed are recognisable to the average person as the type of stone he associates with walling materials and the only difference in the production of stone slates as against certain types of walling blocks is that they are capable of being quarried from stratified layers so that they can be subsequently split along the natural bedding planes often just by the action of frost on exposure and produced in sufficiently strong thin slabs for use as stone slates. The practice of using stone slates for roofing is of long standing, and as with so many of the traditional local materials already discussed dates back to Roman times. On the other hand it is thought that even in the Cotswolds the general use of stone slates did not begin again until the techniques of framing in timber had developed sufficiently far to provide a suitable structure to support the substantial weight involved. The records show that the building of two houses in Gloucestershire roofed with stone slates in 1221 was sufficiently unusual and costly to be commented upon. The 14th century began to see the increasing use of stone slates and from Tudor times to the first quarter of the 19th century stone became a favourite roofing material over wide areas, including parts of Surrey and Sussex, Dorset and Somerset, the whole of the Cotswolds, Northern Oxfordshire, Northamptonshire and Rutland, along the Welsh border and into Wales and throughout all the counties from Derbyshire northwards into Scotland.

The whole difference, however, between slates within the meaning of the previous section and stone slates is that the first are impermeable while stone slates are decidedly not. It is for this reason that stone slates are provided in sufficient thicknesses to form an efficient roof covering. Moisture inevitably penetrates the surface of the stone, particularly with constant saturation in the winter, to a certain degree, but the thickness of the stone is so judged that having regard to its texture this moisture penetration is never likely to be critical.

Thus the sandstone slabs used in Yorkshire are very large and heavy while the oolitic slates seen in the Cotswolds are much lighter, since they are smaller and thinner. The reason however, for the stupefaction of the urban surveyor as he inspects a roof of stone slates is that to his unaccustomed eye it will probably be seen to be in an advanced state of dilapidation. This, however, may not necessarily be the case. The slates may be uneven in shape and Cotswold stone slates are distinguished in this respect, and the natural settlement of the roof timbers under the weight of the heavy covering will no doubt have led to the undulations so beloved of the calendar manufacturer but of questionable charm to the maintenance surveyor. When to this is added the fact that the top surface of the slates may have spalled due to frost action although the underneath may be quite sound and that on this top rough textured surface has grown an impressive brightly coloured array of lichens, the general effect is such that a surveyor who is unaccustomed to roof covering of this type may be forgiven for thinking that the covering is at the end of its useful life.

Nor will inspection from the roof space cause the surveyor much reassurance. The wood pegs by which the slates are usually fixed may be of sound oak but they are more likely to be of unsound oak since a number will inevitably have rotted, be loose, or have broken from stress with slight movement in the roof structure. Alternatively the surveyor may find that the slates are laid on a mortar bed and certain practices which have been acceptable in country districts for centuries may militate most sharply against his careful training in the best constructional methods for new roof coverings.

A good way for the surveyor to keep a sense of balance before contemplating the question of repair, is for him to walk round the village or town where the property is situated and look at all the similar types of roofs that he can see. Such a tour of inspection is often a very good thing since, as on the same principle as the man with no shoes who thought that he was badly off until he met a man with no feet, the surveyor may discover that there are many roofs that show far more dramatic signs of disintegration than the one that he has to deal with and it will be borne in upon him that the very nature of this roof covering is like no other with which he is acquainted. Indeed there is plenty of evidence to establish that well selected stone slates, certainly those of oolitic limestone, will last for well over two hundred years and that despite the external appearance, it is far more likely that it will be the oak pegs and battens supporting the slates rather than the slates themselves which will need renewal, probably at about eighty to one hundred-year intervals.

Having summoned up sufficient nerve to deal with his instructions, the surveyor can look at the slates from a ladder with rather closer attention and decide if these have sufficient body left to be watertight or if they have been worn so thin and have so many fractures that are likely to be fundamental that they can no longer form any useful function. If, however, the surveyor finds that the slates are reasonably sound he may well not be satisfied with the fixings. Fortunately, however, on the relatively shallower pitches the rough texture of the stone and the deposits of lichens may cause the slates to adhere together effectively even if the pegs are rotted, but the surveyor will not wish to take this matter on trust and will want to reinforce the pegs. He may also find that the torching which is traditionally provided to stone slated roofs from inside the roof space is so moist as to be a danger to the pegs so that it might rot them, and indeed this process may be already far advanced.

The weight of stone slates makes their handling difficult and once they are disturbed so that the full weight has to be supported by the rafters and battens the surveyor may feel reluctant to use wood pegs again. Under such circumstances brass screws are probably the best since copper nails may not be adequate. Cotswold stone roofs are of a steeper pitch even than plain tiled roofs and secure fixing of the stone slates is essential. Although the stone slates of Yorkshire roofs are laid to lesser pitches, of probably 30° or thereabouts the slabs of stone are much heavier and secure fixing is just as necessary.

If the stone slates to the roof slopes are clearly so worn and fractured that they are incapable of further life, the surveyor will wish to recover the roof and probably in a locality where this type of roof covering is universal he would commit a dreadful error if he tried to employ, for example, concrete tiles. In an age where, fortunately, the voice of the preservationist is becoming heard a little more often the employment of a modern roof covering would be seen by all to be a mistake and the surveyor would be lucky to avoid being not only run out of the village, but possibly to escape being tarred and feathered as well. There is however, a serious point here, in that the surveyor's normal duty of thinking about cost may not be quite so important as he thinks in a case such as this. If most of the local roofs have coverings of stone slates, this may argue the existence of one or more local firms of builders and craftsmen used to this form of roof covering, so that the economic consequences of using the same material again may not be so severe as he anticipates. There may even be a quarry still in production nearby. The best thing he can do is to interview one or perhaps two of these firms when he will learn a surprising amount not only about techniques but in the economics of the craft as well.

Even if the surveyor cannot understand the terms used by the craftsmen who will lay stone slates since these will have little connection with the slating terms with which he is familiar the surveyor should nevertheless use his faculties to try and retain an independent judgment while conceding that certain areas of such a specialised craft can best be left to those who have been dealing with it for years. In this, of course, he will be lucky in his builder, and it is hoped that his fellow surveyors practising in the vicinity will have enabled a satisfactory introduction to be made in this respect.

When the surveyor examines the sub-structure of a roof he will of course wish to satisfy himself that the rafters are sufficiently strong and inflexible to take the weight of the roof covering. This may often not prove to be the case and the timber structure may well need repair before the roof is re-slated. The surveyor will doubtless take the opportunity of providing reinforced roofing felt as an underlay to the new roof coverings and the additional cost of felt, counter-battens and battens may be accepted by the client.

The lap of stone slates is, due to the fact that stone is porous to a certain degree, rather greater than that for other slates or tiles. A 4-inch (101mm) lap is desirable so that the irregularities in heads and tails of stone slates, which are unavoidable, are not likely to lead to moisture penetration. With stone slates the longest slates at the eaves are likely to be the thickest. An undercourse of heavy slates is normally laid, bedded on mortar at a lesser slope than the remainder, and left to project with an overhang of about 6 inches (152mm) from the exterior wall surface. The next course of slates has an equivalent overhang and there is thus two thicknesses of stone slates at the eaves. Undercloaks are also provided at verges in the same manner as for tiled roofs.

If the surveyor is in luck he will find that swept or laced valleys were provided previously and his client will wish to replace these features. As in the case of plain tiles, valley boards form the angles between the roof slopes but the whole efficiency of valleys such as these, particularly swept valleys, depend on the craftsmen carrying out the work. The shaping of bottomers and skews is a skilled business with stone slates and a successful result is only possible with a craftsman who knows his trade thoroughly.

Ridges to stone slated roofs are of course most likely to be of stone sections bedded in mortar. Half-round clay ridge tiles can alternatively be used if stone sections are hard to obtain. So far as hips are concerned the surveyor may wish to provide mitred angles with lead soakers under, or alternatively carry the ridge material down the hips. In the case of heavy hip cappings the same precautions should be taken as in the case of plain tiled or slated roofs.

(7) *Corrugated Asbestos and Corrugated Iron, Asbestos Slates and Temporary Treatments to Existing Roofs*

A brief word on the subject of corrugated asbestos and corrugated iron sheeting is included at this stage, not so that the surveyor can save his client money by roofing a Georgian mansion with either of these materials, but because there will be occasions when the surveyor will find them extremely useful as semi-permanent or temporary coverings. An obvious example of this is where a dwelling house let in flats is so heavily dilapidated that the existing roof covering is completely worn yet a road widening scheme or redevelopment programme is likely within the next five to ten years so that there is little point in providing a new roof covering of the original material since the cost could not be recouped.

Asbestos-cement is, as its name suggests, composed of ordinary Portland cement and asbestos fibre. Corrugated sheets of this material are non-combustible, durable and in particular, which represents one of the greatest advantages, very light in weight. It is accordingly possible to use this material where the original roof structure is extremely old and fragile. The important matter to watch, however, is the question of the fixing of the sheets, since although the light qualities of the sheeting are attractive from the constructional point of view, it is necessary to make sure that they do not blow away in a gale. Such sheets should always be fixed through the crowns of the corrugations by galvanised screws $4\frac{1}{2}$ inches (114 mm) long, the correct detailing to ensure a watertight joint being a neat perforation in the first instance and a lead dish-shaped washer with an asbestos washer below. Each sheet is secured in six places, two screws being placed at the head, two at the base, and two at the centre point. This, added to a 6-inch (152mm) lap at the head and base of the sheets and a 2¾-inch (70mm) side lap is adequate to secure a safe fixing though it is usually necessary to provide purlins above the old rafters. The use of corrugated asbestos sheets is worthy of attention to detail since a wide variety of accessory pieces are available from the manufacturers such as eaves filling pieces and ridge capping sections and it is obviously worthwhile to employ purpose-made asbestos fittings where possible. It is worth obtaining from the manufacturers a list of the wide variety of special fittings available.

Corrugated iron sheets are also worthy of consideration since they provide, apart from the question of appearance, a tolerable answer to the main defect that afflicts corrugated asbestos sheets. Where corrugated asbestos sheets are brittle and can be fractured very easily, corrugated iron sheets are more resilient, and if any clambering on or tampering with the roof is expected from time to time during its life span, the metal may be a more desirable material under the circumstances.

Whereas corrugated asbestos or iron are suitable for recovering a roof on a property of very limited life where appearance is entirely of no consequence, asbestos slates can be used at somewhat greater cost on those occasions when, even for a few years, some regard must be had to appearance. Such slates are also used quite frequently on garages and outbuildings. They are usually suitable as a substitute for ordinary Welsh slating since the minimum pitch required is 30°. While details for the underlay and most other details are similar to those of true slating, the use of disc rivets is essential to fix the tail of each slate otherwise there is a severe danger of slates being lifted off in heavy winds. In all respects of course the fixing of a proprietary product of this nature should be carried out in accordance with the manufacturer's directions.

A further method of lengthening the life of an old roof for a few years is often adopted and this consists of applying layers of bitumen and canvas. This work is usually carried out by specialist contractors and is often extended over parapet gutters and parapet walls to provide an impervious layer. It is usually also necessary to apply further layers at intervals of every two to three years to ensure that the roof is watertight. While the work is normally covered by a guarantee and can be considered a reasonable method of water-proofing a building for the last ten years of its life, it is exceptionally difficult to trace leaks if any do arise during this period and experience indicates that it is often necessary to invoke the guarantee perhaps more than once until the leak is found. A danger arises with this method since all ventilation to the roof structure is effectively

sealed off and a leak over a period can be responsible in the circumstances for an outbreak of dry rot.

(8) *Thatch*

Thatch in all its various forms has been in use as a roof covering for
as long as the domestic house has assumed a recognisable form but
even by 1200 with the growth of towns it was beginning to go out of
favour for the larger buildings. The decree prohibiting its use for
new buildings in London of 1212 required also that existing buildings
with thatched roofs should have a coat of lime plaster applied to the
thatch. Even so the vast majority of houses continued to be provided
with thatch roofs until Tudor times and the great rebuilding boom,
which lasted from about 1570 to 1640, rehoused all but the poorest
classes. Most of the new houses were provided with roofs of stone,
slate or tiles leaving thatch to persist in those areas where the more
suitable materials, such as reed and straw, were readily available
whereas as before wheat, flax, broom sedge, and heather were all
pressed into service for the purpose. In these areas the thatcher's skill
was prodigious and extended also to the covering of churches and
other buildings as well as houses. Most towns, however, eventually
banned thatch, for example Hull in Elizabeth I's reign, and Cambridge by an Order in Council in 1619, so that most thatch covered
dwellings are situated in country areas, particularly Norfolk, Suffolk,
Cambridgeshire and Essex and in the West Country in Dorset and
Devon where a specially threshed straw known as wheat reed has
long been used as a roof covering for houses built with cob walls too
weak for much heavier traditional roof coverings.

As no thatch, however good, is likely to last a hundred years and
most roofs are likely to need recovering in periods of between twenty
and forty years, there is no question of a surveyor being asked to
inspect thatch of any venerable age.

In spite of its delightful appearance thatch has serious disadvantages as a roof covering, the main disadvantage being its liability to
destruction by fire compared with which its other main disadvantage,
that of becoming infested with vermin, is a secondary one. Thatch
after a dry summer is particularly prone to fire and a plumber's blow
lamp used to unfreeze the pipes in the roof space or sparks from
a nearby bonfire have often proved fatal. Understandably local
authorities do not approve of thatch as a roof covering due to such a
high degree of risk even when this is reduced to some extent by
saturating the reeds in fire resisting solution. In consequence the use
of thatch has declined and there are now few skilled thatchers in the
country. There are, however, some showpiece districts of houses and

other parts of the country where thatched roofs are universally maintained and a surveyor may occasionally be invited to supervise the repair of a thatched roof by an enthusiastic householder. His attempts to point out the difficulties of obtaining the local authority's consent for thatch will probably be countered by the news that his client not only knows that such consent will be forthcoming but also by the information that the chief building inspector to the council lives in a thatched house over the road.

Repairs to thatching will sometimes consist mainly of renewing defective parts in which holes have been made by birds and covering with wire netting to prevent further depredations, but this applies to barns and outbuildings rather than to the main roof of the house. In the repair of the main thatched roof of a house, a traditional method is to strip the dilapidated portion and lay the new thatch starting at the base of the bared square which should disclose the battens, probably 2-inch (50mm) laths at 8-inch (203mm) centres. A handful of thatch known as a yealm, from 4 to 6 inches (101 to 152mm) deep and about 10 inches (254mm) wide is tied at the butt with tarred twine and laid on the roof and tied to the battens or fixed by withies which are nailed to the rafters. The lap of the layers of yealms should not be less than 50 per cent. The second and subsequent layers of yealms should be fastened by laying across them poles or rods which are bound to the rafters with tarred twine. When the area is covered, it is raked down with a wooden rake and the edges trimmed with shears.

At the ridge, the yealms are bent over and weighted with "mixing" which consists of equal parts of slaked lime and earth placed on top of the straw to form a ridge. The ends of the top yealm on the other side are now pressed down into the mixing and weighted down with another coating. A special capping of thatch is then formed and laced with withies to the roof. Verges and eaves should also be laced.

Thatched roofs, however, which are in need of repair, always throw up a strong case for the renewal of the roof covering, either with another material in a non-thatch area, or by a skilled thatcher and his assistant where this is specifically desired. Having given such a warning to his client regarding the risk of using thatch as will satisfy his conscience and having been overruled, the surveyor can then abandon himself to the delight of watching an expert specialist in an old craft produce a perfect result. Needless to say, however, the expert specialist will expect some help from the surveyor not least to see that the rafters are firm and even, the pitch a seemly one and the battens spaced to his needs, and a meeting with the thatcher once the old roof is stripped is a necessity, not just a wise precaution.

The "reed straw" necessary for thatching is difficult to obtain. In modern times straw has usually been bruised by the binder and in the threshing machine and is in consequence quite useless. Good straw or reed having been procured the surveyor will find local variations in the craft. In Dorset, the gables usually droop and are ended in low hipped hoods. In Suffolk the gable end is cocked up and very occasionally is still decorated with a peacock or other bird made in straw.

One of the signs of a well-thatched roof is that little but the stub ends of the thatch show and no straggly or bruised straws can be seen. The covering consists of bundles of reeds or straw lightly packed, secured to battens and rafters. The thickness may be just over or under 1 foot (305mm) and the pitch, according to the views of old craftsmen, should not be less than 52° for a domestic house. Reeds up to 9 feet (2·74m) in length such as those obtained from the Norfolk Broads or nowadays imported from Holland are best used rather than wheat or rye straw. These are formed in bundles laid with their ends pointing towards the eaves.

The thatcher will probably be used to rafters at 2 to 2 ft. 6 in. (611 to 762mm) centres and 2 by 1 inch (50 by 25mm) battens at 8 or 12 inch (203 or 304mm) gauge. In Norfolk the spaces between the sloping rafters of the roof are first of all filled with an interlaced layer of reeds called flaking or basketwork if no battens are in use, but usually battens are preferred. The thatcher then works up from the eaves to the ridge of the roof, laying bundles of reeds side by side in rows, each row overlapping the previous one, working from a ladder from right to left and pushing the ends of the reeds into position with a "leggat". The bundles are held down by horizontal strips of hazel called "sways" in Norfolk, anchored down by iron reed hooks driven into the rafters. Elsewhere in the country withies or osiers (rods of pliable willow twigs) are interlaced through and over the bundles and are secured to the rafters with tarred twine. Sometimes tarred twine (ropeyarn in Dorset) is used instead of withies, bound with the use of a large iron needle. Irrespective of the method used the thatcher will probably use a large iron pin to firstly find the rafters and secondly to hold the bundles in position temporarily.

When the ridge of the roof is reached, it is capped with a thatch of pliable sedge or rushes held down by lengths of hazel or willow called "liggers" in Norfolk, gripped in place by "broaches" which are pointed strips of hazel bent to the shape of a hairpin and pushed through into the thatch. The edges of this ridge thatch are then trimmed with a small knife. The reason for this is that Norfolk thatch is too stiff to bend in ridge sections but elsewhere ridges are formed with straw. The bundles are stretched over the apex and overlap the thatch on both sides until a 4-inch (101mm) long section has been covered to the required thickness. This is then secured with short horizontal withies and staples, pieces of withies bent in a "V" shape. The ridge is completed in sections in this way and the edges then cut with shears or a long-handled knife. If a chimney stack is situated along the ridge line the thatcher begins the ridge each side of it, working towards the hips or gables.

The surveyor should give some attention to details at eaves and verges. At the eaves a tilting filled might be needed to throw the thatch clear of the wall for its 1½ or 2 feet (457 or 611mm) overhang, while the lower thatch bundles should be secured to the wallplate as well as to the rafters. Short horizontal withies are formed at hips and verges at about 2-feet (611mm) intervals fixed with wood staples.

B (1) *Flat roof coverings. Metals*

Metal roof coverings have one characteristic in common. They all depend for their efficiency on the sub-structure below firstly being designed so that it suits the characteristic of the particular metal employed and secondly that the sub-structure remains consistently even and smooth for the length of the life of the metal covering. Failures in metal roof coverings therefore may be due to any one or a combination of the following factors:

(1) Failure of the sub-structure due to either an inherent weakness from a design defect or poor quality materials, or as a result of distortion due to failure in another part of the structure removing support from the roof.

(2) From faults developing in the metal roof covering itself, either by reason of faulty design in laying the roof covering or poor workmanship, or due to the fact that the roof covering has reached the end of its useful life and requires renewal.

(3) Due to a fault or faults developing at angles or abutments of the roof. These can be due to faulty design, bad workmanship or uneven wear on the surface of the metal. Thus a narrow box gutter taking a great volume of water from a roof where the water has a higher than normal acidic percentage will show signs of wear more quickly than the remainder of the metal. Again, metal such as zinc placed in contact with materials containing appreciable amounts of soluble salts such as chlorides and sulphates may, if not protected, show signs of attack and disintegration long before the remainder of the metalwork.

It is suggested accordingly that the surveyor bears these three points in mind when he is asked to undertake the repair of a roof with a metal covering. What the surveyor will find in dealing with flat roofs is that tolerances are very fine and whereas a pitched roof can withstand often quite substantial movement and still remain watertight this is not the case with flat roofs.

The surveyor will find that the use of metal for roof coverings often increases in complexity of design and ambitiousness of execution with the size and grandeur of the structure. He may be asked to repair and maintain a wide range of roof coverings from the elaborate metalwork of a large Victorian country house to perhaps the only slightly less impressive town house which, although smaller, will nevertheless have many metal surfaces and details that will excite the surveyor's admiration, culminating perhaps in cast or wrought ornamentation in iron, lead or zinc, sometimes of intricate and unexpected complexity, with, nearby perhaps, a copper dome over the head of the study used by the fortunate householder. In the case of smaller houses in rows, or terraces, metal roofs become more stereotyped. These either consist of flat tops to houses that have roofs with slated or tiled sides or alternatively simple flat roofs surrounded by brick parapet walls. In the former case where a flat metal roof is surrounded by slated or tiled slopes the structure will be so arranged that a conventional roof space is provided with access to the structural timbers. The surveyor will in all probability find that the top section of the roof consists of joists carrying timber boards on which the metal covering is laid direct. In smaller houses the boards will not be tongued and grooved and the surveyor will, with the aid of his penknife, be able to establish what type of metal is employed for the covering. He will not be able to learn more than this, however, since the condition of the metal can only be learned from the exterior and ladders will be required for a roof of this type since a trap door for access, under such circumstances, is fairly rare. Before he leaves the roof space, however, the surveyor will establish the type of timber structure employed and its condition. Having discovered that the boards are not tongued and grooved but plain edged, the surveyor will nevertheless often be surprised to see how wide the joints are in many cases due to shrinkage of the boards. This, although bad from the insulation point of view, may nevertheless be unintentionally beneficial from the point of view of possible timber diseases. The surveyor will also find that the boards are laid over the joists at right-angles rather than at the diagonal as in the best construction and he will note any peculiarities of design. In particular, however, he will make notes as to the suitability of the surface likely to be presented by the tops of the boards, for example, any shortcomings due to the boards being curled or uneven. The fall of the metal roof as a whole, however, can best be judged from the top surface with the aid of a long straight edge and a spirit level if necessary. The examination of the surface of the metal covering will also be carried out externally but this will be discussed under the appropriate headings used for the various metals. Before the surveyor leaves the roof space however, he is advised to examine in particular the constructional timbers at the junction of the flat top surface with the sloping sides for it is at these points that the joints between roof coverings are often less than ideal and damp penetration occurs. A surprising amount of white crystalline deposits and stains from salts can be seen to the timbers of roofs of this type and the surveyor will note whether there are any new dark damp stains among them which might indicate continual saturation from defective detailing over a very long period. The use of a damp meter is helpful in such investigations, but sometimes the joint between timber is found to be so blackened and spongy as to make further investigation unnecessary.

There is no doubt, however, that the most common form for metal roof coverings to take is when these are provided to flat roofs relying for their support on timber joists built into and suspended between brick walls. These walls generally end in a parapet above the level of the metal covering itself. Such roofs are, of course, frequently found to the main structure and back addition to all types of property and in particular to the urban terraced house. Sometimes when such roofs are employed for the main structure it is not uncommon to see a decorative front slope of tiles or slates employed to provide a particular architectural effect but with virtually the whole extent of the main roof consisting of a single flat slope draining from front to rear and suspended between the party walls on either side. Flat roofs of this type present difficulties to the surveyor but curiously enough there rarely seems to be any difficulty about access to the metal covering itself since the writers have nearly always found that a trap door is provided. In the case of the back addition roofs, of course, access can often be easily obtained from the main structure by means of a door or perhaps a window. The difficulties arise, however, mainly due to the fact that the substructure of the roof cannot be examined since it is sealed between the metal covering on the upper surface and the plaster ceilings of the rooms below which are attached to the undersides of the same joists that support the roof covering. While the first difficulty encountered, therefore, is due to the fact that the structure of the roof cannot be investigated so that the thickness of joists, for example, can only be guessed, the second difficulty is that the surveyor will have great difficulty in endeavouring to judge the effect of any disrepair. Such roofs are, curiously, rarely provided with ventilation between the joists. Sometimes this is due to the fact that ventilation is difficult to provide due to the shape and design of the structure but even where ventilation is both possible and simple, as for example in the case of a simple flat roof to a back addition, it rarely seems to have been thought of. The consequence of this is therefore that the stagnant air which is trapped between the joists, slightly warmed by the diffused heat from the rooms below, forms ideal conditions for dry rot should the covering above admit moisture. This of course, with the wear of the roof covering and flashings, is likely to happen sooner or later in any event, but often this occurs sooner with the distortion of the sub-structure or other defects which can accelerate disrepair. Accordingly it must be with extreme care that the surveyor examines the condition of the covering of the flat roof. Often dampness admitted near a wall giving support to the joists will simply trickle into the brickwork and be soaked up so that no sign appears to the ceilings of the room below. This is perhaps the most potentially dangerous defect of all since the ends of the joists will almost certainly sooner or later be affected with dry rot. Even at the centre of the roof span an inadequate fall or, as happens on occasions no fall at all, will result in water being retained on the surface and penetrating small holes and apertures. Bad detailing can assist water penetration which, by the action of capillary creep will penetrate under the metal and often, by being soaked into the joists, either appear as slight staining some way from the point of entry, or may not even be apparent.

It is for these reasons that the metal coverings to the flat roofs should be examined with great care and any signs of defects, however minor, must be treated with caution. The surveyor, it is suggested, should err on the side of safety under such circumstances and if he suspects that defects exist he should strip part of the covering and boarding below as part of the investigation prior to the repair itself.

It is now therefore desirable to turn to each type of metal used in the covering for roofs in turn, discussing their particular characteristics. We have not finished with the investigation, however, since the surface of each metal examined by the surveyor will present different types of defects with ageing, and develop different faults so that it is as well for each to be discussed in turn.

Metals used in roof coverings

No. 1. Lead

Lead has formed the exterior covering for both pitched and flat roofs for many hundreds of years. There is at present, however, little mediaeval lead left in Britain except perhaps, on the roofs of some churches, since most mediaeval lead was replaced in the 18th or early 19th centuries. Lead sheet is either cast or provided in milled sheet sections. Cast lead sheet is now a craft since the lead sheet is made on an open sand casting table which limits the size of the panels to within a range of approximately 9 by 3 feet (2·74 by 0·91m) to 18 by 6 feet (5·49 by 1·83m). Sheets nowadays can be cast by this method to an accuracy of ½ lb. (0·23kg) per square foot up to 5 or 10 lbs. (2·27 or 4·54kg) per square foot although cast lead in former times was usually made much thicker and therefore heavier. Cast lead sheet was manufactured for centuries by this method but was largely replaced for domestic construction with the introduction of factory produced lead sheeting after the advent of the industrial revolution. Cast lead sheet is now accordingly rarely used in the repair of dwelling houses except for work carried out to buildings of artistic or historic importance by the specialised architect and surveyor and although milled sheet lead becomes the main subject of this section due to its almost universal adoption in the early part of the 19th century, cast lead has a slight advantage in its mechanical properties. Lead sheet when cast on a sand bed provides an attractive texture on the base of the metal which is then used for the exposed surface. It is interesting to note, however, that the mediaeval builder used the cast metal to its best advantage in the form that it was made. The hollow roll was an ingenious way of overcoming the difficult problem of forming a waterproof joint between adjacent sheets and the herringbone pattern of lead panels on church steeples and roofs indicate that the tendency to creep, inherent in the heavier metal, was guarded against, even in the small panels available. The later troubles in Georgian times when mass-produced sheets of large size were used without taking into account the problem of creep on sloping roofs or expansion due to temperature changes took some time to obtain general recognition but at length new constructional details were evolved. The hollow roll, satisfactory enough for joints in cast lead on high and inaccessible church roofs, proved less satisfactory when milled lead sheets of thinner section were used for the roofs of domestic houses exposed to the unsympathetic boots that constant maintenance entailed so that the wood roll was improvised to overcome the problem.

Characteristics of Lead Sheeting

The two main characteristics of sheet lead are firstly that it is extremely malleable and secondly that it is resistant to corrosion against all normal exposure including polluted areas and seaside districts. The reason for this is that lead, once laid, forms a strong self-protective surface on the exposed side due to oxidisation so that a composition which is primarily composed of lead carbonate forms a patina which adheres strongly to the metal base. The advantages of this are many. It means that the life of a lead covered roof is as long as anyone could desire for domestic construction provided that the lead is correctly laid. The other advantage is that the patina will make sure that there is no difficulty from any "run off". The lead will be insoluble to constant rainfall and condensation, and accordingly no particles will be washed on to other metals or stone with the disconcerting results often seen with other metals such as copper. Lead also is virtually proof against electrolytic corrosion when used in conjunction with other metal for roofing work.

Against these considerable advantages there are drawbacks. Lead is of course expensive. It is also heavy. It has moderate mechanical properties but the chief drawback after laying is that it contracts and expands with alterations in temperature to a more marked degree than other roofing metal. The other drawback is that it creeps when laid in large unbroken areas on steeply pitched roofs. Under such circumstances the lead expands in warm conditions but the weight of the metal prevents corresponding contraction in cold weather so that there is an appreciable if imperceptible lengthening causing bunching and ripples leading finally to tears. Accordingly as with all roofing materials lead will only be fully satisfactory if its special characteristics are taken into account in the laying of the material. It must be primarily allowed to expand and contract and when laid on steeply pitched slopes it must be prevented from creeping.

Milled lead sheet for repairs and renewals to roof covering should conform to the requirements of B.S.1178 "Milled lead sheet and strip for building purposes". Lead sheet is specified and known by the weight in pounds of one square foot (or in metric terms by gauge) and lead of less than 6 lbs. per square foot is rarely used for roofs, gutters, high ridges and valleys while up to 8 lbs. per square foot is general for this purpose. Flashings are normally of 5 lbs. lead and soakers are of 4 lbs. lead. Although lead is obtainable in sheets 8-feet (2·44m) wide and up to 40-feet (7·19m) long, sheets larger than 24 square feet (7·32m²) or longer than 10 feet (3·05m) are undesirable.

The Inspection

The inspection of the surface of a lead flat roof should give a good deal of the information on which to base an assessment of the need for repair. The light grey appearance of new milled lead dulls to a polished gun-metal sheen with age and the malleable quality of the material stands to the surveyor's advantage from a number of points

515

of view. The first advantage is that the lead will show depressions indicating any unevenness or sinkings in the boarding underneath from the minor parallel lines indicating that the boards are not tongued and grooved and have warped, to larger irregularities or depressions indicating failure of the structural timbers which, taken in conjunction with other evidence such as damp to the ceiling below, will point to the need for opening up. The other advantage of the malleable quality of lead is that it will respond to a certain amount of bending back and lifting, provided it is not too old and worn, for the surveyor to satisfy himself on certain aspects of the fixing and finishing. Thus flashings can be examined for the nature of the clips and tacks, the splash laps of drips can be raised to ascertain the nature of the lap and fixing of the undercloak, and rolls can often be investigated in a similar manner. The first matter that requires investigating is the fall of the roof surface. A fall of 1 in 120 inches is the recommended standard but there will be cases when the roof surface does not appear to have any fall at all, possibly due to inadequate firring, or alternatively sags at the centre due to deflection of the joists from old age or some more sinister cause. Given soundness of the structural timbers, however, a certain amount of ponding may be considered acceptable provided that the rolls, drips and flashings are sound. If the ponding occurs at a vulnerable part of the roof adjacent to a flashing to a parapet wall or a timber tank casing, the need for modification is obvious, particularly in the latter case where the weight of the tank may be too much for the size and span of the joists. In cases where the ponding is acute however, the relaying of the roof to an effective fall is necessary.

The next points for investigation are the rolls and drips. Wood rolls to flat roofs take a good deal of wear and the lead may be dented and misshapen on the rounded surfaces. Provided that the sheeting is not distorted too badly, or torn, all may be well, but the surveyor may wish to satisfy himself that the splash lap is sufficient, the standard recommended being $1\frac{1}{2}$ inches (38mm) and that the underlap is nailed to the wood roll with flat headed copper nails. The abutments of the rolls with the parapet walls and drips is worth particular note as it is often at these points that insufficient surplus lead is provided to make effectively waterproof joints. It will not be very likely in most cases that the rolls exceed by a wide margin the suggested 23-inch (584mm) intervals but cases have been seen of a narrow section of lead being tacked on to its companion sheet on a lead flat roof by a welt.

Drips, where provided, will not normally vary a great deal from the 7 ft. 6 in. (2·29m) standard interval which may be taken up to

9 ft. (2·74m) with impunity. The detailing of drips is important however as the 1½-inch (38mm) splash lap applies to drips as well as rolls and the 1-inch (25mm) underlap should be dressed into a rebate in the boarding of drips and copper nailed. On rare occasions this rebate is omitted so that the edge of the drip impedes the surface water flow and in the case of lighter than standard lead sheet may lead to tears developing. This detail is worth modification accordingly. Where drips are only 1½ inches (38mm) deep, for this is the absolute minimum recommended, 2 inches (51mm) being the normal depth, an anti-capillary groove should be formed in the vertical surface with the undercloak chased into it.

Lead flashings are worthy of inspection for a number of reasons. These are often too shallow in depth and are badly secured. The upstand at the edges of the roof at the junction of the brick parapet wall should be 6 inches (152mm) high and the lap with the flashing at least 2 inches (51mm), the flashing fitted in maximum lengths of 8 feet (2·44m) with laps of 4 inches (102mm), the top edge being turned into a brick groove for ¾ inch (19mm) minimum and lead-wedged with clips at 2-foot (610mm) intervals and the lower edge being retained with 1½-inch (38mm) lead tacks at 2 ft. 6 in. (762mm) intervals. The clips and tacks are necessary to avoid the malleable flashing being disturbed or torn away.

Parapet box gutters are a never-ending source of trouble in flat roofs. Lead lined gutters are often too narrow and have to be remade. Unless a box gutter has a minimum width of 9 inches (229mm) and is at least 3 inches (76mm) deep at the top end it should be regarded with suspicion. The fall of the gutter and the positions of drips should not be less than the standard recommended for the flat roof itself, and due to design difficulties this standard is sometimes not achieved. It is preferable for the lower end of the gutter to be carried out through the parapet wall by means of a neat rectangular aperture to discharge into a hopper head with an apron of lead. Cesspools inside the roof area are very commonly found with old lead roofs and these are frequently a cause of trouble from blockage, inaccessible leaks, or poor joints with the rainwater pipe below.

The surface of the lead requires particular care in investigations and, if discoloured or covered in deposits, it should be cleaned so as to permit a thorough examination. Pitting or depressions may, on closer inspection, show minor tears nearby, and bulges from buckling or ripples from expansion should always be regarded with suspicion as at these points tears in the lead are extremely likely, particularly if the lead is old and brittle. Blobs of black bituminous compound while exciting suspicions are an exasperating discovery as it often costs more in time and trouble to clean them off and

517

diagnose the trouble than to effect an efficient long-term repair. Previous signs of repair by solder or other means should also be examined, as often a crack will have reopened since the repair was carried out.

There will be cases when the surveyor will decide with some reluctance that the lead covering is so frail and brittle and presents such a tattered patchwork of repaired defects that it cannot be saved. Under such circumstances therefore the whole question of the re-newal of the covering will arise and the next decision for the sur-veyor to place before his client will be one of economics; whether to renew the lead sheeting or whether to effect an immediate saving in money at the cost of providing a covering that will, in all probability have a considerably shorter life. A word of warning might be in-serted at this stage. The renewal of the lead covering itself will be discussed in this Chapter but since it is beyond the scope of this book to indicate how to modify all the types of roofs discussed so as to take the various different types of covering possible, no suggestions as to the way in which this could be done in any particular case will be made. The surveyor should be careful however, that in acquies-cing in his client's decision to save money in this way that he has given due weight to all the circumstances. The decision to renew the covering of a small, high and inaccessible lead flat roof with a covering of an inferior life may well be regretted in some years' time.

The repair of lead flat roofs

If the surveyor decides that the fall to a flat roof is quite inadequate to discharge surface water from the lead covering so that due to old age, poor design and some settlement in the structure or perhaps due to a combination of all three of these factors the roof tends to hold surface water to an undesirable extent there will be no alternative but to strip the lead sheeting from the roof, raise the boarding under-neath and investigate the joists in order to see how a new boarded covering can be provided so as to present a firm and serviceable base for the new lead sheeting. The question of the sub-structure of the roof is discussed under the Chapter dealing with timber, and for the purposes of the present discussion we shall assume that the joists, once exposed, are adequate for the span of the roof and are in sound condition. Notwithstanding this, however, the distortion and settle-ment which have caused the ponding on the roof surface will cer-tainly entail the removal and replacement of the firring pieces. This in itself is not a difficult operation, but it is one that can sometimes lead to problems in detailing. It may well be that the slight variation in levels against angles and parapet walls and abutments of chimney

518

stacks will entail the removal of flashings so that these have to be taken out and formed in the next horizontal brick joint in order to allow them to achieve a sufficient height for the new roof surface. This, again, will not prove unduly difficult in the majority of cases but there are times when an old lead roof is surrounded by a very low parapet wall so that even the slight added increase in height may be difficult to achieve. Under such circumstances the parapet may have to be raised but often the head of the parapet has such short-comings from the design point of view that this is desirable in any event. It is not difficult for the surveyor to square his conscience against the added cost that such work entails when instead of a defective brick-on-edge coping with brick oversailing and no damp proof course the parapet will gain a stone or concrete coping properly weathered and throated with a lead or bituminous felt damp proof course underneath.

It is not an economic saving in cost for the roof boarding to be re-used unless it is of extremely good quality. This will be self-evident in most cases since the boarding will be old and warped, butt jointed and possibly rotted into the bargain. The advantage of specifying new wrot, tongued and grooved boarding, properly seasoned against warping, is obvious. Notwithstanding the fact that the boards are tongued and grooved it is still desirable for the boards to be laid diagonally or in the direction of the fall and an underlay is desirable in all cases particularly when lead coverings are fixed to hardwoods, such as oak and elm, which may corrode the lead if allowed to get moist. The underlay to the new lead sheeting will be probably an improvement over the previous roof design and this is provided not only to allow expansion of the metal when laid so that thermal movement can take place without the lead buckling and becoming distorted but also to enable an insulation barrier to be provided. For this reason a material such as hardboard does not provide the best type of covering, but whatever this insulation should be, the fixings for the lead sheet must penetrate it and be secured to the sub-structure.

The lead sheets, partly bossed into shape are hoisted to the roof surface and before they are fixed to the rolls and drips it is often a good plan for the surveyor to ensure from his own inspection that the surface is in a fit state for the laying operations to begin. No sharp projections should be encountered on the roof surface since all nails or screws should have been countersunk. It is common sense to see that the lead is clean and not filthy from the fact that the bossing operations have been carried out on a flower bed, and it is also desirable to see that the underlay is equally clean and is not sodden from continual rainfall prior to the arrival of the lead. If the surveyor is present when the lead is laid he may give himself up to the pleasure of watching the operation with, it is hoped, the enjoyment that comes from seeing a good craftsman at work. Cut copper nails or gun-metal screws will, it is hoped, have been specified, and simple underlays such as building paper will be smoothed out as each bay is set down. The final operation will be to set up the flashings surrounding the roof and once this is completed the surveyor will make a final check to test that the wedges are firm, that the flashings are rigid and that the pointing up has been carried out in such a way that it will not simply fall out after some months have elapsed. On occasions when a neat cement mix has been used this has been known to happen.

Once the surveyor has had the satisfaction of re-making a lead roof in this manner, he will at least know that barring some peculiar set of circumstances that have been overlooked it should give satisfactory service for a long time to come and probably in excess of his own lifetime.

For the few occasions, however, when the surveyor carries out a repair of the type described above, there will be many other occassions where the repair is only a partial one. It may be that the fall of the roof is adequate and the roof boarding is acceptable apart from perhaps one isolated area and due to some local defect, a partial repair has to be made. Thus an uneven area of boarding which has torn the lead may require repair or perhaps an uneven area on the roof may need rectification following some defect in the sub-structure either by a localised attack of dry rot or, for example, in the case of a single split joist. Under circumstances such as this, it should be possible for one or more bays of the lead covering to be taken up and for the sub-structure to be repaired before the bays are either replaced or renewed. It is important however to ensure that the leadwork forming the bays is sound and this will provide an opportunity for assessing the quality of the lead to the roof as a whole. It is, of course, no use to re-lay lead which is badly thinned or corroded, but it is perfectly in order to re-lay lead which is the subject of one or two local tears due to uneven boarding below but which is otherwise in good order since the tears can be effectively repaired.

Lead sheeting can be repaired either with the use of solder or by burning, that is to say welding new portions of lead into the old. Of these two alternatives burning is by far the best, since the difficulty with using soft solder is that any further distortion in the sheeting may cause a fresh crack to appear in the repaired section. Whichever method is used however, it is vital to make sure that the surface of the lead is thoroughly clean before the plumber makes his repair.

If rolls or drips are excessively distorted due to heavy traffic on the roof, it may be best to burn in new sections of lead sheeting and carry these over rolls which have either been renewed or drips which have been reformed so as to provide satisfactory bases for the lead. This is certainly true of isolated areas of distortion but where the distortion to the roof surface is unusually bad and applies equally to the whole surface of the roof the economics of re-laying new lead and obtaining credit for the old lead must seriously be considered.

Box gutters provide a particular source of difficulty to the surveyor since frequently a lead flat roof is perfectly sound with the exception of the box gutter which is badly designed so as to be far too narrow and to have an inconvenient and potentially troublesome outlet. It is often better to re-build a box gutter and to refashion the outlet so as to be sure that it will not cause trouble in the future.

Maintenance of Lead Flat Roofs

The question of maintenance is an important one with flat roofs of all types but in particular to those covered with lead. It will readily be understood that flat roofs are susceptible to abuses of every conceivable type varying from the heavy wear of workmen's boots, the pitting that follows from the use of steel chairs and furniture on the roof during a long dry summer, and the depositing on the roof of heavy articles such as tanks and flower urns which leave depressions when their position is altered, into which water will pursue its inevitable way so that any subsequent puncture will lead to leakage. Just as important, however, is the fact that flat roofs must, particularly in urban areas, attract a good deal of deposits from various sources. The first and most obvious example occurs in the autumn when leaves will fall and tend to accumulate and choke awkward angles in box gutters. A badly choked gutter outlet will mean that the level of water in the gutter as a result of heavy rainfall will rise so that the level of the upstand is exceeded and leakage may occur as a result. Regular gutter cleaning contracts are therefore desirable in the case of older houses. In addition to leaves, the deposits left by cats and dogs together with deposits from the air will combine together to form a gluey compound which, when washed into the necks of outlets, forms a blockage. This substance, which resembles thick clinging mud, is often quite difficult to remove and consequently the need for regular maintenance of lead roofs, particularly those in urban areas, is most important.

The need for maintenance is underlined when one considers the fact that flat roofs with metal coverings are extremely vulnerable. This is underlined by one case vividly recalled. A complaint of dampness was duly investigated and climbing out onto the flat roof of the back addition of a Victorian house, let in three flats, the surveyor was puzzled to find a number of wedge-shaped holes in the surface of the covering. It was some time before the explanation dawned. What had happened was that one of the tenants, who liked a coal fire, had taken his log and reduced it to kindling on the lead flat, a wood roll providing a convenient chopping block. When the axe missed the wood, as it did occasionally, it made a hole in the roof. It never occurred to the tenant that this method of procedure was anything out of the ordinary.

Pitched lead roof coverings

The size of lead bays to a pitched roof are similar to those of a flat roof. This may not be the case for exceptional structures such as domes or spires, but except for the larger Victorian house these are rarely encountered. In slopes in excess of 15°, however, intermediate support is often found provided in the form of soldered dots, lead-burned dots or lead tacks. The big distinction, however, between lead flat roofs and pitched roofs is that while both types have rolls which run parallel to the slope of the roof, a pitched roof has no drips, the joints across the fall being formed with laps. The following lengths of lap are recommended by the British Standard Code of Practice C.P.143 of 1960 part 3.

For 15° pitch a lap of 23 inches (584mm),
for 20° pitch 18 inches lap (457mm),
for 25° pitch 14 inches lap (356mm),
for 30° pitch 12 inches lap (305mm).

It will only be if the lap is exceptionally big and the position very exposed that copper clips or lead tacks will be required to hold down the edge.

It is usual for the rolls to pitched roofs to be hollow since there is little danger from wear. Sometimes welts may be employed instead but rolls are normally quite satisfactory and have the advantage that they can be dressed down quite easily at the ridge.

The repair of lead pitched roof coverings is complicated when contrasted to flat roofs by the fact that access is generally more difficult and a rather more complicated scaffold often needs to be employed. Against this however, the need for repair is often not quite so acute since pitched roofs tend to be less vulnerable both to traffic and leakage when compared to flat roofs. In the case of pitched roofs the detailing at the ridge sometimes gives trouble. This position is an important one and if there is a ridge roll the capping pieces should extend 3 inches (76mm) down each roof slope on either side and the capping pieces are normally in lengths of up to 7 feet (2·13m). The lap between capping pieces is normally increased to a minimum of 4 inches (102mm) as a protection against driving rain. Each bay should provide a lead tack or copper clip to provide a fixing for the capping. Where there is no ridge roll capping, lead sheets are passed directly over the ridge, the bays being staggered. Wear can occur at the ridge under such circumstances so that burning in a new ridge section could be necessary.

Dormer Windows, Mansard Slopes and Junctions with other roofs

Lead sheeting used for dormer cheeks is commonly encountered. Often, however, the method of fixing is not particularly good since the wiped soldered dot which should be formed on boarded surfaces by means of a brass screw and washer sunk in a depression and covered with solder may be absent. Under such circumstances lead tacks known as secret tacks can be soldered or burned on to the back of the lead sheet and passed through a slot cut in the boarding and fixed to the interior of the dormer window. So far as mansard roofs are concerned lead sheets often merely lap over each other at changes of direction. If this junction proves troublesome the provision of a torus roll is desirable in order to form a proper joint.

A final word might be said about the junction of lead sheeting either from lead roofs or lead gutters with pitched roofs covered with tiles or other coverings. Often the underlap will be found to be totally inefficient and dampness will invariably penetrate under the edge of the tiling. When this is the case correct detailing at this point is important and it may be necessary to reform the junction so that a tilting fillet is provided 6 inches (152mm) up the roof pitch, the lead being carried over the fillet for a further 9 inches (229mm), the edge being folded and the top of the lead being not less than 6 inches (152mm) above the lowest junction with the lead of the flat or gutter.

Metals used in roof coverings

No. 2. Zinc

Zinc sheeting for roof coverings does not have the long association with domestic buildings in England enjoyed by lead. When it was found possible to mass-produce zinc sheeting, following the industrial revolution, it was only then regarded as a cheaper and acceptable substitute for lead, so that its introduction and wide use for new estates of houses was put in hand mainly for economic reasons. Notwithstanding this, however, zinc sheet has proved to be a perfectly acceptable material for flat roofs in most circumstances. It is a basic non-ferrous metal, light grey in colour when it is first used, and of about the same density as steel. When rolled into sheets, the material becomes ductile with good working properties. Once laid, the zinc forms a protective coating of basic carbonate which turns to a deeper matt grey colour which remains constant in rural districts, but weathers to a deeper colour with the soot and deposits in urban areas. It is in such areas that the average recommended life for 14-gauge zinc sheeting of 40 years can be sharply reduced by other factors to about half this period.

The chief drawback of zinc sheeting is that while it is relatively cheap and easy to lay, it is vulnerable to the sulphur acids of industrial and urban areas and it is not resistant to acids or strong alkalis. Corrosive substances will tend to lie on a flat zinc roof and attack the metal over a period of years so that the life of the metal will be much reduced and the urban surveyor is used to seeing the corroded surface of zinc used for a roof covering which has reached the end of its useful life. Zinc is also susceptible to electrochemical corrosion if in contact with copper, so that water from a copper roof should not be allowed to discharge on to a zinc surface. Zinc should also not be laid in contact with, or receive drainage from western red cedar, oak or sweet chestnut. Another disadvantage of zinc sheeting is that it will be attacked when in contact with walling materials containing appreciable amounts of soluble salts, such as chlorides and sulphates. It is commonplace to find the joints of Victorian slated roofs against brick parapet walls formed with zinc soakers but with cement fillets in place of flashings. Under such circumstances all is well if the detailing of the parapet wall is sound, but where rainwater washes on to the cement and trickles down the joint between the slated roof and the parapet, soluble salts will be released which will affect the zinc soakers at the right-angled joint between the slates and the parapet causing corrosion. Condensed moisture trapped against the underside of zinc roof coverings will also be liable to attack the metal. Modern building practice generally avoids such a contingency but this is by no means the case with older roofs.

Zinc has a relatively high coefficient of thermal expansion for which allowance should be made in roofing work. The thermal movement of an 8-foot (2·44m) length of zinc sheet is about ¼ inch (6mm) for a temperature variation of 100°F or 56°C.

The Inspection

Zinc sheeting, unlike lead, does not so readily show depressions indicating unevenness or sinkings in the boarding underneath. A general sag in the roof surface will of course be evident, but minor irregularities and depressions will be less evident. The surveyor may test with the toe of his shoe sections of zinc between rolls which will produce a metallic cracking noise but often it is not clear if this is due to buckling in the zinc itself, or whether it is due to some defect in the sub-structure. Flexing of the roof structure can be ascertained by stamping on the surface but minor irregularities in the boarding cannot easily be traced. Unlike lead sheeting it will not be possible to bend back and lift the metal to a very great degree and although the surveyor can slide off capping pieces and bend back some flashings it is not so easy to make the same type of examination with a zinc roof as with a lead flat roof.

As in the case of any flat roof the first matter that needs investigation is the fall. This should not be less than 2 inches (50mm) in 10 feet (3·05m). Excessive sag should be looked upon with suspicion even more than in the case of a lead flat roof since with the ponding of rainwater there is always a danger that the level may rise to exceed the upstand provided by the rolls. This often happens at times of severe weather when ice may block outlets and melting snow causes a build up of water by the rolls and consequent leakage into the interior. The different construction of rolls to flat lead roofs prevents this happening except in rare circumstances and for this reason zinc roofs have a reputation for poor performance in bad weather. The distance between the bases of adjoining rolls should not be more than 2 ft. 9½ in. (851mm) and the rolls should have a minimum height of 1½ inches (38mm) narrowing to a minimum top width of 1¼ inches (32mm) while being 1¾ inches (44mm) at the base. The reason for rolls to zinc roofs being square edged lies in the property of the metal itself and unlike lead rolls separate zinc capping sections 1½ by 1½ inches (38 by 38mm) are provided over the heads instead of the integral joints formed between lead sheets. The capping pieces allow for the 1½ inches (38mm) turn-up each side of the roll and end bays against abutments are normally narrower to allow for a greater turn-up against the wall abutment. It is undesirable for roll cappings to be fixed in greater lengths than 4 feet (1·22m) although larger lengths will commonly be found. Rolls are worthy of particular examination to existing zinc roofs. Very often these will be found to have distorted badly so that one end may be free from its fixing and investigation will often show that holding down clips are ineffective or absent. Sometimes capping pieces can be pulled away by the surveyor without any resistance from clips and in one case capping pieces which had obviously proved an irritation to a jobbing builder were seen to be nailed at intervals along the top surface in a way that may have solved his immediate problem but could hardly be called a long-term repair. Effective clips are formed by strips of zinc 1½ inches

(38mm) wide and not less than 7 inches (178mm) long. The lower ends of the capping should also be inspected since efficient stop ends can be formed by folding without the use of solder but often a more ad-hoc method is used. The saddle at the upper end of each section should also be formed by folding, again, without the use of solder. Clips to a zinc flat roof should not be less than 2 inches (51mm) deep and are normally spaced at 6 inches (152mm) less than the length of the sheet employed. So far as the top bays of zinc sheeting are concerned the minimum allowance of 4 inches (101mm) to provide a turn-up at the top abutment is sometimes neglected so that the upstand is too shallow. The detailing of drips is worthy of particular inspection at the junction with abutments where corner pieces cut from zinc sheet should be welted to the sheets; a refinement that is sometimes missing. It is however often found with a zinc flat roof that drips are omitted. This is permissible where roofs are pitched at 15° or steeper where single lock welts can be employed, but for lower pitches drips are necessary. Often, however, an entire span which is provided with rolls will have no drips whatsoever and this will mean that the weatherproofing qualities of the roof are entirely dependent on the nature of the welts employed.

Flashings to zinc flat roofs should be of the same gauge as the roof covering itself. These should lap over the turned up edges of the roof sheets and gutters by at least 2 inches (51mm) and should be turned into walls at least ¼ inch (6mm) and be wedged at not more than 2 feet (611mm) centres and pointed. The free edge should be stiffened either with a half bead or a fold at the base. Often flashings will be found to have curled upwards or alternatively to have become adrift at their fixings so that they are ineffective.

Box gutters should not be less than 2 inches (51mm) deep and the minimum fall should be the same as for the flat roof itself. Where the side of a box gutter abuts a vertical surface the zinc lining should have a turn-up of at least 4 inches (102mm). The joints at drips in the gutter and at internal angles, which should be formed with dog-ears, are worthy of inspection and the sides of gutters should also be examined as the folded clips may be absent.

It is not so easy to clean off the surface of zinc sheeting as in the case of lead. Often it will be found to be corroded and pitted from long contact with the atmosphere particularly, as previously mentioned, in urban areas. Added to this there is the risk that the entire surface may have been covered with some bituminous paint or alternatively it may have been treated with a hessian and bituminous compound laid over bays, rolls and drips alike. Under such circumstances the surveyor may reasonably consider that the life of the zinc is either so limited or so problematical as to require renewal of the metal. Zinc sheeting cannot have its life extended so easily as in the case of lead and piecemeal repair is not practicable except under unusual circumstances.

The repair of zinc flat roofs

If the fall to a zinc flat roof is inadequate the sub-structure and timber boarding will have to be investigated, repaired or re-modelled in the same manner as that for a lead flat roof. It is possible also but by no means certain, that as zinc came into general use in the late 1800s, that the parapet wall surrounding a zinc flat roof and the detailing generally may be built to rather better principles than the older parapets surrounding the lead flat roofs of the Georgian period. This does not mean that the parapets should be exempt from scrutiny as any shortcomings in the finishes of copings and their damp coursing should of course be put right. It is possible, however, although again not universally the case, that a higher parapet height may be provided which will entail less basic reconstruction. Against this, however, is the fact that the boarding under the zinc sheeting will almost certainly be found to be subject to short-comings. Zinc was introduced as a cheap substitute for lead and the speculative builder would almost certainly have provided softwood butt-jointed boards underneath with nothing between the boards and the zinc. In the case, therefore, where a roof structure has to be re-made with repairs to joists the provision of new firring pieces and a new timber decking of well-seasoned softwood of not less than 1 inch (25mm) nominal thickness, the boards laid in the direction of the fall and the joints staggered, certain additional precautions will be needed. It will be remembered that zinc should not be laid in contact with surfaces which attract moisture or which allow con-densation from inside the building to become trapped under the metal. With the old roof, the softwood butt-jointed boards will have shrunk over the years since the building was erected and this will in itself probably have provided some measure of ventilation to the underside of the zinc. Notwithstanding this, however, the surveyor may find when the old zinc is raised that there is evidence of corro-sion. It is all the more important therefore with the new roof decking, which will be laid so that there are no gaps between the boards, and where the seasoning of the softwood nowadays is only to a barely acceptable level involving some inevitable additional drying after fixing, that an underlay is provided between the zinc and the timber. A felt underlay is, therefore, desirable or alterna-tively one of the modern types of composition board. The latter have the advantage that a smooth surface is presented which allows the

527

zinc to expand and contract with thermal movement but on the other hand the method of fixing the zinc must allow a secure anchorage and it is important that in doing this the surface in the composition board or slab is not damaged too badly in the process. Where felt is employed it is desirable to ensure as far as is possible that there is little risk of the material adhering to the underside of the zinc sheeting which would inhibit free movement and for this reason felt is best laid butt-jointed and held, if necessary, with galvanised clout nails pending the fixing of the rolls and clips. It is also important to ensure that the felt and the timber are not saturated with rain before the zinc is laid and that the zinc sections which will be hauled, preformed, to the roof, are clean and have no sticky patches. It is also desirable that the box gutters and drop aprons are provided first, followed by the main roof coverings and cappings with the cover flashings being provided last. Laying is commenced from the lowest point and at one side against a wall or a verge and carried upwards until the roof covering is completed.

Where the fall of the roof is adequate and the surveyor cannot see any obvious signs of defects in the boarding underneath he will direct his attention to assessing the condition of the zinc covering itself. Often this will be obviously worn out, being blackened with age and pitted so that the surface presented is like sandpaper. Zinc sheeting, due to the fact that it is thinner than lead, is as already stated not capable of piecemeal repair in the same way, since elaborate attempts to clean off and solder areas will be worthless if the metal is so thin as to need renewal a short time later. However, where damage is found to the surface of a comparatively new zinc roof an antimony free solder of either 50/50 or 60/40 tin/lead compound can be employed, the surfaces to be soldered being cleaned off with spirits of salts. If the zinc roof covering has to be renewed as a whole the surveyor will take the opportunity as already seen, of providing an underlay for the new metal covering but there may be cases where the zinc sheeting may be comparatively new but show signs of buckling or warping due to poor laying or design defects. Under such circumstances one or more bays may have to be lifted to ascertain the reason for this and the necessary repair may vary from the rolls being relaid due to being badly positioned, to the repair of some local defect under the zinc which has caused a partial attachment so that the thermal movement of the metal is hindered, causing uneven expansion and consequent buckling.

Maintenance of zinc roofs

As in the case of lead roofs accumulations of leaves and deposits should be periodically cleaned from zinc flat roofs. Regular inspection to ensure that the detailing of zinc roofs is sound is always desirable since cappings and flashings may become loose and need replacement. Permanent softwood duck boards are desirable to protect the surface of the zinc and objects on the roof such as the bases of "means of escape" ladders should be protected so that they do not pierce the metal. In cases of unusually severe atmospheric corrosion the surveyor may decide that a protective paint could be employed. Copper lightning conductors passing over zinc roofs should of course be protected either by the copper being tinned with a tin/lead solder or coated with an insulating material.

Pitched zinc roof coverings

Pitched zinc roof coverings follow the same pattern as for flat roofs, the joints being either of rolls with cappings or alternatively welted. It is probable that the steeper pitch and the run-off provided by rainwater is more likely to clear impurities from the surface so that the zinc has a longer life than in the case of flat roofs. However, the surveyor will often see unsightly smears and rust marks from other metals and he will have to decide upon closer investigation if this is merely a surface marking or if some local corrosive action is taking place. The detailing of aprons and junctions with other roof slopes however, warrants inspection, as often these joints will be poorly formed.

Dormer Windows

Dormer windows, the sides of which are covered with zinc sheeting over a timber boarded framework, are commonplace. The heads of dormer windows may either be of pitched construction, covered with slates or tiles, or these may have flat roofs of zinc, the design and construction being similar to that of flat roofs. Since zinc, unlike lead, is a comparatively lightweight material, there is not likely to be the same danger of creep or sag that the heavier lead sheeting entails. Similarly as in the case of pitched roof coverings, rainwater washing against the sides of the dormer should carry away impurities from the surface of the zinc. However, it is often found that the bases of zinc sides to dormer windows are corroded or paper thin, and it may well be that due to this factor alone, the zinc sides cannot be saved. Poor detailing at the bases of such dormer windows often leads to considerable damp penetration and only the re-making of the sides and soakers will result in a sound repair. So far as the roofs of dormer windows are concerned where these are of flat construction covered with zinc sheeting it is important to ascertain that the joint between this roof and the pitched roof covering behind is effectively made, particularly since the dormer roof will most probably have been designed to throw the rainwater to the rear, to be drained by the pitched roof covering adjacent.

Valley Gutters

Valley gutters are widely employed formed of zinc sheeting laid on timber boarding. These will often be found to be badly worn and to require renewal. Often the signs of leakage can be observed from the roof space below but the surfaces of the valley gutters will be blackened with age and it is best for them to be renewed rather than patched, since these accept a good deal of the flow of the rainwater from the pitched roofs and any defect will rapidly become apparent in the structure below.

Metals used in roof coverings

No. 3. Copper

Unlike lead and zinc copper sheeting has one particular feature which has caused it to be used for its architectural effect. It is this feature that distinguishes copper sheeting from zinc, since zinc is merely a cheaper substitute for lead, the traditional flat roofing metal which has been used and tried and tested over many centuries. No architect worthy of his salt in contemplating the flat roof of a building of any consequence would dream of using zinc where lead could be employed, since zinc, as we have said, has always been selected for economic reasons only. This, however, does not apply to copper since the same architect might hesitate when asked to choose between copper and lead if the roof slopes were to be visible. The reason for this is that copper changes colour when exposed to the air. The discoloration is due to the formation of an oxide film which incidentally is an important agent in protecting the copper itself. The oxidising process forms a patina, which is usually of a startlingly bright green colour. Under other circumstances in certain atmospheres it might be reduced to a buff, brown or black colour depending on the nature and quantity of the impurities deposited on the surface of the copper from the atmosphere. The British Standard Code of Practice C.P.143 points out, however, that the patina to copper should not be confused with verdigris which is also of a green or grey colour and is formed by different chemical reaction.

Copper, as stated above, is not a cheap roofing material, but it is a very good one. It has good mechanical properties; it is very light in weight and yet it has ample strength for roofing purposes and is very resistant to corrosion by the atmosphere. Under normal circumstances a well-laid copper roof will last as long as anyone could desire, probably 150–200 years. A further characteristic of copper, however, is that it might be described as an aggressive metal since if copper comes into contact with another metal, it will be the other metal that will probably suffer from electrolytic corrosion. For this reason it will be clear to the reader that the nails used to secure copper clips and felt underlay should be made from copper wire and should be not less than 12 S.W.G. being flat-headed and 1-inch (25mm) long and not less than ¼-inch (6mm) diameter. The consequences of using zinc nails might be dramatic under the circumstances and it is important that for copper roofing the whole of the roof including clips, flashing and other details should be made from copper sheet or strip. The only exceptions are the screws used to secure the wood rolls where steel screws are permissible, but where screws are used to secure clips or other components these should be made of brass.

The Inspection

Since copper roofs are found to be provided to mainly the larger Victorian house, the surveyor will not encounter this material as frequently as he will see other roofing metals such as lead or zinc. His inspection may also be complicated by the fact that when copper is used it is often adopted not only for the flat surfaces, but for complicated minor roofs to domes and curved or projecting turrets which it is intended should stand out as features. Occasionally also it will be found as the roofing metal for the graceful shaped balconies of some early Victorian houses.

As in the case of other flat roofs the timber sub-structure should present a firm and inflexible surface. It is likely that this will be the case in copper flat roofs as the comparative rarity of the use of this material for domestic housing and the expense entailed will probably have ensured that some care has been taken in the construction of the sub-structure. The minimum fall for any copper roof is 2 inches (51mm) in 10 feet (3·05m). Where roofs of 5 degrees pitch or less are encountered the drips should be spaced at not more than 10 feet (3·05m) centres and be 2½ inches (64mm) deep.

Copper sheets for roofing are held down to the roof by means of copper clips inserted in the folds between sections. In the direction of the fall the sheets are jointed either by the "standing seam" or the "wood roll". A standing seam consists of a double welted joint formed between bays and left standing upright projecting about ¾ inch (19mm). The wood roll system on the other hand consists of a shaped wood core against the sides of which the edges of copper bays are turned up. The finished height is normally 1½ inches (38mm) for common rolls but a projection of 3 inches (76mm) is required for ridge and hip rolls. Across the fall, the joints between the sheets are flattened to allow water to flow freely over them. Where the pitch exceeds 45° a single lock welt seam is used, but where the pitch is less than 45° a double lock cross welt is essential.

Unlike other roofing metals the maximum width of the bay size selected should be governed by the thickness of the material used and the table of the British Standard Code of Practice 143 is reprinted opposite.

Common rolls, to minimum finished sizes, are 1½ inches (38mm) high by 1¾ inches (44mm) base by 1¼ inches (32mm) across the top. Ridge and hip rolls should stand 1½ inches (38mm) above the top of the common roll. These should be therefore, 3 by 2¼ by 1¼ inches (76 by 57 by 32mm). It is important that the capping pieces are sound and the surveyor should check to see if these are fixed to the side sections of bays by welted attachments.

Drips, normally 2½ inches (64mm) deep, should be inspected to ensure that the lip of the copper at the edge is not distorted or damaged. Excessive foot traffic which continually bends the vulnerable edge of the metal may cause it to crack or tear as excessive working of copper has a detrimental effect.

Flashings to copper roofs need care in investigation as often the vulnerable open ends of standing seams or welts are tucked under them and if the flashing is loose or defective, water will penetrate this tiny detail. Unlike those of zinc and lead, aprons and flashings should consist of an independent strip of copper of not more than 6 feet (1·83m) in length which is welted to the roof sheet. The upper edge should be folded to a depth of 1 inch (25mm) into the wall with a ½-inch (13mm) check welt to act as a water stop and be wedged and pointed. The vertical joints between two apron pieces should be single lock welted. At eaves and the verges, the main roofing sheet should be welted to an independent apron which is firmly fixed by means of a lining plate.

Gutters should be laid to a minimum fall of 1½ inches (38mm) in 10 feet (3·05m). Drips to gutters should be a minimum depth of 2 inches (51mm) and the gutter cheek is jointed to the roof sheeting by means of a single lock welt. Where cesspools are encountered it is preferable if these have been constructed from one piece of copper shaped by dog-eared corners since any joints in the metal to cesspools may constitute a weakness.

Maximum bay widths and lengths to be used with various gauges of copper roofing sheet

S.W.G.	Bay Widths				Standard Width of Sheet to form Bay		Lengths of each Sheet	
	Standing Seam		Wood Roll					
26	21¼ inches	540mm	20 inches	508mm	24 inches	610mm	6 feet	1·83m
24	21¼ ,,	540mm	20 ,,	508mm	24 ,,	610mm	6 ,,	1·83m
23	24¼ ,,	616mm	23 ,,	583mm	27 ,,	686mm	6 ,,	1·83m
22	27¼ ,,	692mm	26 ,,	660mm	30 ,,	762mm	6 ,,	1·83m

The inspection of the surface of the metal will probably reveal that this is, unless unusually badly worn, of an almost polished finish. It should finally be remembered that the use of solder as a means of jointing between copper sheets is bad practice, as the expansion and contraction of the metal will in time break the solder.

The repair of copper roofs

As in the case of lead and zinc flat roofs, if the fall is defective, the surface copper must be taken up and the sub-structure reformed. Once the joists have been repaired with the use of new firring pieces as in the case of zinc sheeting, new boarding of not less than 1 inch (25mm) nominal thickness should be employed, fixed to the same rules as before. The opportunity can then be taken to give adequate ventilation of the voids beneath the decking to minimise the effect of condensation and provide some form of thermal insulation, which, owing to the high conductivity of copper, is desirable. Felt, where employed as an underlay, should be laid with butt joints but in this case secured with copper nails. The sequence of operations for laying the new copper roof is very similar to that employed in the case of zinc but in the case of copper it is particularly important to avoid excessive and repeated dressing of material which might render it brittle.

The detailing of a copper roof is particularly important. Double lock cross welts should not be fixed in line but staggered in adjoining bays and standing seams should be provided with $1\frac{1}{2}$-inch (38mm) wide clips spaced at a minimum of 15-inch (381mm) centres. Where a standing seam meets an upstand the joint should be formed so as to provide a wide webb at the angle. Where upper and lower bays are welted together at a drip by means of a single welt on the drip edge, the turned up edges between the standing seam or wood roll and the upstand of the drip are dog-eared together. Tapered corner blocks are fixed against an abutment such as a parapet wall. Where no drips are provided clips are needed to hold down all cross welts. In double lock cross welts one 2-inch (51mm) side clip is required per bay and in single lock welts two 2-inch (51mm) wide clips should be employed.

Where the fall of the roof is adequate but where the covering is defective the surveyor will decide that it is due for renewal. Under such circumstances he will find an unexpected bonus in the fact that when the copper sheeting is raised, the woodwork below, assuming that there is no underlay, will have attracted condensation which will probably have allowed a weak solution of copper salts to have been formed to act as a wood preservative. In cases where there is local damage to the copper surface it may be possible to renew a single bay or bays or renew details such as cappings. It should be remembered, however, that an excessive use of solder is to be deplored in copper roofs. In the case of new bays provided, any double lock cross welt should be sealed with boiled linseed oil. This is done by painting the edges of the copper with the oil before welting together and is only necessary in the case of flat roofs below 20° pitch.

Maintenance of copper roofs

Copper roofs should require little maintenance apart from the customary clearing of leaves, rubbish and deposits. Duckboards of a minimum width of 15 inches (381mm) are recommended to prevent damage to copper roofing, since it is important that foot traffic does not disturb the patina on the surface of the sheets.

Special features

The surveyor will encounter cases where a tiled or slated roof discharges on to a copper flat roof. Under such circumstances, a copper apron flashing should be nailed to the boarding under the edge of the slates or tiles, taken over a tilting fillet and welted to the junction with the upper end of the copper flat. Where a copper roof discharges on to a slated roof, an independent copper apron with a beaded edge is formed over the top edge of the tiles or slates so that it is stiffened against being raised by the wind, and the apron is then taken to a vertical upstand at the top edge and secured by means of a welt to the lower edge of the copper roofing sheet. All bays of the copper roof covering should be finished at the base with a separate apron piece or gutter.

Metals used in roof coverings

No. 4. Aluminium

It is most unlikely that the surveyor dealing with repairs and maintenance will encounter many existing aluminium roofs at the present time as aluminium as a material has only been used for this purpose comparatively recently. However there is evidence of an increased use of the material, particularly on local authority housing schemes surprising though this may seem in view of its cost.

Aluminium is a comparatively expensive material, although it compares in cost reasonably favourably with copper. In fact the comparison between the two metals is very similar in many ways. Each should have a similar underlay and fall, and the rules for rolls, drips and welts are similar. The only appreciable difference is that since the sheets are normally 6 by 2 ft. (1·83 by 0·61m), the maximum spacing of batten rolls is 1 ft. 9¾ in. (552mm), and of standing seams at 1 ft. 9¼ in. (540mm). The batten rolls should be slightly wider at the top than the base, the top being 1¾ inches (44mm) while the base is 1½ inches (38mm). The height of the roll is 1⅝ inches (41mm). The reason for this unusual shape is that it allows for thermal movement in the metal. Nails, of course, should be of aluminium, and the contact of aluminium with copper, including the run off of water from a copper surface to an aluminium roof should be avoided. Otherwise the detailing to flashings, gutters and aprons of aluminium roofs is similar to copper.

The repair of aluminium sheeting can be carried out by welding or brazing. Small repairs can be carried out with a cold solder but it is of course not desirable to attempt to repair long tears by this method.

The Building Research Station Digest No. 132 of March 1960 discloses a rather unusual and extraordinary feature of aluminium roofing. The drop in temperature on certain clear nights as a result of radiation can cause the formation of ice both on the top surface of the metal and on the underside so that when temperatures subsequently rise, a great deal of moisture drips on to the structure below. This, of course, only occurs where the insulation is not in direct contact with the metal. Where no insulation at all is provided, ventilation alone of the roof space cannot prevent condensation forming on the underside of the sheeting in these circumstances and will only assist in getting rid of moisture by evaporation subsequently. It is not enough, as at first was thought, to treat the underside of the metal with an anti-condensation paint. Instead, sarking, separated from contact with the sheet metal by means of spacers, should be laid under such roofs and carried to the eaves gutters, so that condensation is carried clear of the structure to be discharged externally.

Flat roof coverings. Other Types

No. 1. Asphalt

Asphalt might briefly be described as "a natural or mechanical mixture of bitumen and inert mineral matter". Bitumen, which is the generic term for non-crystalline semi-solid or viscous mixtures of hydrocarbons, provides the essential waterproofing element of asphalt.

Asphalt is of two types. There is first the natural rock asphalt which has to be mined from the ground and which is found principally in France, Italy, Sicily, Switzerland and Western Germany. Secondly there is lake asphalt which is found in a natural state of flow or fluidity such as in the famous lake in Trinidad where it is of unvarying consistency. The whole efficiency of asphalt depends on its blend with an appropriate amount of bitumen. Lake asphalt, after being refined, contains approximately 54 per cent of natural bitumen, while natural rock asphalt has a much lower bitumen content. In order to be accepted this should have a minimum bitumen content of 6 per cent according to the requirements of the appropriate British Standards. The asphalt manufacturers, however, are not dependent for their supply of bitumen on that found in natural rock asphalt or lake asphalt. Natural bitumen may be obtained from other sources and bitumen can also be obtained from petroleum by refinery processes.

Although the production of asphalt appears to be a simple business of mixing bitumen and mineral matter, the blending of the various bitumens and the selection and grading of the inert minerals requires great technical knowledge, skill and control, as well as sophisticated plant and buildings. It is worth perhaps adding that the inert mineral constituent of mastic asphalt is technically described as aggregate. The finely ground mineral constituent is called fine aggregate while added chippings, grit, or particles over a certain size are known as coarse aggregate. Bitumen was known in the Middle East from the earliest times and the first recorded use of the material is given in the sixth chapter of *Genesis*, verse 14, when Noah, building the Ark, was commanded to "Pitch it within and without with pitch". The reference is probably to the native bitumen which seeped from the ground and probably absorbed wind-blown sand and other matter in many parts of the Middle East, and research has said that the term pitch is synonymous with the Greek word "Asphaltos".

The use of bitumen mixed with sand and a fine filler to form asphalt became widespread in the East. Due to the absence of natural stone and timber it was necessary to find other building materials and in time this became an excellent mortar for the frail sun dried bricks and an unrivalled protection against water. Before the birth of Christ and in Roman times asphalt was employed for damp proof coursing, the lining of drains, and the construction of wells, water basins, bathrooms and water closets as well as for the covering of floors.

In spite of the long knowledge of asphalt in its historical context its use was not fully exploited due to the difficulties of large-scale manufacture and production. The first company formed to produce asphalt on anything like a mass scale was probably that of a Mr.

Claridge who, impressed by a visit to Paris in October 1837 to investigate the possibilities of this material, took a patent in the name of "Claridge's Patent Asphalt" and formed a company in this name. Mr. Claridge had the patronage of the great engineer Brunel, and from 1845 asphalt began to be extensively used and by 1860 had become one of the most indispensable materials in the engineering industry. By late Victorian times the use of asphalt had become widespread for a variety of engineering and building purposes and had come into use for domestic house construction for flat roofs, flooring purposes and in particular tanking and waterproofing basements and areas liable to dampness.

Characteristics of Asphalt

Asphalt, when properly laid, provides an excellent covering for flat roofs. It can be laid over large areas without joints and since the upstands at edges of roofs are integral with the surface and the material itself can be taken up vertically or over slopes, the waterproofing sheath can be in continuity with dormer windows or mansard slopes. Accordingly it can provide an unbroken waterproof covering over complicated roof areas where the use of a metal covering would necessitate countless complicated joints. In order to be fully efficient, however, asphalt must be laid on a sound and firm structure whether of timber or concrete.

In addition, asphalt forms a durable and reasonably long lasting surface of about 25 years' duration. It has the virtue that on cooling to normal temperatures it does not immediately become entirely rigid so that small movements in the structure resulting from temperature changes are taken up easily in the asphalt covering without causing cracks.

When asphalt was first produced in considerable quantity a stubborn myth arose that it was not resistant to fire. This, of course, was false, as asphalt has excellent fire-resisting properties, but it took the First World War when incendiary bombs spluttered brightly on asphalt roofs to provide convincing proof of asphalt's qualities as a non-combustible material.

Another advantage of asphalt is that the production of the material and the laying techniques enable the surface to be modified according to whether the roof is expected to take pedestrian traffic or not, since under such conditions a harder top layer can be provided to the roof covering. The fact that asphalt is capable of a certain variation in texture and finish according to the conditions required forms a definite improvement over the metal roof coverings previously described. A final advantage with asphalt is that when

538

roofs are insulated by the use of cork, fibreboard, or any other form of insulation, the mastic asphalt covering ensures that the insulating material is at maximum efficiency as it is kept bone dry.

In view of such splendid advantages it might be enquired why asphalt has not been more widely used for domestic roofs in the past. The answer lies mainly in the fact that asphalting is one of the specialist trades in the building industry, and the application of mastic asphalt is a craft. After being heated to a fluid condition mastic asphalt is applied by the spreader with hand tools which require some dexterity and practice. The spreader of asphalt indulges in what to the onlooker appears to a simple and satisfying operation but in fact the judgment of the temperature and consistency of material requires considerable experience to enable the laying to be as rapid and satisfactory as it seems. Furthermore, mastic asphalt is normally delivered to the site in blocks weighing half a hundredweight each. The blocks are broken into pieces and melted in a cauldron or, preferably, in a mechanical mixer. The melting of the mastic asphalt must be carefully controlled to avoid overheating and so as not to exceed 215°C or 420°F for roofing asphalts. The melted asphalt is then taken in buckets from the cauldron or mixer to the spreader and it is necessary for the buckets to be dusted with an inert dust such as limestone filler to prevent undue adhesion of the asphalt. Accordingly it can be seen that laying asphalt is by no means an easy matter and the process is inevitably an expensive one. This, unfortunately, is the main disadvantage of asphalt as a roofing material, and explains to a large extent why it has not been more widely used in the past. The only other disadvantage is a tendency to creep when laid incorrectly. It should be remembered, however, that while asphalt is, in effect, a stiff liquid and can tolerate slow movement involving the full thickness of the material it otherwise behaves as a brittle solid and is liable to crack under any suddenly applied strain.

One final and rather curious feature of asphalt for flat roofing purposes is that by its very nature it is such a good material that it presents certain dangers. Due to the fact that it forms a completely impervious membrane over the roof area it admittedly keeps the underlay, whether this be insulating material or boarding, bone dry, but this excellence presents the risk element that, where organic insulating materials are used below the asphalt and where there is some danger from moisture building up in the absence of a vapour barrier, the impermeability of asphalt can be a contributory factor in allowing condensed moisture to saturate the sub-structure so that there is a real risk of rot. Where a metal roof covering allows a certain amount of ventilation between the cappings and joints, asphalt does not allow any ventilation whatsoever. This aspect is dealt with under the description of the "vapour barrier" in Chapter 8.

The Inspection

Where the surveyor encounters a flat roof with a sub-structure of timber with an asphalt covering it is possible that this was the covering originally intended but it is perhaps just as likely that the asphalt has replaced an earlier metal covering which required renewal. In order to keep a flat roof covered with asphalt free from standing water a fall is necessary as in the case of any other flat roofing material. The minimum fall in the case of asphalt should be one in eighty or 1½ inches (38mm) in 10 feet (3·05m). In the case of asphalt, however, the need for keeping the surface clear of water is not so acute as in the case of other timber flat roofs with metal coverings. This is due to the fact that asphalt provides an impervious membrane which, due to the absence of joints, is capable of accepting a certain amount of standing water. Should, however, water be retained on the surface of the roof, it is important for the surveyor to scrutinise the asphalt to ensure that it is in good condition. This requires close examination and a certain knowledge of the nature of the material itself.

When roofing asphalt is laid, and when an even surface is formed, a thin skin, rich in bitumen, is brought to the surface by the action of the workman's float, much in the same way as a fine skin is brought to the surface of a plaster finish worked with a steel float. The exposed superficial skin to an asphalt flat roof is more quickly responsive to temperature changes than the body of the material and it tends to heat up in periods of sunshine and will expand more rapidly than the remainder of the material. Conversely the skin will contract more quickly in cold weather. Thus the surfaces of most roofing asphalts even when correctly laid are liable to form a network of fine surface cracks known as "crazing" but this is only a superficial matter and should not affect the durability of the basic material itself. The surveyor therefore needs to assess whether cracking or disfiguring in the surface texture of the asphalt is merely skin deep, so to speak, or whether cracks or fissures run deeper and are due to other factors entirely such as settlement in the building or a defect in the laying or composition of the basic asphalt roofing material. In the majority of cases the surface cracking will not be of any great consequence, but in other cases the surveyor will endeavour to determine if a more fundamental cause has led to deeper cracks which may be sufficiently serious to introduce damp into the sub-structure below. There will be occasions when the surveyor will be informed that an asphalt flat roof is leaking and indeed from the signs below he will himself assume this to be the case, but he will be puzzled on examining the upper surface of the roof to find that the asphalt is apparently intact, although perhaps the surface holds water. The answer may be that the roof is badly insulated and the cold layer of water on top in conjunction with the heated room below causes condensation to form which looks very much like damp penetration.

Many of the defects in asphalt flat roofs are concentrated at the joints between the horizontal roof surface itself and the vertical abutments of brick parapet walls. If the house is of any age it is most unlikely that the asphalt will have been carried up the face of the brickwork, properly bonded into the face and joints of the bricks and then carried through the wall in the form of a damp proof course in the manner recommended with new construction. It is also unlikely that a triangular wooden fillet is provided below the asphalt at the junction of the timber sub-structure and the wall, so that the asphalt can be carried upwards by means of an easy joint. Two defects are likely therefore to be found at the junction with parapets. The first is that the upstand of the asphalt may have come loose from the parapet in a manner which, in the absence of a cover flashing, allows water to penetrate the open joint. The second defect is that a crack may have formed at the junction of the asphalt flat roof and the upstand.

Asphalt flat roofs are vulnerable where sharp angles and corners are presented. These are even found where the timber sub-structure is designed to take asphalt but are very common where the original timber sub-structure was formerly covered with a metal that has become worn out and has since been recovered with asphalt without any modification to take the new material. Thus in the case of some flat roofs, asphalt may have been taken over the sharp angles of box gutters or projections without much thought to the detailing below. This will have resulted in cracks appearing at the edges and the surveyor will notice how temperature changes have caused the cracks at such weak points to open. Finally in his investigation the surveyor will make a note of any parts of the roof area where the asphalt is thin, either by being laid badly in the first place, or by excessive wear and tear. An example of this is often the detail at the eaves of a roof where the asphalt has been tapered down to a narrow edge which becomes frayed and fractured in the course of time. Although the initial hardening of asphalt is slow, it subsequently becomes hard and rigid and any movement in the sub-structure will cause tears. Asphalt therefore needs a firm base.

The repair of asphalt flat roofs

If the asphalt to a flat roof is badly worn and there is a risk of water ponding on large areas, there will be little option but for the asphalt to be taken up and re-laid. It is best for the surveyor to resist the temptation to use the present covering as a base for building up a new layer since stripping the defective roofing provides an opportunity not only to examine and if necessary improve the substructure, but also to put right awkward details that might reduce the life of the new roof covering. The opportunity can be also taken for a lining of insulating material to be provided if one was not present before.

Once the roof covering is stripped the surveyor will be able to take the same steps to decide as to the suitability of the sub-structure as are described under the heading of lead flat roofs. If the boards are not satisfactory new 1-inch (25mm) boarding should be laid, nailed to the edge of each joist, the heads of the nails being well punched in. The boards should, of course, run in the same direction as the fall of the roof where possible and should preferably be tongued and grooved so that the individual boards do not curl. The selection of an insulating barrier will be one of choice but on the basis that the roof is boarded, some additional precautions are desirable before the underlay and asphalt is laid. We have already seen that triangular fillets are necessary at the angles of the flat roof and the vertical brick abutments with parapet walls, but the surveyor should also have regard to the whole area of the roof and ask himself if any other such fillets or detailing should be provided. It is remarkably easy for a last minute tank housing or other afterthought to be set up which escapes consideration in this way so that the asphalt is taken over right-angled boarded junctions or other awkward points with the inevitable deterioration sometime later. If a boarded roof which previously had a metal covering is to be provided with asphalt it should not prove necessary to do away with the drips but these should be provided with triangular wood fillets to give an easy slope to the asphalt. Brickwork to parapets should be thoroughly cleaned off and the joints raked well back so as to allow a sufficient key for the new vertical asphalt. A key can be provided to vertical timber construction by nailing expanded metal lathing at 6-inch (152mm) centres, with galvanised clout nails. A membrane of black sheathing felt is desirable under the lathing. It is also desirable for metal surfaces to be cleaned and painted with a bituminous solution. Metal pipes passing through asphalt roofing require the provision of a special flange collar fitting before the asphalt is applied as otherwise the asphalt will merely shrink away from the pipe after a period, allowing water to penetrate.

It is of particular importance to make sure that the boarding is completely dry to receive the asphalt in the case of this particular material since, as mentioned earlier, it forms a continuous impervious membrane and there will be little opportunity for the wet timber to dry out. So far as the question of an underlay is concerned, black sheathing felt is normally provided, laid loose and lapped at the joints, since it is important that there is free play between the asphalt and the sub-structure. The underlay is normally laid as part of the work of the specialist asphalt roofing contractor.

When the asphalt is laid on the roof surface in two coats to the recommended minimum thickness of $\frac{3}{4}$ inch (19mm) additional grit may be added to the second coat which increases the resistance of the finished roof surface and allows a certain amount of foot traffic. For roofs taking point loads the surveyor will have made some special provision well in advance. Where the asphalt is carried up for the minimum height of 6 inches (152mm) at skirtings or upstands at the edges of the roof the top edge should be well tucked into a groove cut to receive it, so that no ragged top edge is evident. It is true that this will later be concealed by a cover flashing but the importance of this is that the asphalt is not vulnerable to any seepage of moisture should the flashing itself become defective in some years' time. If there is any risk of movement or deflection in the sub-structure the detail shown in illustration 70 is to be preferred.

The metal flashing at the eaves of the roof is a detail that is often provided but is badly fitted. This should be recessed in such a way that when the asphalt is carried to the edge of the roof over the metal of the flashing the depth of the asphalt is not diminished so as to make it vulnerable to wear.

The question of the repair of asphalt flat roofs in part has always presented problems in the past. Where the surface is reasonably sound but where there is cracking or defective detailing the temptation has often proved too much for the builders and it must be added in honesty, surveyors as well, to save the expense of calling in a specialist firm by providing temporary repairs of all sorts ranging from the application of bituminous felt to blobs of bitumen. Most surveyors will have rueful memories of examining roofs that have been treated in this way in very hot weather when the bitumen has liquified and spread, a good deal of it being transferred to the clothes and shoes of the unfortunate who ventures upon the roof surface to inspect it. There is no easy answer to the partial repair of an asphalt flat roof. Asphalt should not be cut when cold and any repair should be carried out by a specialist asphalter only. It is tempting to attempt a partial repair of an asphalt flat roof for an isolated defect in some other way but it is firmly believed that such temptations should be avoided. The following steps are suggested.

Permanent Repairs to Asphalt Surfaces

For the replacement of a faulty area to an asphalt roof, mastic asphalt only should be employed for the purpose, and the most recognised method is that of "poulticing". By this method the area to be replaced is marked out with chalk and hot new asphalt is then laid along the edge of the defective area which is then left until the surface below it is softened with the warmth. The soft asphalt is then scooped away and the underlying asphalt is removed with a trowel. Successive applications of fresh hot asphalt are necessary if the surface proves stubborn. Any old edges that are included in the area being dealt with should not be left but should be treated in the same manner with fresh hot asphalt so that they will provide an effective joint.

Once this is done the hole formed in the asphalt surface is then filled with hot fresh mastic, the joint between the old and the new work being welded by the smoothing action from the asphalter's float. This method is effective for badly worn areas of asphalt to a roof or rectangular areas that are extensively cracked when the remainder of the roof surface is sound. It is a method that is also recommended for wide cracks that are well defined and that can easily be seen due, for example, to some failure of the sub-structure below. It is not necessarily, however, the best method of treatment for fine cracks that can only be traced with difficulty.

Repairs to Asphalt Surfaces by means of Patching

There are occasions where a surface dressing is acceptable to extend the life of an asphalt roof and, particularly where skilled assistance is not available, a surface dressing can often provide a more effective form of repair than unskilled attempts to hack up and fill in the asphalt surface by workmen who are not used to this type of operation. It should be emphasised of course that such a method must be considered as an expedient rather than a permanent repair but in actual practice efficient patching lasts for a considerable length of time unless disturbed by foot traffic or otherwise.

Surface patching is most effectively employed in the case of very fine straight cracks to the asphalt. Such cracks may not justify poulticing and indeed it may be difficult due to the position of the crack to carry out permanent repair work. An application of bituminous paint by itself will not be effective either for a long-term or a short-term repair. The patching method consists of preparing a strip of close textured cotton or hessian about 9 inches (229mm) wide and cut to the desired length. The roof surface is then treated with one of the bituminous waterproofing adhesives suitable for this purpose and the fabric is bedded down upon it in a wet condition. Once the surface has become tacky, a second coat is applied and the surface is then allowed to dry for twenty-four hours whereupon a third and final coat is added. When the final coat is tacky it can be dusted over with fine sand which will give added protection.

With patching it is important that the fabric used should be as closely woven as possible provided that the weave is not so dense as to resist penetration by the waterproofing compound. The fabric should be clean and preferably rot-proofed by a copper or other approved method, and pre-shrunk. The fabric for laying is itself bituminised so that it readily adheres to the roof surface without curling.

If an asphalt roof is very badly worn and it is only desired to extend its life for a limited period of time a suggestion for a short-term repair is to place an overlay of new asphalt ½-inch (13mm) thick on a layer of black sheathing felt over the whole of the roof area, the necessary fillets at wall junctions being provided and appropriate detailing at parapets being dealt with as previously discussed.

Maintenance of Asphalt roofs

Asphalt flat roofs require little maintenance. As in the case of other roofs debris should be removed as it accumulates but this is not likely to be so dangerous to an asphalt flat roof as to the metal coverings for two reasons, firstly that the asphalt forms a continuous membrane so that a build up of water on the surface is not likely to be injurious and decomposition does not occur in the same way. Solar reflecting surfaces of white spar or of marble chippings avoid the build-up of heat to asphalt roofs in warm weather. These can be embedded in the hot and fluid material immediately it has been applied, or they can be applied afterwards, embedded on the surface of the asphalt by means of a special bitumen. Their disadvantage is that they make the tracing of any subsequent faults more difficult. The application of light-coloured paints for reflective purposes is not a satisfactory solution since these tend to cause crazing or cracking in the asphalt surface. A time-honoured solution is the application of a tallow limewash. This however requires frequent renewal in order to retain any efficiency. If the roof is to be used as a terrace the laying of light-coloured asbestos tiles or mosaic provides not only a wearing surface but also helps by way of providing solar reflectivity. The Building Research Establishment Digest No. 144 of 1972 recommends that roof coverings are inspected at least annually by a maintenance surveyor to ensure that rainwater outlets are kept clear and to decide on any action necessary to prevent defects from becoming failures.

No. 2. Bituminous felt

Although bituminous felt roof coverings have been employed for domestic houses for the past fifty years or so the use of this material has only become widespread since the Second World War. It is only really within the last twenty years that effective methods of manufacture and laying have been introduced so that this material can be considered seriously as a roof covering of other than a temporary nature. Even so, the life is limited to 15–20 years and the surveyor will find when he encounters this type of roof covering to houses that the quality of the material and the methods of laying have varied widely so that he must be on his guard to detect imperfections. The early felts were based wholly on organic fibres which were very strong when new but were apt to rot when moisture eventually penetrated the bitumen coating.

The attractions in the use of bituminous felt for flat roof coverings are firstly that it is very cheap compared to other roofing materials and secondly that the plant required for laying it is considerably less than in the case of asphalt. Against this, however, is that it is not resistant to fire and that it is most unsuitable for any foot traffic on the roof surface. Modern practice with flat roof coverings demands a minimum of three layers of bituminous felt so that any lesser number can only be termed a temporary or at the most a semi-permanent covering. The more recent innovation of a top surface of grit or gravel in bitumen or a layer of chippings render the roof rather more acceptable to some foot traffic, but the fact remains that roofs covered with bituminous felt are inferior both in life and quality to any of the roof coverings so far discussed.

The Inspection

Although a bituminous felt roof may be considerably younger in years than any of the flat roof coverings already mentioned, the need for a thorough investigation is nevertheless just as great. The fall of the roof should not be less than $1\frac{1}{2}$ inches (38mm) in 10 feet (3·05m) (1 in 80) if rainwater is to be effectively disposed of from the surface. In addition to this, however, a good deal of other information is required. Not only must the surveyor attempt to assess the quality of the felt but he must try to find out how many layers are provided. Furthermore he is advised to test a corner of the felt covering to see if the bonding compound provides a satisfactory adhesive. In all too many cases the surface of the felt will show bubbles or ripples and where the felt has become brittle and there has been some foot traffic tears and splits will be observed as well. Bituminous felt does have one advantage to the surveyor, strictly it should be added only from the point of view of the inspection, in that it will show up depressions or imperfections in the boarding or insulating material underneath. This advantage also extends to the surveyor being able to assess if the laps between sheets of 2 inches (51mm) at the sides and 3 inches (76mm) at the ends are adequate and if successive layers are laid to break joints. Abutments at angles with vertical parapet walls when inspected will often reveal that there is no triangular fillet at the corner under the felt so that there is a right-angled joint which may have become cracked. The 6-inch (152mm) upstand may be covered with a metal flashing but all too often the surveyor will find that a cover flashing of bituminous felt has been provided which has, in all probability, broken at the top edge. The detailing of aprons, gutters and outlets should be examined as well as the details at the eaves. Sometimes aluminium edgings are employed but often these are not properly fixed or are ineffective.

The provision of a vapour barrier to roofs of built-up bituminous felts is of great importance. The question of the vapour barrier is dealt with elsewhere in Chapter 8 but is stressed here again due to the particular need for vapour barriers in roof coverings of this type. One of the most common defects in bitumen felt roofs is to find that no provision whatsoever has been made for ventilation below the covering material so as to avoid fungal growth. This defect found in combination with an insulating decking of organic material can be lethal and the surveyor must take pains to try to ascertain the nature of the sub-structure. Fortunately in a number of cases with roofs laid comparatively recently, plans are available to show the nature of the original construction but this, of course, is by no means always the case particularly for small roofs of existing additions to houses which may have been laid by a local builder.

The Repair of Bituminous Felt Flat Roofs

If the roof covering is defective in one or more ways, or if it falls short of the modern principles of laying three-ply bituminous felt roof coverings, it is best for the surveyor to advise that the covering be renewed as a whole. The reason for this is that it is often quite expensive to try to effect piecemeal repairs to a roof of this type whereas a new roof covering provided on modern lines will provide a much more satisfactory life.

Once the covering is stripped the decking can be examined. This may be retained and used in conjunction with an insulating material such as granulated cork slabs or fibre insulation board, but where timber is used in the construction the boards should be well seasoned of 1-inch (25mm) nominal thickness and closely clamped together with tongued and grooved joints. Alternatively compressed straw or wood wool slabs may be employed but it is absolutely vital that in this case, particularly where compressed straw slabs are used, that the maker's instructions are followed to the letter. Whatever the decking material used the deck itself must, of course, be stable. The whole structure must be rigid and the construction must counteract the effect of shrinkage, warping or displacement. All the external angles for the built-up felt roofing finishes should be rounded and the provision of angle fillets to internal angles is recommended. The practice of providing an extra strip of felt at corners instead of an angle fillet is not fully satisfactory.

The felt selected should be asbestos based to a timber boarded decking while the subsequent layers may be either fibre, asbestos or glass fibre based. Where the sub-structure is of laminated board the first layer of felt should be either of asbestos or glass fibre based and the subsequent layers may be either fibre, asbestos or glass fibre based. Where the sub-structure consists of a dry insulation board all the layers may be either fibre, asbestos or glass fibre based. The surfacing of roofs that are not used for regular foot traffic are normally of bitumen dressing compound with $\frac{1}{2}$ or $\frac{1}{4}$ inch (13 or 6mm) mineral aggregate up to a 10° pitch or alternatively mineral surfaced felt of types set out in the British Standard Code of Practice C.P.144 of 1968 are recommended.

It is hoped that a good specialist firm would be employed for the work of laying the roof as the bonding of the three-ply covering is something of a specialised technique. The technique of partial bonding of the first layer of roofing felt to laminated board requires some skill while the technique of full bonding of the first layer of roofing felt to dry insulation materials such as insulation board, cork or compressed straw slabs carried out with a continuous coating of hot bitumen applied to the sub-structure (used also to bond the second and third layers of felt) needs to be thorough. The temperature of the bitumen will depend on the air temperature at the time of laying and should be in the range of 200 to 220°C (392 to 450°F). Overheating of the bitumen bonding compound will drive off volatile oils leaving the residue hard and brittle and unsuitable for bonding the layers together. The bitumen bonding compound is poured from a container on to the sub-structure and the felt rolled out. Pressure is then applied to allow the layer of hot compound to soften and weld to the coating material of the felt, any surplus compound squeezed out being smoothed with a scraper as the work proceeds. Only sufficient compound must be poured in front of the roll to allow a thin strip of liquid to be squeezed out at the edges; the other half of the felt should then be covered up and the process repeated, making sure that the layer of hot bitumen is continuous. Alternatively the hot bitumen compound can be spread out in front of the roll of felt by means of mops dipped in a bucket of hot bitumen bonding compound. It can therefore be seen that the laying of ply bonding bituminous felt is not a matter that can be carried out by anyone employed who is not thoroughly conversant with the work.

Detailing to bituminous felt roofs is important. Metal flashings are recommended although felt flashings are often specified. Projections passing through the roof covering and structure such as a vent pipe, should pass through a metal collar having a flat element on the roof structure. The method of waterproofing is to apply layers of roofing felt to the flanged metal collar, the height of this being 6 inches (152mm).

The detail at the eaves is important as a metal drip should be formed permanently fixed between the bonded sheets turned down into the gutter. This strip can be turned up and nailed internally to a fixing batten 1 inch (25mm) forward from the structure. Verges can be finished in a similar manner but the metal drip can be fixed to the top of the first layer of felt allowing a 4-inch (102mm) lap. The metal can be fixed to the nailing batten and succeeding layers of felt can be lapped over the metal and can be continuously bonded with hot bitumen bonding compound, the edge of the top layer being set back 1 inch (25mm) from the face of the drip. Metal drips should not be less than $1\frac{1}{2}$ inches (38mm) deep.

Patching Repairs to Bituminous Felt Roof Surfaces

Where a bituminous felt surface is generally sound apart from a small hole or a minor injury, a patching repair can be carried out by forming rectangular sections of felt cut to give a lap of about 3 inches (76mm) all round the outside area of the hole or injured surface. These patches can then be clout nailed to the boards at the same time that they are sealed into position on to the surface. In the case of concrete roofs it will of course not be possible to nail the patches but these should be fixed and lapped over and sealed to the adjoining felt with hot bitumen. Alternatively the felt manufacturers can provide a bituminous lap cement for cold application.

549

If, instead of an isolated hole or a small area of injury to a roof it is necessary to treat a larger area by patching, it might be possible with care to remove a whole width of felt for the desired length without tearing the adjacent strip and then to replace a new length of felt and fix it in place by lapping and sealing. A new way in which this type of repair can be carried out is to gently warm the joint of the sheet of felt to be taken up by means of a hot iron or blowlamp over about a 3-inch (76mm) margin until the bitumen is soft whereupon the painter's knife can be inserted between the layers of the sheet. These can then be separated and then turned up with the fingers. If this process is carried out carefully it should, with luck, be possible to proceed progressively along the joint without tearing the felt. The defective section of sheet can then be separated from the sheet next to it and detached from the roof surface by further heating as necessary. A new section of sheet can then be inserted between the laps and the joints sealed in the usual way with fresh bitumen or lap cement. The new felts should be sealed and nailed if possible except of course, in the case of concrete, where this is not possible.

Where sloping roofs or exposed positions are concerned, care should be taken to ensure that the lap joint does not end at a vulnerable point where it is likely to be saturated by rain. For example, rather than stop a patching repair near the ridge, it is often better to carry the felt over the ridge completely and in other cases up and under flashings where possible.

Patching repairs, if employed with care, can be effective for a considerable time. It is often possible, for example, to remove and replace existing skirtings and flashings and other vulnerable detailing and replace them but particular care must be taken with the type of bonding compounds used and to ensure that effective laps are provided.

In the case of deterioration of a roof surface due to wear it is often worthwhile to give the whole of the surface a dressing which, when still in a fluid state, can be blinded with sand or fine gravel. Hot bitumen can be blinded with fine grit of mesh size between 14 mesh and $\frac{3}{16}$ inches (4mm) spread at the rate of about 1 pound per square foot ($0\cdot45$kg/$0\cdot3$m^2).

Maintenance of built-up felt roofing

No maintenance treatment is required for built-up felt roofing but periodical inspections should be made and any accumulated debris should be cleared. The Building Research Establishment Digest No. 144 of 1972 recommends that roof coverings be inspected at least annually by a maintenance surveyor to ensure that rainwater outlets are kept clear and to decide on any action necessary to prevent defects from becoming failures.

COVERINGS FOR SOLID ROOFS

It is not often that the surveyor encounters a roof of truly solid construction when dealing with the repair of dwelling houses. Old traditions die hard and it is still the rule rather than the exception for new houses to be provided with timber roofs, usually of pitched construction, but occasionally of flat construction where back additions are involved. Even where the house or a terrace of houses is provided with a flat roof or roofs the construction is more economically provided in timber although on some of the larger schemes there might be a departure into light steel beams and a metal decking covered with bituminous felt. Such roofs are comparatively rare and even more rare are those terraces with a continuous flat roof of reinforced concrete, lightened in weight though it may be, by the inclusion of hollow clay pots. On occasions an old house that has been altered or converted might present such a feature and accordingly one or two factors in regard to the repair of the covering might profitably be mentioned.

If the original roof was provided with an asphalt covering the repair and maintenance of the surface can be dealt with as discussed previously in the case of asphalt coverings for timber roofs. Normally, however, where the surveyor finds a concrete roof which is sound in structure, but where the covering is worn and porous he may wish to consider the number of possibilities for a new waterproof covering which might range from built-up bituminous felt to asphalt or perhaps one of the metals, such as zinc or copper.

So far as the metals are concerned, stripping the original covering to provide a new smooth surface is clearly necessary, and if composition board or bituminous felt is to be specified to provide a new underlay as will not doubt be the case, it is necessary that the fixings for the metal are made by means of clips, and the fixings for the wood rolls are made with composition plugs into which screws are driven. The trouble with timber battens is that these are likely to rot and although the British Standard Code of Practice 143 of 1964 suggests that these be pressure treated with preservative the risk element of using timber under such circumstances is, in the view of most surveyors, too high. The method of fixing of both sheeting and underlay should provide an anchorage at least as secure as that provided with nails or screws driven into sound timber.

Perhaps the best covering for solid roofs of larger span and area is mastic asphalt or built-up bituminous felt. These coverings have the great advantage that they are not dependent on joints as in the case of the metals and although asphalt is undoubtedly the best, bituminous felt has its cheapness to recommend it as a substitute. In the case of asphalt it may be necessary to bring the surface of a flat roof to a fall of 1 in 80 by screeding the surface before any other work is contemplated. The same preparation is also needed for built-up bituminous felt and the British Standard Code of Practice 144 of 1968 suggests a sand and cement screed at least 1-inch (25mm) thick. The screed should not be laid continuously but in areas not exceeding 100 square feet (9m²). Alternatively a lightweight concrete screed may be laid both to give the necessary fall and to provide thermal insulation. Lightweight aggregate concrete should stand a good deal of subsequent wear but where cellular lightweight concrete composed of cement and sand with the introduction of air into the mix is employed, it is not desirable to build this up to too great a height if it is to take any traffic. A ½-inch (13mm) thick topping of four to one clean sharp sand and cement screed should be applied to lightweight aggregate concrete before the felt roofing is laid completed in areas not exceeding 100 square feet (9m²). It should be borne in mind that there is a good deal of moisture in screeds of this sort, particularly thick screeds, which must be allowed to dry out. Where a thick screed is laid and there is continual rainfall which saturates it, the laying of an insulation board of other composition decking is not desirable without the provision of a vapour barrier below. Much of the dampness in new blocks of flats which is commonly attributed to condensation is in reality due to the long slow process of drying out saturated concrete and lightweight screeds where the moisture is effectively sealed in by the roof covering. The pressure on accommodation is so great however that the tenants are moved in on practical completion and it is they, with their heating, who have to dry out the structure. The trouble is that the more heat they use the worse the conditions and this can only be alleviated if they are prepared to live in a perpetual gale with the windows wide open. One's sympathy can be extended to the tenants in these circumstances particularly when they are often blamed for the conditions which arise.

In regard to older property, built before the introduction of reinforced concrete, the surveyor may well find flat or slightly pitched roofs which have the appearance and sound when walked upon of being solid but which are in fact not so. Such roofs occur very widely on Victorian property over bay windows, and the smaller back additions. The construction is usually of ordinary wood joists and boarding but instead of even a cheap metal covering such as zinc the original builders would build up on the boards a thick layer comprising two or three courses of roofing tiles in a thick bed of lime concrete. This would then be topped with a coating of tar or pitch. Whether the original builders ever thought that such a covering would remain waterproof for long is not known but the attempts by subsequent owners to keep water out can usually be seen and range from applications of asphalt bitumen and canvas, plain bitumen down to another layer of cement screeding. The strange fact is that it is not only the cheapest houses of the Victorian period that were provided with such features but some of the most expensive as well. There are even terraces of houses where the main roofs were covered in this manner though in one case seen the construction of the roofs themselves were equally unorthodox, being based on a series of closely-spaced timber arch-like centres joined together and covered with boarding to produce a type of barrel vault.

The great danger with roof coverings of this type is that of slow percolation through the covering which although it may not be visible on the ceiling below is almost certain to have caused rot in the supporting timbers. Experience indicates that this is so in the vast majority of cases when the timbers are exposed from below. In the case of such roofs over bay windows invariably the rot is found to extend to the lintel, if this is of wood, supporting the brickwork of the main wall above, involving its renewal preferably in concrete. If the outbreak is of dry rot, as it usually is in such an unventilated spot, there is no alternative but to remove the whole structure, sterilise the brickwork and to replace the roof in some form in accordance with current sound practice. If the timbers by chance are sound and sturdy there might then be some point in surfacing the top with asphalt in accordance with the recommended details but even so there is a danger of entrapped moisture giving rise to a subsequent outbreak of dry rot if the ceiling is replaced without the provision of adequate ventilation to the timbers.

Chapter 8
Dampness

CONTENTS

INTRODUCTION

THE effects of dampness on the character and temper of the British people would provide a fruitful topic hitherto unexplored, for the more frivolous of academic writers. To a large proportion of the population, however, there is nothing frivolous about the subject. For centuries people have been huddling, complaining bitterly while roofs leak, plaster becomes sodden through rising damp and decorations peel and flake. The incidence even now of dampness is surely a sorry reflection on our skills as builders and designers and a distinct reminder that our sense of priorities has frequently been wrong in the past and may not be much better now. Today throughout the country the labour force available for the repair and maintenance of domestic buildings is concerned to an abnormally large degree with repairing defects caused directly or indirectly by dampness as against other causes. From time immemorial preventative work against dampness has taken up and still is taking up the energies of skilled men, and even then, wrong diagnoses, well-meaning if incorrect efforts at repair, and ingenious but wrong attempts to remedy the effects of dampness are wasting a good deal of the effort of those employed to deal with the problem. Year after year through generation after generation attempts to staunch the flow through defective flashings to chimney stacks and roof slopes are proved to be of no avail when the damp stains underneath mysteriously and exasperatingly reappear. Stains and deposits form to an unexpected degree and with maddening repetition on new plaster and brick surfaces and time after time defective plaster to basement rooms is renewed with the tenant watching in the gloomy knowledge that damp, the old enemy, will probably win in the end. Even with the most expensive house and with the best advice dampness is a formidable enemy but it is by no means exclusively a problem centred round very old buildings. Many new dwellings are also troubled with faults from dampness and very often departure from the old tried methods and the introduction of new materials cause fresh problems to arise which convince the architect or surveyor that dampness as a subject cannot be reserved for the first-year student alone and then forgotten.

The schoolboy is told that Great Britain has a temperate climate. This means, of course, that rain will fall in varying quantities in all parts of the country at all times of the year with the added effects

that driving winds of different strengths provide. It also means that
the sun will not have the full baking effect that occurs with more
extreme climates and moreover the ground will hold an appreciable
proportion of water below the surface depending on the height above
sea level and the composition of the sub-soil. But surely, it is reasonable to ask, a builder should only need good enclosing walls with a
damp proof course at the base and a good watertight roof above for a
house to be effectively dry under all circumstances. This, of course,
is very true but the solution is not quite so simple for the following
reasons:

(1) Different materials forming parts of a building will not
possess similar wearing characteristics and will not be subject always
to equal wear, particularly when the effects of pollution are taken
into account. In any structure of whatever age a wide variety of
materials are employed. Many tiled roofs, for example, are provided
with zinc flashings and in many cases a pitched roof to the main
structure will give way to a flat zinc roof over the back addition.
Particularly in the inner areas of the great cities, acid pollution in
rainwater will cause the surface of the zinc to become corroded and
pitted so that the effective life of this material is reduced to some
20 years as against the much longer life of the tiles to the main roof.
Many houses built at the end of the last century still have their
original back addition roofs which have become worn out but have
been inexpertly preserved with an application of black bituminous
compound often with dire results to the timber underneath when the
damp penetration persists. Acids in the run off from one surface as
against another and acids from marauding cats will also cause light
gauge zinc to deteriorate very quickly indeed. This is bad enough
where it can be seen in the case of flat roofs but often zinc will deteriorate in positions where it can go undetected for some time and
cause a good deal of damp penetration and harm, for example in
the case of soakers and flashings to complicated roofs, abutments and
chimney stacks.

(2) The design of the dwelling house may be faulty. Bad design,
for example, the provision of the damp proof course at the wrong
level, or bad design of solid or cavity walls or damp proof courses
omitted altogether under the copings to parapets will lead to damp
penetration. Similarly a badly designed slope to, for example, a
tiled roof, which allows water to penetrate under the tiles by capillary creep or admit moisture from driving rain can cause the underside of the roof boarding to become saturated. A host of other
irritations from bad design details will lead to effects far beyond their
seeming importance on the drawing board. Small projections without metal cappings and badly designed sills and copings without

adequate projections and check throats and with insufficient weathering may all cause trouble at some future time.

(3) The construction may be at fault. Even a well-designed dwelling house will be vulnerable to dampness if the actual construction is faulty. Facing brickwork formed with snapped headers to save expense, slates laid with an uneven lap and lead roofs and gutters formed with poor rolls and inept detailing are obvious examples. In other parts of the structure, rainwater held in a defective eaves gutter, box gutter or hopper head with an unnoticed defect may be allowed to slowly trickle down the face of a wall. Rainwater acts as a solvent to all conventional mortars but particularly lime mortar, and when it also forms a vehicle for chemicals in diluted form from the combustion of solid liquid and gaseous fuels, interesting results follow. Brickwork, when saturated with driving rain may normally be expected to dry out if the bricks are of good quality and the wall is soundly built to correct principles but the interior of the brick may contain soluble salts which become dissolved with the rainwater, issue from the pores of the brick and appear on the outer surface in the form of a white mould. Under a microscope, this mould can be seen for what it is: a crystalline deposit. Such deposit, known as efflorescence, is not necessarily harmful particularly on new brickwork. In other cases, however, where rainwater is washed from one surface to another, such as a limestone wall surface on to a sandstone plinth, decay will follow.

(4) The original materials may be of poor quality and dampness will ruthlessly search out poor materials. Badly mixed mortar, faulty bricks and cheap tiles will soon be revealed for what they are and if the basic materials of a house are of very poor quality the question of repair work is a problem indeed. It should be stressed that it is dampness not time that is the most ruthless destroyer of poor quality materials. Most materials would be perfectly satisfactory in a warm dry climate without rainfall and most materials such as iron and even wood will suffer total immersion without ill effect. The alternate application of wet and dry conditions however are extremely damaging to a good many types of material but particularly to timber. Prolonged and severe adverse weather conditions such as an unduly long period of wet weather followed by hard frost may also accelerate deterioration. Porous brick will absorb moisture which is normally able to dry out. When the temperature drops below freezing point, however, the water is converted into ice which expands to an additional one-tenth of its original volume, an extra capacity which the brick may not be able to withstand. Thus often the face of a brick will be blown off by this process allowing penetrating damp to soak into and saturate the

softened interior. Surveyors will be familiar with the appearance of the Victorian under-burned red brick where the hard face has been removed in this manner so that the bright red softened interior is then exposed to soak up rainwater like a sponge. Other forms of building material are also prone to this trouble particularly those that have been mass-produced rather cheaply so that they have a hard smooth outside skin but with an uneven texture giving a softer and more vulnerable interior. Some machine-made tiles produced between the two World Wars are an obvious case in point and the reader will no doubt recall a row of houses with which he is familiar where the tiled surfaces have laminated badly in house after house alike. Stone also, if badly selected or badly laid will be vulnerable in a similar way, the resulting lamination and cracks allowing dampness to penetrate what was formerly a smooth and waterproofed detail to a building.

(5) Structural faults may admit dampness. The movement and settlement which inevitably occurs to most buildings of any age may cause cracks to appear in the outer fabric which allow dampness to penetrate. Such movement not only leads to cracks in the outer face of brickwork where it can be seen and repaired but will lead to the shifting and widening of door and window openings. Fractures in pipes in concealed parts of the structure either as a result of movement or as a result of decay may result in dampness under some circumstances and it is often extremely difficult for the surveyor to ascertain the cause in these cases.

It will therefore be appreciated that there are circumstances where dampness can penetrate a structure that appears to be watertight at first glance. Some natural laws of science also form a powerful aid to damp penetration which often lead to the mystified surveyor scratching his head when yet another unusual manifestation from a problem relating to damp arises. We have referred to capillary action which attracts water into porous bricks or assists moisture to creep back under slates and to diluted chemicals in rainwater leading to an adverse reaction of one material upon another perhaps some distance away. Dampened lime mortar for example may produce disintegration in a lead pipe although admittedly only over a long period of time. To these laws must be added the principle of condensation varying from comparatively straightforward problems due to the distillation of moisture from warm moist rooms to colder rooms adjoining to the complex array of more serious problems which can arise from the counterplay of temperature and humidity.

We have referred so far to the question of structural deterioration from dampness but a word might also be said regarding the architectural appearance of the house since this too is of some importance.

The reader will be familiar with the vertical streaks that appear on stone façades from badly designed mouldings or projections due to rainwater channelled down the face of the building in unexpected rivulets. In urban areas such streaks can have a curious appearance against the sooty façade of a building; a refinement that the architect never intended. In a similar manner lack of damp proof courses to stone buildings will cause bad staining to plinths or parapets particularly in cases where limestones are used. Badly designed details or poor damp proof courses will lead to sulphate attacks in brickwork which, if a façade is rendered, will not be discovered until the rendering crumbles in an all too familiar rectangular pattern of cracking, the horizontal cracks being caused by the expansion in the mortar joints of the brickwork behind. The exterior cladding of some newer domestic buildings formed from teak or western red cedar may, although attractive when first delivered and fixed, take on a sorry appearance particularly when the impurities in the atmosphere are washed against the unprotected surface of the wood. A good deal more care in preserving such panels is needed than is generally recognised and unless a linseed oil paraffin wax mixture containing a fungicide is applied annually to the surface of the wood the appearance will suffer since the individual boards in vertical cladding will either reject or absorb water according to their individual grains, thus providing an impressive distinction in colouring as between one board and the next. Copper is sometimes used for roof work since it oxidises in such an attractive manner as anyone who has seen the green copper domes provided by architects over the last three hundred years will agree. Other metals, however, such as aluminium alloys, oxidise extremely unattractively and aluminium used externally requires anodic treatment followed by periodic washing so that pollution does not allow the surface to become black and pitted. Finally in this short list of instances, we might add that rust to cast iron or steel does not only mar façades where it is expected, for example to badly painted railings, but often appears in the most unexpected circumstances. A number of cases have occurred where the ends of reinforcing rods which have been embedded too near the face of a building have been affected by dampness and have subsequently rusted causing disfiguration to the elevation.

IDENTIFICATION

In the question of damp penetration it is, of course, just as necessary as in problems discussed in any other Chapter of this book for the surveyor to have a thorough knowledge of the construction of all the various types of domestic building before he can confidently prescribe a remedy. Experience in other problems allied to dampness will assist the surveyor when it comes to making a proper diagnosis. Very often however, he will find that the damp problem in a house is not by any means new. It may be due to a long standing defect, as a result of which many attempts have been made to effect patch repairs. It will accordingly be useful for the surveyor before he does anything else to find out what steps have already been taken to deal with the problem and an observant occupier can give the surveyor a great deal of information that he could not find from any other source and which may be extremely helpful to him. The surveyor will also be aided by a good moisture meter, although he will appreciate that dense material such as a good quality hard plaster may be drier at the surface than below and that too much information should not be assumed accordingly from a surface reading. Conversely it is possible to obtain a high surface reading under certain conditions while the material below may be quite dry. The surveyor must accordingly learn how to use his moisture meter so as to give him the maximum amount of information and must be aware of its limitations so as not to be trapped into recording a completely unreal reading due to an unusual set of circumstances. Modern moisture meters are becoming increasingly useful, some combining thermohygrometer readings with condensation thermometers as well.

In commencing any investigation of dampness the surveyor is recommended to have regard to the following factors:

(1) He should have regard to the extent of the damp; that is to say, for example, he should ascertain if the dampness is widespread to outer walls, or if it occurs in isolated patches.

(2) He should have regard to the pattern of the damp as it relates to other features such as window openings or chimney breasts.

(3) He should have regard to the time of the appearance of the damp in relation to the date of erection of the building and the prevailing weather conditions. For example he should ascertain if the dampness occurs only after a long spell of rain or when the air is merely humid or after a certain rise of temperature and whether it is persistent or spasmodic.

(4) He should establish the occupational use of the dwelling and decide if dampness follows a change of occupants or a change in their living pattern.

The causes of dampness can be divided into four main categories and it will be the aim of the investigation to assign the problem to one or more than one of the following since the remedies for each category are fundamentally different. The four categories are:

(1) Penetrating damp.
(2) Condensation.
(3) Rising damp.
(4) Extraneous causes introducing damp.

Before we discuss the investigation to categorise the causes of damp in further detail it is as well for the reader to be quite clear that dampness is something that can never be entirely removed from a house structure nor is it desirable that it should be. In a new house the several tons of water introduced into the structure as a result of bricklaying, concrete and plastering will of course, mostly dry out as the house is occupied and heated, but all porous materials in the building will always continue to contain moisture. The moisture content varies widely according to the type of material involved, the content varying from under 1 per cent in the case of plaster to up to 20 per cent in the case of timber. A certain level of natural moisture content is therefore necessary for the correct condition of the building. Anyone who has seen the sudden effect of a central heating system newly installed in an old house with hollow timber floors, doors, panelling and other joinery will appreciate this point. The Building Research Establishment point out that the scientific assessment of dampness is extremely difficult and the term "dampness" is accordingly reserved for conditions under which moisture is present in sufficient quantity either to become directly perceptible to the senses of sight and touch, or to cause deterioration in the decorations and eventually to the fabric of the building.

THE INVESTIGATION

The surveyor will perhaps be called in to investigate the cause of dampness either in relation to a specific fault which has occurred or alternatively to investigate a number of problems relating to dampness throughout the house as a whole, perhaps at a time of general repair and improvement. In either case the surveyor will often be invited to look at certain signs noticed by the householder as being caused by dampness but he will be well advised to look upon the problem as if these observed signs may be only part of the story. A simple and rather obvious case of this would be where a patch of damp penetration is due to the fact that the zinc flashings and soakers to the main roof and parapet walls are perished at a particular point. Presumably, however, the zincwork to the roof as a whole has all perished to a similar degree and further patches of dampness may be expected to appear in other parts of the structure in the fairly near future. It would, accordingly, be extremely short-sighted of the surveyor to renew the soakers and flashings only at the point where the dampness was visible at the time of his inspection and leave the remainder of the roof coverings as they are for further damp penetration to become apparent shortly afterwards. The other reason why the surveyor should not merely look at the signs that are pointed out to him is that the diagnosis of the cause of dampness, while straightforward in some cases, is often no easy matter in others and it is possible that several sources of dampness may be at play at the same time in a complicated relationship. The surveyor accordingly has to make sure in his own mind that he is certain as to the cause or causes of dampness before he seeks to specify what repairs may be necessary. It is for this reason, therefore, that the investigation is of particular importance, and the surveyor is advised when conducting this to consider first, as suggested earlier in this chapter, the extent of the dampness or defects; secondly, to have regard to the pattern of the damp or defective patches in relation to other features of the property and, thirdly, to obtain all the information he can regarding the timing of the appearance of dampness in relation to the date of the erection of the building and to the prevailing weather conditions.

There will, of course, be occasions where the surveyor will need to inspect certain parts of the property only in order to comply with the terms of his instructions just as there will be other occasions when he will feel that it is necessary to inspect the property as a whole. The important factor is to extend the inspection and investigation as far as needed. As it is necessary here to consider all forms of dampness and their likely origins it is convenient to assume that the surveyor would wish to carry out a full inspection of the whole property and we will follow him in this inspection considering at the same time any opening-up for further investigation that may be required. For the purposes of this survey it is suggested that the same pattern might be adopted as that set out by the writers in their earlier volume, "Structural Surveys of Dwelling-Houses". If this course is followed the inspection will accordingly commence at the top floor of the house, each room being taken in turn, the pattern being established in either a clockwise or anti-clockwise direction and followed in a similar manner at each successive floor level until the basement floor is reached. Once this is done the surveyor can then commence his external inspection, taking each elevation together with the respective roof slopes in turn. So far as the inspection of the roof space is concerned it will be assumed that this is carried out in conjunction with the inspection of the top floor but in addition to this the surveyor may no doubt wish to take advantage of the opportunities offered at each floor level to climb out and inspect the surfaces of minor roofs wherever these present themselves with sufficient access but the investigation of inaccessible roof slopes will no doubt be left until the elevations are inspected externally when, if necessary, long ladders can be provided if long distance inspection from the ground is not considered to be sufficient. Investigation from a ladder, particularly in the cases of gutters and outlets, awkward angles and abutments, may be necessary to confirm the surveyor's suspicions.

Many of the most obvious signs of dampness occur from water penetration through defective roof coverings, worn or inefficient flashings to parapet walls and chimney stacks and defective roof gutters, and the surveyor, when he commences his investigation starting at the top floor of the house will normally be invited to assume that any stains that are present to top floor ceilings, cornices or chimney breasts, are due to the fact that the roof is leaking. This, however, may not always be the case. There is often some genuine difficulty in deciding whether a roof is leaking or whether signs of dampness observed to the top floor ceilings may be due to condensation. It is, for example, possible that in certain types of construction, condensed moisture may be transmitted from roof members to the ceilings underneath so that the signs from the room below may appear to be exactly similar to those caused by damp penetration. In certain types of new construction where flat roofs are provided to dwelling houses a vapour barrier or horizontal impermeable layer which resists penetration from condensed moisture may be present to ceilings and where, for example, a foil backed plasterboard or glossy impervious paint may have been provided to the face of the ceilings and where there is a heavy build-up of condensation from bathrooms or kitchens the resulting staining and dripping of moisture may well appear to be due to damp penetration from the roof. It is under circumstances such as these that the use of an electrical moisture meter is of great assistance. It should be emphasised, however, that by merely placing the two points of the probe gently against the surface of a ceiling or wall, a high moisture reading will no doubt result whether the dampness is due to penetration from the roof or to condensation. In order to take the investigation a stage further it is necessary for the surveyor to lightly chip away the surface covering with the householder's consent or, alternatively, to do this discreetly in a corner where it is not likely to be noticed and to press the point of the probe into the shallow sinking that he has formed. If the resulting reading on the dial of the instrument shows that there is no moisture content whatever, the surveyor may be satisfied that the cause of the problem is due to condensation. If, on the other hand, the instrument still records a high moisture reading, neither penetrating dampness or condensation can be excluded as a possible cause at this stage, since it is perfectly possible for condensation over a long period of time to allow certain types of building material to become completely saturated. The surveyor will then have to take his investigations further and determine accurately the nature of the construction and presence, or otherwise, of impermeable layers to the face of, or behind wall and ceiling surfaces, beyond which condensation cannot penetrate from the interior of the house. A thick permeable wall or ceiling material with such a barrier behind can become saturated but if dampness can be found to have affected the structural or walling materials on the other side of this barrier the cause can then only be due to damp penetration.

With older types of flat roofs of conventional joist and boarded construction with a top surface of metal sheeting, condensation is less likely as a cause of irregular staining and a series of blotches to the surface of the ceiling below will probably indicate that the metal covering is defective so that water has seeped down the faces of the timber joists to appear on the ceilings below. This does not always necessarily result in a regular pattern of damp marks appearing along the line of the joists since the moisture will, in certain cases, be absorbed by the ceiling plaster and as a result appears in an irregular pattern on the surface of the ceiling. A regular band of heavy dampness however, below the cornice to one particular wall or across the centre of a ceiling on the other hand is more likely to indicate that a parapet or valley gutter has failed with consequences that are all too evident.

The inspection of a flat roof either to the main structure or to a back addition should involve a particular examination of parapet walls and chimney stacks projecting above the roof level. So far as the inspection of the flat roof surface is concerned this is dealt with fully under the chapter dealing with roof coverings. The particular importance of the inspection so far as dampness is concerned, however, turns also on the consideration of the parapet walls and chimney stacks since these are one of the most common sources of dampness as they act as funnels to introduce moisture into a house structure unless they are designed and constructed with great care. Accordingly the surveyor should inspect such parts of the structure to see if they are upright since signs of leaning may be due to sulphate attack. The disruptive effect of sulphate attack, where damp combined with Portland cement and soluble sulphate salts in the bricks will cause expansion, is that a parapet or chimney stack exposed to continual damp on one side will bend towards the other. Sulphate attack must, however, be distinguished from frost action. Since the remedies for the two types of defects may be different under the particular circumstances concerned the surveyor must of course diagnose the true reason for failure in exposed areas of brickwork.

The tops of parapet walls and chimney stacks should be inspected to see in the former case if adequate copings are provided and in the latter case if the flaunching is in order or if it is loose or badly decayed to the extent that it clearly admits a disproportionate amount of dampness or fails in its duty to provide a bedding for the chimney pots. So far as parapets are concerned the material and construction of copings are of particular importance in keeping out penetrating dampness and the surveyor will be lucky if he finds a stone coping built with a correctly weathered top face, with adequate projections at each side complete with check throats so that moisture does not trickle under the edges of the coping and seep back into the brickwork, and with a correctly formed damp proof course underneath so that any seepage between the joints of the stone sections is prevented from penetrating the top of the wall. The nature of the weathering qualities of the coping, the degree to which it has resisted frost decay or weathering as well as design defects should be noted. Some artificial stone copings are deficient in weathering qualities and are apt to fracture or fragment while many copings have poor check throats which are not sufficiently well formed or deep enough to throw water clear of the parapet below in conditions of severe rainfall. It is, however, far more likely that instead of finding an adequate coping, the surveyor will find an inadequate one. Inverted "V" shaped tile sections placed along a parapet with butt joints are fairly satisfactory from the weather resistant point of view but damp proof courses are rarely found underneath so that seepage between the tiles penetrates the brickwork. The edges of the tiles are also usually insufficient in a large number of cases to prevent water from running down the faces of the brickwork on either side. Brick-on-edge copings with tile creasings often suffer from constructional and design defects, and dampness, penetrating the top surfaces of the bricks and the mortar joints between so that the exposed surfaces become green and stained will eventually penetrate the walling below. Such copings are just not proof against downward passage of moisture. Often no copings will be provided at all and a coating of rendering to the side of the brickwork will merely be carried over the head of the wall which will inevitably admit moisture in time even if a waterproofing mix is provided.

It is of particular importance that the surveyor makes notes as to the existence or absence of any damp proof courses, and if so, how many are provided to parapet walls and chimney stacks. He should note if a damp proof course is provided immediately under the copings to parapets and whether a second damp proof course is provided at a lower level or not. In this connection for reasons that will be mentioned later the surveyor is advised to measure the heights of parapet walls above roof level. Fortunately it is a fairly simple matter to see if damp proof courses are provided or not to parapet walls and chimney stacks since a thick course of cement pointing will often indicate the presence of a layer of damp-proofing material of some sort and the surveyor can usually judge from the age and quality of the house which type of damp proof course is the more likely to be present. If the surveyor finds one damp proof course at high level to a chimney stack he should not forget to search for another adjacent to the roof line. Sometimes there will be doubt since thin layers of bituminous felt can be incorporated without any trace of thickening in the mortar joint and it is on these occasions that further investigation such as lifting coping stones or raking out joints of brickwork must be carried out so as to be certain.

The reader will by now appreciate that it is only on properties built since the First World War that damp proof courses in these positions are likely to be found at all. Even then it is only in the more expensive property constructed between the two World Wars and only on an uncertain proportion of property constructed after the Second World War that the detailing and position of the damp proof courses in parapets and chimney stacks is likely to be correct. Damp stains will, of course, be noted automatically to chimney stacks and parapet walls but on the former feature these should not be confused with the black deposits from condensate which sometimes builds up on the exterior of stacks and is due to the lack of a lining to a flue used by a solid fuel or gas-fired boiler. Finally the condition of the brickwork itself to stacks and parapets should be noted, together with the pointing, and the surveyor should endeavour to form some idea if both are likely to be resistant to frost and sulphate attack. Any cracks or fractures should be inspected closely, and in particular the writers suggest that the surveyor makes notes of any parts of exposed brickwork in these positions where a coating of rendering is provided. Such rendering is sometimes part of the original construction but on other occasions it will have been provided as a palliative to some defect or other which has appeared in the brickwork. A coating of rendering is often provided to soft red bricks which have decayed badly to chimney stacks and parapets above roof level in Victorian houses built about 1880. This rendering should be regarded closely, its texture noted and the surface tapped to see if it adheres to the brickwork or if it is hollow.

With well-maintained pitched roofs widespread damp penetration through conventional coverings such as slates or tiles is not, fortunately, very usual, even where there is no underfelt. However, the most likely case of some saturation arising is almost certainly to the roofs of houses built between the two World Wars where machine-made tiles are laid on feather-edged boarding. Following heavy rain or snow, particularly when the prevailing wind is driving against one or more roof slopes, the whole of a section of the roof boarding may become saturated and a moisture meter will often record a very high reading over large areas of the roof boarding that is accessible from the roof space. If the surveyor carries out his inspection of the roof space when weather conditions are bad, dampness of this type is, of course, sufficiently obvious for him to recognise a cause that is not likely to be misinterpreted. If, on the other hand, the surveyor carried out his inspection of the roof space in the summer, it is hoped that sufficient discolouring, salt stains and efflorescence will be present to the boarding to make him suspect that all may not be well when winter arrives. The need for an investigation in the roof space with a moisture meter is necessary since, in a number of cases, damp penetration to pitched roofs may not penetrate the ceilings to the top floor of the dwelling house. It is, however, just as necessary to trace damp penetration under these circumstances, even if the householder is not inconvenienced, since saturation to the brickwork of gable walls, to take an obvious example, where such walls support structural timbers will almost certainly lead to the timbers becoming rotted over a period of time so that the structural strength of the roof is seriously weakened.

Generally, however, with pitched roofs, damp patches visible in the top floor bedrooms are usually traceable to leakage at features such as valley and parapet gutters, dormer windows and skylights, but parapet walls and chimney stacks as mentioned, can often provide rather more complicated problems of dampness internally. Signs of dampness in relation to these features can appear in rather odd positions and may sometimes seem to be unrelated to what will finally prove to be the main cause. The surveyor again, however, is warned not to take too much on trust and not to assume necessarily that dampness to chimney breasts, for example, is due to the penetration of rain. Dampness may also be due to condensation from flue gases and this defect will often provide damp stains that appear to be exactly similar to penetrating damp. Bearing in mind the rules set out earlier, the surveyor will try to see if he can find a common pattern with other flues but if a pattern is not present it is possible that a solid fuel or gas-fired boiler is employed for the particular flue that he is looking at, and if the house is of two storeys the signs of dampness may appear solely above first floor level and to one chimney breast only. If in doubt as to the true cause of a patch of dampness such as this, the surveyor might investigate the chimney stack in the roof space and ascertain if the flashings which form the joint between this chimney stack and the main roof coverings are watertight or not. If so, condensation will be the likely cause of the dampness but if not, the other alternative should be sufficiently obvious.

As the surveyor proceeds to the next floor level down, he should be able to exclude the main roof as the cause of further damp penetration unless, of course, the signs are very acute and correspondingly more obvious. It is true that chimney stacks cannot entirely be ruled out as a continuing source of dampness either by penetration or by condensation, but consideration now turns mainly to the penetration of dampness through the enclosing walls of the house. This may be due to the design and construction or the maintenance of the walls not being adequate to keep it at bay, or perhaps due to the fact that walls which would normally be adequate are in an exceptionally exposed position in relation to the prevailing wind. Another reason may be that the enclosing walls as a whole are perfectly suitable for their task of preventing the penetration of dampness, but individual faults in external detailing due to faulty design or construction may be apparent which require to be investigated and repaired. Finally, dampness penetrating the main enclosing walls may be due to a structural fault which has developed since the house was built. Very often the shape and position of the damp patches internally assist the surveyor to diagnose the nature and seriousness of the fault when he comes to peer out of a nearby window or to inspect the exterior of the property at the end of his investigation.

The surveyor will not be likely to see, in the vast majority of cases, an even saturation over the whole of an inner face of wall due to penetrating damp in the general sense. Usually the moisture reaches the inner surface at one or more points and spreads out from these so that in time it may build up a series of rings of efflorescence and discoloration. Penetration will, of course, occur most commonly to walls exposed to the prevailing wind. Even in the wetter parts of this country a rendered 9-inch (229mm) brick wall is often thought to be all that is necessary to maintain a dry inner surface under all normal weather conditions, but in abnormally long seasons it may fail and the Building Research Establishment say that there is a limit to the amount of rain that a solid wall can be expected to keep out. The reason, however, why more excessive damp saturation through the countless numbers of 9-inch (229mm) thick brick walls throughout the country does not occur more frequently, is due in part to the fact that relatively few positions are sufficiently exposed to constant and incessant driving rain. Another reason why damp penetration is not on an excessive scale is due in part to the nature of the walling materials themselves.

It is a common error made by the layman that the more dense and impermeable the face of a brick, the better is the quality of the wall of which it forms part to resist damp penetration from driving rain. In fact, the reverse is the case, for if the brick is porous on the exposed face it will absorb a certain amount of moisture which will then be allowed to dry out. Thus stock bricks which form the walling material to a substantial number of houses show very uneven, fissured and rough faces. The reader might enquire why a brick with an impervious face which does not admit damp in the first instance is not equally acceptable. The answer to this lies in the jointing material of the bricks rather than the composition of the bricks themselves. The Building Research Establishment finds that the most rapid penetration of brick walls by dampness usually takes place through the capillaries between the mortar joints and the bricks and the more impervious the mortar and the surface of the bricks, the more serious this type of penetration is likely to be. In one case investigated by the Establishment, a house built in engineering bricks and dense cement mortar proved to be appallingly damp! Water entering the capillaries between bricks and mortar was passing rapidly from the outer to the inner face without appreciable absorption by either material. Such a defect is a major nuisance from the point of view of dampness in the case of even textured dense engineering bricks of good quality, but where the impervious bricks are of less even quality and are of cheap manufacture, having a hard textured face and a softer interior, moisture penetrating through the joints between the bricks may freeze and expand and blow off the faces.

The same peculiarity applies to stone walls. Plain unrendered stone walls are not always proof against the penetration of rain since the often used long stones which go right through the wall from front to back, called through-bonders, act as channels for water or provide direct capillary routes in the mortar surrounding them. Many stones in rubble walls, and this particularly applies in Scotland and the north of England due to the hard stones employed there in building, are often impervious, and due to their smooth surfacing do not always bond to the mortar employed, leaving slightly open joints which attract water by capillary action to the inner part of the wall.

Damp penetration to house walls is, therefore, likely to be most marked where these are exposed to constant saturation from the prevailing wet wind with no dry intervals which would allow the moisture to evaporate, or to walls with the unsatisfactory characteristics set out in the previous paragraph. Penetration also, however, can occur where evaporation is hampered. Thus water intermittently cascading down the exterior face of a wall to an inner light well may not be allowed to evaporate and may penetrate the wall in consequence.

In the case of cavity walls, the reader will appreciate that damp penetration will more likely be due to faulty construction or detailing than to a fault in the design of the wall itself unless some subsequent structural trouble has caused a defect that allows damp penetration to occur where the cavity wall fails. The most usual trouble from damp penetration to cavity walls can be traced to faulty detailing at openings or to mortar droppings lodged on the wall ties, thereby bridging the two leaves of the wall and transferring dampness to the interior. The surveyor should be able to determine by the location of the damp patches internally which of the two is the most likely cause of the trouble. The Building Research Establishment say that the weakest point at openings is probably the sill in most cases but inadequate vertical damp proof courses at the jambs and defective cavity gutters overhead are also found. Again, if dampness is found at ground floor level, assuming that no basement is provided, it is possible that careless construction has allowed mortar droppings to build up at the base of the wall causing a bridge to form over the damp proof course so that dampness is transferred from the outer to the inner leaf of the house.

If hollow block construction is employed the surveyor should also consider from the pattern of dampness if any defects have occurred due to poor detailing in the use of this material. The Building Research Establishment regard this type of construction as being half-way between solid and cavity construction and provided that the mortar bed does not extend from the outer to the inner face, that is to say that there is no mortar on the webs of the blocks, a fair resistance to rain penetration should be achieved. However, due to the fact that quoins and openings are vulnerable with this type of wall, it can never be regarded as fully resistant to damp penetration as can a soundly constructed cavity wall.

In unheated or neglected premises moisture may distil from the outer leaf to the inner leaf of a cavity wall and so enable dampness to occur without the moisture travelling by the usual capillary paths. This is fairly common with industrial or storage buildings but may occur also to a house where this has been left empty for a long period of time. The diagnosis, however, should not be unduly difficult since, if the surveyor knows that the house has been unoccupied for a very long period and his inspection of the external face of the outer leaf of the cavity walls shows him that the texture and jointing is perfectly satisfactory he is not likely to confuse a defect such as this with damp penetration.

In the case of an external wall that has admitted dampness to the interior face at some time in the past, repair work may have been carried out to provide a dense, near impervious rendering externally. Such a rendering is liable in course of time to crack, possibly as a result of shrinkage and of movement relative to the backing during wetting and drying. Once the rendering is cracked, water running down the face gains entry to the interior of the wall and spreads out from the point of entry to provide a pattern internally that can be extremely mystifying. Due to the fact that very hard dense rendering is well nigh impervious, the water is trapped in the wall so that penetration from a defect such as this can be acute. Dense renderings, which will be referred to again later in this Chapter, accordingly should always be regarded with suspicion. They often prevent moisture from drying out far more effectively than they prevent it from getting in, and in consequence, the surveyor is advised to bear this in mind when he carries out his inspection. Rainwater washes down the outside face of the rendering until it finds a flaw whereupon it is drawn into the interior of the wall by capillary action and even if it does not penetrate to the interior face of the wall to cause damp stains it may well be trapped behind the waterproof coating so that in cold weather it will freeze and expand and cause the waterproof coating to disintegrate at worst or at least to become loose.

A surprising amount of dampness can be introduced to the interior face of a wall by bad detailing and design of externally projecting string courses, band courses or other architectural features. Lack of proper flashings and protection can result in dampness appearing internally, often at a point some way from the original source of the trouble, so that the surveyor has to open windows and take measurements and peer outside, upwards and downwards, to be quite certain that he has traced the true cause of the defect. Sometimes he will only convince himself that the penetration is due to a seemingly minor cause such as this by excluding all other possible reasons.

Excessive saturation from a defective gutter or downpipe particularly if this has been allowed to continue for some time should, it is hoped, be sufficiently obvious by the dark circular or oval stains found to wall and ceiling surfaces internally. Minor holes, however, in part of an external pipe nearest to the wall where, by reason of the difficulty of access for painting, neglect may have caused corrosion, can go undetected for some time and build up into a stain that will not appear in such a typical form. Again, rust in neglected cast iron down pipes will expand and crack the collars, probably at the rear nearest the wall, where the crack cannot be easily seen. If the crack is only a small one saturation will occur gradually over a long period so that it is not until the fault reaches sizeable proportions that a builder is called in to deal with the problem. Here again the signs internally may present a different shape from the usually recognisable staining from a defect in a downpipe or gutter.

The surveyor will, accordingly, note the pattern of dampness on the interior faces of main walls to decide if damp penetration is due to a flaw in the make-up of the wall itself or due to localised defects or a single defect in an isolated position so that this information will assist him in his inspection of the exterior of the dwelling house.

Window openings are a frequent cause of trouble and should always be examined with care if damp penetration is apparent nearby. Window openings to old buildings will have become distorted, allowing moisture to penetrate, and wood frames flush with the external face of walls are prone to rot for this among other reasons. War damaged windows, once shifted by blast and never properly reset, may admit dampness if the gap between reveal and frame remains open or the pointing applied to the gap has shrunk and cracked or even fallen out. However, it is to the heads or sills of windows that most faults are found. Victorian soldier arches in particular admit damp either by poor pointing, poor brickwork or bad detailing or a combination of more than one of these factors, so that dampness penetrates and rots the lintel behind. A moisture meter should be employed and the plaster internally opened up in any cases of doubt. Defective window sills are also a prime cause of damp penetration. Lack of check throats and insufficient nosings will allow damp to trickle back under sills and saturate and penetrate the walling below, while bad detailing and weathering will cause deterioration in a stone sill and rot in a wood sill. The examination of external sills and detailing is a matter to be carried out from the interior, particularly in cases of floors above ground level, since it is well nigh impossible even with the aid of binoculars to examine these adequately from ground level externally. The surveyor should also bear in mind that sills before the Second World War were rarely provided with damp proof courses underneath so that fractures which commonly occur are bound to admit dampness.

The movement and settlement of bay windows away from their parent structures is commonplace, and this often leads to outward bowing of the mullions with gaps forming in the reveals and sills in consequence which lead to subsequent damp penetration. The number of windows in a two or three storey bay window can greatly increase the risk element from damp penetration. Unequal settlement or movement in, for example, a tall three storey Victorian bay window will lead to fractures forming above and below the heads and sills of the three windows of one side of the bay. This in itself can present a risk element of damp penetration which is real enough but it should also be remembered that if the bay window is provided with a flat roof and a surrounding brick parapet, the maximum size of the fracture will, in most cases, be at the top of the wall so that the coping to the parapet becomes immediately suspect. Bay windows, however, are also vulnerable from another result of damp penetration. This is due to the fact that most bay windows, and practically all such windows built before 1914, have wood bressumers formed at the head in order to take the weight of the brickwork over. These must clearly be protected from dampness and the surveyor is advised to inspect not only the roof to the bay, particularly if it is of flat construction, but also the joint formed between the structure of the bay window itself and the main structure.

It is not likely that the surveyor will, on an internal inspection, be able to see much of any bond timbers, beams or other timber which form an integral part of the structure. If the house is of such construction that timber forms a structural element in the main enclosing walls the surveyor will not be able to determine a great deal from his inspection of the interior until he carries out his inspection of the exterior of the property. Even then it may be necessary for him to return to verify from his notes the position of any damp stains near parts of the structure that may be composed of timber. In certain cases where damp stains appear to be near some crucial part of the walling, part of which is composed of timber, the surveyor may wish to obtain further instructions from his client in order to open up and inspect the wall by stripping the internal plaster.

As the surveyor proceeds through the interior of the body of the house, it should become clear to him whether condensation is one of the primary causes of dampness or not. Usually if this is the case, the whole area of the walls, ceiling or floor is affected in contrast to the patchiness which results from rain penetration or rising dampness. Sometimes condensation will occur as a result of distillation of moisture from a warm moist room to cooler rooms adjoining and sometimes as a result of the temperature and humidity of the air in the room rising while the surfaces of the walls, ceiling and floor remain at a lower temperature. The condensed moisture is often most noticeable where there is a big heat capacity and an impervious surface, for example on painted, unlined walls or on solid floors with a heat conducting covering. Sometimes, however, condensation is found in patches rather than over large areas and this is where diagnosis can become a difficult problem. Local variations in the texture of wall and ceiling surfaces may occasionally produce what appears to be a patchy condensation since, when an absorbent plaster becomes cracked, areas are commonly repaired with a hard faced impervious plaster. By far the most common cause, however, is the contamination of the plaster by hygroscopic salts. These salts extract moisture from the air at a humidity below that required for condensation on uncontaminated surfaces and the importance of this factor which affords at one and the same time an aid and a puzzle to diagnosis, merits some explanation at this stage.

Among the hygroscopic substances encountered in buildings are nitrates, usually derived from the soil and in certain salts produced by the interaction of ammonia and sulphur oxides present in the condensate from flue gases. However, much the most frequently occurring substances are chlorides such as common salt (sodium chloride) and such chlorides have usually been brought into a building in the sea sand originally used for the undercoat plaster and mortars. Chlorides are, however, often associated with nitrates in rising dampness. Where hygroscopic salts have been introduced into a building in a widely dispersed state during construction, for example, as sea salt in the undercoat plaster and mortar, they rarely remain uniformly distributed for very long since as the moisture introduced during construction dries out, these salts become concentrated more or less unevenly on the surface. In this way, a trace of sea salt in building sand can lead to patches of plaster having 1 per cent or more of chlorides present in the surface layers. The consequences are, therefore, that patches of plaster containing these hygroscopic salts become damp when the air is humid but not so humid as to cause normal condensation. These conditions are frequently encountered just before rain and often the questioning of a reliable witness as to when such dampness appears is the only method of ascertaining the true cause of the trouble.

Persistent dampness from other causes can sometimes aggravate the problem of hygroscopic salts. When moisture is travelling to the inner surface of a building and evaporating there, it usually carries with it traces of soluble salts. In time, as we have said, these salts become concentrated in the surface layers. Most salts crystallise out as an efflorescence but the hygroscopic chlorides and nitrates stay in the plaster unless the atmosphere is abnormally dry. If the movement and evaporation of the moisture go on long enough, the concentration of chlorides and nitrates may become sufficient to cause dampness by absorption of moisture from the air. Such dampness will persist even after the original defect causing the flow of moisture has been remedied. Accordingly the surveyor is recommended to note down all traces of plaster affected by hygroscopic salts and to try to decide at the end of his inspection if replacement of the plaster

577

constitutes a sufficient repair or if there are deeper causes which still need remedy.

As he carries out his investigation of the rooms at each floor level throughout the house the surveyor will try to ascertain with the help of his moisture meter the different types of dampness observed from stains and, where possible, form some opinion as to the cause. If the dwelling house presents a particularly obstinate problem from the point of view of condensation, the surveyor may have to reassure himself more than once by chipping small sections of the plaster away in order to get true readings against the plaster and brickwork below the surface to ensure that his diagnosis is the correct one.

As the surveyor draws near to ground floor and basement level, if there is one, he will, of course, be on the look-out for signs of rising dampness. Before he leaves the interior of the house he should have a pretty good idea from the age of the structure and the presence or otherwise of any damp stains whether the house is likely to have a damp proof course or not. If a damp proof course is provided and the house has no basement the surveyor is advised to note down the various changes in internal ground floor levels so that he can relate these to the exterior ground level surrounding the house. If necessary, the difference between the interior ground floor levels and the exterior ground levels can best be noted by sketches made of each elevation so that the surveyor can judge if the damp proof course is in an effective position on all sides of the house. Often a sloping site will have confused the original builder to such an extent that although the damp proof course is in a satisfactory position at one corner it may, due to the rise in the ground level, be at earth level or in some cases lower, at the opposite corner. During his inspection of the interior the surveyor will make a note of any damp stains at ground floor level that may alert him when he carries out his external inspection as to whether there are any external factors that might tend to rob the damp proof course of its efficiency, such as earth banked against a wall or the provision of paving above the level of the damp proof course which may transmit moisture to the interior face of the wall. Similarly the surveyor will note if rising dampness has occurred from internal causes due to the damp proof course having been bridged by floor screeds or rendering.

The effects of rising damp as seen in many old buildings that lack a damp proof course can take various forms. Usually, there is a fairly regular line of efflorescence which may be several feet above the internal floor level. Below that line the wall is discoloured and there is a general darkening and patchiness and there may in addition be mould growth, loose wallpaper and other signs. Some of the salts brought up from the ground, principally the chlorides and nitrates will be hygroscopic and these will probably have become concentrated in sufficient quantity to cause dampness by extraction of moisture in the air on humid days as previously described. The surveyor should note, however, that the signs of dampness due to the total absence of a damp proof course may be regular in appearance and may be different to the signs where dampness is due to a damp proof course being bridged as the effect in the latter case is likely to be much less regular in appearance. The shape and extent of the affected area usually gives a clue as to the location of the fault, but it would be unwise to be too dogmatic about this since even the total absence of a damp proof course can lead to patchiness.

The surveyor will take particular pains in the case of basements to discover what measures have been taken to prevent rising dampness. In older buildings it will often become all too painfully clear that little, if any, measures have been taken to prevent dampness from the soil penetrating the basement walls and rising sometimes to the ends of the ground floor joists. Fortunately, however, in most older basement buildings, the ends of the ground floor joists are clear of the rising dampness by a substantial margin and the surveyor normally has only the question of the dampness to the basement flooring to consider and the lower section of the walls. Usually, due to the lack of ventilation, a timber basement floor in an older building cannot be saved, but nevertheless, proper investigation with a moisture meter and notes and sketches as to the type of construction to each elevation and investigations, if necessary, by excavation of the exterior soil or paving to ascertain if a vertical damp proof course is provided will be necessary to obtain a true picture of the basement construction.

Ground moisture rising in solid floors is common. Usually this can be attributed to poor design or by the original builders taking a chance on a site reputed to be dry. Concrete on hard core is not a complete barrier to moisture even when the concrete has an integral waterproofer added. The passage of water as liquid may be prevented but moisture can still reach the top of the concrete as vapour and condense at that level if an impervious finish such as linoleum covers the surface so that eventually the linoleum may rot. Certain finishes such as pitch and mastic asphalt form a damp proof membrane in themselves but where neither of these or some similar membrane is present, some rising damp must be expected. Concrete floor and ceramic tiled floors are usually unharmed by the small amount of moisture that gets through to the surface but stuck down finishes such as rubber and linoleum may be loosened and timber as well as linoleum may rot. No type of timber forms in itself an impervious covering but, if exposed to the air, timber can often lose water by evaporation from the top surface as it gains water from below. Because of this a moisture content conducive to rotting, that is to say in excess of 20 per cent, may be obtained only where the timber itself is covered with an impervious membrane. Plastic tiles on concrete will often give satisfactory service without a damp proof membrane if the site is dry, but on wet sites a loss of adhesion and a milky exudation from the joints can occur.

With suspended ground floors there is normally little attempt made to prevent the rise of ground moisture to the surface of the site concrete or its equivalent. To avoid distillation of this moisture from the concrete to the suspended floor and thence to the underside of an impervious covering such as linoleum, the space between the floor and the site concrete must be ventilated by a minimum opening of $1\frac{1}{2}$ square inches (970mm^2) for every foot (300mm) of external wall. Where dampness has occurred, probably discovered by rot subsequently appearing in the timbers, it will usually be found either that the openings originally provided were not up to the recommended minimum, or that they have been partially covered. Occasionally poor distribution of air bricks may have left stagnant areas, particularly in the vicinity of solid hearths or solid floors to adjoining rooms.

Finally, on his internal inspection of the building, the surveyor will endeavour to see if any dampness has been introduced by other extraneous causes. He will often find that a houseproud occupier who frequently washes down walls and floors omits to notice water that becomes entrapped under linoleum laid on a boarded solid floor. Water running through cracks or joints in an impervious floor covering spreads out underneath and may reach areas where evaporation is impossible or at the best, very slow. Prolonged dampness in this manner has been known to cause rotting of floorboards in the vicinity, for example, of sinks. Again, the surveyor will note particularly if dampness is due to any leaks from the plumbing system and this is often more easy to write about than to see as many pipes are chased and buried in walls. A persistent slow leak from a weeping joint can sometimes give rise to effects similar to rain penetration. The surveyor must also, however, be wary of assuming that dampness round a pipe is necessarily a sign that a leak has developed. Many cold water pipes in a building collect dense moisture on their surfaces and this can often accumulate so that water streams down the exterior of the pipe. Condensation is often particularly noticeable on rising mains which bring cold water into the building.

When the surveyor commences his inspection of the exterior of the property, he will already have a good deal of information from his inspection of the interior which will enable him to pay particular attention to specific parts of the external structure. So far as the roof is concerned, by the time the surveyor commences his inspection of the exterior, the main problems should have already been resolved, since in the case of a tall property the chances are that the surveyor will have completed a satisfactory inspection from the facilities provided at roof level and from adjacent advantage points which can enable him to make a thorough examination. In the case of smaller properties the surveyor will again, by this time, know what steps he has to take, since in the case of a small Georgian terraced house with parapet walls at the front and rear he will have realised that there is no practicable alternative to the lack of a roof access roof hatch but to order a builder to attend with ladders. In the case of two-storey houses with simple pitched roofs built since the First World War, it is probably sufficient for the surveyor to examine the roof slopes from the ground. In such a case the surveyor will have gleaned what information he can with relation to damp penetration and the condition of the roof slopes from the interior of the roof space but nevertheless he will find a pair of binoculars extremely useful in examining the exterior roof slopes from ground level.

So far as the enclosing walls of the property are concerned the writers prefer to commence an external inspection by starting with the rear elevation and then carrying out inspections of the sides of the house before completing the inspection at the front elevation. Most of the plumbing is usually concentrated at the rear and sides of the house and any neglect is also more commonly found at the rear of the property than at the front. The aspect of the building however, and the direction of its main exposure to driving rain is important, and the surveyor may like to examine the exposed faces first as an alternative to this suggestion. Such a procedure is worth following particularly in the case of an early oak framed building, the condition of which depends entirely on its exposure to hot sun in addition to rain. If protected from both of these enemies a timber building will last as long as a comparable structure of stone or brick. In general, and there will be exceptions to this, the north side rarely gets any sunshine and seldom any driving rain and in almost every case the timbers of this side of the house will be found to be the original and still sound. The east face of the building does not suffer a great deal from exposure to sun or rain as the morning sun is seldom strong and rain from the east is infrequent and when it does come it is usually a gentle drizzle with little wind behind it. The south face is the one that suffers more than any other. The sun blazing upon it throughout the hottest part of the summer causes the wood to shrink and joints to open. The heavy rains from the south and south-west then drive into the cracks and set up rot in the

581

woodwork. Still more damage is caused by the rain running down the uprights of the frame to the sill and then being drawn by capillary attraction into the mortice holes, where it rots the tenons and the posts from the bottom upwards. The west face suffers in the same way but to a lesser degree. This suffers more than the east face because it gets more driving rain and because the westerly sun on a summer's day is hotter than the morning sun.

During his inspection of a half-timbered property the surveyor is likely to learn a good deal from the most neglected elevation as here the detailing of the timber and plaster will tell him something about the construction. There is a regrettable tendency in this present age to react with such enthusiasm to a half-timbered structure so as to make it thoroughly distinctive by treating exposed woodwork with a dark preservative whereas the original oak was probably lime-washed. Popular enthusiasm for timber framed buildings has now reached the stage where the timber must be exposed externally at all costs and any plaster coating is often ruthlessly stripped away on the grounds that this conceals the historical structure below. In fact the reverse is often the case, since half-timbered work was not always built for display and the coating of plaster was a normal procedure with many of the later ordinary timber framed dwellings throughout the country. Inspection of the faces of the exposed timbers should tell the surveyor if there are any nail holes which might indicate that lathing has been stripped.

Examination of exterior brickwork will tell the surveyor a good deal when his inspection is taken in conjunction with his existing notes relating to the interior. The types of facing brickwork used for each elevation, their texture and porosity having regard to the aspect of the particular wall under consideration can be noted, and in particular the type and nature of the pointing used together with the condition of the joints can be tested. It is suggested that the surveyor, with the aid of his binoculars, starts his examination at the top of each elevation and works methodically to the bottom compiling notes as he goes so that each elevation is dealt with before he commences another. There are times, of course, when this pattern must be disrupted while other information is ascertained, but the writers have found from experience that this is probably the best method. During such inspections the surveyor will scrutinise chimney stacks, copings and parapet walls and make notes accordingly. The rectangular shape of Georgian property should not lead to undue difficulty in ascertaining how the enclosing walls meet the roof structure but in the case of Victorian property the surveyor has to exercise some care since often gables which look impressive as part of the main roof structure are designed simply for display with little cheeks of their own behind, and hidden gutters to drain them which no one would expect to find.

As the surveyor steadily lowers his binoculars down a particular elevation he will examine plumbing details. It is suggested that he takes particular interest when looking at complicated junctions of gutters and downpipes where two different levels meet or an innocuous looking hopper head which he knows from inspection internally must take the discharge from several fittings as well as that from a gutter since this may be a cause of dampness. Very often external examination in a case such as this is more than sufficient to clear up a puzzling damp stain internally. The points where gutters behind parapet walls discharge into rainwater hopper heads is often where trouble begins and the surveyor should see if any signs of damp streaks on the faces on the brick walls below can be observed. The surveyor can note if down pipes are fixed clear of wall faces by means of holder-bats. High sections of rainwater pipes are difficult to maintain on tall buildings and the pipes should project into their respective collars to an extent of only half the depth. Cast iron pipes can only be renewed, not repaired, and if the joints are not too tight, renewal is much easier.

External claddings, such as tile hanging, will be observed together with the detailing and return ends, and window openings will also require scrutiny from the exterior since cracks and distortion above the heads of lintels or below the window sills may be hidden from the surveyor when he examines window openings from the interior. Minor roofs are also worthy of examination for the same reason since inefficient copings which cause stains to the brickwork underneath can often be noted more readily from ground level than by peering over the edge of the coping itself. So far as houses with pitched roofs are concerned the surveyor will decide whether or not it is necessary for him to erect ladders in order to inspect the eaves gutters. Much will depend on the age of the gutters themselves but with Ogee gutters of some age where the backs are probably rusted and in danger of fracturing, care is obviously desirable. Again, early misshapen zinc or soft metal gutters are worthy of inspection from close range.

Projections to main walls consisting of the inserted stone band courses of Georgian times or the projecting cut bricks of Victorian times were often originally provided with small protective lead aprons so that there was no risk of damp penetration. Often, however, the lead work has been removed and moisture has penetrated underneath, leading to deterioration of the projecting feature in a position that cannot be easily seen. Elsewhere, recesses in brickwork can hide downpipes or overflows and the surveyor must use his knowledge of what has been seen internally to enable him to search for the right answer externally. Green stains to external brickwork will, of course, provide a warning sign, but often a darker patch in the texture of the brickwork is the only sign that the surveyor may observe of continual saturation. The condition of the paintwork to wood, stone and metal surfaces should also be noted. This may be a pointer to certain defects which may have been observed elsewhere such as those to the timber of window frames and sills and where the surveyor will have tested with a probe any woodwork which is bare of paint to see if it is sound or whether it is spongy with dampness or alternatively brittle with dry rot.

The surveyor's inspection of the main walls at the base near the ground level will be one of the most important aspects of his investigation. He will verify from his knowledge from the interior of the house what he expects to find by the way of a damp proof course and he will relate this to the internal floor levels measured earlier in his inspection. While it may be possible in most cases to decide as to the measures required to combat rising dampness without the need for further investigation, there are cases where the surveyor will wish to seek permission to open up a section of a wall to investigate the nature and condition of the damp proof course provided. In some cases, the age of the structure and the presence of much rising dampness internally, showing as a fairly regular horizontal pattern, will enable the surveyor to conclude that no damp proof course is provided at all, but in some cases, where the internal pattern is patchy, giving no sign of dampness at one point and heavy saturation at another, the surveyor may wish to investigate the matter more fully. Often, of course, a patchy pattern of this nature has an immediate external cause such as earth built up against the exterior of the wall or a defective pipe near the base of the wall. The remedies here are comparatively simple but in other cases the solution may be a more complex one. The side access paths of large Victorian houses, for example, often incorporate two or more flights of steps, a number of changes of level, and perhaps a low range of brick outbuildings constructed against the side wall. The line of the damp proof course will need to be carefully traced since often it may be bridged at one or more points. Again, the head of a short flight of steps to the side elevation will often not only bridge the damp proof course but will also meet a gulley at the top, which may be defective, so that intense saturation in a basement room internally may be due to heavy penetrating dampness from two sources. It is therefore desirable for the surveyor to note down every part where the damp proof course is inefficient, even to the traditional bridge formed by the Edwardian cement plinth at the base of the main wall. This is not likely to be a serious matter in a property of this age but there are cases in modern construction where a saturated cement plinth bridging a damp proof course can have far reaching consequences. Although it should be easier with more modern property for the line of the damp proof course to be traced, experience has shown that the likelihood of the damp proof course being bridged by a do-it-yourself patio or other structure is more pronounced. This can be rather more serious with modern houses since any defect at the base of a cavity wall which allows moisture to penetrate and set up dry rot in the less seasoned timbers of the present-day presents, in some ways, a larger risk element than when the older seasoned timbers of earlier houses are subjected to the same circumstances.

Finally, in his inspection the surveyor may need to examine the surroundings of the dwelling house to see if there are ways in which dampness can be introduced to the structure from extraneous causes. These may be many and varied and sometimes rather unusual so that it is extremely easy to miss some of the causes, even when the manifestations are obvious. Perhaps the most common example is where a brick wall is built up against the main wall of the dwelling house without a vertical damp proof course so that moisture penetrates the interior of the house. Another example may be due to the run off from the wide eaves of the thatched roof of a house where no gutter is provided so that moisture continually falls onto the ground near the base of the main walls which, having no damp proof course, may be susceptible to seepage from this source. An odd example is where a water butt placed at the corner of a dwelling house developed a leak at the rear and caused an impressive damp stain in a very short time.

Having completed his investigation of the building as a whole, the surveyor will now have identified and diagnosed to the best of his ability the various types of dampness that he has seen and he will now proceed to deal with them as specific problems of repair. We will accordingly now pass to the consideration of the various types of dampness and the remedies available for each.

PENETRATING DAMPNESS

We are informed, says the Building Research Establishment, that in Spain, the rain falls mainly on the plain. In Britain, however, the converse of this statement is more clearly true. The map of annual rainfall resembles closely one showing the elevation of the ground above the sea, with the contour lines enclosing dark blue regions of high rainfall following the contour lines enclosing the brown hilly areas.

DAMPNESS

This simple picture, however, says the Establishment, is distorted by a number of factors. By the distance from the sea, by the shape of the hills and their orientation with respect to the prevailing winds, and above all by the fact that most rain-bearing winds blow from roughly south and north-west directions so that other things being equal, the western parts of the country get much more rain. Another factor is that in the rainier parts of the country it also rains for a longer time than in the drier parts. Around London on average it is raining for 5 per cent of the time; on the western coast of England and Wales this figure rises to 7 or 8 per cent and in hilly districts to over 10 per cent. In north-west Scotland the proportion is even higher, being more than 15 per cent over a considerable area. It would seem therefore that from considerations of rainfall alone, it would be expected that the buildings in the west of England would experience the most trouble from rain penetration. However, rain does not necessarily wet walls in the absence of wind. It is the combination of both rain and wind that gives "driving rain", that is to say, rain driven along at an angle to the vertical, so that it strikes against vertical surfaces. Maps of average wind speed show that the highest winds occur near the coast and especially near west coasts. Inland regions are relatively sheltered but with local increases in wind speed or hills, variations away from the coast line can occur. The measurements made by the Building Research Establishment, using rain gauges set in the walls of buildings, have shown that the amount of rain driven on to a wall is directly proportional to the product of the rainfall on the ground and the wind speed during the period of rainfall. In many parts of the country, most rain will fall with winds blowing from directions between south and west or north-west but this is far from true in places near the east coast of Britain. Thus, while on the west coast it may generally be desirable to pay particular attention to making the walls facing west weather-tight, since the north walls may rarely get wetted, in some eastern districts the north walls may be the ones that suffer most severely from the elements.

The severity of exposure often varies from place to place on a building, and can even vary in intensity on the same wall. This may be due to the fact that part of the wall is sheltered by other buildings or by projections from the wall, but even on a freely exposed wall face there may be significant differences, since as the wind blows past the building the air is deflected from its normal course and is speeded up, particularly around corners and over cornices, where its speed may be twice that of the undisturbed wind. The rainfall intensity is increased correspondingly so that in cases such as this the driving rain index is abnormally high. While this need not affect

586

the general assessment of the exposure of the building as a whole, nevertheless the possibility that certain parts of the structure may be exposed to abnormal conditions in this way is a matter that should cause the surveyor to consider if there are any weaknesses at such points that would make them vulnerable to such abnormal conditions.

One of the main factors as we have seen, that enables 9-inch (229mm) plain unrendered brick walls in certain situations to remain dry year by year is that rainwater absorbed by the porous materials in the construction is removed mainly by natural evaporation from the outside surfaces. The significant climatic influences are solar radiation, wind speed and atmospheric humidity. With such an infinite variety of exposures it is not possible to make precise estimates of evaporation rates from walls but the Building Research Establishment say that in the wetter districts evaporation rates are probably about half those found in the drier districts of south-east England. The net effect, therefore, is that the risk of rain penetration in regions of high driving rain is intensified since walls in these districts have less chance of drying out between spells of rainfall. It is clear that when assessing exposure to a building the surveyor should consider the question of the amount of driving rain to be expected to walls to be the major factor in determining rain penetration.

We will, accordingly, now turn to the question of the repair and maintenance of exposed wall surfaces where these are affected by penetrating dampness and it is both convenient and logical to start by considering the areas at the top of the building since these not only make a convenient starting point for descriptive purposes, but are also in the positions where the maximum exposure to the elements is usually to be expected.

Penetrating Dampness in Relation to Parapet Walls and Chimney Stacks

The Building Research Establishment indicate that according to enquiries they have received, defects are more common in parapet walls than in most other parts of buildings. This is due to the fact that parapets are situated above roof level and are exposed to the weather on all three faces.

Parapet walls, if of porous materials, are likely to become much wetter than other parts of the structure and if water is allowed to drain downwards from the parapet it will travel to the interior of the building by any path open to it. For this reason it is often easier to cure rising damp at the base of a wall than penetrating damp through a parapet, and it should be emphasised that the inclusion of a single damp proof course under the coping of a parapet wall does not necessarily eliminate the need for a further damp proof course at roof level. The first damp proof course will probably provide sufficient protection to prevent failure due to sulphate attack and frost action, but will not keep the parapet sufficiently dry to prevent water penetration into the building. Accordingly, two damp proof courses are recommended, unless the parapet is under 12 inches (305mm) in height and built of bricks of high frost resistance and low sulphate content under which circumstances the upper damp proof course may be omitted.

The same comments in general apply to chimney stacks as to parapet walls. Chimney stacks, like parapet walls as stated before, act as funnels in that they introduce moisture to a house structure unless they are constructed and designed with care and provided with two damp proof courses in the same manner as parapet walls. Although the flaunching to chimney stacks is not as effective as the impervious copings normally provided to parapet walls, and therefore provides a greater risk of damp penetration and sulphate attack, the greater height of the chimney stack probably allows for more drying action to take place within the brickwork so that penetration is not quite so likely as in the case of a low badly designed parapet wall. Against this, however, is the fact that driving rain will penetrate the four sides of a chimney stack and introduce moisture through the sides which will, if the bricks are unsuitable, by-pass the soakers and flashings or cement fillets, causing damp stains to appear in the structure below. One of the main reasons why dampness introduced through chimney stacks and parapet walls is dangerous is, of course, that the brickwork below is often in close proximity to roof timbers. Although with most older properties there is sufficient ventilation through gaps in the tiles or slates of a roof structure to provide sufficient air changes so that the timbers, although badly stained and soft in instances of bad saturation, nevertheless have a good chance of surviving free of an attack of dry rot, in some circumstances, however, where timber is pressed tight against damp brickwork, the risk is correspondingly greater. Perhaps, however, the greatest risk and one of the chief problems in this particular field is that badly formed parapet walls surrounding the flat roofs of domestic buildings may introduce moisture into the joist ends of the roof structure which are built into the brickwork below the parapet. In cases such as this the risk of dry rot where there is damp penetration is very high indeed since ventilation is impossible and the timbers are surrounded and closely pressed against brickwork on every side including the end grain. In a similar matter parapet walls above Victorian bay windows and openings may, if not built to correct principles, introduce moisture into the tops, sides or ends of bond timbers or bressumers with the same danger.

The surveyor will have during his investigation considered the height, position and construction of chimney stacks and parapet walls and will have ascertained by investigation if damp proof courses are provided or not. He will also have determined whether the brickwork is sound enough to withstand penetrating dampness to both exposed sides, and will have formed an opinion as to the resistance of the bricks and of the pointing to sulphate attack. The surveyor will also examine the coping and decide if this has adequate check throats and is likely to present a permanent and impervious surface irrespective of the question of the damp proof course below it. The reason for this is, of course, that the coping must stand up to a considerable amount of wear over the years and not disintegrate under driving rain and frost action. In the case of old brickwork the surveyor will be able to form a pretty accurate diagnosis of what repairs are necessary but in the case of recent or fairly new brickwork to domestic property, the surveyor should try to determine if the bricks are of low sulphate content and high frost resistance, although the writers need hardly trouble to add that this is by no means invariably an easy matter and may involve tests.

The surveyor will often find that in an attempt to repair chimney stacks and parapet walls that have no damp proof courses and are composed of bad bricks or which have been subject to structural faults leading to fractures, that both the chimney stacks and parapet walls are completely encased in cement rendering. This can never be considered an effective method of repair as a long-term solution. Cracks which will inevitably appear sooner by reason of shrinkage, or later with thermal changes, or by movement in the structure or from other causes will introduce moisture which will not be evident for some time but will finally appear in the form of fractures to the exterior in the familiar pattern of sulphate attack. An impervious dense rendering, it is sometimes argued, will keep water clear from the brickwork underneath but it will, in fact, make matters worse, as water penetrating the crack that will inevitably appear at a weak point, will be bottled up inside with no means of escape so that ultimately it will cause a more dramatic defect than if the rendering were porous. If, on the other hand, the rendering is porous, it defeats the purpose of its being applied to the brickwork in the first case as it merely provides a further permeable outer skin to the bricks in the form of a face that is rather too easily detachable under certain conditions.

One of the main reasons why parapets and chimney stacks are so difficult to protect adequately from water penetration is that since they are formed at the top of the building, they are more naturally prone to fractures and distortions that occur from structural faults developing below. The main walls at the base of a dwelling house are rigid under most circumstances but even the smallest movement or settlement will work its way up the structure to finally appear in the form of a fracture at parapet or chimney stack level. Even the smallest amount of movement that is perfectly acceptable and indeed reasonable in an old house will cause cracking to brick parapets and chimney stacks which, if the house is three or more storeys in height may not even be visible to the surveyor with his naked eye from ground level. The central fracture that appears in a great number of party chimney stacks and the gaps formed in brick on edge or stone copings as a result of fractures in the brick parapets below are all too typical. When the surveyor examines his notes, therefore, and considers the question of how to repair chimney stacks or parapet walls that are encased in rendering, some or all of which may have proved to be defective, he should remember that a combination of Portland cement, soluble sulphate salts and water leads inevitably to sulphate attack. Where the surveyor suspects that the familiar horizontal cracking to rendering is as a result of this defect he would be most unwise to contemplate merely renewing the rendering since in doing so it would be extremely likely that the same process of disintegration would continue. It should be emphasised, however, that the three contributory factors mentioned earlier are necessary for sulphate attack which cannot occur in the absence of one of them. Thus if the surveyor is satisfied that no damp penetration is possible, or that soluble sulphates are not present in the particular bricks employed, or alternatively that the amount of Portland cement to be used in a new mix will be small, he may feel that sulphate attack could be prevented. In actual fact where prevention is possible to most other parts of the structure, the removal of the main cause of sulphate attack, which is continual damp penetration, is extremely difficult to parapets and chimney stacks.

Sulphate attack may occur to mortar joints of brickwork where no rendering is employed due to a combination of the three same circumstances. The most troublesome aspect of this is that sulphate attack causes expansion of the mortar joints so that if this occurs on one side of a stack or parapet with continual saturation the brickwork will bend away towards the dry side, and the surveyor must decide whether the stability of the brickwork is affected to such an extent that rebuilding is necessary or whether it is possible to arrest the continuing process of disintegration from sulphate attack by preventing further damp penetration. It is the latter problem that presents the most risk and difficulty.

Sulphate attack should be distinguished from mere frost action, which is more likely to arise with new work or with features which became saturated but because the house was built some time ago (very often before 1914) no Portland cement was used in the mortar for brickwork. We have already referred to the Victorian red brick which, due to its poor manufacture, is vulnerable to frost action and the reader will be familiar with the badly worn red brick walls and chimney stacks which occur throughout the length and breadth of the country due to frost action. Even under circumstances such as this where the bricks may not necessarily have a high sulphate content, rendering is a difficult remedy to apply as the bricks are worn down to a soft and powdery surface which forms a poor base for rendering. It is sometimes possible by forming a basework of expanded metal secured to the brickwork to ensure a longer life for the rendering but this is an unpredictable method and the surveyor cannot guarantee an indefinite length of life by this repair.

It is for all the reasons set out above that the writers feel that the efficient and long-term repair of saturated brick parapet walls and chimney stacks which are affected by structural faults or are the subject of poor design or are composed of poor or unsuitable materials can only be to rebuild them in whole or in part to modern principles using bricks of good quality, of even texture and low sulphate content and of high frost resistance with an appropriate pointing. With the reduction in the use of solid fuel heating appliances and the increasing adoption of central heating there is not always, of course, a need to retain chimney stacks. If they can be abandoned so much the better, but it is far preferable in these circumstances to take the stack down to a point below roof covering level and to make out the roof rather than merely reduce the stack height by a few feet and to cap it off. Provided flues are ventilated in the side near the top, even if it is only into the roof space the former method eliminates all problems for ever more to do with flashings, gutters or dampness penetrating through the brickwork. It is unfortunate that parapet walls cannot be dealt with in a similar way more often, but it is not usually possible to do so because of room height and window head difficulties. In the circumstances and for stacks which have to be retained it does not appear that any palliative attempts at waterproof facings or other short cuts are preferable to rebuilding except as short-term repairs only and even then the money spent may be wasted. In dealing with the repair work in a fundamental way such as this the detailing and the design with particular reference to damp proof courses can be worked out with care and the materials chosen according to their suitability for exposed positions and damp and frost resistance. Most clay bricks contain soluble sulphate salts and although engineering bricks generally have a lower content the surveyor may well recoil with good reason from using engineering bricks in exposed positions such as this. The brick manufacturers however, will advise on the best type of bricks in accordance with B.S.3921:1965 to employ in such situations, and the surveyor should be able to provide himself with a range of choice so that a selection can be made most nearly matching the original; not, it must be emphasised in surface colouring alone, but more properly in the whole basic characteristic and texture of the brick.

For a chimney stack at or near the ridge of a pitched roof and extending only very slightly above it, good weather protection at the top is sufficient in all but the most exposed positions to ensure that the stack is satisfactory. When the exposed part of the stack is more than a few feet high however, a damp proof course is desirable where the stack emerges from the roof. In all other cases damp proof courses are one of the most important elements, if not the most important, to chimney stacks and parapet walls, and it is necessary now to discuss the essential points of such damp proof courses. It should be emphasised however, that this section is restricted to the consideration of chimney stacks and parapet walls alone. Damp proof courses for other parts of the structure are chosen from materials that have different characteristics but which are more suitable for the particular case under consideration.

Essential points in the design of damp proof courses
for parapets and chimney stacks

(1) The material used must form a continuous impervious membrane. A flexible material such as metal, bituminous felt or asphalt is to be preferred over a rigid material in order to avoid damage as the result of thermal movement or other differential movement. Any joints in the damp proof course must be well lapped and sealed or in the case of metals, welted. Slates, engineering bricks or a layer of waterproof cement are not suitable as damp proof courses in parapets or stacks.

(2) The roof covering for a flat roof and the damp proof course of an adjacent parapet wall must form an uninterrupted barrier to moisture either with the continuous use of the same material without a joint, or by flashing the damp proof course over the roof covering. A damp proof course should lap in the same way over the edge of a concealed gutter to a pitched roof hidden behind a parapet.

(3) The damp proof course must extend through the full thickness of the wall including the pointing, applied rendering or other facing materials, or be continued by a metal flashing. The damp

proof course should not finish flush with the wall face for solid or rendered work since water running down the surface from above may seep in below the level of the damp proof course. Thus the damp proof course itself, if of metal, should project, or a metal flashing should be inserted immediately below it. For cavity construction the damp proof course should continue through the thickness of the whole wall including the inner and external leaves and the cavity between.

The damp proof course in a cavity parapet wall should slope across the cavity from the outside leaf to the roofside leaf so as to drain the cavity towards the roof covering. The British Standard Code of Practice C.P.144 of 1968 for bitumen-felt roof coverings recommends the provision of a slate bridging piece to support the felt within the cavity. Open vertical joints should be left above the damp proof course to allow for drainage.

Materials for damp proof courses are listed in British Standard 743 of 1970 and are grouped under three headings: Flexible, Semi-Rigid or Rigid Units. The first category includes such materials as metal, bitumen and polythene sheetings, the second category consists only of mastic asphalt, while the third category includes slates and bricks bedded in cement mortar. Flexible sheet materials with sealed joints are necessary for parapet walls and chimney stacks and although mastic asphalt comes under the semi-rigid classification, its use for a damp proof course to parapet walls as an extension of the roofing asphalt is commonplace and thus merits its inclusion under this section of the Chapter. The flexible materials suitable for damp proof courses to parapets and chimney stacks are as follows:

(a) *Lead*

Lead forms one of the best types of flexible damp proof courses available. It can be dressed to complex shapes, will accommodate a good deal of movement and is impervious and highly resistant to sliding. In order to resist the downwards pressure of water, however slight, in the case of parapets and chimney stacks, joints to lead sheeting should be welted. Lead is resistant to atmospheric corrosion and although fresh lime or Portland cement mortar can cause corrosion, this can be avoided by protecting the metal by a coating of bitumen or bitumen paint of heavy consistency. The mortar bed on which the lead is to be laid is first given an application of paint and the underside of the lead before laying is then coated while the top surface is coated once the lead is in place.

Other excellent damp proof courses are provided by the various proprietary products which consist of lead sheet sandwiched between layers of fabric reinforced bitumen.

(b) *Copper*

Copper is impervious to moisture, is flexible and has a high tensile strength. It will withstand distortion caused by moderate settlements, is not liable to extrusion under heavy pressure and has a moderate resistance to sliding. In the case of damp proof courses to chimney stacks and parapet walls, the joints between the copper sheets should be welted. Copper is not affected by contact with mortars and does not therefore require any protective coating, but it should be remembered that some risk of staining is always present when copper is employed as a damp proof course, particularly where the walls are faced in stone.

(c) *Bitumen Damp Proof Courses*

These are classified in several types, varying from those with a hessian base to those of fibre, felt and asbestos base, with and without a core of lead sheeting. Bitumen damp proof courses are flexible and impervious to moisture. They should withstand distortion caused by moderate settlements but can extrude under heavy pressure. Bitumen damp proof courses offer little resistance to sliding but on the other hand they should be impervious when given 4-inch (102mm) laps sealed with bitumen.

It is interesting that B.S.743 of 1970 says that the efficiency of a bitumen damp proof course with a hessian or fibre base is not impaired should the hessian or felt subsequently decay provided that the bitumen itself remains undisturbed.

(d) *Polythene*

Polythene sheet is flexible, impervious to moisture and has a moderate resistance to sliding. It should be laid on an even bed of mortar and the joints in polythene should be lapped by at least the width of the damp proof course but to resist downward pressure in the case of parapets and chimney stacks, the joints should be welted.

Although polythene appears as a recognised material for a damp proof course in B.S.743 of 1970, the writers feel that its use has not been fully tested over a long period of time and that one of the other alternative materials set out above would be preferable.

(e) *Mastic Asphalt*

This is the only damp proof course included under the semi-rigid category. It is dealt with further under the Chapter dealing with roof coverings and it will be appreciated that the chief advantage of this material is that there are no joint problems. Asphalt is durable and satisfactory but it should be remembered that it can only withstand slight distortion and although it has fair resistance to sliding at

594

ordinary temperatures, it may be liable to extrude under very heavy pressures or under exceptionally warm conditions. It is unlikely that the surveyor will contemplate the use of asphalt as a damp proof course in the repair or rebuilding of chimney stacks for obvious reasons and its use in parapets is likely to be rare, except where asphalt is to be used for recovering a lead flat roof adjoining. Even then the tendency to soften in warm weather and extrude can lead to unsightly dribbles on the surface of the wall below. The flexible damp proof course materials are really superior in these positions.

Copings

Having dealt with the question of the damp proof course a word might be said on the subject of copings. There is no doubt that copings present something of a problem. The joints of stone, brick and pre-cast concrete sections open in time and permit damp penetration, while cast in-situ concrete copings frequently crack and are vulnerable to frost action. It is therefore important that an effective flexible and impervious damp proof course, with the joints well lapped, and satisfying the points set out for parapet walls, should be incorporated under copings in all circumstances. Where severe weather conditions are expected the choice of the material should be made with care. The custom of rendering the horizontal top surfaces of parapet walls in cement mortar does not provide an effective barrier to moisture for the reasons mentioned earlier in this Chapter and this method introduced as a repair cannot be recommended.

The Treatment of Exterior Wall Faces subject to Penetrating Damp

If the enclosing wall of a dwelling house admits moisture from damp penetration over the whole face, the surveyor must consider what basic remedy is best under the circumstances. It may well be that if the pointing has been neglected over a long period so that the joints are open and some of the facing bricks have become defective in consequence, that cutting out and replacing the defective bricks with other bricks of good even texture, low sulphate content and frost resistant properties may be adequate provided that the re-pointing is carried out to the wall as a whole so that the porosity of the mortar for jointing and pointing should approach but not exceed that of the bricks. Before the repair work is put in hand the surveyor should ask himself if this is likely to provide a completely satisfactory solution. In the majority of cases it will be, but it may well be that the dwelling house is in an area of exceptional rainfall and exposure to wind or alternatively that one particular wall is subject to greater rain penetration than the other walls of the house. Under such circumstances other methods may have to be employed. We will, accordingly now turn to the various ways in which damp penetration over a whole wall surface can be remedied.

(a) *Facing with a new brick skin*

Perhaps the best method of treating an exterior wall face that is subject to penetrating damp is to apply a new brick skin over the whole area of the wall. This method can be applied under two separate circumstances, the first case being where an extra $4\frac{1}{2}$-inch (114mm) brick skin is added to the existing wall thickness and the second case being where an outer $4\frac{1}{2}$-inch (114mm) brick skin to an existing wall is replaced with new brickwork. An example of where the second method might be employed is where an outer facing of Victorian red bricks has decayed so badly to a wall that there is no alternative but to renew the facing brickwork to the core of the wall which would entail much cutting and alignment of bricks and involve very heavy labour cost.

It must be emphasised, however, that in either of the foregoing cases the provision of a new brick skin is purely for the purpose of preventing damp penetration and the skin so formed does not form a structural element in the walling material. The new brick skin is attached to the old wall face by means of non-ferrous ties or cramps since, as some damp penetration is inevitable, the ties or cramps will rust, unless formed of an appropriate material, which at some time in the future would lead to the brick skin detaching itself from the main structure followed in the long term by a probable collapse. Where a brick skin is added to an existing wall thickness there may be considerable difficulty in forming the necessary detailing at quoins, window and door openings and at the eaves junction with the roof, but if the problem of the detailing can be overcome in a satisfactory way, there is no doubt that the addition of the further skin of brickwork forms a highly acceptable method of preventing penetrating dampness.

Where an exterior wall displays a facing composed of badly disintegrating red bricks and where the wall thickness is sufficient to allow for this treatment to be provided it may be possible to remove the outer $4\frac{1}{2}$-inch (114mm) skin of red bricks entirely revealing the backing brickwork, probably composed of stock bricks, and prepare this surface so that it is not unduly uneven for the application of the new brick skin. In either event, however, either the skin replaces an existing outer $4\frac{1}{2}$-inch (114mm) brick face or is applied to the existing wall face the new facing bricks selected should be of good even texture, of low sulphate content and sufficiently frost resistant for the conditions that are likely to be encountered. The porosity of the mortar used for jointing and pointing the bricks should approach but not exceed that of the bricks themselves.

(b) *Tile or Slate Hanging*

Tile hanging appeared in England towards the end of the 17th century and is perhaps most commonly seen in Kent, Sussex and Surrey, together with parts of Hampshire and Berkshire. Slate hanging on the other hand is of older origin. This became popular as a wall face at the time of the Stuarts and the use of slate hanging was widespread in the later Georgian age and the Regency. Slate hanging has been in use for very many years in Devon and Cornwall, and in the older seaside towns slate hanging has been regarded as a traditional method of facing houses against damp penetration for some hundreds of years.

When employed as a repair, slate or tile hanging consists of providing a new independent cladding of tiles or slates to the outer face of an exposed wall, the work being carried out in much the same way as on new buildings. However, in suggesting the provision of this type of treatment the writers do so with the strong recommendation for pressure impregnated timber battens to be provided to the brick-work as a base for the tiles or the slates. The practice of nailing the tiles or slates direct to the brickwork and mortar joints by means of nails is not to be recommended as the nails either become corroded and rust or alternatively work loose and allow the tiles or slates to drop. Battens, on the other hand, securely fixed to the wall, provide a much more satisfactory base, particularly for tile hanging, as the nibs of the tiles hang over and are supported by the edges of the battens in a secure manner. It is, however, most important that the whole of the grain of the wood battens is penetrated by an injected preservative as some moisture may well penetrate unexpected parts of the tile hanging and the fixing battens should be prepared so as to cope with at least a limited amount of moisture penetration. The other main advantage with the provision of timber battens is, of course, that they allow air to penetrate between the tiles and the wall face which accordingly provides a complete barrier to damp-ness and has some insulation qualities as well. The ventilation provides a preventative against dry rot forming in the battens.

As with plain roofing tiles, copper or composition nails are best employed since these do not corrode and every course of tiles should be nailed. The variation from roofing practice, however, is that the lap between the courses of tiles can be reduced to as little as $1\frac{1}{2}$ inches (38mm) and at times even to 1 inch (25mm). As with plain tiling there are, of course, three thicknesses of tiles at the lap. In work to existing dwelling houses it is not often possible to do other than to provide horizontal 1½ by ¾ inch (38 by 19mm) redwood battens. There is no doubt, however, that if possible, counter-battens measuring 2 by 1 inch (51 by 25mm) plugged to the wall at 15-inch (380mm) centres to form a base for the horizontal battens are highly desirable, but the difficulty is that the extra projection added to the face of the tile or slate hanging causes difficulties at window and door openings and other details of the elevation. If, however, a plain area is to be tiled the additional cost of counter-battens is well worth while. Sometimes a layer of bituminous felt is provided against the vertical wall surface as a base below the battens on which the tiles are hung but this should not be necessary under normal circumstances since the tile hanging should be adequate to prevent moisture penetration and the ventilation under the surface of the tiles should be sufficient to disperse any moisture that affects the brickwork after exceptional driving rain. One disadvantage of vertical bituminous felt being applied to a wall face is that moisture may be trapped between the felt and the brickwork and not be able to escape. If in addition condensation forms behind the bituminous felt the same disadvantages as those described earlier in the case of cement rendering might apply, although admittedly to a somewhat lesser degree.

Tile or slate hanging is not a cheap solution to the problem of damp penetration as the cost of labour and materials will be high. It is also a solution that must be used with some care having regard to the architectural properties of the building. It will readily be appreciated that an attempt to prevent whole wall damp penetration to a Queen Anne dwelling house with the provision of red machine-made tile hanging would be too horrible to contemplate and the surveyor, if seriously considering a course of action such as this, should not be employed on this type of work at all. It is, however, often possible to hear of sources for second-hand materials and old, but sound, hand-made tiles, can often be acquired and even if the tiles present irregularities that entail the lap being increased to a safe degree the final effect may be far more acceptable over modern hand-made tiles however regular these may be in pattern. Slates present a similar problem and large smooth textured slates should not be employed. An effort should be made whatever the circumstances to try so far as is possible to make the tile or slate hanging appear to be part of the original structure of the house.

Vertical tile or slate hanging follows, apart from the variations referred to, the usual rules for plain tiling or slating. If the vertical tiling or slating is used to cover a gable wall to a projecting bay window the roof coverings at verges and eaves being finished according to normal practice with a suitable overhang, the vertical tiling can be taken up and tucked under the verges and the verge intersection can be made by forming the vertical tiles in a number of different ways, the Winchester cut being a particularly attractive method.

There are some difficulties to be overcome with employment of tile or slate hanging. With tile hanging in particular, angles require care and the best method of overcoming the difficulty of internal and external angles is to make use of the special angle tiles which are available which fit into the courses of the adjacent tiling. Purpose-made right and left handed tiles are necessary for alternate courses and the finding of suitable tiles may be difficult when old second-hand tiles are employed to the remainder of the face of the wall. If angle tiles cannot be procured to give a sufficiently satisfactory match, plain tiles may be cut and mitred at the angles but if so it is recommended that lead soakers are provided beneath at the intersections so as to ensure that the exposed angles are proof against damp penetration.

Another difficulty with tile or slate hanging is the detailing to be formed at the side and head of window and door openings and the sill of window openings. A horizontal projecting tile soffit is necessary at the head of windows or doors to meet the two thicknesses of tile forming the double course at the head of the window or alternatively a tilting fillet or sprocket may be employed. The edges of the tiles at the reveals to door or window openings should be well pointed up and the surveyor should ensure that proper tile and a half tiles are used at alternate courses at the reveals, particularly in exposed positions. The detailing between the sill and tile hanging at windows is most important. Probably new sills of greater projection will be needed but as was mentioned under roof coverings it is not desirable for leadwork to appear too obviously at the detailing of tiled areas. However an apron is necessary below the window sill which is normally fixed underneath the sill and is dressed over the tiles. If the appearance of the lead is likely to conflict with the aesthetic appearance in the case of a building of quality, it is possible for a secret apron to be made, tucked under the sill, and dressed over the tile course nailed to the battens immediately below the sill. A course of short tiles is then bedded in cement or lime and hair mortar spread on the lead apron. The heads of the tiles are inserted in a groove formed under the sill and the tails of the tiles lined up with the general coursing. The lead is scored and scratched so as to provide a key for the mortar on which the tiles are laid.

Tile or slate hanging normally ends well above ground level as the base of a wall is not normally exposed to particularly strong driving rain and accordingly extra protection is not normally needed. Furthermore the risk of damage to tiles or slates near ground level is considerable. Usually tile hanging is finished neatly at first floor level and, at the lower edge, a tilting fillet and under-tile normally laid with the concave side of the camber uppermost to ensure that a weather-proof joint is provided.

Both tile and slate hanging can be successful if skilfully and sympathetically used. The writer has seen slate hanging provided in the form of a downward extension to an original slated roof in order to overcome some awkward and unexpected damp penetration. In the particular case in mind the work was carried out so sensitively that a long look was necessary to make sure that the roof was not originally designed in this particular form.

Before concluding this subject we should mention the practice of securing slates and tiles direct to wall faces with flush joints set in cement mortar. This treatment suffers from the same disadvantage of cement rendering in that any moisture trapped in the wall will provide a risk element with the added disadvantage that if the bedding of the slates or tiles becomes upset, the individual parts will fall away with risk of injury since the adhesion will, in any event, be slight, particularly with slates. Again, water trickling down the face of the tiles and slates will penetrate the butt joints and sooner or later in the writer's view, disintegration is to be expected. The difficulties of specifying an appropriate bedding mix and seeing that this is properly prepared and ensuring that the slates are set up in a firm manner are great and in view of the long-term risks provided by this method, the writers do not advocate its use.

(c) *Weather Boarding*

Clap boarding has been, and is, much employed in the United States, Canada and Scandinavia, to give protection to the external face of a building, not necessarily of timber, against the elements. The same practice is known as weather boarding in this country but it is not generally realised that in the Weald of Kent and in Essex particularly, weather boarding has been employed for years to form attractive finishes to exterior house walls.

The most common form in which weather boarding is found is where feather edged boards laid horizontally to overlap each other are attached to the outer face of the main structure, the lap being sufficient to prevent water creeping between the boards in periods of heavy rain. Oak and elm boarding is often found in its natural and unpainted state but where softwood weather boarding is applied to the faces of buildings as was a fairly common practice in

Georgian times the wood commonly has a painted finish. A variation to this, however, is found with certain houses of the Georgian
period in coastal districts where the weather boarding is covered
with black tar instead of paint. This is a rather disconcerting type
of finish for the surveyor to find as he will, if he sees it, be naturally
concerned about the question of fire risk from the surface spread of
flame.

(d) *Applying a Rendered Finish*

External renderings in cement lime and sand mixes are perhaps
now the most common method of preventing damp penetration to
a whole wall face. The mixes currently recommended are relatively
weak ones which produce finishes that are porous, absorbing water
in wet weather and allowing for evaporation to take place in drier
weather, the action being described by the Building Research
Establishment as rather like that of a thick layer of blotting paper.
We have already referred to the fact that a dense impervious
rendering if applied to copings and chimney stacks while appearing
at first sight to be preferable would, in fact, be less efficient than a
porous one with the passage of time, since water becomes trapped
between brickwork and the rendering with the risk of penetration to
the interior, frost action and sulphate attack. Any shrinkage cracks
that may develop, always a likelihood with dense renderings, will
admit water which will be sealed up and thus either penetrate the
interior as it has nowhere to go or will freeze and blow off the
rendered coating.

It should be said at once, however, that external renderings are
more valid in their application to main walls which are not normally
quite so exposed as chimney stacks and parapet walls, nor are they
subject to rain penetration from more than one side. External
rendered finishes are dealt with fully under Chapter 2 dealing with
Brick Walls, but a few points might be made here in relation to the
specific subject of dampness. The big advantage of a rendering as a
remedy for damp penetration is, of course, its cheapness when compared with, for example, the cost of tile hanging. Unlike certain
types of tile there is also no difficulty in obtaining supplies of the
appropriate sand and cement and lime so that delay is cut to a
minimum. The surveyor, however, should take particular care to
specify the mix in accordance with the principles set out in Chapter
2 and to see that the rendering is applied uniformly over the entire
face of the wall. The application of external rendering is by no means
an easy matter and even under the best of circumstances it is difficult for an even texture to be maintained. There are plenty of
examples to be seen of the efforts of jobbing builders where the

texture changes according to when the workmen leave off and start again. It is also often difficult to restrict a builder from carrying out work of this sort in frosty weather and although it is possible for anti-freezing additives to be employed, the work is so often finished before the labourer's mate arrives panting from the builders' merchant with the necessary package, having stopped to have a cup of tea on the way. The difficulty with additives from the surveyor's point of view is that the makers' instructions have to be followed correctly and only the workmen engaged on the mix can make sure of this.

Waterproofers for spatterdash or first undercoat in conditions of severe exposure can take liquid or powder form. If the surveyor merely specifies the addition of an appropriate waterproofer he is likely to invite the appearance of an ancient and battered tin or package from the recesses of the builder's yard which has no doubt been stored for a long period under damp conditions. The builder's foreman may point to a faded label and say "you can't get this stuff any more" but this, far from being a recommendation will normally cause severe misgivings in the surveyor. In the case of a powder it is perhaps more difficult to include it in a mix particularly in windy conditions but perhaps the greater difficulty is that it needs thorough mixing to make sure that it is distributed evenly. Liquid waterproofers operate on the basis that they fill the cavities and produce a dense and solid mix that becomes impervious to penetration below the surface. The use of waterproof additives, however, in external renderings to general wall surfaces should be limited to conditions where severe exposure exists. When used, a tried and trusted brand should be specified, for mixing strictly in accordance with the maker's directions. Further additives in the form of pigments can be obtained to add colour to the mix but these will no doubt only be employed under special circumstances.

Roughcast and pebble-dash are the traditional finishes to exterior wall surfaces associated in England with the ribbon development of houses built between the two World Wars although both have a rather longer historical background than is generally supposed. Both materials are, like rendering, designed to provide a facing to exterior walls to help resist damp penetration, but unlike rendering both roughcast and pebble-dash make use of gravel or stone chippings as an integral part of the facing. The two terms are used to describe the way in which the constituent materials are combined together rather than any distinction in the nature of the materials themselves. Roughcast has been employed for hundreds of years in England to stone buildings as well as brick ones, not for aesthetic reasons but mainly to cover up uneven or bad construction and to provide at the same time an extra waterproofing face to the building. The English practice thus differs from that in Scotland where roughcast forms a different architectural element to domestic buildings of stone. There is, on the other hand, not much to be said in favour of pebble-dash from the aesthetic point of view, but it should be remembered that the appearance of pebble-dash is not always necessarily the nondescript brown colour used in inland areas. The use of granite chippings instead of washed pebbles provides, for example, an exterior finish to a house that is much more acceptable. Pebble-dash consists of two coats of rendering, the second coat being overlaid with a layer of small stones. The first coat forms the protective covering to the wall and on this coat the efficiency of the weatherproofing really depends. Once it is fairly hard it is scored with a "scratcher" which consists of several pointed laths nailed together in the shape of a fan and dragged across the face of the rendering to form a key for the second coat. The second coat is then applied to a consistency of mortar and before it has had time to set the pebbles are taken in a scoop and thrown or dashed against the surface either by hand or with the use of a machine. The surface is then lightly pressed so that the pebbles are set and the whole face is then allowed to harden. Like all operations in building the difference between a job carried out by experienced tradesmen and the efforts of an amateur is profound. A coating of pebble-dash should be even textured with the pebbles applied in such a way that they cover the whole surface to a uniform finish. The first and second coats and the final application of pebbles should be provided in precisely the right density of mix and time of drying and when efficiently carried out the whole coating will form a perfectly legitimate waterproofing compound. If, however, the workman is not used to this particular operation the surveyor will probably arrive at the site to see that the pebbles vary in density, some areas of rendering being bald while others have areas of densely packed pebbles hastily pressed too far into the top coat. On seeing this the surveyor will wonder if the two coat work below has the proper bond.

Roughcast, called "Harling" in Scotland, has a long and respectable background and forms an architectural characteristic to the Scottish baronial type of house and smaller cottage alike. Traditionally with roughcast a mixture of shingle and slaked lime is incorporated in a mix with a little cement added to give additional strength and adhesion. The mixture is applied to the face of the wall in the same manner as pebble-dash but the lime must be well mixed in so that no pockets or uneven areas are formed in the covering. Modern techniques both for pebble-dash and roughcast are set out in greater detail in Chapter 2.

There are considerable advantages in a rough textured finish to exterior wall surfaces as against a smooth coating of rendering. One of the advantages is that the penalty for a less than perfect mix is not likely to be quite so serious and the weather effects of sun and rain under such circumstances are not quite so severe.

(e) *Temporary Applications of Fluids*

There are circumstances when a damp wall cannot be effectively and permanently treated due perhaps to economics or where, for example, the house is shortly to be pulled down and the area re-developed or alternatively where an occupant may be seriously ill and effective repairs have to wait for a time. There are several waterproofing solutions on the market that are intended for application to the exterior surfaces of main walls.

The drawbacks with surface applications of waterproofing solutions is not only that they are effective for a comparatively short time only but there is also the fact that they may provide a waterproof film over the surface of the brickwork so that water within the brick may be trapped and have to work its way to the interior face of the wall. It is true that the use of such waterproofers have a particular point in the case of hard driving rain but the surveyor must be sure of their effects before he specifies them. Waterproofers recently introduced contain Silicone Resin and Siliconate preparations and are designed to act as water repellents since the purpose of the application is to line the pores of the brick or masonry with a special coating which will cause the combination of surface tension and contact angle to reject the water instead of absorbing it. A drop of water will be repelled and coagulate instead of spreading and thus not penetrate the brick or stone walling. Modern waterproofing solutions "breathe" so that they do not trap moisture behind an impervious skin but specified products are best applied strictly in accordance with the maker's requirements, for example with a pneumatic pressure sprayer when the wall is reasonably dry.

Some modern finishing materials assist the wall to resist moisture. Some of these consist of a base of Portland cement in powder form and require only the addition of water. They are available in a variety of colours and are easy to apply. It should be noted, however, that these products should not be applied to common bricks unless these are dry at the time of the application, and unless the design of the structure affords the maximum penetration against moisture; nor should they be applied over oil paints, distemper, or emulsion paints. The work should be suspended if there is a frost or if the weather is wet. A liquid primer is also available which has adhesive qualities and enables a controlled and uniform surface to be provided to porous and uneven walling with a stabilising solution for dusty or uneven surfaces.

Repairs to Faults in details which admit penetrating dampness

We will now turn to the consideration of repairs to individual defects that are present in the enclosing roof and walls of a house which admit penetrating dampness. The question of the repairs to chimney stacks and parapet walls which project above roof level has already been dealt with and roof coverings are discussed in a separate Chapter devoted to that subject. It is, however, now necessary to refer to the question of cement fillets and flashings.

(a) Cement Fillets and Flashings

For a long time the joints between the brick vertical surfaces of chimney stacks and parapet walls and the roof coverings to pitched roofs, such as tiles or slates, have been formed in lime mortar or cement lime mortar. Since the end of the last century the use of metal flashings and soakers have become commonplace for small houses as well as large. The surveyor will, however, in the course of dealing with the repair and maintenance of older buildings encounter the cement fillet more often perhaps than any other form of protective jointing material. The natural distaste that the surveyor has for the use of the cement fillet should not blind him to the fact, however, that it has long formed a joint that, in spite of its shortcomings, has provided satisfactory service in an enormous majority of cases where cost is important and also to the fact that it was recognised from very early times that the cement fillet by itself was far from perfect.

It was the practice with many early brick and stone buildings to work out the detailing of the projecting chimney stacks and parapet walls with some care. An overhang was formed just above roof level which was designed as a protection for the slates or tiles which fitted neatly underneath. The resulting joint was then pointed up in cement lime mortar. This type of joint formed and still forms an excellent weatherproof detail. Only excessive weathering to the bricks or stone is likely to result in damp penetration and under such circumstances it is best for the surveyor to renew the detail exactly as it was by building-in new sections of brick or stone rather than cut off the projections and provide lead flashings and soakers in their place. Although the latter remedy is adequate from the point of view of damp penetration the reasons against it are aesthetic ones. Other variations have been in use for many years in positions such as this from the use of stone or tile chips set in the cement, to separate sections of stone or tile formed in a continuous line and set in cement lime mortar used as a jointing and bedding compound only. Often detailing such as this is surprisingly durable and there is no particular need for the surveyor to contemplate the replacement of such details with metal sheeting as a matter of principle if the jointing has withstood the elements and the wear and tear of time over many years. Piecemeal repair work may well be necessary, however, involving renewing or rebedding the tile or stone sections and the writers feel that this is perfectly legitimate provided that the use of a mortar that will allow a certain elasticity is employed.

With the introduction of mass-produced slates and bricks, cement fillets were universally employed for cheap housing as the cover fillet between the right-angled junction formed between these two materials. Soakers were only introduced in about 1880 and often the cover fillet formed the only protective covering material. It was unfortunate that the mass-production of cheap cement encouraged a richer mix to fillets which had little hope of adhesion to the new smoother machine-made bricks and smooth greasy faced mass-produced slates. Accordingly, renewal of cement fillets has been carried out at frequent intervals to domestic buildings constructed since 1830. Inspection of the various colourings from white cement mixes, indicating new repairs in almost neat cement mortar, to the brown appearance of saturated fillets of earlier date, indicate to the surveyor that probably more time and money is spent on ineffective repairs by jobbing builders to angles and abutments of this type than any other type of maintenance work to roofs.

The only completely satisfactory way of dealing with the question of cement fillets to buildings of this period and to subsequent buildings where cement fillets are employed is to remove them completely and replace them with a metal cover flashing designed and built to correct modern principles. Soakers should also be provided if these are not already employed, as only the use of soakers in conjunction with an adequate cover flashing can be considered to be an effective long-term repair. The cost of carrying out effective repair work in this way can be recouped by the saving made in perpetual attendances by jobbing builders over a very few years if the cement fillets were merely to be patched. Often when the cement fillets are removed and the abutting slates are examined to a tiled roof of about 1900 it will be found that constant saturation through the cement fillets has caused zinc soakers underneath to become badly perished so that these are in need of complete renewal. Often the end slates are badly perished and these also require renewal, but this, of course, will be considered as one aspect in the decision as to whether the roof coverings as a whole are to be renewed or if certain areas only are to be dealt with.

(b) *Projecting Brick and Band Courses*

Some surveyors regard with genuine affection the large Victorian Gothic villa built with the confidence and flamboyance that were the hallmarks of that particular period. Such villas, however, are notable for the profusion of projections on parapets and chimney stacks and the number of string courses and mouldings and ornamental projections elsewhere. Horizontal ledges, however small, are vulnerable to damp penetration and although the surveyor will occasionally find that string or band courses or ornamental projecting ledges are built with the upper exposed surfaces faced with tile sections which are reasonably weatherproof, there are times where the upper surfaces of projecting brick or stone are badly eroded or were once protected with small cement fillets which have long since fallen away. Often close inspection from a ladder of a stone detail such as this to a Georgian house shows that there is a cavity in the upper angle between the main wall and the projection which permits damp to enter and which cannot be seen from ground level. The surveyor will, of course, specify the renewal of the badly weathered or defective stone or brick sections, but it would probably be well worth while to specify in addition the provision of a lead cover flashing tucked into the brickwork of the main wall, wedged and pointed, and carried over the small ledge formed by the projection. The renewal of cement fillets to form an angle to throw water clear of the projection will only be a temporary expedient since these inevitably crack and fall away in a relatively short time. An exception can be made, however, with the projecting brick courses to chimney stacks since the height of the stacks and the thickness of the brickwork often ensures that any penetrating dampness from this cause dries out before it can enter the main structure below.

(c) *Repairs in connection with penetrating dampness to cavity walls*

Where cavity walls are involved, the surveyor will have decided from his inspection if damp penetration is due to faulty construction on the one hand which has encouraged a build up of mortar in the cavity at the base of the wall or has lodged on the wall-ties, or whether the defect is associated with the most vulnerable parts of the cavity wall construction, namely an opening for a window or a door. Whole wall penetration should not be a possibility in the case of a cavity wall as the whole basis of the design is to resist precisely this type of damp but faults at detailing from poor design or slipshod construction are common.

607

If the surveyor is satisfied beyond reasonable doubt that a build-up of mortar at the base of the cavity due to careless bricklaying is the cause of dampness, there is little alternative but to open up sections of the outer skin just above the damp proof course in separate sections so as to inspect the interior in a number of places. Once this is done it should be possible to obtain or ask the builder to design rakes which will dislodge and collect the loose stuff inside the cavity so that this can be removed by hand. Some of the mortar droppings will adhere with remarkable tenacity to the interior of the base of a cavity but it should be possible working from quoins with a strong beam of light to determine which parts are still likely to bridge the damp proof course and which cannot be dislodged by the method suggested. Under such circumstances further opening up of the outer skin will be required but sections where special measures of this sort are necessary should be left until a later stage so that the previous inspection holes can be made good and allowed time to dry and harden.

In the same manner mortar dropping on wall-ties which introduce dampness to the interior face of the wall can be dealt with by cutting away the outer brick face, carefully cleaning the tie and re-setting the outer brickwork. The whole point of dealing with defects such as this from the outer face is, of course, that it does not involve replastering and redecoration, as would be necessary if the inner skin of the cavity wall were opened up.

Where damp penetration occurs around an opening in a cavity wall the surveyor will suspect that either the damp proof course is defective in some way or alternatively that the detailing is faulty. There is, under such circumstances, little alternative but to open up the brickwork externally in order to ascertain the true cause. Once this is done, it may be found that the damp proof course above the head of the window, which may be of bituminous felt, has failed either by being placed in the wrong position or else having not been provided with adequate laps or stiffening so that it is not sufficiently rigid or alternatively that a great many mortar droppings have collected above the damp proof course and form a bridge between the inner and the outer skins. Defects may be found to the vertical damp proof courses at the side of openings but these are far less numerous since the sides of openings are less vulnerable than the heads.

Mortar droppings above a damp proof course over the head of an opening can be removed as before but a defective felt damp proof course is probably best replaced by metal, such as semi-hard copper, preformed and shaped so that the rear section is at an angle to bridge the cavity with a welt at the top end which can be lightly pushed up against a convenient brick course to the inner skin. The penetration of water through the jambs of windows and doors to cavity walls can be due to one of two reasons. The first and most difficult cause to remedy is that no vertical damp proof course was provided as an insulating barrier to the solid brickwork which bridges the cavity and closes the opening. If no damp proof course was provided the only possible effective remedy is to take out the facing bricks at the sides of the opening and build in a vertical damp proof course, either of two courses of slates set in cement mortar or a flexible material such as bituminous felt. Where ground floor door and window openings are concerned, there is no objection to either material, but at first floor level where some stress from the structure might be expected which might distort window openings, it would probably be best to use a flexible material rather than slate. The second cause of penetration at sides of openings may be through the frame due to the fact that no weather bar or anti-capillary groove is formed between the wood and the brickwork. The only remedy in this case is for the frame to be taken out and suitably modified in either of these ways before being re-set and bedded and pointed up externally with mastic.

Sills to windows in cavity walls give trouble due to two main reasons. The first, and most serious, is that the measures taken against damp penetration may be insufficient so that the sill forms a bridge over the cavity and if this is of porous material dampness will penetrate the inside face of the wall. The removal of the sill and its replacement coupled with a flexible damp proof membrane underneath and behind so that a complete barrier is formed against further penetration is the only practicable way to solve this particular difficulty. The other cause of dampness, which only affects the outer skin is usually where the weathering qualities of the sill are insufficient either because no check throat is provided or because the nosing is insufficiently long to throw off water, so that damp stains the wall underneath which often turns green eventually. The remedy here will be the same as for sills to solid walls, to be briefly discussed shortly. Often the surveyor will find curious external detailing to sills, either by way of bricks on edge or tiles set in cement, and if these have failed, effective repair will probably involve redesigning a new sill with correct detailing.

In order to prevent penetrating dampness, cavity walls must have been constructed so that the inner leaf is entirely disconnected from the outer leaf and if this is achieved all should be well even under the most adverse weather conditions. Where the surveyor has detected in his inspection, however, that some bridging has occurred that is due to a basic defect of design such as a horizontal junction between

609

an 11-inch (279mm) cavity wall with a 9-inch (229mm) upper wall above at first floor or parapet level being formed over a timber wall-plate at the head of the inner skin of the cavity wall he must have regard to the possibility of rot.

There are a number of unusual and unexpected ways in which the cavities to parapet walls can become bridged. Structural faults developing owing to poor design where a concrete flat roof or balcony expands against a cavity wall and pushes one skin of brick-work against another, so that the narrowing space inevitably becomes blocked with droppings or deposits are an example of unex-pected ways in which damp penetration can occur. In such cases the repair work is the consequence of the structural defect and finds no place in this Chapter but nevertheless even when conducting struc-tural repairs to cavity walls, the surveyor must bear in mind the basic principles of cavity construction and always the need for making sure that there is no contact between the inner and outer skins, except where an efficient damp proof membrane is provided.

(d) *Faults to openings in solid walls*

Where dampness penetrates the head of a window or the door to an outer wall the age of the building may give a clue as to the cause of the trouble. It should certainly, however, provide a warning to the surveyor as to the likely consequences. The reason for this is that nearly all brick built buildings, including Georgian houses and those up to late Victorian times, have as a unifying characteristic, an arch formed in the facing brickwork whether of soldier pattern or curved. The materials employed are either the same bricks as those used for the exterior wall facings or alternatively are of red clay bricks or the finely cut and constructed arches of red rubbers set in putty. What-ever the material, however, the arches are for decorative purposes mainly, and have little structural significance, supporting only the outer half-brick thickness of wall. The weight of the remainder of the wall is normally taken by a timber lintel sometimes in better class work with a rough relieving arch over, formed crudely from the walling bricks, the space between the timber and the rough relieving arch being filled with half bats and brick portions cut and discarded during the formation of quoins and angles. Often, even in the better buildings, minor settlement robs the rough relieving arch of its strength so that the weight of the brickwork over the opening depends entirely on the wood lintel as it invariably does always in cheaper work. It is easy to see, therefore, that any damp penetration through the facing arch to the outer face of the brickwork is very likely to set up rot in the timber, due to the poor ventilation afforded. Since even minor settlement can cause cracks to appear in facing arches, there is all the more need for these to be repaired with care. Such arches do not provide an effective bond to the remainder of the brickwork, and Victorian soldier arches are notorious for slipping either in whole or in part, so that they finish up resting on a wrought iron bar hastily provided and built into the brickwork by the local builder. The minor cracks that have appeared above are ignored, not unnaturally, since the problem of repair was seen purely in structural terms of holding up the arch, but nevertheless dampness will penetrate with the consequences of dry or wet rot. Often the jointing material between bricks forming arches will shrink so that moisture can penetrate or the arches may behave oddly at times, cracks appearing at some points and not others due to the variations in the qualities of adhesion between mortar and brickwork. There is little doubt in the writers' view that merely to repoint the face of the arch and surrounding brickwork may not be sufficient to deal with the defect in view of the importance of preventing damp penetration at this point. Pointing, even when a weak mix is provided, must be subject to some shrinkage in the course of time and this method of repair like the application of mastic or the application of a silicone waterproofer must be regarded as a temporary measure which is sufficient for, say, a few years, but will not be permanent. The only permanent way of dealing with the matter is for the arch in the facing brickwork to be carefully taken up section by section and rebuilt. This adds the incidental advantage that the timber behind can be inspected and if any further remedial work is required, the extent of this can be established and appropriate measures taken. If, for example, the lintel is found to be a mass of decay the opportunity will be taken for this to be removed and replaced with either a reinforced concrete lintel or a short section of rolled steel joist wedged and pinned up to the existing brickwork. Where, however, the wood lintel is found to be in reasonable condition, unlikely in most circumstances, it is desirable to build in a metal damp proof course in the form of a right-angled tray to protect the vertical surface of the lintel and the head of the frame from contact with the new facing brick arch before this is rebuilt. The top end of the tray can be tucked in above the wood lintel and the ends of the tray can be dog-eared. This is useful where no weather bar or anti-capillary groove is formed at the head of the frame.

Where driving rain penetrates between a window or door frame and the brick opening which surrounds it, investigation will often show that anti-capillary grooves are not provided in the frame. This can matter considerably at the heads of the windows where the run off from the face of an arch or lintel combined with driving wind and rain can force moisture into a narrow crack. Often the provision of a throating to the lintel or arch soffit externally will limit the amount of moisture penetration so that the sides and head of the frame can then be dealt with in a similar manner. The necessary treatment can consist of either taking out the frame and forming an anti-capillary groove and rebedding, or else leaving the frame in place and providing a groove in the outer face into which a shaped hood fillet can be fitted to throw water clear, fixed to the frame and bedded in mastic to the opening, or alternatively a wood bead can be screwed on to the angle between the flush face of the frame and the brick opening, and bedded in mastic. The last two remedies may be of somewhat limited duration since, with further contraction of the wood and with hot sunlight on the mastic, further shrinkage cracks may be expected but the amount of the penetration may be cut down by this method to negligible limits. The degree of exposure of the opening to prevailing wind and rain must decide the matter.

Where windows with cased frames and sliding sashes are found, particularly those built before the London Building Acts required brick reveals to be provided, the face of the frame will be within 1 to 2 inches (25 to 51mm) from the outer face of the wall. It is most important that dampness does not penetrate behind the face of the outer lining of the cased frame since the unprotected grain to the inner woodwork is vulnerable to dry rot. If the provision of a new outer cover mould set in mastic is not sufficient, a better method is for a metal damp proof membrane to be inserted between the frame and the brickwork, lapped down externally and screwed between the cover mould and the frame then taken internally and tucked into the brickwork, the interior face of the metal having been prepared for being plastered over.

Damp penetration through sills is commonplace but the remedy depends on whether a wood sill only is provided or whether there is a stone sub-sill in addition. With early buildings, particularly timber framed structures, wood sills only are provided and these are normally arranged to sit on the framed opening direct with little or no damp proofing measures. Penetration accordingly occurs between the sill and the timber below. If the window sill has no projection and an inadequate check throat damp penetration may be severe enough to set up rot in the timbers. The best method of repair is therefore to provide a new oak sill properly formed so that there is an adequate nosing and efficient weathering to the top surface and check throat to the lower. This can then be seated on a damp proof course of metal carried over the external face of the wall under the sill and turned up to the inner face behind the sill and fixed in place with a coverbead screwed to the back face of the sill which can be rebated to receive the plaster of the inner wall surface below.

Where a wood sill is provided in conjunction with a stone sub-sill to a brick opening a number of common defects often require remedy. Damp penetration between the wood sill and the stone sub-sill is usually due to the lack of a water bar and often the only effective method of ensuring that penetration does not occur is for the upper sill to be taken out and a weather bar to be inserted. A repair can be carried out by forming a mastic joint to the exterior between the two materials but this will only have a limited life. Effective detailing of the nosing, weathering and check-throating to the wood sill may be lacking in which case one or two methods may be employed. The first is to renew the sill completely and provide another in its place with better design qualities or alternatively, if the wood sill is sound, the nosing can be extended by means of a fresh piece of oak planted on and screwed soundly to the remainder. This additional nosing can be provided with a check-throat and provided that the upper weathered surface is carefully stopped, primed and painted so that damp does not penetrate the joint, a reasonable repair can be effected.

It is commonplace to find, particularly with Victorian and Georgian houses, that stone sub-sills have fractured at the centre point. The cause of the crack is of course structural and in replacing such sills metal or bituminous felt damp proof courses are best provided below them in accordance with good current practice. In addition to this, however, an efficient check throat to such sills is vital to throw water away from the edges free of the walling below. Modern multi-purpose electrical drills make it much easier to adapt incorrect details often found in old sills which are not in such bad condition as to need replacing. Where a sub-sill consists not of stone but of tiles or bricks on edge, the same rules must apply regarding weathering and damp-proofing qualities. A tile sub-sill is only likely to prevent dampness penetrating the actual surface of the tile and unless the projection is sufficient, damp will creep through the joints and underneath the tiles, since no check-throat can be of course provided by this type of sill. Where bricks are employed, dampness may penetrate between the joints and may creep in under the front face, as a projection is not often found, and even if a projection is provided, the lack of a check-throat leads to similar difficulties as in the case of a tile sill.

A brief word might be said on the subject of wood sills. These are the most vulnerable part of the whole window to dampness since they are in the most exposed position, but provided that they are correctly detailed and kept adequately painted, they should last indefinitely. One difficulty is, however, that often the detailing is so poor that they have to be replaced in the manner referred to

613

previously, but even more often than this the paint film wears out and becomes defective before the remainder of the paintwork to the surrounding wood. The reason for this lies in the obvious one of excessive wear from the elements but also in the fact that oak was one of the hardwoods most frequently used in the past for this purpose and tends not to accept paint unless special steps are taken, with for example nowadays an aluminium primer, to ensure that the acid in the oak is separated from the paint film. Because of the difficulty of keeping sills adequately painted a good deal of rot occurs needlessly.

(e) *Penetrating Dampness from Faulty Gutters and Downpipes*

When worn, cracked or rusted sections of downpipe and gutter are removed from the eaves of a roof or the face of an exterior wall, the surveyor should give thought before merely replacing them as they were before to the question of possible future damp penetration. So far as the future maintenance of the building is concerned measures taken at this stage may save endless trouble later on.

An obvious requirement when replacing defective sections of cast iron rainwater pipe is of resetting the whole pipe clear of the wall face with the employment of cylindrical pieces behind the fixing ears of the pipe sections. This improvement not only gives access for painting which, when neglected, is the most usual cause of pipes against a wall face becoming rusty and defective, but also prevents the build-up of dirt and rubbish behind the pipe sections on the ears which in itself can be an irritating minor cause of damp penetration. Some modification with the swan neck to the gutter junction at eaves is necessary but this is not too difficult to overcome. Another obvious reason for making some modification is where the flat back of an ogee cast iron gutter or specially shaped gutter is pressed flat against a stone or wood cornice, the intention being that the gutter section forms an extention of the cornice itself. Before replacing cast iron gutter sections an obvious precaution is to apply two coats of bitumastic paint to both sides of the gutter back and to ensure that the rainwater flows into the gutter with an adequate projection over the rear so that there is no risk of water trickling down between the back of the gutter and the stone or wood face of the cornice. Pains should also be taken with hopper heads and waste pipes projecting from a building to minimise the effects of possible failure as far as possible. Care should be taken to protect new sections so that their life is extended for the longest possible period. Although the consideration of waste pipes, gutters and downpipes does not form part of this Chapter nevertheless the surveyor in considering exterior plumbing should always have an eye to seeing if he can find ways to reduce the possibility of damp penetration in the event of disrepair from lack of maintenance.

CONDENSATION

It does not seem quite fair that a building which has been made proof against all sorts of driving and penetrating rainfall should nevertheless display internally the signs of the most acute dampness. For in certain houses and under certain conditions, water will stream down vertical hard impervious surfaces and will collect in pools on horizontal ledges. Large patches of dampness will appear, disappear and reappear to walls and ceilings with mystifying suddenness and the surveyor is often overcome with a sense of irritation at the way a purely natural set of laws combine with tantalising and malicious effectiveness to provide him with a problem that is not only difficult to solve but is one in which any understanding between himself and his client can only be restored with the ultimate efficiency of his solution.

For the surveyor will have realised that if dampness from penetration cannot occur, or is most unlikely, that the signs of damp that he sees are due to condensation. It is often more difficult than it sounds however, to rule out the possibility of penetrating dampness. The well-meaning attempts of the surveyor to question the householder about the history of the appearance and disappearance of the patches of damp and the area and extent of the severity of the damp may produce some relevant information but may also induce a sense of mutual exasperation in each party. Both will consider that the other has not grasped the nature of the true problem. If it is difficult for the surveyor to be absolutely certain in his own mind as to the true cause of dampness, how much more difficult it is for the occupier of the house to believe that the dampness is not getting in from the outside. He can, after all, see the patches of damp over his head or beside his bed with his own eyes and is certain that he is living in a house that is leaking. Unless he actually sees ladders erected and workmen arrive he is not likely to be impressed or to listen to the proposals that the surveyor may submit with other than scepticism.

In order to discuss possible remedies for condensation it is, therefore, necessary to understand how it occurs. The main fact to bear in mind is that the air around us is never completely dry but can hold and absorb moisture which cannot be seen. For example, steam which spouts from a boiling kettle disappears but the moisture is retained and absorbed by the air. The air remains clear, but its moisture content, known as humidity, has increased. The amount of water that a certain quantity of air contains is ruled by two factors. The first of these is that the warmer the air the more moisture it is able to hold, so that if the temperature of the air of a room rises the moisture content of the air may be increased. The second factor is that at a particular temperature air can only hold a given amount of moisture and when this limit is reached it becomes saturated. The temperature of the air at which saturation occurs is called the dew-point and any cooling below this level leads to condensation. Accordingly, the reader will understand that if the amount of moisture in the air remains the same but the air cools, a temperature may be reached when the air becomes saturated at the dew-point. If the temperature falls below the dew-point, warm moist air will condense and distil onto cold non-absorbent surfaces such as glass or high gloss paint. Condensation will also take place on absorbent surfaces but moisture will not show until the material is thoroughly wet and often the conditions for mould growth on such surfaces are favourable long before any outward signs are apparent.

The great difficulty in endeavouring to assess the degree to which condensation to the interior of a dwelling house will form dampness is that conditions are never the same for very long. Variations in the moisture carrying capacity of air with changes in temperature will be further altered when additional moisture from cooking, washing and bathing is introduced. There are endless complicating factors. A seated person, for example, gives off about $\frac{1}{10}$ of a pint of water vapour every hour and flueless gas and oil burning heaters give out a great deal of moisture, a pint of water being given off for each pint of oil burnt.

We have so far seen that the space available for water vapour as a component of the air in buildings is dependent upon temperature. The moisture content of air at a particular temperature can now be expressed as the relative humidity. This is the ratio (expressed as a percentage) of the amount of moisture contained in the air to the maximum amount it could hold at that temperature. Thus saturated air has a relative humidity of 100 per cent. For example, where air at a temperature of 65°F, with a relative humidity of 80 per cent is cooled to 59°F, so that the air becomes saturated and any further cooling causes water vapour to condense, 59°F is the dew-point. The degree of saturation of air, known as relative humidity, is therefore, capable of definition as the percentage ratio between the given moisture content and that which the air could sustain at the higher temperature. Digest 91 (second series) issued by the Building Research Establishment shows how the risk of condensation may be assessed in the design of new building details and to illustrate this it combines a graphical treatment with worked examples. In the field of maintenance and repair to existing dwellings, however, the field is much more limited although the reader is referred to this Digest or to "Condensation in Dwellings" published by the Department of the Environment[1] in the event of a particular problem arising in new work or where a fuller investigation of the subject is of interest. It should be emphasised however that condensation is an ever-growing problem. About 20 per cent of dwellings in this country are unoccupied and cold during the working day and condensation occurs during the evening. This problem is increasing and remedial work costs the country more and more each year.

Surface Condensation

It will be appreciated that in order to know if condensation is likely to occur on a particular surface it is necessary to know not only the temperature and moisture content of the air but also the temperature of the surface itself, since this will cool the air with which it is in contact. Condensation will only occur on the surfaces of materials when these surfaces are at or below the dew-point of the air which comes into contact with them. Thus condensation is not likely to occur on a panel radiator whatever the other circumstances may be when the radiator is in use. If, however, the heating system is turned off and the house is cold, condensation will probably form first and foremost on the surfaces of cold metal radiators. Cold surfaces or abnormally high humidities will lead to the inside surface of a wall or roof being below the dew-point of the indoor air and water will condense as a result. The amount of condensation will be determined to some degree by the properties of insulation provided by the interior wall surfaces and improving the qualities of insulation will ameliorate the amount of condensation. This is where the difference between modern hard wall plasters and the old softer and more open textured plasters of older houses have made a difference. Fortunately, however, most brick buildings are kept heated and ventilated and where abnormally high humidities are not encountered surface condensation should not be a problem, but where buildings are not heated and the wall surfaces are cold and impervious and there is little ventilation and a good deal of humidity, surface condensation is to be expected. Thus, surface condensation might be expected in the case of a room in a post-1950 house occupied by an elderly person of limited means, the wall surfaces being of hard painted plaster, the temperature being low and there being little ventilation. Add to this an oil stove and some cooking arrangements in the

[1] H.M.S.O. 1971

corner of the room and the likelihood of surface condensation is probably as high as it is likely to be found in domestic property of brick construction except where exceptional circumstances prevail.

The insulation of internal wall surfaces which may ameliorate the conditions leading to condensation in the case of a house with brick or stone walls may not be effective in the case of lightweight structures such as the typical modern additions to dwelling houses where intermittent heating only is employed. In such cases, thermal insulation alone may not be sufficient to prevent condensation in cold weather as once the heating is cut off, the structure will cool rapidly. In order to avoid condensation under such circumstances, continuous internal heating may be necessary.

Ventilation of buildings is of particular importance for two reasons. Firstly it is necessary to remove moisture which condenses on hard surfaces and secondly, it is needed to assist in cases where large quantities of moisture are released into the air for long periods such as a kitchen used by more than one family in a large dwelling house. There will be circumstances where additional heating may not be practicable and no amount of additional thermal insulation can serve a practical purpose. The only solution open to improve matters, therefore, is really efficient ventilation and in every case such as this it may be necessary to consider what steps can be taken to reduce the conditions that are likely to assist condensation. Ventilating hoods over cookers are an obvious example and the fitting of mixing valves to sinks so that water is delivered at the required temperature without the need for cooling.

Rapid changes in the weather will lead to condensation forming in poorly heated buildings or those that are empty and not heated at all. A traditional structure of brick or stone will take some time to warm up and when mild damp weather suddenly follows a cold spell the outer walls will be at a lower temperature for a day or more behind the changes of weather, so that when the warm moist incoming air comes in contact with surfaces which will be below the dew-point, water will condense. As the walls warm up, however, and eventually exceed the dew-point, condensation should cease and moisture should evaporate but the reader will appreciate that in certain heavy stone structures which are left unventilated and vacant, condensation could be a continuing and serious problem for some time. By comparison a more lightly constructed building which warms up rapidly following a change in the weather is less likely to present trouble from condensation when weather conditions improve.

In order to summarise this section dealing with surface condensation it might be stated first of all that adequate and continuous heating of the conventional dwelling house is by far the best means of prevention, since if heating is intermittent, ventilation in itself cannot be a full answer to the problem. Ventilation, however, is a good secondary means of preventing condensation particularly where there is a large build-up of moisture into the air from a particular source, such as a kitchen, and to remove condensed moisture on hard surfaces. The incidence of surface condensation may also be reduced by lining the interior faces of masonry or brick walls or certain roof structures with an insulating board or a plasterboard which can be easily and quickly warmed and this may ameliorate conditions leading to condensation in buildings which do not have continuous heating throughout the year. Some use can also be made of absorbent finishes and anti-condensation paints but these can only be of use where circumstances are such that a speedy return to dry conditions can be expected.

Interstitial Condensation

Every wall of conventional material such as brick or stone contains air in the pores or interstices which in turn holds moisture which may condense when the temperature of the air falls to the level of the dew-point. Such condensation within the thickness of a wall is called "interstitial condensation".

Let us assume for the purpose of considering the question of interstitial condensation an ordinary 9-inch (229mm) brick wall. If the inner face of the wall is at a temperature above the dew-point and the outer face of the wall is at a temperature below the dew-point, condensation may be expected to occur at some point in the wall itself. If the outer face of the wall is permeable to moisture the condensation which may form in the interior of the wall should not be troublesome under normal conditions since the moisture will be allowed to evaporate gradually to the cooler side of the wall, namely to the exterior. If, however, the outer face of the wall is impermeable as it would be, for example, if it were coated externally with a hard impervious layer of painted plaster or stucco, the condensed moisture will be bottled up in the wall and may saturate the walling material if the conditions remain sufficiently static to allow this to happen over a long period of time. In most cases where traditional materials are used interstitial condensation does not present much of a threat, although in the case of a brick or stone wall with bond timbers or wood lintels or bressumers, conditions leading to bad condensation over a prolonged period could cause rot in the wood members particularly at points where the grain is most exposed.

Interstitial condensation can form in a number of ways to different parts of the structure. In the case of a wall with a stone outer face and a cavity and inner permeable lining, warm moist air will penetrate the inner lining and condense on the inner face of the stonework. Other forms of cavity walls are subject to interstitial condensation to a greater or less degree but it is not only to walls that this type of condensation can occur, and it will be appreciated that solid floors may be subject to the same problem. In the case of a solid floor, of, for example, hardwood blocks laid with a damp proof membrane over a 4-inch (102mm) layer of concrete and a 6-inch (152mm) bed of hardcore, the sub-floor will in most cases be damp and cold and the room warm. Vapour accordingly will condense at the level of the damp proof course. A further complication with interstitial condensation is to roofs. With certain pitched roofs moisture vapour will penetrate permeable ceilings and will condense on the undersides of the roof coverings. In severe cases the condensation will drip into the building, but it is more probable that ventilation between the ceiling and the roof covering will remove condensation as it forms. With flat roofs, however, particularly with certain types of modern flat roofs, a much more serious problem arises. Roofs covered with asphalt, bituminous felt or any of the metals are not only watertight on their top surfaces but vapour tight as well and consequently, in cold weather, warm, moist air permeates from below and deposits moisture on the underside of the covering in amounts that will cause very heavy condensation. In traditional roofs of flat construction, the depth of the timber joists and the air space between a traditional lath and plaster or plasterboard ceiling and the undersides of the boards on which the flat roofing material is laid is sufficient in most cases to allow the condensed moisture to evaporate by ventilation, or by absorption into the timber members. The moisture is in most cases effectively dispersed in this manner so that rot is not caused, but often inspection of the undersides of roof boarding reveals considerable discoloration and staining for this reason. It is in other cases, however, where interstitial condensation can present a real threat. Recent developments in flat roof construction have encouraged the use of thermal insulation panels as a decking material instead of the traditional timber boarding. Compressed straw panels are often used for this purpose and insufficient attention is paid to the manufacturer's instructions in regard to adequate ventilation. Where such panels are laid in conditions where dampness cannot disperse, interstitial condensation penetrating a permeable ceiling will form on the undersides of the panels, penetrate the paper surface and will saturate the compressed straw body of the material. The result of this will be that the character of the panel will be changed completely. This may vary from the panel becoming soft and mushy to conditions being created where fungal attacks are set up in the straw.

Remedies Against Condensation

(1) General Internal Measures for Surface Condensation

A. Kitchens and Bathrooms

(1) Cookers and other equipment producing steam but particularly washing machines should be provided with hoods and ventilated to the outside air.

(2) Kitchen and bathroom doors should be well fitting or if necessary draught-proofed in order to prevent moist air from entering other rooms.

(3) Natural ventilation should be provided by means of an opening top light to a window or through a purpose-made ventilating unit.

Alternatively an extract fan high up near the ceiling is the best remedy against an exposed position where the winds may prevent moist air escaping by natural ventilation. An air brick at low level to provide an inlet to maintain a constant flow of air through the window or extract fan is a further possibility.

(4) Kitchens and bathrooms should be kept warm.

(5) Occupiers with the use of common sense can keep the emission of steam to reasonable proportions in their activities. Mixing valves are a considerable help but even if not fitted the running of both hot and cold taps at the same time can reduce the amount of steam in a bathroom.

B. Habitable Rooms

(1) A constant level of background heating should be maintained. The temperature indoors should be kept at a higher level than the temperature outdoors.

(2) Water vapour that can be absorbed by the air in the room should be expelled and all main rooms where flueless gas or oil heaters will be used should be ventilated preferably through a flue or air brick. Where large amounts of water vapour are likely to be released this should be extracted by mechanical ventilation. In other cases natural ventilation through an opening top light or a purpose-made unit should be sufficient with the assistance of an air brick to supply an alternative route for the air to enter the room and thus assist an air change with the help of the windows.

(3) Thermal insulation should be added to cold surfaces. It should be remembered that insulation without heat is not a

621

satisfactory remedy in itself but nevertheless a number of remedial measures can be taken. Double glazed windows with two separate panes of glass in a sealed unit are becoming more and more in use, not only to prevent condensation but to reduce heat loss. Conventional single pane windows can be prevented from misting up by rubbing the inside with a cloth dipped in a mixture of equal parts of glycerine and methylated spirits. The only drawback of this treatment is that it must be carried out afresh every time the window is cleaned. Metal areas that attract heavy condensation can be covered with an absorbent thermal insulation material such as sprayed asbestos. So far as the question of anti-condensation paints and other measures are concerned much depends on the degree and variety of condensation that is to be expected and the question of paints and finishes for walls and ceilings will be discussed below.

Paints and Finishes for Walls and Ceilings in relation to condensation

The application of certain paints and finishes can only help to lessen the consequences of acute condensation when dripping actually occurs from walls and ceilings. They are subsidiary to the methods of reducing or preventing condensation set out in the previous section of this Chapter but on the basis that all practicable steps of that sort have been taken within the bounds of what is possible economically, a good deal of help can nevertheless be provided by the careful selection of the right type of wall finish or paint. The treatment, however, will depend on the severity of the conditions that the surveyor finds. It is of course possible to provide either an absorbent surface or an impermeable surface. In conditions where condensation occurs without sufficiently long intervals for any appreciable drying to occur, there can be no question of the absorption of condensed moisture as walls and ceiling surfaces may run with moisture continuously. Indeed, if an absorbent surface is provided, this could well become saturated and deteriorate rapidly. The most that can be done in these circumstances is to ensure that the surface treatments are of a type that will not suffer under continual damp. Although such conditions are not likely to occur in the house itself, there could be out-buildings that could well come within this category. A large double garage, for example, which is heated intermittently, may well be a case in point and other buildings such as stores, workshops or barns, may suffer from this problem in a similar way. In country districts some larger houses have an impressive range of out-buildings, all of which are used in connection with the house itself or alternatively are used for some ancillary purpose, perhaps as part of a farm.

Where wall and ceiling surfaces run with moisture continuously, brickwork, concrete or concrete blocks are best left untreated, bearing in mind that bricks of high sulphate content may incur sulphate attack and expansion of the mortar, a point to be checked by reference to the durability of the bricks in other parts of the property. Plastering, should this be necessary, is best carried out in Portland cement and sand or Portland cement lime sand mixes. Decoration should be limited to cement based paints applied to either brickwork or concrete or plaster surfaces. Glazed bricks or tiles may be employed provided that they can be used in conjunction with Portland cement mortar to a strong background such as brickwork or alternatively impervious materials such as vitrolite and asbestos cement are suitable, but panels that have to be jointed present the obvious weakness that the jointing material must be as impermeable as the panels themselves, otherwise penetration will occur and the fixings will deteriorate. Whatever the type of wall surface provided in conditions of acute condensation, provision will have to be made for the water that streams down vertical surfaces to be removed.

When dry intervals are sufficiently long to allow most of the condensed moisture to dry away, absorbent treatments may be used provided that the background to which they are applied is not readily affected by moisture. An absorbent rendering based on Portland cement and lime may accordingly be used in such cases. In conditions where condensation occurs for short periods on most days but the surface dries quickly, and remains dry in between these periods, for example, the majority of bathrooms and kitchens, the range of acceptable finishes widens. Gypsum or gauged lime plasters painted with an impermeable paint are suitable, since the paint keeps the plaster sufficiently dry to prevent deterioration that would otherwise occur in protracted wet conditions. Absorbent paint treatments may also be used but only if the backing is not affected by moisture and accordingly distemper should not be used on gypsum or lime plasters. Absorbent surfaces are desirable, however, for ceilings, so that dripping is avoided. Cork-filled and anti-condensation paints are often sufficient to prevent moisture streaming down walls or dripping from projections and porous decorations of this type may be applied to porous backgrounds even when such background materials are of a type that would be damaged by exposure to moisture.

The reader is referred to the British Standard Code of Practice C.P.231 of 1966 "Painting of Buildings" for the answers to many of the points that he may need to know when dealing with painted and other finishes to walls and ceiling surfaces subject to condensation. The following are the major points made.

The first requirement, as always, prior to redecoration, and particularly where condensation is expected, is that the old surface must be thoroughly cleaned down and made good. If grease has been absorbed into a porous surface, more than just surface washing may be required. Grease may be removed by poulticing, that is by the application of a paste of whiting and white spirit which when dried is brushed off and the application repeated if necessary. The second requirement is that the background for the application of the new paint must be dry, particularly with impermeable paints, and painting should be applied by a brush rather than by a spray. The use of blow lamps to remove a limited amount of surface moisture is often permitted but the penalty for incautious use may well involve burning down the house that the surveyor is trying to repair and maintain. The third requirement is that the new decoration must be compatible with the backing and with the old decoration since an emulsion paint would clearly be unsuitable over a gloss oil paint, and a cement paint is unsuitable over an old oil paint or gypsum plaster.

In certain circumstances where condensation occurs, mould or mildew will form. For a slight infection it is often sufficient to apply a fungicidal wash once the surface has been cleaned. Fungicidal paints are particularly useful in preventing the growth of mould during the early stages of the hardening of the paint employed, but will not prevent the growth of mould on deposits of dirt and grease collected on the surface subsequently. Fungicides for the treatment of moulds are to some extent toxic to humans and the manufacturer's directions for application should be followed with care.

The British Standard Code of Practice C.P.231 of 1966 "Painting of Buildings" suggests that on porous surfaces, such as bare plaster where appreciable quantities of water may condense and be absorbed without being noticed, that the plaster be painted with a porous water paint or distemper. In this way the absorbent nature of the surface can be preserved. Water paints and distempers, however, tend to peel or flake off when exposed to frequent repetitions of wetting and drying. Oil paints are less easily damaged by water than are water paints and distempers and some types of flat oil paint are sufficiently porous to allow moderate absorption of condensed moisture. Some plastic paints of high absorptive capacity can be used similarly to absorb condensation although some of these become soft and are best used out of reach.

The Code of Practice C.P.231 suggests that for rooms such as bathrooms and kitchens, the choice of paint will usually lie between a non-absorbent gloss paint, which is easily cleaned but sheds all the water condensed on it, and a porous flat paint or suitable synthetic resin emulsion paint, which may absorb most of the moisture, but is less hygienic and more readily disfigured.

(2) *Remedies Against Interstitial Condensation*

To Walls

We have seen how condensation can form in the pores or interstices of a wall where the external temperature is below the dew-point and the internal temperature is above the dew-point. Remedies to prevent interstitial condensation may be simple or complicated depending on circumstances, but the first and most obvious step is to ensure that the indoor humidity is left at a low level by adequate heating and ventilation. If this in itself, however, is not enough, the surveyor must ensure that the warm air from the room cannot pass through the inner face of the wall into the interior of the walling material. The way in which this done is by the provision of a "vapour barrier". This barrier is placed at or near the inner surface of the wall and impervious materials such as aluminium foil or bitumen papers coated on both sides are employed. If bituminous paints are used, these must be renewed at intervals to ensure that the efficiency of the vapour barrier is kept up. Distempers are almost useless for the purpose of a vapour barrier. A really effective vapour barrier must be impermeable and materials like polythene, bituminous felt, sprayed P.V.C., metal foil and bituminous felt are the most widely used for efficient vapour barriers and since to be fully efficient the barrier must be continuous the joints are normally lapped and welted between sections or made with hot bitumen. A plain lap joint is rarely satisfactory for long. The vapour barrier should be placed on the warm side of the construction and the temperature at the vapour barrier must be higher than the dew-point temperature and to achieve this it is first necessary to fix some thermal insulation on the cold side of the vapour barrier.

If the provision of a fully effective vapour barrier is not practicable, for example where only a limited amount of time and money is allowed for the work, a suggested paint treatment for use on the inside surface under less severe conditions would be for two coats of an aluminium primer to be applied with two coats of oil paint over as the decorative finish.

There will be times when the surveyor finds a framed structure either as an addition to the dwelling house or as part of the basic building. Under such circumstances if a vapour barrier is to be provided it is desirable to ventilate any cavity behind the sheeting to the outside air if possible. The problem with claddings is complicated in that when the outdoor temperature falls at night rapid

625

cooling takes place. This cooling is much accentuated on still clear nights as the cladding is then able to lose more heat by radiation to the sky so that its temperature may fall several degrees below the outdoor temperature. Dew or even hoar frost is then formed on the cladding to the outside and if outdoor air has access to the inner surface moisture will be deposited here as well. The severe cooling of the cladding will, in any event, lead to a heavier deposit of water from inside the building than would otherwise occur. Alternatively this may cause condensation to take place on clear nights when this would not otherwise happen. Fortunately clear nights are often associated with sunny days so that there is generally ample opportunity for the condensation to evaporate during the following day. Water running down the face of the cladding under such circumstances must be tolerated and provision made for it to drain away at the base. There must, however, be no "bridges" to carry water from the cladding to the internal linings.

The Vapour Barrier to Walls

A vapour barrier to the inner wall faces of a dwelling house can be provided by one of the following methods:

(a) With the use of thin sheets of the self-extinguishing grade of expanded polystyrene. These can be stuck to the inner wall face and it is possible to provide a plaster finish if required.

(b) With the use of aerated plastics. These are pumped into a cavity wall through small holes drilled in the outer face.

(c) With linings of fibreboard, plasterboard or asbestos insulation board. These should be built on battens leaving an air space between the wall and the lining. The linings should comply with the requirements of the Building Regulations 1972 for surface spread of flame.

Linings can cause trouble if warm moist air passes through them to condense, possibly in a cavity, causing the deterioration of surrounding materials. It is recommended that humid air entering into the construction should be stopped with the use of materials that are themselves impervious or that can be given an impervious surface treatment such as gloss paint. Alternatively a vapour barrier can be placed immediately behind the lining sheet.

In certain parts of the country where the use of stone for walls is more common than brick, as in most areas of Scotland, a stone wall often has an external absorptive rendering of cement lime or lime mortar or roughcast known as harling. The internal faces of the stone walls have for very many years been provided with linings of plaster fixed on wood straps or laths fixed to "dooks" driven into

626

the walls. Dooks consist of metal or rot-resistant wood sections fixed in the stonework to give a $\frac{1}{4}$-inch (6mm) clearance from the wall face so that the straps or laths are clear of the stone at every point. The straps or laths are nowadays pressure impregnated against rot or plaster lath (plasterboard in narrow strips) is used to form the usual base for plasterwork. If metal lath is used this must be protected against corrosion and hessian is commonly used as a base to prevent the plaster squeezing through the laths to bridge the air space behind. Many different wall linings will be found in country districts and the writers recall instances where the plaster faces of rooms to masonry houses will be flexible to the touch, subsequent investigation showing that these are of plaster on a base of hessian fixed free of the wall surface.

It should be emphasised that the traditional methods are by no means to be discarded or replaced unless circumstances warrant such a step. If there is enough movement of air in the room and the humidity is at a low level and the heating is sufficiently satisfactory and not intermittent, condensation may not be a problem, but in the lack of any of these factors, a vapour barrier and a rather more efficient wall lining is required. Foil backed plasterboard may be used for this purpose but it is suggested in the case of masonry walls which are likely to be damp that small grilles in the skirting should be provided to ventilate the cavity. If a traditional plaster finish is required the vapour barrier could take the form of building paper, but much will depend on the circumstances of each individual case.

Wall linings can also be provided of 2-inch (51mm) concrete blocks fixed clear of the inner wall face so as to provide a 2-inch (51mm) ventilated cavity. The blocks if built with care can be arranged so that the inner face of the lining can be linked with the impervious membrane in a new solid floor, but the chief difficulty with linings of this type, is that they are a little wasteful of floor space and present difficulties of detailing at window and door openings, though these are by no means insuperable.

The Vapour Barrier to Roofs and Ceilings

With pitched roofs of traditional construction built prior to the Second World War there is seldom any need to take special measures against condensation forming at either ceiling level or to the underside of the roof coverings. The reason for this is that even under the worst conditions the plaster ceilings of traditional early pattern are generally reasonably permeable and the moisture laden air penetrating the plaster enters a tall and lofty roof space. Due to the lack of insulation provided by the ceiling, the temperature in the roof space is not a great deal lower than that of the room below and the small amount of moisture that finally condenses on the underside of the roofing material is removed by evaporation due to the penetration of the wind through the eaves of the roof and the components forming the roof covering. The lack of an impervious layer under the roof slopes can be criticised from the point of view of heat loss but there is little prospect of condensed moisture collecting and dripping from the roof slopes on to the plaster ceilings below. The traditional flat roofs of joists and boards with surface coverings of either asphalt, bituminous felt or one of the metals are also reasonably well adapted to resist condensation due to the depth of the air space between the boards below the roof covering and the ceiling and although moisture laden air may permeate the lath and plaster ceiling it is either dispersed in the air space, particularly if this should be ventilated, or partially absorbed by the timber. With both pitched and flat roofs to properties built prior to the Second World War it is now becoming commonplace for insulation to be provided immediately above the ceiling level but the purpose of this is to prevent heat loss and counteract pattern staining rather than to provide an effective barrier against condensation.

It is with modern roofs that condensation can present the most serious problems. Condensation in pitched roofs covered with single lap tiling or slates or sheet materials which do not require continuous support often have an underlay of roofing felt or heavy building paper, the ceilings below being of plasterboard with aluminium foil insulating backing. The outer coverings, however, are not wind tight and the roof spaces above ceiling level become cool. The aluminium foil, being a reflective insulator, resists losses due to radiation which accounts for about half the heat loss through roof spaces but the foil has very little effect on convective or conductive heat loss.

If the roof space is cool and there is a good deal of moisture vapour in the room below, this will rise and diffuse through the plaster to condense against the foil and in extreme conditions will saturate the plaster and thus rob this material of its insulative quality. The ceiling will accordingly remain saturated in extreme conditions but may have wet and dry periods if rooms are in intermittent use such as, for example, a bedroom that is left empty during the day. If on the other hand the foil vapour barrier is omitted and a porous insulator such as loose vermiculite or fibreglass is placed over plain plasterboard the moisture vapour will rise through this into the roof space and condense on the underside of the roofing felt or alternatively penetrate the laps between the felted sections and gather on the colder undersides of the outer roof coverings. It has been found that vapour barriers at ceiling level are seldom perfect and where condensation is still troublesome the roof space should be ventilated. It is recommended that ventilation holes under the eaves on two opposite sides of the building are provided, these holes giving a minimum free area of half a square inch per foot run of the eaves (323mm² per 300mm).

It would seem, however, that the best remedy is to allow a foil vapour barrier to remain at ceiling level and to increase the insulation on the warm side of the barrier by some other means. In cases where penetration is not severe a layer of absorbent ceiling paper coated with water-thinned or emulsion paint may be sufficient while in cases where trouble from condensation is extreme a ¾ or 1 inch (19 or 25mm) thick air pocketed insulation material of a non-porous nature is desirable as a replacement for the ceilings. Lightweight cellulose fibres can be obtained in proprietary forms for this purpose.

If moist air can be excluded from roof spaces vermiculite or glass-fibre can be placed over the tops of ceilings or to the undersides of rafters. Any new insulation, however, must conform to the provisions of the Building Regulations 1972 with regard to the spread of flame. Expanded polystyrene is a substance much in use at the present time and tiles of this material are becoming commonplace as a covering for ceilings, particularly to bathrooms and kitchens. It is extremely important, however, that if this material is employed that the self-extinguishing grade is used.

Where flat roofs or very low pitch roofs covered externally with bituminous felt, asphalt or metal are encountered these will not only be watertight on the top surface, but vapour tight as well. In cold weather warm moist air will permeate from below in the absence of a vapour barrier and deposit moisture on the underside of the covering in amounts sufficient to cause dripping. As mentioned earlier, the big danger is not so much the penetration of water vapour through the ceilings although this can be extremely irritating under severe conditions but the risk of saturation setting up mould growth or fungus in a material such as compressed straw slabs when the manufacturers' recommendations regarding ventilation are not followed. It is recommended that moisture is prevented from entering the roof by the provision of a vapour barrier on the ceiling or alternatively at higher level as shown in Figure 72. Roof ventilators or a ventilated underlay should be provided so that any entrapped water vapour can be enabled to escape. Additional thermal insulation may be necessary under some circumstances and in particular the ceilings if of foil backed plasterboard should be subject to the same treatment as suggested previously.

The Vapour Barrier to Floors

Condensation may be a troublesome matter with floors that are basically of solid concrete construction and which are only heated intermittently, such as dwellings unoccupied during the day, since the floors are slow to warm and if there is a sudden rise in humidity, the floor remaining cold will cause temporary condensation.

Where a permeable floor finish is bedded on a damp proof course such as mastic or P.V.C. sheeting the damp proof course will, in effect, form the vapour barrier. If, on the other hand, the surface of the flooring is impermeable, such as wood blocks covered with a sealer type of polish, the surface of the blocks will then provide a sufficiently effective vapour barrier for moisture to condense on the surface. Since the vapour barrier should be on the warm side of the insulation the latter set of circumstances is preferable to risking the build-up of moisture at damp proof course level since dampness may disrupt the adhesive or cause saturation or decay.

(3) Condensation in Flues

Before leaving the subject of condensation a word must be said regarding flues. The surveyor will already have noted during his inspection any damp patches on chimney breasts or any signs of bad staining which might be caused by the condensation of flue gases. Other stains might be caused by simple condensation inside a flue which is no longer in use and which has been sealed up without any provision for ventilation being made. Undoubtedly, however, the most serious effects to domestic flues are provided from the products of gas fired or solid fuel boilers. The effects go far beyond mere damp and discoloration and extend to complete disruption of the brickwork of which the flue and the chimney stack is composed. Solid, oil, and gaseous fuels all contain hydrogen and the process of combustion is a chemical one which requires oxygen. Hydrogen then combines with oxygen in the proportion of one pound of hydrogen to eight pounds of oxygen to give nine pounds of water. The amount of moisture vapour thus released is, therefore, immense. This is in itself sufficient to cause moisture penetration and damp staining to an irritating degree but another interesting if gloomy aspect of fuel combustion is that carbon dioxide and sulphur dioxide when combined with water can produce liquid acids, both carbonic and sulphuric. These have a disruptive effect on building materials and as the products of combustion from solid fuel and gas-fired boilers rise slowly up the interior of the flue condensation takes place on the inner surfaces and the acids thereupon attack the parging and brickwork behind. Where the flue is part of an outside wall or the stack is very tall it will be appreciated that the conditions for disruption of the brickwork are intensified. Once sulphate attack has got a grip there is little alternative but for an exposed chimney stack to be rebuilt.

Most old flues are, or course, not lined in any way and indeed have probably lost most of their original parging. Many cases arise where new central heating boilers discharge into old brick flues from which the interior parging has mostly departed leaving the brick joints open to attack from the products of combustion.

If substantial repair work and reconstruction is being carried out to a property which involves opening up or wholly or partially re-building an old flue in any event, salt-glazed, stoneware pipes, sulphate resistant cement or high silica (refractory) bricks bedded in fire cement or sulphate resistant cement mortar can be incorporated as the flue is rebuilt so that current sound practice is followed as for new work. Where on the other hand the flue is not to be re-built the surveyor must find an economic method of providing an efficient lining that does not involve opening up the brickwork or alternatively limits the amount of structural work to a minimum. Stainless steel flue linings can be obtained in the form of flexible tubes which can be threaded down from the top of the stack in such a manner that only the pot and top courses will require rebuilding. Other flexible flue linings can be obtained consisting of two sheets of aluminium separated by a layer of building paper or an outer leaf of aluminium with a lead inner lining with a layer of building paper between the two metals. The former is recommended for oil-fired boilers while the latter is recommended for gas-fired boilers.

A specialist method of lining flues involves the use of dense concrete pipes of acid-resistant concrete which are lowered into the flue in sections and end jointed. The area between the circular flue pipes and the brickwork is grouted so that an extra lining is provided that is proof against gas penetration and condensation. More opening up, however, is usually required with this method.

Where metal soot doors are placed externally in flues in a manner that is typical of houses built between the two World Wars the inner face of the metal will attract considerable condensation which will spread into and stain the brickwork underneath. Double skin doors fixed so as to be airtight should improve matters. Where sulphating to stacks has occurred so that stains appear at the junction of a top floor ceiling and wall the formation of hygroscopic salts will mean that condensation is attracted in a manner that will almost certainly suggest that the flashings are defective and moisture is penetrating the joint between stack and roof coverings. If the flashings are found to be sound, however, the renewal of the plaster should settle the matter provided, of course, that the sulphate attacks are completely stopped.

RISING DAMPNESS

In existing dwelling houses of traditional pattern the walling materials are usually porous. It is indeed largely due to this characteristic that the traditional English dwelling house has been able to stand for years, often centuries beyond the life span that might be expected of it, enduring the buffetting of wind and weather and, perhaps, intermittent and haphazard attempts at maintenance. We have seen in the section dealing with penetrating damp how conditions in the British Isles rarely remain constant for long and although some districts are wetter than others there is normally sufficient time for porous brickwork which admits moisture in damp conditions to allow the moisture to disperse by evaporation when times are dry. It has also been seen how one of the qualities of a good brick is an even texture since a brick with a hard face but with a porous interior is a bad brick. Certain walling materials such as granite and engineering bricks are, however, highly resistant to moisture penetration and by no means porous. It has already been seen how, if walling units of this type are bedded in jointing mortar of a porous nature the wall as a whole will not be proof against dampness since moisture will penetrate and creep back through the porous joints to appear on the inside face. The effect of this action is all the more intense as the moisture travels swiftly down the paths open to it since it has little chance of escaping into the almost impervious blocks of which the wall is composed. It is clear, therefore, that one of the main characteristics of a sound wall is that it should be of an even porosity throughout.

We have also seen how dampness can penetrate downwards through chimney stacks, copings and parapet walls, if these features are not constructed according to the soundest principles and with satisfactory materials.

Yet another problem presents itself, however, due to water in the ground reaching the base of a wall. The ordinary concrete of which foundations to houses are composed is porous and, like the bricks above, is of a cellular nature. Ground water reaching the foot of a wall will, therefore, tend to rise in the walling materials and will continue to do so due to capillary action to varying degrees of intensity. This penetration of ground moisture is commonly known as rising dampness and it may not be confined merely to walls but can occur also to floors and other parts of the structure such as internal partitions which are in direct contact with the soil. The severity of rising dampness depends upon a variety of factors, the main three being the supply of water, the composition of the pore structure of the walling materials and the rate of evaporation from the wall surfaces. Sometimes rising dampness occurs to a degree that is simply astonishing even to the hardened surveyor, and in some houses the condition reaches the point where not only is the ground flooring seriously affected, but there are fears for the well-being of the joists of the floor above.

Before proceeding further with the question of repair it is first necessary to consider the question of the damp proof course. Damp proof courses are defined by the Building Research Establishment as barriers so placed in a building that the passage of moisture between the parts they separate is negligible. Such a definition is applied equally to damp proof courses provided to all parts of the structure. In the case of moisture rising from the ground the definition for present purposes can be particularised to refer to a horizontal layer of impervious material placed at the base of a wall in order to prevent moisture rising from the ground into the walling material. Damp proof courses are needed in walls below or at about ground floor level not only to prevent moisture from rising in the walling material and plaster of the ground floor rooms and spoiling the decorations but also to prevent moisture from reaching the timbers of the ground floor if this is of joist and boarded construction and setting up wet or dry rot. Damp proof courses are also needed in the same manner to basement walls and below basement floors and further damp proof courses of a vertical type are necessary to basement walls in order to prevent ground moisture from penetrating the basement rooms in a lateral direction. For the moment, however, we will consider horizontal damp proof courses alone.

Under the Public Health Act 1875 the provision of a damp proof course became compulsory to dwelling houses for the first time. The first damp proof courses provided were not always efficient and in the large number of houses being built at the end of the last century, damp proof courses of slate or of bituminous felt were the most common. Many damp proof courses of this period prior to the outbreak of the First World War are still perfectly satisfactory since these consist of two courses of slate laid in cement mortar. Where, however, slate damp proof courses were laid in lime mortar some deterioration will have occurred and in a great many cases the damp proof courses of bituminous felt provided at the same time will by now prove to be defective. This is partly due to age deterioration and to the fact that the material was not laid to proper laps and joints and partly also to the fact that the methods of production were not fully satisfactory so that the bituminous compound was laid unevenly over a hessian base which subsequently rotted leaving weaknesses that invited damp penetration once the building had been erected. Again, the sub-contract system of providing cheap housing often left the provision of the damp proof course to men who were working against time in any event and considered the incorporation of the bits of slate or felt in the walling material as an irritating and rather unnecessary complication.

Damp proof courses in current practice are required at the foot of a wall at least 6 inches (152mm) above the external ground level and below the level of any woodwork forming part of the ground floor construction. In the case of cavity walls it is particularly important that the cavities are kept clear above the line of the damp proof course. Where rooms or floors occur below the level of the exterior ground the damp proof course must insulate all the walling and flooring materials from contact with the earth. A number of damp proof course materials are suitable against rising dampness and British Standard 743:1970 "Materials for damp proof courses" has already been referred to in the case of those damp proof courses coming within the classification of flexible and semi-rigid. In the case of rigid damp proof courses of slates or bricks, only suitable for use near ground level, the standard emphasises the importance of correct laying since the efficiency of a rigid damp proof course in particular depends as much on the composition of the mortar and the workmanship in bedding slates or bricks as upon the intrinsic quality of the materials. A slate damp proof membrane should consist of at least two courses of slates laid to break joint and a brick damp proof course should consist of at least two courses of brick also laid to break joint, the bricks being to B.S.3921 having no holes or indentations other than frogs. 1:3 cement/sand mortar is suitable in either case.

Once the surveyor has carried out his investigation he will assemble all the information he has obtained. His investigation may have involved taking up flooring, removing skirtings, taking away sections of external plinths and raking out joints to brickwork or masonry. He will have assessed the degree of penetration with the help of his moisture meter and will have formed an opinion as to the degree of moisture in the ground combined with the porosity and qualities of evaporation of the wall. He will have ascertained if a damp proof course is provided or not and if a damp proof course is provided if it has failed as a whole or only in part. He will have decided if failure is due to a sound damp proof course having been bridged on the one hand or, on the other hand, if it has been used under unsound circumstances or alternatively if the material forming the damp proof course itself is unsound. It is for this reason that

634

reference to British Standard 743 is important so that comparison
with the damp proof course provided in an old wall can be measured
against the types of damp proof course which would be specified at
the present time. It may be that a rigid material has proved defective simply because it has been used in the wrong position, for
example at the junction of a main structure and a bay window where
differential settlement has caused the damp proof course to fracture,
and moisture to penetrate the walling as a result. A primary requirement of an effective damp proof course is that it must run
through the whole thickness of the wall and not stop short of the
external face or be either pointed up in mortar or covered over with
a cement plinth. One of the minor exasperations in the life of a
surveyor is that any damp proof course incorporated prior to 1914
like the Victorian and Edwardian underwear of the time was designed to be kept out of sight and a damp proof course was only
thought to be decent if it was covered externally by either a thick
band of pointing or a deep plinth. This habit continued with houses
built between the two World Wars but at least the presence of a
damp proof course was more likely than otherwise at this period and
the type of damp proof course provided is fairly predictable according to the type of house under consideration. Once the surveyor has
formed an opinion as to whether the whole or any parts of an original
damp proof course are worth saving or not he can then consider what
measures are best applied to deal with the problem of rising dampness but before considering the various methods there is one more
aspect of rising dampness which should be mentioned.

If moisture rising in the brickwork from the ground was pure it
would only be necessary in the case of an existing house where no
damp proof course was provided or, alternatively, in a house provided
with a damp proof course which had failed, to provide a new barrier
against rising moisture from the ground. However, it is a fact that
ground water almost invariably contains dissolved salts which tend
to concentrate at the wall surfaces where the water evaporates. The
presence of these salts near the surface of the wall means that even
if the further rise of water is prevented the decorations will still be
spoiled. This is because some of the salts originally drawn into the
wall are hygroscopic, that is to say that they can absorb moisture
from the air so that the surface which contains them tends to become
damp whenever the air in the building is humid. Accordingly, in
addition to providing a barrier against rising dampness the replacement of salt contaminated plaster work is nearly always necessary.
The familiar and gloomy appearance of the horizontal "tidemark"
to the interior surfaces of walls below which stained and flaking
plaster with efflorescence or bleached or peeling wallpaper can be

observed with sometimes unpleasant formations of mould growth if the surfaces are persistently damp will indicate to the surveyor the extent of the plaster renewals to be expected, a generous allowance being added for safety.

There are three ways in which rising dampness can be dealt with. The first is to cure it permanently with the provision of a fully efficient damp proof course. The second is to limit the effects of the rising dampness by reducing the amount of moisture in the wall and by increasing the evaporation from it and thirdly, to conceal the rising dampness. In the third case an additional lining is provided to the wall so that the rising dampness although still there is simply not seen. It should of course be emphasised that the provision of a new damp proof course is the only fully effective way of removing rising dampness completely. The other methods are purely palliatives.

The Prevention of Rising Damp

(a) The insertion of a traditional damp proof course

There has been for a long time an accepted method of providing a new damp proof course to an existing wall. A bed joint in the brickwork is selected as the suitable position for the new damp proof course and this is traced all round the building to ensure that there are no obstructions in the way of the work. Two courses of brickwork are then removed, one above the bed joint selected and one below. It is, of course, never desirable to proceed along the length of one whole wall with this work in a single operation. The brickwork is cut out in alternate sections of 3 to 4 feet (0·9 to 1·2m) much in the same way as underpinning is carried out so that what was in effect a series of piers is left in place to carry the structure while new lengths of damp proof course are formed in the areas cut away. This might be in the form of a sandwich of lead, copper or bituminous felt between new courses of bricks carefully pinned up to the remainder above or as often as not of two courses of slates and a course of bricks laid on edge. These sections are then allowed to dry and the piers in turn are then cut away and treated in a similar manner being provided with lengths of damp proof course so that the whole membrane then forms a continuous line round the building. This method is still valid of course and is still often used but it may be superseded in time by the new techniques for cutting or grinding a narrow slot through a selected bed joint round the building. A cut may be made either by a hand saw or by one of several types of power-driven saw. A selected jamb or corner of the building is marked out so that the cut can be started in a position where it is not necessary to cut out bricks to commence the work. Once the cut penetrates the interior, the work is then often carried out from inside the building as being more convenient than working from the exterior. The Building Research Establishment have developed a chain saw whereby it is possible to mortice into a joint and thus work entirely from one side of a wall. Once the slot is cut the membrane is then immediately inserted and the work proceeds along the length of the wall. For normal domestic work the membrane can be prepared for insertion in lengths of about 1 ft. 9 ins. (0·5m) but in heavily loaded walls or at the junction of cross walls, shorter lengths are desirable.

According to the type of saw available and the type of mortar the surveyor encounters will depend his decision as to the material for the damp proof course that he will employ, but whatever the membrane used it should be wide enough to project about $\frac{1}{4}$ inch (5mm) each side of the wall. It will be understood that a narrow slot produced in a wet and sticky mortar by a thin blade will require a thin rigid sheet as the appropriate membrane for insertion, due to the practical difficulty of trying to insert any other material, but in a dry or crumbly mortar, a wider slot is customary and this will require two layers of a thicker material to fill it. If a thin membrane is prepared and the slot turns out to be thicker than expected it would clearly not be desirable for the difference to be made up in mortar alone and under such circumstances the surveyor is recommended to see that slips of slate are wedged into the joint at intervals of about 12 inches (0·3m). Even when a membrane is a close fit there is inevitably slight settlement as the cut advances and according to the Building Research Establishment who have taken measurements on a test house a settlement of approximately $\frac{1}{16}$ inch (1·5mm) may be expected. If the joint is packed with care, however, the settlement can be limited to only half this amount and the wider slot and packing in this manner is accordingly recommended. Two types of membrane are commonly used for damp proof courses provided in this manner, the first being copper and the second being bituminous felt. Both are satisfactory subject to certain qualifications. Soft copper sheeting for example can be inserted into a wide slot without fear of damage and this is often more cheap and satisfactory in the end result than the half hard sheet required for driving into a narrow slot. Alternatively, two layers of bitumen felt each of 2 foot (0·6m) lengths may be inserted, placed so that the joints are staggered with at least a 3-inch (75mm) interval between the joints in the two layers. Other materials are available for use as a membrane but sheet zinc will only have a limited life of from ten to fifteen years as it is likely to be affected by the action of the mortar. The long-term durability of polythene which can also be employed is not as yet fully known, although it is offered as a suitable material extensively by specialist firms installing damp proof courses.

The types of damp proof course to be employed and the economics of the whole operation depend to a very large degree on the types of saws available for cutting the slot. These are:

(1) Hand saws and power-operated reciprocating saws. Reciprocating saws, hand and power-operated, are of mild steel with teeth tipped with tungsten carbide or stellite. The hand saw has a 42-inch (1,066mm) blade; the 3-inch (75mm) width being preferable to the 4-inch (100mm) wide blade normally supplied. For short periods a hand saw operated by two men is as quick as a power saw although the operation so near the ground is exhausting. Two types of power-operated reciprocating saw have been used; a light pneumatic model, weighing 2·5kg and designed to be held by the operator, and a more powerful type which requires a supporting frame for more continuous work. Other forms of saw may well be suitable such as the larger and more powerful tools used by specialist contractors, one of whom having developed a circular saw claimed to be highly efficient.

A disadvantage of reciprocating saws is that the swarf from the slot is not removed as the cut advances, and after a time this slows down the rate of working.

(2) Circular saws and chain saws. These have the advantage that the swarf is removed by the sweep of the blade but as the chain saws ordinarily used for cutting and dressing stone cut a slot that is too wide for damp proof course insertion a new chain saw blade has been developed at the Building Research Establishment for use with a lightweight petrol-driven chain saw. This unit can be carried and operated by one man and the development of this saw has overcome several limitations of the earlier methods of damp proof course insertion.

Before any work can start it is of course necessary for the line of the bedding course to be traced round the property. There is clearly little point in cutting through one wall if the next return wall has a higher exterior ground level so that it is then found that the section of a higher bed joint would have provided a more effective solution to the problem. Although the minimum of 6 inches (150mm) should be retained as the standard distance between the exterior ground level and the height of the damp proof course, this distance may have to be modified in the case of solid floors to the interior if this height is insufficient to allow an adequate working space for the saw above the level of the floor slab. Certain difficulties are provided by this method with party walls where joint agreement is obviously necessary and particularly in a case of chimney breasts where these are back to back. In this case it is possible to insert narrow widths of membrane around the chimney breast with the fire back in position and this protection combined with the heat from the fire may suffice to keep the chimney breast fairly dry. The Building Research Establishment have found that this technique of inserting damp proof courses by cutting a slot is safe for a wide variety of dwellings provided that care and common sense are exercised by ensuring firstly that all vertical joints immediately above the slot are filled with mortar, otherwise the brickwork may not bridge the slot, and secondly that walls are reasonably plumb and are stiffened by returns or by partitions. Some old walls built in two leaves may present particular problems and where the brickwork is very frail, care is obviously very necessary. The bed joints may be broken and the jointing internally may be found to be very powdery so that as the saw passes, areas of brickwork may become loose and drop. Bricks that are very loose should be removed and then after the membrane is inserted replaced as headers bedded in mortar and wedged with slate. Bricklayers carrying out the work are advised to have several sandbags filled with a dry cement sand mix which can then be prepared quickly to meet emergencies. Again, if any unduly hard areas stand in the way of the saw these should be removed before cutting is commenced, as even the common, if wrong, practice of pointing areas of brickwork affected with rising dampness in hard cement mortar or providing a coating of cement rendering can present a problem as trying to cut through these will cause excessive wear to the saw blades. Areas such as this should be worked on separately with a cold chisel beforehand or preferably dealt with by means of a grinding disc either fitted in an angle grinder or as a separate unit driven by the portable engine which would in any case be necessary to drive the chain saw. A batten on supports fixed free of the wall and aligned with the bed joint provides a convenient method of supporting and guiding the grinding disc. Such a fitting is desirable as a grinding disc makes a much neater job of cutting a groove in an exterior wall face than the saw and in the case of ornamental brick plinths or other circumstances a grinding disc may be of definite advantage. A neat cut about $\frac{1}{4}$-inch (7mm) wide can be obtained when two carborundum-faced grinding discs are clamped to the same spindle.

A very recent development in slot cutting technique employs the use of a grinding disc driven by a portable motor via a flexible drive. The glass fibre discs impregnated with carborundum are up to 24 inches (0·6m) in diameter and are provided with a shield connected to a vacuum extractor. Due to the fact that dust is almost completely taken away the workmen do not have to wear masks and can work in confined spaces. The machine is hand-held and the method has been shown to be satisfactory both with irregularly coursed brickwork and with brickwork set in cement mortar.

The methods described above, both the traditional, which is still ideally suited to a small-scale operation being familiar to most contractors, and the more modern technique using saws, probably more suitable for situations where a number of properties are being dealt with, provide the property with a damp proof course of a type which might have been provided if the property were to be built now. The two following methods which have been developed since the Second World War seek to achieve the same effect of preventing rising dampness by the insertion of a barrier but by entirely different means.

(b) *The Infusion or Injection of Damp Proof Barriers*

A moisture barrier can now be set up in an existing wall by either infusing or injecting water repellent substances into holes drilled at regular intervals along the base of the brickwork or masonry. The most commonly used technique is that of infusions employing a siliconate solution in water which is introduced into the wall by the influence of gravity and changes after infusion to form a water repellent band. Another technique is that of injection employing a siliconate/latex mixture which is forced into the wall under high pressure. Although now widely used these methods are probably best suited to walls which are too thick or too unstable for the insertion of a conventional damp proof course.

The selection of the correct process for individual cases depends on the circumstances. The infusional treatment is well suited to walls which have both surfaces exposed to air and the reliance on gravity feeding of the solution ensures that with correct methods and with normal walling thorough impregnation assisted by capillary action takes place. On the other hand, for a wall where only one side is open to treatment and where perhaps some degree of water pressure is present on the side that is inaccessible the injection process is the better one. There is some danger with injection that the forceful nature of the penetration may result in some parts of the walling being by-passed resulting in an uneven treatment. The injection method is best employed when some counter pressure from another source ensures that the siliconate/latex mixture is forced into all the pores of the walling material.

The infusion of a water based siliconate moisture barrier requires the removal of the skirtings and plaster damaged by hygroscopic salts from the interior surfaces of the main walls. The skirtings are later replaced once the plaster is renewed but in the meantime holes

640

are drilled in the softer parts of the walls near the base in a horizontal line, a 9-inch (229mm) wall either being pierced completely and the holes then being plugged so that the solution is not allowed to dribble out of the wall before it spreads into the bricks.

Alternatively the holes stop short of the opposite face by a short distance. In the case of walls thicker than $13\frac{1}{2}$ inches (343mm) the mortar bed joint is drilled from either side, the ends of the holes overlapping. Cavity walls are also drilled "blind" whereupon injection takes place from both sides. In the case of irregular brick and stone walls or random rubble walls it is not possible to drill the holes in a regular horizontal line. The holes are therefore drilled at the most suitable points at an angle extending downwards so that the solution is effectively retained. If the wall is thick it is drilled from either side or alternatively right through from both sides and in the case of rubble-filled walls care is needed to ensure that the drilling penetrates into the heart of the walling material, even although it may be necessary first to grout the core of a wall if this is very friable.

Once the holes are prepared the fluid is introduced by tubes connected to bottles supported on metal racks. The bottles are at an appropriate height to allow a slight pressure due to gravity and each hole is then topped up with fluid until absorption has ceased or has slowed down to minute proportions. An alternative method in use is to provide small gutters or troughs secured to the wall along the line of the holes which, if kept topped up, ensure that a horizontal line of holes is filled with fluid simultaneously. Once the infusion is complete the gutters or bottles and pipes are withdrawn and the holes are filled with mortar mixed with similar additives to those used for the main treatment and well caulked in.

There are of course complications with this type of treatment, one of which is the irritating habit of holes in a thick wall drilled at a downward angle to become clogged before the tubes can be introduced. Often these have to be washed out with a water jet to prepare the way for infusion. On the other hand, there is no doubt that with rubble walls the infusion method of providing a damp proof barrier presents enormous advantages over other techniques, such as cutting a slot for a membrane since it is not only easier and quicker but is not likely to lead to the difficulties of cutting away and pinning up that that may involve. Again, where there is restricted working space or part of a wall is inaccessible the infusion method presents advantages.

The disadvantages of the infusion or injection methods of providing damp proof barriers are that they rely to a very great extent on the knowledge and experience of the specialist firm concerned and on the thoroughness and sense of responsibility of their workmen. It will be appreciated that the selection of the appropriate method, the way in which the holes are drilled, the efficiency of the fluid and the amount of time that is allowed for its absorption are all crucial matters to the efficiency of the final result and are matters over which the surveyor has no control. Moreover the techniques of infusion and injection change so that if the surveyor remonstrates with the firm regarding, for example, the size and spacing of the holes he is likely to find that he is out of date. The holes which first of all were about ¾ or 1 inch (19 or 25mm) in diameter and spaced at between 2 to 6 inch (51 to 152mm) intervals are now much smaller and are at much greater intervals apart.

There are several excellent specialist firms using these methods and where the surveyor has decided that the insertion of a conventional damp proof course is not possible and it is necessary for the provision of a damp proof barrier by either of these methods he will doubtless apply to a well-known firm who specialise in this work and who will provide a guarantee of the efficiency of their work for a period of at least twenty years. It is, therefore, perhaps rather obvious but nevertheless necessary to suggest that only those firms who are likely to be in a position over a long period of time to provide a firm backing for their guarantee be selected and the surveyor should look into this side of the matter just as a banker would do when assessing the stability of a customer for a Bank loan. The company approached will no doubt be pleased to supply details of their guarantee arrangements and if these have firm backing it will obviously be a comfort for the surveyor to know that in the event of matters going wrong his client has some redress. It is, however, not suggested that once the surveyor has completed enquiries of this sort that he should then wash his hands of the whole matter. Even if the specialist techniques are new to him it is as well for him to watch the operation being carried out so as to compare the different methods available.

(c) *The Prevention of Rising Damp by Electro-Osmosis*

For some time the prevention of the rise of ground water above a certain position in a wall has been possible by electrical means and a number of different systems are in use on the continent and in this country. The systems depend either on electrodes of similar metal being placed in the wall and in the ground and connected together or an electrical potential from an external source being applied between such electrodes. A related system has both sets of electrodes in the wall, one on the outside and the other at a high level inside. Another system has electrodes of one type of metal in the wall connected to those of another type in the ground, the dissimilar metals producing an electrical potential by galvanic action.

A specialist firm has been carrying out work in this field using a patent method for some years and providing a twenty-year guarantee. The firm in question is now able to claim that tens of thousands of houses have been dealt with and many local authorities make use of the firm's services for their own properties. These on the face of it are convincing reasons perhaps for recommending such a system and indeed most reports suggest that the system when installed is immediately effective. Yet despite the passage of some ten years or so the Building Research Establishment still point out that the scientific basis for systems of damp-proofing based on electro-osmosis is a subject of controversy and the system widely used in this country is being investigated.

There is therefore the evidence of many surveyors having been convinced by the immediately successful effect of the method into employing a system which is neither recommended or condemned in whole or in part by the responsible central government agency set up specifically for Building Research. It is not suggested that there is anything particularly unusual in this set of circumstances. After all, clients and their advisers are entitled to make up their own minds but tens of thousands of houses being dealt with represents a lot of money changing hands. It is interesting to speculate what could happen in the future. Obviously if the Building Research Establishment decide favourably on the merits of the system everyone will be happy, but it must be pointed out that they are taking a curiously long time in coming to a decision. Should, however, the systems already installed start to go wrong after, say, 21 years or so, it would have been better if another method had been selected in the first place.

So far the Building Research Establishment say that it has been reported that some of the systems employing dissimilar metals become inoperative after a few years because of electro-chemical corrosion of the electrodes and that it could be expected that similar corrosion would occur when metal electrodes are used in systems employing an external electrical potential. Since neither of these features are common to the method widely used in this country this cannot be counted a very useful comment. It may well be that before the Building Research Establishment is prepared to advise the consumer, in the form of the public on the long-term efficiency of the proprietary method widely used in this country, another twenty years will have elapsed. A responsible surveyor in the meantime, however, must surely discuss all these factors with his client before an electro-osmotic damp proof barrier is employed.

643

The Choice of Damp Proof Barrier

The three types of installation available to combat rising damp in, it is hoped, a permanent manner, have now been discussed. From the above comments it will be evident that the insertion of a traditional damp proof course has the merit of being tried and tested over many years. Installed in the old way of cutting out by a bricklayer and his mate or in the modern manner by cutting a slot it is certain, given good workmanship, to be successful. The other methods have been developed by specialists to meet a demand for this type of work, when the merits of older houses become more apparent, at prices somewhat less than the average builder could manage for the traditional damp proof course, either by the old cutting away method or by insertion in a pre-cut slot. Backed by a twenty-year guarantee the cheaper price naturally has had its attractions although any suggestion that the specialist methods involve less disturbance or are quicker is somewhat facile when it is necessary for a complete job to remove all damp and hygroscopic salt affected plaster whatever method is employed. Of course even the saving in price of the specialist methods is proportionally less when all the other works required, common to all methods, are included.

What sort of advice therefore should the surveyor give at the present time when approached on the subject of rising damp and a permanent cure? From the evidence available in 1972 the insertion of a traditional damp proof course of copper or lead cored bitumen felt must come still as the prime recommendation for any house with a life in excess of 10-15 years. Any work in connection with rising damp will be expensive enough anyway and clients attracted by savings in adopting specialist measures should be reminded that they are just not time tested and therefore the surveyor cannot recommend them, other circumstances being favourable, as there is a risk of spoiling the ship for a "haporth" of tar. Even the Building Research Establishment's approval of polythene as a material for horizontal damp proof courses in walls is suspect for the same reason. Whether it will be possible to vary this advice in a few years will remain to be seen.

The life of the building, economic considerations or the few occasions when technical considerations preclude the insertion of a traditional damp proof course will leave the surveyor and the client to consider what other method can be employed and it is here that the surveyor needs to indicate very carefully the pros and cons not only of the specialist methods but also of those methods to be discussed shortly of reducing the incidence of rising damp and those methods of concealing it. Unless one can be reasonably sure of permanence in the cure the field of choice surely becomes much wider and must embrace these other methods which might well prove to be more economical in the long run.

A word of warning however might suitably be inserted here. Much repair work to deal with rising damp is carried out in connection with the obtaining of Improvement Grants. All local authorities will approve for the purposes of grant the insertion of a traditional damp proof course. Not all authorities, however, will approve the use of the two specialist methods of infusion or injection or the electro-osmotic method for grant purposes. There is therefore a need *always* to check with the local authority concerned which methods meet with its approval and which do not. It is quite surprising how authorities vary and the same divergences of opinion extend to the approval of the various methods of reducing and concealing rising damp shortly to be described. Some favour one method whereas another authority will consider it quite unacceptable but before these methods are discussed a word might be included on replastering.

Replastering

Once a new barrier to rising damp is inserted in an old wall the question of the removal and replacement of the saturated plaster arises. Drying out within the thickness of the wall will immediately commence but the rate of such drying out will be slow and will of course depend on various factors for example the time of year, whether evaporation can take place from both sides of the wall and the amount of heating applied internally. A normal allowance in favourable circumstances is one month per inch (25mm) thickness and while this drying out takes place, hygroscopic salts are continually being brought to the surface. Accordingly it is advisable for the old plaster to be left in position for as long as possible so that the greatest amount of hygroscopic salt is deposited therein before removal. If old plaster can be left for a year or more so much the better but even so replastering should be carried out on a base of 1:6 cement and sand plasticised by means of an air entraining agent rather than a cement lime sand undercoat of similar strength. The aerated mix produced is more effective in impeding the passage both of moisture and salts and the plaster top coat should be finished by a porous form of decoration. It is usual to remove old plaster and re-plaster for a distance of about 2 feet (say 0·6m) beyond the staining for safety.

Limiting the Effects of Rising Dampness

(a) By Atmospheric Siphons

A patent method for the reduction of moisture contained at the base of a wall by drawing it out through a series of porous tubes inserted permanently in the brickwork has been in use for many years. The slight difference in temperature which occurs within the porous tubes is sufficient to enable moisture in the wall to evaporate and be discharged externally but the distance between the tubes and the angles of inclination have to be carefully calculated according to the type of wall and conditions found. Plenty of ventilation in the room is also required. The tubes are protected on the external face of the wall by small triangular-shaped exit grids. It is claimed that a single tube can evaporate and discharge several quarts of water in the space of one month and the method is useful for reducing the amount of water in a wall without, however, necessarily being adequate to eliminate it.

(b) By Drainage and Evaporation

Often cottages or isolated houses in the country are on sloping ground and by altering the sub-soil drainage surprisingly good results may be achieved on reducing the effect of rising damp in walls. Alternatively it may be possible to expose an area of wall below ground level so as to encourage evaporation and allow a larger area for drying out at a lower level in the wall. Impermeable surrounds to houses or cottages in the form of paths to drain away moisture from the walls at the lowest practicable level are also helpful. In the case of country cottages occupied only at weekends the effects of rising dampness may be aggravated by the fact that internal heating is only intermittent.

The reason that country cottages or houses in isolated districts are specifically mentioned under this heading is that whereas these may lend themselves to treatment by the provision of sub-soil drains the position in an urban area may be very different. Sub-soil drainage may have unpredictable results in an urban area particularly where there is a clay sub-soil and even if permission is obtained from adjoining owners and occupiers extreme care would be needed to ensure that the transference of ground moisture from one sub-soil area to another would not cause damage to adjoining buildings.

In the case, however, of a country house or cottage where the foundations rest in waterlogged soil considerable improvement can sometimes be effected by the provision of sub-soil drains. These may discharge into a natural watercourse or, alternatively, into a public storm or foul sewer. The drains themselves consist of porous pipes laid in trenches with hardcore over, the top soil being replaced above. Trial holes are necessary to determine the type of soil and further investigations are necessary to establish the depth of the standing water. A system of sub-soil drains can then be designed completely surrounding the house if the sub-soil water is static or alternatively as a barrier against the direction of flow of sub-soil water if the house is on a sloping site. It is not desirable to arrange the drains so that they are situated too near to the foundations as this could lead to disturbance or settlement of the structure. The sub-soil drains should be connected to public sewers or private drains by means of a sealed water trap ventilated into the open air on the inlet side and rodding eyes should be provided at the top ends of the drain runs so that clearing can be carried out. The methods of reducing the effects of rising damp are of little value carried out on their own but are useful when considered in conjunction with methods to conceal rising damp described below.

The Concealment of Rising Dampness

One of the best known and most widely employed method of concealing rising dampness is by the provision of a patent corrugated pitch or bitumen impregnated lathing which is fixed to the wall once the plaster is stripped. This method is often employed in basement rooms of old properties in multiple occupation with a limited life where the walls are saturated and the cost of removing the rising damp in order to provide a dry surface for decorating would be prohibitive or where difficulties such as unco-operative owners of adjacent terrace properties make the installation of a proper damp proof course impossible in party walls. This particular method is long established and the decorative surface provided once replastering has been carried out is excellent provided that the fastenings and laps are efficiently made in accordance with the maker's directions so that damp does not penetrate to the new decorations through the joints.

A second method often employed in basement rooms where rising damp is prevalent is the provision of concrete block inner skins to walls, suitably separated from any damp structure by a 2-inch (50mm) cavity, or, where it is necessary to make a connection to existing work, by the use of dense engineering bricks. The old plaster is best hacked off from the original walls to allow for better evaporation through the cavity which in turn is ventilated to the external air. Since the new work will either be built off a new concrete floor already provided with a horizontal damp proof membrane or in itself be provided with a damp proof course the newly plastered skin walls present a surface for decoration indistinguishable from new work and rather less prone to damage than that provided on the corrugated bitumen impregnated lathing. The only disadvantage of this method, as already mentioned is the slight loss of space.

Where compliance with Local Authority Basement Room Regulations and Improvement Grants are involved the above methods are often the only two acceptable for concealing rising damp short of the installation of a horizontal damp proof course of traditional type.

Another method recently introduced is for the plaster to be removed to the wall which is then coated with a rubber/tar or bitumen preparation. The wall surface is then replastered using an undercoat that does not shrink on drying such as one part of browning plaster to one and a half parts of clean sand. It is, however, doubtful if this method can be guaranteed beyond, say, ten years and its usefulness must therefore be considered fairly limited.

Another method of concealing rising damp by wall linings in common use is the provision of plasterboard fixed on timber battens. This method has been already discussed in the section dealing with condensation and it is only necessary to stress at this point that it is necessary for the battens to be pressure impregnated with preservative and in cases where rising dampness is acute it would be as well to ensure that mould growth in the cavity is prevented and accordingly the surface of the wall and the backs of the lining boards should be treated with fungicide. There is some risk of interior condensation together with that of driving the rising damp higher with this type of cladding and it is essential that the provision of metal ventilators is specified at the base and top of walls in all cases.

A number of proprietary materials are available for use as barriers for application to interior wall faces affected with less severe rising dampness. These are usually of a heavy paper coated with pitch or bitumastic compound so as to make it damp resistant and sufficiently impervious to prevent penetration by the moisture contained within the walling material. The usefulness of pitch paper is that it can be afterwards hung with ordinary wallpaper. Another proprietary brand of tough paper can be procured which is combined with a metal filling of copper treated with ammonia. Sound adhesion is always a difficulty with all these papers and the barriers probably most favoured at the present time are tin and aluminium foils. These are pasted on the damp portions of walls with a strong adhesive. It is important that the edges should be well lapped and some aluminium foils are now provided backed with a heat sensitive adhesive so that the gentle application with a blow lamp and smooth rolling with a hand roller can produce a perfect application which is quite free of wrinkles. In the lack of any specialist equipment it is quite possible for this material to be literally ironed on to the wall with a hand iron.

Waterproof rendering to internal walls affected by rising dampness has, of course, been a traditional palliative for many years even if it is now somewhat discredited as a result of bad workmanship or its indiscriminate use in basements subject to a degree of water pressure resulting in the damp appearing at a higher level. It has its uses, however, and where rendering is to be carried out the old plaster is stripped to, say, 2 feet (0·5m) above the affected area. The wall surface is then keyed by raking out the mortar joints squarely to a depth of about ½ inch (12mm) and an undercoat of 1:3 cement/sand with, if desired, an integral waterproofer or an undercoat of aerated 1:6 cement/sand is applied followed by a plaster finishing coat. It should however be made clear that subsequent decorative finishes to this plaster should be porous. If the walling material is very old, being of porous stone or soft brick, the strong shrinkage of a dense 1:3 cement/sand rendering can cause damage and the Building Research Establishment suggest the use of a weaker mix of 1:6 cement/sand plasticised by means of an air-entraining agent rather than a cement/lime sand undercoat of similar strength. This aerated mix is probably more effective in keeping damp and hygroscopic salts at bay.

Rising Dampness to Basement or Ground Floors

Having discussed rising dampness to walls it is now necessary to consider the question of rising dampness through basement floors or alternatively through ground floors if no basement is provided to the property. We will first of all consider houses without basements.

In houses built prior to 1860 the surveyor will commonly find that hollow timber flooring is provided to the ground floor, the boards being nailed to shallow joists either laid almost direct on the earth or separated from it by a rudimentary system of sleeper walls, the clearance between the timber and the ground being only a few inches. No damp proof course was, of course, provided. In later houses built prior to 1914 the principles of construction will often be found to be rather better and the joists will be found to have been designed and laid more in accordance with known building practice on brick sleeper walls, a rather more acceptable sub-floor depth being provided, since the principles of ventilation were now beginning to be understood. Unlike the houses of the earlier period ventilators will most probably be found at the base of the main enclosing walls of the dwelling house and although these may not be sufficient in size or number nevertheless they allow for a good deal of air penetration to the sub-floor space. The sleeper walls of these later houses may or may not be of honeycomb pattern and sometimes the beneficial effect of perfectly satisfactory sub-floor ventilators in outer walls will be found to be completely frustrated by a solid sleeper wall built a few inches away from the inlet. Damp proof courses may or may not be found to the main enclosing walls but it is quite likely that wallplates to sleeper walls may be laid on damp proof courses of slate even if a damp proof course is omitted to the brickwork of the main walls.

In the large majority of houses in both the above categories the surveyor will find that no sub-floor concrete is provided. Some houses of about 1900 may have sub-floor concrete but even at this period it was commonplace for the smaller urban houses to be provided with a narrow cellar stretching for only part of the frontage width which was paved in concrete, but the adjoining ground floor timbers, which can often be seen from the cellar, were laid on sleeper walls above the earth.

With houses built prior to 1860 it is often not an economic proposition to repair timber ground flooring since the lack of ventilation due to the absence of any sub-floor space makes it impossible to guarantee any length of life for the timbers. It would cost a disproportionate amount of money to refashion the flooring to correct principles so that the joists and ends of boards are free from damp brickwork and effective principles of ventilation introduced. Although often it seems a pity to take out boarding that appears to be quite seasoned and tough at first glance and on surface examination which appears to be quite dry, investigation underneath often shows a different state of affairs since the joists may well be rotted or sodden on their undersides. With later houses of about 1900 the position may well be different since it is often possible to take certain measures which are relatively inexpensive in themselves but which will extend the life of a timber floor almost indefinitely. Provided that the introduction of adequate sub-floor ventilation can be achieved some of the houses of this period with the good seasoned timber provided at the time and with the deep sub-floor spaces that are often found, can be put into excellent condition for quite modest sums. It is possible with heavy grade polythene sheeting to lay down a horizontal damp proof membrane where the provision of sub-floor concrete would be impossible and once the walls and woodwork are treated against dampness according to the degree that is found to be necessary the surveyor can often leave the property quite confident that all should

650

be well for as long as anyone can reasonably foresee. Since the question of repair of timber is dealt with elsewhere in this book and since the question of the provision of a damp proof course to the main enclosing walls of the property has already been discussed, it is not necessary to devote further space to the preservation of timber ground floors but it is now necessary to turn our attention to the question of basements.

Up and until the beginning of the First World War most houses down to the medium-sized villa were constructed on the basis that servants would work in a basement and sleep in the attic. It is, of course, true that the Georgian and Victorian builders constructed houses without basements, but these were generally in estate schemes involving terraces of houses of cramped pattern designed exclusively for the working population.

It falls to the surveyor's task to maintain and repair the basements of houses even although the word servant provides merely a whisper from the past. Possibly the nearest equivalent, the au-pair girl may have a room in the basement but she would certainly not be pleased if dampstained and peeling plaster is visible round her bed. In the case of the larger mansion whether Georgian or Victorian there is a good prospect that basements will be provided with open areas on each side of the building and once the retaining walls to these areas are repaired, the surfaces repaved and, if necessary new drainage gullies incorporated in them, the surveyor can approach the question of the repair of the basement rooms themselves feeling confident that they will amply repay his trouble. The timber basement flooring may be capable of effective repair and preservation if the level of the area surfacing allows for adequate ventilation to be provided and if the sub-floor construction permits this. In a number of cases, however, the surfacing of the areas will be found to be too high to allow for effective sub-floor ventilation and the lack of any effective sub-floor space would not in any event permit adequate ventilation to be possible. Solid floors are therefore a necessity in these circumstances.

For every Georgian or Victorian basement house with adequate areas outside the basement walls there will be hundreds where the areas are either partial or inadequate. In the case of terraced villas areas may be provided at the front and the rear or, in the case of urban terraces where the level of the ground is lower at the back of the house, areas are, of course, only found at the front. It is usually not worthwhile to carry out elaborate repairs to timber basement flooring to houses such as this since a sub-floor space under the timbers is often totally lacking and again solid floors are a necessity.

One of the major complicating factors however, with detached,

semi-detached and end of terrace Georgian or Victorian houses is
that while areas may be provided to part of the structure the ground
level will be very considerably above the basement floor level and
the lack of any damp proof membrane in the original construction
means that moisture will almost certainly have penetrated from the
earth to the side of the walling brickwork to spoil the decorations of
the basement rooms. Even in the case of large detached Victorian
houses of good quality a side entrance path will often be found to be
provided well above the level of the basement flooring with the result that the walls to the basement rooms adjacent are wringing wet.
Wet basement walls in these circumstances are capable of being
treated by infusion and injection techniques carried out over the
face of the wall requiring treatment but a good many specialist firms
will not guarantee the results and it is therefore necessary to consider the question of vertical damp proof courses.

Vertical Damp Proof Courses

The time-honoured method of constructing a vertical damp proof
course is with the provision of two courses of slates laid to a bond so
that the joints are staggered, the whole set in cement mortar. This
method can still lead to perfectly satisfactory results but it is probably
only best employed for small areas and at shallow depths. The
labour costs of this method of providing a vertical damp proof
course are becoming increasingly high and some care is required to
ensure that the final result is sound. The mortar bedding should be
sufficiently stiff to adhere in its position pending the laying of the
slates and the slates themselves should be well saturated beforehand.
If this is not done the slates will suck up moisture from the mix
which will then be deprived of some of its adhesive qualities. A good
deal of trial and error has been carried out in recent years with
waterproof cement renderings as vertical membranes. Even thick
two coat work, however, with a waterproofing additive suffers from
the disadvantage that any movement in the structure will cause
cracking and lead to deterioration. For this reason rubber-based
liquid or mastic coatings which bond to the interior wall surface and
which provide a key for the plaster finishings have found favour in
recent years. The question of the adhesion of the membrane is of
first importance. Some damp proof coatings will adhere to damp
surfaces better than to dry ones as the moisture allows the membrane
material to penetrate the pores of the wall where on drying it retains
a firm grip. A bitumen emulsion is such a type.

An example of a vertical membrane which does not adhere to a
wall surface is bituminous felt. This material is widely used and is

laid in widths with lapped joints at the edges 3 inches (76mm) wide. For this type of damp proof course a firm vertical surface is first necessary so that when the joints and edges of the bituminous sheeting are heated and bonded there must be no possibility of any wrinkles or depressions appearing in the finished work which might provide a flaw in the membrane.

Perhaps the best known and certainly the most effective vertical damp proof membrane is asphalt. This does not effectively adhere to a vertical walling material without additional support and the provision of an asphalt damp proof course requires care in design and construction. This will be considered under the next heading.

Tanking

A complication in the waterproofing of basements is always the question of static water pressure. The level of the water table is of crucial importance in considering the question of water pressure and where the level of the water table is high and where houses have deep basements the question of water pressure must be considered in conjunction with the type of waterproof membrane proposed. For every foot of vertical depth below the water table the force from static water pressure increases by 0·43 lbs. per square inch (·003 N/mm²). It will be understood, therefore, that the damp proof membrane must either have an adhesive grip sufficient to cope with this pressure or be independently supported by some other means.

The expression 'tanking', therefore, describes the operation of providing an impervious permanent membrane to a basement floor and walls which is capable of resisting the appropriate amount of hydrostatic pressure to be expected according to the circumstances. The basement of the house accordingly resembles a tank in that a complete impervious layer prevents the penetration of moisture from the exterior. The membrane must, therefore, be continuous. It is obviously vital that where membranes are provided to both floor and wall surfaces that these are linked together with an impermeable joint.

Although many types of impervious membranes such as bituminous felt or heavy-grade polythene sheeting are employed there is no doubt that the most effective membrane material for tanking is asphalt. For this to be applied effectively to an existing dwelling house it will be necessary for the room areas of the basement to be slightly reduced since an inner wall lining is necessary either of 4½-inch (114mm) brickwork or of concrete blocks. The existing wall plaster is first stripped from the interior room surfaces of the main enclosing walls and the asphalt is then applied to the face of the walls. The wall lining is then constructed against the asphalt. When this method is adopted, provision should be made for access tubes to allow a liquid grout to be forced into the cavity between the wall and the lining so as to take up any space not occupied by the asphalt. Alternatively another method is for the inner lining to be erected in stages at a distance of ¾ inch (19mm) away from the interior wall face and as the work proceeds liquid mastic is poured into the gap. It is not desirable to provide independent wall linings in this manner to rooms that have a height in excess of 9 feet (2·74m). In heights in excess of this, block bonding is necessary to ensure that support is provided to the lining, recesses for the bond being formed in the inner face of the main enclosing walls of the building which are first treated with liquid mastic and asphalt prior to the brick lining being formed. As, however, it is rare to find domestic basement rooms in excess of 9 feet (2·74m) in height there is little need to enlarge upon this type of treatment.

In order to complete the tanking, the asphalt membrane must run across the floor and be linked to the vertical membranes with a splayed joint which allows for pressure and creep. It is best to incorporate the asphalt floor membrane in a sandwich type of construction, the asphalt being laid on a layer of concrete which might be 3 inches (76mm) thick, in turn laid on hardcore, while a further layer of concrete which would depend for its thickness according to circumstances but might again be 3 inches (76mm) thick is laid over the asphalt. This top layer of concrete is known as the loading floor and is designed to pin down the asphalt membrane so that there is no risk of this being disturbed by hydrostatic pressure.

In the case of houses with basements where the water table is high the surveyor should consider what steps he might take by sub-soil drainage to reduce hydrostatic pressure where possible and in the case of houses on sloping waterlogged sites the absence of any effective sub-soil drains adjacent to the wall nearest to the hill side of the slope will entail much trouble from damp penetration. Accordingly, the opportunity should be taken to divert the ground moisture to each side of the building. In other cases on flat sites a system of land drains may have to be designed by the surveyor but since the cost of efficient site drainage may be relatively cheap compared with the expensive reconstruction of the interior of an old house to provide effective tanking, it is clearly worthwhile to pursue the economics of reducing the cause of hydrostatic pressure before considering what type of tanking to provide.

The whole point about the damp proof membrane used in the tanking process is that it should be continuous. This is not too difficult to achieve with the use of asphalt since the tanking membrane has to be designed as a whole and laid in this way. Difficulties, however, present themselves when the vertical membrane differs in its material and also its characteristics from the horizontal membrane incorporated in the flooring. It is necessary, therefore, that the surveyor gives particular thought to the lapping or welting or other junction that he proposes to form between the two respective materials. It is, indeed, only recently that the importance of providing waterproof membranes to concrete floors has become widely appreciated. It is, therefore, necessary next to consider the question of solid floors from the point of view of damp penetration.

Basement Floors and Solid Ground Floors where no Basements exist

During the housing drive of the 1920s there was an enormous increase in solid ground floor construction due to a shortage of timber. Persistent failures, however, in the wood sections superimposed on such floors as a result of dampness led to the realisation that concrete in itself was not sufficiently impermeable under such conditions to prevent the gradual penetration of moisture. As a result of this, a clause was incorporated in the Model By-Laws of 1937 requiring that wood in contact with solid floors must be protected by a continuous layer, not less than $\frac{1}{8}$-inch (3mm) thick, of bitumen or a suitable grade of coal tar pitch. This was designed to counteract the fact that moisture penetration through solid floors occurs not only by the penetration of liquid on waterlogged sites, but also in other cases by the penetration of vapour. Ground moisture in one form or another will pass through the concrete until it either disperses by evaporation on the surface or reaches a less permeable material under which it will accumulate. For this reason some of the impermeable moisture barriers if badly laid were found to lift or deteriorate because of the build-up of moisture below and it is now recognised that it is not necessary to have an absolutely impermeable moisture barrier. Several new kinds of floor finish and alternative waterproofing materials have been developed in recent years and hot laid damp proof courses are by no means universal. Hydrostatic pressure can, of course, only be dealt with effectively by a completely impervious membrane pinned down to a sufficient degree to counteract the pressure but since it is a by-law requirement that the floor level of a building is at least 6 inches (152mm) above the level of the surrounding ground, this normally ensures that solid floors are not subject to water pressure but have to contend with the question of water vapour only. A modern solid floor is considered satisfactory if it either reduces moisture or vapour penetration to an acceptable level or alternatively, by its construction, tolerates

655

moisture without decay, distortion or loss of adhesion as in, for example, the case of granolithic flooring. Both water penetration and water vapour must be prevented from contact with an ornamental hardwood floor, but on the other hand a permeable material, and this includes, for example, most marbles, can be stained or badly affected with water penetration although moisture vapour may pass through the material such as this without adverse effects. It is true that the moisture may then condense on the surface, but this is another problem entirely and sufficient background heating should prevent this.

It should be said at once that an integral waterproofer incorporated in the concrete or screed to a floor is not a satisfactory alternative to a damp proof layer where an impermeable membrane is required. Damp-proofing materials are referred to previously and in order to decide whether to lay a particular membrane or to incorporate a hot or cold applied membrane, regard should be had to the wetness of the site and the slope of the ground having regard to the depth of the foundations and the temperature to be maintained in the building. We have had one example to show that in a permanently heated building a lower standard of protection against damp in vapour form can be tolerated. Better protection is, however, for example, required where sea salt contamination from the concrete aggregate is such that it tends to keep the floor damp and reacts with lime from the cement and liberates caustic alkali which might attack the floor adhesive or finish.

A damp proof layer in a solid floor must be impermeable to liquid water and, if required, to water vapour, yet be sufficiently tough to survive constructional processes in laying. A widely used modern type of impervious membrane is heavy grade polythene sheeting. This is undoubtedly effective as an impervious barrier, but can be torn or damaged if carelessly laid. In cases where the polythene sheeting has been laid direct over the surface of the hardcore, the concrete being laid on top, the membrane has been pierced by the jagged stones in the hardcore and by the action of laying the heavy concrete on top with shovels. For this reason it is better to lay the membrane on top of the concrete floor underneath the finishing screed. There is the obvious danger that in doing this the screed, if thin, will crack and fracture, since the polythene sheeting offers no key. This is particularly so where too much water is added to the screed and it is trowelled for too long a period with a steel float so that the fine cement is attracted to the surface. A thick screed with a rough textured surface is, therefore, to be preferred.

The surface membranes, such as asphalt and pitch mastic flooring, have the advantage over sandwich membranes in that finishes can be laid without the need for a waiting period while a screed has to dry out. They are subject to possible damage, however, and are best laid just before the floor finish is applied. Hot applied sandwich membranes save time because they can be covered by a screed as soon as they have cooled, whereas cold membranes are likely to require several days to apply and harden. A long delay before laying the finish is unavoidable, however, for all sandwich membranes because the screed has to be left to dry out. This normally takes as long as one month per inch (25mm) of thickness.

EXTRANEOUS CAUSES INTRODUCING DAMP

One of the most common reasons for the introduction of extraneous damp is where a garden wall which has no damp proof course either under the coping or at the base abuts the main wall of a dwelling house and causes impressive stains to appear due to both damp penetration to the top of the wall and from rising dampness at the base of the wall. Clearly the whole boundary wall must be insulated from the main structure by a damp proof membrane and this membrane must be of a permanent type. It is tempting for a simple slot to be cut and bituminous sheeting inserted in the groove, but this will not provide a guaranteed life for anything like the required period. Some of the metals might be employed but there is bound to be an overlap at the edges and if, according to the type of metal used, it oxidises to a different colour than the surrounding brickwork, the effect might be odd. Cutting in sections of an appropriate type of slate in two courses set in cement, the joints lapped, still remains an effective treatment. The same measures can be taken for any small structure built against the dwelling house but where possible any agent likely to introduce damp should be removed, for example, a banked up flower bed. Needless to say, after the example given under the heading of "the inspection" it is preferable to see that water butts are kept well away from the main structure. In country districts, the wide overhanging eaves of thatched cottages present particular difficulties since the run off of rainwater falls on the earth or paving below so near to the main wall as to present a considerable damp problem. It is, of course, not possible to provide anything in the nature of gutters for eaves of this type of roof covering and accordingly attention must be given to the surface of the paving or ground below. A suggested solution to this problem is illustrated on Figure 69.

MAINTENANCE OF HOUSES AGAINST DAMPNESS

The consequences of failure to maintain the ordinary dwelling house against damp penetration are probably more serious than of the neglect of any other type of maintenance. Effective maintenance against dampness is, however, an extremely difficult matter due to the impressive variety of ways that water will find to make its presence felt. It is an easy answer to say that a survey should be carried out at frequent intervals on the lines of the inspection described early in this Chapter, but this really cannot be contemplated as an economic possibility due to the man-hours involved and the enormous number of houses requiring such attention. Dampness must, therefore, inevitably to some degree remain a problem that is dealt with as it arises and for very many years to come surveyors will be gazing at splotches of moisture wondering about the cause and trying to think out methods of repair.

Having said this, however, in case it sounds a counsel of despair, a great many precautions can be taken to cut down the effects of dampness as far as possible. The first and most obvious step is that when a full survey of a building is carried out, say for example, on behalf of a prospective purchaser, the surveyor should try to make the new householder conscious of the steps he can take to avoid the worst effects of dampness. External materials, for example, to roofs, which are likely to wear out before other materials, should be pointed out so that instead of being forgotten about, these are watched and renewed at the appropriate time, and matters of bad design or faulty construction should also be pointed out and remedied. Where it is not possible to escape the effects of bad design so that a complicated network of guttering to the roofs of old houses is bound to be subjected to blockages and overflows, a regular contract for the clearing of gutters should be put in hand with a reliable builder. In smaller more modern properties the owner might be encouraged to clear his own gutters at intervals with the use of a ladder. The importance of external painting again should be made obvious and the owner made aware of the fact that painting, like everything else, has to be done properly, so that scamped work in omitting to paint behind vertical downpipes or in leaving hasty blobs of paint or material to bridge check-throats under sills must be avoided. There is a growing market of magazines designed for the layman and aimed at the young couple in a newer type of house which encourage home repairs and are excellent in informing the householder how to look after the exterior of his property and avoid the worse effects of dampness. It is, however, to the older and larger type of inner suburban house which may be occupied by more than one family that the consequences of neglect are likely to be most severe. It is to these houses that the repair and maintenance against damp assumes its major importance.

Stone cottage c. 1700

Dampness 1

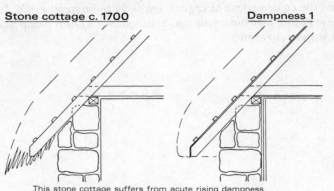

This stone cottage suffers from acute rising dampness
aggravated by the run-off from the eaves of the thatched
roof. An injection method against rising damp is preferred
to the insertion of a conventional d.p.c. since the random
rubble walls are suspect for cutting. Paving with concrete and
clinker below and field drains ameliorate the damp
from run-off and a new concrete floor internally
with hardcore base replaces the old rotted wood floor.
The internal wall lining of damp plaster is replaced
with foil backed plasterboard on impregnated timber
battens. The use of the vapour barrier overcomes
condensation from the stone through bonders. The opportunity
is also taken to renew the rotted wood lintel window and cill.

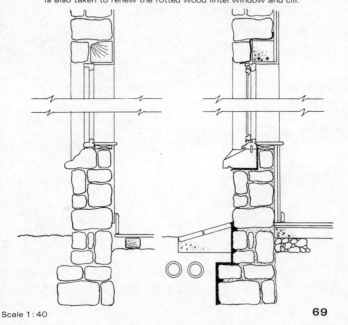

Scale 1:40

69

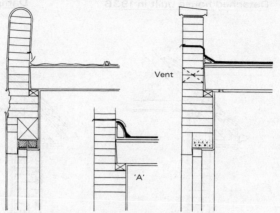

Vent

'A'

The parapet wall of this house had received many attempts
at repair as a result of sulphate attack but the coating
of rendering has done more harm than good. The
existing roof covering of zinc on boards and joists has
failed. The parapet has accordingly been rebuilt using
bricks of high frost resistance and low sulphate content.
The roof covering has been reformed with asphalt reinforced
with X.P.M., 1″ (25 mm) insulating board and a layer of bitumen
felt on a chipboard base. A new ceiling has been formed
with plasterboard on impregnated battens and the roof
timbers are now ventilated. If any deflection is at all
likely in the joists, detail 'A' is preferred, otherwise the asphalt
might crack. Lower down the defective red bricks have been
cut out and new bricks built in and the old fir lintel below
the rough relieving arch replaced in concrete. At ground floor
level a conventional d.p.c. has been put in together with a concrete
floor.

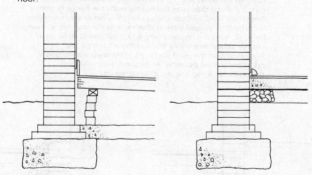

Scale 1:40

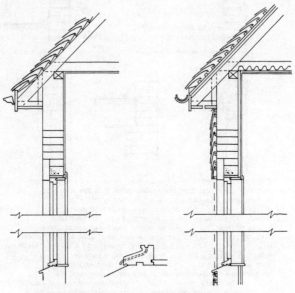

This house, in a very exposed position, proved to be
appallingly damp. The saturation of the feather edged
boarding under the tiles involved re-tiling, using
counter battens, and ventilating the eaves. Whole wall
damp penetration was overcome with tile hanging above
first floor level and condensation to windows ameliorated
by providing condensation channels in the manner shown
by $\frac{1}{4}$" (6 mm) dia. holes every 1'0" (300 mm) lined with
copper tubes. Internally the top floor ceilings are
insulated and the wall surfaces lined with plasterboard
on impregnated battens. At ground level externally
the path, bridging the d.p.c. is removed.

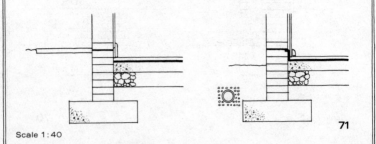

Scale 1:40

71

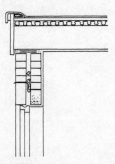
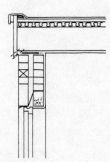

This house had a modern flat roof of built-up bitumen felt
bonded to chipboard nailed through fibreglass insulation
to firring pieces on timber joists. There was a plasterboard
ceiling below. On damp appearing to the top floor ceilings
the roof surface was inspected and the felt and chipboard
were found to be badly distorted due to alternate wetting
and drying periods from condensation. The remedy was to
provide a foil backed plasterboard ceiling as a vapour
barrier and provide for véntilation in the roof void. The
other faults shown are due to poor construction and
neglect. Particles of mortar clung to projections inside the
cavity walls and needed removal. The d.p.c. over the window
lintel was altered and earth against the base of the walls removed.

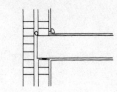
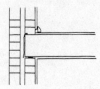

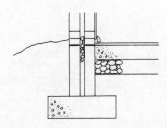
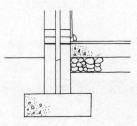

Scale 1 : 40

72

Chapter 9
Internal and General Matters

CONTENTS

INTERNAL AND GENERAL MATTERS

Page

PLASTER

THE research carried out by L. F. Salzman[1] on the builders of mediaeval England shows that purchases of lime and sand are amongst the commonest of the entries in their accounts. This was due to the fact that these materials were used not only in the mortar for stone and brickwork but also in the mix for plasterwork. Plastering had been a skilled craft since early mediaeval times and like many crafts of this period there was a good deal of cross pollination from France. When Henry III visited Paris in 1254 "He took note of the elegance of the houses, which are made of Gypsum, that is to say plaster".[2] Plaster of Paris was made by burning gypsum and the gypsum beds of Montmartre, outside Paris, were famous. It is in records from this period that reference is made to the importation of fine "Plater de Parrys". Mr. L. F. Salzman shows, however, that much plaster of Paris was also made in England from local materials on the Isle of Purbeck, around Knaresborough and in particular in the Trent Valley and this material was used not only for making and finishing of walls, but also for floors and for fireplaces and chimneys where it would stand the heat better than plaster of lime and sand. The smooth white surface of plaster of Paris was much admired and this material was invariably used for good quality work particularly to cathedrals and the castles of the nobility.

Even apart from the use of plaster of Paris the techniques of ordinary plastering had advanced rapidly. Any shortcoming in the surface colour was no problem to the mediaeval builders to whom white-washing was the finishing seal to the larger building. The variety of wall surfaces available was considerable due to the general and increasing awareness and competition among builders to produce attractive finishes. "Some men will have thyr wallys plastered, some pergetted and whytlymed, some roughe caste, some pricked, some wrought with playster of Paris", wrote Horman in 1519. Not a great deal of mediaeval plaster remains in the houses of the period although enough of it can be seen by the surveyor or student in the larger historic buildings or cathedrals to supply convincing proof of the quality of the finish. We have seen, however, in the introductory historical chapter of this book how in Tudor times the interior finishings became much more important and desirable elements for houses across a much wider social scale. Instead of being confined

[1] Building in England
[2] MAT. Paris, Chron. V 481 (Salzman).

668

to churches and castles, the richness and variety of a plaster finish now became commonplace for the houses of merchants and soldiers and a good deal of the plasterwork of this period now remains. Following Tudor times the craft of plastering did not merely remain the province of the skilled tradesman relying only on the extravagance of its patterns and the excellence of its application for its effect. In the 17th and 18th centuries, plastered interiors and particularly ceilings became the legitimate province of artists of talent from Italy and from other European countries, working on the same international basis that the Freemasons were capable of in earlier times. The richness of the plasterwork in the hall of Clandon Park in Surrey, carried out by the Italians Artari and Bagutti and exemplified by the astonishing quality of the modelling of the figures in relief, contrasts with the more restrained design of the ceiling to the Palladio Room from which the emerging ideal for the finishings of the 18th-century English house can be seen. Thus can be seen in one building the sophisticated level which plastering had achieved by this period.

So far as the ordinary home is concerned, however, plasterwork probably reached its peak of excellence in the traditional three coat cement, lime and sand mixes widely used in the better quality Victorian and Edwardian houses. After the First World War the need for a shortening in the time taken for plastering operations due to the rising labour and overall building costs coupled with the introduction of a new range of plasters and backing materials the proper uses of which was, at first, not generally understood, led to a lowering of standards. The urge to speed up building operations has been a tendency which has persisted ever since, not always with satisfactory results as far as the techniques of plastering are concerned.

Defects in Plaster

It is not always easy to diagnose the correct cause of failure in plaster and the more recent the plasterwork the wider is the range of possible faults. In order to carry out an effective repair, however, it is necessary to know the cause of the defect since a partial repair which overlooks, for example, a basic bonding failure between successive plaster coats, will not only entail further repair work at a later stage but may also lead to wasted expenditure in redecoration.

The first matter that has to be decided is whether the failure in the plasterwork is due to a fault in the backing material which supports it or whether the fault is due to the breakdown of the plaster itself either by reason of poor craftsmanship or by the selection of substandard or inadequate materials. In older houses the most likely faults that are likely to arise are cracking as the result of movement in the house structure, defects in lathing, efflorescence due to the presence of soluble salts in the backing material together with the introduction of water due to some fault in the property, while defects in the plaster itself are likely to be limited to mere irregularities in the surface texture. In modern houses the possibility of failure in the backing material is, under normal circumstances, rather less, while defects in the plaster itself due to poor craftsmanship or the unwise selection of materials are more varied and much more likely to occur. Among the latter are bond failure between successive coats leading to hollow patches, flaking or peeling to blistering, where an inadequate key between the plaster coats fails as the result of undue movement between the two due to excessive effects from wetting or drying. An unsightly defect known as popping or blowing occurs where particles of lime plaster or sand in a sand lime mix expand after the plaster has set leaving holes shaped rather like small craters on the moon. Another common defect, which leads to softness or chalkiness of the plaster, can result from a number of different causes, for example either excessive suction of the undercoat, undue thinness of the final coat, working past the setting point or exposure of the final coat to excessive heat or draught during setting. In lime or Portland cement mixes crazing may occur with overworking of the final coat or because of excessive suction from the backing or undercoat but such a defect, if only slight, is often tolerable. A defect in the plaster that is not usually tolerable however is known as "grinning". This is where differences in suction characteristics between the background and the plaster lead to areas of varying texture on the plaster surface. This defect, however, usually arises with one coat work and only very occasionally with two coat work.

Since failure in the backing material is most likely in older houses and since ceilings are the most vulnerable in this respect it is to the consideration of ceilings that attention will first be given.

Ceilings

From early times until shortly after the advent of the Second World War when plasterboard became available in such quantities as to make its use universal for the ceilings of houses, the traditional form of construction had always been lath and plaster. Ceilings were almost without exception formed below timber joists and although some variations in construction will be found, traditional practice was for riven laths $1\frac{1}{2}$-inches (39mm) wide and from $\frac{1}{8}$ inch (3mm) to $\frac{1}{2}$-inch (13mm) thick to be nailed to the joists at intervals of about $\frac{3}{8}$ inch

(10mm) apart so as to provide a good key for the plaster. Riven laths were rent or split from the tree by hand and were considered stronger and longer lasting. For all but the very best work they were replaced by sawn laths produced by machinery in Victorian times and in the very cheapest work the thinnest of saw laths fixed to ceilings often broke under the pressure of the plasterer's trowel. This type of defect together with the common use of nails which eventually rusted would not necessarily be noticed by a purchaster but in the subsequent history of the house a sagging ceiling would not be an uncommon result. Nowadays wood laths are rarely if ever used on new work but if required for either new or repair work they should be in accordance with B.S.1317 "Wood laths for plastering" and the nails used for fixing should be galvanised. Joints should always be butted and the lines of joints broken to avoid long cracks. Early lathing was usually of oak or hazel but later these timbers were superseded by imported softwood. Oak in particular gave rise to tannic acid action on the nails used to secure the lathing to the joists. In the fixing of lathing two common mistakes often arose. The first one was that laths were fixed too closely together. The interval stated above is ideal but if the distance is less than $\frac{1}{4}$ inch (6mm) there is a grave risk that sufficient plaster will not be forced through to form the ideal hook shaped key. A small amount of plaster will obviously give a less than satisfactory key. The other mistake was that lathing was often fixed in part direct to wide timber beams and the like so that no key was obtained at all. Any timber over 3 inches (75mm) in width really requires counter lathing to produce a satisfactory result. The plaster itself has traditionally consisted of three coat work, the first coat known as the lathing coat on ceilings, the rendering coat on walls and sometimes also known as the pricking coat, the second coat being the floating coat while the final coat has been, and still is, known as the setting coat.

The ceilings that the surveyor may encounter in most pre-1930 houses are probably of lime mixed with sand and perhaps, but not often, with a little cement. The mix for the first coat known as "coarse stuff" was probably one-third of a part of cement, if included to one part of lime putty to three parts of sand probably incorporating ox, cow or goat hair to strengthen the final result. The lathing coat, which was approximately $\frac{3}{8}$-inch (10mm) thick was well pressed against the laths so that the plaster oozed into and between the gaps and spread out behind them giving a good key to retain the plaster ceiling in place. The first coat was then scratched and the second coat, consisting of one part of lime putty to two parts of sand was placed on it to a thickness of about $\frac{1}{4}$ inch (6mm). Once the floating coat was in place the setting coat consisting of neat lime putty or equal parts of lime putty and sand, was provided as a skin to provide a final surface of only about $\frac{1}{8}$-inch (3mm) thick to complete the whole ceiling. Lime putty was formed from non-hydraulic or fat-lime slaked by mixing quick-lime, obtained by burning limestone in a kiln, with water.

Many old ceilings will be found where the plaster is considerably thicker in total than the $\frac{3}{4}$ inches (19mm) mentioned above. Cases have been seen, often following unexpected and dramatic collapses of ceiling plaster, where the thickness is considerably in excess of 1 inch (26mm). Often some failure of the plaster key at the corner of a ceiling, possibly following unequal settlement of the structure, or perhaps as the result of a burst pipe, remains unnoticed for years, but eventually an enormously heavy section of the plaster cornice will collapse taking part of the ceiling area with it. This sudden fall of a large area of three coat plaster can be very distressing indeed, particularly when there is absolutely no warning. The weight of a coating say 2 inches (50mm) thick is substantial and fatalities have been recorded. Even though such fatalities may be few, injury must be expected if a room is occupied at the time of a fall since it is a person's head that is usually struck. A surveyor's client is not likely to be pleased if on completion of repairs (such a disaster invariably happens when a contract is completed rather than during its course!) the dining-room ceiling collapses on the guests or the baby in his cot is struck by falling debris. Liability might be difficult to avoid if the surveyor has already expressed a favourable opinion on the condition of the ceiling.

Expressing an opinion on old plastered ceilings is one field on which a surveyor or architect can very easily be caught out. The difficulty arises in that whereas most surveyors know of ceilings badly bulged and cracked which have remained in position for very many years there are also numerous examples of ceilings which have presented no visible indications from below of any defect, which have collapsed completely without warning. If the ceiling was fixed to timber no doubt an examination from above would have shown a lack of key but it is rare indeed for such an examination to be made unless the surface of the ceiling from below can be seen to be bulged and cracked. The presence of damp stains or evidence of fungal attack or woodworm infestation might also suggest the advisability of examination but on the other hand there would not necessarily be any indication whatever of a defect which from two separate causes, for example, may deprive a whole ceiling of its key. One of these causes, the shaking effect of nearby bomb explosions during the Second World War was responsible for depriving otherwise sound ceilings of the entire key. Many such ceilings of course fell immediately after the explosion and some shortly afterwards but there are still many in existence which have yet to collapse. Excessive drying shrinkage of an over-rich first coat can produce the same effect by overstressing the key so that each strip of plaster forming the key fractures. This is a more common cause of loss of key than the fixing of laths too closely which may originally have provided an entirely inadequate key for a heavy ceiling. Such defects may exist for years without anyone being aware of them.

A moment's thought then is sufficient to warn the surveyor that he would be most unwise to give an opinion on a ceiling fixed to lathing unless he has had the opportunity of examining the key from above. Certainly the absence of defects visible from below is no indication of soundness and a frequent examination of old ceilings from above will soon lead the surveyor to wonder why many more do not drop down suddenly than in fact do. The evidence of a litter of broken pieces of plaster between the joists must be sufficient to sound a warning of possible danger at any time in the future. It is academic to ask whether in this case the ceiling has been in its particular condition for a long time or not. Whereas with quite a few structural defects in a house say 100–50 years old some assurance can be gained by mere age this definitely is by no means the case with plastered ceilings.

There is, however, no doubt that ceilings formed in this traditional manner can remain for the most part very tough and sound to this day provided they were properly put up originally and have remained completely dry and undisturbed subsequently. The main disadvantage of the constructional method was, and is still, the rather slow process involved in providing the three separate coats, since each coat is subject to drying shrinkage and accordingly a delay was and is necessary between the application of each of the three coats in order to allow time for this shrinkage process to take place.

Many early plaster ceilings will be worthy of careful repair and indeed in some cases ceilings will be scheduled so that the surveyor is under a statutory duty to preserve them. The reason for preservation is often due to the quality of the plaster ornamentation provided. The repair of the ceiling plaster itself and the steps to be taken in respect of some heavy ornamentation or cornice sections can often be considered as two separate problems.

Failure of a plaster ceiling as already discussed is often due to either rusting of the lathing nails or decay in the laths or by fracturing of the plaster key occurring either in whole or in part leading to subsequent sagging or in extreme cases collapse. In considering the possibilities for the repair of plaster ceilings investigation is first necessary, as always, and often this can be carried out from either a roof space about a top floor ceiling or by lifting boards to upper floor joists from which the laths and key of the ceilings below can be observed. Often an accumulation of black dirt and the dust of centuries will have to be removed and a soft brush is desirable for this purpose or alternatively a small vacuum cleaner. There will, of course, be areas near the cornice that the surveyor is unable to examine in detail but some indication as to the likely stability at these points can be obtained from considering the quality of the plaster observed elsewhere and inspecting and where possible carefully testing, for movement, parts of the cornice from ladders inside the room.

So far as top floor ceilings under ancient neglected roofs are concerned, any of the three above possibilities of failure are equally likely. Damp penetration can be responsible for either the rusting of lathing nails or decay being set up in the laths, while the slender ceiling joists at top floor level are apt to settle and sag over a considerable number of years and differential movement added to this often causes fracturing in the plaster key. In such positions where the structure is frail and where there is no particular reason for retaining ceilings constructed in the traditional manner, plasterboard must of necessity be considered as a possible alternative. Ceilings to top floor rooms are not normally remarkable for their ornamentation or artistic quality and the penalties for the collapse of heavy plaster in ceilings that will obviously be bedrooms is better avoided if at all possible. So far as the ceilings of the rooms at lower levels in the house are concerned these are more likely to require repair in a traditional manner, if they are of quality, but at least they are more likely to have the positive benefit of a stable backing formed by the heavier joists that are provided to support floorboards as well as ceilings.

There is little doubt that one of the primary causes of deterioration or collapse in plaster ceilings is from dampness. Damp penetration from a defective part of the structure or from a plumbing failure is lethal in robbing plaster ceilings of their effective key. Often damp penetration can go undetected for a long time so that a ceiling which is supposed to be sound, and indeed looks sound, can in fact be literally hanging by a thread. A popular cause of disintegration is presumed to be vibration from increased traffic loads on roads adjoining houses but this is not considered likely to be a primary cause except under circumstances such as where the key may have already been damaged by wartime blast. It is, however, probably true that the key of later Victorian and Edwardian ceilings are more vulnerable to distintegration from vibration or other disturbance since latterly the methods of the removal of the hair used in plastering from the animal skins, although quicker, tended to weaken the hair and make it somewhat less fit for use. Experience tends to suggest that the older the plaster ceiling the greater the quality of long good quality hair likely to be present and the greater care likely to have been taken with the slaking of the lime, both factors producing a ceiling plaster better able to resist tensional stresses.

Where a ceiling that is to be preserved has lost its key at the centre but yet the key is effectively retained at the edges and the degree of sagging does not amount to very much, the surveyor may determine to repair it as it stands. It is as well for the surveyor to take care, however, that there are no basic transverse or diagonal fractures hidden below a heavy grade lining paper which may frustrate the object of this exercise. It may not of course be possible to strip such a ceiling before proceeding with the repair work and due to the risk element involved the surveyor's judgment is necessary to determine whether in fact the ceiling can be saved in this manner or not. Once the decision to repair the ceiling is made, vertical and adjustable props are first provided, supporting planks which are carried to within a few inches of the face of the ceiling below the level of any relief ornamentation. Packing pieces with felt pads are then provided so that the weight of the ceiling can be carried entirely free of the relief work. Once this is achieved it should be possible to provide the necessary permanent support by means of brass metal discs, counter-sunk in the plaster, attached by long brass screws to the timber of the joists above. The holes for the metal discs can subsequently be concealed by patching with plaster of paris. If necessary short pieces of timber can be incorporated between the joists into which further screws and discs can be bedded should this be necessary and the intervals between the original joists be large. In the event of a ceiling that has developed a slight bow so that part of the area hangs below the original level, cradling pieces can be formed between the joists as necessary to secure the ceiling in its existing alignment, no effort being made to press it back to its original position.

In lieu of counter-sinking the old plaster for the insertion of brass discs, a similar repair can be effected by adding wood mouldings or battens to the underside of the existing work and securing these with long brass screws to the joists. Fibrous plaster is also suitable for this purpose and appropriate mouldings can be made up to blend with the existing work from a combination of wood, fibre of jute woven into open meshed canvas and plaster of Paris or gypsum

675

plaster. Joints can be stopped and making up to the existing level can be carried out with plaster of Paris.

A common method used in the past for securing sagged and bulging ceilings has been to remove all loose material from above and to spread between the joists a new layer of plaster in which is embedded broads strips of canvas which are subsequently secured to the sides of joists with wood fillets, screwed on so as to obviate vibration. It has been suggested that if there is access to the upper surface of any ceiling that is still in position it is possible for the ceiling to be repaired without it being taken down and in whatever state of disrepair it may be. This statement perhaps is a little too optimistic as even if this were possible there are many ceilings where owing to the mundane character of the ornament, if any, it would be far cheaper and certainly much safer in the long run to employ screws. However, for a very valuable ceiling considered worth trouble and expense and perhaps being the subject of a preservation order the following method of restoration might well be possible and eminently well worthwhile. It would be particularly suitable where, for example, the laths have rotted or have been substantially consumed by woodworm as after sound propping at the existing old level, all broken plaster and the old laths are completely removed. With this method also the plaster is then gently and evenly jacked back to its old position, adjustable metal props being obviously suitable for providing not only the temporary support but also the means of making the necessary change in level. A mixture of plaster of Paris, lime putty and a size made of glue and clean water is spread between the joists and while this is still wet a layer of stout canvas is laid down. When this has set, twisted wads of canvas scrim steeped in plaster are looped over the joists and well dabbed down with plaster on to the canvas at about 3-foot (915mm) centres, the wads being well spread apart to the extent of about 12 inches (305mm). Finally another layer of canvas and plaster is laid over each section between the joists to bond the new work together and when this is completely set the temporary supports can be removed. This traditional method of repair has been adapted since the development of flexible metal lathing and this material can be used to replace the canvas, provided it is protected against rust or is preferably of non-ferrous metal. The lathing can be securely fixed between the joists by non-ferrous wire looped over screws driven into the sides of the joists or alternatively into the top of the joists if access is difficult. Double assurance can be achieved by the addition, appropriate on a relatively plain ceiling, of wood or fibrous plaster moulds screwed through the old plaster on to the joists or alternatively, on a more elaborate and ornamented ceiling, the provision of brass discs counter-sunk into the existing plaster would be advantageous.

Where a surveyor judges that a ceiling to be preserved cannot be dealt with in one or other of the above ways due perhaps to the excessive weight of the heavily moulded ornamentation or more usually where other work, renewal of the joists for example, necessitates it, there is no option but for the ceiling to be cut and the defective areas or sections taken down. The sections can then be overhauled and minor repairs carried out on the ground. Once other repair work has been completed attention can be given to refixing the sections of the old ceiling. This will almost invariably have to be carried out by screwing back to new brackets and cross members secured to the joists. In other words there will probably have to be many more fixing points than previously. Once the sections have been replaced the joints, usually substantial gaps where the cuts were originally made, both in the bed and in the ornamental work, can be made good with plaster of Paris, ready for decoration. If the ornament is perhaps limited to cornice, frieze and a central decorative feature, then of course there is no reason why the bed should not be replastered as for new work leaving the ornamental plaster only to be refixed. Sometimes, however, the plaster ornament will have to be replaced either by being cast from moulds taken from the original or by being formed and pressed into the new work in the traditional manner or alternatively, if the surveyor fears that by using the traditional methods the weight may be too great, there are a number of specialist techniques available with the use of fibrous plaster to produce exact copies of mouldings at a much lighter weight. A surprisingly large array of moulds are now also available from which almost any type of the more usual Georgian or Victorian plaster patterns can be renewed.

With most houses, nowadays, defective ceilings are commonly replaced with plasterboard. It should always be borne in mind that this material should be used in accordance with the manufacturer's instructions and unless proper provision is made, a disconcerting amount of cracking along board joints due to contraction will appear in the skim coat. In particular, nogging pieces between the joists to give all round support to the boards are often omitted and the so called skim coat should not be less than $\frac{3}{16}$-inch (5mm) thick. Gypsum plasterboards and to a lesser extent wood fibre boards lose a high proportion of their strength when wet. If, accordingly, saturation has occurred to a plasterboard ceiling either as the result of a leak to the roof above which has since been repaired, or, alternatively, for example, in the case of a house that has suffered fire damage where water from the hoses has penetrated into parts of

677

the property not affected by the fire, the plasterboard itself should
be examined with care. If the wetting has only occurred once and
has since dried out completely there is a good chance that the
plasterboard will regain most of its structural strength but if there
has been soaking over a long period or there have been repeated
cycles of wetting and drying, the strength of the plasterboard is
probably so badly impaired that it is best for the sheets to be
renewed.

Although not occurring frequently in houses, the need to replaster
concrete soffits is often a matter of some difficulty, and some cases
have been found where the plaster has become detached from the
concrete due to poor preparation of the concrete surface before the
plaster was applied or where too rich a backing coat has been used.
Before replastering is carried out, for two coat work on an uneven
soffit, the surface of the concrete should be cleaned and mechanically
roughened to produce a good key, the best consisting of grooves with
an undercut edge. Preferably however, if the soffit is fairly even, the
thickness of the new plaster should be kept to a minimum, one coat
if possible, and, if necessary, a spatter dash treatment which entails
throwing a wet mix of cement and sand on the concrete surface (one
part in volume of cement to one or two parts volume of coarse sand)
to give a key. A proprietary emulsion of PVA or other polymer
bonding fluid applied to the concrete can also be used to assist
adhesion and has no effect on either the concrete or the plaster. As
to the plaster to be used, one of the low expansion board plasters,
which are only suitable for single coat work, or a special concrete
bonding plaster, both applied neat to the maker's instructions
would probably provide the best adhesion to the soffit where no
special key is provided and the original concrete is smooth enough
to permit single coat work. If the surface is more uneven and two
coats are required the concrete bonding plaster can provide the
first coat to secure adhesion and act as the base for a second coat of
Class B retarded hemihydrate gypsum plaster in a mix with sand
in the proportion $1:1\frac{1}{2}$.

Wall Plaster

It seems an obvious truism to say that generally wall plaster has a
better prospect of long-term survival than ceiling plaster due to the
fact that it has a firm backing. This may not, however, always be
the case even although the effect of a poor backing may not be quite
so spectacular as in the case of ceilings. It must not be forgotten
that on wall surfaces which were not particularly true, such as on
stonework and much early brickwork built with a rough backing to

ensure a good face, a traditional method of plastering was to a backing of battens and lathing fixed to plates and bonding timbers built up with the walling. As an alternative to plastering, principal rooms would often be panelled utilising the same arrangement of battens leaving the less important rooms to be plastered. This was a particularly common method of finishing interiors in both the 17th and 18th centuries in the small better quality estates of town dwellings and may also occur in houses of the 19th century.

Given dry conditions the old method of battening out the interior face of external walls was perfectly sound but to thin walls, exposed walls or walls which are neglected, it can prove to be disastrous when damp penetrates and an attack of dry rot develops since no ventilation was usually provided to the space behind the plaster. The steps to be taken in such circumstances are discussed in detail in Chapter 5 and very often the total removal of all plaster is a necessity in the first instance. When it comes to reinstatement metal channels are best to replace the battens and metal lathing to replace the wood lathing, both treated against rusting, with the plastering carried out in accordance with the section on replastering in this Chapter. Patching is not really a feasible proposition in the same form as on ceilings as it is not usually possible to obtain sufficient access to the backing. Such patching therefore has to be fairly limited and confined to small areas and relatively minor repairs to lathing and plaster.

With plastering direct on to the face of stone or brickwork, dampness, for example, will affect the key just as it does in all other cases, and it is most undesirable for repairs to the plaster to be attempted before the cause of the damp is diagnosed and treated. Another difficulty with damp affected plaster is the presence of hygroscopic salts. As we have seen in the Chapter dealing with dampness the presence of such salts usually results in a persistent appearance of dampness particularly when the air has a high humidity. In considering the replacement of damp affected plaster, therefore, it is not only necessary to ensure that the cause of the dampness has been cured and that a firm backing for the plaster key can be provided but that adjacent areas of plaster which are soundly fixed to the backing but which nevertheless show signs of damp staining are also renewed. It is just not worthwhile risking the presence of such salts in plaster that is about to be newly redecorated. In the case of rising dampness, however, there is a complication. As we have seen in the Chapter dealing with this subject, once a new barrier to rising damp is inserted in an old wall the drying out process commences at once. The rate of drying out, however, will be slow, and depends on various factors, such as the time of the year and whether evaporation can take place from both sides of the wall at once. The degree of internal heating applied is a further consideration. We have seen how a normal allowance in favourable circumstances is one month per inch (25mm) thickness of the wall and while this drying out process takes place hygroscopic salts are continually being brought to the surface. Accordingly it should, in theory, be many months before replastering is carried out after the treatment to cure rising dampness. In practice, however, this may not be possible for obvious reasons and if replastering is urgently necessary it should be carried out on a base of 1:6 cement and sand plasticised by means of an air entraining agent rather than a cement lime sand undercoat of similar strength. The aerated mix is more effective in preventing the passage of dampness and salts and the plaster top coat should be completed by a porous type of decoration as a temporary measure. Where a damp stain ceases it is advisable to cut out and replace the plaster to a distance of about 2 feet (say 0·6m) beyond the edge of the stain for safety.

There may be cases where the surveyor cannot be certain that rising dampness has completely ceased or alternatively where the rising dampness has ceased but due to unusual circumstances, for example in the case of a very thick brick wall, the drying out process is bound to take a very long time. Under such circumstances it is never desirable to replaster straight away even on the lines suggested in the previous paragraph. It is better, therefore, if one of the measures set out in the Chapter dealing with dampness under the heading of "The concealment of rising dampness" be employed in conjunction with the replastering.

Apart from dampness however, failure in the backing material to wall plaster may occur from a number of causes. The most obvious cause is when some failure in the structure comes about which breaks the key holding the plaster in position. It is only when the cause of failure is traced and the structure reaches a new position of repose that replastering can be carried out in the assumption that fresh cracks should not appear. It should be remembered, however, that it is not just structural failure that can cause cracks in wall plaster. Movement by reason of thermal or other changes against backing materials of different types can achieve the same results. For example, the plasterwork to the interior of a half-timbered house may be found to be loose in areas due to the fact that an ineffective key was originally provided between the timber and the plaster while the key between the brick infilling and the plaster has remained satisfactory. Another example of a case where wall plaster becomes defective in older houses is where the plaster is attached to a canvas backing which itself has failed. Even the thermal movement in a house with brick enclosing walls but with stud partitions internally, a type of construction which is, of course, commonplace in urban areas, may result in plaster cracking.

In trying to determine if wall plaster is sound or not there is at least the benefit that it is more accessible than ceiling plaster and the customary method of tapping is still the most satisfactory to determine if wall plaster has a satisfactory key or not. The noise made by tapping plaster which has a solid backing against plaster where the backing is hollow is so distinctive that the surveyor will become used to deciding the approximate areas of replastering that are necessary on the evidence of his knuckle alone.

When considering the question of repair, however, it is of course not merely enough to take down the defective areas of plaster and renew them since some thought must be given to the reasons that led to failure in the first place. It is often found that the use of expanded metal or other reinforcing material is sometimes necessary and in the case of a half timbered house the provision of expanded metal secured to the timber faces should be sufficient to provide a key as good as that formed by the brickwork on either side. Metal lathing should weigh not less than 3 lb./yd.^{2} (1·6 Kg/m^2) for sanded plasters and 2¼ lb./yd.^{2} (1·2 Kg/m^2) for premixed lightweight gypsum plasters and should always be protected by black bitumen paint or be galvanised. The metal lathing should be of ⅜ or ¼-inch (10 or 6mm) mesh and be fixed with the longway of the mesh across the supports. Metal lathing with stiffening ribs can be purchased where the use of this is desirable, for example as a replacement for timber lathing, and a larger guage of metal should be employed if the supports are more than 14-inch (360mm) apart. Distance pieces of round rods, V-shaped ribs or strips of hardwood can be employed where necessary but metal lathing on timber bearers should be fixed by galvanised nails or staples at 4-inch (100mm) centres. The whole point about metal lathing is that it must be firm and taut. Slack lathing, insecurely fixed, will allow later cracking to occur in any plaster coat.

In other cases where, for example, the background is extremely uneven or otherwise unsuitable for the direct application of wall plaster, the application of a background such as gypsum lath, gypsum baseboard ⅜-inch (10mm) thick or insulating fibreboard can be employed. The rules and methods whereby these materials can best be applied are set out in detail in the British Standard Code of Practice C.P.211 of 1966 "Internal Plastering" and the reader is referred to this publication for some very useful information relating to background materials in general. More will, however, be said on this subject shortly.

Patch Repairs to Ceilings and Walls and Repair of Cracks

Before proceeding to a consideration of the factors involved in the replastering of large areas a few general comments on the repair of small defective patches and cracks to ceilings and walls will be set out.

In regard to cracks the mere filling of a narrow crack is useless as eventually the material will drop out. The same will apply if an attempt is made to fill a crack where the plaster on either side has lost its key with the backing. The best practice is to widen a crack as much as necessary until the plaster is found to be adhering tightly or at least to about a ¾-inch (19mm) width and if it is shallow to extend the crack right though to the backing. The sides of the crack should be undercut so as to form a key, all loose material brushed away, existing plaster well wetted together with the backing so as to avoid the repairing material drying out too quickly and the crack fully and firmly filled with a plaster which is quick setting and which expands slightly on setting such as plaster of Paris or Keene's cement.

Fine surface crazing, as distinguished from cracking which normally extends through or nearly through to the backing, is often found. The incidence of crazing seems likely to continue until perhaps it becomes common to include, as is frequently done on the continent, a layer of scrim in the final coat. Crazing can be sealed with a powder filler mixed with water or a diluted emulsion paint. Sometimes a suitably thinned emulsion paint or distemper will be sufficient if well brushed in. In severe cases a lining paper may be necessary to obscure the defect.

A section of plaster which has fallen down and remained in one piece, or a piece which has been left hanging, can sometimes be replaced when all broken plaster and any dust or rubble has been removed, by running plaster of Paris on to the back of the detached portion and pressing and strutting it back into position until set. Again it is essential to ensure that the surrounding plaster is well wetted and of course necessary to ensure that the backing is satisfactory and was not originally the cause of the failure requiring some alteration before the plaster is replaced. On setting the surrounding crack can be dealt with by filling as already described.

Yet another method of dealing with a patch that remains whole is to screw it back into position with brass screws and metal discs, as already described for ceilings in general, either to the existing joists alone or to additional bearers fixed between the joists if this is essential to provide a secure fixing.

For larger patches unless it is proposed to decorate with wallpaper or to use a lining paper, some care is necessary to select a mix which, when dry and hard, will match the existing plaster in appearance and hardness. Fortunately it is neither essential or necessary to be able to identify the existing plaster, although it is to be hoped that most surveyors will be able, from their knowledge of house types and historical forms of construction, to make a reasonable assumption without the need for chemical analysis. Undoubtedly the modern plasters commonly in use at the present time and which will be described in greater detail in the section on replastering provide suitable material for repair work since the work can be completed relatively quickly, the plaster will expand slightly on setting and drying rather than shrink and can be painted much sooner. Plaster of Paris sets too quickly for larger patch repairs and accordingly a mix based on a Class B Retarded Hemihydrate Gypsum Plaster (e.g. Thistle, Faspite, Sirapite Board, Parastone etc.) will usually be found most suitable. For patch repairs in most old houses built before 1930 it will be a case of a repair to lime plaster so that it will probably be necessary to employ a three coat system with proportions for each coat related to the background and on which guidance can be obtained from Table 3 on pages 692–696. Certainly in all cases of repairs to plaster on wood lathing three coats should be used and a check should be made that the lathing is appropriately set out for the type of plaster used.

Class B Retarded Hemihydrate Gypsum Plaster when used as gauging material for lime produces a surface nearer to the characteristics of the lime plaster used in the past, much nearer than would be that produced by the Class A Anhydrous Gypsum plasters, but even so the matching is unlikely to be very good. In the circumstances stripping the old decoration and treating new and old surfaces with clearcole, composed of weak size with a little whiting added to render it less transparent, should serve to even up the suction characteristics and make the new decoration appear fairly even textured throughout. Undoubtedly, however, a much superior finish can be obtained by lining prior to any painting treatment provided the patch is fully dried out. Even with the knowledge that either this lining or patterned paper will be the ultimate covering to new and old plaster, it is still advisable to adopt the plastering method outlined above in view of the time advantage when compared with the use of cement/lime sand plasters.

Replastering

Due to the increasing need for haste in building operations in the 20th century arising from the high cost of labour and materials and the pressure of demand, the old methods of plastering have almost completely vanished except in some remote districts where traditional practices are still maintained. Instead of the traditional three coat layers provided by the render coat, the floating coat and the setting coat giving a total thickness of $\frac{3}{4}$ inches (19mm), two coat work is now quite common, consisting only of a render coat and a setting coat to a combined thickness of $\frac{1}{2}$ inch (13mm). Lime plaster mixed with sand has always been used for plastering and latterly cement has been employed as well. The traditional components for plastering in three coat work are, as we have seen, of one-third part cement by volume to one part of lime putty and three parts sand for the first coat, the mixture being termed coarse stuff, and often including ox or other animal hair. The second coat consists of one part of lime putty to two parts of sand, while the final coat simply consists of neat putty with an equal volume of sand. Non-hydraulic or fat lime was prepared some time before use by burning limestone in a kiln and adding water to form lime putty, the slaking process.

In more leisurely days there was little objection to each plaster coat being allowed to dry before the next coat was applied. The fact that mixes containing lime and cement are bound to shrink on rapid drying means that there is no short cut in the drying process when plastering is carried out by the traditional method. It was in order to overcome the delay in this procedure that modern calcium sulphate or gypsum plasters were mass-produced since these set rapidly to a hard finish within a few hours and two coat work has now become popular in these materials. Lime is still used due to the fact that it can improve the workability of plaster and in some cases accelerate the set of gypsum plasters. The addition of lime however reduces the hardness of plaster and its use in final coats does delay decoration by from six to twelve months if oil paints are to be employed.

It should not, however, be assumed by the reader that three coat plasterwork is outdated. It is true that two coat work has superseded three coat work in the case of new dwellings and new construction generally where there are only minor irregularities in the background or where there is small deviation from the plumb. In older houses, however, considerable variations in the background due to the passage of time and the unevenness of the original materials will be found and under such circumstances the British Standard Code of Practice C.P.211 of 1966 advocates that three coat plasterwork be employed and in particular also in the case of a backing of metal or wood lathing. Three coat work is also necessary where there are considerable variations in suction of the background such as an old stud partition filled with a mixture of different materials. Two

coat work will not be enough, in all probability to overcome the
effects of such variations with certainty. On the other hand,
however, three coat work should never be used for example on
concrete soffits where the plaster thickness should not exceed ⅜ inch
(10mm).

In considering the selection of a plastering system regard must
first be had to the background to be plastered. The background is
obviously of the greatest importance as its strength should never be
less than that of the undercoat mix where cement is employed for
this purpose. Again, the porosity or suction of the background must
be considered as must its ability to provide a bond or key. The
question of the trueness of the background has already been discussed and the question of possible thermal movement in the background is another point that clearly merits attention. Finally the
ability of the background to be completely dry and inert is important
since some forms such as clay bricks can exude soluble salts and a
high moisture content may react badly with some types of plastering
systems.

The British Standard Code of Practice C.P.211 of 1966 classifies
backgrounds under the following groups:

1. Solid backgrounds.

A. Dense, strong and smooth materials such as dense concrete or
high density clay or concrete bricks or blocks. These have low
porosity, little suction and surfaces that offer no mechanical key.
Shrinkage is negligible. These types of background may require
some bonding treatment before the plaster can be applied. This may
take the form of a proprietary bonding agent such as emulsions of
PVA or other polymers or bituminous solutions or emulsions. The
polymer emulsion type of bonding agent is good for use for reducing
suction but the bituminous types while offering resistance to damp,
should not be used on soffits.

B. Moderately strong and porous materials such as most clay or
concrete bricks or blocks, calcium silicate bricks and some medium
density concrete where the background offers some suction and
mechanical key and has variable shrinkage characteristics.

C. Moderately weak and porous materials such as lightweight
concrete either aerated or made with lightweight aggregates or low
strength bricks where a large drying shrinkage movement is to be
expected as well as strong suction characteristics.

D. "No-fines" concrete which forms a class by itself since if offers
a good key owing to the many large voids present but has low or
moderate shrinkage and suction characteristics according to the
aggregate used.

2. Slab backgrounds

Slab backgrounds are those such as wood wool, strawboard and cork slabs. These, when fixed under normal circumstances do not present any serious drying shrinkage risk. Wood wool slab has low suction and provides a good key while strawboard needs a bonding liquid or a fixing of wire mesh or metal lathing before plastering is applied. Cork slab has a low suction and a variable key and a mechanical key can be provided by a brush coating of cement sand slurry and the provision of galvanised wire mesh, stapled to the surface.

3. Boards

These consist of plasterboard, insulated fibreboard and expanded plastics. Expanded plastics have no drying shrinkage movement. Insulating fibreboard has a high drying shrinkage movement but is fixed dry and is easily restrained. It should be conditioned on site before fixing, wetted as little as possible prior to and during plastering and subsequently should be exposed only to reasonable occupational conditions. Plasterboard has negligible drying shrinkage movement. Each of these boards has low suction but affords adequate bond with suitable plasters.

4. Metal lathing

This provides a good key, needs no preparation and is a suitable background to receive most types of plaster coats.

Once the characteristics of the background have been considered such as its strength, suction, bonding properties, liability to shrinkage or thermal movement and probable content of water and soluble salts the design of the plaster coating can be decided. Before passing on to discuss the combination of materials and mixes which can be used a word should be said on the subject of plaster itself.

The British Standard Code of Practice C.P.211 of 1966 divides plasters into two categories; gypsum plasters and thin-wall plasters. Thin-wall plasters are those which normally incorporate organic binders and/or gypsum plaster and may harden either by drying or on setting. They may be used for single coat work or on their appropriate undercoats. Gypsum plasters on the other hand are classified under British Standard 1191 into four classes as follows:

Class A. Plaster of Paris suitable for gauging lime final coats, for patching and repair work and for fibrous plasterwork.

Class B. Retarded hemihydrate gypsum plaster in the following types:

Type (a) Undercoat plaster (browning and metal lathing grades)
Type (b) Final coat plaster (finish or board finish)

Type (a) plaster is suitable for sanded undercoats and Type (b) finish plaster for final coats, neat or gauged with not more than 25 per cent lime by volume in two or three coat work. Board finish plasters are suitable for neat single coat work on board backgrounds.

Class C. Anhydrous gypsum plaster used as a final coat only, neat or gauged with not more than 25 per cent lime by volume.

Class D. Keene's plaster used as a neat final coat plaster only.

In addition to the above classes pre-mixed lightweight gypsum plasters are available either as undercoat plasters (browning, bonding, metal lathing, multi-purpose) or final coat plaster. The lightweight aggregates are usually either expanded perlite or exfoliated vermiculite. Pre-mixed final coat plasters are also available designed for special purposes such as for application to a high suction backing.

Classes A and B

When gypsum is heated and water expelled, a fine white, grey or pink powder is obtained which is known as plaster of Paris. When mixed with water it sets within a very few minutes and thus is not employed for general plasterwork but is very useful for small repairs and gauging purposes. When a retarder is incorporated with the gypsum to delay the set this produces a group of plasters known as retarded hemihydrate gypsum plasters which are suitable for general work including the larger repairs. For undercoat or browning work the normal proportions are one part of plaster to three parts of sand for brick walls and one part of plaster to one and a half parts of sand for concrete surfaces. Hair can be added to the mix. A possible finishing coat is half a part of plaster to one part of lime but a lime mix is normally not employed on plasterboards.

Classes C and D

These plasters are slow in hardening and an additive is necessary in the form of an accelerator to make them suitable for plastering. Anhydrous gypsum plaster when employed for undercoats is normally mixed so that two parts of plaster are added to one part of lime and five parts of sand. Finishing coats can be formed of neat plaster or have a small quantity of lime added to enable the working quality to be improved. Anhydrous gypsum plasters are not suitable for plasterboards as they lack the necessary adhesive qualities. The rather hard dense quality of this type of plaster when used neat as a finishing coat has been responsible for many of the complaints of temporary condensation.

Keene's or Parian plaster is designed for use mainly as a finishing coat to produce a very hard surface. It is much in use for external angles often on a cement and sand base and is useful for the repair of damaged top coats of existing work, for example knocks and abrasions. Keene's plaster, however, is not suitable for a board finish and lime should never be added to the finishing coat.

Essential characteristics and general properties of normal plastering mixes

In the groups of mixes given which are reprinted from the British Standard Code of Practice C.P.211 of 1966, the importance will be readily appreciated of the need to relate the plaster final coat to the undercoat and the plastering process as a whole to the structural background as regards density and strength and liability to expansion or contraction during setting and drying or in subsequent life. Bond failure is to be avoided at all costs. In addition to this, however, the relationship of the various mixes of plaster is important as the conditions for use will vary widely from plaster renewals in an old house, where time may not be of the essence, to piecemeal patching in an occupied house where time is important, but even more vital is the need to select a plastering mix which has little or no drying shrinkage in order to avoid the risk of a crack formation at the boundary of the old work and the new.

For the purposes of obtaining an understanding of the characteristics and properties of plastering mixes such as is necessary for a reasoned choice of materials and for their proper use, the plastering mixes are considered in five groups.

1. *Mixes based on cement, cement and lime, or hydraulic lime*

The traditional plastering mixes containing lime and sand and possibly some cement are characterised by high workability and marked ease of application, properties which become less pronounced as the proportion of any cement increases or when an unsoaked hydrated lime is used. These mixes have a reasonably long working time, a fairly slow rate of strength development (increasing with the amount of cement added) and adequate early strength to withstand modern building conditions. They need moisture to complete the setting process and for this reason, rapid drying in the early stages should be avoided. Shrinkage, partly irreversible, occurs on drying, causing stresses to be set up both in the applied coat and in the undercoat or background; and, in order to avoid breakdown of adhesion between successive coats and cracking of the final coat, it is very important that the drying shrinkage of the first coat should be materially complete before a subsequent coat is applied. Each undercoat should, therefore, be allowed to dry thoroughly. The rate of drying will vary widely with conditions of temperature, humidity and ventilation. This delay to allow for drying also serves to diminish the liability for efflorescent salts to find their way to the final plaster surface, and for drying and maturing shrinkage of the undercoat communicating itself to the finished plaster face over a period of time in the form of map cracking.

Mixes based on the presently available hydraulic limes are comparatively weak, but otherwise their characteristics are similar to those discussed above for cement: lime: sand mixes.

Weak mixes, i.e. those containing little cement or mixes based on hydraulic limes, should not be used in combination with a strong final coat, but they offer certain advantages over the stronger mixes for application to non-rigid backgrounds such as lathing.

Mixes of limes and cement should not, in general, be used for trowelled final coats, as their shrinkage on drying creates a tendency to surface crazing.

2. *Mixes based on lime, gauged with a gypsum plaster*

Plastering mixes of gypsum plaster, sand and lime, are easily worked and have a working time which varies with the type of gypsum plaster used. Gypsum plasters expand on setting and tend to restrain the drying shrinkage of the lime. Sufficient time should be permitted for one coat to dry so that it has adequate suction and strength to receive the next one. The time intervals necessary vary widely.

Mixes of lime and gypsum plaster are used for final coats when a fairly soft finish is suitable and can be used when a reasonable match for old plaster is required. The hardness and strength of the finish increase as the proportion of gauging material increases. Care should be taken to ensure that the strength of the finish is not incompatible with the nature of the backing material.

3. *Mixes based on gypsum plasters*

Plastering mixes based on gypsum plasters show wide variations in properties and require differing treatments for their effective use. Materials covered by British Standards may be divided into two main groups, those based on calcium sulphate hemihydrate (plaster of paris and retarded hemihydrate gypsum plaster) and those based on anhydrous calcium sulphate (anhydrous gypsum plasters and Keene's). The hemihydrate plasters set quickly, the start of the setting process being delayed in the retarded plasters and it is this group which are usually most suitable for use in gauging with lime for repair work. Plasters based on anhydrous calcium sulphate, on the other hand, have a comparatively slow continuous setting process and in practice should not be allowed to dry before the setting process is complete. The setting of all these plasters is accompanied by an expansion which is variable in amount, but when the setting process is complete little further movement takes place during drying. For this reason it is unnecessary to ensure that thorough drying of one coat has taken place before the application of the following coat (a condition essential for mixes containing cement) but sufficient suction and strength should have been developed to enable good adhesion to be obtained. No gypsum plaster should be permitted to remain under persistently damp conditions after it has set as this causes weakening and disintegration.

Most of these plasters may be used, without admixtures, for final coats; when used in this way their expansion during setting becomes an important fact. They set to a hard strong finish which may exert considerable force on the undercoat or background, which should on that account be strong. In this connection it should be noted that when a neat retarded hemihydrate finishing plaster is applied to a non-rigid base, e.g. gypsum plasterboard or fibre building board (insulating board) or to a smooth background of concrete or the like, it is important to use a plaster having a low setting expansion, i.e. B.S.1191,[1] Class B, board finish plaster.

A general feature of gypsum plaster final coats is their relative freedom from surface crazing.

4. *Lightweight gypsum plasters*

Lightweight gypsum plasters are based on hemihydrate gypsum plasters and therefore have the general characteristics described in 3 above and should be used in a similar manner. It is important that only the recommended lightweight final coat should be applied to these undercoats.

5. *Mixes based on gypsum plasters gauged with lime*

Certain gypsum plasters may be used, both for undercoat and final coats, with lime additions which tend to increase workability and to decrease expansion. In the case of retarded hemihydrate gypsum plaster, however, the lime addition also accelerates the set.

In considering the type of materials to be selected in replastering, the question of toughness or resistance of the plaster to knocks may be important since corridors and halls require a greater degree of resistance in this respect than ceilings. Cement finishes are perhaps the stoutest, with Keene's plaster, anhydrous gypsum plaster, retarded hemihydrate gypsum plaster and lime plaster following in order of decreasing surface hardness. The pre-mixed lightweight plasters are more liable to indentation under impact than sanded plasters, but they have a certain resilience which reduces the incidence of more serious damage.

[1] B.S.1191, "Gypsum building plasters".

In conclusion of this section on plasterwork reprinted here are extracts from Tables 3 and 4 of the British Standard Code of Practice C.P.211 of 1966. It should always be borne in mind also that plastering has been and still is a skilled craft where knowledge of the materials and conditions by the craftsman are often vital to the success of the operation. Frequently where alternative specifications are suitable the choice of one familiar to the craftsman will be advantageous. The surveyor can specify the materials with care, and incidentally reference should be made to British Standards 1198 and 1199 for the selection of the correct sand for aggregate (Type 1, 2 or 3) but in the last report the craftsman will make or mar the work and it is a pity that the British Standard Code of Practice, so excellent in other respects, cannot help to select the man to do the job.

Extracts from Tables 3 and 4 of the British Standard Code of Practice "Internal Plastering" 1966

Key to Table 3

Suitable combinations of undercoats and final coats are indicated in the Table. Plastering specifications based on these will normally enable any desired type of finish to be obtained on any background.

The types of plasters referred to in this Table are as follows:

Final coats

Category I. Gypsum. Any Class B or Class C gypsum plaster, neat or gauged with not more than $\frac{1}{4}$ volume of lime. Keene's plaster final coats are *not* included in this category, since they are stronger than other gypsum finishes and require stronger undercoats. Traditionally a 1:3 Portland cement:sand undercoat is used, but this is only suitable for strong backgrounds with good mechanical key, e.g. brickwork or no-fines concrete. A type B undercoat may be used on other backgrounds, but manufacturers of the plaster should be consulted as to its suitability for this purpose.

Category II. Weak lime. This category is restricted to the weaker finishes of lime putty gauged with up to half of its volume of gypsum plaster, to which up to 1 volume of fine sand may be added. The stronger lime finishes, of lime putty gauged with $\frac{1}{2}$ to 1 volume of gypsum plaster, should only be used with stronger undercoats recommended for finishes of Category I.

Category III. Lightweight. Any of the proprietary finishes usually recommended for use on lightweight plaster undercoats.

Category IV. Cement. Types C_1, C_2 and C_3 final coats as for cement-based undercoats shown below. The cement:lime:sand mixes are normally somewhat easier to float to an acceptable finish than are the corresponding aerated mixes.

691

Table 3. Suitable Plastering Systems for Various Backgrounds

Type of background	Type of finish required	Undercoat plasters suitable for these finishes	Remarks	Single-coat work
Solid backgrounds				
Normal clay brickwork and blockwork	I. Gypsum	B_4 or C_2		Not suitable for this type of background
	II. Weak-lime	B_4, C_2, C_3, G or D		
	III. Light-weight	L_1 L_4 or D		
	IV. Cement C_1 C_2 or C_3	Corresponding cement undercoats		
Dense clay brickwork (other than engineering brickwork) and blockwork, calcium silicate or concrete brickwork or blockwork	I. Gypsum	B_3 or C_2		As above
	II. Weak lime	B_3 C_2 C_3 G or D		
	III. Light-weight	L_1 L_4 or D		
	IV. Cement C_1 C_2 or C_3	Corresponding cement undercoats		
No-fines concrete open textured lightweight aggregate concrete or blocks	I. Gypsum	B_3 or C_2		As above
	II. Weak lime	B_3 C_2 C_3 G or D		
	III. Light-weight	L_1 L_4 or D		

Type of background	Type of finish required	Undercoat plasters suitable for these finishes	Remarks	Single-coat work
Solid backgrounds				
	IV. Cement C_2 or C_3	Corresponding cement undercoats	C_1 finishes and undercoats may also be used on strong no-fines concrete	
Aerated concrete[1] slabs and blockwork	I. Gypsum	B_3 or C_2		Sufficiently level surfaces may be plastered with thin wall plasters or with board finish plasters on low suction concrete
	II. Weak lime	B_3 C_2 C_3 G or D		
	III. Lightweight	L_2 L_4 or D		
	IV. Cement C_2 or C_3		When cement finishes are required, the weaker C_3 mixes are preferable on this backbround	
Clay engineering brickwork, dense concrete or close textured lightweight aggregate concrete or blocks	II. Gypsum	B_2	Undercoats based on cement or lime are not normally suitable for this type of background	Sufficiently level concrete surfaces may be plastered with thin wall plasters or board finish plasters; a bonding treatment may be necessary for the latter
	II. Weak lime	B_2		
	III. Lightweight	L_2 or L_4		

[1] Plasters of improved water retentivity have an advantage when the suction of this type of background is particularly high.

Type of background	Type of finish required	Undercoat plasters suitable for these finishes	Remarks	Single-coat work
Solid backgrounds				
Surfaces such as glazed bricks, tiled or painted surfaces, all treated with bonding agents	I. Gypsum	B_2	Undercoats based on cement or lime are not normally suitable for this type of background	Sufficiently level surfaces may be plastered with board finish plasters
	II. Weak lime	B_2		
	III. Lightweight	L_2 or L_4		
Slabs				
Wood-wool	I. Gypsum	B_3		Not suitable for this type of background
	II. Weak lime	B_3 C_2 or G		
	III. Lightweight	L_3 or L_4		
Strawboard	I. Gypsum	Boards surfaced with suitable paper or treated with PVA bonding coats may be plastered with the mixes recommended below for plaster-board. When metal lathing is stapled to this background to provide a key, the mixes recommended below for metal lathing may be applied		Sufficiently level surfaces treated with PVA bonding agents may be plastered with board finish plasters
	II. Weak lime			
	III. Lightweight			

Type of background	Type of finish required	Undercoat plasters suitable for these finishes	Remarks	Single-coat work
Boards				
Plaster-board and insulating fibreboard	I. Gypsum	B_2	Undercoats based on cement or lime are not suitable for this type of background	Sufficiently level surfaces may be plastered with board finish plasters but in the case of expanded plastics the boards should be fully bonded to a firm background
	II. Weak lime	B_2		
	III. Light-weight	L_2 or L_4		
Expanded plastics boards	I. Gypsum	B_1		
	II. Weak lime	B_1		
	III. Light-weight	L_3 or L_4		
Lathing				
Metal lathing	I. Gypsum	B_2 followed by B_3	Mixes for first under-coat should contain hair or suitable fibre	Not suit-able for this type of background
	II. Weak lime	C_1 C_2 or as above		
	III. Light-weight	L_3 or L_4		
	IV. Cement C_3	C_3		

Undercoats

The mix proportions shown below are by volume.

Type G.Lime-sand (1:2–3) gauged with gypsum plaster, e.g. 1:3:9. Class B plaster:lime:sand.

Type B. Class B gypsum plasters and sand.

Class B plaster: Type 1 sand to B.S.1198		Class B plaster: Type 2 sand to B.S.1198
B_1	1:1	1:$\frac{2}{3}$
B_2	1:1$\frac{1}{2}$	1:1
B_3	1:2	1:1$\frac{1}{2}$
B_4	1:2–3, according to density of plaster and manufacturer's instructions.	1:1$\frac{1}{2}$–2

NOTE. The grades of Class B undercoat plaster selected shall be appropriate to the background as indicated in the manufacturer's instructions.

Type L	Pre-mixed lightweight gypsum
L_1	Browning type
L_2	Bonding type
L_3	Metal lathing type
L_4	Multi-purpose type

Type C   Undercoats based on cement

	Cement:lime:sand	Masonry cement:sand	Cement:sand with plasticiser
C_1	1:0$\frac{1}{4}$:3	—	—
C_2	1:1:5–6	1:4$\frac{1}{2}$	1:5–6
C_3	1:2:8–9	1:6	1:7–8

Type D. Pre-mixed lightweight cement.

Proprietary Plasters from C.P.211:1966

Introduction to Table 4. The Classification given in Table 4 has been included to enable the users to identify the types of plasters referred to within the Code. Where a British Standard exists or is proposed for particular types of plaster, the table indicates the British Standard classification.

Table 4. Classification of Proprietary Plasters

| Classification | British Standard classification | | Proprietary name |
	Class	Type	
Gypsum plasters Plaster of Paris	B.S. 1191, Part 1 A	—	C.B. Stucco
Retarded hemihydrate gypsum plaster Undercoat Plaster – Browning Plaster	B.S. 1191, Part 1 B	a. 1	Thistle haired Plaster Faspite haired (Medium Setting) Plaster Thistle Browning Plaster Thistle Slow Setting Browning Plaster Faspite (Medium) Setting Plaster
Metal lathing plaster		a. 2	Thistle Metal Lathing Plaster
Final coat plaster Wall finish plaster		b. 1	Bellrock Wall Finish Plaster Thistle Finish Plaster Faspite (Medium Setting) Plaster

Classification	British Standard classification		Proprietary name
	Class	Type	
Board finish plaster		b. 2	Bullrock Board Finish Plaster Thistle Board Finish Plaster Faspite (Quick Setting) Plaster Bullrock Multi-purpose Plaster
Anhydrous gypsum plaster Final coat plaster	B.S. 1191, Part 1 C	—	Sirapite (Pink) Plaster Sirapite (Grey) Plaster Sirapite Finish Plaster Statite Plaster
Keene's plaster	B.S. 1191, Part 1 D	—	Fine Keene's Cement White Keene's Cement Standard Polar White Gypsum Cement Fine Polar White Gypsum Cement

Pre-mixed lightweight gypsum plaster
  Undercoat plaster
  Browning plaster
	Standard proposed	1	Staunchlite Browning Plaster
			Carlite Browning Plaster

Bonding plaster		2	Staunchlite Lightweight Bonding Plaster Carlite Bonding Coat Plaster
Metal lathing plaster		3	Carlite Metal lathing Plaster

| Classification | British Standard classification | | Proprietary name |
	Class	Type	
Multi-purpose plaster		4	Billingham Lightweight Backing Coat Plaster
Final plaster		5	Staunchlite Lightweight Finishing Plaster Carlite Finish Plaster Billingham Lightweight Finishing Coat Plaster
Pre-mixed cement undercoat plaster	None	—	Thermacote Plaster
Special finish	None	—	LSM Universal Finishing Plaster
Thinwall plasters Undercoat mixes	None	—	Breplasta Render Plaster
Finishes		—	Snowplast Plaster Breplasta 100 Plaster
Acoustic plaster	None		Dekoosto Plaster

Finally a word must be said on the subject of painting new and old plaster surfaces. Since the paint treatment for new plaster varies according to the type of plaster employed, and in particular care is necessary if a mix containing cement and/or lime has been used, some thought is needed to specify the correct materials so as to lessen any risk of failure in the new decorations, an occurrence of unfortunate frequency.

It is, of course, necessary to ensure that the plaster surface is first of all fit for the application of the decorating material. It is hoped that plaster with hygroscopic salts will have been removed but where soluble substances are also present other effects may be seen. If the plaster contains an appreciable quantity of crystalline salts such as sodium sulphate or magnesium sulphate they may form an efflorescence on the surface which will disrupt the decorating film.

Such salts are more commonly associated with brickwork but can occur to plaster and wiping off until they cease to appear is the only remedy before decoration. Portland cement and most hydraulic limes contain caustic alkalis which, when damp, are destructive to oil paint by a process called saponification. The action of the alkali converts oily or fatty matter into soap. Thus an oil paint applied to a damp alkaline surface will become soft and sticky or run down the surface in yellowish streaks.

The biggest danger, however, in painting plaster surfaces is the presence of damp. It is seldom possible to leave new plaster surfaces for a sufficient period to ensure that they are completely dry and accordingly some moisture content must usually be expected. It is only when this exceeds a certain minimum that trouble from blistering and peeling in the decorative film can follow.

The Painting of Lime Plaster

Hydraulic lime plasters and those of high calcium content (non-hydraulic) when mixed with cement are highly alkaline and are therefore liable to cause alkaline attack on the oil in paints and distempers and also the bleaching of certain pigments. Lime plaster finishes have a moderately high suction which has to be counteracted by suitable adjustment of the first coat of oil or emulsion paint or distemper. Such plaster finishes develop efflorescence less frequently than other plaster finishes but surface crazing can occur if the plaster has not been correctly gauged or worked on application.

Lime plaster should be left unpainted for the first few months after application so as to allow it to dry and harden thoroughly. If there is some unassailable objection to leaving the plaster bare, a temporary decoration, if it is proposed eventually to paper, of non-washable distemper can be applied which can be removed at a later date. Otherwise a more permanent decoration of matt finish emulsion paint or a vinyl water paint can be applied which permits evaporation but which does not have to be removed prior to repainting. Whenever oil paint is used the primer employed should be of an alkali-resistant type and preferably two coats should be applied on the bare plaster when dry. Paints and distempers for application to lime plasters should be chosen where the pigments are unaffected by alkalis.

With new lime plaster surfaces non-washable distempers or emulsion or vinyl water paints can, as we have seen, be employed, or alternatively a cement paint can be applied provided that the lime plaster is not gauged with a calcium sulphate plaster. Silicate paint, however, is not suitable if oil paint is to be applied at a later date.

If sufficient drying time is available so that the amount of water in the plaster is small, oil bound water paint or flat oil paint can be employed which forms a suitable base for later treatment with gloss oil paints. If the surface of the plaster can be left unpainted for a considerable time until the work is dry throughout, any type of paint finish can be applied but an alkali resistant primer should nevertheless still be employed. The use of a primer in this manner or of a plaster sealer if surfaces are absolutely dry also takes care of the high porosity exhibited by lime plasters in general and on areas where the extent of trowelling may be variable. Two coats will usually be necessary. With porous first decorations it may be necessary to thin the first coat with water. Paints with pigments liable to be attacked by alkalis such as Prussian blues and Brunswick greens should be avoided. In the case of old plaster surfaces adjacent to repair patches it is necessary to bring these up to a reasonable standard prior to decorating. Any major cracks should of course be cut out and then made good as previously described and if priming paint is applied to the sides of the crack as an alternative to wetting this will avoid undue absorption of water so that when the crack is filled the plaster does not subsequently shrink on drying out. Plaster of paris or a retarded hemihydrate calcium sulphate plaster gauged with about one-third of its volume of hydrated lime is recommended for filling.

Fine cracks can be treated prior to painting by filling them with a mixture of linseed oil putty and white lead or a distemper type of filling composition. If an old lime plaster surface has signs of very fine crazing it will be necessary to first apply a plaster sealer over the whole area.

Where old surfaces have been previously painted their preparation may involve the treatment of mould growth (see the Chapter on Dampness) and the removal of the existing paint if this is perished or shows signs of flaking or saponification. Under such circumstances the paint should be removed and the surface allowed to dry completely. Repainting is then carried out as in the case of new plaster. Individual defective patches can be treated individually, the paint being removed, and the patches then being treated with primer and undercoating before a fresh coating is applied over the whole area to be painted. A leadless type of primer is best under these circumstances. If, however, the existing paintwork is in reasonably sound condition the surface should be cleaned and rubbed down prior to re-painting. Non-washable distemper, however, should always be removed before repainting in any form irrespective of its condition and the surface should be left to dry out thoroughly.

The Painting of Calcium Sulphate Plasters

Where such plasters are properly set and hardened and both the plaster and the backing is thoroughly dry, calcium sulphate plasters can be painted successfully with almost any type of paint. It should be borne in mind, however, that plaster finishes gauged with lime involve a greater painting risk owing to a possibility of alkali attack and it is advisable to take precautions accordingly. The risk, however, is least with retarded hemihydrate gypsum plaster although variations in porosity may still indicate the use of a primer or sealer for satisfactory results.

Neat calcium sulphate plasters have no appreciable chemical action on paint and the paint defects which occur are generally associated with the action of moisture and of efflorescent salts which are carried through the plaster from materials behind the surface, especially from bricks of high soluble salt content. Crystallisation then occurs below or on the surface and causes damage to the paint. This is particularly liable to happen on the denser plasters such as Keenes and if it occurs below the surface stripping and awaiting the disappearance of the salts is necessary. Moisture can cause retarded hemihydrate plasters to "sweat out". This means that the plaster fails to harden or disintegrates either when the backing to the plaster is permanently damp or when moisture is sealed into the plaster by the premature application of an impervious paint film. The remedy in this instance is usually one of stripping and replastering.

Anhydrous calcium sulphate plasters are liable to a defect known as "dry out". This is characterised by a powdery friable condition of the plaster surface which occurs when the plaster is allowed to dry too quickly before it has had time to combine with all the water needed for the setting and hardening process. A "dry out" can be caused by application of a plaster finish to a highly absorbent undercoat, by conditions favouring rapid evaporation or by the premature application of artificial heat. If the plaster has already completely dried there is no alternative but to strip and replaster. Subsequent wetting of the original plaster would cause considerable expansion and lifting.

The painter likes a plaster surface that is not too highly trowelled and non-absorbent. Emulsion paints and distempers adhere less strongly to impervious surfaces than do oil paints. A gloss paint finish shows up any irregularities in the plaster surface and accordingly the plaster should be trowelled only to the minimum extent needed to produce a smooth finish but no attempt should be made to produce a high polish on the plaster prior to painting.

In general the work for the decoration of calcium sulphate plaster finishes is much the same as that for lime plasters. The same precautions should be taken if necessary against alkali attack by the employment of a special alkali resistant primer and pigments liable to be affected by alkalis should be avoided. Once the surface of the plaster is primed or sealed it should be stopped and filled by the painter and the plaster surface examined for signs of efflorescence. For early decoration the same types of paint may be used as have been recommended for use in the case of lime plaster with the exception of cement paint which is not suitable and must not be used. Gloss finishes should not be applied until drying of the plaster and the backing is well advanced.

Anhydrous calcium sulphate plasters, as we have seen, require special consideration on application, in that rapid drying by artificial heat, for example, should be avoided, and as soon as the plaster is set it should be primed at once with a sharp priming paint containing just sufficient red lead or gold size to bind the pigment and consisting of well thinned white lead paste with added driers. The thin coat of paint slightly retards the evaporation of water from the surface, aids hydration of the plaster and prevents "dry out" as previously discussed. It should be said, however, that this method should be restricted to only those plasters which are acid such as Keene's plaster. Once this is done, no further coats of paint should be applied until the plaster and the primer have dried out.

The decoration of old surfaces of calcium sulphate plaster finishes should follow the same practice as that described for lime plasters.

Gypsum plasterboard and fibre building boards are usually finished with one or two coats of retarded hemihydrate gypsum plaster. These can be painted with the same types of paints as those already recommended for calcium sulphate plasters but the surface will be open textured and absorbent and it is therefore preferable to use primings of thinned emulsion paint or plaster sealers before decoration. These reduce the suction making the surface suitable for oil or emulsion paints or washable distemper. There is no danger of alkali attack and with single coat work rapid drying can be expected.

Pre-mixed lightweight plasters, which are increasingly common in use are based on hemihydrate gypsum plasters with vermiculite or perlite aggregates but have a more open texture and contain more water. Accordingly they take somewhat longer to dry out. Apart from this factor they can be treated the same as for the Class B gypsum plasters, there being little risk of alkaline attack unless from the background. One of the problems frequently put to surveyors in regard to calcium sulphate plasters is that of corrosion staining. The most common incidence of such staining occurs on ceilings where the pattern of nails securing plasterboard appears through the plaster finishing coat and often through a distemper or emulsion coat of decoration. The cause is invariably corrosion in the heads of the nails which have not been properly galvanised and is usually accompanied by the omission of the jute scrimming on the joints as well. In such cases probably the best remedial method is to spot coat each stain with a good quality aluminium wood priming paint i.e. one containing a good leafing aluminium powder and then, when dry, to cover the whole ceiling with a further coat. Subsequent decoration should be with an oil paint, probably a flat oil paint if a ceiling is involved and accordingly it may be that a soft distemper or other old decoration unsuitable to take oil paint would have to be stripped first. It is necessary to coat the whole of the ceiling before redecoration as otherwise unequal suction would render the appearance on completion of the work patchy.

INTERNAL PARTITIONS OTHER THAN TIMBER

Where internal partitions rely on timber for their structural make-up, that is to say partitions of trussed design or partitions of stud and lath and plaster, these, whether load bearing or not, have special characteristics of their own and reference has been made to them under Chapter 5 dealing with Timber. No further comments will be made on such partitions at this point but a word should be said on the subject of partitions which do not make use of timber as the main structural element.

In order to determine as to the best means of repair of a defective partition the surveyor must first decide if this is load bearing or not. Brick has, of course, been used as one of the basic materials for internal partitions from time immemorial and while it is probably true to say that up to the end of the Georgian period load bearing partitions were either formed with timber or of brick, non-load bearing partitions were not often of brick due to the expense of this material, timber studs used in conjunction with lath and plaster, being much preferred. With the advent of mass-produced bricks in Victoria's reign, however, it became more and more common for brick to be employed as a material for load bearing and non load bearing partitions alike on the better quality house and indeed, with the increased ceiling heights of Victorian villas and larger houses, brick became more and more into use. The tall five or six storey late Victorian house sometimes displays the use of brick as a material for internal partitions in an impressive manner. The main spine partition will be of brick and will be load bearing and of a substantial thickness corresponding to that of the outer walls. Cross partitions will again be of brick possibly 9 inches (229mm) or 13½ inches (343mm) varying according to the different floor levels. Dividing partitions between rooms that are not load bearing will again be of brick and in particular to the ground floor rooms the heights will be such that 4½ inches (114mm) brickwork is only barely acceptable without intermediate stiffening. The smaller semi-detached or terraced Victorian or Edwardian villa is arranged on much the same lines except that the main spine partition is generally only of 9-inch (229mm) brick construction at the lowest level reducing either to 4½ inches (114mm) or more often to timber studs above while the remaining partitions are either of 4½-inch (114mm) brick or timber stud and lath and plaster construction. Latterly, however, other types of material have been introduced for use in partitions, the most common being breeze concrete blocks which were widely used in the many estates of small houses built between the two World Wars while for the larger houses hollow clay partition blocks were often used. Since the Second World War other types of materials such as lightweight concrete blocks have been introduced to the exclusion of most of the former solid partitioning materials with the exception of brick while the introduction of plasterboard and other boards has replaced lath and plaster used on the traditional stud partition.

In most cases the surveyor will be able to discover from his inspection without too much difficulty whether a partition is load bearing or not. There are, however, cases where this is more difficult than it might appear and under such circumstances only the preparation of careful and accurate plans of the various floors will give a precise answer to the problem of how each particular partition plays its part in the structural make-up of the building. Such complications are, however, more common with timber trussed partitions in Victorian or Georgian houses since often timber trussed partitions will be off-set at the various floor levels rather than directly above each other so that it is often a matter of some perplexity to the surveyor to work out which partition carries what and where, particularly if many alterations have been put in hand to the partitions since the house was first constructed. The main load bearing partitions, when formed of bricks or blocks, will run vertically from top to bottom of the dwelling house, but minor load bearing partitions and certainly non-load bearing partitions will be found off-set from each other at the various floor levels and care has to be taken to ensure if each partition has a structural function or not or if it simply acts to divide a particular floor area into rooms without fulfilling any other purpose.

Failure in partitions can take a number of forms. So far as load bearing partitions are concerned it is a more than commonplace matter to find that the superimposed weights of the various floor loads together with the additional top weight of the roof structure has proved too much for the partition which has settled in consequence. Although we have seen how impressive an array of brickwork can be deployed in the larger type of better quality house for partitions it remains a fact that overloading of an internal partition is one of the most common mistakes found in housing particularly that of the cheaper speculative type. Sometimes a simple timber stud partition with lath and plaster covering will be expected to carry twice the load of even the most heavily loaded external wall. When the construction is of timber with no damp-proofing, it is hardly surprising that wet or dry rot in the base plate or feet of the studs introduces the substantial settlements that have already been described in earlier chapters as severely affecting roof and floor structures. Half-brick thickness at the lowest level with studding above is often only a little better from a structural point of view and it is only when brickwork is used throughout at appropriate thicknesses for the loading that this type of defect occurs to a lesser degree. Even then, however, the foundations and conditions in the sub-soil can undermine the strength of the partition since the same care for matching foundations to sub-soil and loading was seldom taken for internal partitions as was adopted for external walls. Excavation will more than likely show that there is an inadequate foundation or for example that part of the drainage system running under the house has become defective so that water has escaped into the sub-soil and has upset its load bearing characteristics. A further alternative is that the sub-soil was not of an even load bearing characteristic in the first place due to part of the sub-soil below the foundations consisting of made up ground, filled with rubble.

The question of repair of a load bearing internal partition in the main follows closely that already described in the Chapters dealing with Brick and Stone Walls and Foundations. The treatment for a main load bearing internal partition of brick or blocks will follow the same rules relating to inspection, detailed investigation and repair, whether the failure is in respect of the partition as a whole or merely in part. There is some comfort in that an internal partition, being restrained and braced from either side and abutting or being bonded into the main walls of the dwelling house is not likely to show appreciable movement out of the vertical, the movement therefore being mainly limited to straightforward settlement. It is possible, of course, in a house that forms the end of a terrace, that an appreciable movement in the end flank wall may distort a house structure sufficiently to drag an internal partition out of a vertical position but such a case would be rare.

One of the main difficulties in the repair of internal load bearing partitions which have settled badly lies in the question of access. In the case of an external wall access can usually at least be obtained from one side with comparative ease without involving much inconvenience to occupied premises but in the case of an internal partition special arrangements are necessary often involving considerable disruption and the loss of use of one or more rooms. The question of access and time available for repair work can be an important one particularly where the repair work is not being carried out on a change of ownership but is being put in hand while the family are still living on the premises. This aspect can be one which can play a much greater part in the decision as to which method of repair should be selected than in the case of an external wall. If a load bearing partition has settled evenly along its entire length it is likely that the surveyor will select a method of repair that employs the use of horizontal beams worked in under the base of the partition supported at intervals by piers capable of taking the necessary point loads rather than a conventional type of foundation employing the use of concrete. In most cases the surveyor will be satisfied at having arrested the movement since any further settlement should be minimal. With small houses the tendency to throw two small compartments into one large room often requires the substitution of a beam to replace the lower section of a partition. If the partition is load bearing and settling this requirement may well provide the repair necessary to restrain further movement in the partition above and the floors and roof structure which may be bearing on the partition. Even if it is intended to retain the original room pattern the provision of a beam is often a far more simple method of restraining further movement than, for example, underpinning the existing foundations with new. There is far less likelihood of further settlement since pinning up is usually easier. Of course the transference of additional weight on to the walls at each end of the partition is a matter for care but usually all that is required is sufficient dispersion of the load and this is usually achieved by the introduction of concrete spreaders into the existing brickwork. The demolition of the lowest section of the old partition if badly distorted, the making out of the floor, and the substitution of a lightweight non-load bearing partition completes the operation.

In the case of the partial settlement of a load bearing partition the method of repair to some extent depends on the point at which failure occurs; whether this is at a part of the building where access for repair work can be obtained easily, or at a point where access can only be obtained with difficulty.

Defects in load bearing partitions can occur in other ways than by the failure of the foundations or sub-soil. Faults can occur at any floor level due to the fact that too many openings have been formed in the partition resulting in the load being unevenly spread and leading to fractures in the brickwork or blocks. More effective methods of spanning the openings together with the bonding in of the surrounding brickwork can normally be carried out as local repairs provided of course that the condition of the brickwork as a whole is sound.

One virtue of internal load bearing partitions is that due to the fact that they are designed to be plastered on each side, the bond in the brickwork should be effective for the whole thickness. There is not the danger as sometimes occurs in the external walls of finding that a $4\frac{1}{2}$ inches (114mm) external facing skin has a bad bond with the remainder of the wall so that the effective thickness of the wall is reduced by this amount. If, however, the surveyor decides that the partition is too slender to stand the superimposed weights placed upon it there will be little alternative but for it to be rebuilt, as the problem of thickening an internal partition on both sides lies in the difficulty of forming a bond between the old and the new work.

Non load bearing internal partitions present particular problems of their own. Such partitions are normally erected from a single thickness of blocks or bricks and as there is no through bond they are not able to withstand lateral or eccentric pressures that might occur from distortion in a house structure as the result of the failure, for example, of a main enclosing wall. Cases have been seen where, particularly with partitions formed of breeze blocks, unexpected pressures following from failures of other parts of the structure have caused the partition to distort in the form of a curve rather than for the blocks to become compressed. Under such circumstances there will be no option but to rebuild the partition, thought first being given to the choice available from a wider range of possible materials.

Finally, in the consideration of non-load bearing partitions the defect may not be one of failure in the partition itself but of poor accoustic quality. Some remedial measures can be taken by applying a cladding of sound absorbing material or alternatively providing a new partition formed with a cavity or provided with a core of material having the appropriate sound resisting characteristics.

WINDOWS

Windows with glass were provided to the villas of the wealthier Romans during the period of the Roman occupation of Great Britain but, in common with most other refinements of building, vanished with the departure of the Romans not to be seen again in common use for a very long time. L. F. Salzman dates the reintroduction of window glass into England from about 700, since glass workers brought over from France taught the inhabitants to understand and learn the craft at this period. It was a very considerable time however before glass became widely used in the English house. Even in 1500 the use of greased linen cloth for windows was still commonplace and this material sufficed for poorer houses until some considerable time after this date. Most people, including the very poor, would have knowledge of glass since they could see it in churches and cathedrals and some of the richer houses but the cost was, of course, too high for any buildings but the most expensive.

The Romans had perfected a method of casting glass in large sheets, rolled out on a flat surface, and it was curious that this type of glass manufacture was abandoned. Glass in the Middle Ages was produced with difficulty and the resulting sheets were small and of irregular size and thickness. In spite of this we now admire the old hand-made glass that is left to us. It is slightly coloured due to the presence of iron oxide in the silica sand and is of irregular texture which gives a most attractive quality of light. In Tudor times the diamond shaped lattice panes became commonplace to the houses of wealthy merchants and this has since been seized on as a distinctive characteristic of the period, so that no drawing of a Tudor house lacks this particular feature. The small panes of glass were held between strips of lead known as "cames" and "H"-shaped in cross-section which were turned down at the edges and soldered on both sides at the points of junction. The lead was often packed with tallow in order to make the window weatherproof and later a cement of linseed oil, red lead and whiting was brushed on and used for this purpose instead. Once the window was made it was set up in the frame and secured in iron saddle bars with metal rings or strips of soldered lead. Glass windows could either be provided in fixed frames or could be incorporated in opening casements. If set in hung casements these were usually regarded as tenant's fixtures but if fixed in place they were usually considered as part of the property. This distinction was a likely subject of litigation. In a suit of 1535 there was a complaint of a fraudulent sale of "Glasse-wyndows"

709

which the buyer could not obtain as they were "fastenyd unto the frehold and parcell of the said tenement".

From the conclusion of the Middle Ages and up and until the 19th century most clear glass employed for domestic property was Crown Glass. This was manufactured from molten blobs of blown glass spun at a high speed on the blowing iron until spread by the glass blower with a wooden bat into a large disc, the outer sections of the disc being thin and regular and suitable for forming glass sheets while the centre of the disc nearest the spindle retained a hub of thick curved glass which was known as "bottle" or "bullion" glass and was discarded as being useless. It is a curious fact that in order to add an air of authenticity to certain buildings built between the two World Wars in a style that is extravagantly "Tudor", bottle glass was faithfully reconstructed and included in some of the panes. Public houses will be recalled where this ludicrous practice can be seen but the fact that this habit ceased was not due to objections on aesthetic grounds but arose from the more practical reason that the bottle glass often formed a magnifier under conditions of strong sunlight and provided a substantial fire risk.

If the surveyor is asked to repair or maintain a house of a sufficiently early period where the original casement windows have small glass leaded panes he is likely to be given the opportunity by the owner of finding the appropriate skilled specialist assistance that he requires. The casement and frame are likely to be of cast iron or sometimes hardwood and even if the leaded glazing bars are narrow it is often possible for broken panes to be replaced in-situ with hand-made glass by turning back the flanges of the lead cames and reforming them with soldered dots and cement. If, however, the window is badly distorted or buckled, it will be necessary for this to be taken out and the casement reformed while the glazed leaded lights are sent away to a glassworks to be set up and reconstructed on a work table. Where leaded lights in casements are found to properties of much more recent construction built to simulate an earlier architectural style the problem is easier. For one thing the lead cames are much thicker and easier to solder in place and for another the glass will be of plain mass-produced quality and will, of course, be easier to obtain for renewal. It is for this reason that relatively modern leaded casements of this type always look unreal and "dead" when compared to the original casements of the earlier period.

It is suggested that the glass in old windows is always worth some care on scrutiny. A fair amount of Crown Glass can still be seen in country districts and, surprisingly, also in Metropolitan areas in spite of the blast from two World Wars. Crown Glass can be recognised by the faintly visible concentric rings on the surface which may admittedly be difficult to see on a dull day. The texture of the glass, however, has a different quality which may be detected on tracing over the surface with a finger and, of course, wherever possible Crown Glass should be preserved. The light on the façade of a 17th or 18th century house where the glass is almost on the same plane as the red bricks will, particularly when the sun is shining from the correct quarter, ruthlessly show up any pieces of mass-produced glass against the original Crown Glass.

From what has so far been said, it will be understood that the traditional English window from time immemorial has been the casement. This, however, may seem surprising to the town dweller to whom the double hung sash is far more familiar. In fact, the double hung sash has a fairly short history and, like many innovations in building, was an imported idea. "The sash, a Dutch invention", says Sir John Summerson, "had been known for many years, but it's popularity only dates from Queen Anne's time. Then, however, it swept London, and few of the older houses even, suffered, long to retain their transomed and mullioned casements."[1] The introduction of the sash probably dates from about 1700 and in the years that followed first made its appearance in the domestic buildings in seaside towns most exposed to the Dutch influence but a short time after that, at the commencement of the building boom following the Treaty of Utrecht, the sash window became universal for domestic housing to the extent that the casement was completely ousted. So complete was the transformation that the Georgian period of domestic architecture is so bound up with the sash window that it is only with difficulty that one can think of examples of houses of this period with casements. Casements, there are, of course, in towns as well as in suburbs and country districts but the surveyor is so used to automatically dating his buildings by glancing at the windows that very often he is in two minds as he approaches Georgian cottages with casement windows as to whether this is a true Georgian property or whether it is to be suspiciously regarded as a hybrid.

In many parts of the country the sash window was provided almost flush with the exterior face of the brickwork until quite late in Georgian times. In London, however, two famous building Acts forced modifications on the speculative builder for fear of the spread of fire, and transformed the appearance of terraced housing by so doing. These Acts give a useful guide to the dates of certain Georgian terraces and since very often the character of the windows is one of the main features for identifying the date of a house, the London surveyor is lucky in this respect.

[1] Georgian London.

When the sash window was introduced at the beginning of the 18th century the frames were set in square brick openings with no reveals, flush or very nearly flush with the face wall. The frames were wide and the glazing bars, in particular, were thick. In London the Building Act of 1709 stipulated that as a fire precaution the frames of windows were to be set back 4 inches (102mm) leaving a reveal of brick instead of being on approximately the same plane as the wall face. The Building Act of 1774 made a further amendment in that the frames themselves were from henceforward to be formed in brick "reveals" or recesses in the brickwork so that when facing the front elevation only a small strip of the frame could be seen.

Sash windows kept their popularity for practically the whole of the Victorian period but towards the end of Victoria's reign and in the reign of Edward VII, the casement showed signs of returning to favour. Just before the First World War a number of new domestic properties were provided with casements and some houses of about this period have casements at the front and sashes at the back, the evolving changes in fashion being acknowledged at the front only. During the period between the two World Wars the casement, mainly in wood but also in metal, returned to almost universal use for cheap housing due to the fact that sash windows became inappropriate for the small-scale style of building current at the time.

Most surveyors take the view that the accurate repair, maintenance or replacement of windows depends to a large extent on the surveyor having knowledge of the period when the house was built. The thin glazing bars that were universally used at the end of the Georgian period are totally wrong for a house built in the early 18th century for example. With a little care, it is still possible to find many excellent joinery works which will reproduce accurate facsimiles of old sections of glazing bars, and mouldings, and it is a pity to mar the final appearance of a dwelling house for lack of a little research. It is to be hoped in particular that the really dreadful solution to the problem of re-glazing early windows with the use of large sheets of glass entailing the removal of all glazing bars will be resisted at all costs. The appearance of so many fine old buildings has been marred by ill-considered alteration of the original windows, but conversely the appearance of some rather grim old buildings can be greatly improved by thoughtful alteration of the original.

The biggest enemy to wood windows is, of course, damp. Enough is said on this subject in Chapter 8 devoted to Dampness, not to require repetition here except to underline the need for careful maintenance and periodical repainting together with the careful preparation of window sills prior to the paint being applied. Apart from the question of damp however, faults do appear in windows owing to distortion of the surrounding brickwork due to settlement or movement in the structure and the treatment of the window will depend on the steps taken with the basic structure itself. If the surveyor is convinced that the structure has reached a complete position of repose, although distorted, it is legitimate to re-set the frame to take this into account and it is better to take up unevenness at the head of the frame itself rather than to shave the thin top member of a sash in order to enable it to open and close correctly. It should be possible in most cases to reform Georgian sashes with faithfulness and without undue difficulty but problems are sometimes encountered in the repair of Victorian sashes and casements alike. Sometimes sashes and casements to large Victorian houses are found to be enormous. Such sashes are often glazed with a large sheet of plate glass, no glazing bars being provided, and the weight of two sashes hung together in a box frame is considerable. The surveyor should ensure that chains are used instead of sashcords under such circumstances. With large casements glazed in single panes the lack of stiffening provided by intermediate glazing bars causes the casement to warp and after a time this may only open and close with difficulty. If the casement itself is flexible when tested it clearly requires some modification or stiffening but if the casement itself is quite rigid but continually sticks the method of hanging is probably inadequate. For such casements espagnolette bolts were normally provided as the conventional means of closing. These types of bolts were more often than not found to be too cumbersome by householders so that most of them were removed and centre fixings only were provided in their place. The result of this is that the windows are very much less secure when shut than when they were originally installed. The espagnolette bolts gave a secure fixing to the top and bottom of a large casement which is proof against burglars. With a centre fixing only, however, it is easier for a lever to be forced into the edge of such casements so that they can be broken open.

With windows, either casement or sashes, some care is needed to make sure that the wood has not reached the end of its useful life. If the joints of casements or sashes have opened either from lack of effective painting externally, or from structural movement, allowing damp to enter, the wood joint inside may be soft and spongy and the strength may have been completely removed. There is no point in painting over a window of this type as a new sash or casement may be needed. The investigation with a metal probe or a penknife should reveal weakness of this type and the presence of "L"-shaped metal reinforcement to the corners of sashes or casements on the outer faces often gives a pointer to the fact that such investigation is desirable. So far as frames are concerned these are often less vulnerable to dampness although this may not necessarily be the case. For example the commonest type of defect occurs to Georgian or Victorian box frames to sash windows since dampness penetrates into parts of the frame not seen and the timber remains wet for long periods of time, eventually disintegrating. Over a number of years the sash will often be found to have changed its weight characteristics due to either being re-glazed in heavier glass or from other reasons and the sash weights will be found to be inadequate. On other occasions pulleys will be found to be ineffective and missing or defective pocket panels or parting beads are commonplace. Brittle sashcords are obvious items requiring replacement since the penalty for a breaking sashcord to a householder or a window cleaner can be severe often entailing considerable injury.

When examining Georgian or Victorian casements or sashes it is not only necessary to test the woodwork with a sharp penknife to see if it has rotted but it is also necessary to have some regard to the size of the various component members in relation to the glass area as a whole. Some later Victorian sashes, for example, are practically square in shape, with a central vertical glazing bar, but while the top half of the sash is glazed with a number of sections of glass fitted between numerous glazing bars of impressive complexity, the lower sections are of plain glass. This would not matter particularly if it is not commonly found with sashes of this type that the bottom rails of the sashes are unusually thin. Since these are of some length and are inadequately reinforced there is a tendency for them to warp and become defective. Accordingly, it is necessary not only to renew wood members where these are found to have rotted but to consider if these should be replaced or reinforced by sections of larger pattern or of different design.

With regard to steel casements, the first type of metal casements as we now know them were produced shortly after 1900. These were extremely heavy in weight and suffered from the disadvantage that the galvanizing process, as yet in its infancy, was not effective so that casements of this type provided to Edwardian houses of the period have since become a severe liability. These have, during the years since they were installed, become badly pitted and swollen by rust, and in most cases the heavy glass with which they were glazed has cracked. Casements such as this are difficult to deal with and in certain circumstances it is necessary to renew them completely with either wood casements or alternatively new steel or aluminium casements if any can be found or made up of the requisite size. If not of course, it may be necessary to reform the window frames. Fortunately the early casements were often fitted in wood frames so that this is not such a difficult operation as it sounds. Later metal casements vary greatly in efficiency and condition. They are all, of course, subject to the same disadvantage in that they attract condensation which trickles down the inside surface of the window and sets up rust at the base. Effective maintenance is the only sure way of preventing this from becoming a real problem. It is not, however, likely that casements produced between the two World Wars will be so defective as to require renewal unless they are very badly neglected.

Over recent years a thriving specialist industry has grown up to provide purpose-made new windows for older houses. The demand for such windows arises not only from the modernisation aspect, i.e. to improve light and to provide cleaner, less fussy detail, but also from the desire to effect economies in fuel consumption by the elimination of the draughts so frequently encountered with old ill-fitting double hung sashes and casements. Fuel economy is also the main factor in the provision of double glazed units which are offered by some of the specialists in addition to the normal single glazed units. Those operating within the appropriate range of the main airports also arrange their service to include the supply and fixing of suitably spaced units to qualify the purchaser for a noise reduction grant on completion of the work.

As with all items of equipment the purchaser gets what he pays for and the cheapest new windows are not necessarily the best. If a surveyor is asked to advise on the choice of specialist contractor he will be faced with the same array of pamphlets and conflicting claims which beset the client. In the exercise of his critical faculties the surveyor will no doubt reject those fittings which do not follow good canons of design in the provision of proper weatherings and throatings. He may well hold to the view that the adoption of British Standard sections would be preferable. The difficulty will arise, however, when it comes to a comparison of the specialists' price with that of the estimate for the supply (let alone the fixing by an ordinary building contractor!) of the purpose-made windows from a joinery or metal window manufacturer. The specialists will win hands down and with the guarantee that is invariably offered the client will understandably feel inclined to order from the specialists leaving the surveyor to point out the pros and cons as he sees them. These will depend, of course, on the quality of the specialist's product. Some are very good but some are not so good.

DOORS

Many of the doors of Georgian and Victorian houses will be found to be in excellent condition after many years of use and careful repair and renovation will often result in a spectacular difference in appearance at little cost. The front doors and the doors of what were originally the main reception rooms of even the average Georgian and Victorian house may well be sturdy in construction, the stiles and rails and muntins being at least 1½ inches (38mm) or 2 inches (51mm) thick, or even thicker, and the panels, since these doors are normally of the panel type, being in good condition apart from some expansion splitting and blurring of detail from successive layers of paint surrounding the mouldings. There may also be scarring to the middle rail due to different types of lock, either mortice locks or rim locks having been fitted neither wisely nor too well in the past, but in general many of these doors are square and true in shape when opened and closed and the surveyor will obviously wish to retain them. If such a door is taken down and the bolection mouldings removed and the whole of the woodwork stripped and prepared with care, any holes or indentations from old locks being carefully pieced in with new wood, careful repainting and the replacement of the bolection mouldings will often result in the door appearing as good as new. It can then be re-hung. Many such doors are beautifully formed from hardwoods such as oak or mahogany and skilled treatment is well worthwhile to bring them up to the spectacular standard that can, with care, be achieved. Even when the doors are of softwood it is frequently pine or a similar wood of high close-ringed quality.

It is as well if doors of such quality can be repaired, as to replace them is a very costly matter. Such doors will probably not be of standard size and a new framed and panelled door if made by hand to such a high quality will involve the owner in a sum of money that will not only surprise him but will probably surprise his surveyor as well. It is, therefore, worthwhile to take pains to preserve well made doors wherever possible and it is to be hoped that the client will reserve a sufficient sum of money for the correct locks and fittings. Good quality locks and fittings accurately matched to the requirements of a particular period can be obtained from one or other of the various firms who specialise in manufacturing and supplying these articles and although they are costly when compared to the mass-produced fittings available nevertheless such cost is more than justified in the final appearance.

Not all doors, however, should be automatically preserved. Very often in the same house that we have just been discussing the doors to the upper and attic rooms may present a rather different problem. These will invariably be of softwood, the members being much thinner, so that warp may have caused sufficient distortion for them to be difficult to open and shut with ease. Such doors are more

716

likely to be fitted in openings that are nearer a standard size and the replacement of doors such as this is often a practicable possibility. There are an enormous number of mass-produced machine made doors available on the market at the present time and the cost is so low that replacement is often more economical than incurring the labour costs of trying, for example, to repair a door that has become badly warped by taking it to the joiner's shop and laying it out between cramps. Often replacing doors that are sub-standard is not only cheap but it is also beneficial from another point of view. Advantage can often be taken of qualities that are available in modern-mass produced doors, for example where a particular standard is required of resistance against fire, or for use in a house where central heating has just been put in so that a certain standard of resistance against warp and shrinkage is desirable.

STAIRCASES

The surveyor will encounter staircases constructed of many different materials. These will vary often from the attractive stone geometrical staircases formed in London houses in late Georgian and early Victorian times to the timber staircases found in the majority of houses or the reinforced concrete or wrought or cast iron stairs occasionally found to the more utilitarian Victorian houses.

In considering the question of the repair of a late Georgian or early Victorian geometrical staircase, the surveyor must first of all have regard to the design. Often careful inspection will show that geometrical quarter turn or half turn staircases with cantilevered stairs and an open well which are seemingly secured by the built-in ends of the spandril steps and stone half landing sections are, in fact, reinforced by an arrangement of rods and straps or alternatively steel channels and beams mostly hidden under the soffits which may have been provided as part of the original structure or may have been provided since in the form of simple reinforcement. The repair of a staircase of this type will therefore come under two different categories. It may be possible to renew stone spandril steps by straightforward replacement but if the trouble is not so much wear on particular treads but distortion of the staircase as a whole, more radical measures will be required. It may well be that settlement of the surrounding brick structure has caused an open well staircase to become distorted and this may have grave consequences to the spandril steps and half landing sections. The seating for the steps is all important and since the bedding of the half landing sections relies on the seating with the surrounding brickwork, it is often first necessary to chip away at the wall plaster and brickwork to determine the exact nature and extent of the seating of the stone sections before considering any other measures. If this is found to be sound, however, attention must often then be next given to the sections of stone forming the half landings. These depend for their support on the joggle joints formed in the stonework and in cases of severe wear or settlement the joggle joints may be robbed of some of their efficiency. If, therefore, the surveyor feels that he cannot rely on the natural joints between stone sections or the bedding between half landing and spandril steps with the brick wall surrounding them he is well advised to consider a system of discreet reinforcement with mild steel beams to reinforce the half landing and steel channels formed under the soffits of the stairs and connected to the channel so as to take the weight of the structure. The channel sections are best formed at the free ends of the steps and from the aesthetic point of view, these can be boxed in and plastered and whitened to match the soffit of the staircase.

One of the difficulties with stone staircases of some age is that the balustrade often needs some attention. Such balustrades are often of wrought iron, the iron or wood handrail being screwed to the balusters which are set in the stone in a socket filled with solidified lead which was poured into the joint in a molten state, the top then being plugged with cement to conceal the lead. The efficiency of the balustrade depends in a number of cases on the curved bracket balusters, which are taken under the tread at changes of direction of the balustrade and are plugged to the sides of the spandril steps with lead joints, a cover plate being formed between the baluster and the jointing material. If the balustrade as a whole is loose it may not be possible to do very much about the individual balusters particularly if these are situated too near the edge of the treads so that cracks are visible indicating that the stonework has fractured from constant vibration. One method of dealing with the matter is to increase the number of bracket balusters so that these intermingle at even distances with the remaining balusters, the bracket balusters being formed of the same pattern as the original, so that the new reinforcing balusters appear to be part of the original staircase itself but are nevertheless the main points of support for the balustrade as a whole.

The Building Regulations 1972 in Section H5 are as follows in respect of the guarding of stairways and landings:

Guarding of Stairways and Landings

H5. (1) Any private stairway or common stairway shall be guarded on each side by a wall or securely fixed screen, balustrade or railing extending to a height of not less than 840mm measured vertically above the pitch lines.

(2) The side of any landing or similar space forming part of a stairway or directly overlooking a stairwell shall be guarded by a wall or securely fixed screen, balustrade or railing extending to a height above the floor of such landing or space of (in the case of a private stairway) 900mm or (in the case of a common stairway) 1·1m.

(3) Any flight of steps in a private stairway or common stairway with an aggregate rise of more than 600mm shall have a continuous handrail fixed securely at a height of not less than 840mm nor more than 1m measured vertically above the pitch line:

(a) On each side of the stairway, if the least width of the stairway is 1m or more; or

(b) On one side of the stairway, in any other case.

Reinforced concrete stairways are not often seen in domestic property but are encountered in the larger house of the Edwardian period or later. It is not likely that such stairs will have become badly defective although it is possible that some rusting or deterioration of the steelwork and concrete may be apparent, in which case appropriate repair by painting and patching is necessary as described in Chapter 2 for repairs to concrete lintels. The most probable defect is likely to be that the treads, where the fine concrete will have gathered to the surface by means of the steel float when the staircase was formed and laid, will have become so slippery that they are a menace. It is possible to improve the staircase from this point of view by cutting out a portion of each tread and forming a non-slip nosing either of tile or rubber according to the client's preference. There is certainly one point about concrete staircases which is to some extent an advantage and this is that their appearance is usually so repellent that considerations for repair work can be simply related to function and economy.

A later Georgian or early Victorian dwelling may, as well as an internal staircase, have external steps. These may vary from the impressive entrance steps to the main front door of the house to the not at all impressive stone steps from the pavement down into the front basement area. In the first case it should be possible to repair sections of worn or damaged stonework quite easily since these steps are usually of solid construction and thickness and rely for their support on brickwork on either side. A note of caution is, however, necessary with regard to the handrails and balustrades. These often follow the same design and pattern as the internal balustrade to the main staircase, namely that they are composed of wrought iron, in this case with a wrought-iron handrail, the balusters being set in recesses by means of lead joints. The difference, of course, with external balustrades is that they are exposed to rainfall and continual rainwater trickling down and lying at the top of the lead joint is likely to interfere with the paint film so that any lack of maintenance will result in the iron work rusting and expanding and thus splitting not only the lead joint but the end of the tread apart from its parent structure. If the surveyor finds that signs of this type of defect are evident it is best to take out the balusters completely and repair them by "tipping" with non-ferrous metal and reset them in the restored stone treads by means of bronze bushes.

The external area steps to Georgian or Victorian houses will normally be found to be of thin stone slabs, the treads and risers being formed of separate individual thin stone sections resting on an outer bearing wall of brickwork. These staircases are always suspect. In most cases a right-angled bend with winders is formed in this area staircase and the support provided at the junction of the two outer bearing walls is a poor one since at the connecting point the stone treads and risers will rely upon each other for their support rather than on brickwork. The unexpected collapse of steps of this type is not unusual.

The vast majority of the internal staircases that the surveyor will encounter, however, are constructed of timber. Perhaps the simplest type that the surveyor will see is the straight flight stair which is commonly found in cottage property and consists of a single flight from the ground to the first floor landing which, in a small cottage, normally gives access to both the front and rear bedrooms. This type of stair is probably as functional as could be desired and due to the fact that it is built and supported against two internal partitions it is sturdy and the risk of the timbers becoming affected by dampness is remote. The only disadvantage of a staircase of this type in small cottages is that due to the limited going of the flight, the depth of tread may barely be within acceptable limits. Due to the restricted room available it is not usually possible to do much about this except by a reconstruction of the staircase within the existing ground and first floor total area and this is outside the scope of this book.

The dog leg staircase is a sound design, since if the half landing is properly supported and the flights are provided with effective strings and carriages the construction should be sturdy. With the open well staircase, however, the rather more complicated design and layout producing one or two changes of direction entails the need for correct trimming and detailing of the bearers and joists generally and distortion or sagging may occur if bad joints are formed as described in Chapter 5.

Perhaps the greatest enemy to the lowest flight of staircases in the older Georgian and Victorian houses is dampness. Very often the wall string of the section of a staircase leading from the ground floor to the basement is placed against a wall which is wringing wet from rising or penetrating dampness. Deterioration of the wall string and the ends of the treads, where the grain is vulnerable to penetration, may soon become pronounced, leading to the whole of the lower length of the staircase having to be renewed. Clearly the staircase cannot be replaced in its existing form without the most stringent precautions being necessary both to eradicate rising damp from the wall on the one hand and to ensure that if timber is used again that it is pre-treated, separated from damp brickwork and allowed the benefit of full ventilation, however restricted the access may be. Even so, there is no possiblity of a successful replacement unless the surveyor is absolutely certain that all the strands from any previous attack of dry rot have been completely eradicated by chemical or other means as fully discussed in Chapter 5.

Many minor defects and irritations occur from the fact that treads and risers are not properly notched and screwed together as they should be, or alternatively that carriages are omitted. If the owner or occupier is particularly conscious of creaks and other shortcomings from such deficiencies it may be possible to insert a carriage or carriages, or, as an alternative, remove the old treads and risers and replace them with treads and risers that can be screwed and notched together. It is, however, sometimes possible for wood angle blocks to be placed under the joints of the existing treads and risers. These, if screwed in place, usually provide a sufficiently satisfactory answer and avoid the need for the treads and risers to be taken out completely and afterwards replaced. A guide to the number of carriages that should be provided is that one carriage is needed if the staircase is 3-feet (914mm) wide while an additional carriage should be provided for every extra 15 inches (380mm) in width.

The rules for private and common stairways in the Building Regulations 1972 under Section H2 and H3 are worth repeating here. They are as follows:

Private Stairways

H2. Any private stairway shall be so constructed that:

(a) Between consecutive floors there is an equal rise for every step or landing; and

(b) Between consecutive floors there is an equal going for every parallel step; and

(c) Over the whole width or (in the case of tapered steps) the notional width of the stairway there is:

    (i) Headroom of not less than 2m, measured vertically above the pitch line; and

    (ii) Clearance of not less than 1·5m, measured at right-angles to the pitch line; and

(d) The nosing of the tread of any step or landing which has no riser below it, overlaps on plan the back edge of the tread of the step below it by not less than 16mm; and

(e) The sum of the going of a parallel step plus twice its rise is not less than 550mm and not more than 700mm; and

(f) The rise of a step is not more than 220mm and the going of a step not less than 220mm; and

(g) The pitch of the stairway is not more than 42°; and

(h) The stairway contains no tapered steps, except as permitted by regulation H4 (2) or (3).

Common Stairways

H3. Any common stairway shall be so constructed that:

(a) It complies with Regulation H2 (a), (b), (c), (d) and (e); and

(b) The rise of a step is not more than 190mm and the going of a step is not less than 230mm; and

(c) The pitch of the stairway is not more than 38°; and

(d) The stairway has not more than 16 risers in any flight; and

(e) The stairway contains no tapered steps, except as permitted by regulation H4 (2).

Clearly in the case of repairs to an existing dwelling house the surveyor will not wish to embark upon design improvements unless these are inevitable and he will normally decide as to what repairs are necessary on the basis of the existing structure. If, however, the staircase falls badly short of basic modern requirements, re-design may be necessary but a number of ameliorative measures can be taken which, together or separately, might provide a sufficient answer to the problem. The lighting of the staircase for one thing might be improved since bad lighting to a staircase is a frequent cause of accidents. It is also possible to improve unsatisfactory headroom by altering the position of the trimmer to the joists above by providing a slightly more complicated shape of soffit and it is also worthwhile to re-plan and alter parts of existing staircases by taking out winders or remove the two quarter space landings separated by a single riser, common causes of accidents, and replace them with something else.

Faults to the balustrades to timber staircases occur when an excessive length of balustrading is provided between newel posts and the balusters are slender and fragile. Discreet metal reinforcement under the handrail and in between successive pairs of balusters screwed to the outer string may provide a palliative treatment but this is only possible where the newel posts themselves are sound and firm. If the newel posts are flexible the chances are that the double tenoned joint between the newel and the outer strings of the staircase may have become defective and the dowels loose. If the timber is quite sound, new dowels can be provided and the joints re-glued, but if weakness has developed in the timber, new posts will be necessary, notched and secured to the existing trimmer, and firmly fixed to strings and handrail.

WALL PANELLING

The custom of providing hardwood or softwood panelling as a decorative internal finish to wall surfaces is one that has flourished for many hundreds of years. Early plain or linenfold panelling is unmistakable in character, the panels themselves being small and probably of oak, the muntins and rails being tenoned together and secured with wood dowels. A good deal of such early panelling still exists and is usually a subject for preservation. On examination, however, the surveyor may find that early oak panelling itself is intact but the timber grounds fixing it to brickwork or masonry may have rotted as the result of dampness and poor ventilation and the panelling should accordingly be carefully dismantled and stored for later re-erection. It is probably best in most cases to refix such panelling with metal distance pieces away from the wall face but to first, of course, ensure that dampness is removed from the wall as discussed in Chapter 8 devoted to this problem. Metal distance pieces can be fixed to the back of the panelling in such a way that is not easily apparent by means of screws which are recessed and then covered with pellets which are small carefully selected pieces of timber having the same general appearance as the adjacent wood and in a way looking like the original pegs. It is best, even when dampness is eradicated from the wall, for the metal distance pieces and the back of the panelling to be treated with an appropriate preservative, but in addition to this the surveyor is well advised to try and find some discreet method of providing ventilation behind the panelling so as to allow a current of air to circulate between the timber and the brick or masonry as the case may be. This might be acheived by a false dado rail or by the provision of small bronze grilles at the base or at the corners of the panelling according to circumstances. Much will depend however on the character of the room and the number of return ends provided to the panelling as to how this can best be achieved.

With true oak panelling little should be needed to bring the surface treatment to a satisfactory standard. The panelling should have achieved a satisfactory patina over the years and rather than varnishing which gives a hard and unreal gloss to the surface it is best for natural oak to be treated with the application of a little softened beeswax in order to bring up its true texture.

Later, as already mentioned in the section of this Chapter dealing with plaster repairs, brickwork on the internal faces of walls together with stonework tended to be battened out and then either covered with softwood panelling or lath and plaster. This type of construcion persisted for over 200 years from about the early 17th century to the middle of the 19th century since it was difficult to obtain a good surface, other than on face work, for plastering, with the misshapen bricks normally used for the backing of external walls. Even more so than in the case of hardwood panelling, the back faces, being unventilated and in close proximity to wall surfaces which may be affected by damp, can prove to be a veritable breeding ground for dry rot. Procedures for coping with such an outbreak are set out in Chapter 5. Once the outbreak has been dealt with and the sound panelling is being replaced perhaps the most important aspect as before is to provide adequate ventilation behind the panelling so as to avoid any re-occurrence.

Many houses built between the two World Wars are provided with an impressive array of wood panelling, the ultimate in this being the mock Tudor mansion with its simulated baronial hall. The surveyor will find, alas, on investigation, that the panelling is likely to be of plywood and that this may have become corrugated by damp, attacked by rot, or riddled with Anobium wood-boring beetle. It is in these cases that the surveyor should seriously consider whether panelling of this type is worth replacing or not. Much will depend upon circumstances not the least of which being his client's taste in such matters but the easiest way of dealing with the problem is often simply to strip the panelling out completely. Such panelling can be replaced and preserved with one of the appropriate fluids available for this purpose but although this may sound something of a heresy it is nevertheless possible to replace sections of this type of panelling rather better with one of the modern plastic substitutes if the owner is bent on preserving a mediaeval influence in a modern house.

PAINTING, REPAINTING AND DECORATING

Wherever possible and where it has been deemed appropriate various sections of this book have been extended to include the special factors which need to be taken into account in painting repaired work or repainting existing work. Thus in Chapter 2 the painting and repainting of external rendered finishes is included. Chapter 5 includes a section on painting and other treatments for timber surfaces, the Chapter 8 on Dampness incorporates various comments relating to decorative works and already in this Chapter special precautions on painting new plaster have been discussed. These aspects need not be repeated here but even so a substantial area remains to be covered particularly on the painting of walls and metalwork in a subject which has changed rapidly over the last twenty years and where the rate of change appears to accelerate rather than slow down.

The development of many new resins and some new pigments has made it possible to produce a number of new types of paint and to improve a number of the older types. More people than ever are prepared to turn their hand to painting and decorating and this has acted as a great incentive to the industry to produce materials which are easy to apply, less messy, quicker drying and with a harder finish than those which were available say 25 to 30 years ago. The professional decorator in some respects tends to turn his nose up at new materials often continuing with the processes and the materials of a generation previous as long as they are available. As much of the sucess or failure of a painting or decorating job depends on the preparation, and it is on this aspect that the main effort should be expended, the professional may well be wise in the circumstances since he cannot afford a failure which might arise with the adoption of a new material unless he is fully exonerated from the responsibility for its use. On his own home the do-it-yourself handyman will often achieve a standard superior to that of the routine professional because it is on just the aspect of preparation that he can afford to spend a long time and devote much effort. Whether on completion of the preparation he then proceeds to chance the final result with a new paint for which extravagant claims are made is his affair but if he does so and it is a success everyone gains by the experience and usually hears about it in distinct contrast to a failure which is quickly forgotten. Even when there is a satisfactory appearance on completion, however, this can only be considered an initial success. There are the long-term factors to be considered such as the ability of the painted surface to stand up to normal use and weathering and ultimately its ability to take further coats on a weathered film when the time for redecoration arises or alternatively to be stripped off should that need arise.

As the Building Research Establishment points out (Digest No. 21 Second Series) the performance of new types of paint cannot be evaluated fully until there has been some years' experience of their use under practical conditions. Although accelerated tests can be carried out and are useful for checking modifications to established types of paint such tests can be misleading when applied to entirely new types of paint. Practical trials in the field are necessary to deal with not only the long-term factors set out in the preceding paragraph but also the performance of a paint under less than ideal conditions such as arise when painting an indifferently prepared surface during adverse weather conditions. All this tends to suggest that in the normal course of events the surveyor should tend to adopt the attitude of the professional decorator and risk the accusation that might arise of excessive conservatism. There may be a time and occasion depending on the surveyor's position *vis-à-vis* his client or employer where he might be able to advise and indeed recommend the trial of a new product. As the Research Establishment advises, however, such a trial should be in a position where premature failure would have no serious consequences. One of the difficulties with specifying the use of paints is the comparative shyness of the manufacturers to disclose, certainly on the cans and in the ordinary retail trade literature, the precise type and category of their product. The manufacturers no doubt have their own reasons for this and it is not suggested that reputable makers refuse to give such information on written enquiry. They usually do with alacrity and are often most helpful in advising on which of their products is suitable for a particular purpose. On very large contracts they have been known to assist on the preparation of the specification and to examine the work during its progress. The trouble is that in bandying about trade names the surveyor requires an encyclopaedic memory to remember which product fits a particular category. It is hardly surprising then that the wise surveyor tends to continue to specify a paint that he has found to give satisfactory results in the past for certain purposes. The danger is that eventually the manufacturer will change the constituents and type of paint without changing the name (if the maker does alter the name it is likely to be merely the addition of "New Super . . . " to the old) or alternatively the contractor will report that it is no longer available and the surveyor will find himself left behind by the times.

As always, guidance for the younger surveyor or a surveyor seeking to keep abreast with recent development in the field of painting is best obtained from official publications or alternatively from experienced colleagues. Currently the British Standard Code of Practice C.P.231:1966 "Painting of Buildings" gives guidance on the painting of different materials, paint types, preparation and paint systems. Despite its size and price, 150 pages and £2·87, it does not claim to be a comprehensive treatise on all matters dealing with painting and is confined to the circumstances most commonly arising, for example, in housing and school work. For painting new work or substantial reinstatement the Code must constitute the principal guide and while its cost may preclude its purchase by everyone dealing with building work on an individual basis, it should certainly be in the possession of every office. The Code of 1966 as far as types of paint is concerned was overtaken by events to an extent and some of the newer types developed at about that time are discussed in Building Research Establishment Digest No. 21 (Second Series) "New Types of Paint" 1966 (reprinted in 1970) as already mentioned. In the British Standard Code of Practice C.P.231:1966 the terms relating to materials are set out with explanatory notes and a detailed summary is given of fifty-eight paint types with descriptions classified into sections, sixteen paint types relating to pre-treatment priming coats for metal, wood and plaster, fourteen paint types relating to undercoats and finishing coats, eight paint types relating to water paints and seven paint types classed as chemical reaction coatings. The remaining paint types, totalling 13, form a miscellaneous section consisting, for example, of knotting, wood stains, imitation stone, stoppings, fillers and clear finishes for wood. The fifty-eight types mentioned in the Code coupled with those described in the Digest provide a substantial range, the mere size of which probably contributes to some of the current failures. The wide range of types provides a greater possibility for error.

It will be understood that there is a need for proper preparation of a surface prior to painting but the need to relate paints and primers to each other is not so obvious and tends to be overlooked. It is, however, just as necessary to ensure that each coat in a paint system should be chosen so that it is in proper relationship with the other coats as well as with the surface to be painted. For example, where good durability and protective effect are required, the finishing coat has to be tough and elastic, but a coating of this nature will tend to shrink unless the priming coat and undercoats have sufficient strength to resist this tendency. Again, says the British Standard Code of Practice, the paint for any surface should possess such elasticity and adhesion that, when dry, it adapts itself to any slight movements of the building materials without becoming detached. Although on drying most paints harden well, not all of the newer types of paint possess this elasticity.

The main requirement of the first coat of paint applied to the surface to be decorated is that it must adhere firmly to the surface and provide a suitable base for the next coat of paint. If this sounds obvious it should be remembered that the first coat or priming coat may have to be selected to comply with very different conditions. It may on the one hand have to reduce the suction of a surface such as wallboards or plaster by sealing the pores, or fulfil a quite different function such as to prevent corrosion on a metallic surface and at the same time have good adhesive properties since the metallic surface will probably be a very smooth one. Alternatively the primer may have to have qualities that enable it to be used on a surface that will become heated so that it retains its adhesion and does not become discoloured. Again, as we have already seen in a previous section, the main duty for the primer might be to protect the pigment or the oil medium in paints from attack by alkalis in new plaster. It can be seen therefore that the selection and correct application of a priming coat is extremely important and in this respect hurried workmanship should obviously be avoided. Application with a brush rather than spray application is recommended as a general rule by the British Standard Code of Practice.

The function of the paint selected for use as an undercoat is a different one to that of a priming coat. An undercoat should obscure the surface already primed, and provide a fresh surface of uniform texture and of a colour approaching that of a finishing coat. The undercoat should also help to build up a layer of paint sufficient in type and thickness to protect the material painted, according to the conditions of exposure, when used in conjunction with a suitable finishing coat. Undercoats may be selected to comply with the requirements of the paint coating as a whole for example if this is to be heat resistant, and if the paint system has to be durable, flexible and water resistant as in the case of, for example, the painting of external woodwork, the undercoats should be of a type to match these requirements. In the case of external painting it is usual to select undercoats that are of a different colour but which are not so widely different from the colour of the finishing coat that they are liable to show through and alter the colour characteristics of the exposed paint film. The reason for this is that on outside work it is of vital importance to make sure that the protective quality of the paint film comes first and foremost and the different colours enable the surveyor to see that the correct number of undercoats are provided and that each undercoat is of good overall quality and has not been scamped. So far as inside work is concerned the quality of

INTERNAL AND GENERAL MATTERS

the decorative finish comes first while the protective qualities are secondary and here the undercoats will be chosen first and foremost so that they do not conflict in any way from the colour quality of the finishing coat. The surveyor should take care to ensure that undercoats and finishing coats are supplied by the same maker otherwise they may not be compatible. It is worth remembering that paint for undercoating has a comparatively large proportion of volatile thiners and a reduced binder content so as to dry nearly flat. This favours hardening and enables light rubbing down to be carried out between successive coats.

The finishing or final coat in a paint system provides not only the particular colour required but also the degree of gloss or texture needed. It can only do this, however, if the previous work has been carried out properly. Gloss paints are usually employed for external use since they are more durable than flat paints as they contain a higher proportion of binder. Flat oil paints were once used extensively on interior surfaces such as broad areas of plastered walls but have now tended to be replaced by either flat emulsion paints or in kitchens and bathrooms by a satin finish paint. The avoidance of a high gloss from the plastered wall surfaces of an old house is one that is often employed purposely by the surveyor so that any irregularities of the plaster surface are not unduly emphasised.

Water paints and distempers now also displaced to some extent by emulsion paints are used for decorating interior surfaces of walls and ceilings because they are cheap and provide a useful initial decoration on new plaster. British Standard 1053 "Water paints and Distempers for interior use" provides for two main types of material.

(1) Water paint, washable, oil bound, in which the binder is in the form of an emulsion of drying oil or oil varnish.

(2) Distemper, non-washable, oil-free, in which the binder is usually glue or starch.

Of these two types, the first resists washing but distempers of the second type are not resistant to washing or rubbing and are therefore generally used for ceilings and surfaces beyond normal reach or where it is intended that they should be subsequently removed. Water paints and distempers offer less resistance to the passage of water and water vapour than oil paint films. They accordingly allow a damp material to "breath" and are able to absorb moisture condensed on the surface of a material. Water paints and distempers are, however, more readily damaged by moisture than oil paint and if too frequently exposed to condensation they tend eventually to peel or flake off. Such paints are more brittle than oil paints and are therefore best used on rigid and moderately absorbent surfaces

729

such as plaster, concrete or brick. They have little or not protective effect and are not normally employed on wood or metal. The coatings are thicker than those of oil paint and where an oil paint system may need four coats in all, a water paint system rarely consists of more than two coats. The first coat thus has to combine all the functions of the primer and undercoats of an oil paint system which means that it must adhere strongly to the surface and equalise any variations in suction. With soft non-washable distemper where it is not desirable to apply two full coats the surface is first treated with clearcole to deal with the question of suction prior to the distemper being applied. With some water paints, however, suction can be controlled by thinning the first coat of paint with a suitable proportion of petrifying liquid. Surfaces to be decorated with washable waterpaint should not, as a rule, be sized or clearcoled.

Where a surface previously decorated with a "soft" distemper, i.e. non-washable, is to be redecorated, the original coating should be washed off completely and the surface allowed to dry. In the case of washable paints and distempers it is not necessary to remove the paint if the coating is in good condition and it can be redecorated either with the same type of paint as was originally used or with oil paint. Repeated re-coating with water paint or distemper, however, builds up an increasingly heavy coating which eventually tends to flake. Five or six coats are usually considered about the maximum but a coat of oil paint, well thinned with white spirit, if applied before this stage is reached, will penetrate and strengthen the accumulated coatings and thus provide a sounder foundation for further coats.

Although oil-bound distempers and water paints have been considerably improved in recent years they have been widely supplanted by synthetic resin emulsion paints in nearly all cases except for the cheapest work and where it is desired to paper walls within say a year or eighteen months of plastering. Emulsion paints are easier to use, they dry rapidly, are odour free or very nearly so, they wash well and are longer lasting and there is a better range of colours and finishes available.

Synthetic resin emulsion paints are dispersions of resin particles in water, pigmented with white pigments, extenders and selected colouring pigments to give opacity and colour. The paints are complex with many additives to impart stability and frost resistance in the can, good application properties and water resistance, bacteria and fungi resistance in the dried film. By varying the pigment/binder ratio and the correct selection of emulsion, paints with a sheen ranging from matt to fairly glossy can be produced. The darker colours however are somewhat less satisfactory than the lighter shades and in places exposed to wear tend to take a "polish". The permeability of the film is equal to that of the distempers and water paint.

The original synthetic resin emulsion paints based on polyvinyl acetate (homopolymer) incorporating a plasticiser have been largely replaced by copolymers which are sufficiently plastic in themselves. More expensive types based on acrylic resins offer better resistance to weathering and alkalis and are more suitable for outdoor use.

In order to cheapen the product and bring the cost of emulsion paint down to a level comparable to that of the traditional distempers, special ranges of "vinyl water paints" or "vinyl distempers" are produced. These are in effect highly pigmented emulsion paints and are almost always copolymer based. They are produced in a limited range of colours and have good opacity but they are less able to take frequent washing. Accordingly their use is restricted to the less demanding of positions.

In addition to the character of the surface to be treated and the degree of exposure to be expected, the paint type to be selected will depend upon the aesthetic effect desired and also the amount of cleaning and handling that the work will be called upon to withstand. In some cases the protective quality is so important that all other considerations are secondary, for example in the cases of ferrous metals and external woodwork. Since all building materials are subject to movement, however small, all paints should possess some quality of elasticity and adhesion which can adapt to this. The requirement is more marked when considering the protection of external woodwork which will expand and contract to a considerable degree as against such materials as plaster or concrete which are less subject to movement. Hard gloss (oleoresinous or alkyd resin based) or oil-gloss paints are normally selected for external woodwork as they are the most durable types available that are suitable for this type of surface but even the best exterior quality gloss paint may not retain the full gloss for many months when exposed to strong sunshine. The important matter, however, is that the surface will not break down and it will be two to three years and often longer before repainting is necessary. Bituminous paints are also used as protective finishes for iron and steel in conjunction with an effective anti-corrosion primer. Such paints have good water resistance but will break down rapidly on exposure to direct sunlight. The range of colour available in bituminous paints is poor and the appearance dreary so that they are seldom used now on domestic work.

So far as interior work is concerned paints are usually selected that will keep clean under normal conditions of use. Full-gloss paints and enamels provide the most hygienic finish and the widest range of colours for woodwork but distemper, water or emulsion paints or flat oil paint will meet most requirements for walls except in kitchens and bathrooms where steamy conditions may exist. Where a choice lies between a flat oil wall paint and a distemper, water paint, or emulsion paint, the question of cost has to be considered. The initial cost of a flat oil paint system is greater than that of either a washable distemper or an emulsion or oil bound water paint but flat oil paint will last longer, being much more resistant to condensation, and can be cleaned more effectively for a much longer period of time. Flat oil paints usually offer a wider choice of colours than distempers though not necessarily nowadays than with emulsion paints. The textures between the finishes vary and the choice is to some degree a matter of preference.

If the plaster surface is uneven, emulsion or distemper can be seriously considered as a choice for a decorating material particularly over a textured lining paper as it will mask an uneven surface rather better than a flat oil paint. Emulsion and water paints are generally of a finer texture than soft distemper and are produced in a wider range of tints. Water and emulsion paints and distempers are, as already seen, much more permeable to moisture than flat oil paints and are more suitable for early application to newly plastered surfaces On the other hand flat eggshell or satin finish oil paints are less readily affected by frequent condensation of moisture than either emulsions or water paints and distempers. Oil paint is not so likely to peel or flake under moist conditions and should be capable of being repeatedly recoated.

There has never been such a wide selection of paint types and pigments available as there are today. A very wide range of colours and tints are produced by the various paint manufacturers and many of the colours correspond with those shown on the standard colour cards issued by the British Standards Institution. B.S.381C "Colours for specific purposes" gives a range of ninety-six colours and B.S.2660 a range of 101 colours.

In selecting a colour or tint, the surveyor is well advised not to rely merely on the usual small colour cards produced by the manufacturers. Most manufacturers produce books of larger samples and separate large cards of the colours comprised in both B.S.2660 and B.S.381C are available from the British Standards Institution. Without recourse to larger samples such as these a minute paint sample as on the average card, which, in itself may not be completely accurate, will not only give a poor impression of the exact pigment but will also give little impression of the possible overpowering effect of a dark colour on walls or ceiling as against a light colour since the former will reduce a sense of space while the latter will increase

732

it. It is a fairly common cry when the painter is engaged half way through the finishing operation, for the owner or tenant to cry "Oh it is much too dark". If as much as possible can be done to acquaint the occupier with the likely final effect before the finishing coat is applied much time and temper will be saved. Fortunately at the present time the range of colours is so wide and all embracing that it should not, with luck, be necessary to mix paints to find a particular hue. Just after the Second World War decorating was subject to immense difficulties when the choice of colours was severely limited. Anyone with an interest in colour usually wished to mix the available paints to produce an individual hue although often with dire results. Not only did the final colour vary as the painter's enthusiasm for mixing waned once the owner or occupier had left the site, but the surveyor suffered many painful experiences in trying to act as a buffer between two parties with conflicting points of view. The client might wish to capture "an azure, not a silver azure but more of a darker hue, but yet with a certain translucent quality". The painter on the other hand has a more simple desire; that of getting the paint on the wall as quickly as possible in view of the fact that the morning had been spent in everybody gassing and nobody getting anywhere.

Thanks to the glossy magazines everyone is an expert on interior redecoration these days and indeed, it must be said in justice, that in recent years most of the formerly accepted ideas of what constituted an acceptable internal colour scheme have been upset. Times and fashions change rapidly and discussion of such changes although interesting, regrettably must play no part in this book. Whenever possible these writers gave up producing colour schemes for other people many years ago but the surveyor should, however, if possible, try to ensure that the owner or occupier at least knows what they are likely to get even if he himself disagrees violently with a suggested scheme. This should at least help to avoid the "You should have told me" type of comment afterwards.

In painting and decorating it is not always possible to choose the correct time of year and many painting contracts for external work often run dangerously into bad weather. Normally, however, the surveyor tries to minimise the effects of climatic conditions as far as possible in his specification particularly since moisture is the chief enemy of a paint film as it prevents proper keying of the paint to the surface, delays the drying process and is a common cause of subsequent peeling and blistering. Painting should strictly, therefore, not be commenced until a surface has been allowed to dry after a period of rain or damp weather. This applies to exterior and internal work alike since condensation of moisture internally can have an equally bad effect as that of rainfall externally. It is also, however,

733

equally undesirable to carry out repainting in conditions of extreme heat.

So far as external work is concerned the surveyor should take account of the particular circumstances. If the dwelling house is exposed to wind which by its erosive action will cause deterioration in the paintwork, special paints, or extra coats of normal paint may well be necessary. Houses near the sea are also exposed to wind and rain but in particular the atmosphere will be salt laden and paint should be of the highest quality and contain pigments not likely to fade. Alkali-resistant types of paint are often found suitable for use in seaside positions. So far as urban areas are concerned rain often contains acids in solution which attack some pigments, and fog and smoke may be detrimental to paint in a similar manner. Most fumes are harmful to paint both during and after drying and oily soot particles may delay the drying of paint as well as disfigure the paint film.

Preparation for Repainting

The careful examination of an old paint film prior to repainting is a necessity in order to decide upon the scope of the preparatory work.

In the case of paintwork on internal wall surfaces, defects in the structure affecting the paint film should, of course, be eradicated prior to the redecoration. Paint on walls can be affected by penetrating and rising damp and also by excessive condensation. Remedies for the basic cause of such defects have already been discussed in Chapter 8 but if it is not proposed perhaps on grounds of expense or because of the property's limited life, to deal with such defects then the probability of subsequent failure in the paint film must be accepted. The likelihood of such failure being too pronounced and correspondingly noticeable can be reduced by the use of permeable paints to permit evaporation of moisture and the deposit of salts on the surface which can be brushed off.

If repairs have been carried out then it is of course necessary to be sure that the surfaces and the body of the plaster and wall structure are dry. Salt contamination of plaster may need dealing with as described in Chapter 8 but there is no use trying to seal back dampness by impermeable paints or by a lining such as lead or aluminium foil unless there is a clear alternative path for the moisture to escape. Even then there is a risk of failure since the heat of a room will tend to draw moisture towards the internal face which may cause paint to flake or the adhesive for foil linings to fail either by reaction or the mere effect of moisture.

Mould growths or mildew are a frequent occurrence in properties which have been neglected and penetrated by damp over a period.

734

The usual form is of black or various coloured spots and may occur either on the surface in or below distempers, emulsion or oil paints or wallpaper. Microscopic examination will confirm their character. In order to prevent the re-occurrence on redecorated surfaces of whatever form it is necessary to remove the source of the dampness and allow the stripped surfaces to dry out thoroughly. Ventilation should be improved in the room or area affected as a matter of prime importance and the surfaces sterilized with a fungicidal wash. Various types of wash have been found effective among them aqueous solutions of sodium pentachlorphenate, sodium ortho-phenylphenate or sodium salt of salicyl anilide which are available under proprietary names and which should only be used in accordance with the manufacturer's directions. When the wash has completely dried redecoration should be carried out with a paint which will not support mould growth. For domestic purposes paints containing non-toxic fungicides are necessary but often if, by improved ventilation, the re-occurrence is minimal, the use of a paint insensitive to water, for example a chlorinated rubber or epoxy resin finish, will be sufficient.

Sometimes a problem arises with mould growth on sound paintwork which may not be in need of renewal. Assuming the causes giving rise to the damp conditions producing the mould can be cured, paintwork can be scrubbed with a detergent and then washed with a fungicidal solution with the likelihood of no further trouble. Failing the ready availability of an antiseptic wash the use of one of the proprietory domestic bleaches has achieved satisfactory results.

An apparently sound paint film should not from a cursory glance be considered satisfactory for further coatings. New paint films almost always shrink on drying and this shrinkage can exert a force sufficient to detach a weakly adhering original film. This is more likely to occur where the original paint is water based and less likely with oil paint but since the effect is inclined to be apparent only some time after recoating the selection and painting of a trial area is an ideal precaution to take but this has to be done some months before to obtain the full benefit.

Painted wall surfaces, when viewed to decide on preparatory work, can present the full gambit from sound unbroken surfaces to vast areas of flaking paint with all those subtle gradations in between that can make the choice of preparation a difficult one. Flat oil or oil gloss paints or paints with an oleoresinous or alkyd resin base if free from flaking or cracks present little difficulty. The normal cleaning process to remove dirt and grease can be adopted with the use, preferably, of synthetic detergents, mild soap powders or emulsified paint cleaners or alternatively highly diluted solutions of soda or soft soap. In either case as soon as the dirt is loosened the cleansing agent should be rinsed off with clean water, the water being frequently changed during this operation. If a gloss finish has been used previously it will probably be necessary and certainly wise to rub down to remove any remaining gloss in order to improve the adhesion of the new coats.

The difficulty may arise where there is some flaking and blistering but not enough to suggest total stripping. The use of water with a cleansing agent can be dangerous in such circumstances as it is likely that the water will be absorbed by the bare plaster and penetrate behind sound paintwork. Alkaline from the cleansing agent may then begin to attack the original film from behind even if the moisture itself does not cause subsequent blistering. Dry rubbing down with abrasive paper is preferable in these conditions with dusting off to remove all the loose and powdery remaining material on completion. Although this method will remove all the old loose blistering and flaking film, some paint is almost sure to be firmly adhering to other parts of the wall. To leave these areas is dangerous since the flaking shows that a weakness existed which may extend to the sound parts subsequently. Accordingly every effort should be made to remove the whole surface of a particular wall or section unless it can be shown that the flaking of an area of paint had a specific cause which has been satisfactorily cured.

In addition, with oil or alkyd resin painted wall surfaces where the film exhibits deep cracking, the whole surface should be stripped as it is difficult to overcome the pattern of the cracking on repainting, where a high standard of finish is to be expected. Sometimes films showing hair cracks can be filled with a knifing stopper or even by well brushing the undercoat into the cracks but it is a difficult matter to decide whether this will be entirely successful without preparing a trial area preferably about a year in advance. Similarly slightly blistered or wrinkled paint, provided it is well hardened, may sometimes be left in place after rubbing down to a smooth surface. In both the latter cases, however, the risks involved should be carefully weighed and it would be appropriate in the circumstances to offer a full explanation of the reasoning behind the advice which is given by the surveyor, not so much as to avoid criticism but so as to fully acquaint those who may have to pay the bill of the steps taken if success is not achieved.

As far as washable water painted walls are concerned, washing down prior to recoating is not recommended since the adhesion of the original coat is liable to be disrupted in the process. A dry rubbing down will not only clean the surface and remove any loose material but will also reduce the thickness of the old coatings and improve the key for the new coat. Worn, washable soft distempers should be washed off completely, allowed to dry, and the plaster surface repaired by cutting back and filling if wide cracks exist. Fine cracks should also be filled if washable water paints are to be used but if oil paint is proposed it is often better to defer filling until the priming coat has been applied and then use an oil filling or putty as appropriate. This is, of course, the normal preparation for painting new or fairly new plaster.

If the decorations are entirely removed from old lime plaster the surface usually exhibits very fine crazing due to long standing overall shrinkage. Although this is often hardly visible until the plaster is wetted it may be conspicuous after painting or distempering owing to absorption of the medium at the cracks. The best way to reduce this absorption is by the use of an akali resisting plaster primer as a sealer, brushed well into the cracks. Since the crazing can sometimes involve sharp lipped edges from which new paint may recede, best of all is the method of lining prior to painting.

In view of the differing composition of emulsion paints a trial area should be prepared prior to general preparation of plastered surfaces previously coated with this material. Emulsion paints vary considerably in their water sensitivity and porosity and assuming that the paint film is unbroken and accordingly does not require stripping a test of these characteristics is essential. Where the water absorption approximates to that of an oil bound water paint it is better to prepare the surface by dry rubbing down with an abrasive paper. Those emulsion films which soften to the extent of easy removal with a stripping knife under the effect of hot water will accordingly require careful attention and alternatively cleaning with cold water or again dry rubbing down. Other emulsion films will stand a good scrub down with hot water much in the same way as oil painted surfaces and accordingly the preparation in these circumstances may be similar to that adopted for oil paint.

Decorations applied to plaster on building boards sometimes exhibit typical defects which require attention when the time for redecoration comes round. Methods of dealing with the stains from nail heads have already been dealt with in the section earlier in this Chapter covering the painting of calcium sulphate plasters but cracking along the joints due to the absence of jointing tapes or strips when the boards were originally fixed may also require filling. Where the decoration finish is of oil paint the cracks should first be touched up with oil paint and then filled with an oil filler or putty. Where water paint has been used a water filler should be used but it should be remembered that such fillers are rigid and the cracks may well reopen to some extent subsequently. A much superior finish can be obtained if, after filling, a stout lining paper is applied before subsequent redecoration. Where oil paint is to be used a prior coating of weak glue size on the lining paper will improve the finish by evening out and reducing the suction characteristics.

The preparation of external wall surfaces for recoating where these have previously been painted follows along somewhat similar lines to that of internal wall surfaces. The material to which the decoration has been applied in the past, however, will be different, since there is a likelihood in more recent work of the presence of Portland cement rather than, say, the calcium sulphate plasters which are never employed externally. Where external surfaces have previously been painted with oil paint on a cement rendering, normal preparation consists of thorough cleaning and rubbing down wet, and the removal of any small sections of loose paint. These areas and any cracks should be primed with an alkali-resistant primer and filled with hard painter's stopping or with a non-bleeding mastic which may however require a few days to harden before the application of paint. Broad areas requiring filling should be similarly primed and then filled with an oil-based filler obtained for knifing or brushing as required. Where the existing paint accumulation is thick and it is desired to fill the defective area flush, the filling should be applied in several coats, allowing adequate drying time between each. Often however, it is considered adequate to fill them merely to smooth the surface, relying on feathering the edges of the existing paintwork to overcome any poor appearance. Filling should be primed of course and brought forward with undercoating prior to the application of the general undercoat.

When the general adhesion of an old oil paint system is weak or the work badly crazed or flaking over a wide area, complete removal of the paint is advisable as described in the section following. When continual repainting for many years has built up accumulations of considerable thickness there is a tendency to these faults. On stripping, any residue of former repairs carried out in plaster, often found, should be removed and any dust from such material removed. All cracks disclosed on the rendering should then be repaired in accordance with the advice given in the section on repairs to existing rendered finishes towards the end of Chapter 2. Repainting must be treated as for new work.

Water based paints, applied externally, should be prepared in the same way as for internal surfaces, but it is important to remember that repairs to cracks should be carried out in cement and not in oil putties if water based paints are to be used again. Cement based paints tend to form a hard brittle or powdery surface to which even successive coats of cement based paint do not adhere well unless the surface is brushed down and given a prior coat of sealer.

Oil painted brickwork sometimes exhibits failure along the line of the mortar joints, particularly if painted too soon after construction. Wire brushing can be used to remove flaking paint along the joints and if they are subsequently treated with an alkali-resistant primer the trouble should not be repeated.

In the domestic field the repainting of metalwork does not assume quite the same degree of importance as it does elsewhere but even so there are gutters and pipes, balustrades and sometimes fire escapes which require recoating. If paintwork is allowed to deteriorate on ferrous metals so that it no longer fulfils its function as a protective measure then the process of removal of the old paint, the removal of the rust and the cleaning of the surface is difficult, laborious and expensive. On the other hand very old paint surfaces from which it can be said that all the useful life has long since been extracted provide an unsatisfactory base for a new paint film even apart from the damage which may have been caused to the metal itself. This is particularly so in the case of ferrous metals. New paint applied to cracked, checked, flaking or peeling paint will probably fail quickly due to the stresses set up as the new paint system dries, ages and weathers, the dimensional changes so produced causing constant stressing at the surfaces of the paint in contact with the metal.

If repainting is carried out early enough and no rusting is visible it will be sufficient to clean down the paintwork by washing with detergent, rinsing off, drying and apply two coats in the usual way. If rusting has started in only a few places these should be cleaned by wire brushing either by hand or mechanical means and coated with red lead primer to B.S.2523 or metallic lead followed by one coat of an oil based air-drying anti-corrosive paint. The surface should then be brought forward by such stopping and filling as necessary to bring the surface to the level of the existing work or alternatively the surrounding sound paintwork should be flattened down at least. If, however, the metalwork has become extensively rusted the whole of the old paint should be removed leaving a surface ready for priming and painting in accordance with the requirements for new work once pre-treatment has been carried out by either manual, blast or flame cleaning or by one of the chemical processes now available.

The painting of non-ferrous metals does not feature very largely in the domestic field at the present time although the use of such metals is on the increase. Most, for example the aluminium used for external windows, are left unpainted, having already been

739

provided with a protective chemical coating such as anodisation. Later, however, in order to brighten the dreary appearance of weathered anodised surfaces, painting may be resorted to in which case the continued repainting will be a regular requirement. In these circumstances if flaking of the paint has occurred only on a limited area and the adhesion of the rest is sound it is usually sufficient to remove loose paint and any corrosion products and to patch prime, or prime overall, at once. If the paint film is left exposed to the weather after cleaning down, further loosening of the sound paintwork is a possibility. Removing loose paint and the products of corrosion must be done very carefully so as to avoid the danger of damage to the anodised coating.

In the external maintenance of pre and post Second World War housing the repainting of galvanised steel in windows and doors figures prominently. Very often neglect removes not only the paint film but the non-ferrous coating as well leaving the base metal exposed. After cleaning to remove all corrosion products it is advisable to choose the pigment in the primer to inhibit the corrosion of both the base metal and the coating, for example an etch-primer or one based on calcium plumbate in the case of galvanising on steel or zinc chromate for aluminium on steel.

The preparation of wood surfaces for repainting is dealt with fully at the end of Chaper 5 with the exception of stripping old paintwork which for the sake of uniformity is dealt with in the following section.

Removal of Defective Paintwork

The development of many new types of paint over the last twenty to thirty years has been accompanied by an almost equal amount of activity devoted to the introduction of new chemical paint strippers. When it is desired to strip some of the newer paints a special formulation is required and the selection of the correct type of stripper is an important factor. There are indeed now available paints which cannot be stripped except by abrasive means, the reverse aspect of the claim that the paint is "waterproof and heatproof". When the claim as it can be nowadays is extended to "scratch and impact resistant" as well the difficulties of stripping, even by mechanical means, can be well imagined yet some paints for which such claims are made crack and look dull remarkably quickly.

Where it is desired or necessary to remove for preparation purposes dried films of oil alkyd or oleoresinous paints or varnishes the choice lies between burning off or employing liquid paint removers. Where the heat of a flame is liable to cause damage to surrounding or underlying surfaces paint strippers must be used and also where the coating itself is highly inflammable as with some cellulose enamels. Skill and care is required in the use of both methods; with burning off to prevent the outbreak of fire and with strippers to prevent damage to surrounding surfaces, to the operative himself and in the case of volatile products to obviate the danger of fire and explosion as well as the inhalation of toxic fumes.

Burning off is usually the quickest and most economical method of removing paint from wood surfaces but it is often less effective on metals and other heat conducting materials. Owing to the risk of cracking and disintegration it should not be used on plaster and cement rendered surfaces unless the coatings of paint are sufficiently thick to soften without transmitting excessive heat to the surface. A blow lamp is seldom used for removing paint from metalwork although on larger contracts cleaning with oxy-acetylene equipment is sometimes adopted.

Chemical paint strippers fall into two separate types but both require to be used carefully and in accordance with the maker's directions to be fully effective and economical in use:

(a) *Alkaline*: These are applied and maintained in a damp condition until the paint is soft enough and able to be removed with a knife. After removal the surface has to be rinsed many times with clean water and the use of neutraliser such as vinegar or acetic acid is advantageous in the rinsing water. The difficulty of removing all traces of the stripper particularly from porous surfaces has led to the development of the second type.

(b) *Solvent*: Both spirit-rinsable and water-rinsable organic solvent types are now available to B.S.3761. Some are available for specific types of paint only but the instructions of the manufacturers are usually clear as to suitable purposes. After softening and removal of the paint with a scraper, surfaces must be swabbed with white spirit or water as directed to remove any residues of a waxy nature before repainting. These types of paint stripper are much more satisfactory in use than the alkaline types but even so the reaction on the more complex resin media types of paint and varnish can be limited. On oil, alkyd or oleoresinous painted wall surfaces and external rendered surfaces the water rinsable organic solvent type of stripper is to be preferred to the alkaline in all cases as the latter can be absorbed by the plaster or rendering to the possible detriment of a new paint coating even if the plaster surface is primed with an alkali-resistant primer. This also applies to wood surfaces where it is not possible, for example near glass, to use a blow lamp.

As has already been seen it is not usually necessary to remove entirely washable water paint systems on plastered walls but when

741

this need does arise most respond well to steam stripping appliances the use of which enables even the heaviest accumulations to be removed. On the other hand, polyvinyl acetate emulsion or vinyl water paints may only need the application of hot water to render them sufficiently soft for removal by a stripping knife. The differing compositions of such paints make trial and error the only way of ascertaining a suitable method of removal in the absence of knowledge of the precise type used originally. However, special organic solvent strippers are available for the removal of emulsion paints which cause the resin or varnish binder to swell.

An accumulation of many layers, perhaps of different types, of water based paints on external rendered surfaces may prove difficult to remove by ordinary wire brushing or scraping and it may be necessary to use mechanical means, such as rotating steel brushes or abrasive discs. Heavy absorbent accumulations will sometimes yield to steam from a steam stripping appliance but more often, however, the need to remove such layers can be avoided by the use of a special sealer or a thin oily paint liberally applied to impregnate them as deeply as possible and to act as a stabiliser as described earlier. If oil and water based paints have been used on the same surface in the past and the accumulation consists of layers of both, burning off might have to be employed to assist removal, but great care in the circumstances would be necessary to avoid too great a heat being applied to the surface otherwise cracking and crazing may occur.

Manual or mechanical wire brushing, hand scraping or the use of mechanical grinding machines are normally used for the combined removal of the remains of old paint films and the cleaning of ferrous metal surfaces before priming and repainting. The work is laborious but few contracts in the domestic field will justify the use of blast-cleaning or flame cleaning so that the only alternative would be a chemical stripper which would probably in any event leave the cleaning still to be carried out by abrasive methods of one sort or another. There would probably therefore be very little saving and if ferrous metals are allowed to fall into a state where entire stripping is necessary heavy expense must be anticipated.

Where non-ferrous metals are used the likelihood of surfaces requiring the same treatment as above is remote and the use of an organic solvent type of paint remover is recommended so as to minimise any damage to the anodised or other chemical coating that may have been applied to the metal and which will remain below soundly adhering paintwork. By using this type of stripper only the minimum of scraping will be needed.

As discussed, most paints in common use can be removed either by burning-off, by softening with a solvent or by the use of a steam appliance but in recent years paints have been developed which are chemically resistant and develop a very hard surface. These paints are mainly of the epoxy or polyurethane systems and are supplied in two parts, a base and a hardener which are mixed just before use. They set in a few hours and harden to a tough film. While they are useful as floor paints and furniture finishes they are not recommended for exterior cladding and if used incorrectly so that subsequent removal is necessary this can only be done by mechanical means. Unfortunately their very hardness makes a subsequent adhesion with a coating of a different type very problematical so that stripping is normally a necessity.

Repainting

In repainting it is always best to recoat with the same material as formerly used if this has given satisfactory results. Unfortunately it is not always possible to consult records or to establish accurately the composition of the previous coating and it may accordingly be necessary to send a sample to a paint consultant or to the Building Research Station Advisory Service who will analyse and report back for a small fee.

On other occasions it may be desired to change the appearance to produce a different decorative effect or perhaps to increase the protective qualities of the finish and a different paint has to be selected to be applied over an existing finish which is not to be stripped. There are certain dangers in such a procedure although nowadays the range of compatible finishes is extending. Perhaps the greatest danger arises in the application of oil (or water paints) over old bitumastic coatings. Unless these latter coatings are very thin, old, and have fully oxidised, there is a great danger of "bleeding" into the new paint film. As a result the recoating of soil and waste pipes, rainwater pipes and gutters and very often fire escapes in bitumastic paints is usually a necessity if they have once been painted with that material. Such painting was common at one time in the mistaken belief that it proved better protection against rust than an oil paint system. A sealing treatment might conceivably be used if it is absolutely essential to make the change but the danger here is that hard drying sealers and paints are prone to crazing when applied over a softer bituminous coating.

Undoubtedly the increasing and now almost universal use of the alkyd resin paints has tended to bring with it problems in the repainting field. Their slightly less flexible nature has led to an increase in the amount of cracking and flaking where they have been used over a lead based or oil gloss paint. Accordingly it is far better (if a lead based paint is now unacceptable owing to its toxic nature) to use the oil gloss paints to B.S.2526–27 and undercoats to B.S.2525 which, although they have been altered slightly in 1968 by the incorporation of some alkyd resin in the oil medium, still retain in the main the characteristics of the older oil based paints which are not now available. The temptation in repainting to apply a new paint with a very hard and supposedly weatherproof finish is great but it is one that should be resisted as there is evidence to show that a combination of a new different paint over an old film of different character is seldom wholly successful.

On the other hand there is ample evidence in regard to plastered wall surfaces to show that emulsion paints, particularly of the newer copolymer and the acrylic types take quite well both over washable distempers provided all powdery material is removed and also over old gloss paints provided these are well washed down with detergent and wet abrasive paper. Apart from the earlier emulsion paints which tended to lose adhesion under damp conditions in kitchens and bathrooms, for example and which therefore might continue to suffer in this way if recoated with oil paint, most emulsioned surfaces provide a satisfactory base for practically any type of redecoration.

Oil bound distempers can, of course, be recoated with similar material as described above but there is a limit to the number of coats which may be expected to adhere, with possibly six being about the maximum in dry situations. The application of a binding down primer and dry rubbing down helps to prolong the need for stripping, however, as already seen.

The practice of using emulsion paints as an undercoat for interior work is fairly common particularly over existing oil paint and permits final coating the same day. There is no evidence at present to suggest that this is a bad practice but certainly it should not be permitted in bathrooms and kitchens or for work outside. Copolymer and acrylic types of emulsion paint are used and the practice permits walls and woodwork to be undercoated together with a resultant economy in costs. Provided existing surfaces have already been previously oil painted or suitably primed there is no objection to the use of emulsion paint on woodwork or metalwork if it is desired that these have the same finish as the walls, although where handling is concerned it is not thought that quite the same appearance or length of life will be sustained as would be the case with oil paint.

The difficulties of recoating bitumen painted surfaces with a different type of paint have been touched upon but there is a group of paints, of which bitumen and size bound distempers are but two, which are troublesome to recoat in themselves. Normally size bound distempers are washed off but with bitumen paint, removal is not normally necessary so that the difficulty arises on re-coating when it is difficult to apply a fresh coat without picking up the previous one. Chlorinated rubber and cellulose paints are two other paints in this group which are relatively simple products since the dissolved binder in the paint is deposited unchanged when the thinner evaporates and consequently remains dissolvable by the thinner in a new coat when this is applied.

For external wall surfaces there has been a tendency in recent years to replace the traditional limewash (see Chapter 3 for aspects of limewash in regard to its use on stonework) distempers and cement paints with emulsion paints of an exterior quality and even more recently by solvent-based paints with various synthetic resins as binders. The resins are usually of the alkali-resisting (non-saponi-fiable) type and include isomerised rubber, styrene/butadiene (synthetic rubber) and acrylic or vinyltoluene/acrylic polymers. These products are useful on cement renderings to resist efflorescence and they shed water better than most water thinned paints, thus reducing dirt collection and algal growth. They normally have an initial slight sheen but this soon chalks, a necessity to enable them to resist dirt accumulation in grimy atmospheres. These paints are inappropriate for use on stucco which although not originally intended to be bright and glossy (see Chapter 2) has now after a hundred years or so acquired a traditional appearance of that character.

The specialist painting contractor offering house-owners a guarantee is a new breed on the building scene but has been in evidence for the last few years. The concentration is on the owners of houses with rendered elevations and the paints used are thicker film compositions with sand, mica, coloured glass or minerals as filler based on oleoresinous, emulsion or polyurethane binders. The thickness alone plus the protection given to the binder by the aggregate gives such paints a high resistance to weathering but, as with all paints, they require correct surface preparation and use to be fully effective. The Building Research Establishment indicates that the elasticity claimed for some types is unlikely to be able to cope with cracking in the background which seems to be hinted at in some of the publicity. In the circumstances it is considered that such paints ought to be thought of in exactly the same manner as other paints and not as an all-embracing panacea. Certainly the use of a type with a pronounced aggregate is an unmitigated disaster as far as appearance is concerned on stucco work.

745

Defects in Paintwork

If paintwork is left for such a time that general stripping is required merely because of old age, i.e. paints eventually crack and flake as their normal breakdown process rather than wear away, there is little point of speculating on whether the original work was carried out well or not. There will be sufficient problems to solve in considering how to deal with the new painting without considering the past. On the other hand just occasionally the surveyor or architect becomes involved in the inspection of paintwork which is not so very old but which has yet failed. He may well have to diagnose the reason for failure and prescribe a remedy to prevent a re-occurrence of the defect. This can be a difficult matter and it may need the assistance of a painting consultant of which a few exist, to carry out microscopic examination and laboratory analysis. It will be readily appreciated that the causes of defects are very numerous. They can, for example, emanate from the backing, they can arise in the workmanship, they can be due to the incorrect use of a particular paint or be due to a failure in the paint itself, though this is rare indeed in view of the control exercised nowadays by the large-scale manufacturers of the better known brands. On the other hand the actual physical defects can be categorised into a few groups.

The most frequently occurring group of defects arises from loss of adhesion, manifested by blistering, peeling and flaking of the paint film. Flaking is distinguished from peeling by the brittleness of the paint film as it is detached resulting in small "flakes" rather than the "strips" of flexible material which become detached on peeling. Blisters are usually brought about by entrapped moisture below an impermeable paint film and may be a result of poor workmanship or the wrong choice of paint. Of the former the remedy will be to remove the loose paint, allow the surface to dry and repaint but if there is a possibility of dampness penetrating the backing from behind then clearly a decision will have to be taken on the use of a different paint system of a permeable character if the damp penetration cannot be cured, such as a porous alkali-resistant paint.

In repair work much peeling paint is due to bad preparation, particularly the failure to remove dirt before repainting or painting over damp surfaces. The remedy will be to strip the affected surfaces, prepare them properly by the removal of all dirt or powdery material, dust, etc., allow to dry thoroughly and then repaint. The moral to be drawn is to employ reputable firms of contractors since the surveyor cannot be on site to supervise all the time. Even the most reputable firms, however, can be let down by their workmen at times but there is less risk of this with the older established reliable firms than with others. On the other hand the specifications and price must be of a character to allow sufficient time for proper preparation.

The cracking and eventual flaking of paint is, as already stated, the way in which many paints eventually break down in the course of time rather than by chalking and wearing away. Some modern paints have a tendency to a high drying shrinkage which has accentuated this process to a considerable degree thus necessitating a much earlier recoating than would have been considered necessary a few years ago if stripping is to be avoided. In work of recent origin cracking may be the result of error in that a hard drying gloss paint has been applied over a soft undercoat not compatible with the finish, or alternatively over the correct undercoat which has not properly dried and hardened. The importance of using undercoat prepared by the same maker as that for the finishing coat is emphasised by the former defect while in the second instance the interval between the application of separate coats should always be related to drying conditions as well as the maker's instructions. Obviously loose paint must be stripped when a remedy is being prescribed and strictly speaking this should apply when paintwork seems to be adhering even although it is cracked, particularly if it is not too long since the painting was carried out. If, however, some two to three years have elapsed it may be possible to rub down to remove crazing or "checking" (the forerunner of cracking before the entire paint film is severed) by rubbing down dry and also filling and stopping any cracks in the paint film provided no defects exist below the paint film. The main guarantee for a reduced incidence of such a defect, however, is the choice of paints with a low drying shrinkage, for example stucco work to be repainted with a lead based paint to B.S.2525 or a lead free paint, if essential, to B.S.2526-7.

Many of the other causes giving rise to blistering and peeling are associated with painting on new surfaces and while these are perhaps more properly considered in the subject of new building they are briefly mentioned here as possibly arising in consequence of substantial repairs. Earlier in this Chapter advice was given in regard to the painting of new plaster and the consequences of defects such as "Dry-out" where the plaster mix loses its water before hydrating. "Delayed expansion" where plaster in "Dry-out" state subsequently takes up more moisture and "Sweat-out" where set gypsum plaster remains wet for long periods and looses its strength. Decorations on all such plasters will fail rapidly and the only remedy is usually to replaster and subsequently re-coat properly as for new work. The absence of or incorrect use of primers will have similar effects on paintwork. Very often undercoats and finishes are so badly affected in a short space of time that stripping is necessary but on other occasions if it is a matter only of differential background character-istics the use of an anti-suction primer over sound paint and bare background will even up the conditions and enable a new film to be applied.

Repeated condensation will sometimes be found to be a problem and in particular will cause swelling and shrinkage of the bonder especially with distemper and fresh coats of paint although satin finish or hard gloss oil paints will withstand limited condensation well when dry. Increased warmth and ventilation, see Chapter 8, is a prime remedy although anti-condensation paints applied to adhering dry old paint will make intermittent light condensation inconspicuous.

Paint will sometimes be affected itself by way of the formation of a soft sticky film with watery blisters or yellow oily runs occasionally with some bleaching or discoloration. This is invariably caused by alkaline substances attacking an oil paint or oil bound distemper applied over cement or lime plasters or where on painting over an old stripped surface a residue of alkaline paint remover has been allowed to remain. Precautions to avoid such a defect have already been fully discussed but if it has already happened the only remedy is to strip the affected paintwork entirely and start again taking into account the recommendations for new work.

Efflorescence will often produce patchy deposits on painted surfaces if permeable, or push off decoration if impermeable. The remedy on existing painted surfaces is to strip, allow to dry and redecorate preferably avoiding water-thinned paints or using them over porous alkali-resistant primers if the surface is heavily con-taminated with salts. It is better to use thin coats of permeable paints such as some of the emulsion paints which offer a better chance of allowing the fluffy efflorescence to form on the surface without disturbing the paint film. If drying conditions are good with ample heat and ventilation so much the better.

The increased use of lightweight plasters has brought about a certain amount of staining where these have been applied over some types of brick, especially if underburnt, or over clinker blockwork. The advantage of using these plasters in repair work is considerable but if emulsion or vinyl wall paint is used faint brown patches have become rapidly apparent. The way to overcome the staining is to apply on top of the existing base an anti-suction or alkali resistant primer plus further emulsion paint or flat, eggshell or gloss oil paint. It is difficult to anticipate such difficulties with paintwork as this in the same way as it is with patchiness of colour or sheen brought about by uneven trowelling of plaster producing variable density and suction. As will have been seen, however, anti-suction and alkali-resistant primers provide useful palliatives when such defects do arise.

Paper-hanging

Wallpapers are the present-day successors to the tapestries and woven or leather coverings once used to decorate the walls of houses of quality. Today, it is possible for anyone to purchase at reasonable cost papers not only of a wide range of design but papers also produced to simulate other materials which they do with a terrifying degree of accuracy.

Wallpapers, as the term is generally understood, are either machine-printed or hand-printed. The latter are printed from blocks wholly of wood or from lino or rubber covered wooden blocks each colour employed usually involving a separate block. Hand-printed papers are expensive and the number of colours employed governs the price. On the other hand special designs can be produced by this method that would be impossible by mass-production and the slight differences in texture and variation of pattern are their most pleasing quality. Hand-printed papers can be distinguished from machine-made papers by the blank unprinted ground at either end of each roll. There are other methods of producing wallpapers by hand such as by stencilling or the silk screen method of printing.

The varieties of patterns and types of wallpaper available today are innumerable. Embossed papers enable a raised effect such as canvas or linen or various types of weave to be reproduced. Flock papers are one of the most attractive which have come back into fashion and these consist of an imitation of a velvet-like cloth which was one of the earliest types of wallpaper and highly popular in the 17th and 18th centuries. The modern method of reproducing a flock paper is to print a ground design with a mastic and while this is still tacky dust silk, wool, nylon or cotton flock on to the surface. The flock can of course be coloured to any desired tint and such papers are often flocked more than once to increase the height of the pile. In addition to flock papers, leather papers, marble papers and grass papers are produced. Other papers which have been given metallic effects or papers which have been printed with a mixture of finely ground mica thus giving rise to a satiny sheen to the ground are also made.

Moires which give water silk effects and Jaspes which give an irregularly brushed soft line effect are also obtainable. In addition to the satins and satinettes which are papers with a shiny surface produced by polishing with rotary brushes and french chalk or mica, the old-fashioned anaglipta hardened embossed paper and the lincrusta papers are still available. Added to the range in recent years are a whole group of vinyl and other papers which are quite different in their basic composition to conventional wallpapers.

"Think first of the walls; for they are that which makes your house a home" said William Morris. The bewildered house owner tries to follow this precept faithfully but the heap of pattern books often confuses more than it helps. As with paint colours the larger the interior to be covered with paper, the less intense the colour should be for all normal circumstances. Wallpaper backgrounds should be less commanding in general colour than the objects which are to appear against them and the normal result of the selection of papers by one member of the family is for another to decide that there is little alternative, once the paper is hung, but to order a new and complete set of furniture as the old looks so "impossible" against the background. This is a forgiveable mistake, but the surveyor, if he has any feeling of compassion for fellow human beings in trouble, can try to avoid this contingency by suggesting that a mockup of the room is made before the paper is finally ordered. Venturing on criticism is not always easy but the surveyor is surely entitled to point out to the over enthusiastic that they might not relish living in a simulation of a Malayan jungle for ever, or that a particular type of strong patterned paper might be one they might grow tired of rather quickly. The writers in particular recall a type of paper selected some years ago by a client which consisted of red spots on a white background. When the paper was hung it induced a sense of complete vertigo and the memory of the experience remains with the writers even to this day. Another common error made is that of failing to relate the size of the pattern to a particular room or to the fabrics and the furnishings. It is always best if, after the paper is purchased and before it is hung that the owner or occupier and his wife are asked to look at the effect of the unwound roll draped over the painter's steps. The difference between this and the appearance of the small pattern in the book is often a marked one.

FIREPLACES AND FLUES

In the great majority of cases fireplace openings to old dwelling houses are nowadays no longer required. Main bedrooms and attic rooms, once the bedrooms of servants, all had their fireplaces in the past as an open fire was the only means of heating but these will probably now be sealed and heating will be by means other than that of an open fire. The brick chimney breasts and the flues will normally be retained except under exceptional circumstances since to remove these would be an expensive business. In addition to this aspect the householder may still require open fires for decorative purposes, if not actually for use with smokeless fuel or wood, to the main ground floor reception rooms and possibly utilise the existing flues for unit gas heaters in the bedrooms. It is likely therefore that the surveyor will be instructed to give orders for the flues to the bedrooms to be sealed up. The surveyor will probably decide to do this by means of a skin of bricks or concrete or tile blocks built into and pinned up to the existing opening but he should also remember that effective ventilation must be provided by means of a fibrous plaster or metal grille to each fireplace opening as near the floor as possible to ensure for example that the requirements for habitable rooms regarding ventilation are obeyed on the one hand, if this is not already complied with by other means, but primarily that the conditions leading to condensation forming in the flues are prevented on the other. Ventilation of course must also be maintained at the top of the flue.

With regard to fireplaces that are to be kept for their functional purpose the surveyor will find many different conditions according to the type and age of the house. There are cases of houses built about 1650 where the fireplace openings resembled caverns into which the surveyor gingerly poked his head to be rewarded by the sight of sunlight from the sky above. In such cases the flue is often straight and sometimes the "withs" or brick dividers between the respective flues for different fireplaces have crumbled or burned away and vanished long since. In addition to this the lintel carrying the brickwork over the fireplace opening is likely to be formed of timber which will have been smouldering merrily over the years since the house was built so that its inner surface is charred and brittle. Parging to the flue is probably not only non-existent but probably vanished about the time that Napoleon started his Russian campaign.

Not all fireplaces and flues depart from established principles to the above extent but in fact very often little needs to be done unless particular requirements are made by the client except the most obvious repairs. First of all, however, the lintel must be replaced in an incombustible material as discreetly as possible and the repair of any particularly bad or crumbled brickwork inside the flue must be given consideration. Sometimes it is worth providing a rigid or flexible flue lining in such cases but by no means is this invariably necessary. It should of course be explained to the client that there may be difficulties from down draught and rain hissing on to an open fire at certain times of the year but if the owner is prepared to accept these shortcomings and most are, since this type of fireplace provides a focal point and much character, and usually the alternative to leaving the flue is a matter of major expense, some amelioration of the conditions can sometimes be obtained with cowls. Even this, however, may not be particularly desirable in a house of historic or artistic importance and more often matters can be left well alone. There is, however, one other aspect of the matter that it is important should be considered. This is to make sure that there are no structural or other timbers near enough to the flue to present a continuing fire hazard. It is highly likely that the structure will be rather odd so far as the flooring and roof timbers are concerned where these abut the brickwork surrounding the flue and if investigations show that these press against an insufficient thickness of brickwork at a critical point steps should be taken either to re-trim the surrounding timber so that it is set away from the brickwork or alternatively to provide a layer of incombustible material between the brick and the timber.

In most cases it is likely that with the fireplace opening to a reception room of an old building the house owner will keep it mainly for decorative purposes as an adjunct to the room. He may make use of it occasionally and it is possible that he will find a hob grate for this purpose but the surveyor should, under these circumstances, investigate the hearth. The Building Regulations stipulate that the hearth in front of a fireplace shall project at least 20 inches (500mm) beyond the front of the jambs, have a minimum thickness of 5 inches (125mm) and extend at least 6 inches (150mm) beyond each side of the opening. No combustible material is to surround the hearth. In practice of course this ideal set of circumstances may not occur to an existing fireplace. The hearth may be of insufficient projection or may simply consist of a stone flag much worn and laminated from long use. This flag will often have to be replaced in concrete and a larger piece of stone selected for use so as to bring the hearth up to the required standard.

If instead of merely being a decorative adjunct to a room a fireplace opening is to be used constantly the surveyor might consider doing what he can to make it more efficient than it already is. The opening itself might have to be reduced with the use of old bricks to match the existing and the lintel lowered. A new fire back will inevitably be required with a brick backing formed to bring this forward to provide a suitably narrow throat for the flue. The fire grate will be ordered to match the new depth of the opening provided and in general it is possible normally to alter an old fireplace into one that complies with good practice.

Not all fireplaces used for open fires and flues to old houses present problems but sometimes unexpected difficulties occur. Old alterations or, indeed, modern alterations, may have interfered with the run of a flue, and cases have been known where, once the building has been occupied, the first fire to be lit has resulted in clouds of swirling smoke vomiting into the newly decorated drawing room This is obviously to be avoided if possible and a test of each flue to be used with an open fire for soundness is a prudent precaution. Cases have also been known where the lack of parging to old flues and the rough brickwork laid between old floor joists has resulted in gaps in the flue which, although very small, will be enough to give a slight penetration of smoke in a bedroom where the fireplace is not in use. Such circumstances are, however, mercifully rare but occasionally do arise. Extensive defects in the parging and pointing of a flue may necessitate the provision of a flexible metal inner flue connected to the appliance to be used and fixed to a plate at the top of the main flue. There are two other methods of effectively making an old flue smoke and fume tight without pulling it entirely apart. Both of these methods however are utilised by specialists who if it cannot be said that the principle is patented certainly use equipment which probably comes within this category. The older of the two methods which has been in use for many years consists of pulling through the flue a spring loaded appliance which forces a parging mortar into all gaps in the existing parging, pointing or brickwork. Obviously the flue must be cleared first by abrasive sweeping of all loose and dusty material but once this has been done a sufficient thickness of parging can be built up. This method is similar to that used for applying an internal lining to old drains which is referred to in Chapter 10 and is carried out by the same firm or their licencees and under their patents. The second method introduced much later, utilises a flexible liner as temporary shuttering while a lightweight insulating mortar is pumped in under pressure to fill up the whole of the space between the temporary lining and the parging and brickwork of the old flue. This provides a much thicker lining to an old flue than does the coring method described above and of course the result is that a square flue is reduced to a much smaller circular flue. The insulating qualities of this form of lining can of course be advantageous in reducing the risk of condensation from the flue gases of slow burning solid fuel or gas-fired appliances. If a large gas-fired boiler is being installed in an old house it would of course be essential with this method of flue lining to check that the size of flue remaining on completion of the work is satisfactory and large enough for the capacity of the boiler.

DOMESTIC ELECTRIC WIRING

The up-dating of electric wiring installations to houses often involves the total renewal of the whole wiring system. There are a
number of reasons for this, the first and most obvious being that
any wiring installations provided more than about thirty years ago
are by now out of date when judged in comparison with present-day
requirements. A tall Victorian house, for example, may well have an
electrical installation put in about 1920 that is designed to feed
2 amp. two pin skirting lighting points with the very occasional 15
amp. power point only and this system can never form an effective
basis for the power circuit that will be required to feed the numerous
appliances that are likely to be needed by the present-day householder. The second reason for complete renewal of an installation is
concerned with the life expectancy of the system. A wiring installation may be adequate as it stands at the time of inspection and
indeed may pass a test but the surveyor may well decide, in consultation with his electrical engineer that as the cables and fittings are
beginning to show signs of age and are becoming brittle, the system
cannot be guaranteed for more than a year or two at the most so
that renewal of the wiring is best under the circumstances. In the
case of a house built before the Second World War, for example, the
installation may be fit for use for some time if undisturbed, subject
to a few minor repairs, but if the rubber covered cable shows signs
of becoming perished the surveyor should think seriously about the
question of re-wiring. Most householders have the best of intentions
to carry out work after they have purchased a property but once
they have moved in, interest and enthusiasm in the idea of modernisation may wane, as indeed may the money for the project, and the
wiring installation may have to serve for a considerably longer time
than the surveyor or the owner expected. Electrical wiring systems,
even those of comparatively modern design, have a short life when
judged against the life span of an average dwelling house and the
renewal of the installation in cycles of, say, twenty or thirty years
enables advantage to be taken of the advances in the standards of
materials and design since the last re-wiring was carried out. The
modern electrical installation, like the central heating or hot water
system of a modern house, is now quite different to the type of
system provided a comparatively short time ago. The accepted
methods of design and practice change so rapidly that in order to
take advantage of them the surveyor has to adopt a completely
different approach to wiring installations as against the main integral
parts of a house. It is suggested therefore that the wiring installation

is seen as an element in the building that is not permanent and that in considering the question of repair and maintenance as against renewal this factor is taken into consideration.

If it is felt that what has so far been said represents a rather callous attitude towards the owner's pocket it should be remembered that one of the enormous advantages of present-day electrical wiring installations is that they are relatively cheap. Cheap, that is to say, when compared with the cost of the repair and maintenance of most other parts of the dwelling house that have so far been discussed. The benefits of an up-to-date wiring installation as against an old one are so enormous from the point of view of convenience, quite apart from the question of electrical shock or fire risk from an old installation that when compared to the modest sum that is often at stake the decision to renew is probably one of the most worthwhile investments in the whole range of present-day building economics. Besides, if a dwelling house is repaired and maintained with patience and care it would hardly be possible to neglect the wiring installation which if it proves to be defective will present one of the most serious risk elements of all.

Before discussing the question of the repair, maintenance and renewal of electrical wiring installations it will be necessary to refer briefly to the types of wiring installation likely to be found in houses in contrast with the types that are available today. First, however, must come a description of the methods adopted in the testing and investigation of a wiring system whether it be new or old.

Testing and Investigating an Existing Installation

The Electricity Boards are empowered under statutory regulations to refuse to connect a supply to any consumer unless they are satisfied that all apparatus and conductors are constructed, installed and protected so as to prevent danger. The tests laid down in the regulations to determine the efficiency of a system are as follows:

(1) Tests for Polarity. These ensure that all accessories to the wiring system are correctly connected.

(2) Tests of the effectiveness of the earthing of the system.

(3) Tests for insulation resistance which are made between each conductor and the earth and between the conductors themselves.

(4) Test of ring-circuit continuity which ensures that all conductors (including earth-continuity conductors) are electrically continuous.

It is at this stage that it may well be asked, with some reason, if it is necessary to embark upon ground which is clearly a specialised matter and where a little knowledge is a dangerous thing. Surely the appointment of an experienced and qualified electrical engineer should relieve the surveyor of all worries and the surveyor need no more than take his advice. This may be so but there will be occasions where the surveyor will not know the electrical engineer who may perhaps be separately appointed. If an owner has great faith in a particular electrician who has done work for him before, the surveyor may merely be presented with a report that he has to evaluate. Without some knowledge of what is required by way of tests and investigations the surveyor will be in no position to determine if all the necessary steps have been taken or not. The surveyor should not hesitate to cross examine an experienced electrician on his report and if the questions are put in a manner which shows that the surveyor understands the principles involved the discussion should be mutually profitable.

Several types of testing apparatus are available to carry out the tests for polarity and continuity. As already stated, polarity tests are made to ensure that the correct connections have been formed at all junctions, switch, socket-outlet and lighting-point positions. They also ensure that all fuses and single-pole switches are connected in the live conductor and that there is no break in the conductors. Whatever apparatus is chosen for the polarity test the main switch must be turned off so that the circuit is dead at the time of testing.

The bell-and-battery set forms the simplest apparatus that can be used to carry out tests of polarity and continuity. A dry battery and bell are connected in series and the circuit is completed by two test leads so that when the test leads are joined together the bell rings. An electrical engineer will carry out a test of conductor continuity by connecting the bell set across the two leads connecting to the meter, closing all light switches and socket switches and then shorting out the live and neutral contacts at lighting points and socket outlets. The bell rings as each pair of contacts is shorted out. The engineer also determines correct polarity by using one long fixed lead and one short test lead. The fixed lead is connected to the red live lead which is normally connected to the load side of the meter and the bell set with the short test lead is taken to each lighting point and socket outlet position in turn. The test lead is connected to the live terminal and the bell will ring when the switch is closed and stop when the switch is opened. At unswitched socket outlet positions, the bell rings when the test lead is connected to the live terminal.

Polarity and continuity tests, including earth continuity resistance, can be made by using a hand driven generator type of testing instrument which can produce voltages up to 1,000, known as the "Megger" or a battery operated testing instrument which has a transistorised converter producing up to 500v. Perhaps the best known and most popular type of insulation and continuity tester is the "Megger" which is a trade name for a series of instruments manufactured by Evershed and Vignoles Ltd. Other comparable makes are available but the "Megger" has almost become the standard term for insulation testing. The 500v. model of both hand driven and battery type instruments is normally used for all tests on domestic wiring and these are provided with two scales; an ohms scale for continuity testing and a megohms scale for insulation testing. The battery operated type of testing instrument is increasingly used since it can be operated with one hand and is also more compact. It is often supplied with a rechargeable battery and in order to compensate for any drop in battery voltage during use, all models have an adjusting screw.

Tests to see that the earthing is effective are more numerous and complex than this short description implies. There are at least two main tests to be carried out on earthing systems known as tests of earth continuity conductors and earth loop impedance. Two other tests may also be required—tests of consumers' earth-electrode resistance and earth-leakage circuit-breakers.

Every earth-continuity conductor must be checked to ascertain that it is mechanically and electrically continuous and that its impedance is sufficiently low to enable a satisfactory earth-fault current to pass in order to operate the protective devices. There are three methods of carrying out a test for this purpose; by means of the A.C. test or secondly by means of the reduced A.C. test if this is preferred with the use of a hand testing machine when it is desired not to apply a test at the full current as is employed with the A.C. test. Alternatively a D.C. test may be employed.

Every installation whether old or new or partly new must be tested to ensure that the insulating resistance is high enough to prevent leakage or create danger. Two tests are made; on the first the resistance is measured between all poles or phases and earth, and in the second the resistance between poles or phases is measured. Tests of insulation resistance are carried out by applying a test voltage approximately twice the normal working voltage. The insulation tests between conductors and earth should be made with all switches closed, all fuse lengths in position and all poles or phases of the wiring electrically connected together. At all distribution fuse boards or switch-fuses the fuses should be in position and, if possible, the main switch from the supply side of the installation should then be connected together. The insulation tester is then connected between the linked phase and neutral leads, or contacts, and the consumer's earthing terminal. The insulation resistance to earth should not be less than one megohm. After a section of wiring has been tested and proved to be faulty it is always advisable before an attempt is made to remove or replace any of the wiring to test all switches, ceiling roses, lamp holders and connecting flexes because the fault may well be in these fittings, particularly if the insulating covering of the cable appears to be sound.

The Repair and Maintenance of Electric Wiring Installations

Once the various tests have been completed the surveyor can then assist to decide in the light of the results as to the extent of the repairs or the renewals required. Even if the tests are satisfactory, it must not be assumed that this is necessarily the end of the matter as there are other points that the electrical engineer may wish to bring to the surveyor's attention. Since a fault or accidental damage may cause live conductors to come into contact with the metal casing of apparatus or other accessible metal parts of an installation, it is often better to earth the metalwork or remove it completely. Electrical engineers, for example, always recommend that the old and rather attractive brass covers to light switches in Edwardian houses be removed and replaced with non-metallic switch covers. Again, even if the main circuit is in order, the client may well prefer a ring circuit which can be employed for wiring socket outlets employing fused plugs. The object is to provide sockets in all positions where portable apparatus is likely to be required, thus avoiding the use of long flexible cords, always a hazard when trailing across a room. Individual fixed appliances such as water heaters, inset fires and wash boilers may be connected to a ring circuit, provided suitable fusing arrangements are employed. It may be desirable therefore from sheer convenience to provide a separate ring circuit to a part of or the whole of a house. Again, the client may wish to add a bell-circuit or an open or closed circuit burglar alarm wiring system to the existing electrical installation. Another matter that the engineer may bring to the surveyor's attention is the question of fuses. The simplest type of fuse in general use is the rewirable type which consists of a base and carrier of incombustible material such as porcelain or moulded plastic and which encloses the fixed contacts to which the incoming and outgoing cables are connected. The link or carrier has two contacts, connected by means of screws or nuts to the fuse wire. The fuse wire is usually enclosed in the porcelain link or in an asbestos tube, to prevent damage being caused by the arc and the resulting hot gasses when the fuse wire melts. The disadvantage of rewirable fuses, other than their limited breaking capacity, is in the fact that a blown fuse wire is capable of being replaced by one of an incorrect size, which may often involve an increased hazard from fire. For this reason an electrical engineer may prefer to recommend the incorporation of a new fuse box designed to take cartridge fuses. These consist of a tube with two end caps to which the fuse element is attached, and a filler. The tube or body is normally made of porcelain and is of high strength and is resistant to intense local heating. The end caps of tinned brass or copper are attached rigidly to the body of the fuse so that they do not blow off when the fuse operates and elements are either of wire or strip metal, often with a section of low melting point at the centre. The cartridges are usually filled with quartz sand to absorb and extinguish the arc. The renewal of a cartridge fuse is simply a matter of removing the old one from the holder and replacing it with a new one of the same rating.

As an alternative to a distribution fuse board, small automatic circuit breakers are available which can be mounted on a distribution board in much the same way as fuses. These miniature circuit breakers are really switches designed to open automatically when the current passing through them exceeds the value for which they are set. The electrical engineer may also advise the installation of a consumer's control unit adjacent to the meter position. These units usually comprise a 60 amp. double-pole switch and a distribution board made up of two or three 30 amp. fuses or circuit-breakers and a number of 5 amp. fuses or circuit-breakers. A neutral bar is also included and the whole unit is enclosed in a metal or insulated case. A metal clad unit is normally used for conduit systems while an insulated case of incombustible material is used for sheathed wiring systems. A screw or bolt is normally provided on the side or bottom of the unit so that it can be connected to earth.

The Electricity Board customarily install their cutouts and meters on a wood or fibreboard backing which is screwed to the wall, porcelain spacers or wood battens being used to give approximately a 1-inch (25mm) clearance at the back. This wooden board is the property of the Electricity Board and normally no other equipment is allowed to be attached to it. The consumer's control unit is normally mounted on a separate board adjacent to the meter board. This not only prevents rusting at the back of the unit but allows sheathed wiring which is normally concealed under the plaster to emerge and be taken into the box in a neat manner. Conduit tubing is normally terminated in metal clad fuse boards with a smooth brass bush to prevent abrasion of the cables. Where sheathed cables enter metal clad units, a rubber grommet or brass bush with locknut is inserted for this purpose. The grommets should be tight fitting and any unused conduit entries should be blanked off in view of the requirement of the regulations that all fuse boards shall be totally enclosed to prevent the ingress of dirt or moisture or accidental touching of the live parts. One of the obvious deficiencies in many old houses is the condition of the wiring nearby, usually under the stairs, where a number of exposed cables enter out-of-date boxes. There is an obvious need for these to be removed even if the remainder of the wiring installation is sound. Switch fuses or splitter units may be employed on small domestic installations, to control extensions such as for example a circuit requiring separate metering for an off-peak heating installation.

If an existing wiring installation is sound but is of some age, it is extremely likely that the switches, together with the lighting points and power points, will require renewal. Wall switches will probably now be mounted at a modern recommended uniform height of 4 ft. 6 in. (1·37m) above floor level. In normal domestic supplies single-pole switches which make-and-break only one conductor of the supply may be used generally where the neutral conductor is connected to earth. Double-pole switches must, however, be used for fixed heating appliances where the heating elements can be touched. Switches for wall mounting may be of the tumbler or rocker type and may be surface, semi-recessed or of the flush pattern. They are available in single or multi-gang units. The projecting or operating part of the switch is known as the "dolly". Tumbler operated switches have a protruding dolly with a positive up and down movement whereas rocker type switches have a centre pivoted dolly which is, although easy to operate, much less likely to be damaged if accidentally knocked. These type of switches are coming more and more into use. It is a requirement that any switches controlling lights in a room containing a fixed bath or shower must be situated out of reach of any person using the bath or shower. Under such circumstances the switch may either be placed in a suitable position outside the door or it may be of the type operated by a cord. In damp conditions the switches should be of the damp and dust-proof type and cable entries must be provided with glands or bushings or be suitable to receive screwed conduit. In circumstances where inflammable vapour or gas is likely to be encountered the switches must be of the flame proof type. The reader is referred to Part 1 of Code of Practice C.P.1003 for recommendations on the installation and maintenance of flame proof electrical equipment.

A very popular method in present-day domestic wiring practice is for wall switches to be mounted flush. This entails the box of the switch being let into the wall so that the cover plate when fitted is flush with the face of the plastering. Either plate switches can be employed where the switch mechanism can be attached to the back of the surface plate or the gridswitch system can be employed where the switch mechanism either clips or is screwed into the grid which is in turn screwed into the recessed switch box. Boxes may be of cast iron, steel, plastic or hardwood. Metal boxes are essential under certain circumstances. It should be noted that switch boxes are available in a range of different sizes to suit the possible plaster depth to be found. Although a deep box must be used for a large diameter conduit and a shallower box for plaster covered P.V.C. it is irritating for the surveyor to observe on the inspection of an installation that a box $1\frac{1}{2}$ inches (38mm) deep has been employed so that the face projects beyond the plaster when in fact a $\frac{5}{8}$-inch (16mm) box could have been used instead. In older houses surface type switches mounted on wood blocks will often be found, the older type of surface switches being fitted to a circular wood block which is drilled for cable holes and fixing screws. Modern blocks are normally rectangular in shape and moulded and metal boxes are available which enable rectangular flush type switches to be surface mounted.

A ceiling rose is necessary to make a safe and efficient connection between the flexible wires of pendant lights and the circuit wiring of an installation. Very often the surveyor will find that flexible pendants are worn out and ceiling roses are inefficient while the remainder of the wiring circuit is satisfactory. Under such circumstances there is no alternative but for the roses and pendants to be renewed.

Most modern ceiling roses are of moulded plastic with an integral mounting block. The unsheathed cables can be enclosed within the fitting and there are no exposed metal parts. An earth terminal should be provided, in common with all lighting points. A number of types of ceiling rose are available but broadly two categories are provided; the two terminal type or the three terminal type. The latter type can be employed where the rose is installed directly on to the surface of the ceiling with a break ring to cover any irregular holes. Where ceiling roses do not have integral bases they must be mounted on blocks. Semi-recessed ceiling roses are constructed of porcelain or moulded plastic and are intended for mounting on a small conduit box and these are available in two or three terminal types.

It is present-day wiring practice to ensure that the lighting outlet is made in the ceiling adjacent to a joist so that a good fixing for the fitting can be obtained. Often, however, with old houses the ceiling point will hang equally between two joists in which case precautions should be taken to provide a bearer board, fixed between the joists in order to take the strain of the lighting fitting. Longer wood screws than usual should be employed so that the rose can be attached through the ceiling to the bearer board.

The connection between the pendant and the lamps of a light fitting is made with a lampholder. These are generally of the bayonet type and have retracting contacts of either the solid plunger or spring plunger type. They often require renewal as frequently as the flexible pendants in positions where lights are kept on for long periods at a time.

With regard to power and lighting points or socket outlets as they are more correctly termed, the sizes available are 2 amp., 5 amp., 13 amp. and 15 amp. They can be surface or flush mounted and switched or unswitched. The 13 amp. rectangular section three pin, non-reversible socket outlet with its accompanying 13 amp. fused plug top is the standard fitting now employed for new wiring in domestic premises. The other types of sockets supplied are now obsolete, but they will be found in widespread use and replacement parts are still available. All plugs and socket outlets should conform to the appropriate British Standard and two pin plugs are not recommended nowadays for any apparatus other than electric clocks and razors for which special socket outlets can be obtained. It will be no surprise to learn that the British Standard specifications for socket outlets and plugs go into the matter in considerable detail and a number of important safety features have to be incorporated so that it is not possible for the fingers to touch live metal when taking out or inserting a plug in a socket. Exposed metalwork in connections to socket outlets must be connected to the appropriate earth continuity conductors. Unfortunately there are still many installations not complying with such requirements in existence.

Flush type socket outlets are fitted into a box set into the wall or plaster in a similar manner to that already described in connection with flush switches. Both metal and insulated moulded boxes are available and steel or cast iron boxes to B.S.1363 should be used with metal conduit systems. Where metal conduit systems are employed, an earthing terminal must be fitted to the box and a bonding loop connected between it and the socket outlet earth terminal. Moulded surface type socket outlets are normally deeply recessed at the back and do not need a block if fitted to an incombustible surface. Where they are fitted to skirting boards or combustible material a back plate is desirable. Metal clad surface mounted socket outlets should be installed with surface metal conduit in positions where mechanical damage is likely. These are obtainable with brass or steel cover plates, the steel boxes normally being finished in aluminium stove enamel. All switched types are available with a pilot light if required and many have a choice of tumbler or rocker operated switches.

Wiring Systems

Should the wiring installation prove to be so out-of-date and defective under test that there is no alternative but to renew it, the surveyor must have regard to a number of circumstances when considering the replacement of the system. To enable him to reach a sensible decision a knowledge of the wiring systems in present-day use is desirable. Before proceeding to a discussion on the types of wiring available, however, it is first suggested that the surveyor gives some thought to the question of the installation as a whole before he starts to compile his specification. The reason for this is that it is all too easy for the surveyor merely to specify a wiring installation that, while admittedly forming an improvement as the material and equipment will be of modern pattern, nevertheless provides no new benefit from the point of design. It is suggested that thought at the outset can often provide considerable benefit to the owner/client or occupier from the point of view of the ease and convenience of the new system as against the old.

The nature of the new installation will very much depend on the number of units of accommodation provided in the dwelling house. If the house is merely in one single occupation consideration can at once proceed to the positioning of points for the convenience of the owner/occupier but in the case of a large house occupied as separate flats, the question of metering and access must be first decided. Electrical re-wiring in these circumstances should have in mind not only the user but also the aspect of maintenance, since access may not be easy and since the number of occupants will be high, more wear and tear on the new system must be expected. The question of resistance to fire must also be considered seriously and under such circumstances a durable system must be employed with socket outlets, switches and accessories preferably of metal to withstand wear and tear and to require the least possible maintenance. If the house is occupied as flats, the surveyor, in considering the number and position of switches and socket outlets, must have regard not only to how each flat is being used at the particular time he carries out his inspection but as to what is likely to be a sensible arrangement for the future as well.

So far as lighting points are concerned the purpose of each room and the use to which it is put must be considered when determining the position of points and switches as additional lighting is often required in kitchens or living rooms. The question of additional fixed points to ceilings is one that often causes some difficulty in the client's mind but the surveyor can always reassure himself that if all else fails a sufficient number of socket outlets will allow the client to

763

make use of table or floor lamps. Halls and stairways need at least one lighting point, normally controlled from two or more switch positions. In houses let in flats or in multiple occupation time switches may be employed and the more permanent and trouble free the switches, the better will be the wear and tear on tenant's and landlord's nerves. Dark staircases are often best permanently lit as the cost is relatively small while a central time switch is usually a better proposition than individual time switches on landings.

In rooms with two or more doors or in passages, halls, staircases and landings, and possibly bedrooms, the question of more than one switch point should receive full consideration.

There are basically two methods of arranging lighting circuits known as looping or jointing, and in either case it is usual to arrange a number of switches and lamps in parallel on the same circuit, the switch feeds being all connected to one main and the lamp feeds to the other main. The importance of connecting switches to the live, non-earthed or phase side of the mains must be underlined. This will ensure that switch feeds are the only permanently live parts of the installation and that all other parts of each circuit including lamp holders are "dead" when the switch is off.

With regard to power supply, the ring circuit is formed by wiring the "live" neutral and earth conductors of a power circuit in a complete ring. The two ends of the live conductor are brought back to the same fuse on the distribution board, and the two ends of the neutral and earth conductors are brought back to the appropriate terminal blocks. Only 13 amp. socket outlets conforming to B.S.1363 may be used on a ring circuit in conjunction with 7/·029 inch cable (7/1·78mm) and a 30 amp. fuse, or circuit breaker, at the main fuse board. In domestic premises a ring circuit may serve an unlimited number of points but must not serve an area of more than 1,000 sq. ft. (100m²). With premises of greater area than this, two or more ring circuits must be installed. Each ring circuit must be terminated at its own 30 amp. fuse, or circuit breaker, and the socket outlets and stationary appliances should be reasonbly distributed among the rings. The rating of the cable is normally about 20 amp. but the fuse must be of 30 amp. rating.

Socket outlets are installed to provide an easily accessible and convenient method of connecting portable electrical apparatus to the supply. The socket outlet is permanently connected to the circuit cables and should have entries which are so shaped that they allow only the correct type of plug to be inserted, the plug being connected to the portable apparatus by means of a flexible cord. The surveyor should note that in various rooms particularly living rooms and kitchens, more than one appliance will be in use at the same time.

This should be allowed for in the number and position of points and indeed this rule should be followed throughout each room. It is necessary to ensure that the householder avoids the use of long and inconvenient cords joined together from temporary connections formed often with much ingenuity from old and out-of-date fittings. Not only present but future needs should be envisaged by the surveyor so that there is no encouragement for the do-it-yourself enthusiast to plunge into ill-advised electrical work in order to extend the installation.

As a general rule it is not desirable to install socket outlets in living rooms where they are likely to be masked by furniture. Socket outlets in kitchens should be approximately 6 inches (152mm) above working surfaces for portable appliances and at hand height for major appliances. In bedrooms socket outlets should be provided each side of a single or double bed and at each side of or in between twin beds. Sockets for heaters, lamps and other appliances should be placed at the opposite corners of the room. Where fixed inset heaters are set up, switching from the bedside might be a convenience. No socket outlets may be installed in bathrooms except shaving points.

With regard to fixed appliances a separate circuit should be installed to supply a cooker, run from a separate way on a fuse board or switch fuse. The cable ends at a cooker control unit which comprises a double pole switch for the cooker circuit and a switched 13 amp. socket outlet intended for the connection of a kettle. For all radiant, convector and fan heaters, correct wiring and earthing is obviously necessary and special precautions are needed for heaters in bathrooms. A heating appliance having heating elements which can be touched should not be installed within reach of a person using a bath or shower. Any fixed heater must have a cord operated switch and portable heating apparatus should not be taken into bathrooms. Heaters recommended for use in bathrooms are wall mounted, cord operated "Infra-red" radiant types.

In considering the question of which wiring system to employ, the surveyor must bear in mind that these may first of all be divided into categories. There are those which are suitable for sunk work, that is to say for use under the plaster surface and those that are basically surface systems. Perhaps the best-known wiring system is the steel conduit system and this will be discussed first.

Steel Conduit Systems

In steel conduit systems, steel tubes are fixed to the internal structural members of the house and cables which may either be P.V.C (polyvinyl chloride) insulated or V.R.I (vulcanized rubber insulated) taped and braided are drawn through them afterwards and connected up. The chief advantages of this system are the degree of protection afforded to the wiring whether or not the conduit is buried in the plaster and the ease with which re-wiring can be carried out. On the other hand to install conduit in an existing building and to bury it in plaster involves a great deal of cutting away to form chases and making good. It is very obtrusive if left exposed.

Steel conduit is obtainable in two classes. Class A which is light gauge, is a plain conduit intended for grip type fittings and Class B, which is heavy gauge, is screwed conduit.

Conduit is supplied in standard lengths of about 12 to 14 feet (3·65 to 4·27m) and is manufactured to B.S.31. Class B screwed conduit is supplied with both ends of each length threaded. Class A conduits are joined together by a clamp type grip fittings and sockets. Class B conduits are screwed together by means of threaded sockets, tees, elbows, etc. In either case the whole system must be electrically continuous when it is completed so that a current applied to any part of the conduit will be conducted to earth.

Class A conduit is made up of light gauge steel strip which is formed into a tube and the seams are butted or close jointed, brazed or welded. Close joint conduit is cheaper than any other but suffers from the disadvantage that when bent a gaping seam is produced on the bend. Special bend fittings are therefore necessary at changes in direction. Brazed or welded tubes, however, can be bent satisfactorily.

Light guage conduit can also be obtained in an oval shape. The object of this is to provide a shallower depth so that the wiring can be hidden within the thickness of wall plaster. Sometimes where normal circular conduit is employed it is sometimes possible to trace the lines of the conduit through wall plaster. This is obviously undesirable. Oval conduit is available in close jointed and in brazed grades and is rather more expensive than circular tubes. Other types of conduit are also available, for example waterproof conduit can be set up, but only if screwed fittings and joints are specified to a waterproof grade. Most conduits are available either galvanized for external use, or sheradized for either external use or internal use in wet or damp situations. Conduit can also be obtained enamelled for internal use in dry situations. Some conduits can be obtained in a light silvery grey finish for internal use where surface systems are to be employed. They are supplied in this manner so that they can be easily painted if required or remain reasonably unobtrusive if left unpainted.

There is not doubt that heavy gauge screwed conduit is the

soundest system. It affords the best protection for the cables and the screwed joint is more secure both mechanically and electrically. The light gauge conduit system is less costly and is not so strong but nevertheless is normally considered to be a safe and efficient system. With both systems of conduit tubes the installation is set up before the wires are inserted and threaded through. The point for the surveyor to watch is that cables are not overcrowded in the conduit tubes. Excessive strain when drawing cables into the tube may fracture some of the strands with unfortunate results and the installation should always be designed so that sections of cable can be replaced without undue difficulty. It is customary with installations of conduit tubing for drawings to be prepared showing exactly where the runs of tubing are to be provided. A wide range of junction boxes and accessories is obtainable and there should not normally be any difficulty in making sure that the wiring can be inserted without strain and that junctions are trouble free so that repair and maintenance in the future is relatively easy. Saddle shape fittings and clips are employed to fix the sections of conduit tubing to the wall surfaces or the undersides of floor joists and multiple saddles are available for runs of conduit where several tubes are adjacent to each other.

When conduit runs across floor joists the joists must be recessed at every point of crossing. Excessive cutting of joists should obviously be avoided. Notches in the joists should never be made in the centre or too near the bearings. A notch not exceeding $\frac{1}{8}$th of the depth of the joist may be made not more than $\frac{1}{4}$ of the span away from the bearing or nearer the bearing than $\frac{1}{8}$ of the span, in joists not exceeding 10 inches (254mm) in depth.

When conduit is fixed to vertical wall surfaces crampets or pipe hooks are employed driven into the joints of the brickwork at intervals. The conduits should be covered by at least $\frac{1}{4}$ inch (6mm) of plaster. Nailing conduit is a bad practice and is to be deplored.

Other types of conduit can also be employed. Aluminium conduit may be manufactured from strip aluminium alloy formed into a tube and then welded along the seam or extruded. It is softer than steel and not so strong to resist accidental damage but it has a resistance to corrosion that could be important under certain conditions. It can easily be cut and screwed together and is light and easy to handle. Threading inserts between sections of aluminium conduit should always be of aluminium since precautions are necessary to prevent electrolytic action.

Non-Metallic Conduit Systems

While steel conduit provides the best form of protection against damage coupled with earth continuity when initially installed it presents difficulties in the long term from condensation, rusting and corrosion. It is also possible that the earth continuity can be impaired. Non-metallic conduits on the other hand are highly resistant to corrosion by water or acids, are unaffected by plaster or concrete, do not age or deteriorate, provide a good protection against combustion and have very good electrical properties. Most types of non-metallic conduit are of P.V.C. compounds and two separate types are available; rigid and flexible.

Rigid non-metallic conduit made of "unplasticised" P.V.C. is either available in a standard gauge or a light gauge. Flexible plastic conduit which comes in coiled lengths is used for sunk or concealed wiring where appearance does not matter. The chief advantage of flexible conduit is that it allows awkward bends to be dealt with and in the case of an early house with a complicated timber frame structure, its use could be a real asset. The conduit also readily adapts itself to irregularities in wall surfaces and is of sufficient strength to withstand stresses and strains of workman's boots and barrows while awaiting the covering of a floor screed. Oval conduit can also be obtained. Non-metallic conduit should not be used where temperatures fall below minus 15°C (5°F) or are likely to exceed 60°C degrees (140°F). An example of this at the upper end of the scale might be in close proximity to a central heating boiler.

All-Insulated Sheathed Wiring Systems

There are two types of cable available: the first is P.V.C. (polyvinyl chloride) insulated and sheathed cable; the second being T.R.S. which has vulcanised rubber insulated conductors surrounded with tough rubber sheathing. Various types of single core, two core and three core cable are available. Sheathed wiring cables are used for surface wiring systems and are designed to be buried in plaster or concrete. They will resist attack by most oils, solvents and acids, are not greatly affected by the action of direct sunlight and are not inflammable. P.V.C. sheathed cables are by far the most commonly used at the present time.

The big advantage of P.V.C. sheathed wiring is that it can be used and adapted so easily for so many types of purpose. It can be used for surface wiring in properties where repairs are carried out but where these are only partial or it can be hidden under wall plastering. The cables are normally fixed at intervals with special clips or saddles and tinned brass buckle clips are perhaps the most common. Non-corrosive clips and brass nails or screws should be used in damp situations. A P.V.C. moulded saddle fixing is also available. Where cables are installed in inaccessible positions and are unlikely to be disturbed, for example under floorboards or behind partitions no fixing is necessary for horizontal or vertical runs less than 15 feet (5m). Junction boxes are still a desirable fitting for use with P.V.C. cables. Moulded insulated accessories and fittings are available and should be used, and all switches and ceiling roses should be fitted with an earth terminal. Where a cable passes through walls or ceilings the holes made must be made good with an incombustible material to prevent the spread of fire. A short length of bushed conduit or sleeving should also be used to prevent sharp edges on the brickwork from chafing the sheathing. The tubing should also be filled at these points with an incombustible compound. Where cables are installed under floors they should be run in positions where they are not likely to be damaged by contact with the floor or the fixings. Where they traverse a wooden joist under floorboards the holes should be drilled so that the cable, when installed, is at least 2 inches (50mm) deep measured vertically from the top of the joist. The floorboards should preferebly be screwed over the wiring and a screwed section of board, to provide an access panel, should be placed over each junction box or other position where access is likely to be necessary at some future time.

Lead Sheathed System

This type of wiring is now practically obsolete. It will, however, be found in many older properties and may require maintenance or repair. The cables for this system are vulcanised rubber insulated, taped and sheathed with a lead alloy, usually lead with a small amount of tin or antimony. Three varieties are used containing one, two or three cores within the lead sheath and a twin cable is also available with a bare earth continuity conductor within the sheath.

Lead sheathed wiring was designed for surface work and by fixing with clips. Where cables are concealed beneath plaster there is always some risk of corrosion between the lead and the plaster itself. The big disadvantage, however, of re-wiring in lead sheathed cable is that the lead sheathing makes it awkward to unroll and slip cables through the structure as easily as, for example, with P.V.C. wiring. Great care has to be taken for the cable not to be handled too much as if it is too sharply bent or twisted the lead sheathing can easily be damaged. It is very often the pulling around of an old cable to

769

make some alteration, probably quite small, that can cause a subsequent fire.

Mineral-Insulated Copper Sheathed Wiring System

This wiring system consists of solid copper conductors insulated with a highly compressed covering of magnesium oxide powder and sheathed with a seamless malleable copper tube. The system is robust, non-inflammable, easy to bend and impervious to condensation, oil and water. The system should last indefinitely and the cables are comparatively small in diameter for the capacity required. The cables are fixed by copper clips and saddles and can be laid under floors or buried in concrete or plaster. They can even be buried in soil. An example of an excellent use for cable such as this is where the wiring is made semi-permanent but is sufficiently pliable to enable occasional movement for maintenance and inspection.

Prefrabricated Wiring Systems

Prefabricated wiring systems which are at present coming into use are mainly intended for new buildings and do not accordingly warrant a description in this book.

We will now pass to the consideration of certain other aspects relating to electrical wiring for specialised heating purposes which has become much more popular in recent years.

Off-Peak Systems for Central Heating

Electric central heating is normally carried out by three basic methods: the first is underfloor heating, the second is by means of storage radiators and the third is with the use of warm-air circulation. All three systems use the thermal storage principle, which has been evolved to make use of the Electricity Board's off-peak periods. A mass of energy retaining material is heated during this period and then emits stored heat throughout the day. This ingenious system allows off-peak electricity to be provided at half the normal peak rates.

Floor Warming Installations

Floor warming is often installed in new premises and can be installed in existing dwelling houses which are undergoing substantial repair and modernisation. The thermal storage properties of concrete enable this method to be successful and under it the concrete floor is heated by special cables embedded in the concrete screed just

770

below the floor surface, so that when a current is passed through them the heat is conducted into the surface which radiates into the room. The system lends itself to operation on the off-peak supply and is popular for that reason.

It is, of course, necessary that the ground floor of an existing dwelling house is virtually reconstructed to allow for these systems being set up in complete safety. It is unnecessary to say that the cables must be laid with extreme care as the consequence of inefficient workmanship can be well imagined. Cases are known of under floor heating systems going wrong almost at once and the whole floor having to be taken out with pneumatic drills shortly after the premises are occupied.

Under this system the hard core or aggregate is covered with a layer of concrete and allowed to harden. This provides a sub-floor. A damp-proof membrane and perimeter insulation is then applied to the ground floor slab. Cable spacers are then fixed to the sub-floor 6 inches (152mm) from, and parallel to the opposite walls over the area to be warmed and the cable is then run across the sub-floor from spacer to spacer, not being strained or pulled in any way, and extreme care taken to see that it is not damaged by being trodden on. A "megger" must ensure that the installation is satisfactory before the final screed is laid.

Floor warming circuits will usually be controlled by a separate main switch. A meter and time switch will be installed by the Electricity Board for off-peak circuits and each separate floor warming cable is usually controlled by its own thermostat.

Off-Peak Storage Radiators

Off-peak storage radiators consist of free standing metal cabinets which contain blocks heated by elements passing between them or embedded within the thickness. The blocks absorb heat overnight and allow it to be gradually emitted throughout the whole of a following day. Most heaters have a device to control the input and output according to the weather conditions and some heaters have fans to assist heat output with or without thermostats.

Storage radiators are not normally installed below windows but rather to one side or in between. The number, size and positioning of such heaters is most important and this of course determines the wiring circuit. The biggest disadvantage of storage radiators as a heating system is that they are bulky and the blocks inside the heater case are extremely heavy. Care therefore has to be taken in their positioning. A further serious disadvantage is that they are not capable of that fine control which is advantageous on sudden changes

771

in the weather. At such times they can be either overpoweringly too hot or entirely inadequate on a sudden drop in temperature.

Ducted Air Heating Systems

The Electricaire heating system, which is the name given to the Electricity Council's specification, is based on a centrally sited thermal storage heater with a high storage capacity and very good insulation to retain heat until it is required. The unit, as before, is charged during the Electricity Board's off-peak periods. A built-in fan which is manually or automatically controlled by room thermostats delivers the heat in the form of warm air. This is carried from the central unit through concealed ducts to outlet grilles in the walls or floors. This system can be installed in existing properties provided there is a sufficient cavity beneath the floorboards to conceal the ducting. The size of the Electricaire unit of a capacity normally required for most domestic properties can be accommodated in a cupboard approximately 2 ft. 6 in. square (762mm).

The metal ducts are normally rectangular in cross section but other types and shapes can be obtained. The components are normally fixed together by pushing one end of a duct into another and fixing with screws or clamps, then sealing round the joints with heat resisting tape. When the ducts have been laid in position and the components fitted the whole length of each duct is then wrapped with an insulating material to prevent heat loss. It is, of course, necessary that the heating unit itself is effectively lagged.

Electric Water Heaters

There are two main methods of providing domestic hot water by electrical means, the first being by self-contained thermostatically controlled storage heaters and the second is by means of immersion heaters or circulators, i.e. an immersion heater with a draught tube. Immersion heaters are the most widely used.

There are four versions of storage type heaters available which are as follows:

(1) The non-pressure (open outlet) type. This type of heater is used when only one point is to be supplied with hot water. A swinging spout can be used to supply two adjacent points as an alternative. The water control is on the cold water inlet and the hot water, displaced by cold water, emerges into the bath or basin. Small heaters of three gallon capacity and under can be connected direct to a cold water main but above this size supply from a cold water cistern is often insisted upon by the water authorities.

(2) Pressure type. Pressure heaters are generally used for supplying a number of taps. These are always fed directly from a separate cold water ball valve feed cistern and not from the mains supply. The heater is located so that the shortest run of pipe is to the sink, where most of the hot water is needed. A vent pipe must be provided, running to a position over the cold water storage cistern. To avoid heat loss, the runs of hot water pipes to taps should be kept as short as possible.

(3) Self contained cistern type. The cistern type of water heater saves the cost of piping from the cold water cistern serving the rest of the house as is required by other types. It must be fixed above the highest draw-off point and will feed any number of taps satisfactorily provided that the runs are as short as possible.

(4) The two in one heater. In the dual heater, advantage is taken of the fact that the full heating capacity is not continuously required. Two heating elements each with its own thermostat are fitted, one near the top to keep some water available for immediate use, while the other is at the bottom and switched on when larger quantities of hot water are required.

The reader is referred to the British Standard Code of Practice C.P.324:202 of 1951 "Domestic Electric Water Heating Installations", for information as to the design, storage temperatures and capacity and layout of such installations.

Combined Fuel Fired and Electric System

Under this system a pressure type heater can be employed in conjunction with an existing hot water supply system. The hot water passes through the heater on its way to the hot taps and the electric water heater takes over completely when the fire goes out. Changeover valves allow the electric heater to be by-passed when it is desired to use only the fuel fired system and it is essential that these are fitted otherwise the full benefit will not be obtained in the winter months.

Electrically heated water should not circulate through towel rails or radiators for obvious reasons of expense. These should be connected so that they only operate when the solid fuel boiler is in use.

Immersion Heaters with Solid Fuel Systems

There are times when a combination of a solid fuel fire with an electric immersion heater or circulator can provide a simple arrangement at reasonable cost for the conversion of existing installations.

773

The tank or cylinder into which the heater has to be inserted should be in good condition and must be efficiently lagged. It is necessary that the hot water pipes feeding the taps are all taken from the vent pipe or the top of the tank not from the flow pipe. The pipe to the kitchen sink from the hot tank should not be more than 20 feet (6m) if in steel or 35 feet (10·6m) if in copper. In soft water areas a copper cylinder and pipework should be employed and in hard water areas a galvanized steel cylinder or square or rectangular tank is more likely to be used and once the water is alkaline and the risk of electrolytic action minimal no particular restrictions need to be placed on the metal used for pipework. The advice of the water authority should be sought if doubt arises.

COLD WATER SUPPLY

Most dwelling houses are served with a single mains supply of cold water, which enters under the front boundary of the property where it is usually provided with an accessible stop valve on the owner's land. The water supply is then taken to the interior of the building where it rises to feed the cold water cistern which is situated at the top of the building either in the roof space if the roof is of pitched construction or alternatively on top of the main roof or back addition roof if this is of flat construction. In older urban terraced houses, one stop valve only will usually be found and this is normally situated under the floorboards of the hall just inside the front entrance door. The supply pipe in its vertical position inside the building is known as the rising main and since the water in it is under pressure the question of both repair and maintenance is important since the consequences of a leak will be severe. If the leak occurs inside the house, water will spray out under high pressure and even if the section of the supply pipe under the front garden of a house becomes defective the effect will be dramatic as pools of water will appear in no time at all requiring urgent attention.

It is understandable therefore that the by-laws of local water undertakings permit only one draw off to be taken from a rising main and this is usually to the kitchen or scullery sink. Branch pipes feeding sanitary fittings or fittings to supply hot water are taken from the cold water cistern.

Supply pipes are normally to be found in either lead, cast iron galvanised steel or copper. Lead supply pipes are commonly found to existing dwelling houses but copper is perhaps the material most favoured for present-day use and has been for the last twenty years or so. In the event of the failure of a supply pipe it is advisable for the reason for failure to be investigated while the fault is being repaired as obviously no delay can be tolerated. It is possible that a lead pipe may have burst due either to the fact that the lead itself has become old or brittle or perhaps due to a local defect such as a tree root growing in the front garden and disrupting the pipe. Pipes should be laid at a minimum depth of 2 ft. 6 in. (760mm) under front gardens or paved areas but often the depth of old pipes is much shallower and on some occasions supply pipes are taken round bends or projections. Strictly the supply pipe should be laid on a flat bed with a layer of fine sand but this refinement is usually lacking and after some years the pipe itself may follow a serpentine course and may well fail. If the pipe is likely to have a limited life due to a reason such as this it should be re-laid at an even and adequate depth and bends and angles should be avoided.

In the older basement properties of Victorian times one never ceases to be amazed at the way lead supply pipes enter under the threshold of the front door and then pass through the cellar area only being casually restrained at long intervals by pipe hooks. In between the hooks the old lead has sagged appreciably and very often joints in the lead of a hair raising simplicity show that new pieces have been inserted. It is obviously not worth retaining a length of supply pipe that is likely to prove defective and it is best if the whole pipe is replaced in copper subject of course to the surveyor being sure that any joints between different metals are properly formed.

Distributing pipes which are taken from the storage cistern to feed the various sanitary fittings together with water waste preventers and hot water supply units should always be provided with stop valves. The pipes should be run to simple falls and should not be formed in too complicated a manner as otherwise air locks and water hammer will occur. Distributing pipes under old timber floors should preferably be run alongside joists and fixed to them but if this is not possible and the joists have to be cut the pipes should run near the ends of the joists rather than at the centre point and the cut should be made in the top third of a joist where the consequences of cutting will be least likely to rob the joists of much of their strength, as already described in Chapter 5.

Distribution pipes are often found nowadays formed of polythene tube. This is a material that has both good and doubtful points. It is resistant to corrosion and is of light weight and is flexible. The surveyor, however, should make sure that the familiar kite mark appears on the pipe, either for British Standard 1972 where polythene tube complies with the requirements for cold water services or British Standard 1973 where the tube is for general purposes only. The tubes under the two standards vary in thickness and different methods of jointing are required. It should be noted however that polythene tube is not suitable for hot water supply pipes.

The question of maintenance of distributing and supply pipes is mainly a matter of periodic checks to ensure that the joints particularly at junctions with stop valves and the stop valves themselves are not leaking. This is a more necessary precaution than it sounds, since the consequences of drips from supply or distributing pipes and valve joints in concealed positions can be severe in an old house where there is much timber. Lead pipes encased in plaster should be regarded with suspicion and if a good deal of repair work and redecorations are in hand, it is best if these are removed as inevitably the reaction between the lead and the plaster will cause pin holes to appear with subsequent staining and dampness. The need for lagging exposed sections of service and distribution pipes in exposed positions, for example, under eaves, is an extremely important item of maintenance, and a material with appropriate protective qualities that does not attract vermin should be employed.

The surveyor will see very many different types of storage cisterns in old houses. These will vary from slate slabs which are bolted together, the slate sections having bevelled joints so that they are watertight, to lead cisterns either on their own or contained inside timber cases. All these old cisterns due to their weight and the risk of water contamination should be taken out and replaced with a modern cistern most probably of galvanised steel or polythene. If a steel cistern itself is found this should be drained down and examined for traces of rust marks and if there is any doubt about its suitability it should be renewed. The economics of this are sufficiently obvious to make it clear that it is not worth risking a defective cistern where repairs are being carried out to a house since failure might involve considerable water damage. The cost of replacement is probably less than £20 and this is not a large sum to pay for safety. Cisterns should be placed well above the highest fitting to be served, a minimum of 6 feet (1·8m) being desirable and the question of an overflow or warning pipe is important. This should be larger than the incoming main supply and never less than ¾ inch (19mm) in diameter. The overflow pipe must be fixed so that it projects over an exposed and conspicuous position where, if it starts to discharge, it can readily be seen. The end of the pipe should be protected by a light hinged metal flap. The cistern should be provided with an effective cover, and a stop valve is essential to the rising main and at the outlet of each down service so that the cistern can be replaced easily if required. The junction between the metal pipes and the cistern should be carefully formed.

776

So far as the capacity of cisterns is concerned the Metropolitan Water Board require a minimum actual capacity of 25 gallons (112·5 litres) for the tank to a small house or a flat where this is used for cold water only. If the tank is to serve both hot and cold water supply the minimum required capacity is 50 gallons (225 litres). These minimum figures are simply multiplied in the case of larger units so that for example in the case of a house containing four flats where the supply is required to serve both hot and cold water appliances a tank (or tanks) with a total actual capacity of 200 gallons (900 litres) is necessary.

If the repair work being carried out to a dwelling house entails the complete replacement of service and distribution pipes some thought should be given to their future position. It is best if these are arranged internally and are not fixed to external walls from the point of view of frost damage but if an exposed position is unavoidable the pipe should be held free of the brick wall surface by means of extended brackets to enable insulation to be carried behind. Water pipes should not if possible be placed near the eaves but should enter the roof space at some other point. Cisterns should be effectively insulated whether these are standing on the surfaces of main or back addition roofs or whether they are situated inside roof spaces. Finally the stop valve to the supply pipe itself should be well protected against frost at the point just before the supply pipe enters the building.

DOMESTIC HOT WATER SUPPLY

Hot water supply to dwelling houses can be produced by one or a combination of the following types of appliance:

(1) Back boilers
(2) Cooking Stoves
(3) Independent Hot water supply boilers
(4) Heating boilers
(5) Gas heaters
(6) Electric Heaters.

Back Boilers and Cooking Stoves

In most houses built between say 1880 and 1914 back boilers situated behind the grate of an open fire have provided the main source of hot water. Such back boilers are often found behind the fireplaces of kitchens to the back addition on the ground floor of the smaller type of terraced house while the flow and return pipes are carried up vertically, parallel to the side of the chimney breast, to feed a galvanised steel tank or cylinder installed in the cupboard of the bedroom above or in a cupboard on the landing adjacent. Such systems are now normally removed, mainly because the large section pipes are furred and also because the back boiler and tank are inefficient and the system is of limited use and is incapable of being developed to provide the quantity of hot water that is now required by a modern family. It is also a drawback that an open fire is needed before hot water can be obtained. Not everyone wishes to consider lighting a fire during the summer months.

On the other hand, however, the system is an economical one since, if a fire has to be provided in any event, hot water is obtained as a useful by-product. In some cases a system such as this has been retained with hot water for the summer months provided by an immersion heater fitted to the tank. Back boilers have been much improved in recent years and a high output back boiler has now been developed which is capable of supplying a few radiators in addition to the hot water draw off supply needed by the household. A further development is in the use of a high output back boiler in conjunction with a closed stove or room heater which supplies convected and radiant heat to the room in which it is situated together with hot water supply to an indirect cylinder together with radiators in one or two rooms. It should be noted that an indirect cylinder is necessary where a system serves radiators as well as providing a hot water supply for sinks, basins and bath.

When the surveyor encounters a back boiler hot water supply system in an old house, he may well decide, on having the sections dismantled and investigated, that it is beyond saving and must be taken out. This does not mean to say, however, that he must discard the idea of the system completely when advising his client. It may well be that, suitably modernised, with up-to-date equipment this type of system would provide an economical and easily maintained source for hot water and partial central heating that might suit his client's needs admirably. A modern back boiler is quite capable of heating a 30 gallon (135 litre) cylinder for hot water supply and the high output back boilers have on average a heating capacity of approximately 18,000 B.Thu.Us. per hour (6 kW). For heating the 30 gallon (135 litre) cylinder a minimum of 8,000 B.Th.Us. per hour (2·7 kW) should be allowed and this leaves 10,000 B.Th.Us. per hour (3·3 kW) available for heating one or two radiators and the connecting pipes.

Solid fuel stoves will also be found which act as combined cookers and water heaters. These are usually of the continuous burning type, effectively insulated to give stable heat conditions and economy of operation but these are not suitable for providing more than the hot water draw off supply.

Independent Hot Water Supply Boilers

Between the two World Wars the provision of independent solid fuel boilers became commonplace to small and large houses alike. It was normal to site the independent boiler in the kitchen, usually in a tiled alcove, where it formed a focal point and radiated heat to make the kitchen a light and cheerful place in the winter months and purgatory in the summer unless an immersion heater was also fitted to the tank or cylinder.

The attraction of independent hot water supply boilers is that, if of appropriate size and used in conjunction with a sufficiently large hot water storage cylinder, they can be made to meet the needs of any size and shape of dwelling house. Generally the boilers provided were of sturdy construction and have a long life unless there is some peculiarity such as, for example, in a soft water area where neglect to provide a boiler with the Bower Barffing process had led to premature corrosion.

So far as modern boilers are concerned, the present-day range available is extremely wide. In addition to hand fired solid fuel boilers automatic control boilers are available with either gravity feed, forced draught feed or feed by mechanical stoker.

Boilers are classified as either direct or indirect. A direct boiler contains and heats the same water that is drawn off at the taps through a direct cylinder while an indirect boiler heats the draw off water in an indirect cylinder by means of a primary closed circuit of pipes. The direct type of boiler has wide waterways and differs from an indirect boiler by the flanges found on the shoulders of each section and on the side of each section near the level of the grate. These are clearing lids to enable lime deposits to be removed.

Direct boilers are available in a range from 20,000 B.Th.Us. to 700,000 B.Th.Us. rating per hour (6·7 to 233 kW). If the surveyor finds on reading the report from his hot water engineer that the output of the existing boiler in a dwelling house falls woefully short of the heat likely to be required, having regard to the size of the house and the number of people living in it, he will have recourse to a wide range of pamphlets all of which give alluring details of the type and sizes of boilers available at the present time. As in the case of electricity, it is suggested that the surveyor tries to avoid the trap of merely falling into a replacement frame of mind without first considering the whole aspect of the matter including his client's needs and possibly prejudices as well. It is possible that the surveyor

779

might be instructed to remove a boiler working on the direct system which although operating adequately, nevertheless does not supply a particular client with the heat output that he requires. The surveyor might possibly be required to provide a heating system (by transatlantic clients in particular) which has an output which is well above what he himself might normally consider to be desirable. This is not of course to say that the final result is any less perfect for that. It is often here that the surveyor must have regard to his own prejudices as well as his client's.

If it should be decided to retain a direct hot water supply system and boiler, it is obviously necessary to have the system investigated. Often a low heat output is due to the fact that the pipes are badly furred and although the usual treatment of spirits of salts can effect some improvement, nevertheless, it is not worthwhile persevering with a system of pipes that are appreciably affected in this way as, even if the boiler is efficient, there will be much waste of heat. Even if the pipes are satisfactory, however, there are other points that should be checked by the heating engineer. He will note for example if the open vent pipe which rises from the top of the cylinder is carried horizontally for a little way above the cylinder. This horizontal run which should not be less than 18 inches (457mm) is designed to prevent heat loss, particularly where an immersion heater is provided to the cylinder as an alternative to the boiler. If the vent pipe is not extended in this way, one pipe circulation within it can occur whereby a circulation is set up so that a core of hot water rises up the centre of the pipe becomes cool and then returns down the outside. This is barely acceptable utilising solid fuel but is vastly wasteful of electricity with an immersion heater. In these circumstances a circulator should be fitted. The primary flowpipe from the boiler should leave the cylinder near the top to ensure that water at the highest temperature is available quickly at all the draw-off points even before the whole of the water in the cylinder may have been completely heated. There must be a safety valve on the primary flowpipe as near to the boiler as possible and a drain cock should be fitted to the primary return pipe near the boiler with an accessible loose key. It might be added that the drain cock is, of course, only necessary for emptying and draining down the system and must never be touched while the boiler is in operation. If a secondary circulation is provided in connection with a direct system of hot water supply, which is often done in order to provide a heated towel rail, for example, and to enable taps to be heated more efficiently since the branches to each tap from the secondary flowpipe are very short, the return of the secondary circulation must enter the storage cylinder at a high point. If this is not done, cold water from the feed connection passing up the secondary return to the draw off taps is possible.

The direct system of providing hot water supply has the advantage that rapid heating up of the boiler is possible for sudden and unexpected demands upon it, but on the other hand there are a number of disadvantages. The first is the likely deposit of scale in the boiler and in the cylinder and primary and secondary circulations which is greater with this system than with the indirect system. Perhaps however the greatest disadvantage is that heating circuits should not be taken from a direct system and accordingly with the current vogue for installing central heating the direct is becoming relatively obsolete. The reader is referred to the British Standard Code of Practice C.P.403:101 of 1952 "small boiler systems using solid fuel" for further information including a range of tests for systems.

Heating Boilers

A heating type of boiler for use with an indirect hot water supply system normally has a primary circulation passing through an inner cylinder with a separate feed system to allow the water to circulate. However, primary circulation and inner cylinder are arranged merely so that the water in the outer cylinder is heated and the actual heated water from the boiler is not therefore drawn off. This of course has the advantage that the boiler should not require descaling which means that its life is likely to be prolonged. The biggest advantage of the system is undoubtedly that heating and hot water supply can be supplied from the same boiler. On the other hand the boiler is not responsive to an urgent demand as it is in the direct system, but this is usually found to be a small matter compared with the enormous benefits obtained.

The capacity of boilers is based upon the British Thermal Unit (watts or kilowatts) and heat loss calculations are based upon transmittance factors (U values in either British or metric units). Hot water boilers used to be rated for heating as having a capacity for warming so many square feet of heating surface but this method is now obsolete. Boilers for heating are now rated at about 4,500 B.Th.Us. per hour per square foot (roughtly equivalent to 1½ kW for every tenth of a square metre) of boiler heating surface, the heating surface of a boiler being that part of the interior which contains water and which is exposed to the furnace flames and the flue gases. The cast iron sectional boiler has been widely used in recent years and has many desirable qualities. The boiler can be transported in sections and built up in the boiler house but the biggest advantage from the point of view of repair is that a fractured section can easily be replaced by a new piece instead of a complete new boiler having to be provided. Many boilers of this type can also be enlarged by new sections being added. Sectional boilers are also manufactured from mild steel so that they are able to withstand greater pressure while retaining the same advantages with regard to ease of handling. Most small domestic boilers nowadays however are of the "package" type. These are of welded construction being oil or gas fired, of the three or four fire tube type, and are mounted on steel chassis and are complete with burners, forced draught fan, control panel and all necessary equipment so that they are ready for use once they are delivered to the site.

Gas and Electric Heaters

Gas heaters can be specified as instantaneous or storage heaters. Instantaneous heaters are those ranging from single point outlets for a basin bath or sink, up to multipoint heaters supplying several fittings. The difference between the two types is mainly that the rate of flow from instantaneous heaters is slower than from storage heaters as the water has to be warmed as it passes through the fitting. In the storage type the water is already hot inside the fitting and stored until required. Although such fittings, particularly the instantaneous type, are in wide use due to the fact that they are relatively inexpensive to install, they require to be adequately maintained in order to provide a sufficient amount of hot water even for comparatively limited purposes. On the other hand they are under continuous development and improved models regularly appear.

Electric heaters are also either of the instantaneous or storage type and the qualities of these heaters have already been fully dealt with under the heading of Electric water heaters.

The Need for Hot Water

It has always been difficult to ascertain the likely demand for hot water in any building. Any estimate arrived at can only be approximate and any system suggested must be related to the needs of the house as a whole. Thus where a demand is likely to be heavy over a short period only, and at infrequent intervals, such as where a family are out all day and only arrive home in the evening, the surveyor in consultation with the heating engineer will arrange for a large storage capacity and a lower boiler power.

In spite of all the uncertainties one or two facts are generally accepted as guides to assessing hot water needs. 140°F (65°C) should be the essential temperature at kitchen sinks although lower temperatures will often be found. In the Guide to Current Practice issued by the Institute of Heating and Ventilating Engineers the maximum daily demand for hot water in respect of a dwelling house is estimated at 30 gallons (135 litres). It is normal to provide a 35 gallon (157 litres) capacity cylinder as standard for a three bedroom dwelling house of about 1,000 sq. ft. (92m²) of floor area and the following is given as a guide for the probable demand for hot water at a temperature of 140°F (65°C).

Baths (2 per hour) 40 gallons (180 litres)
Lavatory basins   5 gallons (22½ litres)
Sinks   10 gallons (45 litres)
Showers   20 gallons (90 litres)

The heating capacity of a boiler and the storage capacity of a cylinder is normally based on the maximum volume of water which may be required in one hour. In the case of a small house with bath, sink and lavatory basin the estimate for capacity would be 55 gallons (247½ litres). A storage cylinder with a capacity of 35 gallons (157 litres) and a boiler with a heating capacity of 20 gallons (90 litres) per hour would accordingly provide a draw-off limit of 55 gallons (247½ litres) in one hour. The boiler manufacturers' catalogues normally give the rating of hot water supply boilers, both in gallons per hour and B.Th.Us. per hour (litres per hour and kilowatts).

In all but the most simple cases the heating engineer will, once the principles of the system are decided, proceed with the layout drawings and decide boiler and cylinder sizes, pipe dimensions and other matters. The surveyor should approve the drawings, however, since layouts that often appear ideal on paper are by no means so when translated into practice in an old house with walls that are by no means square and with many changes of level. Nothing is more unsettling to the client's eye than to see a length of heating pipe projecting from a plaster soffit or appearing from floorboards before vanishing into another room.

Central Heating by Hot Water

In all the changes in the development of the British house none has perhaps been so widespread and so sudden as the introduction of central heating systems using hot water. Central heating systems with boilers and radiators came into fairly widespread use between the two World Wars but more recently and particularly in the last decade, heating by a gravity system for even the smallest property has been replaced by the electrically pumped systems that are now commonplace and which use smaller bore pipes. In addition to this, the types of heating units themselves have changed radically. Cast iron sectional radiators employed where the static head does not exceed 100 feet (30·5m) are not seen so frequently now as steel radiators are available and special types of steel panel radiators have been developed in recent years for the domestic market for use in conjunction with small bore heating systems. These are being installed in enormous quantities all over the country.

Another type of heater is the skirting heater which consists of a continuous strip 6 to 9 inches (152 to 229 mm) in height provided at skirting level. These comprise a finned element in a metal case and are either designed as radiant panels or are designed to be part radiant and part convection. Convector heaters are available consisting of finned heating elements placed at low level within a case so that a current of air passing through the element is warmed and heats the room by convection. Fan convectors make use of the same principles and these are similar to normal convectors apart from the fact that one or possibly two electrically driven fans are suspended under the element and a high controlled outlet of air is passed through the heater and becomes warmed on the way. Unit heaters consisting of a battery of grilled pipes through which hot water is circulated used in conjunction with an electric fan are obtainable but these are not so common in domestic use. The convector radiator, however, is intended for domestic use, and this consists of a louvred case hiding tubes through which the hot water flows, the louvres in the case assisting convection.

When a surveyor nowadays finds a gravity fed large bore heating system that is less than perfect this will probably not be required to be retained by the client. Even if it is in perfect condition, highly unlikely in the circumstances, the chances are that the client may wish to replace it due to the enormous benefits that can now be obtained from small bore pump driven systems which promise not only maximum efficiency but enable the old bulkier sectional cast iron radiators and large pipes to be removed. Should the client wish to retain the existing system, however, it is as well for this to be tested.

Tests of central heating systems are fairly elaborate affairs. While it is possible to gain a good deal of information from inspection of boilers, cylinders and various parts of the installation and while it is also possible to learn a good deal from the measurement of radiators and pipe surfaces so as to gain some idea of the heat output, nevertheless the only way to assess the value of a heating installation is to put it into operation and observe it actually working over a set period of time. It is often not easy to arrange for this to be done.If a vacant house, for example, is being repaired in the height of summer and no fuel is on the premises there will be a marked reluctance to take the steps necessary for a full test. If the house is being repaired in the depth of winter, however, the surveyor's suggestion of a full test will probably be considered in a different light and instead of being thought to be unnecessary will probably be accepted as a positively sensible suggestion.

In considering the question of a new central heating system, however, there are one or two points to be thought of, the first one being the question of fuel. Much discussion has been centred in recent years around the question of the various types of fuel and so far as the economics and long-term prospects of any particular fuel are concerned the surveyor and his client might just as well read the daily and Sunday papers, the latter in particular, than technical books on the subject. One aspect of the matter, however, is a more technical one, and this concerns the question of storage. The solid fuels such as coal, anthracite or coke obviously take up storage space but solid fuel at least has the advantage that it can be ordered in deliveries ranging from tons to single bags. Oil storage on the other hand needs the provision of a tank of sufficient size to achieve the aim of this type of fuel which is to provide a reserve against a period when supplies may run short. One month's supply is generally considered to be normal. Oil tanks should comply with B.S.799 and must be provided with a surrounding catchpit of 10 per cent greater volume than the tank itself. The obvious reason for this is to contain the oil should a leak develop in the tank. The tank must be installed with some care so that it is supported on brick piers and arranged to a fall to enable it to drain to one end. An oil level indicator is obviously necessary. Unless storage for oil fired heating is arranged with care it defeats the whole purpose of the exercise and if space is restricted or access is unduly difficult another type of fuel burning boiler must be considered.

When the heating engineer calculates the amount of heating surface that will be required in a new installation by means of radiators or the length of piping of a given diameter he uses a table of the coefficients of heat emission. The heat emission from water in radiators to the air surrounding them varies according to the difference between the temperature of the water and the temperature of the air itself. The tables of coefficients are normally based upon tests and the simpler tables assume a temperature difference of 100°F (38°C). In addition to this, however, the heating engineer must take other factors into account. Heat is continually lost through the structure of a building and additional heat must be provided to allow for such losses according to the type of structure under consideration. Heat loss coefficients are again employed and tables are consulted which give the coefficients against most types of material. Under certain conditions where the building is exposed, allowances from 10 to 15 per cent are added, and where a building is only used very intermittently, a total of up to 30 per cent can be added to the heat requirements to allow for this. Otherwise heat requirement calculations are normally based upon a temperature of 65°F (18°C) in a room when empty where the temperature outside is 32°F (0°C) while allowing for 1½ air changes per hour. Bedrooms, however, can be allowed a somewhat lower temperature of 55 degrees F (13°C) or living rooms can be accorded a slightly higher figure of 70°F (21°C). Halls and staircases can be put at 60°F (15½°C).

In considering the question of the layout of pipes and radiators the plan of the building and the position in which the radiators can be most usefully and conveniently fitted will determine the type of system selected. In the single pipe system a primary flow and return pipe forms a continuous circuit from the boiler and radiators are connected directly to this ring main. If the property is a large one, however, this layout may be undesirable since the radiators near the end of the circuit may receive water that is much cooler than those that are fixed near the commencement of the flow pipe. The two pipe system offers a better answer since the flow and return pipes are not provided in a form of ring main but are kept distinct, branch connections being taken from the flow pipe to radiators, and the return connections from radiators being carried to the main return pipe direct. The cool water is therefore conducted directly back to the boiler by means of a separate route.

Where there is a basement to a building this normally provides a logical position for the boiler. Where a property does not have a basement the boiler is often placed in a small chamber specially built for it externally and although the position of the boiler does not matter where a pumped circulation is introduced, there is the problem with gravity systems that the ground floor radiators will be on the same level as the boiler itself. Accordingly a drop system of heating is normally adopted under such circumstances which can be arranged by taking the main flow pipe direct to the roof space venting this from the highest point and then forming branches with dropping pipes either on a single pipe or two pipe system to feed the radiators. The return pipes are then collected at ground floor level and connected to the boiler. Gravity systems are now obsolete as far as new installations are concerned.

The small bore system of heating has been widely adopted everywhere in recent years. The main reason that enabled this to be done was the introduction of small electric pumps which are capable of a high and efficient performance with quiet running and little maintenance. Copper is now chosen as almost the universal material for pipes and generally sub-circuits can be run in tube with as little a diameter as $\frac{1}{2}$ inch (13mm). Where the one pipe system or radiator layout is employed the pipes are normally fitted to the skirting boards and other than drilling through walls and ceilings there is very little disturbance. The two pipe system on the other hand is normally installed under the floor and if this is of timber the joists are notched to take the pipes. If a floor is of concrete this must be designed and set out so that ducts of adequate shape and depth are provided to enable the pipes to be insulated and buried. There is nothing worse than a small shallow wavering groove in a concrete floor designed to take copper heating pipes as, unless the duct is adequately formed, later expansion and contraction of the pipes will break through and cause a disturbance in the screed.

Boiler units for small bore heating systems are available which incorporate the pump within the boiler casing, the pump itself being matched to the boiler rating. With the small bore heating system thermostats can be employed fitted to the boiler, although this is normally worked at a constant temperature, and thermostats can also be employed to stop and start the pump or alternatively thermostatic valves can be fitted to each individual radiator. An indoor or outdoor sensing element can operate a mixing valve fixed in the heating flow pipe adjacent to the boiler. The mixing valve incorporates a by-pass which allows the cooler water from the return main to be blended with hot water, leaving the boiler in the flow main feeding the radiators. In this manner the temperature of water flowing through the radiators may be reduced in mild weather without altering the boiler temperature.

Air for combustion must be allowed to reach the boiler otherwise it will not operate correctly. A grille and a trunk under the floor adjacent to a boiler in a kitchen can be provided or alternatively sufficient air inlets should be incorporated in the walls. The area of opening should be about twice the cross sectional area of the flue outlet on the boiler. With an external boiler house louvres can be fitted to the access door at the top and bottom. While regulations have tended to increase the requirements for combustion air in recent years leading to draughty conditions in boiler compartments the development of balanced flues have eliminated this requirement for smaller boilers. Both the flue and the aperture for combustion air are reduced to a small louvred box fitted to an opening in an external wall adjacent to the boiler, the appropriate channels being connected thereto.

In considering the question of the provision of a new central heating system either as a replacement for an older system or as an improvement to a dwelling house, the surveyor should finally consider the likely consequence of a vastly increased heat output. Woodwork will contract, particularly to framing and panels, and doors, if not sturdy and of the required standard, will warp. It is worthwhile taking some pains to ensure that joinery is sufficiently well formed and of an appropriate quality to withstand contraction and that mouldings are formed so that such expansion is allowed for and can occur without forming unsightly cracks in new paintwork. This is not always possible particularly where modern design calls for flush surfaces but this factor should nevertheless be borne in mind so that the consequences of such contraction will not be too unsightly to a newly decorated interior. In an existing house which is otherwise being left unaltered the occupier needs advising to keep temperatures relatively low for the first season and if care in this respect is taken much of the damage can be averted.

Maintenance

Periodic maintenance to hot water and central heating systems is an obvious necessity and this will usually be carried out by a specialist firm. During the first months after the installation of a system a close watch must be kept on pipe joints to radiators and fittings so that any leaks can receive attention and if the system is well fitted and installed teething troubles of this sort should very soon cease. There is one particular aspect of maintenance, however, that is most important. Should the house be vacated in the winter months it is vital for not only the cold water tank but also the whole of the central heating system to be completely drained. Severe damage can be caused on the bursting of radiators and pipe joints. On the other hand, it is often better to leave the central heating on at a lower temperature if a property is to be vacated for a short period only.

Chapter 10
Drainage

Contents

791

A. INTRODUCTION

STRANGE though it may seem, a visitor to the museum of Roman
excavations at Verulamium can see in the glass showcases accurately
formed tapering earthenware drainage pipes, yet sanitation as a
science and the whole system of water-borne sewage and drainage
as we know it today sprang into being, virtually overnight, no more
than a hundred or so years ago. That this is so was due not only to
the fact that medical knowledge had found a firm link between
excretia and disease but due equally to the ability of mass manufacturers to produce cheap impervious drainage pipes. The microbiol-
ogists found the necessity and provided the urgency for waterborne
drainage and the large manufacturing firms enabled the solution
to be introduced but it was the late Victorian engineers and
surveyors who worked the transformation. For a transformation it
certainly was. The vast programme of providing sewage disposal
and house drainage to newly established principles in urban areas
occurred simultaneously with the legislation that controlled and
provided checks on new building work and on every type of existing
manufacturing place, shop and residence. It was a unique programme
pushed by reformers in every field with a co-ordination and speed
for which it is difficult to find a parallel even at such a time renowned for great invention and an exuberance of ideas. Early books
of the period have lists of advertisements and patents, some of which
have lapsed and some of which have survived unchallenged. In the
edition of W. H. Spinks and E. H. Blake, published in 1903, we have
not only Hassall's and Stanford's drainage pipe joints, but Leem-
ing's, Turley's, Wakefield's and Green's as well. Sutton's single and
double seal patent flush jointed pipes occupy a full page advertisement. One wonders vaguely what has happened to Jennings' impermeable capped stopper, the "reversible commode" or Gordon's
Patent Disconnecting Syphon and one is impressed by the amount
of ingenuity. The other remarkable feature of drainage in Victorian
times is the permanence of the work. Well before the First World
War commenced the principles of house drainage were established
for the next sixty years almost completely without modification.
The excellence of the drainage systems provided in these years is
too often now taken for granted and the absence of diseases which
can be attributed to lack of sanitation never thought of as anything
particularly remarkable. It is as well, sometimes, to recall the
terrible diseases which occurred in the past and which still occur,

due almost solely to defective sanitation, in many areas of the world.

In the middle of the 14th century the main and perhaps most well remembered horror occurred: the plague called the Black Death. Starting in the East it reached Sicily in 1347 and swept through Italy, France and Germany and the remainder of the continent to reach England in 1348 when two ships arriving in Melcombe, Dorset, from Gascony, brought the seeds of the disease. It then proceeded to rage through the West Country and the South before ravaging London, and then swept through the Midlands, the North, Wales, Ireland and Scotland. The Black Death in its original form was Bubonic plague which was endemic in Western Arabia, Northern India and the Gobi desert. The bacillus found its home in the stomach of a flea which lodged in the hair of the vagabond black rat which, introduced by ship travel, eventually arrived in Britain. It should be mentioned, however, that plague is by no means extinct. In the first 30 years of this century it killed millions of people in Asia and from the East has spread and is still spreading in parts of the globe.

Plague is a disease of the circulatory and respiratory systems resulting from an invasion of the body by a minute organism, the "Bacillus pestis". The disease exists in two forms:—Bubonic plague and Pneumonic plague. These differ both in their mode of infection and by their symptoms. In Bubonic plague the blood is infected but in pneumonic plague the lungs are infected with the bacilli and the ensuing symptoms closely resemble that of pneumonia. In either form the results are usually fatal in a vast number of cases. This dreadful disease is one that belongs essentially to rats and the peculiar species of fleas infesting them. The rat fleas feed on the blood of an infected rat and then pass on to another rat. Their bite forces infected blood into the system of the new host. Although overcrowding in the cities has always been intense so that in the 14th century the poor in London often slept a dozen to a floor, beds being an unheard of luxury, dirt and inadequate sanitation were not the main reasons for the plague although bodies weakened by dysentery were more vulnerable to it. Warmth and dirt provided the best environment for the rat. The black mediaeval ship-borne rat became quite at home in the timber mediaeval houses and this was the source and bearer of the plague. The symptoms, given in accounts of the time were grim. When the familiar bluish black spots appeared on the thighs or elsewhere, the sufferer was expected to die within five days. The alternative symptoms, sudden coughing of blood, meant that death would follow in two or three days. "Ring a ring o'roses" sang (and still sing) the children, "a pocket full of posies, a'tishoo a'tishoo we all fall down". Posies, however, although kept on the bench of the Old Bailey for years, were incapable of warding off the Pneumonic plague from children and judges alike and the sudden sneezing of blood and subsequent "falling down" of the victim were, to the mediaeval mind, quite incomprehensible.

Rats crouching in the early latrines and rubbish of the crowded houses saw to it that Bubonic plague was never entirely kept at bay but could break out again at a moment's notice. It is little wonder that mediaeval writers saw the plague as an evil black cloud hanging over the doomed area. Even in the time of Nelson a high walled compound was built at the entrance of the harbour of the Port Mahon in Minorca to prevent disease from spreading from infected sailors to the town through the air.

The eventual decline of Bubonic plague in England was achieved by two main factors. First, the improvement of building and the removal of the surrounding filth. As brick replaced timber the rat was kept more out of the structure of houses and guards and nets over sewer and latrine pipes assisted to this end. The second factor, however, and the more important one was that the brown rat that we know today achieved a physical superiority over the black rat and all but exterminated it. Black rats are now rare and are confined to sea ports and certain areas where the sanitary conditions are below normal.

With the passing of the Black Death the next most fatal disease, cholera, stayed for several hundred years and finally required the united efforts of the population to bring it under control. The germ in this case is the spirillum known as the comma bacillus of Koch. It is not directly contagious but is conveyed by faeces and contaminated water. It arrived like the plague, by the trade routes, from India and in the insanitary overcrowded cities it spread rapidly, accompanied by vomiting, cramps and collapse. In 1831 no less than 50,000 people died in London, due to pollution in the Thames, one of the main sources of the city's drinking water.

Another type of disease, typhoid and paratyphoid, the bacillus typhesus, has always been liable to recur. There were some cases among holiday makers headlined in the newspaper while this Chapter was being written. The disease spreads from contaminated water and contaminated soil from defective drains or cesspools. It arrives in the form of a fever with accompanying rash and diarrhoea and is particularly difficult to eradicate as persons who may be typhoid carriers have to be traced and found.

The need for the disposal of faeces in the Middle Ages was not, of course, understood, due to the absence of medical knowledge. Underground pipes for the disposal of waste and storm water were known and used, but faeces were then regarded as rubbish is looked upon today, as something of a nuisance, to be removed only when convenient, and sometimes to be pushed on to a neighbour's premises if the possiblity of being found out was not very great. From Norman times the sight of brown stains and heaps at the base of white castle walls was seen as commonplace and without alarm. A blockage in a castle chute was viewed with irritation rather than concern. As clothes were kept in a "garderobe" in the 14th century it was found to be convenient to incorporate a latrine in the same place and thus the word "cloakroom" came into the language later on. Closets were accordingly not planned and the building was not set out as it is today with emphasis on the sanitary requirements as one of the main elements. Elsewhere public latrines or "gongs" were often built over streams as this seemed a convenient way of disposing of sewage and in the case of town houses the easiest course to pursue was that commonly adopted. A complaint in the early 14th century against persons with overhanging latrines in a lane called Ebbegate said gloomily "quarum putredo cadit super capita hominum transeuntium" which evidently added a new peril to the other risks of the road. "Guardez loo" called the citizens of Edinburgh as they slung the contents of the chamber pots from their high multi-storied buildings on to the crowded street below. It was considered quite legitimate for citizens everywhere to dispose of sewage by piping it into a common drain in the centre of the street and if not legitimate at least a minor offence for citizens to allow rubbish and filth to pile up in heaps. At the London assize of nuisances in 1347 it was found that two men had been piping their ordure into the cellar of a neighbour. This was only detected when the cellar began to overflow. This illustrates the common feeling that the only offensive thing about sewage was its smell. It was otherwise just a nuisance. "A wyse builder" it was said "wyll set a sege (seat) house out of the way from syght and smellynge."[1] The make-up of sewage is now, however, known to be a complex one with a high percentage of nitrogen and ammonia heavily charged with dead organic matter. It changes its nature to being harmful due to putrefaction or fermentation, the organic matter being attacked by bacteria.

In 14th-century England those fortunate enough to possess a private latrine would also have their own cesspool. In theory these had to be placed $2\frac{1}{2}$ feet from a neighbour's land if stone lined or $3\frac{1}{2}$ feet if not. There was, however, much bad construction, seepage and contamination. Thus the unfortunate Richard the Raker vanished through the rotten planks of a latrine and perished unspeakably. In parts of England and London in particular, conditions

[1] Horman.

were abominable. An inquest into the state of the Fleet prison ditch in 1355 revealed that though it should have been 10-feet wide and deep enough for a boat laden with a tun of wine it was choked by the filth from eleven latrines and three sewers. So deep was the sludge that no water could flow around the prison moat. In 1282 thirteen workmen were employed for five days cleaning the "Cloacam" at Newgate.

In addition to sewage, the disposal of offal and refuse was a problem. Blood from butchers' killings in Stratford and Knightsbridge ran down the streets and bowels and entrails of the slaughtered animals were cast into the Thames. The stench was unspeakable. Not only slops but garbage and soiled rushes were emptied into the streets from upper storeys. The gutters in the centre of narrow streets and at each side of wider streets were often blocked as were the few open sewers which ran down to the river. Scavengers to remove filth were at last appointed in cities and a city raker for each ward in London and a penalty of two shillings was imposed for defiling a street, a householder being deemed responsible for the mess outside his house unless he could prove his innocence. These measures helped but large banks of refuse on the banks of the Thames were a perpetual problem.

Although the edicts of the Wardmotes in London and the provision for scavengers in the towns curbed the worst excesses of piled up rubbish, effective drainage of sewage remained practically non-existent for several hundred years. We have seen in Chapter 2 how plague and sickness resulted in panic measures to try to stop the rate of building in London.

The Georgian age saw the introduction of a better system of rubbish disposal since the trim terraces leant themselves to better organisation than the jumbled half timbered and brick houses of earlier years. A beginning was also made on a rudimentary drainage system in urban areas. A "bog-house" was provided to each dwelling either at the end of the garden or attached to the back of the house. A brick lined circular pit was constructed under this and connected to a cesspool in the garden. Later a brick drain was laid under the house and carried to a Public Sewer under the road. Rainwater was simply dealt with by being carried from the roof in lead pipes connected to branch drains which were taken to join the main drain. The traditional method of removal of sewage, however, in all areas, particularly in country districts was by the dry or conservancy system. This involved the use of privies or earth closets of which there were a number of different types. The most notorious were the midden privies which consisted of a fairly large pit sunk in the ground under the seat either lined with stone or brick or, most often, not lined at all. By-laws passed to limit the sizes of such privies and insist on their being watertight ameliorated to some extent a thoroughly insanitary invention which should by now be extinct. The situation was marginally better when the privy was combined with an ashpit in which the ashes were mixed with the excrement thus acting as a deodorant. Often, however, rubbish and vegetable matter was mixed with the ashes resulting in an insanitary mess. The pail closet was an improvement to the privy in that a removeable metal container was substituted for the pit but the difficulty was, of course, in the removal of the pails. Ultimately local authorities formed special vans in the Midland towns and elsewhere to remove the pails for treatment and subsequent sale as earth manure. The Earth closet was rather more satisfactory than the privy. The construction was basically similar, but the application of dry earth on the excrement was carried out mechanically, the act of sitting on the seat operating a rather primitive mechanism releasing a certain quantity of earth. Other types had levers or handles which could be operated to the same effect. With the use of dry and loamy earth and a fixed or moveable receptacle the earth closet was universally used for many years.

The traditional methods of dry conservancy served for many generations in agricultural areas and with close supervision under enlightened local authorities in the growing cities. However, the growth of the larger urban complex and in particular the rapid growth of the industrial town where no control in practice existed resulted in the awful conditions noted by Engels. It was clear that the dry conservancy system was becoming increasingly hard to adapt to crowded conditions. Further attempts however were made to make the dry conservancy system work by improved fittings such as Goux pails which had absorbent linings to absorb the liquid and iron covers with rubber rings to make an airtight joint. These, however, required constant disinfecting and cleaning.

Howson's ashpit door, Brodie's patent ash bin used in Liverpool, and Dr. Quine's ash bin were all attempts to make the removal of the excrement easier and less messy. In spite of this, however, the sanitary conditions of cities were generally appalling and in country districts conditions were only slightly better by reason of the lower density. Even at the end of the 19th century, Francis Wood, at one time Borough Surveyor of Fulham, reported drains from numbers of houses running into fields within two or three yards from other dwellings for years without any attention, so that the places became unwholesome masses of filth. In one case the drains from about twenty houses discharged into the front gardens of some cottages which became, in consequence, some six inches deep in sewage.

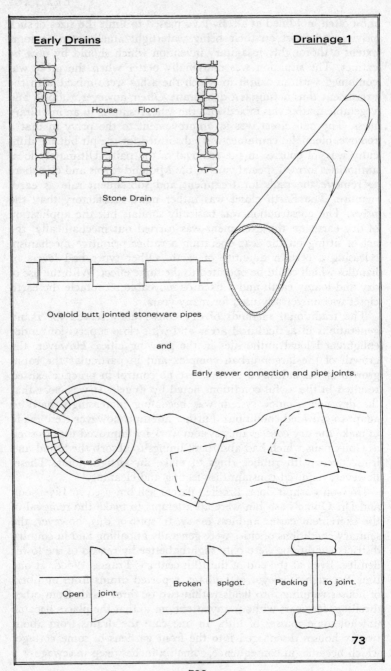

House   Floor

Stone Drain

Ovaloid butt jointed stoneware pipes

and

Early sewer connection and pipe joints.

Open   joint.   Broken   spigot.   Packing   to joint.

73

The means often used of disposing of sewage from houses was a brick culvert except in the north where rough ashlar culverts were used, particularly in Lancashire, Yorkshire and the Pennine Range. These can be seen still under the floors of cottages although not, it is hoped, still in use, since they were hopelessly insanitary as they were invariably full and formed reservoirs of foul air (Fig. 73). Flushing was no answer due to the open joints in the ashlar and the fact that movement of the sewage along the length of the culverts was non-existent or, at best, extremely sluggish so that the culverts became breeding grounds for all types of bacteria, and were, in this respect, worse than the pits of the dry conservancy system. However, the culvert formed the first basis for the removal of excrement. The factors that enabled water borne drainage to become an accomplished fact were firstly the universal extension of the Victorian piped water supply and secondly, as mentioned previously, the mass-production of gradually improving pipes for drainage. Without either of these factors water carriage drainage as we know it today could not have become a practicable possibility.

The possibilities of the system of water carriage drainage were very probably first prompted by such inventions as the slop water closet. Here a three to four gallon capacity tipper was fed with the discharge of slop water and balanced on a pivot so that it automatically drained into the closet immediately it became full and carried the solids away. Alexander Cummings' patent water closet in 1775 and Joseph Bramah's valve closet, patented as early as 1778, were the first means of proving that the mechanically operated water closet was an advance on what had gone before. These patents languished for years however and without the mass-production of suitable pipes the water carriage system would probably have been abandoned as impracticable.

As the production and delivery of pipes of different sizes became feasible and the cost became cheaper, surveyors and engineers grew bolder and were able to experiment more freely. The combined system of drainage consisting of one large sewer pipe taking all types of discharge from soil and waste fittings and surface water as well was replaced by the separate system in which the parallel sewer pipes were installed, the first taking surface water and the second taking other drainage from soil and waste fittings. When it was then found that the foul drain was apt to become insanitary due to insufficient flow, a partially separate system was devised in urban areas where the surface water sewer took the discharge from main roofs and gullies while the soil and waste sewer took the rainwater from back addition roofs and rear paved yards to assist the drainage flow.

Pipes for drainage were, however, the fundamental innovation of the time and it is with the development of pipes that Section B commences before proceeding to trace the evolution of the remaining constituent parts of the underground domestic drainage system likely to be found in houses built up to about ten years ago, and indeed for many built since. Up to about 1960 good modern practice in this field was exemplified in the British Standard Code of Practice C.P.301 (1950) "Building Drainage" and this provided a yardstick to the surveyor in charge of repair or maintenance work to houses whereby older systems could be judged. Although the basic principles of the water carriage system have remained constant since Victorian times there have been changes in detail with the result that many of the systems of older houses lack features now considered essential and incorporate fittings or constructional details that now are proved to be suspect. However, around 1960 doubts as to the traditional constructional methods for drains were aroused by studies carried out by the Building Research Establishment and which resulted in Digests Nos. 124 and 125 (First Series) suggesting that considerable modifications were necessary in current practice in drainage design and construction. In particular the study of the pipe line as a structure suggested that methods of jointing and support for drains advocated in the Code of Practice were unsound and might give rise to the problems of soil infiltration, blockage of drains by tree roots and damage to foundations all brought about by broken joints and pipes. It was stated in Digest No. 134 (May 1960) which dealt with the problems encountered, that the Code of Practice C.P.301 (1950) was in course of revision and the revised Code was in fact produced in 1971 and not only incorporates C.P.301, but also C.P.303 "Surface Water and Sub-soil Drainage".

The background to the 1971 Code of Practice was that as a result of the work undertaken by the Building Research Station the Ministry of Housing and Local Government set up a working party in 1964 to initiate and co-ordinate further experimental and research work on the subject and "to investigate the practical application of structural theory to the design and construction of buried pipe sewers having due regard to structural stability, to watertightness and to economy in capital, operational and maintenance costs; to consider and advise on the relative merits of flexible and rigid construction over a range of ground and loading conditions commonly occuring in practice; and to initiate and co-ordinate research and experiment directed towards the production of reliable design data and the co-ordination of design and construction".

Until comparatively recently it was general practice in this country to provide additional strength to sewer pipelines, which had

to support the weight of backfill and surface loads transmitted through
the soil to the pipes, by means of concrete bedding, haunching and
surround, subject to some general rules which were set out in the
Ministry of Health Form K29. Since these rules were devised many
years ago, a working party under the Chief Engineer to the Ministry
of Housing and Local Government was set up between April 1959
and February 1961 to consider the basic theories for the determination of loads on buried pipelines, originating from studies carried out
at Iowa State University (U.S.A.) in the light of which the adequacy
of the K29 requirements could be assessed. It was decided by the
working party that the K29 requirements should be amended to
provide for the use of the method of design incorporating these
theories as an alternative to traditional practice. It was also decided
that since this method of design had not up to that time been extensively used in this country, some preliminary guidance in the
form of an agreed document should be provided to enable suitable
mention to be made of the alternative in the revised Form. In order
to fulfill this purpose, the Building Research Establishment produced
National Building Study No. 32 which included information on the
basic factors recommended for general use where detailed design
criteria were not available and simplified tables incorporating these
factors. The study was intended to serve the purpose only temporarily until research and experience could provide more information
regarding the extent and effect of loads likely to be encountered,
and until the detailed method of design became better known. For
this reason the design criteria suggested in it were intended to be
generous and to provide a factor of safety in the worst conditions
likely to be encountered. The new Form K29 and National Building
Study No. 32 were issued in December 1962 with a circular 62/62
intimating that more detailed reference to the new method would
probably be incorporated in the British Standard Institution's Code
of Practice for sewerage, currently in course of revision.

The Code Drafting Committee appointed by the British Standards
Institution to review the Code of Practice encountered difficulties and
requested the Minister to set up a special committee to initiate
and co-ordinate research and experiment on the structural design
and construction of pipe sewers and a similar request was made by
the National Salt Glazed Pipe Manufacturers' Association. The
Building Research Establishment, the Ministry of Public Building
and Works, with consulting engineers and local authority engineers
confirmed the need for further study and investigation of the subject.
The present position is that local authorities are now permitted by
Form K29 to use the traditional rules for protection, to design from
first principles by the Marston Theory, or to use the simplified table

provided by the National Building Study No. 32. The latter in many cases results in the use of substantially stronger pipes than those called for by the traditional rules, a situation which has led to some doubt and confusion in the minds of designers. So far as Code of Practice C.P.301:1971 is concerned, the Code Drafting Committee considered that it would be premature to expect a sudden change of method to be adopted forthwith and was prepared to accept the view of the Ministry that traditional methods of design are acceptable and would continue to be used.

The absence of unanimity at the present time in relation to standards for new drainage systems, makes matters rather difficult for the surveyor in charge of repair and maintenance work to house drains. The 1971 Code of Practice C.P.301 admits the validity of both new and traditional methods while the Building Research Establishment gives advice which is irreconcilable with traditional methods. The radical alteration in methods proposed by the Building Research Establishment may find difficulty in obtaining general acceptance as they concentrate on some aspects of pipe line construction to the exclusion of others but the conclusions of the Establishment certainly cannot be ignored and these are referred to in this chapter where it is thought that they are of value within the scope of this book such as, for example, in certain aspects relating to renewal work and in the diagnosis of faults in pipe lines, one of the Establishment's undoubted strong points. In general, however, the Code of Practice C.P.301 "Building Drainage" of 1971 is drawn upon as being the basis for sizing up the merits of older systems and where necessary and where this does not conflict with the 1971 Code, the older Code C.P.301 of 1950 is also used.

That an older system lacks some features or incorporates fittings or constructional details now considered incorrect, is not necessarily of consequence. For the drains of the ordinary dwelling house, there is not normally the abuse or sudden mass use that occurs in other establishments and provided the system functions satisfactorily and there is no leakage in normal use, repairs are not necessarily required. It is when something goes wrong, either by way of frequent blockages, leaks causing insanitary conditions or damage to other parts of the structure, that it becomes necessary to ascertain what has happened and why. Once this has been established, steps can be taken to repair or reconstruct either in whole or in part to a standard approaching that commensurate with current knowledge.

(B) PIPES AND FITTINGS ETC. FOR DRAINAGE BELOW GROUND UNDER THE WATER CARRIAGE SYSTEM

(1) *Evolution of mass-produced pipes*

The modern highly glazed circular stoneware pipe is the successor of the pipe of egg shaped section. Even this pipe was unknown in 1840 which shows the speed of progress. The early salt glazed stoneware ovaloid pipes were, however, not successful as a vehicle for sewage. There was, firstly, excessive friction due to the inter-section of the long side arcs at the base which slowed the velocity of the flow and caused a build up of deposits, and secondly there was the even more disadvantageous reason that the pipes had no sockets. This was a most grave defect as the joints were open and apt to become easily blocked by rubbish. There was constant leakage into the sub-soil and the reader will imagine how subsequent settlement and distortion of the drain line could result in the whole system becoming clogged. "There are", said Mr. W. M. Spinks in 1897, "still many thousands of yards of these egg shaped pipe drains and whenever they are examined there is inevitably found a great amount of deposit in them . . . " By 1900 glazed circular socketed pipes were in universal use but as E. H. Blake said significantly at this time, "there are pipes and pipes". The methods of mass manu-facture were still not perfect and it was easy for a pipe to get damaged in the green state when drying. Pipes could miss the glaze when in the kiln, or get cracked or twisted by sudden extreme rises in the firing. All such imperfect pipes were known as "seconds" and in the absence of any enforceable standards were often used by the speculative builder.

At this time the Public Health Amendment Act 1890 empowered every urban authority to make by-laws but it was not until some time later that these dealt with pipes. It was, however, not only the method of manufacture that was at fault. Junction pieces were, at that time relatively more expensive than today and it was a fairly common practice for a 4-inch (102mm) drainpipe to be hammered into the side of a 6-inch (152mm) pipe or sewer with no proper con-nection, the ragged aperture formed being filled with pieces of slate or broken brick. Some pipes were often run into others without reducing sockets. Moreover, at this period the later insistence on inspection chambers at every change of direction in a drain was not by any means generally adopted and pipes were often laid in curves by the drainlayer knocking a piece of pipe off the spigot end with a trowel and forcing it home in the socket as shown in Fig. 73.

The need for a calculated fall for drainage pipes was known but did not have universal acceptance and in the absence of supervision the individual drainlayer interpreted this according to his own ideas so that many a drain wound its own serpentine way underground. Another difficulty at this period was in respect of traps. The principles of traps were also appreciated but the difficulties in manufacturing satisfactory quality fittings were great. It was then that a double check on the possibility of sewer gas entering the house was devised, in that an interceptor trap at the foot of the drain formed a first barrier while the trapped gullies formed the second line of defence. In practice, however, this theory often proved to be an illusion. Early gullies were terribly inefficient and the first types of interceptors introduced, known as "manhole traps" consisted simply of a shallow bend in the pipe with an unreliable water seal and a removable stopper at the top. Needless to say this trap was not particularly effective as it was apt to become clogged and was then extremely difficult to clean out. Joints also between the drains and soil vent pipe or other pipes were often badly formed in clay. Rainwater downpipes were also often connected with drains direct without an intervening gulley and with poor or almost nonexistent joints.

The best period of drainage for the surburban speculative house was probably from 1890 to 1914 until a halt was called by the First World War. It is doubtful if such excellent drains were laid again, even after the war ended, for the new suburban estates were laid out in a different pattern calling on other factors as we shall discuss later. In the period before the First World War, excellent mass-produced pipes were made from the clays taken out of beds lying in the coal measures in mining districts and known as "fireclays" which were either of a red brown or a blue grey colour. These pipes were extensively used in northern areas while stoneware pipes were available from the clays produced in Dorsetshire and the use of these pipes was primarily confined to southern regions. As this second type of clay was more tenacious, thinner pipes of one-twelfth of the whole diameter in thickness could be produced of an equal strength to the fireclay pipes which were one-tenth of the whole diameter in thickness. Stoneware pipes were, and are, a pale creamy buff in colour. Both types of pipe were glazed by means of salt being thrown into the kiln when they were being fired, the pipes then becoming salt glazed. This had the dual effect of increasing the life of the pipes so that constant abrasion did not wear them away and also increased their hydraulic efficiency. The advantage of stoneware pipes was that unlike fireclay pipes they were not porous when the glaze was chipped. Nevertheless the fireclay pipes were extremely strong and capable

804

of being tested up to 200 lbs. per square inch pressure (1·38 N/mm²).
It is interesting to note that a leading writer at the end of the century
viewed with suspicion the word "tested" indented into pipes due
to the fact that this could only have been done when the pipes
were "green" and therefore not capable of being tested. This was
before British Standards and more sophisticated production methods
were established. There was, of course, good reason for suspicion
with the manufacture of pipes at this time. Until recently no really
satisfactory way of moulding the complete pipe was known and
weaknesses existed in many pipes between the shoulder and the
barrel since the sockets were sometimes added by hand after the
pipes were formed.

Fortunately, however, the present-day surveyor has few of the
qualms and fears about new pipes that worried his forbears at the
beginning of the present century. He might, no doubt, tap a stoneware pipe to hear the metallic ring and impress the foreman in
charge of the work to keep an eagle eye open for flaws. He might
also on large jobs order a pipe to be immersed in cold water,
gradually raised to the boil and left for an hour to see if the pipe,
subsequently re-weighted, has absorbed more than its due weight of
water (6 per cent to 10 per cent according to thickness). The surveyor
will, however, be confident that the modern manufacture of pipes by
firms of repute to British Standards relieves him of the sort of worries
that plagued the Victorian surveyor. If the drainlayer is a man of the
old school and the pipes are stoneware he might approve of the
surveyor breaking a piece off the pipe and applying it to his tongue
to see if it is too porous, but he had better be sure of his man as the
modern drainlayer would probably look at him as if he were some
ancient eccentric—a part hard to keep up for the remainder of the
contract. For the surveyor can be sure of British Standard 65 for
salt glazed ware pipes which is comprehensive and the presence of
the familiar kite mark of the British Standards Institution is his
greatest safeguard, signifying that each pipe is inspected after
manufacture.

The reader may note, however, that there are two classes of
pipe specified under B.S.65; "British Standard Pipes" and "British
Standard tested pipes". In the case of the tested pipes each single
pipe has been subjected to a hydraulic test before delivery of 20 lb.
per square inch (·138 Nmm²) for a period of at least 5 seconds
without proving defective while only 5 per cent or thereabouts of
British Standard pipes are so tested. The only area in which ceramic
pipes are unpredictable is in crushing strength as there is as yet
no guarantee against damage from unduly heavy loading but this
point will be referred to under a later heading. British Standard

tested pipes are so marked in indelible black on each pipe, "tested and approved". In Scotland there is a long tradition of using fireclay pipes given not only a salt glazed treatment but a lining in addition of glass (vitreous) enamelling and these are covered by B.S.540.

Cast iron pipes are manufactured to British Standard 437 and are used for conditions that might cause a ceramic pipe to fracture, for example where drains have to be carried, suspended through basements on brackets or piers, or near roads subject to heavy traffic vibration and loads. Cast iron pipes should always be used under buildings although they are by no means always found by the surveyor during repair work. A wide range of pipe lengths is now manufactured but normally six-foot lengths are preferred for domestic work. British Standard 437 provides tables of weights and dimensions for pipes in 9 feet (2·7m) lengths from 2 inches (51mm) to 9 inches (229mm) diameter, but no hydraulic pressure test is demanded of cast iron pipes. A coating with a composition having a tar base is specified and the reader will recall that cast iron pipes need such a protective solution to prevent corrosion which should be adequate for normal conditions. Abnormal conditions such as discharges from factories containing acids which would strip the coating and need special protective measures for the pipes are not within the scope of this book but conditions involving severe external corrosion on cast iron pipes when laid in soils permeated with peat waters or containing appreciable quantities of sulphates should be borne in mind. Traditionally however cast iron pipes have been treated with Dr. Angus Smith's solution. This consists of a mixture of coal tar, resin and linseed oil and the pipes are prepared and dropped into the liquid at a temperature of between 290°F and 330°F (143°C and 166°C). The alternative method is the Bower-Barff process where the pipes are brought to a white heat and then played with superheated steam for some hours until a protective coating of black magnetic oxide is formed. The British Standard for cast iron pipes, however, includes a protective element. In B.S. 1130, standard diameters for a large range of bends, junctions and fittings for use with pipes to B.S.437 are given and centrifugally cast (spun) pipes are dealt with separately under B.S.1211. Concrete cylindrical pipes and fittings are dealt with under B.S.556 and as in the case of ceramic pipes two classes of pipe "Tested" and "Standard" are specified. They are considered by the Code of Practice to present an alternative to ceramic pipes but only for drains over 6 inches in diameter and must not be used in conditions where there is a likelihood of attack by acids on either the outside or inside of the pipes.

Types of pipe other than those above are not really within the scope of this book since there is as yet no British Standard for Ductile Iron pipes and Unplasticised P.V.C. and plastic pipes are only of recent introduction. Pitch Fibre pipes, however, now included in C.P.301:1971 have been in use in the United States for about half a century. The pipes are manufactured from wood cellulose fibre which is pulped with water and moulded. The pipes are then oven dried and impregnated with hot coal tar pitch. The pipes are manufactured in 8 feet (2·4m) lengths and are jointed without any material being needed. A coupling adaptor is slipped over the tapered end of one pipe and this is hammered home with the aid of a wooden dolly to receive the blows. The tapered end of the next pipe is then hammered into the other end of the adaptor and the pipes when connected are then at once ready to receive a test. The advantages of pitch fibre pipes are obvious. The pipes are light to handle and are unaffected by fungus and proof, it is claimed, against penetration by tree roots. The joints are fewer and uncomplicated compared with other pipes and there is no jointing material to cause obstruction in the bore under the junctions. The pipes are supplied with a wide range of bends, junctions and adaptors so that they can be used for the most advanced types of house drainage systems and can be connected to ceramic spigots and sockets with conventional cement and gaskin joints. The pipes are also tough and slightly flexible so as to withstand minor unequal settlement. When subject to British Standard 2760 they are approved by the Building Research Establishment for most purposes in connection with house drainage in spite of some misgivings by local authorities. Some reports of failure investigated in the U.S.A. were finally traced by an officer of the Building Research Establishment to deficiencies in laying rather than in the pipes themselves. The Establishment indicates however that pitch fibre pipes should not be laid on or surrounded with concrete in open ground but that the pipes must have an even uniform bed of sand, fine gravel or ashes, free from large sharp stones. Backfilling around the pipe and for some distance above is to be carried out with similar material.

The mention above of concrete and pitch fibre pipes does not alter the fact that in the province of repair and reconstruction the likelihood of finding these pipes used for existing systems is indeed remote. They are included here in that they may in some circumstances prove suitable for a major reconstruction scheme, perhaps involving a number of dwellings. In the past and certainly up to the Second World War the choice lay between ceramic and cast iron pipes for schemes of domestic drainage. As the use of cast iron pipes doubled the cost of any scheme, and still does for that matter, it can

be imagined that cast iron found very little favour among speculative developers and it will be only in the very best work that this
material will be found to have been used. It is not very likely that
a complete drainage system in cast iron pipes will be found to be
defective as the best work is usually well thought out, designed and
constructed under close superivsion. Invariably the surveyor investigating a defective system will be confronted with ceramic pipes laid
within the last hundred years or so, the quality of the pipes not
necessarily being consistent with the character of the house. There
are two main reasons why a lack of consistency should arise. In the
first instance with houses built before about 1870 the drains would
have been installed subsequent to the original construction and
secondly drains being below ground level provided ample opportunities for the unscrupulous to effect those savings on initial outlay
which would increase the profit on a speculation at the expense of
the innocent purchaser. Notwithstanding this factor, however, it is
not necessarily the pipes themselves which will be at fault although
this is always a possibility. The next two sections will show how the
workmanship and the design of the system can have a distinct
bearing on its satisfactory functioning.

(2) *Joints of various periods*

For many years after they were first produced ceramic pipes were
always jointed with clay. In 1878 Mr. Benjamin Latham said "We
seek the most impervious materials wherewith to construct our
sewers and often spoil their effect by the indifferent manner in which
we put the materials together. A soft yielding substance like clay is
about the worst possible material that can be used for jointing pipes
as it is clear that clay is liable to get washed out of the joints, both
from the action of the water escaping from the pipe or of water
flowing from the subsoil into the pipe. Apart from this a soft yielding
material when used for jointing, notwithstanding however perfectly
the work may be performed will lead to failure, as the weight of the
earth covering the pipes causes the clay to be squeezed out of the
lower part of the socket of the pipe, leaving an aperture in the upper
part through which sewer air and sewage may escape or water and
sand be carried from the subsoil into the sewer. These serious defects
in jointing not infrequently lead to the disturbance of the line of
pipes and destroy the regularity of their bed." Mr. de Courcy
Meade, Surveyor to the Hornsey Local Board, pointed out in 1893
the dangers arising from this material, especially from cracks due to
shrinkage and from the danger of hurried piecework when work to the
bottoms of the pipes was scamped and then hidden. In spite of this,

however, clay jointing went on merrily into the 20th century and probably continues today in country areas. A drainlayer has been heard to comment recently that clay jointing was better than any of the other methods, so that the writer would not be surprised to find clay joints where they are least suspected; in the heart of towns.

The supporters of clay joints had, at any rate, a good deal on their side when the early types of cement joints were analysed. All the criticisms made by Mr. de Courcy Meade applied equally to the early cement joints with the added difficulty that wet cement slurry, when too moist, travelled down to the invert, was forced up through the joint and set in a ridge, forming an obstruction in the pipe. The use of the badger did not entirely remove this difficulty even when the impressive invention of Mr. Fred Lynde, A.M.I.C.E., comprising wood rubber edged discs connected with a steel spring, was developed. Most of the difficulty however was overcome with the introduction of the tarred gaskin inserted all round the spigot and driven home into the rebate of the socket, the annular space being completely filled and the work being done with a proper caulking tool cranked for a hand hold. The joint was then completed with a mixture of four parts of Portland cement to one part sand and a fillet was formed to project beyond the socket to a distance equal to the thickness of the socket and neatly bevelled to 45 degrees. An alternative recommended was one part of hydraulic lime to one part sand with hair beaten into the compound. The difficulty however with the gaskin joint arose owing to the need for supervision to ensure that it was made fully satisfactory. It took just over five minutes for a 6-inch pipe to be laid, centred, caulked and pointed against half that time for a slapdash joint. This hardly commended itself to the speculative builder. Even at the best of times care has always been needed to ensure in a Portland cement and gaskin joint that the whole space round the spigot is evenly filled. Cement is always lavished on the upper surface and beautifully finished but often close inspection reveals gaps below and care is needed to supervise joints. Modern cement mortar joints recommended by the Code of Practice C.P.301:1971 suggest a mix of 1:2 cement to sand on the basis that a richer mixture could lead to damaging expansion although a mix of 1:3 might be better in this respect. Concrete pipes are jointed in the same manner as glazed ware pipes but the spigots and sockets must be thoroughly wet before the jointing is carried out.

Due partly to the difficulty of supervision in the making of cement joints, the time needed to make the joint and the insatiable inventiveness and ingenuity of Victorian sanitary surveyors and engineers, many patent joints were evolved at the beginning of the century or around the end of the previous century, some of which are still going strong. The Stanford joint was and remains perhaps the most well known. The patent for this ran out in about 1900 and it was widely adopted afterwards in slightly different forms but at its early best, however, it was made by Doulton's. Basically the joint consisted of the spigot end of the pipe being cast with a ring of asphaltic solution and with a similar bevelled lining inside the socket end. The pipes then having been greased were pushed together. At its most effective the joint, as manufactured by Doulton's, was set up with machine jigs to keep an accurate alignment of the pipes. Before the solution was applied, consisting of one part of clean sharp sand, one part of boiled tar and one part and a half of sulphur, the glaze was carefully chipped away so as to afford a strong key for the composition. This accurate manufacturing process was vital for the efficiency of the joint. It will be appreciated how in the lack of such a process a do-it-yourself application by a plumber of an imperfectly made up solution, indifferently mixed in a cauldron previously used for some other unspeakable purposes, the end-product being applied to the glazed spigot end of the pipe by the mate, is hardly likely to result in a satisfactory joint.

Doulton's must have been not only extremely busy but also inventive at the end of the century as they produced not only the self-adjusting joint, which bears their name, but also a double seal joint and an invert shoulder joint. The self-adjusting joint was an ingenious method of overcoming the disastrous effects that even minor settlement could cause to the normal orthodox rigid joint and was made up of two composition rings of a bituminous material. One ring was attached to the inner face of the socket end of the pipe, reaching from the extreme end to the butt. The other was formed round the external face of the spigot end of the pipe. The socket ring was of equal thickness throughout its length but the ring on the spigot end was slightly cambered in the centre, so as to remain tight while allowing for a certain degree of movement on the principle of a ball and socket joint. By comparison to this the other two joints were comparatively orthodox. The double-seal joint consisted of an ordinary Portland cement joint with two small composition rings, one on the spigot and the other in the socket taking the place of the gaskin, while the invert shoulder joint was designed to overcome the problem of the spigot end of the pipe sinking below the invert line when a soft cement joint was used. In this joint, the pipes were manufactured so that the butt end of the internal face of the socket was made in the form of a rebate into which the spigot end of the pipe could be fitted neatly and tightly thus securing true and steady alignment. This idea was an extension of the "free flow" joint by Knowles and others in which splays formed on the spigot and socket ends of the pipes were designed to enable a true alignment to be incorporated automatically in the pipe run. The invert shoulder joint was undoubtedly the better as the splays on the pipes for the free flow joint were not only more difficult to manufacture than the conventional butt end, but were subject to the disadvantage that they were more vulnerable to penetration from a wet cement joint with a poor gaskin.

Hassall's single lined and double lined joints were among the best known of all patent joints for stoneware or fireclay pipes. In the case of the single lined joint which was not dissimilar to the Stanford joint, the sockets were, however, formed to a greater depth and allowed for two bitumastic rings, one in the socket and the other on the spigot, with liquid cement being poured in through apertures in the side of the socket while the end was temporarily caulked with clay. Hassalls double lined joint, however, was and is, a really impressive one. It consists of two composition rings one in the socket and one on the spigot bevelled in shape to interlock accurately, separated by a space of about $1\frac{1}{2}$ inches (38mm). This space is filled, when the pipes are laid, with a grout of five and a half parts of neat Portland cement to three parts of water which is poured in through a hole in the top of the collar. A second hole near this enables air to escape and a check to be made as to whether the cement has penetrated all round the joint. The advantage of Hassall's double lined joint is that it can be made effectively in soil where the water table is high. The method of manufacture, however, described in the *Contract Journal* of June 7, 1893, was then complex, requiring careful preparation of the spigot and socket ends with several stages in the process, and much centering and adjusting of steel circular dies to ensure an exact fit of the separate bevelled rings of composition. The laying is still complicated as plastic cement supplied with the pipes has to be carefully smeared over the composition material (but on no account the aperture between) so as to ensure that the inner and outer annular linings are airtight and watertight so that they do not attract the Portland cement grout by capillary action at the final stage of the laying. Even then this final stage has to be carried out with care so as to ensure that the grout is thoroughly run into the collar of the pipe all round the spigot. A tin-dish or funnel is necessary for this to be completed with any hope of success. It can therefore be seen that the Hassall double lined joint, excellent when well constructed and laid, is subject to a number of serious disadvantages if badly laid. Carelessness in alignment or a lumpy grout could render it less effective than a conventional joint. It must be added, however, that with skilled drainlayers an appreciable saving in time is possible with the Hassall joints.

The reader might be excused for thinking that the Hassall double lined joint catered for every possible contingency. Apparently not however, since we find that in some conditions a lateral stress or rocking movement takes place. The "Scientific" joint was designed to overcome not only longitudinal but lateral movement as well. It consisted (the past tense is used only as the writers have not heard of it recently) of two bands of composition, jointed with plastic cement and a central band into which a cement grout was poured. The difference however was in the fact that in the "Scientific" joint the cement band was of spiral form instead of being a truly circular ring. The advantage of this modification seems to be evident and its virtues were extolled at the time of its introduction with illustrations as to its use and notes as to places where it was used. If any surveyor should ever be concerned with the main drainage layout of Sitting-bourne he may confidently expect to come across the "Scientific" joint. Another joint that had some regard to lateral stress was the Sykes joint which, with a combination of a screw thread and a cement composition achieved something of the same purpose except that the joint was possibly more vulnerable to water penetration in waterlogged soils.

The number of patent joints on the market at the end of the last century was infinite and the ingenuity exhibited inexhaustible. The Archer, the Solus and the Secure joints were variants of the Hassall joint and the Grouted Composite and the Parker joints were variants of the Stanford joint. Other joints such as the Rubite joint were referred to in textbooks very cautiously at that period as "being necessary to be made with the greatest care and should be placed in the hands of the patentees and subject to a guarantee of efficiency". Others are of little concern except for the sanitary historian of the period but the practising surveyor may in the course of being asked to carry out repairs to a drainage system, stumble across joints in pipes which may be new to him, whether they be effective or not.

A word must now be said about joints to cast iron pipes. The method basically has not changed for 70 years. After the inner 2 inches of the socket (51mm) is filled with white spun yarn and well rammed home, the remaining space is filled with molten lead using a jointing ring fitted and clamped to the pipe, the molten lead being poured through a hole at the top of the collar. Once the lead is set the jointing ring is unclamped, the lead well rammed in with a caulking tool to make up for the shrinkage of the metal on cooling and finally trimmed off. Lead fibre or asbestos fibre should only be used with the consent of the Public Health Department and even then in only exceptional conditions, as there could be danger of seepage of air through the joints if these should be carelessly made. For example in very wet conditions lead fibre joints can be approved and are recommended in the former British Standard Code of Practice C.P.301:1950 as against molten lead under such circumstances. Approval can be given under these circumstances since unless pipes are perfectly dry before lead run joints are made, blow holes may occur in the lead and injury result to the pipe jointer. The appropriate quantities of lead, gaskin and lead fibre for both types of joints are given in C.P.301:1950.

A recent innovation in jointing is the use of rubber "O" rings. Although these have been used for concrete and asbestos cement pipes for many years and have proved their efficiency they have only recently come into favour for other types of pipe. A new slide-in multi-lip rubber ring is now available for concrete pipes and an adjustable roll-on rubber ring has recently been introduced by the British Ceramic Research Association for ceramic pipes. A slide-in rubber ring is now also available for spun iron pipes which is now approved by the British Standard Code of Practice C.P.301:1971. The Building Research Establishment also advocates the use of such rubber joints but subject to certain reservations. Firstly only rings supplied by or through the pipemaker must be used; secondly the ring sizes must be exact lest burst sockets or leakage occur through the insertion of oversize or undersize rings and finally the waste and the sub-soil must not contain any unusual elements if the rubber to B.S.2494 is to be used. It should be noted that the sockets for use with ceramic pipes should not be grooved. It is also undesirable and unnecessary for the annulus outside the rubber ring to be cemented up. Puddled clay or fine soil performs this function more adequately as elasticity of the joint is retained, coupled, as for pitch fibre pipes with an absence of a concrete bed or surround in the laying.

Nowadays flexible joints to ceramic pipes are still produced on the same principles as before but polyester mouldings and rubber "O" ring gaskets are used for the Naylor "polyester" or Hepworth "Hepseal" joints, and plastisol P.V.C. sealing units in the case of the Doulton "Drawflex" joint. Ideas for flexible joints are as prolific as ever, the Oakes joints for ceramic pipes, the "Tyton" joint for cast iron pipes, and the Stanton-Cornelius joint for concrete pipes all being now produced, but the surveyor is unlikely to discover these joints in existing domestic systems of any age although he may specify them in pipes for repair work in certain circumstances where the manufacturer's recommendations can be strictly followed.

The whole subject of joints for drainage pipes is be-devilled by the element of dispute at the present time. It must be remembered that up to around the turn of the century designers and builders were limited to stoneware or fireclay pipes and even after the introduction of cast iron pipes their cost made them an uneconomic alternative for much of the new work in the domestic field. In a physical sense the advantages of cast iron pipes were undoubted in that fewer joints were required and even those joints were immensely stronger than any joint that could be made for ceramic pipes. We have already seen that the weakest point in a below ground level drain run in ceramic pipes occurs at the joints, hence the vast amount of ingenuity expended in endeavouring to improve the quality of jointing right up to the present time. It is considered that so many of the patent joints of the past have enabled builders and designers to feel secure in using ceramic drains in adverse conditions, whereas this security has proved in retrospect to be quite unjustified. Much of the ingenuity might have been better channelled into stressing the need for a better understanding of soil conditions and the likely circumstances of damage to shallow underground drains from external pressures. Many drains laid on poor or non-existent beds with patent joints which have subsequently failed, would have been better laid on a proper bed, perhaps with some reinforcement to the concrete, with ordinary cement and gaskin joints and encased in concrete if necessary.

Even today the Building Regulations lay stress in regulation N10 (c)(ii) that joints be formed so that they remain watertight under all working conditions including any differential movement as between the pipe and the ground. This is likely to require builders to consider a patent joint rather than give thought to the problem of providing suitable support to the drain so as to avoid differential movement arising in the first place. There is no specific reference in the Building Regulations to the British Standard Code of Practice where consideration is given to such matters. The Code indicates that there are special joints for glazed ware pipes and acknowledges that the majority of these joints give satisfactory results. It goes on however to give equal emphasis to the standard joint, which, if carefully and properly made under suitable conditions, gives results equal to these special types of joint.

The introduction in recent years of new materials in special joints for drainage pipes should perhaps be given some thought. The use of perishable rubber and plastics in a position so inaccessible as a drainage pipe joint might give some cause to doubt the long-term efficiency. Possibly a consideration of the feasibility of all other economic methods of constructing a suitable system based on flexible joints, using traditional materials, should be gone into first before a final decision is taken. Although the Building Research Station are prepared to say in regard to a number of couplings and the materials used in the joints that the life "should" be satisfactory there is no artificial way of ageing materials. It would seem far more likely that the life of these materials is probably limited. Even although the Department of the Environment are prepared to approve schemes using such joints for thirty-year loan sanction and for improvement grant work, that period is not long in regard to the life of a building. Perhaps the use of such jointing materials should advisably be confined to those cases where a house has a definite limited life or where given the alternative an owner is prepared to take the undoubted risk.

Part of the confusion at the present time lies in the different advice given by the British Standards Institution in their Code of Practice and detailed research carried out by the Building Research Establishment. The former undoubtedly is a result of the distillation of long experience but the research carried out by the Building Research Establishment which will be referred to later under Types of Faults to Pipes (C)(2) and Preliminaries to works of Renewal D(3) arose out of many reports of failures in drain runs (it is perhaps significant that these reports came after a series of long dry summers) and has produced some radical thoughts on the consideration of drain runs as structures adopting ideas from other structural fields. There is, however, surely a basic flaw in paying over much attention, as do the Building Regulations and the Building Research Establishment to accommodating differential movement in the joints to maintain their watertight characteristic at the expense of the principle that drains are laid to an even fall to be self-cleansing. When gradients are so shallow it is of little value to have watertight joints when an upset along the line of the drain for some reason or other, causes repeated blockages.

(3) *Bed, support, fall, velocity and ventilation of drains*

The early pipes for drainage, all of which would be classified as "rigid" today, have no bed or support in the manner that is now understood. The ground was merely opened up, the pipes were laid and the trench back-filled. There was, possibly, an attempt to take out and refill with compacted earth any areas obviously not suitable for pipe laying, such as a pit with decayed vegetable matter, but no particular need for a separate bed for drain pipes was contemplated. Indeed, if the pipes were laid deep enough and the sub-soil was of uniform bearing capacity, there was no particular reason, nor is there now, why a bed should be necessary. The difficulty was, of course, that these ideal conditions very rarely applied. Accordingly, it later became usual to lay drainage pipes on a bed of hardcore later followed by a bed of concrete. At first the bed was regarded as a convenient way to make up soft ground and, as a side benefit, a method of providing a fall for pipes without too much levelling and ramming. It is not surprising therefore, that the bed usually proved to be extremely uneven in thickness and often in consequence caused failure in pipes due to fractures from unequal movement. It has now been learned that if a bed is to be provided, then the most necessary factor is that it shall be of constant thickness otherwise it may do more harm than good.

In recent years the alternative methods of constructing pipe lines have increased largely due to the introduction of flexible pipes and joints, all of which were, of course, unknown in Victorian times. In addition to this however, as we have seen, the traditional method of design for rigid drains has come under scrutiny and the Building Research Establishment has suggested a new method of design known as the Computed Load Method based on investigations over a number of years and has produced Digests explaining the new principles. The British Standard Code of Practice C.P.301 of 1971 was brought out in circumstances of considerable difficulty in that the new method of design was irreconcilable with the traditional method and there was a body of opinion to support each. The Code Drafting Committee accepted the view of the Ministry of Housing and Local Government that traditional methods of design would continue to be used and in fact both methods are presented in the Code as alternatives. Accordingly, the new Computed Load Method, set out as Design Method A, relates the load carrying capability of the drain as laid underground to the maximum vertical loads likely to be imposed on it and aims, by means of flexible construction, to mitigate some of the effects of the secondary forces (e.g. soil movements, thermal effects) to which it may be subjected. The Code specifies the following:

(1) Computation of the total effective external design load, caused by the worst combination of the maximum fill load and the maximum surface surcharges, which is likely to be imposed simultaneously on any particular length of the drain.

(2) Selection of a rigid pipe having a safe crushing test strength and of a standard class of bedding having a known bedding factor which, taken together with an adequate factor of safety, will provide the load carrying capability required.

(3) The use generally of flexible joints for rigid pipes to make the drain sufficiently flexible and extensible without loss of watertightness.

The computation of the total effective load coupled with the selection of a rigid pipe having a safe crushing strength and of the appropriate bedding factor, are inter-related and Design Method A is too long to be included in this chapter and readers are referred to Building Research Station Digests 130 and 131 of June and July 1971 Parts 1 and 2, for rigid and flexible pipe lines respectively.

In the Code, Design Method B for rigid pipes relies upon the provision of additional support, where necessary, by concrete haunching or surround of approved quality and specified dimensions to suit varying depths of cover. It allows the use of either rigid or flexible joints.

The surveying student has been taught until very recently that the total width of a concrete bed should equal the external diameter of the pipe, plus 12 inches (300mm) and that the thickness of the concrete bedding below the barrel of the pipe, should not be less than 4 inches (100mm) for pipes under 6 inches (150mm) in diameter and 6 inches (150mm) for pipes of 6 inches (150mm) and over. In the Metropolitan area of London, this latter figure is specified as a minimum under all circumstances. The student will also remember that haunching consists of a concrete bed in all respects similar to that just described, but with the full width of the bed carried up to the level of the horizontal diameter of the pipe. From this point the level is carried up, splayed, on both sides of the pipe from the full width of the bed to meet the pipe barrel tangentially. In certain cases pipes are completely encased in concrete, the concrete known as the surround which is, or should be, square in section with a minimum thickness outside the barrel of the pipe of 6 inches (150mm). Accordingly, until recently, drain pipes were provided with a bed or were haunched or provided with a surround according to the diameter of the pipe. The British Code of Practice C.P.301 of 1971 however, in Design Method B for rigid pipes, relies upon the provision of additional support according to the varying depths of cover provided above the drain pipes. The suggestions which are in accordance with the current requirements of the Department of the Environment refer to pipes of up to 30 inches (750mm) in diameter, but the provisions for pipes up to 13 inches (200mm) in diameter are as follows:

(1) Pipes with 20 feet (6m) and more of cover in trenches to be surrounded with at least 6 inches (150mm) of concrete.

(2) Subject to (1) all pipes with over 14 feet (4·3m) of cover to be bedded on and haunched with at least 6 inches (150mm) of concrete, to at least the horizontal diameter of the pipe. The splaying of the concrete above that level to be tangential to the pipe.

817

(3) Subject to the provision below, all pipes under 12 inches (300mm) diameter and with less than 14 feet (4·3m) of cover, may be laid without concrete, if the joints are of the socket or collar type.

(4) All pipes with less than 4 feet (1·2m) of cover under roads (except roads formed of concrete) or 3 feet (0·9m) not under roads, to be surrounded with at least 6 inches (150mm) of concrete.

The Code concludes the section by saying that in all cases the filling or concrete support should be well rammed and consolidated at the side and haunches of the pipe. Selected filling should be used up to at least 12 inches (0·3m) above the top of the pipes. Where conditions are abnormal in the case of made up ground, reinforced concrete or piles may have to be employed although such conditions are mercifully rare. In basements where pipes have to be carried or suspended, piers should be built just behind the pipe sockets with further additional intermediate piers being provided if necessary. In certain circumstances, for example in the case of a suspended concrete ground floor, the cast iron pipes carried through a basement can be carried partially by metal clips built into the concrete when the floor is formed. This will save some of the cost of providing inter-mediate piers, but these arrangements are not common in domestic buildings.

The aim in arranging the fall of house drains, described more gracefully in early textbooks as "inclination" has for long been so as to produce a self-cleansing velocity. The velocity depends upon the fall of the drain taken in conjunction with the hydraulic mean depth, which is the cross sectional area of the stream of waste water divided by the wetted perimeter, i.e. the length of the pipe surface in contact with the stream. Thus when the inclination remains the same, the greater the hydraulic mean depth the greater therefore is the velocity. This is because the friction between the flowing liquid and the surface of the channel with which it is in contact influences the flow. Should this surface be large and the depth of the stream be slight its velocity is reduced but if the surface is small and the depth increased the friction is lessened and the velocity therefore increased. It is possible to ascertain other information by varying the calculation. Thus the quantity of liquid passing through the pipe is ascertained by multiplying the sectional area of the stream by its velocity. The student is advised to look up and test the simple formulae given in drainage textbooks for determining the gradient of a drain necessary for any particular set of conditions and the velocity produced by any particular gradient. This is most easily ascertained with the aid of Chezy's formula using varying co-efficients. The student might be reminded, however, that there is a difference between bottom velocity which imparts the greater motion, from mean velocity. Thus the greatest discharge from a circular pipe is when it is not quite full.

The question of fall is of the utmost consequence in the design and layout of drains. A drain only requires such a rate of fall as will carry off the sewage and the greatest quantity of rainwater coming into it and for the sewage alone a moderate fall is better than a steep one. The liquid should carry the solids along and not run away from them and the velocity should be equable and constant so as to prevent deposits forming and adhering to the drain. Early drains were not always fully planned with these principles well in mind and speculative builders were inclined to over-do the fall so that the maximum efficiency was lost. The writers have inspected a large number of drainage systems, however, belonging to terraced houses built between 1890 and 1910 and have found that the fall is generally adequate and well calculated. The reason for this is probably that where new terraces were laid out exactly parallel to a road with a sewer beneath it, the question of the fall for each individual house drain which would be almost the same in each case, could be considered at the time of the original layout by the builder, surveyor or architect in charge. This is not invariably the case however with re-drained terraces of Georgian houses. Between the wars also, apart from ribbon development, many housing estates were built on different lines in an attempt to get away from the rigid uniformity of previous periods. They were accordingly laid out in crescents and curves and in circles surrounding cul-de-sacs. It is under these circumstances that the writers have found that the fall of drains goes awry. Instead of a firm policy laid down at the outset as has been previously described for Victorian and Edwardian houses, the house layout was often considered independently of the system of sewers so that the outlet points and the sewer depth were already predetermined with little thought having been given regarding the fall. The result of this is that drainage systems of the inter-war period do not invariably work satisfactorily. Alternatively in an attempt to induce a correct fall, many a speculative builder has allowed the top inspection chamber to be so formed that the invert level of the channel is only a matter of inches below ground level. He has not, however, at the same time departed from the normal bed for the drain so that fractures and defects under these circumstances are commonplace.

Acceptable gradients have been arrived at for many years by adopting the rough rule of thumb known as Maguire's rule which simply consists of multiplying the diameter of the pipe in inches by 10. This is as follows:

For a 4-inch (100mm) pipe gradient equals 1 in 40.

For a 6-inch (150mm) pipe gradient equals 1 in 60.

For a 9-inch (230mm) pipe gradient equals 1 in 90.

The minimum satisfactory gradient depends in practice on the quality of construction of the drain, the method of jointing the pipes and other factors. The design should be such that the daily peak flow should provide a good flush. The British Standard Code of Practice says that when the laying of drains is to a high standard of workmanship, and with satisfactory joints, the gradients can be reduced from the above standards to 1 in 80 for a 4-inch (100mm) pipe or 1 in 150 for a 6-inch (150mm) pipe. This assumes that steady flows will occur when the gradient should be such as to give a minimum velocity of flow of 2·5 feet (760mm) per second when flowing one-quarter depth full, which is a self-cleansing velocity. When flows are small, or when there is a good deal of solid matter, steeper gradients are necessary and the standard laid down in Maguire's rule should be adhered to.

It is important for the surveyor to keep in touch with the latest standards in the design of drains and to make use of the fruits of research where possible. It should be remembered, however, that within the scope of this book we are discussing the repair and main-tenance of drains to houses, most of which will be single units and of considerable age. Most research carried out in the field of the design of drains relates to vast schemes of dwellings where the construction is new and where over a vast area with enormous runs of pipes, a slight change in gradient or an alteration in constructional methods or in jointing, may effect a high saving in cost. Within the scope of this book the cost element is relatively less important due to the fact that the pipe runs in most cases are relatively short and the savings to be obtained by varying the gradient or bed are small. On the other hand drains often have to be laid in their original positions under or near buildings and the penalty for errors is much greater than a short-term saving in cost.

In the field of the repair of single houses therefore, tried and tested methods are best, and savings in time or materials by the employ-ment of new products can be bought dear some years later.

The primary requirement in the repair of drains is to find out what went wrong in the first place and this applies to an isolated fault or a major repair alike. To say that tried and tested methods are best is not to imply that if a tried and tested method, provided when the house was built has failed in the first place, the same con-struction should be slavishly followed. It is under such circumstances that the benefits of new materials and techniques are available to give the surveyor alternatives to help him, but the choice and decision will be his alone.

The question of flow is of obvious importance in connection with the repair and maintenance of houses since conditions will vary widely on how a particular house or houses are occupied and used. Often the use of a house will change and the flow characteristics will be completely different from those originally contemplated. Efforts to tinker with the problem are not always successful and in certain cases complete re-design of the drainage system as a whole becomes necessary where, for example, an estate of larger houses occupied in flats is under a single ownership. Re-design however, is not nearly so likely in the case of single houses but conditions for adapting the drainage system to changed circumstances are rarely ideal and there is always a temptation to consider expedients rather than to consider repairs from fundamental principles. For example, in cases where falls are restricted, the practice of using a larger diameter pipe than is required by the normal quantity of flow to justify laying at a flatter gradient, does not result in increasing the velocity of flow but reduces the depth of flow and for this reason is deprecated. On the other hand it is undesirable to employ gradients giving a velocity of flow greater than 10 feet (3m) per second.

In assessing the likely peak flow in a foul drain, the British Standard Code of Practice C.P.301 of 1971, suggests that the following points are considered.

(1) Number and type of appliances to be connected.
(2) Likely peak frequency of use of the appliances.
(3) Average duration of discharge of the appliances.
(4) Rates of discharge from the appliances.
(5) Any foul flows other than domestic sewage.

Where appliances will be used continuously, the maximum rates of discharge should be taken but the likely peak rate of flow of applicances used intermittently can be determined by a statistical or probability study, an aspect which is dealt with in C.P.304 by the allocation of a discharge unit value to each type of appliance. The number of discharge units which may be connected to 4 inch (100mm) and 6 inch (150mm) nominal bore drains laid at varying gradients are given in C.P.304.

So far as foul sewers on the separate system of drainage are concerned, a basis of 6 times the 24 hour average flow, determined by the water consumption per head of population, generally provides an adequate factor of safety. An approximation of the peak flow rate for a water consumption of 40 gallons per person per day (180 litres/person/day) would be 1/40 of a cu. ft. per minute (1/80

821

litre/second). Other approximations of the peak flow rates are given in the Code.

So far as surface water is concerned, the method adopted for the assessment of the peak rate will vary according to the area of the land and buildings. For areas which require a main surface water drain not more than 600 feet in length (180m), a rainfall intensity of 2 inches (50mm) per hour may be adopted. The peak rate of discharge for larger areas is described in C.P.2005 and reference may be made to this Code. It should be noted that the whole of the rainfall on impervious areas should be assumed to reach the drains. The impervious areas should include the horizontal projection of the roof areas and all paved areas.

From time immemorial smells from rudimentary drains were accepted as commonplace and as part of the Englishman's lot. It was not until the 19th century that the advance of sanitary science became so successful in dealing with this matter that the problem came to an end. It did not end however without some considerable argument and discussion to establish generally accepted principles for the ventilation of drains. Sewer gas to the Victorian household of 1890 was rather like the tiger in the jungle. It was worse in imagination than in fact; it was not known when or where the gas would strike and the consequences of attack, although unpredictable, were generally held to be grave. For some years therefore, particularly when trade sewage and effluents were not controlled, the tendency was for sewer gases to be kept out of house drainage systems at all costs. It might, after all, be added in fairness that Section 19 of the Public Health Act 1875 was the first clause regulating the construction, ventilation and emptying of sewers so that in the Victorian age there must have been those with long memories of unspeakable conditions. Accordingly at this period it was considered essential to disconnect the house drain from the sewer by means of a proper intercepting trap. Some of the early patterns of traps however are so extraordinary and so obviously inefficient that it is not altogether surprising to find a textbook published in 1903 earnestly advocating "a reliable method of sewer ventilation with a mechnically induced current from the house towards the sewer". The object of this was to repel the sewer gas and to avoid the need for an interceptor trap but any such method devised must have been very expensive even at that time.

It is now recognised however that an essential of good drainage is the maintenance of equilibrium of pressure inside and outside the system achieved by through ventilation. It is accepted that where intercepting traps are omitted from house drains, and the British Standard Code of Practice suggests that they are omitted except when local by-laws require them (often in central areas where the authority is aware that its main sewers contain an unduly high concentration of offensive gasses) adequate ventilation to the drain or sewer will normally be provided through the vertical soil stacks on each house without any other provision, as long as such stacks are carried up beyond fittings as vents. Where the intercepting trap is provided on the house drain however, one of the following three methods of ventilating the house drains is recommended.

(1) A high vent near the head of the drain e.g. a soil stock and a low vent or fresh air inlet near the intercepting manhole.

(2) A high vent near the intercepting manhole and a low vent near the head of the drain.

(3) High vents near both the head of the drain and the intercepting manhole.

It is suggested that method 3 should be adopted wherever practicable and low vents should be regarded as undesirable due to a danger that they might inadvertently act as foul air outlets and have a tendency to become damaged and sometimes even buried. It is also suggested that the diameter of vent pipes should not be less than 3 inches (76mm) and that a high vent pipe should in all cases be taken to a point above the level of the eaves or flat roof and not less than 3 feet (914mm) above the head of any window within horizontal distances of 10 feet (3m) from the vent pipe. In the case of branch drains the lengths without separate provision for ventilation, i.e. a branch connected to a trapped gully should not exceed 20 feet (6m). Effective ventilation of an interceptor manhole is essential unless at least one well ventilated branch enters the manhole in addition to the ventilated main drain. A separate fresh air inlet should always be provided. This may consist of a 4-inch (102mm) pipe taken through the wall of the manhole about 1-foot (305mm) below the cover and leading preferably to a shaft not less than 4 inches (102mm) in diameter or to a stout fresh air inlet head with mica-valve. Ventilated covers should not be used on interceptor manholes.

(4) *Inspection chambers*

Inspection chambers, so termed in the Building Regulations but known as manholes in the B.S. Code of Practice were a comparatively late arrival on the drainage scene. The need for proper access to drains for repair and cleansing was not really recognised universally up and until about 1900. Before this time many house drains had been installed and many Georgian houses redrained without inspection chambers being provided and with changes in direction between straight drain lengths being formed with curved pipes below the surface of the ground. Even today many a surveyor is disconcerted to find on arriving at an inner suburban house to investigate the drains that there are no inspection chambers whatsoever and that his plumber has to be sent away without a chance to exercise his talents. After the value of the inspection chamber had been established and proved however, there was a tendency to incorporate very many of them on new drainage systems to houses after the First World War. The writer has seen ordinary semi-detached houses with as many as seven inspection chambers often in clusters or within short distances of each other. The modern tendency in new work is to explore ways in which too many inspection chambers to a drainage system can be avoided due to the present high cost of building and drainage systems to older houses are also re-designed with care to eliminate, so far as is possible, the need for too many inspection chambers by means of straight drain runs and the use of clearing eyes. The British Standard Code of Practice says that a rodding eye may now serve the purpose of a manhole at the head of a shallow drain and recommends that the use of manholes be reduced to a minimum. Even so, however, the writers feel that manholes should never be omitted where they serve a useful purpose and the guiding principle in their location is that they should be so situated so as to allow every length of drain to be accessible for clearance and testing but on straight runs the maximum distance between manholes can be 300 feet (91m) according to the Code although the writers consider 200 feet (61m) a better maximum. Manholes should generally be provided at all changes of direction of a drain, at all changes of gradient and at all junctions where cleaning is not otherwise possible. They should also be provided at either the point of connection of a drain with a main drain, private sewer or sewer, or on the drain at a point within 40 feet (12m) of such connection. Lastly a manhole should generally be placed at the head of each length of drain. The whole point of a manhole is that a man must be able to work within it. Clearly this does not matter where the invert depth is less than three feet (914mm) but it should be remembered that deeper chambers should be such as to allow a man to stoop and kneel and to bring down and insert his stoppers and drain rods. This demands a surprising amount of space where the invert level is below a man's height, say below six feet (1·83m), and an L- or T-shaped chamber may be required under certain circumstances. The width should be increased for a manhole on a bend or junction and the minimum internal dimensions of the access shaft in a deep manhole should be not less than 2 ft. 3 in. (680mm) square where step irons are used or 2 ft. 7½ ins. by 2 ft. 3 ins. (800 by 680mm) in shafts containing vertical ladders. Where a number of branches into the chamber are involved an estimate of increased size may be made as follows:

Length: 12 inches (300mm) per branch on the side with the most branches for 4 inch (100mm) diameter pipes and 15 inches (375mm) per branch for 6 inch (150mm) pipes with an adequate allowance on the downstream end for the angle of entry.

Width: 12 inches (300mm) for each side with branches, plus 6 inches (150mm) or the diameter of the main drain whichever is the greater.

Most manholes will be of rectangular section and of brickwork. The Building Regulation N.12 requires them to be made of brickwork, concrete, or other not less suitable material. The B.S. Code of Practice recommends that the brickwork should be of English bond not less than 9 inches (230mm) thick. The bricks should be Clay engineering bricks Class B to B.S.1301. This is important as only surface water manholes in separate systems may be built in ordinary building bricks. In deep manholes, all pipes exceeding 6 inches (150mm) diameter passing through the manhole walls should have a brick-on-edge relieving arch over them. The chambers in such manholes should be roofed by means of a brick arch of not less than two rings of special radial bricks set in cement mortar or by means of a concrete slab not less than 6 inches (150mm) thick. The access shaft should be corbelled inwards on three sides at the top to reduce its size to that of the cover frame. Such corbelled work should be in headers and the oversail in any course should not exceed 1½ inches (38mm). The cover frame should be bedded in cement mortar. It is clearly important and the Building Regulations require that the inspection chamber must sustain any imposed loads. It must also be watertight.

Manholes can also be formed of concrete, either in-situ or precast. The former are advantageous in cases where a large number of similar chambers are required as purpose-made repetition shuttering can be used. Precast concrete manholes, on the other hand, while perhaps cheaper than ordinary brick manholes, should conform to B.S.556 before they are set up and need to be surrounded with 6 inches (150mm) of concrete. The concrete sections also need particularly careful attention with regard to jointing. Cast iron manholes are made but their cost is high.

In specifying channels and branches to new manholes which should, of course, be glazed, regard should be had to B.S.65 and 540 (1952) and B.S.539 (1951). Bends, needless to say, must be in the direction of the flow of the drain and should be bedded in cement mortar. Benching in inspection chambers must under the Building

825

Regulations provide safe foothold and should rise vertically from the edge of the channel pipe to a height not less than that of the soffit of the outgoing sewer, and be sloped upwards to meet the walls of the manhole at a gradient of 1 in 6. The surface should be floated to a smooth, hard surface with a coat of cement mortar 1 : 1. The level of the soffit of the pipe of a branch drain entering a manhole should not be below the level of the soffit of the main drain at its point of entry into the manhole.

Step irons and ladders should be carefully specified and planned to B.S.1247, B.S.556 (for concrete manholes) and B.S.51 (wrought iron ladders). Manhole covers and frames are specified in B.S.497.

(5) *Interceptor traps and gullies*

We have already referred to the fact that interceptor traps should be avoided where possible in new or reconstructed work but it must be remembered that some sanitary authorities insist on an interceptor trap between the sewer and the house drain. In any event the interceptor trap in existing house drainage systems should always be examined as some of the more ancient and insanitary traps remain. If any of the early siphon or manhole traps are found these should be replaced as they are obviously insanitary and inefficient. Such traps are little more than 2-inch (50mm) dips and allow sewage to lie in the dip without being cleared. The early Buchan trap although better should also be replaced as its shape is inefficient and it cannot be scoured out and the writers apply the same comment reluctantly, having regard to so much ingenuity, to Browns and Stidders traps and the "Quick motion" traps of Mr. Slagg.

Modern intercepting traps are to B.S.539 for glazed ware traps and Figs. 29 and 30 of B.S.1130:1943 deal with cast iron traps. The means of access to such a trap should always be in the form of a manhole, the trap itself being set on a 6-inch (150mm) concrete base projecting 4 inches (100mm) on every side. There should be a drop of at least 3 inches (76mm) from the invert level of the manhole to the water level in the intercepting trap. Stoppers in the rodding arm should be of the lever locking type with a suitable rust resisting chain secured to a ring in the manhole as shown on Figure 34 of B.S.1130, although these will seldom be found on older systems.

There are, as might be expected, numerous patterns of gullies in existence to be found working merrily with varying degrees of efficiency for anything up to 90 years. It is of course known that a gully should be self-cleansing, have a seal of at least 2 inches (50mm) and a flat base. Many that the surveyor will find will not comply with these requirements. Some are square or rectangular in shape with square corners, and some with detachable sludge boxes will still be found. Others still will have insanitary connecting channels. A warning is moreover necessary in regard to the difficulty in ascertaining if some gullies have traps or not. The "Cecil" for example is a trapped gully while the Hellyer gully, similar in appearance, has no trap. It was supposed to have been used in connection with a separate "P" or "S" trap but this may have been omitted.

Modern gullies are to B.S.539 (glazed ware gullies) and B.S 1130 (cast iron gullies). They should be fixed as near to the surface level as possible and the distance from the ground to the water level should not exceed 2 ft. 6 in. (760mm). In order to preserve the trap seal a branch drain should be ventilated as for a sanitary fitting if its length exceeds 20 feet (6m). Pipes should be connected to a gully below the grating or cover but above and as near as possible to the water level in order to reduce the area that can become fouled.

Types of gullies are as follows:

(1) Open gullies (i.e. those fitted with a grating). These should only be used outside a building where they are required to take waste or surface water.

(2) Sealed gullies: These are for use within buildings.

(3) Access gullies: Used in all cases where it is possible to dispense with an additional manhole.

(4) Yard gullies: To take surface water from the maximum possible area. These should be of the access type. For a single private garage washdown however, a deep gully trap with perforated lifting tray is recommended.

(5) Trapless gullies: Suitable only for surface water when not connected to a foul drain or sewer.

The surveyor is well advised before starting any drainage repairs to obtain a manufacturer's catalogue of fittings to see how all-embracing is the range provided and in the case of gullies in particular with back and side inlet extensions and ancillary fittings, the range is enormous. Such a catalogue is a great comfort when considering a difficult repair. It should be mentioned at this stage that in normal domestic drainage, grease traps are not necessary.

(C) THE REPAIR OF DAMAGED PIPES BELOW GROUND FOR ISOLATED FAULTS

(1) *Investigation and diagnosis of the area of fault*

Repairs to house drains may be required because of a single isolated fault or due to a more fundamental flaw from bad construction as a result of faulty workmanship, poor materials or ignorance of local conditions when the drain was laid. In the latter case, renewal of the complete drain run or runs could be entailed since the flaw will most probably be integral to the whole system. If bad layout and design so warrant, reconstruction of part or the whole of the system may be necessary. Repairs to a drainage system may again be needed as a result of other faults entailing subsequent repair work to the house structure, for example as a result of settlement followed by underpinning.

By far the most common occurrence, however, is for the surveyor or managing agent of residential property, to receive a telephone call from a houseowner or tenant as the case may be, that the drains are blocked and that water is flooding into the yard or garden. To this is added a request for the surveyor or agent to do something about it, quickly! The houseowner will possibly ask the surveyor if he could recommend and instruct a suitable builder while the tenant will merely expect the work to be done.

This forms a convenient starting point to commence a discussion of the investigation of defects and the repair of drains and we will accordingly follow the movements of an agent or surveyor who first becomes involved in this way. There are, of course, other ways in which a surveyor becomes responsible for repairs to drainage systems; following a full scale survey for which he is paid, for example. But probably most drainage problems are started by someone other than a surveyor observing a fault or by having the problem forcibly thrust under their noses (in some cases literally). It is therefore a convenient vehicle for this Chapter to assume as a commencement such a set of circumstances.

The surveyor or agent will probably, upon being notified, now instruct a small local builder who he knows deals with drains, either by telephone or by calling at the builder's yard, and possibly may go to the extent of watching two men, a plumber and his mate, wobble off towards the property on bicycles encumbered with drain rods and the bulky paraphernalia of their trade. The surveyor or agent will then promptly forget about the matter in the rush of other clients' activities until the account for clearing the blockage arrives. On some occasions, however, the surveyor will be reminded about the matter rather earlier than this, possibly on the afternoon of the same day, by finding the builder and one of his men waiting for him in the office with expressions indicative of the fact that the news, whatever it is, will not be good. The builder will then explain in graphic terms of the herculean efforts to clear the drains without success and will then spring into an impressive mime suggestive of a man hauling on a rope. He will indicate his colleague who will by this time be leaning against the doorpost in an attitude cleverly suggestive of physical exhaustion. The surveyor, for the agent becomes a surveyor at this point, recognises that he has to visit the property and stifling an exclamation of annoyance will look at an overloaded diary in order to detach a sufficient period to deal with the matter at short notice. He will then probably ask the builder and his assistant to meet him at a given time at the scene of their labours and ask them to add any equipment that might help. Mirrors and a torch may be useful and bag plugs might be added as well as 6-inch (152mm) and 4-inch (102mm) stoppers. The surveyor also might enquire if the drain cleaning rods have lock fast joints. The rods usually consist of Malacca canes, usually in 3-foot (914mm) lengths with screw joints, although lengths from 2 foot (610mm) to 6 foot (1·8m) are available, and in attempting to clear a blockage on a long drain run the violent twists in the rod may cause the end section to become unscrewed. This can be more than a mere irritation as often the only way of retrieving the lost section is by opening up the drain. Lock fast joints are accordingly worthwhile. Special fittings for the rods should include a brass cleaning wheel for heavy work in shifting a mass of spongy matter and a double worm screw in addition to the ordinary single worm screw with wheel attachment to keep the screws in a central position in the drain. A coring iron with a supporting wheel is also useful, which is nothing more than a chisel-shaped spike. Finally drain brushes are required, in the hope that if the stoppage can be cleared the resulting mess can be cleaned and flushed out of the pipes leaving, it is hoped, no damage, and a flexible spring rod for use in traps. There are one or two firms in most large urban areas that now run drain clearing units in the form of radio controlled vans equipped with power operated appliances such as electrically controlled cutters and borers and often a pump for clearing flooded areas. The principles of operation are the same and their use merely takes out some of the hard work. The real value of such firms is the fact that they are generally readily available. There is not however usually much difference in the cost of clearing a blockage by either method and it is always important for the surveyor to be informed of the cause of the blockage. This information is often more easily obtained from a small local builder who is concerned with the maintenance of the property. If the blockage is caused by the improper use of the drains then advice can be given to owners and tenants. Persistent blockages arising out of ordinary usage of the drains even though they can be cleared can be an expensive item and will often involve the subsequent investigations for an isolated fault as one described below for severe blockages which cannot be cleared.

On reaching the house the surveyor will first of all use the evidence of his own eye to assist him. He will, as he opens the garden gate, register in his mind what age and type of house he is dealing with and what the layout is likely to be. He should then quickly ascertain how the main drain or drains together with the surface water drains run and where they discharge into a sewer or cesspool. He will then join the builder who will give him the latest blow by blow account of progress. The surveyor will ask for operations to be suspended while he ascertains from the workman how many lengths of rod he has down the drain whereupon the surveyor can clip the end of his tape to a handle of the inspection chamber from which operations are being conducted, and will run off a similar length above the ground. This will give him the position of the blockage but not its extent. Accordingly the surveyor can then ask for the drain rod to be passed up the drain run from the other end using another inspection chamber and repeat his measurement to find how far the ends of the blockage are apart. He can next question the man handling the rods as to what the blockage feels like. He will ask if it is hard and unyielding or spongy and soft and may with confidence expect the reply which always seems to be given: "sort of middling". The surveyor can then go to the ground over the blockage and look about him. He will see if there are any outward signs of possible causes of failure. A patch of sunken ground or paving in a corresponding position over the position of the blockage may tell him part of the answer, while a nearby tree of a type the surveyor knows to have a marked root growth may suggest another. Often, however, there will be no sign at all. The surveyor will try to ascertain by means of mirror and torch the material and quality of the drain. Having taken such notes as he can he will now measure and order an area of drain to be opened up having satisfied himself that no other simple solution is possible. He will then calculate the probable invert depth at the point of blockage so as to enable the builder to assess what time and labour he will require and will no doubt arrange to return at an appropriate time.

It is, of course, possible that after the builder's first visit to the property he may telephone the surveyor to say that he can do nothing at all as there are no inspection chambers and after making sure the gully which is overflowing is unobstructed by means of a steel spring he can only assume that the fault must lie in the drain. The final outcome will be the same, however, as the drain will need to be opened up at a gully or some other suitable point first of all so that rods can be put down to find the blockage.

Once the drain is opened the surveyor will be in a position to gain a good deal of information from inspection of the pipes. He should at once be able to ascertain if the blockage in the drain has been caused by some unexpected pressure independent of the drain run or if the blockage has been caused by some defect in the manufacture of the pipes or bad construction or design in the laying of the pipes. A list of possible causes of stoppages is as follows:

(a) *Solid objects accidentally passing down the drain run and lodging in pipes*
It is rare that such objects cannot be removed with rods but bends in old drains beyond the reach of clearing eyes or inspection chambers are vulnerable to this cause of blockage, as are certain early types of trap.

(b) *External local conditions which affect the drain run*
    (1) Tree root pressure or penetration.
    (2) Local settlement due to moisture changes in sub-soil, local weakness in sub-soil or heavy traffic over.

(c) *Bad construction*
    (1) Badly aligned pipes causing a projection in the pipe run leading to a blockage.
    (2) Pipes being affected by settlement where they pass through or under walls.
    (3) Bad quality pipes being used for the drain run.
    (4) Bad craftsmanship in the laying of pipes due to ignorance, i.e. jointing failures and overloading
    (5) Bad craftsmanship in the laying of the bed due to ignorance of requirements for the bed or sub-soil or scamped work.

(d) *Design failures*
    (1) Pipes with too large a diameter so that liquids run quicker than solids, and solids are held up at bends.
    (2) Insufficient fall or back fall so that solids are held up.
    (3) Insufficient flush so that solids are held up.
    (4) Flooding of sewers by storm water thus causing back pressure and preventing the drain clearing its contents.

The surveyor will, of course, be fortunate if the excavation reveals nothing but a plastic part of a child's toy wedged in the drain and holding a mass of accumulated rubbish behind it. The remedy here will of course be simple but the surveyor should be warned that what will happen once could happen again and if there is any possibility of this the provision of a clearing eye or inspection chamber is desirable at this stage as the cost of providing such access at once is much reduced due to the excavation already carried out.

Perhaps one of the most common causes of blockage is from tree roots. This may either take the form of pressure from the roots themselves or from the penetration of the drain joints by a web of tiny roots which in due course bunch up and join together so that they become an impenetrable mat so that no attempt at clearing with ordinary drain rods is likely to be successful without causing damage to the drain itself. In cases where a drain pipe is dislodged by pressure from the roots of a tree the roots can of course be cut back before the drain is repaired but it will be a short-sighted surveyor who does not give instructions for something to be done about the tree itself. This problem must be treated with some care as it may not be the correct answer for the tree, if it happens to be a large one, to be cut down and the roots killed by sodium chlorate dissolved in an equal weight of water injected into the bole. If we are to assume a rule of thumb calculation that the root spread of an average tree reaches a radius of one and a half times the height, most drain runs and indeed house foundations as well will rest on a sub-soil that is penetrated by a great mass of roots. Sudden removal of the tree may cause an uneven and violent alteration in the moisture content of the sub-soil and may cause more harm than good. The surveyor accordingly, if in doubt, should choose a time of the year for pruning or lopping the tree with care and if uncertain as to the best course to pursue should consult an expert. Fortunately, however, most cases of blockage are due not so much to disturbance from root pressure as from the penetration of tiny roots into pipe joints which have already, due to some other reason, become defective. Another danger from tree roots is that they absorb moisture from the ground particularly to clay sub-soil in a dry summer and cause settlement so that drains, particularly shallow drains can become defective. This fault, however, is of a more fundamental nature than that caused by tree root pressure or penetration of roots between joints and the method of investigation and repair is dealt with later in this Chapter.

A blockage in a drain may also be caused by an unexpected weakness appearing in an area of sub-soil under the drain. Possibly an old pit may not have been compacted properly before the drain was laid, or alternatively some freak conditions of excessive moisture may occur with the same result causing settlement of the bed and failure of the pipes above. Under such circumstances of course no method of repair can be considered satisfactory that does not take into account not only the removal of the cause but the satisfactory strengthening of both the sub-soil foundation and the concrete bed of the drain. Blockages due to heavy traffic over drain runs can occur in housing schemes where shallow drains run under estate roads or parking areas or where the forecourts of urban houses are used for cars, an increasing practice. Very often the garages and forecourts of houses built between the wars are badly sited in relation to the drains so that shallow drains running under may be fractured.

A different but equally effective cause of blockage might be due to careless jointing of a particular pipe, or failure in the jointing material of one or more pipes, so that the spigot of one drain pipe will drop in the socket of another causing a lip or raised projection to appear which will trap sediment and allow a gradual build up of waste or soil to take place which will eventually block the drain. The writers have found cases where a junction piece of incorrect size has been inserted in a drain run producing the same effect. This is a piece of carelessness which only comes to light some time later with inconvenient and expensive results. Again the lack of a relieving arch in a brick wall over a drain run may lead to fracturing of the drain should the wall settle.

(2) *Types of Fault to Pipes*

It is however a sobering thought to realise that many of the faults in drains from blockages and failures occur from fractures by loads and forces some of which may even arise before the pipes are buried. So many enquiries and reports of failures were reported to the Building Research Station by 1959 that a series of Digests were prepared to deal with the problem which are extremely interesting to the surveyor in charge of repair or maintenance work. The Building Research Station for the purpose of the Digests classified pipes as flexible or rigid. Flexible pipes are those in which the increase in horizontal diameter under vertical loading is large enough to enable lateral soil pressure to assist the pipe in resisting the vertical load. Flexible pipes are therefore, for example, of steel or pitch fibre. Brittle or rigid pipes on the other hand are those in which the increase of the horizontal diameter under vertical loading is too small to enable lateral soil pressure to assist the pipes significantly in resisting the vertical load. Such pipes are of salt glazed ware or other ceramic material as well as plain concrete or cast iron pipes. These pipes fail suddenly with a brittle fracture. The Building Research Station found in addition that not enough attention was given to the structural aspect of pipe line design and construction. The essential requirements of pipe line design as a structure are:

(1) That the field strength of the pipes (other than ceramic pipes) shall be at least equal to the maximum effective primary load caused by the backfill and surface surcharges which they will at any time have to carry or, with ceramic pipes, at least equal to 1·5 times this load.

(2) That the pipe line remains watertight at all times, hence that

it has adequate axial flexibility and extensibility or is so supported by its bedding and foundation as to avoid fracture by secondary loads and forces.

(3) That the materials used in pipes, jointing and bedding are, or are so treated as to be, and remain, chemically inert in both the internal and external environments to which they may be exposed.

Many brittle pipe lines do not begin to comply with such requirements. It is thus difficult to take any drain on trust even if it operates satisfactorily or appears to do so, without applying a water test. Careless backfilling may cause structural failure while top soil movement to pipes at a depth of less than about 5 feet (1·5m) may have the same result.

Other stresses in pipe lines may arise from damage in handling and stacking of pipes before they were laid and by inadequate supervision in allowing a defective pipe to be used. A very common source of failure to ceramic pipes is from burst sockets when temperatures rise or fall or a rise in the moisture content occurs when the jointing moisture swells to a greater extent than the ceramic pipe socket, causing it to break. Thermal cracking occurs after jointing and before backfilling, but moisture cracking occurs an inconveniently long time after backfilling and may go undetected for years. Even cast iron pipes are not excluded from defective laying as the collars can be burst by unskilled caulking. Distortion fractures may also occur to ceramic or concrete pipes when left laid on the site before use. Sharp falls in temperature can produce fractures in ceramic and concrete pipes which when left exposed on the site, may be dry on top and wet at the base in a similar manner. The Building Research Establishment have diagnosed and clarified types and causes of fractures in brittle pipes and it is of value for their findings to be stated here as it is necessary for the surveyor to recognise the types and causes of fractures before he can attempt to provide a remedy.

(a) *Overload Fracture* (see Fig. 74). This is caused by excessive vertical load or inadequate bedding and the remedy requires a higher bedding class (see B.R.S. Digests 130 and 131 of June 1971), or a stronger pipe or concrete surround.

(b) *Burst Socket* This is caused by a differential thermal or moisture expansion of the jointing mortar. The defect can be prevented by using a more resilient jointing material which does not cause excessive radial pressure in the socket.

(c) *Distortion Fracture* This is caused by differential heating or cooling or moisture content. It can be prevented by protecting uncovered pipes against sun or extreme cold or damp conditions.

(d) *Beam Fractures* These are caused by uneven resistance of

Types and causes of brittle pipe fractures   Drainage 2.

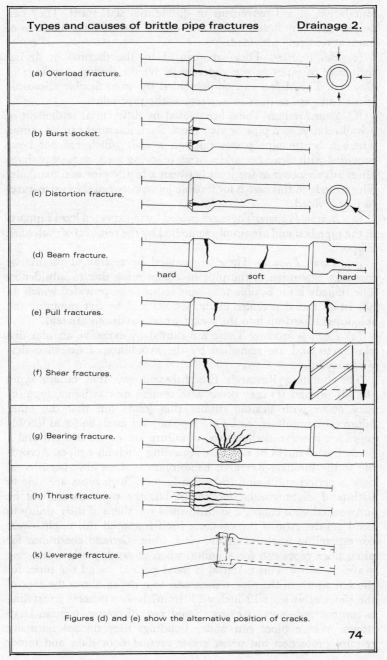

(a) Overload fracture.

(b) Burst socket.

(c) Distortion fracture.

(d) Beam fracture.

hard   soft   hard

(e) Pull fractures.

(f) Shear fractures.

(g) Bearing fracture.

(h) Thrust fracture.

(k) Leverage fracture.

Figures (d) and (e) show the alternative position of cracks.

74

835

foundation or soil movement or differential settlement. They can be prevented by flexible joints being used and uniform hardness of foundation being provided.

(e) *Pull Fractures* These are caused by the thermal or drying shrinkage of pipes or site concrete or by the drying shrinkage of clay soil. This defect can be prevented by using flexible telescopic joints and gaps in the site concrete at the pipe joints.

(f) *Shear Fractures* These are caused by differential settlement of a wall relative to a pipe or vice versa. Such fractures can be caused where a brittle pipe passes through a wall which has not been provided with clearance and a brick relieving arch, or may perhaps alternatively occur at the joint between a brittle pipe and manhole. The remedy in this case is for flexible joints between the two features to be provided.

(g) *Bearing Fractures* These are caused by unexpected hard supports in the pipe bed and are simply remedied by the removal of such hard supports.

(h) *Thrust Fractures* These are caused by restrained thermal or moisture expansion of the pipe or compression due to subsidence. The remedy is for flexible telescopic joints to be provided which do not cause radial pressure in the sockets and by not ramming the spigot held hard up into the socket when the drains are laid.

(k) *Leverage Fractures* These are caused by excessive angular displacement and are remedied by the avoidance of excessive slew when laying.

The Building Research Establishment say that failure types (b) (d) (e) and (f) may occur with cement mortar joints, type (k) may occur with flexible rubber ring joints but that the other failures are uninfluenced by the type of joint used. So far as flexible pipes are concerned the causes of failure are not so marked and a further word might be said here regarding pitch fibre pipes. According to the Building Research Establishment these have been tested over a period and found to be satisfactory. Such pipes are able to withstand slight ground movement but the pipes should not be surrounded with concrete as this would rob them of their ability to bend gently. Also if the concrete itself fractured this might cause corresponding fractures in the pitch fibre. Ground conditions for pitch fibre pipes call for a uniform bed of sand, sandy loam, fine gravel or ashes. This material is hand packed round the pipes for the full width of the pipe trench and to a depth above the tops of the pipes of at least 12 inches (304mm) before general backfilling is commenced. Such packing should not, of course, contain large stones. Where pipes run under buildings they do not normally require protection but when under ground floor slabs and under suspended floors protection need only be given if any part of the pipe line is at or above ground level. Where a pipe passes through a wall a clearance gap at least 2 inches (50·8mm) over is required. The advantages of pitch fibre pipes are obvious but it should nevertheless be stated that some failures have arisen and these have been attributed to over driving at the couplings when the pipes were laid.

(3) *Notice of Repair under Section 48 of the Public Health Act 1936*

This section will be brief but nevertheless necessary. The whole or the partial reconstruction of a drain must be notified to the local authority as follows:

"In a Borough or Urban District, and a rural district or contributory place in which Section 39 of the Public Health Act 1925 was in force immediately before the commencement of this Act no person shall:

(a) except in case of emergency repair, reconstruct or alter the course of any underground drain which communicates with a sewer or with a cesspool or any other receptacle for drainage.

(b) Where in a case of emergency any such works have been executed without notice cover over the drain or sewer without giving to the Local Authority at least 24 hours notice of his intention so to do.

While any such as aforesaid is being executed the persons concerned shall permit the surveyor or sanitary inspector or any other authorised officer of the Local Authority to have free access to the work."

It is usual for the builder to give notice to the local authority but the surveyor should see that this is done.

(4) *Repair of Isolated Pipes to part of Drain Run*

When the broken pipe or pipes have been exposed and the fault found to be a local one the surveyor must now consider the best manner in which the repair work can be carried out. Several methods can be adopted for removing and replacing a broken pipe. Very often three or more pipes are taken out; the broken one and the one on either side of it, or if two or more pipes are broken then the damaged pipes and the sound ones at each side. The joints have then to be carefully cut out and the bed investigated. Assuming this is sound, fresh joints are made roughly, the new pipe fitted in to replace the broken one and the three pipes pressed down firmly into position when the joints are completed in the ordinary way.

Although this is a method commonly used the writers view it with some suspicion since however careful a drain layer may be there is bound to be a certain amount of cement oozing from the joints to the insides of the pipes. This is difficult to remove in a completed drain unless there happens to be a clearing eye within easy reach for the insertion of flexible rods fitted with cleaning rake and Turk's head. It is also often difficult to obtain a true gradient under these circumstances. The use of plain pipe, spigotted at both ends and a loose collar goes some way towards overcoming the objections to this method but, on the other hand, in the absence of nearby access there is no way of checking that the inside of the pipes is clear of jointing material and accordingly this method also remains open to doubt.

A second method is merely to cut out the joints between the damaged pipe or pipes and the sound ones on either side and replace the broken pipe with two half section channels. In such a case the invert section is first laid, the spigot end being inserted in the socket of the old pipe, and the socket end of the channel slipped under the spigot end of the one on the other side. The two bottom halves of the sockets are cemented in the usual way before the half section is inserted and left rough. A joint has to be formed on the top edge of the half section channel. The end joints on sockets and spigots are also completed in the rough and then the top channel is pressed into position. The formation of the horizontal joint is difficult since there must be sufficient material to ensure that the pipe is watertight but if any surplus cement is squeezed into the inside of the pipe it will harden and eventually cause a blockage and on a pipe run of any length there is no satisfactory way of avoiding this defect. A third method is perhaps the best. In this case an access pipe is inserted in place of the broken one with, as usual, the sound pipes being taken out and replaced either side. Before the fresh joints are made, two tightly compressed rag cleaners attached to strong cords are placed in the old pipe well beyond the position of the new joints and the cords brought through the access eye. When the joints have been made, finished off and allowed a sufficient time to partly set, the cords are pulled so that the internal joints are wiped smooth and any excess cement may be scooped out. The access pipe makes it possible to use a small hand mirror to show if the joints have been properly cleaned and also makes the use of inflatable air bags possible to permit of an adequate test being applied to the renovated section. When this has been done the stopper is fitted into the eye and sealed with a neat cement joint (Fig. 75).

A word might be said here regarding leaking joints. These are usually caused by faulty workmanship or the use of bad materials but occasionally unexpected chemical conditions in the soil may

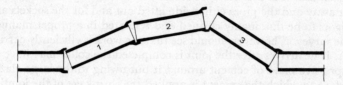

'A'   The broken pipe (2) and pipes (1) and (3) are
carefully removed. A new shortened pipe (2)
is provided and the three pipes pressed down
upon the bed with fresh jointing material. The
drawback is that jointing material is left in the pipe.

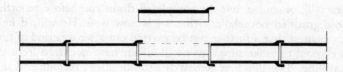

'B'   The broken pipe is cut out and replaced with
two half section channel pipes, the invert
section being laid first. The drawback is
that too much jointing material is needed and
too many jointing surfaces are presented.

'C'   The third and best method is for three pipes
to be taken out, the centre one being
replaced with an access pipe. Rag cleaners
with strings are placed in the pipes when
laid which, when withdrawn, wipe the pipes
clean.

75

lead to leaks. If the defect is a local one it may have allowed tree roots to penetrate and block the drain leaving the pipes and bed perfectly sound. Clearly, however, if the leak were to continue the bed would be rendered defective sooner or later. Under such circumstances it is best for the surveyor to have the joints either side cut away and the pipes either side lifted out and for the sockets and spigots to be thoroughly cleaned and rejointed in a proper manner. The surveyor, however, should see that the work is efficiently carried out. If he arrives after the joint is completed the collar may have an impressive band of cement around it but owing to the large glazed surface to which the cement is applied the shrinkage of the jointing material will merely cause the joint to crack and leak again.

In dealing with repairs to damaged pipes and isolated faults of cutting away and replacement, the work must obviously be done as delicately as possible and the surveyor must be satisfied that all is well before he passes the work and supervises careful backfilling.

Before completing his task and sending in his account the surveyor will, of course, test the completed drain run before reporting to the gratified householder that all is now well. He will, if he is wise, suggest that a further test be carried out after a period of time has elapsed to make sure that no ill effects have occurred from the backfilling. The Building Research Establishment recommend that a year should elapse for new drains to make absolutely sure that all is well but in the present case, assuming the bed to be sound, it is not necessary for this length of time to elapse and a period of say 6 months should be sufficient.

If the surveyor is thorough he will now suggest to the house owner or to his client, if he manages the property as an agent, that he carries out a sanitary survey and test of the system. Often his suggestion will be declined on the basis that lightning does not strike twice in the same place but the surveyor will have satisfied his conscience that if anything more goes wrong he has done all he can to prevent it happening.

THE REPAIR OR RENEWAL OF DAMAGED PIPES BELOW GROUND FOR MAJOR FAULTS

(1) *Investigations and Tests*

It may be the surveyor's misfortune on opening up the drain to find that not one but every pipe within sight has failed due, for example, to overload fractures or burst sockets in the ceramic pipes used for the drain run or that there are other fundamental signs of bad construction. Under such circumstances the consequences are likely to be serious as it is more than probable that most of the drainage system is similarly affected and the owner must be notified that more fundamental repair work must be considered. Alternatively the surveyor may find that the design of the pipe run is faulty so that pipes of an incorrect size to an incorrect fall are not self-cleansing and blockages gradually build up. It is at this stage therefore that a sanitary survey and test of the drainage system becomes essential as the surveyor cannot possibly give full advice on the little that he has already learned. He will, however, cause the blockage that led him to discover the trouble to be remedied and he will see that the account of the smaller building firm is paid at this stage as it is probable that the rest and larger stage on the contract will be entrusted to a bigger firm with more resources.

Assuming the surveyor has obtained the necessary instructions he will then proceed with a survey to ascertain all the information he can about the system as a whole. The writers under such circumstances carry a foolscap pad with a clip and a number of sheets of blank paper. This enables a plan of the drainage system to be made on which the outline of the house can be sketched with appropriate measurements and on which every pipe run and the position of every inspection chamber together with the position of the interceptor can be noted. First of all the surveyor should determine if the drainage system is combined, that is to say if all the pipes for soil, waste and rainwater discharge by means of a single main drain into a single sewer, or alternatively if the drainage system is separate, a single sewer being provided for rainwater and another for soil and waste water. If the house in question forms one of a comparatively modern estate the system may be partially separate, the water from road gullies and public paved areas being taken to a surface water sewer while a separate sewer takes the soil, waste water and rainwater from roofs and yards of private houses. The pipe runs can then be measured and the invert levels in inspection chambers noted. The purpose of this is quite simply to ensure that the fall of each drain is adequate and self-cleansing as it is no good repairing or relaying a drainage system if the fall is inadequate without considering if anything can be done to remedy the situation. Of course if the ground is undulating it may be necessary to relate all levels to a common datum so that the existing fall of drains can be accurately gauged, although as a water test will be carried out the gradient of drains can be determined between chambers by using a calibrated glass gauge which is much easier. Certainly in this form of investigation the approximations involved by estimating difference in ground levels between chambers should be avoided as likely to introduce inaccuracies. The surveyor will also note on the plan the outlets from the property and the gullies and their various purposes. This will enable him to obtain some idea of the volume of flow and to indicate information for any alterations which he may consider necessary. He will next consider the question of ventilation and note on his own drawing the position and type of fresh air inlets, soil vent pipes and vent pipes to any unusually long branches. He will then inspect each gully in turn noting whether it is in any way defective or of a pattern that is obsolete and trace each branch drain to its junction with the main drain. He will note on his plan if the branch drains join the main drain without the benefit of inspection chambers and where inspection chambers exist he will measure them and put them on the drawing with at least two tie measurements to the main building so that the inspection chamber can be plotted on a plan if necessary. The surveyor will then note the condition and position of each chamber as it relates to the drain. He will decide if the inspection chambers occur in the correct positions and if there are enough of them. He will inspect the interiors of inspection chambers noting whether there is any defective rendering or brickwork, and whether the benching is adequate for the flow and well shaped and if the chamber is big enough to allow a man to work. In the case of a deep chamber the surveyor will check on the condition of the brick arch or concrete cover to the lower extension and will no doubt find out by personal investigation and possibly misfortune if the step irons are rusted through. The surveyor will also take notes at inspection chambers noting any covers that are rusted or where the handles are worn away and he will not of course forget the interceptor trap including the condition of the stopper, the depth of the trap and its age together with any other relevant matters that strike him.

The surveyor will now be in a position to make closer examination by mirrors and lamp and to apply a water test to the whole system of main and branch drains. The writers do not propose to discuss any of the other tests available since they consider that the water test is the only one of real practical value so far as the question of condition of drainage systems is concerned. It should be noted that the prohibition applying to a water test under Section 48 of the Public Health Act 1936 does not apply to an owner or his surveyor carrying out a water test to the drains on his own property. The water test will be carried out in the normal manner by a plumber and his assistant working from the head of the drain to the base. It may also be necessary to have labourers in attendance if access to the drains is limited or alternatively excavation works may have been put in hand previously. Each length of drain and branch drain should be separately tested, the stoppers being applied and with-drawn in such a manner that the same water can be used for the next lower section of the drain. This simple precaution saves hours of time. The plumber will certainly need to have bag plugs with him as well as the conventional disc stoppers as with old property many of the drain outlets into inspection chambers are clogged or cracked and an unnoticed trickle of water under a disc plug into the inspec-tion chamber can completely nullify the accuracy of a test. The writers consider that for old drains the head of water to be adopted at the top of each drain during the test should be 2 feet (610mm) equivalent to about 1 lb. per square inch (·007 N/mm²) for ten minutes to allow for absorption in the joints and then for a further ten minutes at least if the drain is sound or as long as necessary if the drain leaks. As it is mainly on the result of the water test that the expenditure of a considerable amount of the owner's money is to depend, a substantial degree of care in regard to accuracy must be taken. After all it is this investigation which will determine the extent of the work necessary and therefore a greater attention to the finer points is required than might be the case in the more simple water test applied for a prospective purchaser on a structural survey merely to establish whether the drains leak or not. The condition of the interior of inspection chambers is seldom ideal particularly at the joint between the channels and the benching and accordingly reliance should not be placed on taking levels in the upper chamber. After all it is a simple matter to repair the inside of a defective cham-ber and a water test is hardly necessary to prove that the chamber leaks. Far better is to confine the test to the drain lengths alone by using a glass water gauge attached to the lower plug and a topping up container or a pipe with elbow bend at the head of the drain, always ensuring that there is no air locked in the drain. By using these means a suspect drain to which there is no access from cham-bers at either end can be water tested, provided the ground is opened up at each end. The need to do this often arises not only when the drain is suspect but also where it is desired to add more fittings, for example a bathroom on an improvement grant scheme, and the local authority insist on the drains being sound as well as the provision of suitable access.

Having established that the drain leaks the surveyor must pursue his investigation further. Does every joint in the drain leak, exten-sively or slightly or is the leak confined to one spot only or for that matter more than one spot? Whereas the facts which postulated this investigation as set out in an earlier section of this Chapter were based on a previously excavated section of drain which was found to be generally defective in some respect, indicating the likelihood of

DRAINAGE

similar conditions elsewhere this might not always be the case. In the previous example it is likely that all joints in the particular length will be found to leak but this could be verified by floating a bag plug down the drain, inflating it and testing various lengths at a time. Total or substantial loss of water from all lengths tested would confirm the diagnosis and the degree of leakage would determine whether a method of repair to be discussed later or excavation and relaying was necessary. The writers would always advocate complete verification on these lines before a client was advised to incur the considerable expenditure of relaying.

In other cases, assuming that we are dealing with lengths of drain between chambers, the water gauge attached to the plug at the lower end may remain steady after the level has dropped for a period. This would indicate that the drain below a certain point was sound and knowing the distance between chambers, the fall of the drain and the level of water in the drain, by simple proportion the approximate position of the end of the sound portion can be ascertained. By carrying out the further test of floating down a bag plug to within say six feet of the sound portion from the top end it may be possible to isolate the leaking section to within reasonably narrow limits. Some indication of an isolated leaking section may have already been ascertained from an examination of the drain with a lamp and mirrors before water testing, an essential pre-requisite. Apart from leaks along the length of a drain between chambers, there are two distinct danger spots which always repay attention. These are where the drain passes through the walls of the inspection chamber and should be considered both by asking the plumber to feel along the drain from each end to detect defects and also by carrying out water tests on the small sections of drain involved particularly at the lower end where, for example, the use of the water gauge in testing the whole length of drain might indicate that the whole length was leaking whereas in fact it was only the last few feet that were defective.

In regard to branch drains the same danger point arises as mentioned above but even more so at the top ends of branches where they may be connected to gullies or the base of soil pipes or ground floor W.Cs. The top ends of branch drains are of course nearly always at or near ground level and accordingly are more subject to movement and external pressures. In addition gullies are often defective themselves and the connections with gullies, etc. are frequently badly made. If there is no access by a cleaning eye to the base of a soil pipe to enable a water test to be carried out, it may be necessary to remove a section of pipe temporarily for the purpose. As to connections to gullies, use of the water gauge will indicate whether it is to the joint at the head of the branch drain that there is a defect in most cases, but if there is also a leak near the chamber in addition it may be necessary to break out the gully so as to get at the top of the drain to enable a more precise test to be carried out. Similarly on a branch to a W.C., the pan may need removal for the proper testing of the drain.

It is by close attention to the detailed operation of testing that will enable a surveyor to say either that the bulk of the drains need relaying or alternatively that a scheme of local repairs, perhaps coupled with the re-lining process which will be mentioned later, will restore the drains to their original watertight condition as good as new. All too often one hears of drains being entirely relaid at great expense because someone said that they leaked. An experienced surveyor can on occasions save a client considerable expenditure by not only finding that drains leak but also finding precisely where they leak and why. Additional time spent on a really detailed investigation can be amply repaid.

On completion of water testing it may be necessary to restore the system to use, by making temporary joints and connections, so as to enable the surveyor to consider the results of the tests and later to prepare his scheme for repair or renewal. However if there is likely to be much renewal involved, before the surveyor considers that his enquiries are completed, he should consider other factors, the answer to some perhaps only being capable of ascertainment away from the site. He should find out the nature of the sub-soil where possible, not only from the point of view of excavation of deep drains and manholes although this is important, but also from the point of chemical composition since some joints are not to be recommended in acid soils. The flood levels and depth of the water table are obviously important and the nature of the effluent from a private house while reasonably assumed to be inocuous nevertheless might show some odd characteristics if the occupier should be either a scientist with a laboratory at the rear of the garden or a second-hand car dealer.

Finally the surveyor should note if any nearby buildings or structures, not necessarily on his site but adjacent to drain lines near boundaries and belonging to adjoining occupiers, are likely to be affected by any work that he may wish to carry out. If so the surveyor might make enquiries of the appropriate names and addresses so that notification can be made at the proper time.

The surveyor should now evaluate and consider the efficiency of the drainage system against the modern principles which have been established. He will know by now if the pipes and joints are satisfactory and although he will not know of their precise quality he will be able to accept pipes and joints that pass a water test of this order as being sound. The surveyor will also have ascertained if the gradient and diameter of the pipes is correct so as to ensure a self-cleansing velocity and if the pipes have adequate means of access and are laid in straight lines. He will have learned if the ventilation system is adequate. He will have formed his own opinion of the layout of the drains noting if branch drains are kept to a minimum and if the junctions to the branches are made in the direction of the flow. The surveyor will also note if there are any trees which will be likely to interfere nearby with drain runs and will know or later ascertain if local by-laws require an intercepting trap or not. He will also have ascertained whether there are any drains run under the building itself and will note down any inlets to the drainage system from inside the building. The surveyor will lastly note if any inspection chambers inside the building have single seal covers in which case they should be removed and double seal inspection chamber covers and frames provided.

Before the surveyor begins to draw up a specification of the necessary work required he should clarify the ownership of all drains within the curtilage of his client's property and will decide whether each pipe is a drain or a sewer. It may accordingly be convenient if the difference between the two terms is restated here. The reader will recall that an underground pipe is either a drain or a sewer but which depends on a number of factors. The rules are different in the London area as against other districts. Outside London any pipe taking sewage or surface water from within the curtilage of one property is a drain and as such is in private ownership. All other pipes apart from these are sewers. The responsibility for the repair and maintenance of a drain does not end however at the boundary line of the property but extends up to the point where the drain connects to a sewer. Sewers however fall into two categories, public and private. Private sewers can only be found outside London with groups of properties constructed after the 1st October 1937. In every matter of maintaining, renewing and cleansing, private sewers are the responsibility of the owners concerned, the proportion of liability being fixed at the time of construction by the local authority. All other sewers are now public sewers be they below land owned by the local authority or below private land. However, where such sewers before the 1st October 1937 were classed as "combined drains" the local authority although responsible for carrying out the work can recover from the owners of those properties which utilise the sewer any costs of repair renewal or improvement, but not the cost of cleansing.

In London, however, the position differs in that a drain not only includes a pipe used for the drainage of the premises within the same curtilage, but also a pipe used for draining a group of buildings, provided the drain was constructed after 1848 with the sanction of the appropriate authority. Thus it will be seen that any combined drain serving properties constructed before 1848 has become a sewer and is the responsibility of the local authority both as to any works required to it and to the payment of costs. After 1848 any pipe constructed by private owners to drain a group of properties remains a combined drain repairable by those owners unless taken over by the local authority. Since 1937 the local authorities in London have been empowered to make an order requiring new groups of properties to be drained by a combined operation in which case the combined drain so constructed remains the responsibility of the owners concerned. However, the order does not specify the proportion of liability as between owners for the cost of any necessary work, leaving a wide margin for possible dispute. There are no "private sewers" by definition in London. Pipes in this category within the London area are known as "combined drains".

The surveyor is accordingly advised to ascertain and verify the nature of all pipes and sewers and to enquire from the local authority as to the position and depth of their sewers, together with any other useful information in connection with both the sewers, local conditions and any difficulties which the local authority may have been experiencing in the area.

Nothing has been said so far on the length of drain between the last inspection chamber of the house system and the connection with the local authority sewer. Although the owner of a property is liable for the repair or renewal of this length of drain, it can perhaps be considered in a rather separate manner from the remainder of the house drains. The connecting drain is normally situated at a reasonable depth below ground to render it relatively free in comparison with the house drains from outside pressures. On the other hand there are occasions when it is affected by road subsidence or vibration and in particular roots of trees planted in the footpath have been known to cause substantial movements. More often than not a defect is brought to the attention of an owner by an unclearable blockage in the connecting length, immovable either by rodding from the interceptor chamber or by the council's sewer men from the sewer. If the defect and blockage is caused by tree roots sometimes the authority's insurance policy can be invoked so that the expense of the necessary work of relaying will be defrayed by the insurance company on a firm line being taken by the owner that the council is responsible. If the blockage is due to any other cause then the house owner is likely to have to bear the cost of the work.

Although local authorities can insist that the connecting length of drain should be watertight, in the writers' experience as long as the original connection was passed they do very little to check on this point subsequently. Even then the question of testing house drains arises on an owner's intention to make substantial alterations. From the owner's point of view it is possible to test the connecting length to the sewer for watertightness by floating down a bag plug from the interception chamber. As, however, the surveyor carrying out such a test cannot examine this length of drain with a lamp and mirror beforehand, the possibility of serious upsets in the line of drain causing the bag plug to jam (thereby putting the system out of operation until the roadway is excavated, often to a substantial depth) the whole operation is somewhat fraught with danger. The attitude of most owners would be that they were not really concerned if this section of drain leaked into the ground below the footpath and roadway, provided it did not affect them. Reprehensible though this may be it is understandable and it would be wise for the surveyor to check with his client whether he wished the investigation to extend to this length of drain if it has not given trouble in the past particularly in view of the likelihood of additional costs and the average owner's viewpoint.

As to the repairs that may be necessary for the relaying of a new connection to the sewer although the owner has to pay the cost it is seldom that he or his adviser has any say in what is done. Most local authorities, but particularly those in urban areas, reserve the right to carry out the work themselves or by their own nominated contractor and to standards which they prescribe. If they do not do the work they are still certain to prescribe the standard. These are normally unexceptional but in these cases the surveyor can at least consider whether the requirements are sound in all respects and discuss any amendments that he may consider necessary. The Code of Practice C.P.301 (1971) sets out in Section 4.15 the methods of connection and factors to be taken into account. The actual connection to the sewer either by saddles, junction pipes or to joinder junctions is covered by the Code but it is more likely that the local authority will lay down how this is to be done.

Before concluding on the subject of tests and investigations it is appropriate to mention that on occasions the problem will be one of infiltration into the drain of ground water, bringing with it soil particles which might cause blockages. In such circumstances the ordinary water test for old drains to the pressure previously discussed is unlikely to reveal a leak. Whether infiltration is occurring or not will depend on the type of sub-soil, a heavy clay being the most likely culprit, and whether the seasonal highest point of the ground water is above the invert of the drain. An examination of the drain in the winter when the water table is high and all fittings are not being used will usually reveal whether there is any flow into the drain and the presence of soil or muddy water would be confirmatory. Repairs to make the drain watertight would have to follow the same procedures as described before and subsequently in this Chapter but detailed tests to establish the precise location of leaks might have to await a dry season when confirmation of the water table at a level below the drains could be obtained.

(2) *Repairs for Major Faults*

Although a surveyor may have started out on a major investigation with a belief that the result of water testing would have meant almost total relaying he may as we have seen, end up with a programme for a series of local repairs all probably involving some excavation but nothing like the trouble involved in total relaying. The taking out and removal of pipes in a drain run has already been dealt with and the need at the same time to establish the cause of the defect and to take remedial measures also covered so as to avoid a repetition of the problem. In regard to the types of other local repairs which have been established as a result of the investigation the same principles apply. For example in renewing a defective gully, the new gully and its connection to the drain should be set in concrete with additional support if it is established that soil movement (such as on a shrinkable clay) has been the cause of the original movement. The same set of circumstances might also apply to the connection at ground level between a soil pipe and a branch drain. In regard to defects arising where a length of main drain or a branch drain connects to a chamber, these are usually associated with a differential movement between the structure of the chamber and the drain. Since the channels by their very nature are part of the chamber and not part of the drain run there is a good case in this instance for not only providing a relieving arch over the point where the drain passes through the wall of the chamber but also a flexible joint between drain and brickwork and a further flexible joint between the two sections of drain nearest the chamber.

With drains passing below a building, the drain run can at least be considered a separate structure apart from the building. Usually defects arise because of the much greater initial settlement in a building after its construction than there is with a drain. On repairing drains to an old building this initial settlement will have occurred many many years ago and can now be discounted but it is still necessary to make some allowance for possible movement after the repair. If the drain penetrates brick walls above foundation level so often the drain is cemented in where it passes through the wall. It is this rigid connection that causes the trouble and in repair there is no reason why three inches should not be left all round the drain with no packing at all provided provision against rodents is made, although it may be necessary also to introduce a small lintel in the brickwork above the opening. If the drain is below foundation level then it is important to ensure that there is a suitable gap between the underside of the foundation and the drain and that any material left between the two is of a compressible nature. Very often, provided the remainder of the drain below the building is laid to a suitable even fall, repairs of the nature carried out as just described and the drain re-lined, the disturbance and expense of taking up floors internally to relay drains can be avoided. It would probably be necessary of course to provide new chambers, if none already exist, at the ends of the sections passing below the building but it is quite unnecessary, if the drain can be made watertight in this manner, to relay in cast iron or glazed ware pipes encased in concrete just because the original drains were not laid in either of these ways. After all the ground below the central areas of most buildings is eminently stable in most cases, being unaffected by climatic conditions and beyond defects at the extremities there is often very little wrong other than the materials of early joints breaking up and corroding through being often eighty to one hundred years old. It is only fair to point out however that occasions do arise when there are settlements in the foundations to internal partitions and breaking up and movement in solid floors above drains which can complicate matters and involve the necessity for more fundamental work even apart from design faults which are just as likely to arise with drains below buildings as elsewhere. Notwithstanding this, however, there is much that can be done giving due attention to the principles set out in the Code of Practice to avoid total renewal of drains both inside and outside buildings.

The advantages of a system providing for the repair of drain runs without the need for the excavation involved in relaying is obvious. Such a process was evolved many years ago by a London-based firm and consists first of cleaning and disinfecting the drain, the disinfectant applied under pressure so that it also treats the ground surrounding any area of past leakage. An appliance is then passed through the length of the drain containing cement grout which is forced under pressure into defective joints or any cracks in the pipes, to set leaving the bore of the pipe undiminished and clear of any obstruction. It may be necessary to repeat the operation before all defects are sealed but on completion the specialist contractors are satisfied that the drain so dealt with will withstand a water test and are prepared to guarantee the work for six months. This method has been tested over many years and is approved by most local authorities, and indeed used by them on their own properties when necessary.

While the advantages of the coring process described above are obvious, the limitations should also be apparent and the specialists will not carry out the process until they are satisfied that it will be successful (they are also specialists in drain reconstruction themselves). Obviously the method is totally impracticable where there have been substantial disturbances to the drain run throughout its length and even if the disturbance is limited to a few points in a long length these would have to be dealt with separately before the lining process was carried out. Ideally the method has been found suitable for old drains laid at a reasonable depth, more than say 2 feet (610mm) below ground level or more than 4 feet (1·2m) if the sub-soil is clay, in drains not subject to excessive vibration or external pressures and in those well away from any interference by tree roots. As will be seen drains below buildings, particularly those below basements are usually within this category.

In a scheme of repair work such as has been envisaged in this section of isolated excavation to deal with specific defects and re-pairing the remaining lengths of drain it may also be necessary to overhaul and repair chambers or to provide new chambers. New chambers have been referred to earlier in this Chapter but repairs to old chambers may be extensive or relatively slight depending entirely on their condition. Sometimes repairs to fractures or even rebuilding of the walls may be necessary but much more often it is a question of repairs to benching and rendering and repointing which is required. Occasionally new channels and bends are required and almost invariably with neglected systems covers will require attention, usually by way of renewal. Where systems have been added to at some time in their history it is amazing how often the connections in the chamber are badly made. Often a soil branch is allowed to discharge at quite a high level in the chamber fouling an extensive area of benching. This was often done so as to avoid undue excavation in connecting a new shallow branch drain to a deeper chamber. There is seldom sufficient room for a ramp to be formed, particularly when there has to be a sharp bend in a hori-zontal plane as well, so that it is usually necessary to form a vertical drop on the outside of the chamber so that an ordinary three-quarter bend or other appropriate channel can be used. The introduction of a vertical drop is always necessary if the difference in level is appreciable and if any improvement is to be achieved the correct detailing should be studied in C.P.301 of 1971 irrespective of whether it is being added to an existing chamber or whether it is a feature in a new relaid drainage scheme.

Finally in a scheme of repair of this nature it goes without saying that all work would be tested before backfilling and that backfilling would be carefully supervised so as not to disrupt new work from old. Provided existing ventilation is satisfactory and improvements in this regard are not usually difficult, an owner would not have a fully watertight modernised drainage installation but still basically the same one as before and all at much less cost than an entirely new system. Since most of the features will have been in the ground for a long time, subject to proper care being taken in the investigation diagnosis and repair work carried out, there is really very little risk of the system failing again subsequently. Indeed rather less than with an entirely new system.

3. *Preliminaries to works of renewal*

In considering the question of repair work which will involve the renewal of one or more drain runs regard should first be given to the principles referred to earlier in this Chapter and the matters discussed in particular in Sections B and C(2). Further points now, however, need consideration and these will be set out in turn.

Minimum cover

Pipes should not normally be laid with less then 4 feet (1·2m) cover under roads or 3 feet (0.9m) in the case of fields or gardens. If a lesser depth in each case is unavoidable, a protective slab should be designed over the pipe but not in contact with it.

Consideration of gradient

Once the surveyor has decided on the nature, material and design of the new pipe run to replace the old he will start to prepare his plans and Specification of Works. Before these are commenced, however, it would be as well to say something further on the subject of gradient. The British Standard Code of Practice C.P.301 of 1971 deplores the custom, as already mentioned, of increasing the pipe diameter where the available fall is less than the minimum since the velocity of flow is thereby decreased leading to a tendency for deposits to accumulate but there are bound to be circumstances where the outlets from fittings and the sewer depths are fixed and no amount of ingenuity in raising the level of the top manhole or altering the positions of fittings will be enough to ensure a satisfactory gradient. Under such circumstances it helps to deprive the main drain of gradient in order to give the best possible gradient to soil pipe branches. It also assists the situation if the water from baths, sinks or basins can be arranged to enter the drainage system at the highest possible point so as to assist in flushing the drain. However, where all measures which could assist the problem are exhausted and the gradient of the drain run or runs are still clearly unsatisfactory the installation of an automatic flushing tank should be considered. Field's flushing tanks have been made for many years and many others have been on the market at different times working on different principles. The size of the tank, which is normally regulated to discharge once or twice in 24 hours, will depend on the length and bore of the main drain and the recommendation of the manufacturers should be followed.

Where the existing fall of the drain to be replaced is far too steep, the new drain should be laid at a correct gradient. This will, however, bring the outlet to well above the invert level of the last manhole or interceptor chamber. Where this is the case a back-drop manhole can be constructed from the existing chamber if there should be one or, perhaps better, a chamber and back-drop constructed from new materials. If the difference in invert levels is appreciable the vertical drop is best constructed outside the manhole in order to overcome the problems of confined space and adequate support inside the chamber. In any event for pipes larger than 6 inches (150mm) nominal bore the pipe should be encased in concrete outside the manhole wall with a 90° bend into the chamber. The drain run itself should be carried straight through the wall of the manhole with a swept back-drop junction section to join the vertical pipe. Where pipes are less than 6 inches (150mm) in diameter the British Standard Code of Practice C.P.301:1971 says that the back-drop may be formed of cast iron inside the chamber provided that this does not obstruct access or adequate working space. The support for the back-drop pipe would also have to be satisfactory.

Flooding

In areas likely to flooding the surveyor must remember to install an anti-flooding ball valve interceptor. This is a cast iron fitting that arrives in one piece with access plates and it should be tested before use. Cast iron anti-flooding ball valve gullies are also available.

Double seal manhole covers

It is to be hoped that the surveyor can avoid the need for a manhole inside a building but if this should not be possible a double seal manhole cover is essential.

Notice

Before he makes arrangements to carry out any work it will be necessary, however, for the surveyor to give notice to the local authority of his intention to repair the drainage system under the provisions of the Public Health Act 1936. In order to do this he must obtain the appropriate forms from the council concerned and in the case of the London area the forms will be framed according to the by-laws made by the Greater London Council under Schedule 9 of the London Government Act 1963. In order to provide an illustration we will briefly examine the form issued by the London Borough of Hammersmith. These are issued in duplicate and require certain information to be provided in the event of the construction, repair or alteration of the drainage system. The form is framed in the nature of a certificate whereby the applicant gives notice that he intends to either carry out new drainage works or alter the existing drainage arrangements on the premises that he must describe. The form requires the submission of plans sections and elevations of the house or building showing the drainage arrangements on tracing linen or other durable material. The size of each drain and branch has to be distinctly figured in the plan of the building to not less than one sixteenth of an inch to a foot or $1:192$ ($1:200$ in metric terms). The existing drainage arrangements are to be shown in blue lines and the proposed alterations are to be shown in red lines. The public sewer and connection of the drain with it must, according to the notice, be shown in both plan and section and in addition to the plan of the building, a block plan or plan of the locality must be provided at a scale which is not to be less than 88 feet to 1 inch ($1:1,056$ although $1:1,250$ is now acceptable). The form also asks for a detailed description to be provided by the applicant of the size of drains together with notes of their material and inclination. Other questions cover the size and description of the intercepting trap, inspection chambers, soil and ventilating pipes as well as the method of connection of W.Cs. to soil pipes and their flushing arrangements, the materials, sizes and description of waste pipes, traps and anti-syphonage pipes. There are also questions as to the ventilation of W.C. compartments and lobbies and as to whether the drainage system is combined with other premises or not. The form also deals with an application for permission to construct, use or connect with a system of drainage for the purpose of draining by a combined operation into the sewers which come within the local authority's jurisdiction. It should be mentioned however that it is preferable that details of inspection chambers should be drawn to a scale of $\frac{1}{4}$ inch to 1 foot or $1:48$ ($1:50$ in metric terms). Once the forms and plans have been completed and submitted, seven days at least must elapse before any alterations are commenced and either during this period or later one set of documents is certified and returned to the depositor, the other being filed in the Public Health Department for future reference and it is perhaps worth stressing that the execution of the drainage arrangements is under the supervision of the Medical Officer of Health of the local authority. Once the surveyor has submitted his plans and proposals and received back the consent form stamped and signed by the Public Health Inspector he can normally heave a sigh of relief. The builder, however, is still charged with the obligation of giving notice before he actually commences the work.

It can be seen, therefore, that application to a typical local authority is made by means of a set type of application form that covers all contingencies. In the case of re-draining or the complete renewal of a drain length the applicant is not relieved from the responsibility of providing full information in the same manner as will be necessary in the case of a completely new layout so far as the local authority is concerned.

4. The renewal of the whole of a drain run or runs

Assuming that a drain has to be relaid as there is no prospect of the methods of repair set out previously being adopted the surveyor must consider the steps necessary to do this. Before the work commences, however, he will have formed an estimation of the nature of the ground. This is of great importance as it will rule the cost of the contract according to whether the ground is classified as good ground which does not readily collapse, or bad ground where close and continuous support is necessary. On this factor will depend the amount of timbering necessary to trenches, which can be a fairly expensive item. In good ground, timbering to the sides of trenches may not be necessary up to a depth of 4 feet (1·2m) but some skeleton timbering is desirable below this depth. For bad ground close sheeting is necessary to prevent the infiltration of loose material from behind the boards as a running trickle of unfirm material may lead to cavities which might cause a sudden and unexpected collapse. Often one reads in the papers of some unfortunate man who is trapped or killed in a trench and, with lives at stake, a surveyor cannot be too careful in his supervision of a contract for drainage repairs if the trenches are of any depth. The width of the trench will of course be determined by the size of the drain and having regard to the need to allow an adequate working space. A minimum width of 1 ft. 9 in. (533mm) or the external diameter of the pipes plus 12 inches (305mm) whichever is the greater is normally taken to be the minimum width between the sheeting of the trench, not merely the trench sides, but intermediate staging is necessary involving wider trenches below depths of 5 feet (1·5m) since a man cannot throw earth with a shovel above this height, but once having paid due regard to such factors trench widths must be limited as far as possible not only for economy in excavation but also to minimise the load on the pipes.

There are occasions, in the case of good ground, when dealing with drains below the level of 10 feet (3m) where it may be more economical to excavate in heading, that is to say by means of tunnel rather than to dig a trench, but these are relatively rare in domestic construction. Circumstances which are not rare however and for which the surveyor must always be on his guard are that the excavation may reveal other pipes running transversely across the trench or pipes laid alongside at shallower depth for other services such as gas, water or electricity, and any service pipes uncovered by the excavation should be well supported by temporary strutting. The surveyor must also take care if the trench is to be excavated alongside any building where the foundations are bound to be uncovered to take any precautionary steps that might become necessary. It should be remembered that the overall direction and supervision of the work is in the hands of the surveyor so that any trenches that are dug carelessly near proximity to other adjoining structures and which cause local settlement as a consequence may well involve him in an awkward situation so far as liability is concerned unless he had specified measures to deal with such a contingency. He would be wise under such circumstances to agree a Schedule of Condition with the adjoining owner.

In re-laying a new drain to replace an existing one the line of the trench will be known and the invert levels at each end of the drain will be predetermined. The British Standard Code of Practice recommends that excavated material should be stacked 18 inches (450mm) from the edge of the trench and the size of the spoil bank should not become too large. Excavation then proceeds to reveal the old drain which it is useful to see along its total length to confirm faults before it is removed completely along with the remains of any bed before the ground is disinfected. In most domestic drainage works hand excavation will be sufficient without mechanical hoisting being necessary, the final 3 inches (76mm) being removed carefully to give a true line. It should be mentioned here that trenches once excavated should be kept dry for the next operation of laying the concrete either by pumping or by forming sumps clear of the drainage work. There are many difficulties in excavating trenches in the varying types of soil including rock and the reader is referred to C.P.2003 where the various methods are described.

Once the excavation is completed, the bed for the pipes is prepared. The recommendation of the British Standard Code of Practice C.P.301:1971 given earlier in this Chapter and the bed for the pipes will, by design method B for rigid pipes, depend on the size of the pipe, the depth of the cover and the nature of the ground. In cases where no added bed is necessary, the nature of the ground being sufficiently sound so as to allow the pipes to rest on the trench bottom, 2-inch (50mm) joint holes should be scooped out to ensure that the pipe lengths can be effectively jointed while remaining on a sound bed. It will be understood that it is vital that the pipes must rest on the true compacted sub-soil. It would be disastrous for inadequate packing to be added to compensate for a trench bottom that is untrue. Where this occurs or where the sub-soil is suspect or subject to infiltration by ground water further excavation is desirable to allow for an added layer of 4 inches (100mm) of granular bedding material extending for the full width of the trench, any soft areas first being taken out and replaced with broken stone or gravel and any hard rock projections being removed. Granular bedding can be employed for both rigid and flexible pipes but in the case of pitch fibre pipes further granular filling is necessary at the sides of the pipes to assist in preventing lateral deformation.

When providing a bed of concrete for rigid pipes the trench bottom, once prepared and levelled with soft areas replaced with broken stone and any hard projections removed, should be covered with a layer of concrete 2 inches (50mm) thick. The pipeline is then set up, the pipes being supported by concrete blocks behind each socket with an additional support at the spigot end in the case of long pipe lengths. The clearance under the barrel of the pipes before placing the concrete should be not less than 4 inches (100mm) for pipes up to 12 inches (300mm) nominal bore and the concrete bed or haunch should extend at least 4 inches (100mm) on each side of the pipe.

Joints to pipes should be provided with care. Where rigid pipes with flexible joints are used in conjunction with a rigid bed to ensure the strength of the drain, simple constructional flexible joints should be provided to the concrete bed as well. In all cases where flexible joints are employed the maker's instructions for fitting them should be closely followed while in the case of rigid joints to rigid pipes correct and careful construction is vital. Not only must gaskets to clay pipes be well tamped in but ends of pipes must be wetted and any intrusion of mortar into pipe joints quickly removed. In the absence of any of these provisions the joints will be likely to be defective and the surveyor is well advised to inspect the workmanship.

The surveyor will also keep a keen eye on the method of laying out the drain run. Sight rails are necessary since merely transferring levels by means of a straight edge and spirit level is not accurate on a long drain run. The surveyor should inspect the boning rods and traveller to see if they are purpose made or hurriedly run up for the occasion when their lengths should be checked. It is always more satisfactory to see properly painted sight rails set up, as if they mean business, into drain pipes filled with fine sand. The reader will recall that sight rails are at a height equal to the length of the traveller above the invert level of the drain. Pegs are driven in the trench floor until the top of each peg is at the exact level required for the invert level of the pipe line. The pipes are then laid with the sockets leading uphill so that they rest on solid and even foundations for the full length of the barrel. The pegs are withdrawn as the pipe laying proceeds. To obtain a true line on the horizontal plane a side line is used strung tautly between steel pins set in the walls of the existing chambers at each end of the pipe line to be re-laid.

In the case of short lengths of branch drain where sight rails would be inconvenient, pegs are driven into the floor of the trench and their tops boned in with the aid of three equal boning rods. Two of the rods are held at the inverts of the pipes to be connected, the third being used on the peg to be driven and lined in. Additional pegs and probably the use of a side line establish the run of the branch drain. For cast iron pipes a boning rod provided with a bottom shoe is desirable which rests on the invert of the pipe being laid.

Once the pipe line is laid it should be tested for watertightness by means of water pressure maintained for a period of one hour or otherwise as agreed with the manufacturer. The tests should be applied before the pipes are haunched or covered in and carried out from length to length. The construction or repair of the manholes normally follows that of the drain runs so that these are tested separately once the work is completed.

The reader should remember that it is necessary to take care to draw off the confined air in all traps prior to testing by means of a rubber tube. In the case of a new drain run a test pressure of at least 4 feet (1·2m) head of water is recommended for glazed ware at the highest point of the section under test with a minimum of 8 feet (2·4m) at the low end. A knuckle bend and vertical pipe section above may be necessary in the top inspection chamber to provide the required head of water. The surveyor should, of course, supervise the test himself and may expect to see a slight amount of sweating but excessive moisture forming and dripping will indicate a defect. He may also wish to test the pipe run for straightness and obstruction by means of a smooth ball of a diameter of ½ inch (13mm) less than the pipe bore. The ball should, of course, run down the pipe and emerge at the other end. The writers, however, prefer to employ a mirror at one end of the drain line and a lamp at the other. This gives an accurate idea of the straightness of the pipes whereas the ball test does not.

Once the first test is completed the backfilling is commenced, the timber strutting being removed as backfilling proceeds. This is an operation that needs great care. In the absence of concrete haunching fine material is packed and tamped around the lower half of the pipes so as to give good lateral support. The filling then continues to 12 inches (300mm) over the top of the pipe using selected fine hand-picked material watered and rammed with a wooden rammer. Filling then continues in layers not exceeding 6 inches (150mm) in thickness, each layer being watered and rammed. Larger stones can be kept on one side until the backfilling has reached nearer to the surface. The backfilling to any new brick manholes should preferably be carried out with concrete 1:20 and carried out uniformly on all sides to avoid lateral stress.

Once the drain is completed and backfilled it should be tested again as before to ensure that the backfilling has not caused damage. A further test is also recommended sometime subsequently to ensure that settlement has not damaged the drain run. This test should ideally be one year after laying but this period may have to be shortened to six months under the terms of the contract.

(5) *Suggestions for repair of individual drainage systems of various types and periods*

This section is best dealt with in the form of illustrations, see Figures 76 to 81.

A terraced house built in 1880

Drainage 4

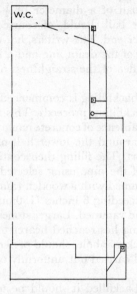

W.C.

This house has a combined drainage system but the existing layout was found to be inadequate. The rear section of the stoneware drain ran under the back addition where it was found to have failed and there were no inspection chambers. The ventilation was inadequate.

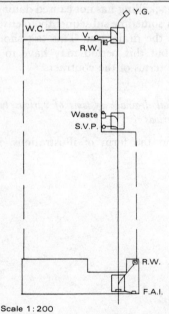

W.C.

V.

R.W.

Y.G.

Waste

S.V.P.

Investigation revealed that the existing drains could be made sound and as local bye-laws required the provision of an interceptor trap this was provided in the front chamber. Two further chambers were also provided and a new vent pipe set up at the rear since the drain run between the two rear chambers and rear W.C. is long enough to warrant this. A fresh air inlet to the interceptor chamber was fitted although a vent pipe would have been preferred. The new rear yard gully helps to flush and cleanse the drains.

R.W.

F.A.I.

Scale 1 : 200

76

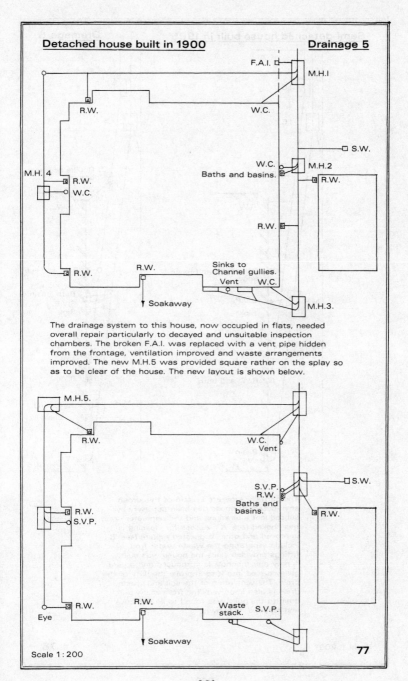

Detached house built in 1900

Drainage 5

F.A.I.

M.H.1

R.W.

W.C.

S.W.

M.H. 4

W.C.
Baths and basins.

M.H.2

R.W.

R.W.

W.C.

R.W.

R.W.

R.W.

Sinks to
Channel gullies.
Vent

W.C.

Soakaway

M.H.3.

The drainage system to this house, now occupied in flats, needed
overall repair particularly to decayed and unsuitable inspection
chambers. The broken F.A.I. was replaced with a vent pipe hidden
from the frontage, ventilation improved and waste arrangements
improved. The new M.H.5 was provided square rather on the splay so
as to be clear of the house. The new layout is shown below.

M.H.5.

R.W.

W.C.
Vent

S.V.P.
R.W.
Baths and
basins.

S.W.

R.W.

R.W.
S.V.P.

R.W.

R.W.

Eye

Waste
stack.

S.V.P.

Soakaway

Scale 1 : 200

77

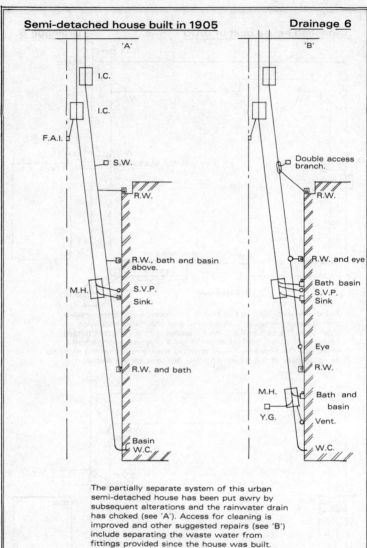

Semi-detached house built in 1905

'A'

'B'

I.C.

I.C.

F.A.I.

S.W.

Double access branch.

R.W.

R.W.

R.W., bath and basin above.

R.W. and eye

M.H.

S.V.P.

Sink.

Bath basin
S.V.P.
Sink

Eye

R.W. and bath

R.W.

M.H.

Bath and basin

Y.G.

Vent.

Basin
W.C.

W.C.

The partially separate system of this urban
semi-detached house has been put awry by
subsequent alterations and the rainwater drain
has choked (see 'A'). Access for cleaning is
improved and other suggested repairs (see 'B')
include separating the waste water from
fittings provided since the house was built.
A new rear manhole is introduced and a yard
gulley turned into it to improve the flow of the
drain. The ventilation of the soil and waste
drain is also improved. The front rainwater
drain to the gully was found to be defective
and repaired as shown.

Scale 1 : 200

78

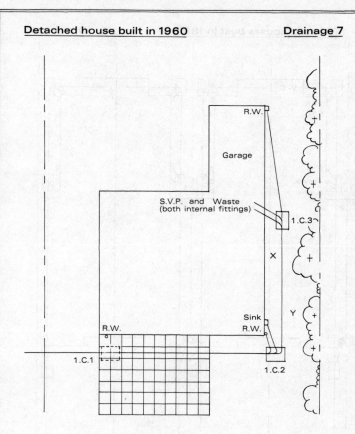

This detached house had to undergo the renewal
of the drainage system to a greater depth. The
invert levels were as follows: No 1 1′ 9″ (530 mm),
No 2 1′ 0″ (300 mm), No 3 6″ (150 mm) and this
shallow depth was quite unnecessary since the
sewer depth was much lower. The drain was
disturbed by tree roots at X and Y and 1.C.
No 1 covered by a terrace laid by the owner
since the house was built.

Scale 1 : 200.   **79**

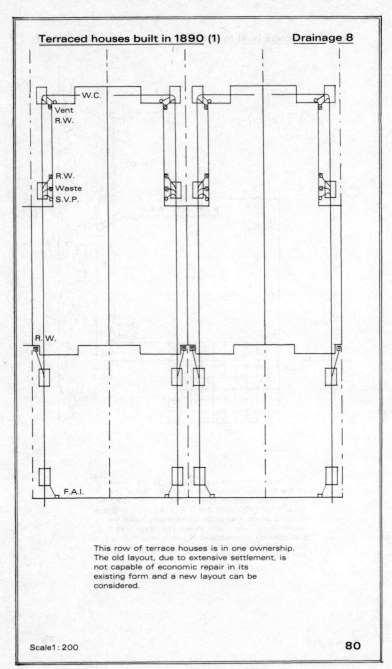

W.C.

Vent
R.W.

R.W.
Waste
S.V.P.

R.W.

F.A.I.

This row of terrace houses is in one ownership.
The old layout, due to extensive settlement, is
not capable of economic repair in its
existing form and a new layout can be
considered.

Scale 1 : 200

80

Terraced houses built in 1890 (2)

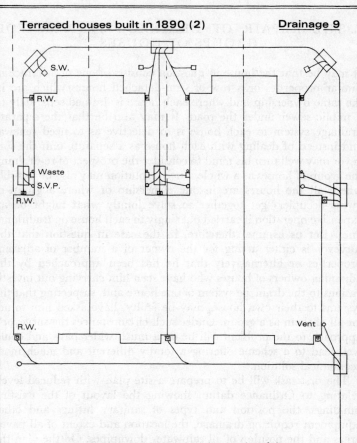

S.W.

R.W.

Waste

S.V.P.

R.W.

R.W.

Vent

The new drainage scheme involved the retention of the
combined system due to local sewer arrangements. The
outlets at the rear were linked in the manner shown and
the external W.C.'s dispensed with since they were no
longer required, and turned into utility sheds. Due to
the past history of settlement, drain pipes joints and bed
were chosen with care and the number of manholes
provided for were considered worthwhile. The front
rainwater drains were linked in the manner shown
clear of the underpinning work for the front walls.

Scale 1:200   81

E. THE REPAIR OF DRAINAGE SYSTEMS FOR GROUPS OF HOUSES

It may be that the house in question consists of one of a terrace of similar properties or a row of semi-detached houses which are in the same ownership and where each house is drained separately to a public sewer under the road. It may also be that the separate drainage system to each house is so defective as to need renewal and instead of dealing with each house as a separate unit the surveyor may well turn his mind to consider the prospect of re-draining the group of houses as a whole. Such a solution may also be possible where all the houses are in one ownership or where a group of owner-occupiers get together to solve jointly what might be an expensive operation if carried out singly to each house on traditional lines. Let us assume, therefore, in the case in question that the surveyor is either acting for the owner of a number of adjacent properties or alternatively that he has been approached by the adjoining owners of houses who have seen him carrying out investigations to the drainage system of one house and, suspecting that the systems to their own houses may be faulty, have asked him to act for all of them as a group. Under such circumstances the surveyor's approach to the problem will be on a much wider basis and could well lead to a scheme offering a totally different and much more economical solution.

The first task will be to prepare a site plan with reduced levels relating to Ordnance datum showing the layout of the existing buildings, the position and types of sanitary fittings and other equipment requiring drainage, the location and extent of all paved areas and the position of all rainwater downpipes. On the plan the surveyor will note the presence of any sewers whether they be public or private, with, of course, information as to their depth and size which can be obtained from the local authority together with any information regarding joinder junctions. The surveyor will then study the local by-laws relating to drainage and sewerage and obtain the information regarding each individual house that will enable him to calculate peak discharges. He should also note any areas that take a weight of traffic from an estate or side road that might interfere with his plans should he intend to provide a sewer or drain at a shallow depth only. It should also be ascertained if part of any sewer or drain will pass under a highway that the requirements of the highway authority are met. The building owner or owners will be responsible in such cases for the maintenance of the surface of the highway and the cost until permanent reinstatement can occur. In some cases the permanent reinstatement can also be carried out by the owner to the satisfaction of the highway authority after a suitable time has elapsed for proper consolidation of the filling to take place. In the case of highways the surveyor is advised to obtain any agreement from the highway authority in writing and the nature of the surface reinstatement in particular should be agreed before any work is put in hand.

It may be that the surveyor may wish a sewer to cross land in other ownership. Under such circumstances he will be responsible for negotiating the way-leaves (easements) concerned. He may have to prepare a way-leave plan for the adjoining owner showing manholes, so that the right of access can be included as a specific element in the way-leave agreement. The terms of the way-leave agreement should also be notified to the contractor so that he understands the position.

Once the surveyor has amassed the necessary information he will proceed with the remainder of his investigations in the manner previously described in this Chapter. We should mention, however, that in the case of a group of buildings a block plan of the site is preferable to a lesser scale of 1:500 as against the 16 feet to an inch (1:192), for a single dwelling house. The block plan should indicate the following:

1. Details of the whole of the site within which the buildings are situated with the existing buildings and drains shown upon it together with the environs and any buildings upon adjoining land.

2. The north point of the compass, the scale of the drawing and the date of submission.

3. The names of the streets or roads in the immediate vicinity or adjoining the curtilage.

4. The location and size of all paved areas and the total area of roofs and the curtilage itself.

5. Ground levels reduced to Ordnance datum and the lowest floor level in each building.

6. The size, invert level and direction of flow of all existing sewers.

7. The size, direction of flow and levels of any water course into which the surface water drainage is being taken.

8. The size, direction of flow and mode of construction of all proposed drains or sewers together with the invert levels at each proposed manhole.

9. Every manhole with a distinguishing number or letter for each.

In addition to the foregoing a layout plan is also essential on which all proposed lines of sewers and drains are shown. The purpose of each drain or sewer should be indicated briefly by colours as follows:

Foul water—red
Surface water—blue
Existing work—black

The layout plan should be drawn so that the north-south axis is parallel to the left-hand edge of the drawing. In addition to the plan itself longitudinal sections of all proposed sewers should be prepared, the longitudinal scale being equal to that of the layout plan while the vertical scale is larger than that of the longitudinal scale. The existing ground level is simply indicated by continuous straight lines drawn between established levels along the line of the sewer. The invert level of the proposed sewer should be indicated at each manhole and the gradients between manholes stated, and all levels should be tabulated at the foot of the section. The position of existing sewers or services intersecting the line of the proposed sewer should be shown where known and the nature of sub-soil indicated where established from trial holes. The beginning and end of each section should be marked by a key number or letter for reference to points on the block plan and layout plan.

It should be mentioned that one of the functions of proper plans is not merely to obtain consent for drainage work from the local authority but as a record for the building owners in future years. For this reason it is important if any deviation should take place from the plans when the work is carried out that the plans are amended accordingly.

The surveyor will, of course, carry out his site investigations for such a scheme in the normal way but he may come across the problem of unknown drains. It is highly desirable that all his investigations are complete and that every drain within the boundaries of the scheme he has in mind is known about and plotted. It may be that the existing buildings are in the form of an ancient crescent of irregular layout and that the drains are so intermingled as to be extremely difficult to follow. Under such circumstances the writer advises the use of drain tracing sachets. These are made by a firm in Ashton-under-Lyne and supplied in boxes of a dozen. They consist of strong fluorescent dyes in the colours of green, red, yellow and purple and each sachet contains enough dye for a thorough test. The dye is especially manufactured and is the strongest obtainable for the purpose.

The relations between the site of the buildings and the layout of the existing drainage should now be considered. Often minor changes can lead to much saving in drainage costs but the use of the private sewer can achieve a dramatic reduction alone. The use of a sewer where the connection from a number of houses are joined to it instead of individual connections being made to the main public sewer will show savings in:

(a) the total length of drain required
(b) the number of connections to the main sewer
(c) the amount of opening of roads in some cases
(d) the number of manholes.

The Building Research Establishment suggests that manholes in branch drain connections are unnecessary and uneconomic provided that suitable access is made at the bends in the private sewer but the writers feel that this is too ambitious and that the Code should be followed as to manhole positions for repair work. The new layout should, however, be ruled by the following considerations:

1. The layout of the drainage system should be as simple and direct as practicable and should make full use of the natural slopes of the ground.

2. The drain runs should be laid in straight lines in both vertical and horizontal planes at constant gradients and the use of bends should be avoided except where unavoidable, i.e. at the foot of a vent or vertical discharge pipe.

3. If the sewerage is on the combined system all surface water from impermeable areas can be taken into it. If the sewerage is on the separate system care must be taken to ensure that the run off from impermeable areas is rigidly excluded from the system and separate arrangements made for its disposal. In the former case traps must be provided to prevent the ingress of sewer gas into the surface water drain and in the latter case drainage of the surface water must be into:

(a) Adequate soakaways, being pits of jointed honeycomb brickwork, laid dry or perforated precast rings filled with hardcore and covered with slabs of stone or concrete.

(b) A watercourse, i.e. a nearby stream or river where, if possible, the invert level of the outfall should be about the same as the normal water level in the watercourse. The outfall should be protected against floating debris by a screen and a non-return flap should be provided if there is any danger from flooding. The banks of the stream should be protected each side of the outfall against the risk of erosion.

(c) Storage vessels. These may accept the water from rainwater pipes but the vessels should be raised to a convenient height above ground and be provided with ventilating pipes, draw-off taps and overflow pipes.

4. Where two or more drains are laid beside each other or in the same trench, care must be taken to ensure firstly that there is no danger of pollution of the surface water from the foul drain and secondly that the position of the pipes does not prevent future connections being made. When the drains are laid at different levels in the same trench the support and loading on each drain must be correct.

5. The flow from branch drains should never be permitted to enter the main drain at right-angles to or against the flow.

6. The laying of drains under buildings should be avoided wherever a practical or reasonably economic alternative is available. Where unavoidable however the possible effects of differential settlement between the building and the drain must be considered and measures such as lintels or relieving arches where drains pass through main walls with an annulus of 2 inches (50mm) round the pipe are necessary together with the consideration of the use of flexible pipe joints.

7. Connections inside a building should be made only at a sealed manhole or inspection chamber, except where suitable alternative access is provided to ensure that the branch connection to the drain can be effectively cleansed.

8. Ready access for cleansing must be provided to all parts of the drain runs.

Since the maximum amount of flow from a group of houses is not precisely known, specific recommendations on the maximum number of houses that a drain of given material diameter and slope can serve have not yet been given by the Building Research Establishment. A minimum gradient for a drain of given diameter is sometimes specified with the object of ensuring an adequate self-cleansing velocity. The velocity of flow however, depends on the quantity of flow as well as the gradient for a drain and there is little point in specifying the minimum gradient for a drain without specifying the flow load to which it applies. Similarly the practice of limiting the number of houses to a drain, irrespective of the gradient, is unsatisfactory according to the Building Research Establishment. The general practice in this country regarding both the minimum gradient allowed and the number of houses that may be connected to a drain is nowadays found to be conservative. The Building Research Establishment say that it is acceptable for as many as 20 houses to be connected to a 4-inch (102mm) drain laid at a gradient of 1 in 70 and that the number could be increased where the gradient is steeper. If a 6-inch (152mm) drain is placed at a fall of 1 in 150 the drain could be expected to serve up to 100 houses. It may well be that such a statement will horrify the reader brought up in the tradition of Maguire's rule, but the findings are endorsed by the British Standard Code of Practice C.P.301:1971. The Building Research Station also say that there is little danger of scour for short lengths of foul drain even when they are laid at very steep gradients. Back drop manholes are useful to save excavation but they are rarely needed on drains or private sewers purely to check velocity. Surface water drains should be designed to dispose of a rainfall intensity of 2 inches (50mm) per hour falling on the areas of roofs and other impervious areas served by the drain. It will, however, be necessary to take precautions against flooding from storms of greater intensity. Under such circumstances several small soakaways are preferable to a single large soakaway and possible discharge into a watercourse as mentioned earlier is suggested as an acceptable alternative where permitted by the appropriate river board or other authority.

F. MAINTENANCE OF BELOW GROUND DRAINAGE SYSTEMS

It often strikes the writers as remarkable that drainage systems, often of vulnerable antiquity, operate satisfactorily with no maintenance at all for many years. Ideally, of course, drainage systems should not be left to chance but should be inspected at intervals. Regular cleaning should be put in hand and the discovery of any defects should not be left without some action being taken. Any signs of infiltration should be noted and the cause ascertained. It is not enough for all lengths of main and branch drains to be rodded and flushed with clean water. The covers of inspection chambers and manholes should also be removed and the interiors, benching and channels of chambers scrubbed. The covers should then be replaced and bedded in suitable grease. If an intercepting trap is provided this should be plunged and flushed with clean water and the stopper and rodding arm overhauled and checked. The covers of the access plates to all gullies should be removed and the traps plunged and flushed out thoroughly with clean water.

It should be borne in mind that the deposits of clearing should where possible be extracted and not flushed into the system direct. The British Standard Code of Practice recommends that domestic drainage systems in normal use should be inspected at regular intervals. The Building Research Station recommend a water test every two to three years.

It may be that where drains are corroded or have been partly blocked for a long time that spirits of salts may have to be applied and suitable disinfectants are desirable. The chemist will recommend a suitable disinfectant once the conditions are made clear to him.

G. SOIL AND WASTE DISPOSAL PIPES
FOR DRAINAGE ABOVE GROUND BY THE
WATER CARRIAGE SYSTEM

Surveyors will be aware of the principles of the two pipe system where soil and waste are piped separately and the one pipe system where they are conveyed together. Both these systems entail the use of ventilating pipes. The reader will also know that the even simpler single stack system is now in use for housing purposes in which separate ventilating pipes are not used. Within the province of this book, however, the writers would like to warn the reader against a too ambitious approach to solving the problems of vertical plumbing by the removal of practically every vertical pipe within sight in the hope that very much fewer pipes can, if cleverly planned, perform the function of the tangle of pipes provided with such abandon in Victorian times. The whole point of any plumbing system if it is to operate satisfactorily must be to ensure that the traps to the various appliances remain sealed in all conditions, otherwise there is a risk of odours penetrating rooms in different and unpredictable parts of the house. A seal can only be broken if the pressure changes in the branch pipe leading from the trap are of a size and duration to overcome the head of water in the trap itself. Such pressure changes can be brought about by liquid flow in the main stack, that is to say by induced siphonage or back pressure, or by liquid flow in the branch pipe, that is to say self siphonage. Induced siphonage depends on the flow load in conjunction with the diameter and height of the stack while self siphonage depends on the design of the appliance and the length, fall and diameter of the branch pipe. Both the old two pipe system and the fully ventilated one pipe system virtually eliminated the risk of seal breakage, the first by interrupting the continuity of the system at hopper head and gully, the second by ensuring, with the help of vent pipes, that the pressure in branch pipes never deviated appreciably from atmospheric. With the single stack system the soil stack alone is relied on for ventilation and the system needs to be of good design and workmanship to ensure that it functions correctly. This system is now much in favour for new small dwellings of one or two storeys particularly on larger estate schemes due to the saving of pipe material and the "one pipe" and "single stack" systems are coming so universally into favour that the term "discharge pipe" is beginning to replace the term "soil and waste" pipe.

The two pipe system

In houses of some age the surveyor will invariably find the two pipe system. This of course involves the soil stack taking discharges from the W.C. or W.C's. and the downpipe or pipes taking the waste from the baths and basins. This system ensures that the sewer gases cannot enter the house. The ventilated soil stack and the double break at the hopper head and at the gully to the waste pipe with its trap, provide all that is necessary for an effective barrier. Even so, however, the surveyor will appreciate that the hopper head often becomes foul and offensive and the same criticism has also been levelled at the gully. It will, accordingly, be necessary therefore for the surveyor before carrying out repairs to devote some time to carrying out a survey of the waste and downpipes to the property together with the connections to gullies or branch drains. A procedure of inspection is recommended commencing at the head of the drainage system embracing a description of each branch drain together with a description of the purpose of each gulley which will include an inspection of the particular downpipe concerned to the point where this is taken through the external wall of the building.

Perhaps the category of building that will need least radical repair will be the two-storey semi-detached or terraced house of post-1900. Under such circumstances, the need for redesign prior to repair will be unlikely as the two pipe system will probably be functioning perfectly efficiently. The soil stack will no doubt have the appropriate L.C.C. embossing to denote heavy metal and may have a bend at first floor to avoid a window and to link up with the first floor W.C., but this, apart from the swan neck for the pipe to avoid the eaves gutter, will be the only complication in a relatively simple layout. This soil vent pipe will probably only take two outlets at most and probably only one. The surveyor may wish to satisfy himself with a smoke test that all is well with the joints but it is not often found that much basic repair work is necessary apart from the fact that the top vent section may be loose and that the wire baloon grating is often missing. If caulked lead joints have been employed these may need recaulking if the pipeline has been subject to thermal or other movement such as settlement of the wall to which it is fixed. If the pipeline has to be dismantled the condition of the internal surface and any protective coating can be ascertained. In other cases the top section alone can be dismantled and examined as this is the most vulnerable part. The fixings of the lower sections to the brickwork of the main walls should also be examined. The reader is reminded that the Building Regulation N.7. states that the vent pipe should be carried up to such a position and height so as not to transmit foul air prejudicial to health or nuisance and be fitted with a durable iron cage. The Code of Practice recommends that high vents should in all cases be taken to a point above the eaves or flat roofs and not less than 3 feet (900mm) above the head of any window within a horizontal distance of 10 feet (3·0m) from the vent pipe.

The surveyor will not moreover find much to complain of in houses of the type mentioned in the design of waste downpipes. These will have a hopper head at first floor level and a gully at the base and although each may be subject to the criticisms set out earlier in this Chapter some elementary care and cleaning by the householder is cheaper than an expensive effort in redesign. The important aspect of the matter is that the foul air is effectively kept at bay from the interior of the house. Repair will therefore include the renewal of any of the cast iron sections that might be cracked and in particular the hopper head, which is always particularly suspect from this point of view, should be examined from a ladder and any sections of light metal pipe should be removed and replaced with appropriate B.S. material. The surveyor will complete his inspection of the vertical plumbing of houses in this category by checking that unusually long branches are provided with separate ventilation but even this feature is often found to be provided. Care is also necessary to ensure that access to pipework is available for future maintenance and that in certain special circumstances insulation against noise or freezing is incorporated.

Where care in redesign is called for in particular, however, in the writer's experience, is in the case of houses older than in the previous category, or alternatively in houses of approximately the same period which are above two storey in height. In particular houses of the inner metropolis often comprise basement, ground and possibly three upper floors and these might be discussed briefly in turn.

Older Houses

The old lead soil pipes which were commonplace up to 1880 will still be found operating satisfactorily after many years of use. Much will depend on how many W.C's. these serve and as to the weight and condition of the metal as to whether they will be retained or not, provided the soil pipe has a minimum diameter of 3 inches (76mm). Lead is an acceptable material in one major sense in that it adjusts itself to movement more easily than cast iron. The weight of a 4-inch

(102mm) diameter modern lead soil pipe should be 22·8 lbs. per linear yard (10·33 kg per linear metre). It might be mentioned that one of the reasons for retaining lead soil pipes where these exist is to preserve the architectural quality of the building. It is often better to accept that such pipes are sufficiently satisfactory than to replace them with a modern equivalent however superior from the point of view of sanitary design. The only difficulty with lead piping is of course that it is more prone to distortion than other types and for this reason the base of the pipe is normally protected with a sheath. If any of the soldered joints are unsatisfactory they can of course be renewed by a skilled plumber who should also ensure that vertical fixings are not at a greater distance than 4 feet (1·2m) apart, spiked to plugs let in the wall, the surplus tacking being turned over the heads of the nails as a protection. Astragal joints should, in the writers' view, be replaced with wiped joints. Finally it should be remembered that lead pipes are resistant to acid attack but can be attacked by Portland cement, lime and plaster, so that where they pass through or are in contact with walls they require a coating of bitumen.

Should the lead soil pipe be beyond hope of saving however, cast iron pipes to B.S.416 which covers three grades of pipe, extra heavy, heavy and medium, can be employed instead. Caulked lead jointing is to be preferred to lead wool where possible, but access and other circumstances must be taken into account, together with weather conditions. The provision of a new soil pipe will provide the opportunity for distance pieces to be used between the back of the pipe and the wall face so that repainting is possible. The surveyor should however take care to ensure that the joint at the base of the pipe, which will be caulked lead to a cast iron soil pipe or a cement joint with tarred gaskin to a stoneware drain, is properly made, as this will not be capable of inspection once it is set up.

The older property will, upon inspection, be found to have a number of independent waste pipes with probably little provision for ventilation. If the house is not more than two storeys in height not much harm will occur but a tangle of waste pipes discharging into a single hopper head should be altered by the provision of a new waste vent pipe with anti-syphon pipe if necessary and the provision of access junctions is recommended where possible. The lower end of the waste pipe must be treated with care to disconnect it from the underground drainage system. It may be taken to discharge over the grating of an ordinary trapped gully but preferably it should be taken into a back or side inlet gully below the grating but above the water seal. Main waste pipes for external use are normally of cast iron to B.S.416.

Taller Buildings

Where the two pipe system will be found to be chiefly in need of redesign will be in taller buildings consisting of basement, ground and perhaps three or four upper floors with sanitary or waste fittings to each floor. Here the waste pipes may often combine with rainwater pipes by means of a number of hopper heads, one at each floor level. These will often be found to be in need of renewal which will involve the consideration of redesign. Under these circumstances the existing layout is unsatisfactory, as the top hopper heads are well beyond the reach of regular maintenance and will be found to be insanitary and liable to blockage. The risk of overflow with the resulting smears often seen to exterior brickwork are a telling indication of the sort of defects which can occur over a long period of neglect and may also be indicative of rot internally, a point always worth investigation.

The surveyor will therefore wish to replace the present waste pipes with new waste and anti-siphon stacks complete. In the London area the Greater London Council By-Laws express a distaste for hopper heads. A single hopper head to a two-storey house will probably be tolerated but if the circumstances just described apply to larger houses the Council will probably insist that the hopper heads are removed and the waste and anti-siphonage stacks set up to modern principles.

One Pipe System

In the one pipe system introduced on multi-storey buildings between the wars the omission of the gully and the hopper head throws the whole burden of ensuring an effective barrier to gases from the sewer on to the seals in the appliances and it is necessary to ensure that the traps are kept adequately filled. Trap water seals of 3 inches (76mm), as against the $1\frac{1}{2}$ inches (38mm) which is effective in two pipe plumbing, are considered necessary, together with the venting of all traps except the highest to prevent any siphonage or blowing of seals. Although often more expensive than two pipe work for two-storey houses, the one pipe system has increasingly tended to replace the two pipe particularly in houses of more than two storeys on improvement schemes and nowadays with the Building Regulations requiring pipes to be run internally and total abandonment of waste hopper heads it must be considered standard for such work. It is particularly suitable where there are bathrooms one above the other in three, four or five storey converted houses and kitchens can be arranged adjacent.

876

The single stack system

Single stack plumbing (i.e. a true one pipe system, with the appliances ventilated only by the stack), an innovation since the Second World War, becomes comparable in cost for two pipe work on the old style with hoppers and no trap ventilation but it is vital that the seals remain intact under normal conditions of use. The Building Research Establishment now say that the risk of siphoning and back pressure are not so great as had been thought but single stack plumbing is mainly suitable for single units of not more than two storeys and will only achieve its full value and economy when used in a large estate scheme of single or two storey houses. The saving in cost in normal domestic construction is not nearly marked enough to automatically invoke its use within the realms of maintenance and repair of ordinary domestic single houses which drain separately into a public sewer. There may, however, be a case for its use to be adopted if a terrace or row of houses is to be re-drained as one unit on the private sewer principle. It is possible however, that, as for the one pipe system, a surveyor will be faced with a problem of an incorrect installation. It is here that the Code of Practice of 1968 will be of value for checking an installation against the good practice recommended today. An earlier edition of C.P.304 dated 1953 and entitled "Soil and Waste Pipes Above Ground" dealt with the two pipe system in addition but this is now out of print. The 1968 Code is an extensive one covering all sizes of buildings in the domestic field. Every practitioner should have a copy available since, as with so many of the Codes, it provides a rational basis for the design of new installations and the renewal of installations for that matter, departing from the rules of thumb which have tended to serve for so long in the past. It also covers the necessary correct arrangements to overcome a particular problem of recent years, that of foaming detergent. This problem has not arisen much on single family units but on the larger house converted into flats it has caused much annoyance to the occupiers of the lower flats in the building either by soapy yards in the case of the two pipe system or by foam backing up into fittings within the building if on the one pipe system.

It should be borne in mind however that the recommendations of the Code as a whole are based on the most modern application of sanitary pipework above ground in so far as new work is concerned and in particular in the wider modern application of the one pipe and the single stack systems. It must not be assumed by any means therefore that every two pipe system must necessarily be redesigned with the recommendations of the Code solely in mind. The reason for this is that with the single stack system the position of the sanitary

877

fittings is regulated to very narrow limits. Each fitting has a minimum critical length away from the stack and even with the provision of deep seals the recommended length must not be exceeded. The reader will understand therefore that, particularly in the case of Victorian houses which are subject to a good deal of change and alteration during their lives, it could be unduly restricting for the single stack system to be set up in order to cater for a particular set of sanitary fittings at a given time. A surveyor has often regretted even changing from the two pipe to the single pipe system when further sanitary fittings are required which were not originally contemplated when the one pipe system was provided in place of the more flexible two pipe system set up as part of the original building.

Certain provisions of the Code however are of interest in the field of repair to houses in order to bring existing systems up to standard and these are extracted and repeated here.

Traps

A trap which is not an integral part of an appliance should be attached to and immediately beneath its outlet and the bore of the trap should be smooth and uniform throughout. All traps should be accessible and provided with adequate means of cleaning and there is advantage in providing traps which are capable of being readily removed or dismantled.

The internal diameters of traps should be $1\frac{1}{4}$ inches (32mm) for basins and bidets and $1\frac{1}{2}$ inches (38mm) for sinks, baths and shower trays. Traps of W.C's. should have a minimum water seal of 2 inches (50mm); traps of other appliances should have a minimum water seal of 3 inches (76mm) for pipes up to and including 2 inch (50mm) diameter and a 2 inch (50mm) minimum water seal for pipes over 2 inches (50mm) diameter.

Discharge Pipes

The internal diameter of a discharge pipe should normally be that of the trap to which it is attached, and in no case less. The fall of a discharge pipe should be adequate to drain the pipe, the minimum desirable fall being 1 in 48. All bends, branches and offsets should be of easy radius and there should be no restriction to the bore of the pipe.

Prevention of cross flow

To prevent the discharge from a W.C. branch backing up the bath waste the latter should be connected to the stack so that its centre line meets the centre line of the stack, or at least 8 inches (200mm) below it but not less than this distance.

Design of single branches and fittings

Branch discharge pipes serving waste appliances should have a uniform shallow fall and the inlet to the stack should, if swept, have a sweep of not more than 1-inch (25mm) radius. Any bend on plan should be of large radius.

Detailed recommendations for the design of single branch pipes and fittings are now given.

Component	Design recommendations	Possible troubles to be guarded against
Bend at foot of stack	Bend to be of "large radius" i.e. 6 in. (150mm) minimum root radius or, if adequate vertical distance is available, two "large radius" 135° bends are to be preferred. Vertical distances between lowest branch connection and invert of drain to be at least 18 in. (460mm) for a two-storey house and 30 in. (760mm) for taller dwellings. Where this distance cannot be achieved, ground floor appliances should be connected directly to a drain	Back pressure at lowest branch, foaming detergents
W.C. branch connection to stack	W.C. connections should be swept in the direction of flow with radius at the invert of not less than 2 in. (50 mm). Cast iron fittings to be to BS416.[1] Fittings in other materials should have the same sweep as cast iron fittings. Unvented W.C. branches up to 5-ft. (1·5m) long have been used successfully	Induced siphonage lower in the stack when W.C. is discharged

[1] BS 416, "Cast iron spigot and socket soil, waste and ventilating pipes (sand and spun), fittings and accessories".

Component	Design recommendations	Possible troubles to be guarded against
Basin waste 1¼-in. (32mm) trap and 1¼-in. waste pipe	"P" traps to be used. The maximum fall of the waste pipe to be determined according to the length of the waste, any bends on plan to be not less than 3 in. (76mm) radius to centre line. Waste pipes longer than the recommended maximum length should be vented. As an alternative 1½-in. (38mm) diameter waste pipes longer than 10 ft. (3m) have been used successfully, but maintenance may be necessary to maintain bore	Self-siphonage
Bath waste 1½-in. (38mm) trap and 1½-in. waste pipe	"P" or 'S' traps may be used. Owing to the flat bottom of a bath, the trailing discharge normally refills the trap and the risk of self-siphonage is much reduced. Waste pipes 7 ft. 6 in. (2·3m) long at a fall of 1¼° to 5° (¼ in./ft. to 1 in./ft., 1/48 to 1/12) have been used successfully. Position of entry of bath waste into stack to be as illustrated in the Code	Self-siphonage
Sink waste 1½-in. (38mm) trap and 1½-in. waste pipe	"P" traps to be used. Owing to the flat bottom of a sink the trailing discharge normally refills the trap and the risk of self-siphonage is much reduced. Fall not greater than 5° (1 in./ft., 1/12) for lengths up to 2 ft. 3 in. (0·7m). For longer lengths up to a maximum of 7 ft. 6 in. (2·3m) fall not greater than 2½° (½ in./ft., 1/24)	Self-siphonage

NOTE. Where the length or fall of the discharge pipe serving a waste appliance is greater than the recommended maximum in the Table above, the discharge pipe should preferably be vented or a larger diameter discharge pipe could be used. This should have a maximum length of about 10 feet (3m).

880

Diameters of branch ventilating pipes and stacks

Diameter of branch discharge pipe or discharge stack (D)	Diameter of ventilating pipe
Smaller than 3 in. (76mm)	2/3 D
3 in. (76mm) to 4 in. (100mm) inclusive	2 in. (50mm)
Larger than 4 in. (100mm)	½ D

Plastic pipes

A wide variety and range of thermoplastic pipes and fittings are now available. The most common are probably those of unplasticised P.V.C. (polyvinylchloride) but these should not be employed where large volumes of water are discharged at temperatures exceeding 140°F (60°C). Some washing machines discharge water in excess of this level. Jointing of unplasticised P.V.C. pipes is usually by means of synthetic rubber ring joints or by solvent cementing, in which case expansion joints must be incorporated in the system.

Thermoplastic pipes are also available in polythene, polypropylene and acrylonitrile butadiene styrene (A.B.S.). These pipes are more resistant to higher temperatures and are more flexible than unplasticised P.V.C. pipes particularly polythene pipes which are less liable to damage from impact and are more resistant to damage from freezing. All polythene pipework needs to be adequately supported however and the maker's instructions for this and for jointing need to be followed.

Thermoplastic pipes are light in weight and easy to handle. They are also highly resistant to corrosion. The chief danger, however, is that their coefficients of expansion are much higher than those of metals and they are not invariably suitable for use without great care in selection and fixing.

Joints

The joints between pipes of the same material such as caulked joints for cast iron pipes, wiped joints for lead pipes and the compression and capillary joints for copper pipes are well known but the following is a list of joints between pipes of different materials recommended by C.P. 304:

(a) Joints between cast iron, galvanised steel or asbestos-cement

881

pipes and ceramic drain pipes should be made with yarn and cement/sand mortar not stronger than 1:2 and not weaker than 1:3.

(b) Joints between lead pipes and cast iron pipes should be by wiped or lead-burned joint on to a copper-alloy sleeve which should be caulked with yarn and lead, into the cast iron socket. The copper-alloy sleeve can be protected from corrosive effluents if the lead pipe is inserted into it for its full length.

(c) Joints between lead pipes and ceramic pipe sockets should be by wiped or lead-burned joint on to a copper-alloy sleeve which should be jointed with yarn and cement mortar consisting of one part of cement and two of sand, into the ceramic socket. The copper-alloy sleeve can be protected from corrosive effluents if the lead pipe is inserted into it for its full length.

(d) Joints between lead and copper should be made by wiped or lead-burned joint to a short copper-alloy connector attached to a normal copper joint.

(e) Joints between lead and galvanised mild steel tubes should be made by wiped joints to the spigot and of a copper-alloy connector screwed to the steel pipe.

(f) Joints of copper pipes to cast iron pipe sockets should be by means of a compression, capillary or brazed joint to a copper-alloy caulking bush which should be caulked with yarn and lead or cold cementitious caulking compound into the cast iron socket.

Joints of copper pipes to threaded bosses on cast iron pipes should be by means of a threaded copper-alloy connector, preferably of the type which can be readily disconnected.

(g) Joints of copper pipes to ceramic pipe sockets should be by means of a brazed or soldered joint to a copper-alloy sleeve which should be jointed by means of a yarn and cement mortar consisting of one part of cement and two of sand into the ceramic socket.

(h) Joints of pitch fibre pipes to ceramic pipes should be spigot and socket joints, and, if made with yarn and cement mortar, the mortar should consist of one part of cement and two of sand. Connection between pitch fibre and other types of pipe may be made by means of the special adaptors manufactured for this purpose.

(i) Joints of galvanised steel to cast iron should be made with a cementitious cold caulking compound or be caulked with lead.

(j) Joints of uP.V.C. pipes to ceramic pipe sockets should be by means of purpose-made metal sleeves jointed as in (a) above.

(k) Joints of uP.V.C. pipes to cast iron pipe sockets should be by means of purpose-made cast iron sleeves jointed with firmly caulked tarred yarn and not less than 1½-inch (38mm) depth of run molten lead, or fibrous lead yarn.

(*l*) Joints between polythene pipes and pipes of other material should be made in accordance with the polythene pipe manufacturer's instructions.

Testing

The Code of Practice devotes three pages to tests for sanitary pipework above ground. These are necessary for testing completed new work and although too lengthy to set out here in full, briefly provide for an air test to ensure that the system is watertight and performance tests for establishing that trap seals are not broken when fittings are used. The precise methods of test should be followed for new or renewed work and of course the addition of smoke is necessary on the air test if a fault is to be detected.

In the field of investigation for repair, tests may be of use depending on the circumstances. However while it is of value to know that a new system will not leak when it is put into service, a leak in an old installation is usually only too evident, both as to position and cause. On occasions it may be that a leak is difficult to trace to its source but even then it is probably easier to expose hidden pipes to track down than apply air and smoke tests which would not necessarily give a closer indication of where the leak occurs than visual observation. However, the smoke test is available if it can be of use in such cases.

Tracking down the source of unpleasant odours and eliminating them can be quite a trial of the surveyor's knowledge and tests may be of assistance here. If the system is two pipe it may be a simple matter related to a gully or a hopper head, the cure being either a closer attention to maintanence or alternatively some, perhaps minor, alterations. With a one pipe or single pipe system there are two possibilities. In the first instance it may be that a joint or joints on the system although not giving rise to a leak are not airtight while in the second instance there may be some defect in design layout which gives rise to siphonage in a trap. An investigation would of necessity have to proceed from the building owner or tenant's grumbles as this would, with luck, isolate the matter to a reasonable area. Cross examination might elicit whether the unpleasant odour is very intermittent or of a more permanent nature. One might even be able to associate the occurrence with the operation of a particular fitting even though this was elsewhere from the compartment affected. A physical examination of the system and some performance tests as laid down by the Code should reveal whether a trap can be deprived of its water seal and if so the remedial measures would have to be appropriate to the circumstances.

If the odour is persistent then it is more likely to be due to a defective joint and if this is not readily found by close examination of all visible joints then it is conceivable that a smoke test will be of assistance in locating the source. When found the remedy is obvious and in this case much cheaper.

The successful solving at reasonable cost of the "nasty smell" problem can work wonders for the surveyor's public relations, particularly if others have attempted to solve the problem before him and have failed to do so.

Support and fixing of pipes

External pipes requiring painting or other protective coating need a free space for access all round the pipe. The clearance with the wall should be $1\frac{1}{4}$ inches (30mm) and it is not desirable for pipes to be set in angles or in chases. The walls of Victorian houses are often so formed that pipes are tucked in angles where they are exceptionally difficult to inspect, let alone to maintain. In extreme cases such as during the repair or maintenance of inaccessible pipes where these are situated in hidden corners or very high positions redesign may be called for if the surveyor suspects that the pipes as a whole will not receive regular maintenance. Where pipes pass through walls or floors or other parts of the structure they are best provided with an aperture formed with a sleeve of inert material to protect them.

Many existing pipes are not provided with adequate support. The most vulnerable are of course horizontal pipes of polythene or lead, but the fixings of pipes should not present much of a problem provided particularly that in the case of thermoplastic pipes, the maker's instructions are followed. Cast iron pipes are normally fixed by means of ears on the sockets with or without distance pieces. Lead pipes require double or single cast lead tacks, soldered or lead burned to the pipe, fixed to the structure with galvanised nails or gun-metal screws while sheet lead milled tacks are also used. Asbestos cement pipes are fixed with galvanised mild steel holderbats for building into or screwing to the structure. Copper pipes may be fixed with copper alloy holderbats or strap clips.

Maintenance

Regular maintenance of pipework above ground probably pays higher dividends than many other areas of this necessary function. Vertical ventilating pipes, particularly those of cast iron, accumulate rust at bends and offsets and rust will appear elsewhere externally on pipes if the protective coating is neglected or scamped. When access covers, caps and cleaning eyes are removed care is necessary to replace damaged packings and washers before replacing the covers. Defective pipes, particularly those which are cracked at the back and blocked and overflowing hopper heads are one of the frequent causes of dry rot outbreaks in buildings. Moisture soaks into adjacent brickwork and as the construction of timber floors above ground level is often unventilated there is a distinct danger whenever a pipe leaks for any length of time in outbreaks occurring in adjacent floors or other timber features, such as skirtings, window frames and linings.

H. RAINWATER PIPES AND GUTTERS

The surveyor will find a surprising complexity of shapes and materials for gutters and downpipes. These will vary from cast iron half round or O.G. gutters to specially shaped gutters in soft metal such as zinc to the more modern materials available. Often several different patterns of gutter will be observed on the same house.

It is of first importance when considering the repair of gutters and downpipes to consider their adequacy for the task they have to perform. The reader will be familiar with the 3-inch (16mm) cast iron downpipe attached to the outside wall of a tall building which proceeds with perhaps several bends along its length to carry the rainwater from top to bottom. It also nonchalantly collects the rainwater from additional and subsidiary roofs at various levels. In conditions of abnormal rainfall many of the gutters will overflow so that these either drip in a visible manner or alternatively tip the rainwater to the interior of the gutter edge so that it forms a dark stain in the brickwork below the eaves, with a consequent danger of rot developing in adjacent timber. Accordingly, it is, when considering repairs, necessary to know the maximum flow load for which provision must be made and the capacity of gutters and downpipes of various sizes.

The flow load for a gutter depends on the area of roofing discharging into it taking into account the pitch of the roof and the peak rate of rainfall. The angle at which the rain falls when it is at a peak together with the duration of peaks are also material factors. It is interesting that the Building Research Establishment feel that a simplified approach to rainfall statistics can be valid in estimating gutter flow. Regional differences are not significant in relation to peak intensity and accordingly the number of important features in the rainfall pattern is reduced to three, the average intensity of a fall, its duration and the frequency of occurrence. The average intensity suggested as a basis for general design purposes for eaves guttering is 3 inches (76mm) per hour. This intensity is found to occur, in any given locality, over a period of five minutes about every other year, and over a period of ten minutes only once in about eight years. As an approximation for roof pitches up to 50°, the area of the roof surface may be taken as the basis for calculation ignoring the pitch and angle of the rain. This gives the flow load as 2·6/100 times the actual roof area in square feet (gallons per minute). A slightly more accurate formula is necessary for pitches over 50° which is that the flow load equals plan area times $(0{\cdot}026+0{\cdot}12 \tan A)$ where A is the angle of pitch.

A flow capacity of a simple straight gutter, i.e. the amount of water in gallons per minute it can carry, depends on its area of cross-section, its shape, length and slope. Quite a slight slope increases the capacity although there is a limit to the advantage that can be achieved. A level 36 feet (11m) length of 4½ inches (114mm) half round gutter can dispose of 15 gallons (68 litres) per minute; when laid to a slope of one in 216, however, it can dispose of 26 gallons (118 litres) per minute. The Building Research Establishment suggests that too big a fall should be avoided as too wide a gap between roof edge and gutter may cause some water to miss the gutter altogether. Length has little influence on the flow capacity but it determines the area of roof drained and therefore the flow load. A right-angled bend reduces flow capacity if it is near an outlet. If the bend is within 6 feet (1·8m) of an outlet a 20 per cent reduction in capacity should be assumed when the bend is sharp cornered but this is reduced to 10 per cent only if the bend has a corner rounded to a 1-inch (25mm) radius. For sloping corners the reduction should be taken as 25% for both rounded and sharp corners. If the bend is within 6 to 12 feet (1·8 to 3·6m) of the outlet half these reductions may be assumed.

The shape, size and position of the outlet and downpipe also affect the flow capacity of a gutter. Round cornered outlets give a smoother flow than sharp cornered ones and this has an effect on gutter capacity with the smaller outlet sizes. The area of cross-section of outlets and downpipes may be smaller than that of the gutter because this rarely flows full at the outlet and the speed of flow increases markedly at this point. Downpipe sizes commonly used are unnecessarily large, but with smaller downpipe sizes it is necessary for joints to be sealed to avoid leakage. Swan necked offsets, bends and shoes do not appear to affect the capacity of the gutter. The position of the outlet however has a big effect on the flow capacity of a gutter since when an outlet is placed centrally along the length of a gutter the gutter capacity required is only one half of that needed when an end outlet is employed.

The manner in which water leaves the edge of a roof varies with the kind of roof covering and this has a bearing on the fixing of gutters. In a slated roof the water leaves the edge with very little spread to front or rear. The gutter may therefore be placed centrally under the edge but not more than 2 inches (50mm) below. With some roofs, however, such as clay pantiles with sharp upper corners, the water leaves the edge with a wide spread and the gutter must be close to the edge with its centre slightly forward of the under edge of the roof. When the lower end of the roof edge is rounded the water may be deflected more to the rear and the centre of the gutter should then also be placed slightly to the rear. The most satisfactory roof edge is the one with the upper corner round and the lower corner sharp.

When assessing the sizes of gutters and downpipes and deciding if the present system is adequate or if new gutter lengths are required the surveyor must have the fall very much in mind as a practical element in the work. The suitable choice and fixing of gutter clips must be studied and only those recommended by the makers for the particular purpose should be employed. Unsuitable clips which lead to a sideways tilt of the gutter can, of course, reduce the capacity. An insufficient number of clips leads to sagging and inefficient falls which will affect the performance of the gutter and put a strain on joints which can affect its durability. The surveyor should be particularly careful to ensure that gutters are as rigid as possible as there is always the possibility that a ladder placed against the gutter for roof maintenance or some other task may cause it to become distorted and may thus affect its efficiency.

Maintenance

Gutters below trees should be cleared at least once a year after the leaves have fallen and the surveyor must consider if wire balloons can assist in preventing the blockage of downpipes if leaves are likely to be a problem. Some types of tree, for example cedar trees, are particularly difficult to deal with, as a mass of fine needles will be allowed to fall into gutters causing considerable problems. These will have to be cleared at regular intervals. With cast iron gutters, rust should be scaled and two coats of bitumastic paint should be used for the gutter interior. If the surveyor is in any doubt about the suitability of a gutter length so far as its state of repair is concerned once he has estimated its flow capacity, he might well decide to take the section down and have it set up to a proper level rather than take its state of repair on trust. In this way he can be certain that the joints are effectively remade and that there are no cracks hidden on the inside edge of the gutter that might cause hidden seepage to the brickwork behind.

I. SANITARY FITTINGS

A surprising range of ancient sanitary fittings will be found in older buildings. With the mass-production of cheap, effective modern fittings to British Standard requirements, the obsolete types of W.C. pan are fast disappearing and although some valve closets may still be seen, their renewal with a modern fitting is not a very expensive matter. Ancient pans with "D" traps or of the long or short hopper variety or even the washout pan, if seen, will cause a surveyor pleasure, not because of any intention to retain them for they are now very obsolete, but purely due to the entertainment of seeing a rare specimen of a vanishing breed. Washdown closets and siphonic closets are available in a range of ceramic finishes to B.S.1213 and washdown closets may have either a P or S trap. The outgo of this fitting should be above floor level for easy connection to a soil pipe or a drain. Siphonic closets are generally satisfactory but the surveyor should satisfy himself that the pattern chosen has a good lasting and efficient action. The W.C. flushing apparatus should also be matched to the pan in use. The high level cast iron painted cisterns of former years with their noisy actions and subtleties of operation (except to the initiated) are now also obsolete. Considerable corrosion takes places inside and tell-tale rust marks externally may indicate that the cistern has reached the end of its useful life.

The joint between a W.C. pan and a cast iron soil pipe still gives a remarkable amount of trouble. All surveyors will be familiar with the shaky timber floor in the W.C. compartment and the leaking connection between the fitting and soil pipe. The circle becomes vicious in that the floor, besides being highly insanitary, develops dry or wet rot becoming shakier in the process and causing a larger leak to develop. The difficulty lies in the normal formation of a rigid joint between pan and pipe giving no allowance for vibration or movement in the floor to which the pan is screwed. The advocacy of a flexible joint for this connection has been strong for many years but perhaps the writers have been unlucky since these have been found to be equally unsatisfactory and even experienced plumbers find them difficult to make in a watertight manner. It is considered that with more attention paid to ensuring that a timber floor is reasonably free from any vibration and there are plenty of ways of doing this, the ordinary cement and gaskin joint properly made still provides the best connection and will continue to do so until some form of improved coupling can be developed. The case for easy removal of the W.C. in the event of blockage and which is facilitated by the use of a non-rigid flexible joint as recommended by the Code of Practice are of course strong but on the other hand access for clearing any blockage can usually be provided nearby from the soil pipe.

Cast iron baths with porcelain enamel finishes and white glazed fireclay baths are abundantly available. The latter due to their high cost and weight are less frequently used. The surveyor will be able to judge for himself if the type delivered is satisfactory. One of the points to observe when replacing an old pattern of bath is that the floor and surrounding area which may have been covered up by ancient panels and coverings are free from any rot or disease. A slow drip from a defective fitting may have persisted and remained undetected for years. Glazed earthenware or vitreous china lavatory basins are of suitable pattern for domestic use and the surveyor is invited to consult his client's preference when advising as to type and pattern since these vary considerably.

Overflows from W.C. flushing cisterns should be piped and taken through an external wall to discharge at a convenient point in the open air. The whole point of an overflow is to give a warning that the ball valve system has broken down and needs repair. It goes without saying that the overflow should project in a position where, if it is used, it does not saturate the surrounding brickwork, but it is surprising how often this happens. The overflow should be fitted with a hinged stopper arranged above the splayed end to the pipe so that it does not freeze in cold weather.

J. DISPOSAL

Up to now in this Chapter it has been assumed that disposal of sewage and surface water will be to a local authority sewer. It is now necessary to deal with those circumstances where this is not the case and where sewage has either to be stored for collection in a cesspool or is taken to a small domestic treatment plant, with waste and surface water taken to a sump or soakaways.

(1) Cesspools

Cesspools are very often used, particularly in country districts, for one or two isolated buildings of insufficient size to justify a treatment plant. Their use however should be discouraged for more than say ten persons. Cesspools are, of course, employed due to the fact that drainage to sewers is not possible within easy reach but the chief difficulty with cesspools is that they have to be emptied at intervals and in considering whether to retain a cesspool or contemplate the cost of piping drainage to a nearby sewer, the surveyor should check up on the nature of the services provided by the local authority for emptying, together with details of their charges.

The British Standard Code of Practice C.P.302:200 recommends that cesspools be tested by filling with water, allowing the water to stand for 24 hours and then topping up if necessary. The water test is then left on for 48 hours following and if the fall of the level during this period exceeds 1 inch (25mm) the test is not deemed to be satisfactory. It is, of course, probable that many existing cesspools will fail a test of this stringency, and the surveyor may have to consider whether to repair the existing structure or whether to renew the whole installation. Before deciding he should consider first of all whether the existing structure satisfies current require- ments and if the existing location is the best position. The first requirement is clearly that access to the cesspool from a main road or a side road is as near as possible, subject of course to the neigh- bours not being offended if the prevailing wind should not be kind. The site should be lower than the dwelling house with the ground sloping away in the other direction as an obvious and elementary precaution in case of flooding. A minimum capacity of 4,000 gallons or 640 cubic feet (18,184 litres or $18 \cdot 1 m^3$) is required by the Building Regulations while the Code of Practice suggests a minimum capacity for 45 days which can be reduced if commensurate arrangements to empty the cesspool at more frequent intervals can be made. The water usage of thirty gallons per head per day is often taken as a basis for calculation for cesspools which should not really exceed 10,000 gallons (45,460 litres) in capacity as an economic size to build.

The surveyor should bear in mind that the local authority is empowered under the Public Health Act 1936 to examine and test cesspools in their area. The provisions of the Act include such matters as repairing or cleaning overflows or leaking cesspools by default or requiring this to be done. Building Regulation N17 requires a new cesspool to be impervious both from within and without and sited so as not to pollute any source of water likely to be used for drinking or domestic purposes. The regulation requires a cesspool to have access for cleaning and not to be so near a building that it constitutes a nuisance or a danger to health. The cesspool must be properly covered and able to be emptied completely. It must have a suitable manhole cover for the purpose of inspection and cleansing and have adequate ventilation. The Building Regulations also require that the cesspool is not provided with any outlet for overflow and discharge other than to provide for emptying or cleansing. It used often not to be considered a particularly serious crime in the remoter country districts for an overflow pipe from a cesspool to be taken out on to neighbouring fields which, particularly as they belonged to a neighbour, was considered highly beneficial to the soil, as indeed it was. This is not now permitted so that suitable access from a road is of prime importance. If renewal is decided upon as the best procedure then both Building Regulations and the Code of Practice should be followed. If on the other hand all the requirements are basically provided but the cesspool under test is not satisfactory then it should be emptied (it would have to be emptied to obtain the size in any event) and the structure examined. It is possible even then of course to find the rendering severely cracked and on the removal of this throughout that the brickwork is so fractured and distorted that much rebuilding is required. Here the opportunity would arise to establish the constructional details since there is little sense in rebuilding to the same form as before if this has been proved by time to be inadequate. At this stage it would be necessary to consider all constructional details as it might still prove cheaper to build afresh rather than expend money on part rebuilding a defective structure.

More often than not however the internal defects causing leakage will be confined to cracks in the rendering and probably loose areas as well. Hacking off the rendering, raking out joints to form a key and re-lining would be the answer in these circumstances. The merits of re-lining in asphalt as against cement rendering would seem to be considerable, particularly since the aspect of water penetration from outside should have been taken care of in the outer lining of puddled clay or concrete in the original construction and there should therefore be no question of the asphalt being forced off the inside.

A check on such items as covers and frames and ventilation to the cesspool and the adjacent interceptor chamber and the remedying of any faults could complete an operation to restore a cesspool to a condition almost as good as new.

(2) *Small Domestic Sewage Treatment Works*

All surveyors will have no doubt learnt at some time in their career the principles behind sewage treatment and many would no doubt be able to draw a reasonably approximate section through a septic tank, filter bed and humus tank, since it is a frequent enough examination question. Notwithstanding this, however, it is doubtful whether many surveyors really have sufficient contact with buildings where treatment to sewage is carried out to be really familiar with the requirements for successful operation. It is a field which borders on the specialist and a study of British Standard Code of Practice C.P.302:1972 entitled "Small Domestic Sewage Treatment Works" shows why. There may well be surveyors who have proceeded beyond the normal ambit of the general practice or building surveyor to study the subject of sewage treatment from the municipal engineer's point of view and they would certainly be qualified to deal with testing and supervising repairs or renewal to a small treatment works. For the general surveyor, however, it is outside his scope and such matters should be entrusted to a specialist. This would apply also to surveyors in the public service whose Council purchased, say, a large country house for institutional purposes where such plant might exist, though he at least should have the facilities of the Borough Engineer's Department to fall back upon. The Code itself indicates that it is no substitute for the taking of skilled engineering advice based on a knowledge of sewage works practice and of the local conditions.

In regard to an existing system functioning and in use it is of course possible that it may have been installed by specialist contractors and be maintained by them. Such a firm would no doubt be able to advise a surveyor or owner on the present condition. On the other hand it may have been installed to the specification of a consultant by a general contractor. If the consultant is recalled, he or his firm could be asked to report on the performance and present condition. If there are no indications of this nature available then the local authority itself may be able to advise on the selection of a reliable specialist contractor in the area or of a consultant familiar with local problems.

Although in these circumstances a little knowledge can be a dangerous thing and specialist contractors or a consultant should be responsible to the client a few salient points could well be set out in regard to maintenance tests and one or two special points so that the surveyor will be familiar with the problems and if necessary instruct contractors on behalf of the client.

As to maintenance regular weekly inspection should be made giving particular attention to the filter bed which may become clogged with organic matter so that the liquid does not percolate, causing ponding. If loosening of the surface of the bed does not overcome this other lines of investigation and treatment are needed together with further consideration as to whether the septic tank has been de-sludged at sufficiently frequent intervals (normally about every six months), whether there has been an excessive use of detergents, which have now become a problem in sewage treatment, or whether the filter capacity is adequate. Distributor pipes require cleaning with sufficient frequency to prevent obstruction to the flow of effluent.

The same type of test can be used for any tank used in a sewage treatment plant to ensure that it is watertight as for a cesspool. In addition it is desirable for some means to be available whereby a sample of the effluent can be taken for testing.

The Building Regulations require a septic tank to have a minimum capacity of 600 gallons ($2 \cdot 7m^3$) and, as for cesspools, to be impervious from within and without and to be sited having regard to various factors (see Regulation N17). It is probably in regard to suitable siting in relation to local conditions and in the specification of a suitable plant taking these factors into account that the skill of specialists or consultants are fully exercised.

(3) *Surface Filtration*

The disposal of waste water from baths, basins and sinks together with surface water when domestic sewage is taken to a cesspool or septic tank is usually by means of the surface filtration method. This involves taking these categories of waste water in ordinary jointed pipes to a sluice box and from the sluice box through a series of open jointed agricultural drains to a sump. The method is also sometimes used for the final disposal of effluent after treatment from a small domestic sewage treatment plant. Consideration of site conditions again is vital as it is essential to avoid pollution and the system must be in open land away from trees, otherwise the roots will quickly clog up the system. Care is necessary too in laying to prevent the system of agricultural soakaway drains from becoming silted up, the sluice box being used to divert water along the different lines of drain. It is difficult however to ascertain the amount of land required for this method and to observe the results. The level of the underground water table has a distinct bearing on the performance and if it is nearer the surface than 6 feet (2m) in winter it is inadvisable to adopt this method. Since access is seldom provided the indications of trouble would be waterlogging of the ground and a too frequent necessity to bale out the sump. There is little that can be recommended in the way of repair, apart from cleaning if access is provided, otherwise a reconsideration of basic principles in accordance with the current British Standard Code of Practice would probably be required with a view to re-laying.

(4) *Soakaways*

Although it is far more preferable for rainwater and surface water
to be taken to either a combined or separate local authority sewer,
in many cases of estate development where a combined drain is
the method adopted at the rear to pick up the discharge from each
house, rainwater from roof slopes at the front and surface water
are taken to a soakaway below the front garden.

Failures in the arrangement and performance of these soakaways
are usually indicated by flooding or a waterlogged condition and
sometimes also by subsidence if the structure of the soakaway fails.
In the unlikely need for a new system of such soakaways (perhaps on
re-draining an old terrace of houses on a new combined drain in
lieu of former individual systems for each house) a body of information exists in the current Code of Practice on which to base the
design. Some of the other factors to be taken into account have
already been touched upon previously in this Chapter in regard to
the assessment of rainfall and run-off, the permeability of surfaces,
areas to be drained and the necessary calculations for the size and
gradient of pipes to give a velocity of flow of not less than 2·5 feet
(760mm) per second. As surface water drains should not be less
than 4 inches (102mm) in diameter such calculations are not
normally necessary for a single house but where the discharge is to
be taken together from a number of houses, they may well be essential.

A soakaway can only be of use in a pervious sub-soil such as
gravel, sand, chalk, or a fissured rock. To avoid collapse the pit is
usually lined with brickwork laid dry or perforated precast concrete
rings or segments laid dry or alternatively filled with hardcore and
should be covered with a slab of stone or precast concrete. Soakaways should not be constructed within 10 feet (3·0m) of a building,
20 feet (6m) if the soil is clay or in such a position that the ground
below the foundations is likely to be affected. The size of a soakaway is governed by the amount of surface water it will have to deal
with and the rate of percolation, but a common method of assessing
size is to allow a water storage capacity equal to at least ½ inch
(13mm) of rainfall over the impermeable area.

If the suitability of the ground is in doubt, absorption figures can
be obtained by digging trial pits and measuring the rate at which the
water soaks away. Alternatively, disposal to a watercourse or by
means of storage vessels might be considered.

K. SUB-SOIL DRAINAGE

The drainage of the sub-soil is essential on certain sites and in certain soil conditions to divert the natural flow of water away from foundations, particularly on the uphill side of a house, or to reduce the level of the ground water. Four reasons are given in the British Standard Code of Practice 301:1971 for the drainage of sub-soil water which is water occurring naturally below the surface of the ground (the upper surface of which being the "water table") in contrast to surface water which consists of the run-off of natural water from the ground, whether paved or not. The four reasons are:

(1) To increase the stability of the ground
(2) To avoid surface flooding
(3) To alleviate or to avoid causing dampness in basements
(4) To reduce the humidity in the immediate vicinity of the
    buildings.

In the province of repair work a surveyor may be consulted on any of the above matters, except probably the last. In the construction of a building the question of sub-soil drainage may or may not have been taken into account. If it was and adequate drainage at the time of construction was provided, confirmation of this might be obtained by the presence on the site of a soakaway, a catchpit with pipe discharging into a ditch or watercourse or a connection through a reverse action interceptor to the local authority surface water drainage system. If the building is not too old the local authority may have records of what was done originally. What is unlikely however is that there will be any record of the run of the drains or any access to them. Field drain pipes or French drains consisting of a shallow trench filled with rubble or clinker are notorious for becoming clogged with silt or obstructed by tree roots and the absence of access for ensuring that they are free of blockage often means that over a period of years the system either in whole or in part ceases to function effectively. The result may well be a return to those conditions existing on the site before the work was carried out with the consequences of possible structural damage to the building, surface flooding and unpleasant conditions for the occupants. Although the evidence of flooding would make the diagnosis of this problem relatively simple there can be cases where there is no surface flooding and if sub-soil water movement is suspected as being a reason for structural damage, the surveyor would need additional evidence before being certain. This will involve ascertaining the depth of the water table and the direction of flow of the sub-soil water. This information can best be ascertained by the digging of trial holes. The depth of the water table varies with the season, the amount of rainfall and the proximity and level of natural drainage channels. It is desirable to ascertain the level of the standing water in the trial holes over a considerable period so as to enable the seasonal variations to be recorded, but in particular the highest water level, and it may conceivably be possible to relate structural movement to periods when the water level is at its maximum. The movement of sub-soil water can usually be inferred from the general inclination of the land surface and confirmation obtained from the trial holes.

If the problem is verified as being one of inadequate sub-soil drainage the solution will probably lie in the provision of a new system, of a necessity as the old system, assuming one exists, will almost certainly be inaccessible for repair. New sub-soil drainage systems are described in British Standard Code of Practice C.P. 301:1971 "Building Drainage" to which reference should be made as necessary. The design considerations are covered together with five systems of laying pipes, one of these being particularly apposite to the repair field called the Moat or Cut-Off System designed to intercept the flow of sub-soil water and thereby protect the foundations of buildings. The choice from the remaining systems will depend on the character of the site but in particular on whether the whole of the site need be drained or whether it is only a problem in relation to the building. If the whole site is being redrained then it is important to divert carefully into the new system any of the drains of the old system that may be cut in the process because it is likely that parts of the old system still function to some extent however slight.

Chapter II
Running the Contract

CONTENTS

897

INTRODUCTION

HOWEVER skilled a surveyor may become in correctly diagnosing the faults that occur to buildings and in specifying remedies for those faults, this knowledge alone will not in itself ensure that the building is repaired in a manner both aesthetically and economically satisfying and which leaves not only the owner but also the builder and all the many people who will have had an interest in the repair work contented at the termination of the contract. For the business aspect of the actual carrying out of the work is as vital to all concerned as any other aspect and this Chapter, accordingly, will be devoted to a subject which, for the sake of brevity, has been called "running the contract".

It will be understood however that there is far more to this subject than these simple words imply. If the survyor's duties in repairing houses consisted merely of selecting a builder or builders, deciding what type of contract to employ and then "running" it, with all the blissful ease suggested by that attractive word, the changeover of personnel in the profession would be much more rapid since the swollen intake of recruits could be catered for by the early retirement of the senior members in easy circumstances. For many of the matters that affect the outcome of a building contract and make it either a success or a failure lie outside the literal meaning of these words and, in ways in which it is hoped will become clear in this Chapter, the surveyor's relationship with the builder is no less important than his relationship with his client, the building owner, be he a private individual, a group, a committee or a government department. The surveyor's relationships also, moreover, extend to a host of others such as engineers and specialist experts of all types, sub-contractors whether nominated or otherwise, Planning Officers and Public Health Inspectors, the Local District Surveyor if in the London area or the Building Inspector elsewhere, Council Officers dealing with grants, representatives of statutory undertakings or Highway Authorities and the surveyors acting for superior landlords and adjoining owners. The surveyor may also in the course of his duties perhaps deal with a number of solicitors acting for various parties since the repair of buildings on land either in towns or in the country often involves some legal work. Each of these many persons referred to can be assumed to be expert in his own field but each will be concerned only with his own specialised viewpoint which might well conflict with that of the surveyor who will need a combination

901

of firmness and tact to ensure that his own scheme and his client's interests are not put badly awry. Conversely however, it is hoped that the surveyor will have the common sense and humility to grasp that certain suggestions which may be put to him might improve his scheme and result not only perhaps in a saving of money but possibly in a better repair in the end.

Although the surveyor will doubtless have available the benefit of the advice of his client's solicitor should the need arise, he clearly cannot keep troubling a busy man over small points of law, to say nothing of increasing his client's expenses by way of legal costs. The surveyor must therefore have a sound knowledge of the basic law that will be required to see his repair work successfully through to completion. This will cover not only the law relating to building contracts but the whole web of legislation affecting buildings from the Building Regulations to the Town and Country Planning Acts, Drainage By-Laws and, if in London, the London Building Acts and By-Laws. The surveyor will be expected to keep abreast not only of Acts of Parliament but the Statutory Regulations following from such Acts and to be aware of regulations affecting, for example, underground rooms, means of escape and like matters. There are, in addition to those statutes directly affecting buildings, others that effect them indirectly such as the Clean Air Act 1965. Knowledge of the law for the surveyor however does not even end here. It is just as important for the surveyor to know what may be expected of himself by his client involving, for example, the degree and extent of supervision which is considered necessary for the contract on the site and to understand what the law requires of him before the professional relationship with his client can be said to be satisfied. For it should be remembered that it is not only statute law that has changed rapidly in recent years. Case law has also changed a number of aspects of the surveyor's work, among other matters his relationship with his client, but, just as important, has also made a fundamental difference in the relationship between the surveyor and other parties. It is important therefore for the surveyor to inform himself of these matters. This is, of course, by no means as easy as it sounds, particularly when the pressure of work continues to increase enormously. A good deal of information can be obtained from professional and other journals but probably just as important is the need to read the daily papers. If, for example, the surveyor is contemplating applying for an improvement grant on behalf of his client, he may read in the press that a White Paper is about to be published setting out proposals for a much more generous grants system and under circumstances such as these the surveyor's client may well be prepared to wait and take advantage of the improved legislation on the surveyor's advice that matters be delayed until the proposals can be studied in Bill form.

It is a convenient starting point for this Chapter to assume that the surveyor has so far received authority to complete his initial investigations and that he will have formed an idea as to what suggestions to submit to his client. He now, accordingly, has to make his report advising as to the extent and type of repairs that he considers necessary together with an opinion of the approximate cost. There will be, however, cases where the surveyor is in no position to report to his client even with preliminary information since he will first need to refer back for consent to spend money on further investigations. An example of this might be, for example, the digging of trial holes, or the need for removing casings or panelling to examine parts of the structure that are hidden. There will be a number of occasions when the cost of further investigations such as these may be considerable. Even in minor cases the cost of preliminary investigations appears rather awkwardly as disbursements on the surveyor's account and it is, of course, best for these to be known in advance rather than at a later stage. It should always be remembered that irrespective of any other professional connection with his client, the surveyor, when he spends money on his client's behalf is merely, in the eyes of the law, an agent acting for his principal. There are certain exceptions to this such as, for example, where the surveyor is empowered to act under the terms of the contract as a "quasi arbitrator" in order to decide simple disputes. This will be referred to later but in general the surveyor is an agent for his principal. It is worthwhile, therefore, to pause briefly at the legal relationship of principal and agent.

An agent is one who is invested with a legal power to set up a contractual relationship between his principal and third parties. The creation of the relationship of principal and agent may be set up either by express appointment on the one hand or by implication of the law on the other which might arise from a number of different circumstances. The relationship of principal and agent may also be established by the subsequent ratification of an unauthorised act. There are other ways in which an agent may be invested with power to act for his principal but these are outside the scope of this Chapter. In most cases relating to building contracts, a contractual agency is set up, that is to say one based on contract and it is only in rare cases that an authority to an agent is given under seal. This is known as a Power of Attorney. In the case of a building contract an agent would be described at law as a special agent that is to say one who is appointed to perform a particular act after which his authority comes to an end. In certain circumstances, however, for example, in

903

the case of an agent who manages an estate of property for his client, and who not only collects the rents but gives orders for the repairs, he would be known at law as a general agent since he has a continuous authority to act in the disbursement of money and his authority indeed, may date back over a considerable number of years.

An example of where an agency may be set up by implication of the law arises from the nature of the circumstances known as "An Agency of Necessity". An authority may be conferred by law in circumstances where property is in jeopardy, and, at the time of the emergency, the owner is either away, or ill and his instructions cannot be obtained. In such circumstances the law can imply that the owner has consented to the creation of an agency in order to allow the surveyor to act so as to prevent a dangerous situation arising. The conditions necessary for an agency of this nature to arise are obviously that there is a real emergency on the one hand and that it is impossible to obtain instructions from the owner on the other.

The position of the agent so far as third parties are concerned where his principal is either named or otherwise is also of interest. Where the surveyor makes it clear that he is acting in the capacity of agent and gives the name or description of his client to a builder, the general rule is that the agent himself incurs no obligations. The contract is assumed at law to be between the principal and the third party and the legal effect is as if the principal had made a contract directly with the builder. Where the agent does not disclose the name or sufficient description of his principal but nevertheless makes it quite clear that he is acting purely in the capacity of agent, the legal position is generally the same as where the principal is named, so that under these circumstances also the agent should not incur a personal liability. It is where, however, an agent who is given proper authority to act by his principal does not disclose that he is acting as agent so that the third party does not know of the existence of his principal that the position is more complex. In these circumstances, the doctrine of the undisclosed principal will apply. Under this doctrine the third party, if entitled to take action, may elect to sue either the agent or the undisclosed principal if he can be found. Clearly, however, if a third party obtains a judgment against the one, he is not able to proceed with his case against the other. If, on the other hand, the undisclosed principal has a cause of action against the third party, his rights are limited to some degree since he can only take action if the agent's authority existed at the time of the original contract. Also the agent must not have contracted in terms that are incompatible with his agency, for example, he must not have described himself as the owner of the property.

The agent owes a number of duties to his principal, the first being to exercise diligence and to exercise whatever skill he professes. He must render accounts as required and he must never let his own interest conflict with his obligations to his principal; for example, he must never take any secret profit or bribe from any party with whom he deals on behalf of his principal. If this should occur the contract between agent and principal is voidable at the option of the principal. An agent must also not make use of confidential information obtained during the course of his duties as agent and further should not delegate his duties to a sub-agent without express or implied authority. Finally the agent must comply with his principal's instructions and notify him when it is not possible to comply with them. However, if an agent is given instructions that are ambiguous, he is not liable if he interprets them otherwise than as intended by the principal.

The principal also has obligations to the agent. He is bound to pay his remuneration and expenses as may have been agreed, or, failing that, a sum that is customary under the circumstances, or, in the lack of any evidence as to this, a sum that is considered reasonable at law. The principal is also bound to indemnify the agent against losses arising from the execution of his authority and is also bound to indemnify the agent against losses and liabilities arising out of an unauthorised act that he subsequently ratifies. An agent, however, is not entitled to be indemnified against the consequences of his own negligence, or breach of duty.

An agency may be terminated either by notice or revocation given by the principal to the agent or by notice or renunciation given to the principal by his agent. Otherwise the agency is terminated by the completion of the transaction in the case of a special agency or by the expiration of the period stipulated in a general contract of agency. Alternatively an agency can be terminated by mutual agreement, by death, lunacy, or bankruptcy of either the principal or the agent, by dissolution where the principal is a corporation, by the destruction of the subject matter of the agency, i.e. in the case of a fire completely destroying the house being repaired, or by the contract becoming unlawful. It should be stated, however, that summary action by the agent to terminate his contract, or, for that matter by the principal, may be in breach of contract, and damages may be awarded against the party revoking or renouncing. However, if no period of notice is stipulated in the contract of agency, either party is entitled to give reasonable notice at any time. An interesting situation might occur when a principal terminates an agent's authority but where the agent still continues to act. Under such circumstances the principal will still be bound by the acts of his agent unless he has given notice of revocation to all third parties.

Where it is generally true that the act of an agent is binding upon his principal, this pre-supposes that the agent has due authority to act on his principal's behalf. If he has no such authority, however, the principal can deny any liability. The surveyor must therefore take pains to ensure that at the outset of his relationship with his client he is granted authority to act and to spend money on behalf of his principal and must take care to obtain further authority to act should their relationship change to envisage matters not contemplated when they first met.

Quite apart from the legal duties of the surveyor as agent, it is obviously best if the preliminary transactions between himself and his client are dealt with efficiently so that their relationship can start on a basis of trust. Early misunderstandings and the need for subsequent explanations are to be avoided wherever possible and agreements confirmed in writing are a better aid in this respect.

Once the surveyor has completed his preliminary investigations, he should then consider the best method of reporting to his client. Clearly one of the most necessary elements in his advice will be the question of cost but here the surveyor should avoid entering too early on the obtaining of building estimates and the preparation of full contract documents, such as plans and a detailed specification, before he has discussed all the alternatives fully with his client. At too early a stage he will have no authority for doing so and might accordingly not be paid. This may sound obvious but an experienced surveyor will always avoid falling into this trap. Nothing is more depressing to a surveyor who has devoted many hours in preparing a scheme of repair work to see his client's downcast face as he turns over the papers with his comment that the cost is totally beyond him. In comparatively simple maintenance contracts for repainting and repointing for example, the surveyor may feel justified in proceeding with the preparation of his specification to obtain prices before reporting to his client, particularly if he has carried out work for that client before, but in the great majority of cases dealing with repair work there are invariably several options open to the building owner in how work can be carried out and it is for this reason that a preliminary report is recommended, perhaps in the form of a long letter, setting out the various alternatives including perhaps very approximate prices which, the surveyor should make quite clear, can be little more than wide approximations at this stage based on his experience. There are, of course, some clients who will much prefer to deal with the preliminaries by way of an interview only but the writers feel that there is a place for the preliminary report even under these circumstances and it could perhaps be best dealt with by way of a letter subsequent to the discussion which confirms the various points made at the meeting. In other cases, of course, where the surveyor is acting for a client, who is in a fiduciary capacity to someone else, for example a banker or a trustee, a preliminary report is most necessary and if not provided would probably be asked for in any event. As an example of a very common type of repair one might take the case of a severe outward movement to the flank wall of a Victorian semi-detached or end-of-terrace house. It is possible that in a case such as this that the surveyor may wish to set out two alternatives; the first being that the wall could be restrained and made stable in its present position by means of steel rods incorporated in the structure and channel sections bolted on the outside face of the wall. This, while providing an effective repair at moderate cost, would, nevertheless, have the grave disadvantage that it would be unsightly and make it obvious to all and sundry that some defect in the structure had occurred so that the ultimate resale value of the house would likely to be affected adversely. On the other hand the best method of repair would undoubtedly be to re-build the wall and although this would preserve the full value of the property and dispose of the question of repair once and for all, it would obviously be more costly.

One of the advantages of early contact with the client for discussion is that the surveyor is more easily able to assess what type of man or woman he is dealing with and in some cases, fortunately rare, it will enable him to withdraw from proceeding further with the work without too much loss. If, for example, the client is only interested in entertaining a very cheap type of superficial repair where the surveyor knows that the work will have to be done again in a few years' time, he may wish to withdraw from the transaction altogether from the point of view of professional risk. Even if he states in a letter that he considers the work to be a temporary measure only, it is not possible to be sure that he is adequately safeguarded professionally should his client later accuse him of having carried out an ineffective repair and having wasted his money even if his client merely sells the property shortly afterwards leaving the new owner to deal with future defects. Again the surveyor may find that his client is completely uninterested in the architectural characteristics of the building in question and may wish to take short cuts in repair work that will destroy its character. Under such circumstances, the surveyor may wish to take the opportunity to suggest to his client that he might be best served by someone else. On the other hand, of course, the surveyor should try to avoid pressing one particular point of view only on the grounds that he must be right by virtue of his appointment alone and must hold himself open to give genuine thought to any reasonable alternatives that are suggested to him.

Having arranged with his client in outline the nature and approximate extent of the repair and maintenance work to be carried out, and having confirmed this in writing, the surveyor should next, before he does anything else, examine his notes to make sure that he has all the necessary background information to enable him to proceed with the detailed scheme and the obtaining of approvals and estimates. If the work involved is on a comparatively minor scale and only includes the preparation of a specification with the subsequent supervision of the work in progress, the surveyor will adopt the basis of engagement for this type of work set out in the scale of charges issued by the Royal Institution of Chartered Surveyors whereby his remuneration will be on the basis of a percentage on the actual cost of the works. It should at this stage be emphasised however, that if the work is more complicated either in nature or extent, or both, over and above the simple application of this scale, for example if drawings are necessary, the conditions of engagement issued by the Royal Institute of British Architects at once become applicable since the scale of the R.I.C.S. endorses these conditions and adopts them for use accordingly. No surveyor should therefore be without a copy of the R.I.B.A. Conditions of Engagement which covers both new work and work to existing buildings. In the case of small-scale works where the simple percentage basis for the preparation of a specification and supervision of the work carried out does not quite cover the circumstances, it is best for the R.I.B.A. Conditions of Engagement to be employed since these can normally be telescoped with agreement of the building owner in the case of works to existing buildings, so that the full stages recommended need not be adhered to but can be adapted to suit the circumstances. Otherwise, of course, all the stages should be followed in a large scheme in the manner set out in the conditions.

The R.I.B.A. Conditions of Engagement are set out in nine parts with an appendix. Part 1 relates to general conditions of engagement and applies irrespective of the nature or extent of services to be provided and the level of percentage fees or time charges which are applicable. Part 2 of the conditions describes the normal service provided in respect of building works and it is important to note that the normal service is divided into stages which mark the progress of the work, each being an integral part of the process so that none may be omitted save when the engagement is terminated in accordance with the required notice. On completion of each stage an instalment of the cumulative fee is payable in accordance with the percentages laid down in the conditions. Part 3 of the conditions describes variations in fees from the normal service and is of great interest to the surveyor practising within the field covered by this book since part of it deals with works to existing buildings. A separate scale, Table B, of fees as a percentage of construction costs shows that such fees are calculated at a higher percentage for works to existing buildings than for work of a similar value on new buildings.

Parts 4 to 8 of the conditions are also of consequence since they deal with additional and special services, time charges, out-of-pocket expenses, partial services and abandoned work and the detailed calculation of fees and charges.

Having given thought to the conditions of his engagement and having discussed and agreed these with his client, the surveyor must now give thought to the nature of the approvals that he must obtain. These arise from either legislation on the one hand or from other persons to whom the building owner or his surveyor may owe an obligation either at common law or statute law.

A brief summary of such matters which might be used in the form of a check list, is set out below, but it should be remembered that this can only cover the ground in very broad outline and cannot fully be comprehensive in regard to every aspect that might arise.

APPROVALS

1. *Town and Country Planning Consent*

Repairs to existing houses may well involve the seeking of consent under the Town and Country Planning Acts. In most cases of simple reinstatement this may not of course be necessary but there will be cases where the use of different materials alter the appearance of a property or where the advanced decay or failure of a structure entails reconstruction in a different manner to the original. In such cases town and country planning consent will be necessary. Again, should the building, once repaired, be intended for a change of use this also will involve planning consent.

The Town and Country Planning Acts that have been introduced since the Second World War are numerous and detailed but the provisions of those Acts relating to this section have been re-enacted and consolidated in the Town and Country Planning Act 1971. Parts III, IV and V of this Act deal with planning control, planning permission and its enforcement, the powers of the Minister relating to these matters, the revocation or modification of planning permission and appeals. Sections 96–101 of Part V of the Act deal with enforcement control in respect of listed buildings which have been extended and widened over recent years as will be seen later in this part of the Chapter.

It is a sobering comment on the rate of growth of our present-day society that the increase in population and in particular the increase in motor traffic entails the constant revision and amendment of our planning laws. Since 1962 two Town and Country Planning Acts were found to be necessary. These are the Acts of 1963 and 1968 which amended and modified the earlier legislation. The main purpose of the Act of 1968 was to provide for a new system of development control by means of structure plans and local plans to be prepared by local authorities. In addition to this, however, a speedier system for planning appeals was introduced together with a new enforcement procedure for planning control. There was also an improved procedure for the preservation of buildings of special historic or architectural interest which will be referred to later. Parts III, IV and V of the 1971 Act are of interest under this section, however, since they deal with the enforcement of planning control and with appeals. Section 22 in particular defines "development" which requires planning permission and under paragraph (2)(a) certain works of maintenance improvement or other alteration of a building as set out are to be taken as not involving development.

2(a) *The Building Regulations and the London Building Acts*

The surveyor should next have regard to the statutory rules and requirements that relate to building work and considerable emphasis is now thrown upon the Building Regulations 1972. These are, broadly speaking, little different from the Building Regulations 1965, although the provisions relating to staircases etc. are not the same as previously. The Regulations are divided into 15 sections (Parts A–Q) with 12 schedules. It is thought that an index to the main parts of the building regulations might be helpful and this is as follows:

Part A—Interpretation and General.
Part B—Materials.
Part C—Preparation of site and resistance to moisture.
Part D—Structural stability.
Part E—Structural Fire Precautions.
Part F—Thermal insulation.
Part G—Sound insulation.
Part H—Stairways and balustrades.
Part J—Refuse disposal.
Part K—Open space, ventilation and height of rooms.

Part L—Chimneys, flue pipes, hearths and fireplace recesses.
Part M—Heat producing appliances and incinerators.
Part N—Drainage, private sewers and cesspools.
Part P—Sanitary Conveniences.
Part Q—Ashpits, wells, tanks and cisterns.

The local authority is responsible for the administration of the Building Regulations, but the Minister has power to delegate to local authorities the ability to relax building regulations with a right of appeal should a local authority refuse to do so. This power, however, is given in the Public Health Act 1961 and not in the Building Regulations themselves. Extending to 188 pages, the Regulations provide a comprehensive code of requirements for all new buildings or works to existing structures and are applicable throughout England and Wales (separate Regulations being made for Scotland) apart from the Inner London boroughs where the London Building Acts apply.

The London Building Acts are of obvious importance to surveyors in the London area. The main Act, the London Building Acts (Amendment) Act 1939, extends the Acts of 1930 and 1935 and deals in Part III with constructional matters such as certain rules relating to party walls, bay and oriel windows, roof drainage, precautions against fire in certain buildings and in particular provisions relating to the "uniting" of buildings whereby the making of openings in the party walls between two adjacent buildings or the connections of these buildings together is only allowed under certain conditions. Part III also deals with the separation of buildings, the ventilation of staircases and certain matters relating to public buildings. Part IV of the Act deals with special and temporary buildings and structures and Part V, which is of particular importance, deals with means of escape in case of fire. Part VI of the Act dealing with the rights etc. of building and adjoining owners is referred to later in this section but Part VII deals with dangerous and neglected structures and should be noted. Parts IX to XII of the Act dealing with the fees of District Surveyors and others, by-laws, legal proceedings and miscellaneous matters are of less direct importance to the surveyor but it is as well to know where the authority for such matters can be found.

The London Building Acts 1930–1939 empowered the London County Council (now the Greater London Council) to make by-laws to regulate the construction and conversion of buildings in London and at the time of writing the principal group are those entitled the London Building (Constructional) Amending By-Laws No. 1 1964 running to 80 large pages. Some of the 1952 London

Building (Constructional) By-Laws are however still in force and there are further amending by-laws of 1964 (No. 2) and of 1966. The curious survival of by-laws from 1952 arises out of a dispute between the Council and the then Minister of Public Building and Works over revised by-laws relating to ceiling heights and window-less kitchens. Agreement could not be reached and accordingly the old by-laws remained in force. Fortunately all by-laws in force are at present grouped in one publication with a separate booklet for exact metric equivalents. It is understood that a revision is in course of preparation when the opportunity will be taken to round off the metric values.

2(b) Public Health legislation, by-laws and regulations

The real beginning of the basic legislation affecting sanitation is the Public Health Act 1875. This Act was the start of the close interest taken by the Legislature in the law relating to dwellings right through the present century until the appearance of the latest statute, in the direct line of issue so to speak, the Public Health Act 1961. Part 1 of this Act substitutes the National Building Regulations for the various building by-laws throughout England and Wales as already discussed except for the Inner London Metropolis. Local authorities under this Act no longer have power to make their own by-laws. Plans deposited under the Building Regulations, however, continue to be approved by local authorites and the penalties for those who contravene the regulations are heavy. These changes were dealt with in Part II of the Act which, in sections 61–70, replace parts of the 1936 Public Health Act. Sections 12–23 of the Act deal with sewers, drains and sanitary conveniences and the contribution to sewerage works to be paid by frontagers where a local authority construct a new sewer in a public street and the houses on each street have thereby increased in value. Powers are also given to local authorities in asking for contributions from land owners when a public street is laid out and there are specific provisions relating to drains and powers are given to a Medical Officer of Health to examine and test drains without the local authority having to autho-rise such an act together with powers as to stopped up drains and defective drains, including the disconnection of drains and fines for improper construction. Sections 24–33 of the Act deals with buildings and structures including dangerous and defective premises and neglected and dilapidated buildings. Section 28 of the Act is entirely new since it now enables a local authority to ask the owner of a newly built tall building which renders the chimney stacks of the buildings on either side inoperative, to raise such stacks where it is practicable to do so. Section 29 of the Act is worth noting since it gives the local authority power in relation to demolished properties to serve notice on the building owner to ask him to shore up adjacent buildings, weatherproof exposed surfaces, remove rubbish, disconnect and seal off drains, and remove sanitary services and any work disturbed. Section 30 of the Act prohibits the construction of undergound rooms and cellars where these are below the sub-soil water level without the permission of the local authority and Section 31 deals with provisions for compulsory food storage accommodation in new houses while Section 32 deals with the same problem in existing houses where the storage facilities are inadequate. Section 33 of the Act deals with the question of the compulsory provision of bathrooms in every new house being a separate dwelling with an appeal to petty sessions in case of difficulty. Sections 34, 35, 36 and 37 deal with the prohibition of rubbish heaps on vacant sites, with filthy or verminous articles or premises and the prohibition of the sale of verminous articles by dealers and hawkers. Parts III to VII of the Act make important reading but in general deal with matters that are outside the scope of this volume.

The surveyor should finally check through the relevant Public Health and Drainage By-Laws including, if relevant, regulations as to underground rooms issued by the local authority of the area in which the house is situated so that he is as certain as he can be that there are no aspects of the matter that he may have overlooked which might alter his scheme and cause unnecessary delay and expense once the building work has started. As a final check he might consider any statutes that while not affecting building legislation or sanitation directly nevertheless do so indirectly. An example, given earlier in the Chapter is the Clean Air Act 1965. There is obviously little point in elaborately reconstructing period fireplaces for the wrong type of fuel but this is an example of the sort of trap that an experienced surveyor will take pains to avoid.

3. *Superior Landlords*

In the case of Leasehold property, there will, in general, be no obligation on the lessee to notify a superior landlord where the repair and maintenance of the structure is within the terms of the lease and where the work contemplated is in conformity with the repairing covenants. Improvements, however, clearly require consent but it is possible that even in repairing a house, the surveyor may infringe, even marginally, some provision in a lease; two obvious examples being firstly the need to rearrange structural timbers due to some basic defect where there is a clause in the lease not to "cut,

913

maim or injure" such timbers or where the surveyor has to adapt or alter an external covering material to main walls or roof surfaces where the original material has become badly worn and cannot be replaced satisfactorily in its existing form. An application for consent to carry out the work from the superior landlord is always desirable at an early stage under circumstances such as these and in all cases of doubt the surveyor is well advised to ask to see the lease.

4. Rights of Building and Adjoining Owners in respect of Party Structures, Easements and Servitudes

The repair, maintenance or alteration of party structures separating buildings, or for that matter land and buildings or purely and simply two plots of land, can become bedevilled by complications of ownership and responsibilities. The economic necessity to make the maximum use of land and to build right up to the boundary led very early on to difficulties between adjoining owners and consequential actions at law. As will be recalled from Chapter 1 local legislation can be dated from 1189 in London to regulate building upon boundary lines as well as other matters of building construction but this was exceptional and outside London common law rules ameliorated by equity applied until the Law of Property Act 1925 took the matter in hand to some extent.

Prior to the Law of Property Act 1925 and in the absence of any local statute most party walls were walls of which two adjoining owners were tenants in common and in the absence of any evidence to the contrary the law would construe that situation even if there were no records establishing the point. In the circumstances either tenant in common could repair a party wall as the common property but there was no right of contribution from the co-owner. The repair could extend to the demolition and rebuilding, or the underpinning of the wall without legal objection from the co-owner provided the co-owner's use of the wall was not jeopardised. On the other hand, a co-owner could not impose additional loads on a party wall which might impede its stability since this would damage the common property. As can be seen each of the two owners had a half interest in the whole wall, what is known as an undivided moiety of the wall, and this situation persists in London where matters of repair are controlled by local statute and in one or two other cities, Bristol for example. Elsewhere Sections 38 and 39 of the Law of Property Act 1925 altered the situation so that all walls that were at that time considered to be owned by tenants in common and any in future purported to be vested in that manner were deemed to be severed longitudinally along the centre line as between the two owners, each party having such rights of support and user over the half of the other owner as existed on January 1st 1926 or which might have existed but for the Act. As a result each owner now has a divided moiety in the wall and can more or less do what he likes with his own half without reference to the owner of the other half provided he does not interfere with the adjoining owner's user rights and rights of support. There would however, now still be a right to repair the other half of the wall at one's own expense even without the co-operation of the adjoining owner and an owner would not have to await damage before a remedy could be sought.

Alternatively in case of difficulty an owner could apply to the Court, which, under the Act, is now empowered to settle any dispute as to rights and interests in a wall on the application of any interested party.

The whole point in regard to party walls where there is no local legislation is that matters have to be dealt with by agreement with the adjoining owner as to how the work is to be done and how the cost is to be shared. Failing agreement an owner can work wholly from his own side and within his own boundary so as to effect the necessary repairs but this may not always be possible and in these circumstances he may be forced to take legal action to obtain the court's declaration. In serious cases of disrepair another remedy may lie in reporting the condition to the local authority so as to enable the authority to exercise its statutory powers.

In London the procedure laid down in the London Building Acts (Amendment) Act 1939 must be followed but it should be noted that the Acts only apply to the former London County Council Area. The Greater London Council which has existed since 1963 has entirely replaced the London County Council and the authority of certain other County Councils in regard to certain areas and 32 London Boroughs have replaced 28 former Metropolitan Boroughs and other outlying areas as well. The changes have been extensive and part of the new Metropolitan area is now outside the control of the London Building Acts.

Under the London Building Act 1930 and the London Building Acts (Amendment) Act 1939, statutory rights are defined for both the "building owner" the person who is proposing to carry out work to a party wall and the "adjoining owner" who is the person affected by the work. The legislation is extremely detailed and the definition given to the parties and the other terms used in the Act are important. A party wall is defined in Section 44 of the 1939 Act as (i) a wall which forms part of a building and stands on lands of different owners to a greater extent than the projection of any artificially formed support on which the wall rests and (ii) so much of a wall

915

not being a wall referred to in (i) as separates buildings belonging to different owners. Each owner has an undivided moiety in the whole wall and nothing can be done to any part of the common property without due notice being given to the co-owner, a point which often escapes those unfamiliar with the principles.

The Act deals with the rights and duties of the building owner and adjoining owner and deals in detail with the question of expenditure to be incurred by each and other matters relative to party walls such as special foundations and underpinning. In particular it is worth noting that under Part VI of the Act Section 50(1) states that where a building owner:

(a) proposes to erect within ten feet from any part of a building of an adjoining owner a building or structure independent of the building of the adjoining owner and any part of the proposed building or structure will within the said ten feet extend to a lower level than the level of the bottom of the foundations of the building of the adjoining owner; or

(b) proposes to erect within twenty feet from any part of an independent building of an adjoining owner a building or structure any part of which will within the said twenty feet meet a plane drawn downwards in the direction of the building or structure of the building owner at an angle of forty-five degrees to the horizontal from the line formed by the intersection of the plane of the level of the bottom of the foundations of the building of the adjoining owner with the plane of the external face of the external wall of the building of the adjoining owner;

he may and if required by the adjoining owner shall subject to the provisions of this section at the expense of the building owner underpin or otherwise strengthen or safeguard the foundations of the building of the adjoining owner so far as may be necessary.

In particular, however, the 1939 Act sets out a code of procedure to be followed by a building owner for putting work in hand to a party wall or party fence wall and for settling disputes with an adjoining owner which has worked moderately well provided a reasonable amount of goodwill exists on both sides. While the application of a similar code of procedure to the remainder of the country would be advantageous and is being actively considered it is hoped that various defects in the London procedure would be first remedied.

Very briefly, where the surveyor contemplates carrying out work to a party wall he must serve two months in advance on behalf of his client, the building owner, a notice under the 1939 Act giving brief details of the proposed works and the date on which they are intended to commence. Forms for such a notice can be obtained from the Royal Institute of British Architects, but there is no obligation to use such forms. The building owner and the adjoining owner each appoint a surveyor to act on their behalf who normally arrange to meet together fairly quickly and consider the proposals and any plans submitted on the site. The lack of a reply to the notice within the statutory period of fourteen days implies dissent to the proposed work by the adjoining owner and a difference is then deemed to have arisen. One of the first acts of the two surveyors is to appoint a third surveyor to decide further differences between them in the the case of a disagreement. Such appointment must be in writing but in fact the nomination is not taken up in the majority of cases since most party wall matters are settled between the two surveyors acting for the respective parties. Once basic agreement is reached, the draft party wall Award, together with any necessary drawings, is prepared by the surveyor to the building owner who then sends it for approval to the surveyor for the adjoining owner. The draft is then agreed and the Award in two parts is drawn up and both parts are signed and witnessed by the two surveyors. The work in progress is then supervised by the building owner's surveyor and is watched, no doubt with an eagle eye, by the adjoining owner's surveyor until completion to ensure compliance with the terms of the Award.

One matter that often arises at the same time as the question of the Award is that of a schedule of condition of neighbouring premises. Where work to party walls is contemplated, it is extremely important to have a record of the condition of the structure including decorations and finishings on the adjoining owner's side of the wall so that any deterioration as a result of the work carried out can be determined and assessed on completion of the work. It is highly desirable for the surveyor to the building owner to suggest at an early stage in the proceedings that a schedule of condition is prepared in good time before the work is put in hand and this should be drawn up, approved and signed by the respective surveyors to the building owner and adjoining owner and then forms part of the Award so that the two documents together comprise the whole settlement. It should also be borne in mind that photographs and drawings can also play an important part in recording the condition of premises at a particular date.

In Scotland also, the proprietor of property has to take into account the interests of his neighbours so far as common structures are concerned. Where there is a common dividing wall either proprietor may object to the other carrying out operations which might be injurious to it. The position, however, is unusual in the case of a flatted or tenement building where each house is owned separately. Here the external walls of each property may belong to individual proprietors but each proprietor has a common interest in the whole and may not interfere with his own walls in such a way that might damage other properties. Similarly each proprietor is sole owner of his floors and ceilings down to the centre point of the joists but he must not cut into or weaken them in such a way that might damage his neighbour's floor or ceiling. The roof of a tenement property belongs to the owner of the top storey but the other owners clearly have an interest in seeing that it is kept watertight and undamaged and may compel the owner to keep it in repair and prevent him from damaging it. With properties in Scotland it is always best to check the feudal titles since an express condition in the titles may well prevail over the common law rules.

In both England or Scotland the surveyor is advised to have regard to the question of easements or, in Scotland, servitudes. The natural expectation of support to buildings for example is a fundamental right that can be acquired by adjoining owner or proprietor alike and can only be ignored at the surveyor's peril since the removal of earth from the base of a wall without prior consultation or consent is likely to lead to the application for an injunction to stop the work by the injured party. The same conditions apply to all natural rights if these are infringed and, in particular any easements relating to drainage, for example, should not be ignored. Although in England there is in general no right to support from underground water which can be extracted without liability, no surveyor would feel happy in allowing the extraction to occur knowing that this would change the sub-soil characteristics and lead to grave risk of damage to adjoining buildings. Mining subsidence is now dealt with by statute and compensation is paid to house owners.

Rights of light to a defined aperture in a permanent building can be created by grant or by prescription. The surveyor is less likely to encounter problems over rights to air or rights in water but rights of way are worth some thought at this stage in the contract preliminaries since it could be awkward if these become blocked by scaffolding or builder's materials.

5. *Listed Buildings Consent*

The term "listed buildings" refers to the procedure laid down under various Acts of Parliament for protecting special buildings of "Architectural or Historic Interest". Although the Department of the Environment and its predecessors have been listing·buildings of special architectural or historical interest since the end of the Second

World War and the process is continuing at the present time, the desire to prevent the wholesale wastage and destruction of ancient monuments and historic buildings finds its roots at the end of the last century. In 1877 the Society for the Protection of Ancient Buildings was formed but probably the first statute that caused genuine controversy was the Ancient Monuments Act of 1882, a modest enough measure which related to burial mounds, stone circles and objects of antiquity. The formation of the Georgian Group in 1937 and the Victorian Society in 1958 have reflected growing public interest in the preservation of old buildings and this has also been reflected in statute law by the various measures passed which have tried to find an acceptable way of preserving the best buildings of the past.

The first Town and Country Planning Act that gave power to planning authorities to make building preservation orders to prevent the demolition of buildings of special architectural or historic interest was passed in 1932 but it is the much better known Act of 1944 in which the real basis of effective action in this direction can be found. This Act charged the Minister of Town and Country Planning with the duty of preparing lists of buildings of special architectural or historic interest in England and Wales and in 1947 the list and notice control machinery came into operation whereby owners were required to give two months' notice of works that might materially affect the character of a building that had been listed by the Minister. The list in fact took 20 years to complete and listing is, of course, still in progress, but the provisions with regard to notice have since been changed by subsequent legislation.

The list of buildings prepared by investigators employed by the Department of the Environment is issued under grades. Buildings included under grade 1 have always been those where it was felt that their destruction should not be allowed under any circumstances, while under grade 2, buildings were included whose preservation was regarded as being paramount subject only to being set aside for more important considerations. Buildings listed under grade 3 were of lesser importance, but it was the list comprising buildings under grades 1 and 2 that become the "statutory lists" for the purposes of the Planning Acts. The list of grade 3 buildings became the "supplementary list". Unlike the statutory list the supplementary list had no statutory force. Under this system when an owner gave notice of his intention to alter or demolish a building on the statutory list, the planning authority, if they opposed his intention, could make a building preservation order which was subject to confirmation by the Minister, such confirmation, however, only being granted after the Minister had heard any objections.

The real trouble with the planning procedure for listed buildings prior to the middle sixties was, however, that an unscrupulous owner could drive a coach and horses through the legislation as it then existed. Few local authorities had the staff or the means to deal with matters adequately and only a few had the resources to cope with the battles over the listing system with its narrow margins for the service of notices and the means not only to make a building preservation order, but the intention and resources to push it through. Perhaps, however, the greatest drawback was that public opinion was not yet convinced of the need for firm action to protect old buildings and there was nothing like the support for preservation, not only of buildings but of the environment, that has emerged in the last few years.

The Civic Amenities Act, 1967, and the Town and Country Planning Acts, 1968 and 1971 (which came into force in April 1972) have built on the earlier legislation and have amended and consolidated it to form the system of listed building consent that we know today. The procedure relating to the old type of building preservation order no longer exists and the onus is now on the owner of the building to obtain consent for any works of demolition or alteration to a building on the statutory list or an unlisted building which was formerly the subject of a confirmed building preservation order. The virture of this new system is that it is much more clear cut since a planning authority simply issues its decision on an application submitted by a building owner who has the right to appeal to the Minister if he feels any sense of grievance. The fact that applications have to be advertised and some, including all applications for demolition notified to the Secretary of State for the Environment who may direct that the application be referred to him for decision, provides a much stronger system and the increased fines and penalties have a far more deterrent effect than under the previous legislation. A completely new feature of the later legislation is that planning authorities are now able to identify areas of special architectural or historic interest as "conservation areas". The provisions are largely contained in the Civic Amenities Act 1967 and offers a completely new approach since it enables the authorities to take steps to preserve or enhance areas where historic buildings are grouped together.

The reader may wonder why it is necessary for the listed buildings procedure to be mentioned within the scope of this book at all, since the only reference so far made has been to demolition or alteration. However, listed buildings are now automatically protected under Part IV of the Town and Country Planning Act 1971 and any unauthorised interference with such a building is a criminal offence. Sections 54–58 and 96–101 of this Act provide that the demolition or alteration of a listed building is an offence if it "would affect its character as a building of special architectural or historic interest" and no such works will be authorised unless the local planning authority have granted a "listed building consent" specifying what these are to be. The imposition of conditions in a listed building consent may include any which require "the preservation of particular features of the building" or "the use of original materials so far as practicable". The importance of these provisions so far as the surveyor dealing with building works to repair and maintain a house of artistic or historic importance is self evident. The surveyor should take pains to ascertain if the house in question is listed or not and, if so, how it is listed and then give proper consideration as to whether the work that he intends to put in hand requires consent or not. In cases of doubt, a preliminary interview with the planning authority concerned is always valuable and indeed much information and benefit can often be obtained by such a meeting.

Section 4 of the Historic Buildings and Ancient Monuments Act 1953 provides that grants of money may be made by the Secretary of State for the Environment for the upkeep or repair of a building of outstanding historic or architectural interest subject to the blessing of the Historic Buildings Council, a body set up to advise the Secretary of State under this Act. The 1967 Civic Amenities Act extends the powers of the 1953 Act to enable the Secretary of State to make loans as well as grants subject to Treasury approval. If the surveyor is dealing with a property of outstanding historic or architectural interest, he should consider the question of applying for a grant under the terms of Section 4 of the 1953 Act as extended by the 1967 Act.

It is perhaps worth adding that sections 114–117 of the Town and Country Planning Act 1971, deal with the duties given to a local authority to look after a listed building that has become neglected. In this event a "repairs notice" can be served on the owner of the building giving him notice of certain specified repair work which must be carried out. In the case of the owner's default, the local authority have power under the Act to acquire the building compulsorily, provided that this is not an ecclesiastical structure or an ancient monument.

6. *Improvement Grants*

Although most works of repair involve improvements to some extent, "improvements" as commonly thought of to houses are outside the scope of this volume and it might appear that a consideration of Improvement Grants is unnecessary. However, the discretionary grants cover a wide range of matters such as the eradication of rising damp, electrical re-wiring and the like which the surveyor quite properly regards as being within the province of repair and maintenance work. Consideration of the present system of available grants, therefore, is worthwhile.

The grants system was first introduced in 1949 and since that time well over a million older houses have been improved with the aid of subsidies. In April 1968 however, a White Paper "Old Houses into New Homes" was introduced by the Minister of Housing and Local Government which admitted that some powers and grants which were adequate when they were introduced, were no longer enough and which set out proposals for improved powers for local authorities and increased grants for the general public to improve older houses. Following on from the White Paper, the Housing Act 1969 was passed which introduced a new and more generous grants system. Under this Act three types of house improvement grant are now available though local councils as follows:

(1) Discretionary grants for improvements to single houses or conversions, to which the Council may contribute at their discretion;

(2) Standard grants for the provision of certain standard amenities to existing dwellings set down in the Act which the Council are obliged to pay.

(3) Special grants which comprise assistance for the provision of basic amenities for the benefit of houses in multiple occupation payable at the discretion of the local authority.

Part 1 of the Housing Act 1969 sets out a new code for the Grant Aided Improvement and Conversion of Houses in England and Wales. It also provides local authorities with additional powers to bring about the compulsory repair of houses. Part II of the Act is concerned with area improvement where councils are given the power to declare "general improvement areas" so that the environment as well as houses can be improved, for example, where streets can be turned into pedestrian precincts and play spaces and garden areas can be created. The effect of improvements on rents is governed under Part III of the Act, but for the purposes of this Chapter, it is Part I of the Act that is important. This enacts that improvement grants of up to £1,000 (£1,200 for conversions or for properties in excess of two floors) can be payable at the discretion of the local authority for works of a high all round level for the improvement, conversion and repair of properties with a good life ahead of them. Standard grants of up to £200 in most cases can be obtained by owners, as of right, for the installation of standard amenities in cases where the dwelling has an estimated life of at least 15 years; and otherwise at the authority's discretion subject to Ministerial directions, except in general improvement areas, while special grants are

922

available at the local authority's discretion for the installation of standard amenities in houses in multiple occupation at the rates set out in the first schedule to the Act.

The new grant code is flexible since it applies to a wide range of houses and is limited by a minimum of statutory requirements. In the case of improvement grants, Ministers are empowered to specify requirements as to the level of works and the estimated life of the dwelling where the works have been carried out, but local authorities are left with a wide discretion. Local authorities may relax the strict statutory conditions relating to standard grants subject to any directions from Ministers, but special grants are only intended to be used in exceptional cases. Authorities are also enabled under the Act to fix a limit for improvement grants higher than the figure of £1,000 (£1,200 in the case of flats) with the approval of the Minister or Secretary of State in particular cases. The amount of grant is limited to 50 per cent of the whole amount of work approved for grant purposes up to the maximum limits and accordingly to obtain a grant an owner has to have or be able to borrow an amount equal to the grant so that the expenditure can be matched.

It is important when making application for a grant that approval is sought before the work is commenced. Model forms are set out in Appendix E to the Act and duplicated forms in accordance with this Appendix are now generally available from most local authorities. It should be remembered that a local authority is normally not allowed under the Act to approve an application where the works specified have been started, unless the authority is satisfied that there are good reasons for the commencement of works before the approval of the application. Improvement grants may be paid either after the completion of the work, or by instalment as the work proceeds with the balance becoming payable on completion. Where part of a grant is paid by instalments, the aggregate of the instalments paid can at no time exceed one half of the total cost of the works already carried out.

It is important to note that in order to qualify for a discretionary grant, the dwelling must, where practicable, after improvement or conversion, meet what is known as the 12 point standard set down in the Act. The points are that the dwelling must:

(a) Be in a good state of repair and substantially free from damp.

(b) Have each room properly lighted and ventilated.

(c) Have an adequate supply of wholesome water laid on inside the dwelling.

(d) Be provided with efficient and adequate means of supplying hot water for domestic purposes.

(*e*) Have an internal water closet if practicable; otherwise a readily accessible water closet.

(*f*) Have a fixed bath or shower in a bathroom.

(*g*) Be provided with a sink or sinks and with suitable arrangement for the disposal of waste water.

(*h*) Have a proper drainage system.

(*i*) Be provided in each room with adequate points for gas or electric lighting (where reasonably available).

(*j*) Be provided with adequate facilities for heating.

(*k*) Have satisfactory facilities for storing, preparing and cooking food.

(*l*) Have proper provision for storing fuel (where required).

A local authority, however, may waive any of the above requirements if any of these appear to be impracticable. It is interesting to note that the dwelling, once improved, is expected to provide satisfactory housing accommodation for a period of 30 years but this period can be reduced to 10 years under the Act at the discretion of the local authority. It is recognised under the Act that the conversion or improvement of buildings of historic or architectural interest often involve higher costs if the new work is to blend harmoniously with the old. Under such circumstances, Ministers are prepared to consider proposals for higher grants.

7. *Trees*

It is possible that the surveyor who is contemplating carrying out repair work to a house may have to decide what to do about trees affecting the property. In many urban districts the types of trees selected for planting in the estates built during the building booms following the First and Second World Wars were unsuitable and often become an embarrassment since they are often situated very near buildings and their continual and rapid growth gives rise to problems. No surveyor wishes to remove trees from urban areas where this can be avoided, but there are times when it is necessary. Trees have figured largely in town and country planning legislation since the Second World War and Section 60 of Part IV of the Town and Country Planning Act 1971 re-enacts the procedure in making and confirming tree preservation orders. It is, accordingly, essential for the surveyor to find out if any trees that he proposes to deal with are the subject of such an order, but it is worth remembering that there are statutory grounds for the removal of an order on the owner's application should the tree be causing damage to buildings.

FORMING THE CONTRACT

INTRODUCTION

A building contract, like any other contract, is simply an agreement that is enforceable at law and the term "building contract" has no particular significance to a lawyer who, in the event of a dispute, will try to ascertain what was in the minds of the parties when the contract was made and will apply the basic rules relating to the law of contract in order to determine how the parties stand in relation to each other. Most contracts are simple contracts, that is to say contracts not made under seal and building contracts are no exception. Contracts under seal are known as speciality contracts and are, for example, contracts entered into by a corporation or a contract for the sale of land.

Accordingly, a building contract, like any other contract must comply with certain rules to be binding. The parties must have reached genuine agreement or be subsequently deemed to have done so; they must also have had a firm intention to create a legal relationship and must intend that some advantage, known as consideration, must move from one party to the other. The contract must also contain the two elements of offer and acceptance. Each of these must be definite, that is to say complete and final and without any ambiguity. Thus in simple cases a building tender which is an offer to carry out work for a certain sum as distinct from a mere estimate of the cost must be shown to have been accepted by the building owner either by his conduct or in writing in order for a contractual relationship to have been set up. Just as the tender must be complete and final, however, so must the acceptance. If the tender is not certain clearly the acceptance cannot make it so but the acceptance itself must be certain which implies that it must not only be complete and final but it must also be effectively communicated. A firm tender is effectively accepted at the moment that the building owner posts an unconditional acceptance and where a builder wishes to withdraw his tender he must do so before acceptance is an accomplished fact. On the other hand however, a building owner cannot rely on the tender being open indefinitely. If the building owner does not accept a tender within the time limit stated by the builder or alternatively within a reasonable time the offer will lapse. Alternatively the offer may be rejected but only if notice of this has reached the offerer. Rejection, however, can also be implied by law where the offerer makes a conditional acceptance. Thus where a building owner replies to a tender saying that he accepts it but subject only to further conditions that he wishes to impose, these conditions may well imply a rejection of the original offer.

Where a party to a contract neglects or refuses to honour the terms of a contract there arises what is known as a breach of contract which gives the aggrieved party a right of action against the other. There are two remedies for breach of contract, the first being damages, i.e. the award of a sum of money designed to put the aggrieved party in the position that he would have been in had the contract not been broken and specific performance being the second where the Court may order the party who breaks the contract to actually carry out his promise. It should be understood at once, however, that specific performance is never awarded where damages will suffice so that if a builder who has submitted a tender for repairs which has been duly accepted by the building owner subsequently refuses to carry them out, it is extremely unlikely that a Court will order the builder to carry out the work under the equitable remedy of specific performance. The Court will probably decide on the amount of damages that flows from the breach of contract, damages in such a case being dependant on the amount of the loss suffered by the building owner. It should be emphasised, however, that damages will only be those reasonable and foreseeable as a result of the breach.

It can be seen, therefore, that certain basic requirements are necessary before a contract can be set up which is enforceable at law. Even if these are present, however, a number of circumstances can effect its validity so as to render it void or unenforceable, the main examples being as follows:

(a) *Mistake*

Where two parties to an agreement both suffer from an identical misapprehension as to its terms, known as common mistake, or have been negotiating at cross purposes so that a mutual mistake may occur, the Courts may declare the contract void at common law or declare the contract voidable, that is, liable to be set aside on such terms as the Court thinks fit, which is an equitable remedy. Even where there is unilateral mistake where one party only to the contract is mistaken, the Courts may declare the contract void or voidable but the other party must know or be deemed to know of this mistake.

When there is a mistake of fact which prevents the formation of any contract at all, known as an operative mistake, the Court will declare the contract void. Operative mistake is an exceptional occurrence, but an example might be mistake as to the identity of the person with whom the contract is made or mistake as to a fact that is fundamental to the entire agreement. Where, however, the contract is good at common law, that is to say where a Court would not declare it void for operative mistake, a person may still have entered it under a misapprehension and may be able to obtain equitable relief from his obligations.

(b) *Misrepresentation*

This word means not only a false statement but the act of making it as well. Misrepresentation may be innocent or fraudulent and it is necessary to distinguish between the two as a fraudulent misrepresentation is a tort and is often described as deceit. A tort is a civil as opposed to a criminal wrong for which damages is the usual remedy but any misrepresentation not defined as fraudulent must be innocent, that is to say where a representation is made with an honest belief in its truth. In the case of fraudulent misrepresentation the party who has been deceived may sue for damages in tort for deceit and may either affirm the contract or disaffirm it. In the case of innocent misrepresentation a party who has been misled may seek his remedy at common law or in equity or under the terms of the Misrepresentation Act 1967. The remedy under the Misrepresentation Act is a recent one since this Act was designed to alter the common law rule that damages are not awarded for innocent misrepresentation.

(c) *Duress or undue influence*

This is where direct or subtle coercion is brought to bear on one of the parties to a contract. Where a person is coerced into a contract so that he does not enter it of his own free will he may apply to the Court to have it avoided or set aside. His remedy lies either in common law in a case of duress, i.e. where a party to a contract is threatened with violence to himself or a member of his family, or in equity where the coercion amounts to undue influence, whereby a party to the contract is under any kind of influence which prevents him from exercising a free and independent judgment.

(d) *Where one or more of the contracting parties does not have full contractural capacity*

The contractual capacity of a corporation depends upon the manner in which it was created but in the case of all natural persons (i.e. those other than corporations) almost everyone has a full contractural capacity. Of the few exceptions it is unlikely that the surveyor will set up a contract where one of the parties to it is drunk or insane (although cases have been known) but he may well have difficulty over the case of an infant.

The Infants Relief Act 1874 provides that "all contracts, whether by speciality or by simple contract, henceforth entered into by infants for the repayment of money lent or to be lent or for goods supplied or to be supplied (other than contracts for necessaries) and all accounts stated with infants, shall be absolutely void". It is obviously likely to be difficult to prove that "necessaries" include the execution of building works and it is therefore worth some care for the surveyor to ascertain if his client is an infant. It is not thought likely that the builder would fall into this category but in these days of the youthful tycoon one cannot, of course, be sure.

It might perhaps be added in the hope that this may assist a surveyor in an awkward position that although a contract was voidable if one of the parties to it was incapable at the time it was entered into, it is not voidable if a lunatic makes a contract in a lucid interval or where a drunkard, having made a contract when intoxicated confirms it when sober.

(e) *Where the contract is illegal*

Illegal contracts are those against public policy, i.e. against the policy of the common law which contain a wrongful or illegal element. Examples are rare in relation to building contracts and these mostly occur in time of war when emergency regulations are in force.

(f) *Where the contract is partly or wholly void under a statute or is partly or wholly void at common law as being against public policy*

The distinction between a void and an illegal contract is that a contract which is void does not give rise to rights and obligations, but the full consequences of illegality are not present. A contract may be void for example if there is a statute that declares contracts of that particular class to be void or where the contract is void at common law. A contract may also be void where the Restrictive Trade Practices Court declares that it is against the public interest.

(g) *Where the contract is of a class requiring formalities and these are absent*

We have already seen that some contracts are unenforceable unless evidenced by writing and although these are rare in the case of building contracts they apply very much to the sale and leasing of land and buildings. Nevertheless there are cases where the absence of proper formalities affect the law of building contracts particularly in the case of contracts with corporations.

In conclusion of this introduction it can again be stated that every building contract, however complex, follows the law of contract. A building contract can, for example, be rescinded by mutual agreement of the parties or it can be assigned but again only by mutual agreement of the parties. In every case of difficulty the surveyor must try to decide what the original intention of the parties was in the first place and ensure that all the elements of a valid contract are present before he decides as to the extent of any further work to be carried out by the builder or any claims for extra payment that should be met by the employer.

Having said that every building contract must follow the ordinary rules of contract we must now proceed to examine the different types of building contract and different methods of contracting. It will be obvious that a contract for the repair or for maintenance work on a house is different from most other contracts to deliver goods or supply services. In the first place the highly complicated and technical nature of the operation usually requires that the two contracting parties deal through professional representatives who not only translate the requirements of the building owner into technical language, so that the contractor will know the precise extent of the work contemplated, but will supervise the work as well. Furthermore, due again to the complexities found by long experience to occur in a contract that relates to building operations, difficulties may be foreseen before they arise so that matters which might prevent another type of contract being fulfilled are dealt with by way of agreed variations to the building contract as it proceeds so that it stands a good chance of successful completion no matter what type of troubles occur. Examples of such difficulties are where the weather affects the progress of the work, or where genuine difficulties arise over the nature, quality or extent of the work. A building contract may also differ from any other type of contract in that the rules relating to the goods supplied by the builder on the land of the employer may not be subject to the rules governing goods normally supplied in a commercial transaction. There are, accordingly, a number of ways, known to the surveying, architectural and legal professions alike, in which recognised contractural methods may be employed to suit different circumstances and we will now turn to a brief consideration of these types of contract.

TYPES OF BUILDING CONTRACT

(1) *The Lump Sum or Entire Contract*

In the case of a lump sum contract the building owner or the surveyor on his behalf may contract with a builder to have works carried out for a lump sum. It does not affect the basis of this contract that progress payments may be agreed as being payable at intervals or that the specified sum is subject to extras or omissions incurred within the terms of the contract since the final payment is conditional upon the whole of the works set out in the contract having been completed. A lump sum contract may be set up, for example, by an exchange of letters between a surveyor on behalf of his client and a builder for the repointing and repainting of a single dwelling house for a certain specified sum. Alternatively, the surveyor may have prepared and obtained the execution of a contract in a form of words printed by the Royal Institute of British Architects, either with or without quantities, for repairs to a house for which the builder has given a tender which has been accepted. In either case the form of contract is a "lump sum" or "entire contract". Each is a simple contract, that is to say a contract not under seal and in each case there is valid offer and acceptance. It is true that in the latter form of contract, there are more printed provisions which lay down terms that would guide the contracting parties in the event of difficulties arising, but nevertheless it must be remembered that both are lump sum contracts where payment is conditional upon the whole of the work being carried out.

Although an entire contract is one where the entire fulfilment of the promise by either party is a condition precedent to the right to call for the fulfilment of the promise by the other, it is not necessarily the case that in order to qualify under the definition of an entire contract, that the exact amount of money to be paid has to be known beforehand. There are four varieties of entire contract of which only the first qualifies for the definition of a lump sum contract. These are as follows:

(a) A contract to carry out the whole of the works in consideration of payment of a fixed sum of money. This is a true lump sum contract. Under this type of contract a builder cannot recover for work, labour and materials carried out on a quantum meruit basis, since the effective completion of the contract will only allow him to receive the pre-arranged sum.

(b) A contract to carry out the works in consideration of a specified price made up of a separate payment of each separate part of the whole. An example of this type of contract might be where several different buildings are to be repaired and separate prices are agreed for each.

(c) A contract to carry out the whole of the works without mention of any price. In such cases the contractor will be entitled to payment at reasonable rates but it should be emphasised under this heading that the extent of the work must be clear since the contractor is under an obligation to complete the whole of it otherwise the work would not be classified under the heading of an entire contract.

(*d*) A contract to carry out the whole of the work for a price to be subsequently ascertained on a fixed basis for example by a schedule of prices. Here again, of course, the extent of the work must be pre-determined beforehand.

(2) *Measurement and Value Contracts*

A measurement contract is one that provides for the execution of proposed work on the basis that payment is to be made entirely on measurements taken as the work proceeds and at the rates quoted in a schedule of prices by the contractor. Such contracts may or may not be entire contracts depending upon whether the amount of the work is known in advance or not.

(3) *Prime Cost Contracts otherwise known as Cost Plus Percentage Contracts*

In this type of contract which may or may not be an entire contract depending upon whether the extent of the work is known beforehand or not, the employer may contract to pay the builder the actual cost of his labour and materials, plus in addition some allowance for his overhead charges and a percentage for profit.

There will be circumstances where more than one type of contract is in use for building work at the same time or where some new form of contract is substituted for an existing contract either between the same parties or different parties, the original contract being discharged. This is known as Novation. It must be emphasised however, that while Novation is a form of assignment in which, by the consent of all parties, a new contract is substituted for an existing one, the original contract must be completely discharged.

Apart from cases where a new contract is set up by agreement, there will be cases where a new contract may be implied from events. If the original contract has to be abandoned or circumstances contemplated by it have become so changed that the conditions are no longer applicable, the work may proceed in a manner in which a new contract may be implied. It is probable that payment will be on a basis of quantum meruit in the lack of any specific terms between the parties, but it must be emphasised that this is only so where the substitution of something totally dissimilar in its character from the previous contract is in progress. Mere variations do not warrant a quantum meruit basis of payment for the whole contract unless a variation goes so deeply to the root of the contract so as to alter it

931

fundamentally. Whether this is so or not depends very much on the individual circumstances of each case.

It must be said that the basic legal requirements for the satisfaction of an entire contract is a stern one. If the builder abandons the work or is unable to go on with it, he has no right of action as against his employer under the contract, nor is he able to claim payment on a basis of quantum meruit for that part of the work that he has completed. There are, of course, circumstances where the builder will be able to show that he was frustrated by unforeseen circumstances in carrying out the contract or that the employer on his part has been so much at fault that the builder has been totally unable to fulfil his bargain. If, for example, the area in which the dwelling house is situated is cordoned off due to some police emergency for a considerable period of time or alternatively if the employer in fits of completely irrational rage orders the workmen away from the premises continually and without good reason, the builder clearly cannot be held accountable for the failure of an entire contract. Conversely, however, if the builder cannot show that there are any circumstances to justify his failure to complete the contract, he will not only be unable to recover payment for the incomplete work; but he will also be liable in damages to the employer for breach of his contract to complete, so that, for example, if the employer is dependent upon the work being finished in order to let the premises for a specific period, the employer's action could well include his loss of rent as one of the heads of claim.

If a contractor undertakes to carry out work outside the terms of an entire contract he is able to recover payment for such work on a quantum meruit basis, although he may not have completed the new work in hand. Clearly however, for this to occur, the employer must have authorised the additional work or have subsequently confirmed that it was in order for this to be carried out.

If a builder undertakes to carry out a certain amount of work under the terms of an entire contract, the whole of the work to be completed for a fixed sum the contract remains, as has been seen, an entire contract, even if progress payments are laid down in the contract at certain specified intervals. On the other hand, however, if payment is specified not at certain intervals but only in respect of individual parts of the work, the whole of the work no longer comes within the category of an entire contract since it is in effect split into a large number of smaller contracts.

In most cases where an employer contracts to employ a person to do jobbing repairs to his house, the implication will be that the contract is not entire. However, a contract for repairs can be made entire by express words and even if there are no such words, a Court may decide that the contract is an entire one if it is clear from the intention of the parties that this was the case. These distinctions are important as upon the interpretation of the type of contract, a Court will judge the rights and duties of the parties. For example in the case of an entire contract, a Court will have little patience in listening to a builder who says that he was unable to carry it out as the sub-soil was partly rock instead of what was expected. A builder would be expected to carry out whatever preparatory work is necessary as part of a contract as a whole, unless, of course, this would impose a condition that was so unreasonable as to be obvious as where blasting or excavating would lead to a grave danger of subsidence or cliff fall. A Court would also be unlikely to listen to a contractor who argued that as a result of using better materials for the work he should be entitled to an extra payment over the lump price. In the lack of any authority from the employer, a contractor is normally unable to recover a higher payment than the lump sum figure agreed upon in these circumstances. A Court is also likely to reject an allegation by the builder that the building owner has received something as good as that for which he bargained to justify the fact that the entire contract has not been strictly completed. Completion of the original contract is a condition precedent to the right of payment except when the employer waives this right or where a new contract is set up which may enable some payment to be made.

A contract to carry out building work implies a condition that the work shall be done in a good and workmanlike manner and by workmen having the ordinary amount of skill possessed by those exercising the particular trade or calling. This is, of course, in the absence of any other stipulation in the contract, although it is unlikely that anyone will contract for a lower standard than this. There is also an implied obligation that the work shall be reasonably fit for the use intended and, so far as materials are concerned, there is an obligation on the builder to supply materials that will be of good quality and reasonably fit for their purpose. Finally however, on the contractor's side there is the right for him to carry out the whole of the work in his own way provided that this is consistent with the terms of the contract and to have free and uninterrupted use of the site and access thereto.

Where no particular time is specified for the completion of a building contract, it can be inferred that a reasonable time for completion is allowed and what constitutes a reasonable time is a matter of fact according to the circumstances. The nature of the work to be carried out obviously plays a large part in the decision as to this and a judge will probably take into account the time that a reasonably diligent contractor of the same type as that employed under the contract would allow for work of a similar type and he would no doubt accept expert evidence on this point. Even if a time for completion is specified in the contract the contractor is not necessarily liable for damages for failing to complete within this time.

An employer is not normally able to release himself from liability under the contract if the builder does not complete the work within the time specified but he may be entitled to damages should he suffer genuine loss in other ways, for example pecuniary loss in having to pay rent for premises without being able to take up occupation. If, however, the work is subject to undue delay and the contract time has ceased to be binding, the employer may serve notice to complete within a fixed reasonable time and if the contractor overruns this period, the employer is then justified in refusing to allow the contractor to proceed further with the work. Where time is not of the essence of the contract, one party has a right to limit the time against the other in cases of unnecessary delay and upon further default to abandon the contract.

Where time is specifically made a fundamental condition of the contract so that it is the essence of the contract, the employer is released from the contract by non-completion within the stipulated period. It should be borne in mind, however, that simply inserting words in the contract making time of the essence will not alone be effective if these are inconsistent with other terms of the contract. Thus time cannot be of the essence of a contract where there is provision for the payment of a penalty of liquidated damages for delay, for example, or where the parties contemplate a possible postponement of the completion date. Where the contract expressly makes time of the essence of the contract however, and gives a power to determine in the case of non-completion within the stipulated time limit, then, in the absence of any other provisions, the contractor can recover nothing unless he completes within the time specified which is midnight of the day fixed for completion.

THE CHOICE OF THE METHOD OF CONTRACTING

In most cases of small building works, either works of repair or more particularly works of maintenance to houses, it is usual for an entire contract to be set up and it is common for this to be a lump sum contract as well. The advantages of this are obvious since both the employer and the builder know exactly where they are since the terms of the contract are defined both as to the extent of the work and the amount of the consideration to be paid. It is not usual in most cases for time to be specified as the essence of the contract, although there may well be exceptional cases where time is of fundamental importance. Where time is not specified as the essence of the contract however, the employer does have some remedies against an extremely slow or inert builder and these have already been referred to.

We have already seen that there are four varieties of entire contracts only one of which can be strictly described as a lump sum contract. Provided the extent of the work is known, most of these types of entire contract are in ready use. It is quite common for a contract to be arranged where the price is to be subsequently ascertained on some fixed basis for example by a Schedule of Prices, since there are occasions when the extent of the work may be known to the various parties but circumstances make it so difficult for the builder to quote a lump sum price beforehand that if he is pressed to do so, his figure could operate unfairly against either himself or the employer. An example of a case such as this might be in respect of the renewal of large areas of defective plaster throughout a large house that has been neglected for many years. It is possible to define the extent of the work by the surveyor merely specifying that areas of loose, unsound or otherwise defective plaster be taken down and renewed, but this is of no great assistance to the builder in trying to compile a lump sum price. It is of more use to the plasterer on the site since he knows what to do in broad terms although he should properly seek advice over doubtful areas of plaster. However, we are not concerned under this heading with the problems of the plasterer but with those of the builder and employer. If the builder makes an attempt to compile a lump sum price, this can be little more than a guess which may be wildly astray, and from his point of view once the work starts, he may realise with a sinking feeling as soon as areas of plaster start to come rattling down, that he is going to lose money. The reader might suggest that this results in a good bargain for the employer, but the writers emphatically take the opposite view. Under such circumstances the builder can be forgiven if he tries to press the work through in the shortest possible time and take short cuts where these are not likely to be noticed. Once the decorations are applied, and these may be expensive, the results of hurried workmanship may not become apparent for a time, but some months afterwards bulges, distortions or cracks may appear behind or through the wallpaper or the lining paper to the ceilings, indicating that although the lump sum contract price appeared to be favourable at the time, it was by no means the bargain that might have been thought. There is, however, another reason why such a situation is not desirable. It should never be the surveyor's duty to try and enforce a harsh bargain against a builder or to try and make a profit out of him on behalf of his client. The surveyor should try to hold the scales fairly balanced between employer and builder so that a good and workmanlike repair is achieved at a just cost. It is not only morally obnoxious for the surveyor to attempt to drive hard bargains unnecessarily, but it is extremely undesirable that he should attempt to do so since his efforts will merely rebound on his own head.

The lump sum contract and the entire contract where the price is to be subsequently ascertained by a schedule of prices have been discussed, but the other two forms of entire contract where the extent of the work is known and there is a single price made up of a separate payment for each separate part on the one hand, or whether no price at all is mentioned on the other, are rather more rare. It is possible that in a group of cottages for example, an extensive repair contract that is negotiated for a single price might specify that payment is to be made on completion of the work to the individual dwellings, but the writers feel that this is a rather clumsy way of managing the matter and it would be easier if progress payments were arranged on a normal basis. It is extremely rare in the writers' experience for no price to be mentioned at all and even more rare for no way being specified of ascertaining the price. The latter would appear to be an extremely undesirable method of proceeding with the contract, although the writers are prepared to believe that there exist somewhere extreme circumstances that would justify taking such a step.

It might be thought that the above methods of contracting cover every possible contingency but this is not so. There are many occasions particularly in the repair of older structures which may be extremely complicated so much so in fact that the surveyor is quite unable to arrange an entire contract. Circumstances may arise where he has to advance on the property with the builder armed only with a schedule of agreed prices. The writers might instance the case of structural repairs to an Elizabethan house where the structural timbers are not only hidden from view but where they are very badly worn and decayed. An entire contract may be completely impracticable under such circumstances and the builder will follow the surveyor's directions as the work proceeds. Under circumstances such as these however, the question of the subsequent ascertainment of the price is of grave importance. The client will have accepted the surveyor's advice that no other form of contracting is possible or desirable under the circumstances but he will want to know that his interests are being safeguarded and the surveyor has therefore two choices to make so far as cost is concerned. He may either, on the one hand, agree with the builder a schedule of day work charges and overheads or, on the other hand, he may prefer to have the costs subsequently assessed by valuation and measurement by a quantity surveyor. When one says that the surveyor may prefer it, the builder on the other hand may emphatically not, since this leads to an area of uncertainty so far as he is concerned if the quantity surveyor is unknown to him. Problems of this type are generally overcome by nominating a quantity surveyor between the parties but the builder will try to press a day work basis on the surveyor and his employer as this represents much the best and safest form of contract so far as he is concerned. For one thing he knows that all his expenditure and overheads with an allowance for profit will be paid and that whatever the difficulties encountered, he can take his time to them since he is not penalised if he drags his feet. Again if certain parts of the work prove difficult to complete, there is no reason why the builder should not have a second, third or even fourth chance at the repair since he knows that he will be paid. In the case of subsequent measurement and valuation he will certainly be paid for the work that he has completed but he will not be paid for having had two or three shots at it.

Having said this however, there are occasions where a day work basis will suit the surveyor and the employer as well as the builder. An obvious example of this is an isolated but small cottage in the country where the repair work, although complicated, is not very large in extent and both the surveyor and the employer, both of whom live locally, know and trust one particular firm of builders and would be hard put to it to find another. Not only do they feel safe in the builder's hands, but they might feel that the introduction of a firm of quantity surveyors from some way away might prove unnecessarily costly and difficult under the circumstances.

DOCUMENTS FORMING THE CONTRACT

It will be recalled that the great majority of building contracts are simple contracts, that is to say those that are distinct from speciality contracts as in the case of an agreement with a corporation which is under seal. It is also perhaps true to guess that the vast majority of building contracts are contracts by word of mouth when one thinks of the number of occasions that frantic householders or surveyors may telephone plumbers to ask that an urgent repair be carried out to leaking pipes or defective tanks. Clearly, however, for slightly larger and more costly repairs, some better form than this is necessary. Possibly an exchange of letters which satisfy the conditions of offer and acceptance and set up a lump sum contract can be sufficient between the surveyor to the employer on the one hand and the builder on the other, to deal with a straightforward single repair such as the rebuilding of the top section of a chimney stack. The surveyor might embody in the letter two or three simple specification clauses each of a few lines which are sufficient to describe and delineate the amount of the work to both his and the builder's satisfaction. If the work, however, is more extensive than this, the next and most common document is probably the specification and this will now be considered under a separate heading.

The Specification

A specification is a detailed and particularised description of every item of work required so as to put the contractor in possession of definite priceable data. Specifications for more complicated sets of circumstances will be referred to later, but at this stage the writers wish to confine themselves to a simple specification for repairs or maintenance to a house where the specification itself, together with its accompanying letter and the subsequent exchange of letters between the builder and the surveyor, form the only documents that define the contract.

The specification for small repairs and maintenance of dwelling houses can be conveniently divided and set out under four parts all of which are equally important. These are as follows:

Part 1 General preliminaries and conditions of contract.
Part 2 Materials and workmanship.
Part 3 Provisional sums and prime costs items.
Part 4 The works.

The first section under the heading of "preliminaries" deals with the conditions under which the work is to be carried out together with special points that need to be made and these preliminaries should be drafted with care as they will form the contractural basis of the agreement between the builder and the employer. It is always desirable to commence the preliminaries with a brief statement as to the extent and purpose of the work and whether the premises are to remain occupied or not and then to deal with those points that seem to be of particular importance for the type of contract envisaged. Thus in the case of a house facing and overlooking a busy main road, the need to carry out repairs to the front elevation may make the subject of scaffolding an important one and the need for the builder to seek the appropriate consents and supply lighting at night, is of some consequence. The surveyor might also think it wise to stress that the builder must allow access to callers and even more importantly, point out that the question of insurance in the case of damage or injury to third parties is a matter for him alone and one on which the employer bears no responsibility. Most competent firms of builders are well aware of their duties in the case of work of this type but it does no harm for the surveyor to stress the points that he considers to be important since it directs the builder's attention to them on the one hand and makes it absolutely clear what the respective rights, duties and obligations of the parties are, should the matter ever unhappily proceed to Court in the event of some difficulty developing. In the case of another type of property, for example, an isolated cottage in the country, the question of water supply for the repair or maintenance work might be of consequence and the surveyor could do well to define who is responsible for supplying it if it cannot be obtained from natural sources. Again, in the case of a large property that is let in flats, the surveyor should specify if access is difficult or restricted at given times and make it clear to the builder what the position really is. It is not only that the builder in the lack of any other information has the right to free and uninterrupted access to the site, but it is obviously helpful if the surveyor provides the builder with as much basic information concerning the contract as he can. Another example of this might be where one dwelling house abuts directly on the site of another and the surveyor knows that access is extremely difficult on the adjoining land so that special arrangements have to be made for some repointing. Full information on points such as this make for much better relations between the employer, the surveyor and the builder and forethought in trying to overcome the particular difficulties of each case always pays, since it is fair to assume that every case will have some particular point of difficulty about it.

The writers are conscious of the fact that, when advocating the use of selected preliminary clauses, they are open to the suggestion that this can lead to danger. An example of this is where the surveyor foresees some fairly commonplace difficulty which he then proceeds to deal with at some length, but completely overlooks a much more fundamental problem to which no reference is made at all. It is clear therefore, that thought must be given to the arrangement and balance of the preliminary clauses in small building works, and even at a somewhat lower level, that of common sense, the surveyor should cast his eye through the clauses once he has drafted or dictated them to see that they sound reasonable and complete as a whole. It is, for example, only too easy to specify the panel pins in detail but to omit all reference to the panels! It has been seen however, that a great many points in elementary building contract law are inferred at common law or in equity and it is not considered that the use of selected preliminary clauses presents as much of a risk as may be feared. Predominantly the major advantage of this course of action is that it provides a flexible and reasonable method of presenting a small contract without overloading it to a ridiculous degree. It is possible in theory for the surveyor's office to have prepared, duplicated, copies setting up standard preliminary clauses in great detail and for these to be attached to every small building contract that the surveyor is asked to carry out. This is a quite unacceptable proceeding as firstly the builder on seeing a vast array of clauses may attach far too much importance to them and increase his price accordingly and secondly it is just plain ridiculous to have preliminaries in respect of "treasure trove" or "antiquities" when dealing with the repointing of a dwelling house.

So far as the second part of the specification is concerned, dealing with materials and workmanship, this must be as full as necessary where a number of tenders are being sought from builders who are not known to the surveyor. Where, however, the contractors who are asked to tender are known to have high standards and are appreciative of the opportunity to submit a tender and look for future contracts, then possibly some relaxation might be permitted since they will know the standard of materials and workmanship that will be required. It should be emphasised, however, that the firms must not only be known to the surveyor but also be used to dealing with contracts of the type and nature of the one under consideration.

Part 3 of the specification, dealing with provisional sums and prime cost items, will be referred to again in greater detail later. At the time that the specification is drawn up the surveyor may not always be able to describe in detail a number of articles that are to be provided and fixed to the premises or perhaps the surveyor has not quite made up his mind how to deal with some knotty problems. It may well be that the client wishes to delay the selection of various goods such as sanitary fittings and door furniture until the works are in progress when he, or more accurately his wife, will be duly despatched to a large firm of builders' merchants who will assist in the selection of not only hardware, but wallpapers as well. A list will be provided giving the "p.c." or "prime cost" sums that the surveyor has allowed against each item so that more expensive fittings or wallpapers will become duly authorised extras of the contract. It should be remembered however, that as few p.c. sums as possible should be used. It is far better and safer for the client to select the goods in advance since it is possible for the client's wife to return, wreathed in smiles, announcing that some type of fitting has been selected that nobody expected, but that it is definitely the last word in taste and design. The consequence all too often is that the last word in taste and design has several awkward features about it which upsets the surveyor's careful arrangements for plumbing and involves all sorts of complications leading to increased cost. It is accordingly advocated that wherever possible prime cost sums are avoided and also that provisional sums are reduced to a minimum. It is all too easy in a busy office when getting out contract documents is a race for time, to take the easy way out and specify provisional or prime cost sums in order to get over an immediate problem only to find that they lead to trouble and difficulty at some future time. It is desirable in this part of the specification to define the two terms and to set out what is included and excluded from each as various interpretations exist. This matter is discussed again later in relation to Bills of Quantities.

So far as part 4 of the specification is concerned, dealing with the works on site, the writers feel that for small repair and maintenance contracts, the work is perhaps best described in a logical sequence of operation following operation under groups collected together and described under various parts of the structure, rather than trade headings as is common with specifications for new works. It is thought that this makes a more logical basis for the builder to arrive at his quotation since he can visualise the work easily in the absence of any other supporting documents. There is, of course, the disadvantage under this method that it is relatively easy for the surveyor to omit all reference to a fairly vital part of the operation. It is possible for example, in the repair of a door opening set in a brick partition to deal faithfully with the jambs and threshold, together with replastering and redecorating and include full details of the door and frame, but to forget the question of the lintel entirely. It is thought, however, that constant practice will overcome this type of error.

There is little doubt that the ability to draft a specification for small building works is something of an art. It is however, well worth the surveyor's practice and concentration in order to acquire the ability to write such a specification well. One of the vital factors is that the surveyor should put himself firmly in the builder's shoes and visualise the work as his builder would see it for the first time and endeavour to describe the various stages shortly and in plain and simple language with consistent stages so that one operation logically follows another, with nothing omitted of any great consequence and, almost as important, nothing repeated. It should be remembered that the layout and wording of a specification that might be suitable for estimating by a very large firm of contractors who might have a number of different processes in their estimating department dealt with by different people under various trades might not suit the small working builder who has two or three men on his staff and who will compile the estimate himself, going over the property with the specification in his hand, marking amounts in pencil beside each item.

On a minor point it is worth perhaps stating that as many copies of the specification on a single typing, usually six, should be procured since it is invariably the case to find that more copies are needed than is expected for sending to competing builders, the client and various authorities. It is customery to produce specifications of this type on good quality flimsy paper for this reason, but if the surveyor suspects that he is likely to need more copies than this, almost invariably if an improvement grant is involved, stencils should be cut and the specification duplicated in the first instance or a master copy prepared for ready photo-copying when required.

The Specification with Quantities

In larger works of repair, the surveyor may decide to include quantities with his specification purely to assist tenderers and to avoid the waste of time and expense that would be involved in a number of building firms having to produce quantities independently. In these circumstances of course, the quantities will not form part of the contract as a separate document and it should be made quite clear by the surveyor's conduct that the specification takes precedence in any conflict in the text between the two documents.

The Specification where Quantities form part of the Contract

In large contracts for repair and maintenance the quantities form part of the contract and are a separate contract document. The bill of quantities is sent to the contractors and the specification does not override the bill of quantities if there is any discrepancy between the two documents. The specification can be considered as ancillary to the bill of quantities under these circumstances and cannot impose any greater obligation on the contractor than is contemplated in the bill of quantities.

In large building works where plans and quantities are necessary, the specification takes on a rather different form than was referred to earlier in the case of small building works. It may well be drafted under trade headings and allow the drawings to perform the task of describing the nature and extent of the work graphically rather than by verbal description in a manner that can be understood on a first visit to the site. Often the specification is incorporated within the bill of quantities.

Prime Cost and Provisional Sums

Prime cost and provisional sums have already been referred to in relation to a relatively small contract where they would be included in Part 3 of the Specification. Where these terms are used in a bill of quantities they have specific meanings.

The Standard Method of Measurement of Building Works 5th Edition 1963, General Rules A7, paragraph 2 defines a prime cost sum as follows:

> The term Prime Cost Sum shall mean a sum provided for work or services to be executed by a nominated sub-contractor, a statutory authority or public undertaking or for materials or goods to be obtained from a nominated supplier. Such sum shall be deemed to be exclusive of any profit required by the general contractor and provision should be made for the addition thereof.

In general and in basic terms, the position is that when a prime cost sum is stated in a specification this is the maximum that the building owner can be expected to pay and in the absence of any stipulation to the contrary, the contractor is not entitled to the benefit of either trade discount on the one hand or cash discount on the other. If the contractor has been offered the benefit of trade discount or cash discount, these should be passed to the building owner. If any variation is to be made concerning this rule, therefore, the surveyor should make this clear when the specification is prepared. In actual fact this rule is often substantially varied in most specifications and bills both for goods and for services. Where prime cost sums for electrical or other specialist work are carried out by a nominated sub-contractor for example, a cash discount, normally $2\frac{1}{2}$ per cent, is generally allowed to the general contractor.

The R.I.B.A. Contract form in clause 11 (4) (c)(ii) states that where work cannot properly be measured and valued the contractor shall be allowed, in the absence of day work rates "the prime cost of such work calculated in accordance with the 'Definition of Prime Cost of Daywork carried out under a Building Contract' last before issued by the Royal Institution of Chartered Surveyors and the National Federation of Building Trades Employers together with percentage additions to each section of the prime cost at the rates

943

set out by the contractor in the Schedule of Rates and recorded in the appendix to the conditions. Under sub-clause (c)(iii) to the same clause the form states that 'where the work is within the province of any specialist trade and the said Institution and the appropriate body representing the employers in that trade have agreed and issued a definition of prime cost of daywork, the prime cost of such work calculated in accordance with that definition as last before issued together with percentage additions of the prime cost at the rates set out by the contractor in the Schedule of Rates and recorded in the appendix . . .' " shall be allowed to the contractor accordingly.

So far as provisional sums are concerned, these are defined by the Standard Method of Measurement of Building Works 5th Edition 1963 as follows:

The term "provisional sum" shall mean a sum provided for work or for costs which cannot be entirely foreseen, defined or detailed at the time the tendering documents are issued.

It may often be the case in contracts for the repair of houses that it is not possible to specify every item of work in detail. It may well be that the extent of certain work, such as repairs to many window frames has not been decided upon in advance and the surveyor may wish to allow a contingency sum against such work, the exact cost of which will be ascertained later either when the work is carried out, the balance of the provisional sum, once the actual cost is deducted from it, being due to the building owner. Sometimes of course the work exceeds the provisional sum allowed and therefore an extra becomes due to the contractor.

A common provision in every specification and bill is that the builder shall provide a provisional sum for general contingencies, this sum to be spent only on the direction of the surveyor. This is designed to cover unforeseen extra expenditure within the terms of the contract and it is not designed to cover extra items over and above those contemplated in the specification. A contingency sum of 10 per cent of the surveyor's approximate total envisaged expenditure is considered reasonable on a well thought out and carefully specified scheme of repair.

Once a provisional sum is included in the surveyor's specification or the bill, it becomes strictly part of the contract. If, in the unusual circumstances of no expenditure being required for any extras, the money is not spent at all, the whole of the provisional sum will be due as a credit to the building owner at the end of the contract. On the other hand, if the provisional sum is to be spent on work within the contract terms, it would appear that the work cannot be omitted and given to another contractor without rendering the employer strictly liable for damages for loss of profit.

The Bills of Quantities

A bill of quantities is the name given to a schedule with prices of the actual amount of work, labour and materials which are calculated to be necessary under the terms of the contract. The bill of quantities is normally presented under separate trade headings so that the work, labour and materials of, for example, the trade of bricklayer, is presented separately to that of drain layer, quite irrespective of the sequence of the work as it proceeds on the site. The object of this is to collect and describe the extent of each trade so that each contractor who tenders for the work can put his price in the appropriate blank money column on the bill and thus arrive at a total for the work on the final page.

Until recent times it was one of the accepted methods of forming a contract for a building surveyor or architect to prepare his own quantities which he delivered to the tenderers together with the specification. In such a case where the specification was intended to take precedence over the quantities in defining the contract, the bill of quantities was produced purely to assist contractors and to save several firms the waste of time and expense involved in duplicating hours of unnecessary work. In general under this procedure the building owner was not liable for inaccuracies appearing in the bill of quantities made by his surveyor or architect unless, as was extremely unlikely, they were guaranteed as being correct. It was far more common for the contract documents to specify that in the case of error or inaccuracy, the employer was under no liability to the contractor. This state of affairs would not apply, as we have seen, in the case of mutual mistake or a gross error in calculation made by the contractor which is obvious to the employer. In general terms the contractor is not expected to take a bill of quantities prepared on this basis on trust and must merely see it as a guide to enable him to arrive at his calculations on the same basis as other tenderers. Accordingly he must check the bill to his own satisfaction.

The procedure where a surveyor or architect provides a bill of quantities in the manner outlined above is still carried on in certain parts of the country. The writers feel, however, that the procedure is an unsatisfactory one since the person preparing the bill does not take the ultimate responsibility for errors. It is now, however, becoming an almost universal practice for a quantity surveyor to be employed since it is recognised that it is far more satisfactory to make the maximum use of the services that he can provide and it is more usual for the bills of quantities to then be made part of the contract. In these circumstances the builder may be entitled to extra payment for additional work involved through omissions in the bill of quantities but it should be emphasised that this follows from the form of contract itself, not merely because a quantity surveyor provides the bills of quantities.

Although the National Federation of Building Trade Employers decided in 1956 to recommend that contracts in excess of £4,000 should be supplied with bills of quantities, it should not be assumed that this is invariably the case. The Federation themselves exempted works of repair, painting or decorating from this rule and the question of when to provide bills of quantities either as assistance to the tenderers only or as part of the contract is very much one for the surveyor to decide having regard to the particular circumstances of each individual case. Where a large amount of comparatively straightforward work is to be carried out to a vast house and a number of firms are to be asked to tender, bills of quantities are obviously helpful but in the case of a smaller and more complicated repair to a dwelling house where the matter may be complex but the cost is relatively low, the need for the preparation of a bill of quantities diminishes to the point where it merely adds to expense without much benefit being gained.

Drawings

The preparation of drawings that will form part of the contract and which are produced in such a way that they are intended to be signed by the parties to the contract is commonplace to illustrate points referred to in the specification and the suggestion that any drawings produced should be clear, accurate and on durable paper is an obvious one.

Before he embarks on the preparation of drawings, the surveyor should give some thought to them beforehand. He will probably wish to employ a scale that is in common usage such as, for example, 1:100 for his floor plans while he might wish to produce detail drawings to a scale of 1:20. The advantage of using scales that are in common use is that the drawings can be readily understood by all persons experienced in the building trade. Drawings to odd scales can lead to blunders being made in a builder's or surveyor's office particularly when the staff is under pressure from a great deal of work.

The surveyor should first decide if it is more desirable for the drawings to be produced on linen or tracing paper for the purposes of later reproduction. Tracing paper is perhaps most widely used but linen is desirable if the drawings are likely to be exposed to much wear and tear from continual reprinting. If for example in the case of repairs to a large estate of dwelling houses, extending perhaps over a period of years, a key plan of the estate is included automatically with every batch of fresh applications for tender, this plan is best drawn on linen in the first place. It is on the other hand, however, hardly necessary for linen to be employed if one or perhaps two batches of reproductions are to be produced and no further copies apart from an occasional print are likely to be required subsequently. Under these circumstances tracing paper is preferable and once provided with an edging tape, drawings can be numbered and filed away in case they are ever required again. Prints of all drawings as sent out should be retained by the surveyor and all revisions noted.

In the case of drawings for repair work to existing buildings, it is, of course, necessary that the plans are accurately drawn to scale but it is not usual for dimensions to be figured on the plan as in the case of new work where dimensions are, of course, absolutely vital. All drawings for repair work to existing properties should carry a note to the following effect: "all measurements are to be taken on site and not scaled from this drawing". The onus for measuring in advance on the site for the work to be carried out, for example the provision of joinery fittings to be installed, is therefore placed squarely on the contractor's shoulders instead of those of the surveyor. This sounds at first sight rather unfair but it should be remembered that contractors well used to carrying out this type of operation in fact would prefer, on detailed work, to ensure accuracy by measuring themselves. In any event, however well the drawings are prepared, the limitation exists with old buildings that existing faces are seldom true and level and new work notwithstanding has to marry up to the existing.

Drawings should also show, by details, all fittings duly installed with, in the case of sanitary appliances, all pipe runs and outlets etc. This gives added reason why, as mentioned earlier in this Chapter, prime cost items should be kept to a minimum by ensuring the client's agreement to the selection of appliances and to the design of fittings to be built in.

The surveyor should always remember that mistakes have to be paid for. If they arise because of errors in the drawings or specification, the employer will feel justified in refusing payment when the contractor presents his account for the altered work and this leaves the surveyor or architect holding the bill. Mistakes of this nature in both new work as well as repair work are now giving rise to substantial claims under professional indemnity liability policies of amounts in any one year that are probably far in excess of those being made in connection with the failure to discover defects on structural surveys. This is a situation which has only developed in the last few years and has resulted in a substantial increase in the premiums for cover in regard to design work on buildings. It must also not be forgotten that a mistake not only involves payment to the contractor when he remedies the matter on the site but may also involve an extension of time under the contract which will render the surveyor liable to the penalty envisaged under its terms, should there be one, rather than the builder.

The surveyor is advised to find a good firm of printers for his tracings as near his office as possible, since he will use them constantly. After a while his decisions on whether to employ ink or pencil for example, will be based largely on his knowledge of the quality of copies that can be produced by the particular firm concerned under the various processes available. In addition to this however, a good firm can offer enormous assistance to a surveyor in advising him how difficult printing tasks can be accomplished. Occasionally old plans or ordnance sheets will have to be reproduced and the surveyor should be able to rely on the judgment of the firm as to not only the best method of achieving a good result but also as to the comparative costs involved by the different processes that they recommend.

The publication "Architectural and Building Drawing Office Practice" by the British Standards Institution is recommended in regard to layout etc. of drawings.

The Agreement Form and Conditions of Contract

The Royal Institute of British Architects produces a standard form of building contract which is very commonly used and its terms are reasonably familiar to those concerned with the building industry. The contract consists of the agreement form which is signed by both parties to the contract with the conditions of contract and there is provision for the embodiment of the specification and drawings. There are other forms of contract which are produced and used by local authorities and government departments which have regard to their own specialised requirements but it is to the R.I.B.A. form of contract that reference will mainly be made in this Chapter.

The Royal Institute of British Architects provides the Standard Form of Contract in four different versions. There is firstly the Local Authorities Edition in alternatives either with or without quantities and secondly the Private Edition either with or without quantities.

In addition to the above form of contract, it is also possible to

948

procure forms of sub-contract with a nominated sub-contractor and also a form of agreement for use where the sub-contractor is not nominated by the architect in those districts where it reflects local trade practice.

In June 1968 the R.I.B.A. under the sanction of the Joint Contracts Tribunal, issued a new Form of Agreement and Conditions for Minor Building Works. Although minor building works are not defined either in scope or by reference to a contract sum, this Form of Contract goes some way to meeting the objections that the normal R.I.B.A. Form is somewhat overpowering and too detailed in its conditions when the works are relatively small in scope. The Form is for use where a specification or a specification and drawings have been prepared, where the works are to be carried out for an agreed lump sum and where an Architect/Supervising Officer has been appointed on behalf of the employer. The conditions are set out in two pages in contrast to the twenty-two required for the Conditions in the R.I.B.A. Standard Form. Yet all the main items likely to arise on small contracts for repair or maintenance are covered in comparatively simple language. Such conditions can, of course, be varied or extended according to requirements and in agreement with the builder. Although comparatively new and not yet well known this Form of Agreement for Minor Building Works is likely to become much more frequently used and will probably tend to replace the Conditions assembled together for each individual job found necessary for small works at present.

If forms of contract are employed by the surveyor he should take great care to ensure that these are completed in a proper manner. Messy deletions or amendments are undesirable; these should be neatly typed or written in clearly and legibly and must then be initialled by both parties to the contract. In particular it should not be forgotten that the agreement must be stamped, an ordinary stamp stuck on the printed form which is subsequently cancelled being sufficient in most cases, but, where the agreement is under seal, the stamp must be impressed by the Inland Revenue within a time limit of 30 days. This is a more expensive process. An ordinary stamp is supposed to be affixed to the agreement within 14 days of the first signature being made. It is, however, reassuring for the surveyor to know that a late stamping does not invalidate the agreement. In fact, failure to stamp an agreement is never fatal to it. A Court will accept an agreement as evidence, even if it is not stamped on an undertaking being given that it will be stamped. The Commissioners of Inland Revenue have power to impose a penalty of a fine up to £10 in the case of stamping being omitted, but this is often remitted or reduced.

PARTIES CONNECTED WITH THE CONTRACT

(1) *The Employer or Building Owner*

The employer or building owner can be coldly described as the person who employs the contractor to execute work upon buildings that he owns for a consideration. Both terms are in common use, the term "building owner" being more usual in the London area since it appears in the London Building Act 1930 Section 5(A). Although the term is mainly used in connection with party walls, the expression "building owner" is a convenient one and is widely used.

Whether he is known as the employer or the building owner the surveyor's client will come in many forms and in many different ways and the introduction might be due either to the fact that the surveyor's firm has built up a reputation for the type of work required for many years or to the fact that the surveyor's personal reputation has encouraged the client to seek him out. The introduction, again, can be made through social contact or friendship but in this last case a client who is a personal friend is by no means an unmixed blessing. The writers advise extreme caution in accepting instructions from personal friends since the whole relationship is wrong from the start of the matter. The personal friend and surveyor alike both commonly contribute to a breakdown in relationships at some time during the contract, the first by an inability to establish the fact in his own mind that he is entering into a change of relationship with his friend and the second by a distaste to establish the correct safeguarding procedures both to the contract and to his own position that he would normally employ with another client. If the surveyor says that "of all the jobs that I have running this one has to go wrong" subsequent enquiry generally reveals that the job that has gone wrong is being carried out for a friend and that the surveyor has not been as firm as he should have been in either the procedure for setting up the contract on the one hand or administering it on the other. True the client himself will have contributed grave faults but he will not have been solely responsible for the unsatisfactory nature of the outcome. The surveyor will complain of the fact that the client has telephoned him at all hours with constant changes of plans and the client will deplore the surveyor's stiffening of manner after the friendly relationships at the outset and the growing difficulty of finding him on the telephone. Both parties will have a common grievance in that the other has become ungrateful with a lack of understanding about the true position. Both are probably about half right.

It should also be borne in mind however that the employer can, apart from an individual, be a small or large company, in the latter case with a property manager answerable to a board of directors. Again the employer can be a local authority or statutory board who might well appoint a project manager in the case of larger contracts. Finally the employer might be a committee possibly one of the hardest clients for the surveyor to advise, particularly in the absence of a strong controlling chairman or secretary since old rivalries and grievances are then likely to rule the committee decision rather than a clearsighted approach to the true problems.

As a last word on the subject of the employer the surveyor should be wary of the creative layman. The self-styled ability to have an "instinctive feeling for houses" or "an inborn ability to do anything with buildings" should be treated by the surveyor with inward suspicion not outward scepticism. The suspicion is purely on the grounds that confidence and flair are often words that can be more aptly if cruelly translated as rashness and ignorance and in a prolonged muddle the surveyor will be hard put to it to defend his own position. The employer who allows the extras to run away unchecked will round on the surveyor at a later stage and imply that the situation has somehow arisen as a result of his laxity with the builder and the surveyor's only hope of dealing with the contract effectively is to exercise a firm grip over events or if he cannot manage this to resign his position. Having uttered these harsh words however, it should be added that the surveyor will be quite wrong to see such signs in the vast majority of clients who, encouraged by the glossy magazines, have the natural and delightful wish and often the very considerable ability to reflect their own personalities in their surroundings with the use of many of the attractive new furnishings and materials on the market in a way that does no violence to either technical or financial considerations or to the character of an old building. This in the last analysis is the hallmark of the good employer.

(2) *The Builder or Contractor*

The term "builder" has been defined as referring to a person who builds either upon his own land or that of another for profit. He is commonly the person who is responsible for the execution of work by artisans under the instructions of a surveyor or architect. As we have seen the builder must exercise reasonable care and skill in execution of the work and must complete it within a reasonable time if no precise period has been agreed between the parties. He is also bound to enter upon his employment without undue delay and

951

has to be industrious and diligent in the performance of his duties. He must also exercise due care.

There is probably no difference at law between the term "builder" and "contractor". The latter term envisages a person who sets himself up as willing to contract for works on a large scale and possibly the difference between the two terms, if there is one, relies solely on the scale of the operations envisaged. The term "builder" is customary in small building works while the term "contractor" is more common in large-scale building operations.

(3) *The Surveyor or Architect*

The principal corporate bodies for the training of surveying and architectural students are respectively the Royal Institution of Chartered Surveyors and the Royal Institute of British Architects. Members of these corporate bodies are entitled to designate themselves as Chartered Surveyors or Chartered Architects but it must be remembered that under the Architects (Registration) Acts 1931–1938, no person practising or carrying on any business under any name, style or title containing the word "Architect" can legally do so unless he is recorded in the Register of Architects. Both Chartered Surveyors and Chartered Architects have to qualify for membership of their respective bodies by examination and are subject to rules of conduct and disciplinary proceedings if these rules are broken. Both are restricted in a number of ways for the good of their profession as a whole in such matters as undertaking not to enter into transactions relating to trade or commerce and not to enter into unlimited personal advertising to further their advancement.

So far as the Royal Institution of Chartered Surveyors is concerned, there are a number of sub-divisions relating to the very different areas of work undertaken by Chartered Surveyors. For the purposes of this Chapter however, it is assumed that the duties of surveyor and architect are synonymous except as will be referred to later and both engage in the duties of preparing the contract documents, arranging the contract and supervising the work in progress that is envisaged within the scope of this volume. In addition, of course, the surveyor or architect's duties will include the certifying of interim and final payments to the builder and ensuring that the contract is completed satisfactorily from all points of view. The word surveyor on its own will henceforward be used in this context alone.

The surveyor is required at law to supply the fullest information that he can to the contractor. He is not, however, expected to give constant supervision to the work while this is in progress, but is only bound at law to give such periodical supervision as is necessary to ensure that the works are being executed in general accordance with the contract. Thus he is not, for example, responsible to the building owner for the failure to notice that defective workmanship has been carried out which is not obvious, for example, defective joints to pipes laid under a floor which are subsequently covered up, but on the other hand he has a duty to advise as to what constitutes effective supervision in any set of circumstances. Thus, for example, in the case of a large repair contract where a good deal of day work is unavoidable, he might recommend, for example, the employment of a clerk of works. He might also feel that regular site meetings should be arranged attended by the main contractor and principal sub-contractor and any other persons whose presence is desirable.

As we have seen earlier, the surveyor is appointed by the building owner to make arrangements to have the work put in hand and completed on his behalf and is under most circumstances simply his agent. He thus has authority to act on behalf of his employer but not to exceed his duties so that while he will no doubt arm himself with appropriate authority to make minor variations, subject to written notification to the employer, any major variations in the contract that are entirely unexpected should be referred back to the employer for his consideration. Much, of course, depends, as we have seen on the terms of the surveyor's appointment and in particular on the type of agency involved for example if this happens to be either a special agency or a general agency.

There is one way in which the surveyor acts other than as agent of his employer. This is where the building contract contains a covenant giving him power to decide all differences between the parties to the contract as arbitrator. This in fact is a situation that is becoming increasingly rare since modern standard forms of contract provide for the appointment of an independent arbitrator. Notwithstanding this however, in modern forms of contract the surveyor is empowered to act between the parties in certain minor areas of dispute and as such he might be described as a "quasi-arbitrator".

The surveyor is expected at law to possess the requisite amount of skill in his profession since he held himself out for reward. He must use a reasonable amount of care and diligence in the carrying out of the work that he undertakes and must exercise due skill. It should be stressed, however, that he is not expected to exercise an extraordinary degree of skill. The fact that a practitioner of greater experience might have carried out his duties in another way does not necessarily imply that the surveyor has not carried out the work with the necessary skill required at law. He is only negligent if it can be proved that there has been such a want of competent care and skill that this has led to a bad result. It is interesting to note, however, that while a surveyor might be liable in negligence to his employer, he cannot be liable for negligence in his role as "quasi-arbitrator" when he acts in deciding minor disputes between the parties. Otherwise, however, the link between employer and surveyor arises as a contractural one so that privity of contract exists between the two parties concerned. Thus it was difficult to envisage circumstances where a builder might recover damages should he be misled by faulty plans for example, but in the recent case of Hedley Byrne and Co. Ltd., v. Heller & Partners (1963), the principles laid down by the House of Lords have extended the duty of care widely so that it is now thought likely that a builder might be able to recover damages from a surveyor under such circumstances although in such a case the employer could not also take action.[1] In general however, the surveyor has hitherto been liable to the contractor only for breach of warranty of authority where, for example, he exceeds his authority in ordering additional works of the contractor, or for fraud.

The contract between the surveyor and his employer is a personal one so that he cannot delegate his duties entirely. He is not, however, bound to carry out every detail of the work personally and can make use of others to assist him. It should be remembered however that he is responsible for the acts and defaults of subordinates and this may include the clerk of works. It has been established that a surveyor cannot rely implicitly on the judgment of a clerk of works even although the clerk of works was appointed by the employer in the first place. The surveyor may still be liable for the negligence of the clerk of works, in particular if he is relying on the clerk of works to carry out part of his own duties under the contract.

As the contract of employment between the surveyor and the employer is a personal one, it becomes dissolved by the death or disablement of the surveyor. The employer, however, is not entitled to rescind the contract where the surveyor has a temporary illness except under unusual circumstances. Similarly of course, the death of the employer puts an end to the contract so far as the surveyor is concerned, provided of course that the contract is of a personal nature between the parties.

As we have seen earlier in this Chapter if a surveyor acts without due care and skill the building owner is entitled to dismiss him and the surveyor is unlikely to recover any remuneration. A surveyor is expected to ascertain and comply with the requirements of all Acts of Parliament regulating buildings or works in the locality in which the repairs are being carried out and to know about and comply with

[1] "Emden & Gills Building Contracts and Practice" 7th Edition.

by-laws. He is likely to be dismissed therefore if he is so far lacking in skill and knowledge that he fails to comply with regulations that he should have observed. He is not, however, automatically liable in every case, for example, if the contractor fails to notify the District Surveyor or Building Inspector before putting work in hand, this is not a matter firstly that affects the relationship between the surveyor and employer and secondly since that statute places a prima facia penalty upon the contractor, the surveyor is not likely to be involved. However, in the early case of James v. Masters (1893) it was held that where work was no longer proceeding in accordance with the deposited plans, that the respondent was bound to submit fresh plans in accordance with the change of his intention and having omitted to do so was liable to conviction under Section 157 of the Public Health Act 1875.

(4) The Quantity Surveyor

The quantity surveyor takes out detailed measurements and quantities from plans prepared by the surveyor to enable builders to calculate the amounts of money necessary to enable them to submit tenders. In practice of course, the quantity surveyor covers very much more ground than this. He can advise on cost and tendering procedures and contractural arrangements generally and in particular he can value building works executed so as to enable an interim or final certificate to be issued. A Chartered Surveyor who is recorded on the Register of the Royal Institution of Chartered Surveyors as having qualified in the Quantities Sub-Division of the Institution's Examinations has the right to use the designation "Chartered Quantity Surveyor".

The surveyor in charge of larger contracts for repair work employs a quantity surveyor to extract the quantities for the work proposed. He will of course notify the employer as to the fact that he is instructing a quantity surveyor but such authority would be implied where the employer either knew of this fact or had tacitly acquiesced in the surveyor's action. An awkward set of circumstances might occur where the surveyor appoints a quantity surveyor to produce quantities without his employer's knowledge knowing that the employer had only a certain sum of money to spend. If the tenders subsequently are very much higher than the upper limit that the employer has to spend upon the property, and he has not ratified the quantity surveyor's appointment, he might be justified in refusing to pay the quantity surveyor's fees who could thereupon in turn look to the surveyor for payment. It is therefore always wise for the employer to be consulted and the quantity surveyor to be appointed at an early stage in the proceedings.

The quantity surveyor, like all professional men, has a duty to act with reasonable skill and care. His position, however, is an unusual one as he will probably have little direct contact with the employer on the one hand and he has not privity of contract or legal liability with the contractor on the other. However, the relation of employer and employed arises between the building owner and the quantity surveyor and any provision that a contractor tendering for work is to add the amount of the quantity surveyor's charges to his tender, does not alter this relationship. The position is of course different where the contractor employs a quantity surveyor to assist him to arrive at his tender. In this case if the quantity surveyor fails to exercise due care, he will of course be liable to the contractor in negligence.

(5) *Engineers and Consultants*

There will be occasions when the surveyor, in the course of the repair and maintenance of houses, will wish to avail himself of the services offered by Engineers and others. Engineers for the purposes of this Chapter can be sub-divided into two groups as follows:

(1) Structural Engineers, i.e. those concerned with steel or reinforced concrete.

(2) Mechanical and Electrical Engineers, i.e. those concerned with heating and ventilating, the provision of hot water and all electrical services.

It will be appreciated that not only is the function of the two separate groups of engineers entirely different so far as the work they do is concerned, but equally their relationship with the surveyor can differ widely. In the field of repairs to houses, the structural engineer is likely to provide services of an advisory nature in connection with problems that are out of the ordinary where, for example, part of an old structure originally intended to be load bearing can no longer, due to age, be guaranteed to provide this function so that the loads have to be transferred elsewhere, the building nevertheless giving the impression that nothing has changed. Alternatively, the surveyor may wish to bring in the engineer to check his calculations and to reassure him that what he proposes to do in a conventional situation in steel or reinforced concrete, is adequate and sound. In either case the engineer might simply provide advice for a fee or alternatively he may take a greater part in the matter by drawing up a specification for steelwork, supervising the work on the site and certifying payment. The mechanical and electrical engineer on the other hand is far more likely not only to provide advice, but to specify the best type of installation for use under the circumstances concerned, and to supervise the work in progress and certify payment. Where the structural engineer may be, in most cases, working on behalf of the surveyor so that he is unlikely to have direct contact with the building owner, the mechanical and electrical engineer on the other hand may have a much more fundamental part to play and may well be brought in at the outset of the matter not only to advise on costs and alternative schemes, but will have an important role to play in the whole question of maintenance which will include not only the question of operating and running costs, but also ease of access for maintenance and the appropriate periodic intervals that maintenance should take place and what should be done on these occasions. The function of mechanical engineers where larger mansions are concerned can be such an important one that the selection of the right man is of considerable consequence and where a large house is opened to the public, the complications of heating, ventilating, electrical and other services may entail a total cost which exceeds the work of renovation.

Other consultants used by the surveyor may be experts in the field of piled or raft foundations and soil mechanics. These will be indispensable in certain cases and although in the case of soil mechanics the function may most often be limited to that of advice in the case of structures where the sub-soil characteristics are extremely unusual or may have altered completely due to some extraneous cause, the surveyor may decide that an expert should design and supervise the provision of the piles or raft that may be necessary for an effective repair to be carried out.

Finally in the consideration of consultants, one should not forget the landscape design expert who, particularly in the case of larger houses, is becoming more and more established, not just to provide an attractive garden, but to advise on the whole question of layout of grounds, tree preservation, planting programmes and the like. Gardening maintenance costs are high and the provision of one type of garden or landscape as against another may drastically affect the entire maintenance programme.

The surveyor will probably wish to see that his engineer or consultant is a member of the appropriate professional body that represents the best standards entailed by his particular branch of work. The engineer or consultant will normally be a professional man and will have his own recognised scale of fees which the surveyor should call for before entering into any arrangements for work to be carried out. In a small case where an engineer gives advice to the surveyor, it is possible that the surveyor may wish to absorb the engineer's fee in his own charges rather than pass them on to the client, but in most cases the consultant's fees will have to be a separate matter and this will have to be explained to the building owner. It is interesting to compare the arrangements, recently having undergone some alteration, in the scale of fees recommended by the Royal Institute of British Architects. The scale no longer includes a clause providing for reductions in architects' fees when consultants are employed. This is due mainly to the fact that new modern buildings are highly complex and the employment of consultants is no longer an abdication of the architect's role, as it used to be regarded, since with certain types of modern structure the architect's duties may even be increased rather than reduced by an ambitious scheme however much the design and execution of the work falls into specialised hands. A new scale of fees does, however, permit architects at their discretion and by prior written agreement, to reduce their fees by up to one-third of the percentage fee on the cost of the particular service, provided that the architect's total fee is not reduced by more than one-sixth.

The advantage of the independent consultant or specialist as a professional man is that he in turn can obtain quotations for steelwork, heating layouts or electrical services from as many firms as he thinks proper. His professional standing ensures that the surveyor may expect to receive advice that is completely independent irrespective of commercial considerations. It will be known however that today in an age of specialised techniques there are a growing number of commercial firms who provide consultancy services and it is necessary to give such firms some consideration.

The growth of the specialist contracting firm to provide consultancy services has been rapid not only in the engineering fields, particuarly the mechanical engineering field in such matters as heating and ventilating, hot water and electrical services, but also in the case of foundation and sub-soil specialists and landscape design as well. Even more firms can be found who will advise and provide specialist materials for floors and roofs, for example, while other firms specialise in almost every field where the surveyor is likely to need advice and will provide a commercial service to follow. Many of the firms that offer advice together with a design and supply service are excellent and the reason for the growth of many of them over recent years has been that the service they have provided has been based on their own patented methods apart from being also expert, rapid and competitive in cost. In cases where, for example, there is an extremely bad outbreak of woodworm in an old structure, or where investigation of a large and advanced structural failure has revealed that the foundations are sadly defective having regard to the load bearing characteristics of the sub-soil, the introduction of a specialist firm who will not only provide advice, but carry out the work swiftly for a lump sum and subsequently provide a guarantee to the building owner, has a great deal to be said for it. The alternative method of preparing an independent specification and calling for tenders from recognised firms of general contractors may not only merely be a longer process, but may be more costly in the long run and with a more uncertain end-product so far as the building owner is concerned. In certain cases it is true that skilful design or a well drawn specification placed before a first-class firm of general contractors may result in a rather cheaper alternative proving equally satisfactory, but this is by no means always the case and specialist firms, who act in a consultancy capacity and provide a commercial service as well, have established their place in the field of repair work to a substantial degree.

Having said this, however, it should be recognised there are certain disadvantages in the employment of such firms. The introduction of such a firm, even if well known, does mean that the building owner is presented with a single solution only. It is perfectly true that it is possible in theory to obtain the separate advice of one or two firms of this type but this is an unwieldy and cumbersome process and the comparison between the recommendations suggested by each is difficult and worrying firstly because there is no common specification of what type of work is required and secondly because the recommendations put forward may be fundamentally different. The surveyor may find difficulty in trying to persuade his client not to allow the consideration of costs alone to influence him where the figures are set out boldly and alluringly in the individual quotations submitted by the respective firms. It is perhaps reasonable to suggest that it is the surveyor's duty to translate the advantages and disadvantages of each proposal to the building owner but it is considered that this point of view although plausible on the surface, does not hold water. The whole point of obtaining a specialist firm is that it will provide advice and services in a field where the surveyor is most probably not himself an expert. It therefore follows that if the surveyor has to decide as between several proposals submitted to him in a highly technical and specialised field in which he is not an expert, he exceeds his function and may exercise the wrong choice. Added to this is the fact that it is often counter-productive to ask too many firms to submit different schemes and quotations since the end result may be more bewildering than helpful to the building owner. Another disadvantage in employing firms of this type is that it is fair comment to say that there must be a certain conflict between the professional approach on the one hand and the commercial approach on the other. It is easy for an expert to become fond of his own methods and products and indeed he must feel full confidence in them for his firm to survive. This outlook can, however, lead to a rather blinkered approach and he may well be intolerant of the benefits of other methods or the employment of other techniques. It is true that by having a commercial approach his firm survives on keeping abreast of its competitors, but the basic approach and basis of survival of the firm will be a commercial rather than a pro-fesional one. Specialist contractors, though not all by any means, can be guilty of adopting a short-term viewpoint.

(6) *The Clerk of Works*

In larger contracts or where constant supervision of works is re-quired, the appointment of a clerk of works is desirable. Unless anything is stated to the contrary in the terms of his employment the surveyor is not expected to exercise constant supervision on a personal basis and the appointment of the clerk of works is normally made on his advice by the employer. The clerk of works is normally a man of mature years who has had experience in one or more recognised trades, probably bricklaying or the like, where he has probably been appointed a general forman. His experience and general standing lead to recognition and subsequent employment as a clerk of works. He may be a member of the Institute of Clerks of Works or may hold a building inspector's certificate of the Institu-tion of Municipal Engineers or may have passed the Clerk of Works Examination of the Association of Building Technicians.

The duties of a clerk of works are to ensure that his employer's interests are protected insofar as the quality of materials and work-manship provided comply with the terms of the contract. He is therefore in the opposite relationship to the builder's general foreman and although this may appear to be a situation that could cause conflict to the detriment of the work, such occasions do not often arise and if they do, it is the surveyor's task to try to mend matters. More often both the clerk of works and the general foreman will be men of considerable experience and with mutual respect for each other and on many contracts the clerk and the foreman become firm friends on the one hand while well able to preserve their loyalties to their employers on the other. A good clerk of works will be every-where on the site but will be unobtrusive and will exercise an admirable amount of tact in rejecting sub-standard materials or workmanship. He will certify the day work sheets when work is carried out on a day work basis and will sign them to the effect that they are correct. A clerk of works is obviously of enormous assistance in a contract that depends on day work and the benefit of a constant check on the times spent by craftsmen and labourers is obvious. In lump sum contracts the value of a clerk of works is that he will be able to verify the contractor's submissions for variations due to extras and will also be able to look out for savings, a task to which the contractor will normally apply himself with rather less enthusiasm. The clerk of works is also of great assistance to the quantity surveyor or the surveyor in charge of the work in being able to describe accurately the nature and extent of works subsequently covered up such as foundations or pipes for services.

(7) *The General Foreman*

No summary of persons concerned with the contract could exclude the general foreman. These men, like the clerk of works, were probably originally tradesmen who by their special qualities have been appointed to the post of general foreman by the contractor. They are, of course, employees of the contractor and their duties are straightforward in that they are the contractor's representative on the site and responsible for the day to day running of the work. It would be true to say that the character of the general foreman can have a profound influence on the running of the contract. A good foreman with substantial knowledge of the type of work being carried out will anticipate difficulties and by his general attitude will inspire the confidence not only of the building owner and surveyor but also the men on the site. His advice can be invaluable in bringing a contract to a successful conclusion. Unhappily the converse is also true but fortunately very rare.

(8) *Sub-Contractors and Nominated Sub-Contractors*

It has always been usual for general building firms to enter into sub-contracting arrangements for specialist services such as steelwork, heating and ventilating or electrical works. In recent years however, the sub-contract system has increased to a very large extent and it now includes traditional trades such as joinery. In order to illustrate this trend, for example, one can reflect that it would be highly unusual for scaffolding not to be sub-contracted in metropolitan areas whereas this was by no means the case just after the Second World War.

As a general rule, sub-contractors are firms or persons offering specialist services who are employed by the contractor direct and who are responsible to him alone. As a sub-contractor is not a party to the contract between the employer and the main contractor, he cannot bring an action against the employer as there is no privity of contract between them. For the same reason the building owner is not responsible to the contractor for the extra expense incurred by any delay or faults caused by the sub-contractors to the builders. Accordingly a sub-contractor has no general right to expect money due to him to be paid by the employer in the event of the builder's default, unless such a provision is made in the contract.

There are many occasions in building contracts, however, where the employer or his surveyor will wish to employ a particular specialist firm which is unknown to the builder. Clearly it would be cumbersome and unworkable for such a firm to be engaged by the employer direct since there would be many points of conflict of responsibility with the main contractors and the custom has become accepted for the specialist firm to be employed by the main contractors as their sub-contractors. In these circumstances, the specialists are known as "nominated sub-contractors". It should be emphasised however, that nominated sub-contractors are not, generally speaking, in any different position to other specialist sub-contractors, even although the employer or his surveyor may have had a hand in their selection. Similarly, acceptance of work completed by a sub-contractor by the employer will not generally imply that the employer has made a contract with the sub-contractor. On the other hand, however, where there are dealings between the employer and a sub-contractor direct which amount to a contractural obligation either express or implied, for example that the employer will pay the sub-contractor a certain sum of money, the position is much more complicated at law and the question would arise as to whether the promise is collateral to the contract between the contractor and the sub-contractor or whether it is a direct promise to pay on the part of the employer.

Unless there is any stipulation in the contract between the employer and the main contractor that prevents him sub-letting part of the work, for example, should the employer particularly want the main contractor to carry out certain work on a personal basis, the contractor has a right to sub-let portions of the work to sub-contractors and expect payment for this work by the employer. However, the contractor then becomes liable in his turn for defective workmanship carried out by his sub-contractor and on the same basis, should the main contractor default under the terms of his direct contract with the employer, the sub-contractor will have a remedy against him. The main contractor will normally see to it that any arrangements between himself and his sub-contractor reflect accurately the terms by which he himself is bound to his employer and should there be any special terms in the main contract, for example the question of liquidated damages, these will no doubt be reflected faithfully in the sub-contract.

Where an employer or his surveyor nominate a firm to act as sub-contractors to the general contractor, the general contractor clearly has a right to object to the appointment if the conditions of the employment of the other firm conflict with the terms of his own contract with the employer. The sub-contract procedure is laid down by the form of contract issued by the Royal Institution of British Architects and in normal circumstances, nominated sub-contractors are on the same basis of payment as other sub-contractors since the general contractor passes on payment as this becomes due under the respective certificates, the only difference being that amounts due to nominated sub-contractors are usually stated clearly in the certificate when these are issued by the surveyor. The general contractor makes payment to the nominated sub-contractor when the certificate and money are in his hands and is customarily allowed $2\frac{1}{2}$ per cent cash discount if payment is made within 14 days of the receipt of the certificate.

Rights and duties of the employer, main contractor, and sub-contractor are set out in detail in the R.I.B.A. standard contract form when this is used. The position however, can be complicated in larger building disputes and the provisions of the R.I.B.A. contract form were recently criticised in the House of Lords as being "confused and obscure" and there have been one or two cases both in the House of Lords and the Court of Appeal on points of difficulty arising between main contractors and sub-contractors. In one case before the House of Lords[1] the nominated sub-contractors under an R.I.B.A. contract form went into voluntary liquidation and the liquidator refused to perform the contract. The employers refused to nominate a new sub-contractor and the main contractors completed the sub-contract work themselves but at a cost of £900 more than the original tender submitted by the sub-contractors. The main contractors contended that the employers should have nominated a new sub-contractor and that having failed to do so, they were liable for the increased cost of the work, while the employers on their part argued that the main contractors were under a duty to complete the work themselves at the price originally agreed by the sub-contractors. The House of Lords decided that the employer had a duty to nominate again, should the first nominated sub-contractor repudiate his contract and they found for the main contractors and

---

[1] *North West Metropolitan Regional Hospital Board v. T. A. Bickerton & Son Ltd.* (1970). Estates Gazette May 23rd 1970, page 973.

dismissed the appeal with costs. In another case[1] an R.I.B.A. form of contract provided for liquidated damages to be paid by the main contractors at the rate of £1,800 per week but stated that if in the opinion of the architect the completion of the works was likely to be or had been delayed "by delay on the part of nominated sub-contractors", the architect should "make a fair and reasonable extension of time for completion of the works". What happened was that the sub-contractors completed their work within the time laid down under the contract and withdrew from the site. Nothing appeared to be wrong until a month later when the work carried out by the sub-contractors was found to be defective. The sub-contractors carried out remedial work, but in the meantime the main contract work was delayed. The legal dispute that then arose was between the employers and the sub-contractors, joining the main contractors in the action, since the sub-contractors were ulti-mately bound to pay any damages due because of their liability to reimburse the main contractors for liquidated damages paid to the employers. The sub-contractors then found themselves in the curious position of seeking to establish that there had been "delay" on their part so that an extension of time should therefore have been granted to the main contractors and accordingly no damages were due. It was found, however, that the sub-contractor was in breach of contract rather than causing delay and that there were no grounds for the application of a rather odd condition in the main contract under which the sub-contractor might benefit from his own default. It was accordingly found that the sub-contractors were not guilty of delay and the appeal by the employers was allowed. In a third case, on this occasion heard in the Court of Appeal,[2] sub-contractors under the usual R.I.B.A. printed form were due to start certain work but were delayed, although this was not, as they claimed, through their own fault. Eventually they completed the work and questions about the workmanship itself arose subsequently. The main con-tractors, however, held back money due to the sub-contractors under interim certificates on the grounds that they had been injured by the acts of the sub-contractors and the matter went to Court. The case turned primarily on the construction of the clauses of the sub-contract which contained an explicit provision dealing with the payment of interim certificates. These had to be paid within 14 days less the retention money, cash discount and amounts previously paid. It was plain in the ordinary course of business that once a certificate

[1] *Westminster City Council v. J. Jarvis & Sons Ltd. and another* (1970). Estates Gazette May 23 1970, page 974.

[2] *Dawnays Ltd. v. F. G. Minter Ltd. and another* (1971). Estates Gazette July 31 1971, page 585.

was issued, it had to be paid save only for the permitted deductions, but the employers had argued that claims for delay were deductable even although these had not been fully ascertained. In the sub-contract it said that "the contractor shall, notwithstanding anything in this sub-contract, be entitled to deduct or set off against any money due from him to the sub-contractor (including any retention money) any sum or sums which the sub-contractor is liable to pay to the contractor under this sub-contract". The main contractors sought to rely on this clause, but Lord Denning, the Master of the Rolls, found that it was not legitimate under the terms of the contract to deduct sums which were unliquidated and simply matters of claim and disputed claim. The appeal by the sub-contractors was accordingly allowed.

Following criticism of the Royal Institute of British Architects in the Courts for their alleged failure to make amendments to the R.I.B.A. form of contract, the Institute produced a statement in which it pointed out that the standard form of building contract is amended by reference to the Joint Contracts Tribunal and the R.I.B.A. is only among eleven bodies who together form the Tribunal which is responsible for any amendments. The Institute said, moreover, that if it was solely responsible for production of the contract as had been suggested, it would indeed be an entirely different document, and it was because the Institute failed to secure the agreement to certain changes, that it found it necessary to publish forms of warranty for the protection of clients in August 1969. It might be far better perhaps from the point of view of the R.I.B.A. to suggest a change of name away from the R.I.B.A. form to perhaps something like the "Joint Tribunal Form of Contract" and acknowledge the fact that it is a form hammered out by all sides of the industry.

(9) *The Arbitrator*

An arbitrator is the person appointed under the terms of a building contract to hear and determine a cause of difference between the parties. He is a man selected for his specialised knowledge and is normally a chartered surveyor or chartered architect. Many arbitrators are selected from the list of the Institute of Arbitrators founded in 1915. Arbitration clauses in building contracts are now governed by the provisions of the Arbitration Act, 1950.

The position of arbitrator under the terms of a building contract should not be confused with the role of the surveyor as "quasi-arbitrator" in deciding small matters of dispute in the course of the contract itself. A formal reference to the arbitrator appointed under a building contract is required before his appointment can take effect.

THE TENDERS

The surveyor will select with care the building firms to whom he decides to issue invitations to tender. These may be perhaps three local firms in the case of a small contract for repairs or in larger work six tenders may be desired from medium or large sized firms some of whom will probably be in the area concerned, while others may be further afield It is always as well to include the name of one firm out of the district where the work is to be carried out, particularly if this firm has carried out work for the surveyor on other occasions and has his trust.

Once the names of the firms have been selected, the surveyor should write to them giving them notice that he proposes shortly to ask them to tender for the work and he should ask them if they are in a position to carry it out. Busy builders' offices are used to receiving a bundle of documents at short notice asking them to provide a quotation within, say 14 days, and any prior notice comes as a welcome change to them. From the surveyor's point of view preliminary notice to the builder that he will be asked to tender is a desirable precaution as it has the advantage of lessening the risk element of some tenders failing to arrive in time.

The surveyor is well advised to try and obtain firms of roughly comparable size for whatever type of job he has in mind. He should also bear in mind the irritating, if time honoured practice, of builders to send in an inflated tender rather than to turn down the invitation to tender if they are too busy. This, together with other possible causes of difficulty or delay, mean that the number of tenders required may be cut down. If the surveyor has to report prices to a committee who are expecting, say, four tenders, it is embarrassing to say the least of it, of the surveyor to have to admit that only one actual tender arrived, two others being ruled out on the ground of time and the fourth being so grossly inflated that it was not worthy of consideration. The surveyor is, therefore, well advised to ask for six firms to tender if he is expected to produce four prices in this way.

An invitation to tender is a mere attempt to ascertain whether an offer can be obtained within such limits as the building owner requires. It is therefore in effect an "offer to receive an offer". An employer may revoke an invitation to tender at any moment and is not normally responsible for expenses incurred by persons in connection with the making of a tender. A person making a tender on the other hand is entitled to withdraw it at any time before actual acceptance, but if he does not do this, it remains in force until it is either accepted on the one hand or lapses by effluxion of time on the other.

The surveyor should remember that the documents that he sends out together form the contract and a covering letter to each builder is desirable which refers to all the contract documents sent, i.e. plans, specification and quantities, it being made clear on what basis the quantities are provided. The letter might also refer to any particular points that are important at an early stage that are set out in the contract documents so as to assist the builder. A bald announcement in the preliminaries to a specification tucked away in clause 21 on page 3, to the effect that access for inspection to compile a tender can only be made on Thursday afternoons, is hardly helpful to a builder who, pressed for time and having left his inspection until the last week prior to the tenders being due for delivery, has another engagement on that day. Arrangements for access should in any event be channelled through the surveyor so as to avoid the risk of competing contractors meeting on the site.

Under the rules that bind certain public authorities, it may be necessary for the surveyor to advertise a contract publicly. This miserable process has been subject to some criticism in recent times. The offer encourages many inexperienced firms to provide tenders and to undercut their more established rivals in the hope of obtaining the business of the public authority in the future. This has reached such a pitch in some areas that the more established firms refuse to tender under these circumstances and the surveyor has the unhappy task of trying to decide what advice to give the appropriate committee when this meets to consider the tenders submitted.

The covering letter enclosing the documents that together form the invitation to tender should state the date, time and place that tenders will be opened. Tenders are normally opened by the surveyor but in the case of public authorities, the clerk to the authority concerned will probably deal with the receipt of tenders himself. The documents that form the invitation to tender are normally accompanied by a suitable envelope addressed to the surveyor or otherwise as the case may be, marked with the word "tender" clearly on the face so that the envelope will not be opened in error by the surveyor's office staff before the appropriate day concerned. It is no longer customary for the surveyor to open the tenders himself in a ceremonial manner in his office with the representative of the various firms of contractors grouped around him. On the other hand, however, the time at which tenders will be opened must be strictly adhered to and the surveyor is well advised to stick rigidly to the rule that no late tenders can be accepted. If the surveyor accepts late tenders even under the best of motives, the same firm tendering again on another job may feel that they need not take quite so much pains to comply with the strict time limit as they were forgiven last time and might expect to be forgiven again.

Once the surveyor has opened the tenders, he will then report to his client with a list giving the amounts of the tenders in order of price. He should take special care, however, to make sure that he does not overlook any conditions in any of the tenders that vary the terms to a substantial degree. If it is obvious that the lowest tender is so low as to make it certain that an error has been made, the surveyor is well advised to telephone the firm concerned and ask them simply if they are prepared to stand by their tender or not. This will at once acquaint an experienced firm of the fact that there is something badly wrong with their price and they will hastily go through their calculations to see what has happened. The surveyor should never say for example, "your price is far too low since it is £1,208 below the next lowest tender", as if he does this, the firm of contractors will find that they have in fact made an error amounting to £1,200.

If the surveyor is satisfied that the prices can be reported to his client, he can now send the appropriate letter setting out the results of the tenders with his comments. It is also good practice to notify the various firms of contractors of the results of the tenders at this stage and a letter can be written to each setting out the amounts of the tenders in descending order of cost. It is undesirable, however, for the names of the firms to be included in most cases and it is best for the surveyor to merely set out the individual tenders as A, B and C etc., since invitations to tender on future occasions make it politic that competing firms know as little as possible about each other's existence so far as this can be arranged. In certain circumstances it is necessary to publish the amounts of the tenders with builders names but these are rare. It should be added that if the tenders are all in order the surveyor should do all he can to see that the lowest price is accepted even where he reserves the right for his client to accept the lowest "or any other" tender. The surveyor should try to prevent the building owner from accepting one of the other tenders on the grounds, for example that the difference in cost is trivial and he "liked the look" of the other builder or that he has just discovered that one of the other builders has just carried out some work for a friend. Builders take a great deal of time, trouble and expense in preparing tenders and they would have every justification in looking on a surveyor with a jaundiced eye should he tamely submit to his client accepting any tender he chooses. On the next occasion that the surveyor invites a firm to tender that has been disappointed in this way he may be taken aback to find that they politely decline his offer.

Having obtained the approval of the building owner to the lowest recommended tender, the surveyor is now free to write that his acceptance on his client's behalf is unconditional. In the absence of any revocation there is now a binding contract, but this is not the end of the matter since the surveyor should ensure that this is completed in proper form. The printed forms of contract should be completed, signed and stamped and in the case of his client being a Corporation, the contract should be completed under seal. Finally as a last precaution the surveyor should make certain that all the insurances are in order to the premises being repaired whether these are in part occupation by the owner or not.

Now that a binding contract has been made, we will pass to the consideration of the works in progress. It will be appreciated that all the other attributes of a binding contract must be present; for example, that the acceptance by the surveyor as agent to his employer must be authorised and that there is no misrepresentation. The element of time for completion of the contract will presumably have been dealt with but if this is not referred to in the contract documents a realistic completion date should now be agreed with the builder.

THE WORKS IN PROGRESS

(a) *Commencement*

When the day appointed for the commencement of the work finally arrives, the surveyor and the building owner will wait with keen anticipation for lorry loads of materials accompanied by vans full of keen and enthusiastic men whose one thought will be to execute the work as quickly and as completely as possible. In this innocent expectation they will both, nine times out of ten, be disappointed. One case is recalled when, waiting with his client at a house for the builders to arrive to start a contract that was very much a race against time, the surveyor watched a small aged man arrive on a bicycle with a diminutive ladder. Suspecting him to be a window cleaner, the surveyor observed him with idle interest as he opened the gate and laid the ladder face downwards with some ceremony in the centre of the front garden. The man then favoured the assembled company with a gap toothed smile and withdrew with simple dignity but without explanation. It was some time before it was realised that this was the builder's advance force and when this fact also dawned on the building owner and his wife, they were not very pleased, particularly as no further action occurred for not only the remainder of that day but the following day as well. One learns eventually that the ceremonial placing of ladders is as much a part of builder's folk lore as the presentation of an inflated tender so as not to cause offence. It is assumed by builders that providing ladders is not only evidence of good faith in starting but also stakes a claim to the contract so that if there is subsequent delay and the building owner threatens to cancel the contract, the action taken has cleverly blocked any such manoeuvre. It also enables some relaxation while the builder begins to think about selecting a labour force from his hard-pressed team or more likely nowadays starts to approach his various sub-contractors. It is perhaps unnecessary to add that this is, to say the least of it, an over-simplification of the legal position but the arrival of ladders or in larger contracts, the provision of the hut for the foreman and the clerk of works, is an act of deep significance to the builder while being less than satisfying to the other parties concerned. The delivery of ladders is, however, perhaps better than another alternative that is recalled. On this occasion while waiting with his client at an empty house which was to be extensively repaired, the surveyor was gratified to observe a lorry drive up and a team of men leap out all clad in snowy white overalls directed by a particularly fearsome foreman who bellowed loudly at each man telling him where he should go and what his duties were to be. The surveyor, needless to say, was relieved and his client was delighted and when they both left the property half an hour later, they were both convinced that an excellent start had been made. However, feeling that with such an example he might as well complete the detail drawing relating to the kitchen layout that would shortly be required, the surveyor called back at the house later in the day and was mystified to find that it was entirely empty. Not a single white clad figure remained. Enquiry of a gardener working at the adjacent property elicited the information that the whole team had piled into the lorry and left 10 minutes after the surveyor and his client had themselves left. Fortunately the contract was for a lump sum and the writer, after some misgivings, decided not to disturb his client's peace of mind by telephoning him and, as it happened, the contract ended perfectly satisfactory in due course of time.

In most building contracts within the scope of this book, there will be no clerk of works and most contracts will of course be on a lump sum basis. Under normal circumstances such as these, the surveyor's first visit to the site after the work has started may or may not be by formal arrangement. In either event however, the surveyor should seek out the site foreman and make himself known. The foreman will then either express a wish to accompany the surveyor or will leave him to make his own inspection. On a formal arrangement for a visit the surveyor will ask for the site foreman to accompany him, but he has no general authority to do so on every occasion. If the site foreman is engaged in superintending the delivery of complex loads of materials or in deciding the allocation of labour, the disruption of his activities may well mean considerable loss in time and efficiency. The surveyor should therefore use his judgment before he adds to the pressures of what may well be a day of heavy work for the foreman in any event. It should here be emphasised that the surveyor should endeavour to strike the right relationship with the site foreman as soon as possible. Nothing is more exasperating to a foreman in coming across one of his men having a long conversation with the surveyor about the desirability or otherwise of carrying out a particular operation. The foreman has every right to feel aggrieved, particularly if this is his first encounter with the surveyor just as an unfortunate commencing act from the foreman will make the surveyor wary of the man he is dealing with in precisely the same way.

In larger contracts the surveyor will normally arrange regular site meetings which will be attended by the general contractor, his general foreman, representatives of sub-contractors engaged in the work, the clerk of works if there is one, and representatives from the offices of professional men also engaged in the work such as quantity surveyors or engineers. The first meeting will be arranged shortly after the work commences and at this and subsequent meetings, the surveyor will draw up an agenda of points for discussion and take notes at the meeting which will subsequently be typed and sent to the various parties. Even in small lump sum contracts where the only people present at the meeting are likely to be the surveyor, the builder, his foreman and possibly one or more sub-contractors, the same practise of compiling notes and having them subsequently typed and sent to the various parties concerned should be adopted. It may or may not be desirable for the surveyor to ask the building owner if he will attend such meetings depending on the circumstances of the case. In other contracts, for example, cost plus percentage or day work contracts, a different arrangement is preferable. Occasional meetings are not on the whole sufficient since the surveyor may be in effect employing a direct labour force. As mentioned earlier, there are circumstances where the advantages of this outweigh the disadvantages, but some arrangement must be found for an independent check to be made of the time of tradesmen and labourers' attendance either by someone at the house or alternatively by continual visits from, say, a junior working in the surveyor's office The employment of a clerk of works removes the need for this but the contract must be a large one to justify the extra expense.

The first visit of the surveyor to the site may most likely, however, be at the builder's request. In repairs to old houses, the preliminary work of dismantling or opening up part of the structure is normally attended by surprises, often disagreeable ones, which are rapidly conveyed to the surveyor with the least possible delay with a request asking for an urgent inspection. The busy surveyor's life is full of such requests and he must fit them in to his working pattern as best he can since the need for his attention to requests of this sort from the builder is obvious. Brickwork marked on a plan to be taken down and re-built may reveal that the structure adjoining, thought to be sound, is in fact not sound at all so that further work is required. The contractor who has had the duty of notifying the District Surveyor or Building Inspector that the work has commenced, is also likely to have another interested visitor so that the surveyor when he arrives will know that his suggestions must not just satisfy himself and the builder, but the District Surveyor or Building Inspector as well. The surveyor should never let it seem as if requests for visits of this nature are troublesome. They may very well be so in his crowded calendar but nevertheless the hallmark of a good builder is to notify his surveyor under circumstances such as these and the surveyor should be glad to know that he has a builder who will take the proper steps if he runs into any difficulty instead of trying to deal with the matter himself. If the builder uncovers badly fractured or disintegrating load bearing brickwork or stumbles across a bad attack of dry rot or a load bearing partition badly affected with wood-boring beetle, the surveyor is not likely to jump for joy when the news is brought to him but discoveries of this nature are very likely in old houses and a site inspection can result in prompt decisions being taken for the correct remedial action. More than this it can determine the extent of the unknown work so that in any claim for an extra the builder will know that the surveyor has had the opportunity to register the extent to which extra work is required. The surveyor's willingness to attend when a genuine difficulty of this sort occurs is of value to the building owner since not only are difficulties correctly solved, but the builder is the less likely, once the work is completed, to submit claims for extras on the basis that he discovered some trouble, put it right, and subsequently covered up the work without troubling the surveyor as "he knew that he was so busy at the time". This, particularly if the surveyor feels that the builder is genuine, presents an awkward moral dilemma. However, the main point at stake is that the builder must under no circumstances be encouraged to attempt to deal with defects that he uncovers on his own account without notifying the respective parties. If he does so it can lead to untold trouble and while a good builder will never do such a thing from the point of view of his own liability, a smaller and inexperienced firm might take an unwise course of action in the genuine belief that they are saving trouble all round and they are more likely to do this if the surveyor's attitude has been a rather unapproachable one. Subsequent cracking or a bad outbreak of dry rot may teach a sad lesson.

(b) *Temporary Work and possible risks*

The surveyor should remember that temporary work is as much part of his province as the permanent work that follows and he should not merely abdicate from responsibility completely and leave all scaffolding and shoring to the builder. In the case of Clayton v. Woodman & Sons (Builders) Ltd. (1962) 2QB 533, the Court of Appeal found that the builders alone were liable for the absence of adequate timbering since the architect had not taken it upon himself to order the plaintiff to carry out work that was potentially dangerous, nor had he assumed the responsibility which remained the builders, for cutting a chase in a safe matter. However, since this date the position has been radically altered by a case that has been referred to before, that of Hedley Byrne & Co. Ltd. v. Heller & Partners Ltd. (1963) 2 All ER 575. This case, applied in the case of Clay v. Crump & Sons Ltd. (1963) 1QB 533[1] heard in the same year, held that an architect's duty was not confined to his contractual duty to the owners of a dangerous wall which had been left purposely standing after demolition and which had collapsed, injuring a builder's workman, but that his duty extended to all those persons who would be so closely and directly affected by his acts and omissions that he ought reasonably to have them in contemplation as being so affected In this case the Court of Appeal found that the architect ought reasonably to have foreseen that the builder's workman would be affected by his carelessness He was held 42 per cent to blame, the demolition contractors being held 38 per cent to blame and the workman's employers being held 20 per cent to blame.

In the recent case of Dutton v. Bognor Regis Urban District Council[2] the law of negligence was extended to a new area when a local council was held liable to the purchaser of a house which developed defects some years after it had been built because the Council's building inspector had been negligent in approving the building at foundation level and had failed to see that it was being

[1] Also reported in the Estates Gazette 21st September 1963, page 835.
[2] 1972, 1 All ER462.

built on an old rubbish tip. In this case Lord Denning said that "it was also submitted that the (Councils) inspector, like any other professional man, owned no duty to a person who did not employ him but only took the benefit of his work; but since Hedley Byrne and Co. Ltd. v. Heller & Partners (1964), it was clear that the professional man who gave guidance to others, owed a duty of care not only to his client but also to another who he knew was relying on his skill to save him from harm . . . but the duty of a professional man who gave evidence on the safety of buildings, machines or materials was to all those who might suffer injury if his advice was bad." Lord Denning added that house foundations were in a class by themselves. Once covered up they would not be seen again until the damage appeared and the inspector ought to know that. Accordingly Lord Atkin's test of "who is my neighbour" in the famous case of Donoghue v. Stevenson (1932) 2 AC 562 580 has been widely extended by the Hedley Byrne case.

The surveyor therefore does well to recognise that when he visits the site and carries out an inspection after work has been opened up or cut away, that the lack of adequate struts or support or temporary work that might lead to subsequent collapse is very much his concern as well as that of the builder and if he feels that there is any element of danger, he should say so at once and ensure that the necessary steps are taken to put matters right. It is best to be on the safe side. The builder may smile at the surveyor's concern, but modern adjustable tubular supports can be employed at much less cost than the carpenter's work involved in the traditional practise of forming a framing with braced struts, and worthwhile precautions of this nature are still mercifully today one of the cheapest items in building work. It is always worthwhile for the surveyor to point out weaknesses that might affect the safety of passers-by or workmen. Wooden ladders should be left unpainted so that any flaws can be detected at once and the ends of ladders must always be tied to the scaffolding or the structure. Scaffolding boards should also be secured and properly laid so that there is no tendency for them to "see-saw".

Where the employer or his surveyor have enaged a competent contractor, and have parted with the day to day control of the work, the contractor will, as a general rule, be liable for injuries caused to others by the carrying out of the works or by the negligence of the workmen that he employs. The question of liability is decided by reference to the general law on the subject and there is no special law applicable to building contracts. For example, the well-known rule in Rylands v. Fletcher might apply to a building contract where the contractor keeps something on the employer's land that is potentially dangerous. In such a case he keeps it at his peril, and, if he fails to take precautions he is liable for damage caused as a result of its escape. For example a highly toxic chemical that is inefficiently stored and is allowed to escape, causing damage or injury to health, might well come within this category.

If the contractor while working on the site, causes noise and vibration, he might be liable to neighbouring persons if this becomes a nuisance. His best defence is that he has taken what steps are open to him to alleviate the noise or vibration by the best means possible. The Courts have tended to accept the fact that a neighbour altering or repairing premises cannot help making a noise during normal working hours and this is acceptable provided it is consistent with normal work.

The passing of the Occupiers Liability Act, 1957, has altered the law relating to persons entering the premises except in the case of trespass. As the act of trespass is wrongful, a contractor owes no duty to a trespasser but he must not intentionally injure him and must not commence dangerous work when he knows that a trespasser is on the premises. The Act, however, was passed to regulate the duty which an occupier of premises owes to those who may legitimately call upon him and the former common law rules relating to invitees and licensees have been merged together and clarified under the Act under a new term: that of "visitor". Under the Act an occupier owes a common duty of care to all visitors, but this applies only to normal risks and accordingly if a visitor calls at a site where demolition operations are in progress and is duly warned of the danger by a notice, he proceeds with his inspection at his own risk. However a builder cannot contract out of the Act to avoid his normal duty of care to visitors. He cannot, for example, merely pin up a notice which denies responsibility for his duty of care to visitors engaged on their normal day-to-day occupations.

Any surveyor who supervises the work of a particular firm of contractors on more than one occasion will be regarded by the tradesmen of that firm, and certainly by the site foreman, as being a little unbalanced on certain points. It will be noted for example, with tolerant amusement, if he is obsessive about inspecting undercoats before finishing coats are applied, or if he gets angry if he sees large slots cut in floor joists for electricians to instal their wiring. It is therefore sensible that the surveyor's eccentricity may as well extend to the area of safety so that if this peculiarity gets well known there is at least the chance one day that a life or a building might be saved. Thus, it does no harm if the surveyor has some words to say about all aspects of this subject where breaches meet his eye. If he asks for inflammable materials to be properly stored, or for work with blow lamps to be limited to certain specified conditions or insists that where scaffolding is over a public way passers by are properly protected from falling debris while work is in hand and the scaffolding is lit by safety lamps at night, he may note that glances are exchanged between the general foreman and the foreman of the various groups of tradesmen concerned, but nevertheless every one of these instances has caused death and destruction at some time or another and the surveyor can at least know that he is doing his duty to limit accidents as much as he can.

Once the surveyor has inspected the works that have been opened up, has satisfied himself as to the safety of the structure and the temporary work and has arranged with the contractor as to the extent of any further work required, his next step will be to seek authority from the building owner for the extra variation in cost. It may well be that the surveyor has such authority already, either by the nature of his agency employment with the building owner or alternatively under the terms of the contract that has been drawn up for the work. Again, the variation may turn out to be a saving rather than an extra as certain work originally specified when offset against the cost of the work now proposed in the light of the changed circumstances, might result in a credit being due from the builder. Accordingly, it is now perhaps an opportune moment to look at the question of variations on the contract.

(c) *Variations*

As we have seen earlier in this Chapter, building contracts are peculiar in that while they have the attributes of any other contract, they nevertheless allow for an element of uncertainty since provision is generally made for the variation of the work as it proceeds and for adjustment of the price to be made accordingly. The reader will understand, however, that variations in this sense refer to lump sum or entire contracts since the whole basis of a contract that is not entire and is carried out by day work or subsequent valuation of the work is not subject to variations being dealt with in the same way. Again, it is assumed that in accordance with the principles set out earlier in the Chapter, that the variation is not so fundamental as to go to the root of the contract and to change its nature, or so as to make nonsense of the original agreement and frustrate it completely. Most variations in normal building contracts are relatively minor when their cost is compared to the contract sum but there are, of course, circumstances where due to some set of unforeseen events or a complete mistake, they are so large as to imperil the basis of the whole contract. We will, however, for the purpose of this section, assume that the variations are of a type often found in contracts for the repair work of old houses for which provision is made in the terms of the contract.

The Standard Form of Contract of the Royal Institute of British Architects provides that all variations must be the subject of a written order. This sensible rule is one that should be followed in all building contracts whether the standard form of contract issued by the Royal Institute of British Architects is employed or not. The R.I.B.A. contract also states that if the contractor gives notice to the architect in writing confirming verbal instructions, and the architect does not dissent in writing from such notification within 7 days, the variation is assumed to be agreed and is sufficient authority for subsequent adjustment of the price. In most cases, however, the surveyor will wish to issue what are termed "variation orders" or "architects instructions" as these are now preferred to be known by the Royal Institute of British Architects and it is suggested that a proper form addressed to the contractor giving the requisite information about the name of the job and the nature of the variation, dated, numbered and signed by the architect, is desirable practice. The advantage of using forms is that several copies can be typed for use by quantity surveyors and others as necessary and the final copy, if tinted, will stand out in a surveyor's file so that all the copies can be collected at the end of the contract when the final account is being considered. Although it should be indicated on the form if a variation is an addition or an omission, it is not necessary for any reference to be made as to price or for any other information to be added. The order or instruction, whichever term is preferred, merely provides a continuous record of how the contract is altered day by day as it proceeds. Subsequent costing is another matter entirely and the procedure for this varies according to the nature of the contract and the parties to it. The valuation of variations to the contract is made in one of three ways, either by a definite price being agreed with the contractor on the spot or alternatively by subsequent measurement and valuation by the quantity surveyor or on a day work basis, checked by a quantity surveyor if there is one, or by the surveyor in charge of the work if there is not. It is always a prudent precaution for the surveyor to ensure that the contractor will have quoted day-work rates before the contract commences with appropriate agreed percentages to be added to the prime cost so that subsequent valuation is made easier in that there is a lesser area for argument.

(d) *The Permanent Work in Progress*

Once the preliminary difficulties are out of the way, the building work should start in earnest and the surveyor must then consider the extent of the supervision that he must provide, bearing in mind what has been said on this subject earlier in the Chapter. Much, of course, depends on the surveyor's experience not only of the type of work being carried out but also as to the capabilities of the contractors employed. The latter consideration is a most important one since the miseries of attempting to carry out a contract with a bad builder are so many and so all-embracing that they affect the question of supervision to a fundamental degree. The surveyor must feel that he can take on trust work that is being carried out while his back is turned and this is why the employment of a firm that he knows and trusts with a general foreman that he respects and has worked with on other occasions is the biggest comfort of all. Such a firm will see to it that work is not covered up before it is approved and that the surveyor has ample opportunity for inspection at the correct times. The difficulties that are entailed by the practices of some firms who cover up work and adopt an air of injured innocence when the surveyor takes issue with them or who telephone the surveyor's office at 4 p.m. on one day to notify him that they are dismantling the scaffolding at 8.30 a.m. the next morning, for example, are too numerous to mention and the surveyor is advised to adopt an uncompromising attitude right from the outset as to how he expects the contract to be run. Even so it should be said that it is simply not possible to "win" against a bad builder. They are just to be avoided. One of the biggest services that the surveyor can provide to his client is at the outset of the whole matter when he advises as to the names of the contractors to be invited to tender.

Although most formal site meetings are made by appointment, there are other occasions when the surveyor will wish to and should make a brief if rapid inspection on his own account without prior warning. Contrary to general belief, this is by no means an underhand proceeding. It is one that is welcomed by the builder and his general foreman alike as it enables them to feel that there is a degree of interest and control in the work and it enables the general foreman to say with truth "if the surveyor came round and caught you doing that you would be in trouble". This threat is an empty one if the tradesman knows that the surveyor rarely visits the site and even then only does so by appointment.

Before entering a house itself, the surveyor is well advised to have a look around the grounds or the immediate environs of it, particularly at the rear where the contractor's men may like to disport themselves in the lunch hour away from the rude stares of the public on the one hand and the obstrusiveness of the building owner and his representatives on the other. The surveyor will accordingly find the customary bunch of cronies in the potting shed sitting in a fug that will make his head spin while they discuss and solve the problems of the world at the same time. This is quite normal but what may not be normal is that they may be brewing up "and using as a table" a piece of selected hardwood that was specially imported by the building owner and for which the contractor sent down a special van to the docks. Tea stains may not harm it but, on the other hand, they might and the surveyor could mention this point which will be received by the collected company as an interesting factor which had not occurred to anyone before. At the same time the surveyor might cast his eye round the open ground and his gaze will generally be rewarded by some piece of thoughtlessness. Bags of cement may be placed up against the garden fence and admittedly covered with a tarpaulin but resting on soggy ground instead of on a raised platform that is completely dry. The coarse sharp sand for concrete may have been delivered next to the "soft" sand used for plastering, the two being completely different both in texture and appearance, but nevertheless in all probability being jumbled in rough proximity to each other so that they tend to intermingle. Again, softwood for joinery may be left in the open either soaking up moisture from the ground or open to the weather so that by the time that it is ready for use, its moisture content is excessive. In the same manner all sorts and types of materials can be left in the open without proper covering and on damp ground, ranging from plumbing and heating pipes to extreme cases where the sophisticated components of heating and ventilation systems are left unprotected and open to the rain.

It is also worth the surveyor's time to examine the materials that are being used in the work and let it be seen by everyone working on the site that he hopes to see materials delivered exactly as specified and that he expects an explanation to be forthcoming for any variations. There is a constant battle between builders' merchants and their delivery men on the one hand and site foremen and their tradesmen on the other. In times when certain materials are hard to come by or in short supply, the builders' merchants will try to foist off alternatives by delivering them at the site and the general foreman will feel tempted to accept them unless he knows that the surveyor has strong views about being fully informed of any variations in materials whatsoever. Practice will tell the surveyor when to reject hardcore with too much questionable material in it of a soft, vegetable or crushable nature, bricks or tiles that obviously have some manufacturing flaw, facing bricks with most of the faces badly chipped, rusty reinforcing bars, timber with an excessive number of knots or an excessive amount of sap-wood, timber scantlings that are badly warped, or rainwater goods or plumbing fittings that although specified to a British Standard Specification nevertheless do not have the familiar kite mark, and, upon subsequent investigation, turn out to be not to the requisite British Standard although resembling it very nearly. There will be cases when the identification of the correct materials is difficult or almost impossible. The surveyor should always, however, feel that he has the right to ask questions and examine and feel materials that he can see since constant practise in this direction builds up his knowledge. While it is true that the presence of a first-class builder's foreman will save him much worry, this alone never replaces the surveyor's own judgment and one of the techniques that he does well to try and acquire, and one which in turn will give him pleasure, is the constant assessment of the materials that he specifies so that after a while he has a genuine knowledge of them and they are not merely words in his sets of standard specification clauses.

The basic trades of bricklayer, carpenter, concretor, roofer, plasterer to name just a few, take some years to acquire to a skilled degree and if the surveyor is lucky enough in his earlier years as a student to see work carried out by skilled tradesmen, this will teach him a good deal and he will soon recognise inferior work when he sees it on other occasions. A skilled bricklayer will watch a young surveyor with some amusement while he checks that the bed joints are straight and the perpends above each other and will smile as the surveyor puzzles out the detailing of quoins, reveals and detailing of brickwork as he sees it on the site. A skilled bricklayer will often unbend to a sufficient degree to explain mysteries that are not apparent; how, for example, he is able to "lose" some millimetres in an awkward detail by skilful manipulation of the bed joints that the eye cannot see where no other solution can be found. When the surveyor sees the same work carried out badly on another occasion the difference will be all too apparent as will the fact that half bats incorporated in the walling without attention to the bond have been used to finish up a batch of bricks rather than the remnants being returned to the store. The good bricklayer will lay his frogs upwards and not use an excessive amount of water unless the bricklaying is being carried out in high summer. Bricklaying should, of course, cease in frosty weather completely. Even if the surveyor knows that the craftsmen employed on a job are competent and experienced, he should not be afraid to ask questions. If he asks the bricklayer how he proposes to "pin" brickwork up to the underside of a beam for example, to ensure that it is quite tight and sound, the bricklayer will proceed to show him. This has the happy advantage of all parties being satisfied. The young surveyor learns something; the bricklayer, secure in the knowledge that he is giving instruction in a field that he knows all about will do a particularly good job, and the building owner would no doubt be happy if he knew of the matter, although of course he will not.

The surveyor will watch concrete being laid on many occasions and although it is becoming the custom for concrete to arrive ready mixed for use on the site, this is by no means universally the case in small building jobs and the need for competent concretors who can achieve a sound blended mix to the correct specification and, just as important, keep this up throughout the whole of a day, is a vital one. The trade of concretor, rather like that of painter, is one that is rather devalued by the bricklayer and carpenter, since techniques and materials have altered to assist the tradesmen far more in the former trades than in the latter. The ability to form a lintel "in situ" or to form a concrete floor ready for its screed is by no means as easy as it sounds. Inspection of new work often shows the lintels of weird shape due to bad construction or concrete floors that when broken up prove to be shallow at one point and very deep at another with the consistency of the mix varying widely. With the trades of carpenter and roofer the surveyor can learn a good deal from watching so that he can, after a time, tell a good tradesman from an indifferent one. The joints in carpentry should always be examined, not only because these form important structural elements but because they give a very accurate indication to not only the carpenter's ability but to his care as well.

The roofer, particularly in urban areas, is an elusive bird. He is most likely nowadays to be a sub-contractor and once the groundwork is ready and he has been notified of this fact, he will appear one morning in his van with a screech of brakes and leap out with his assistants and complete a vast amount of work in a very short time. By the time the surveyor thinks that it would be a good idea to inspect the roofing work while in progress, he normally arrives to find that the roof is completed and that the vast pile of tiles which have been piled in an awkward position for weeks obstructing everyone's access, have mysteriously vanished. Those roofers who are sub-contractors normally know their job very well and over plain areas of slating or tiling will provide a very adequate finish in most cases to the specified gauge and lap. They are, however, not likely to be deterred from fitting in a job to their time schedule by hearing that it has been raining and that the underlay is saturated. Rather than try to instruct the builder to tell his sub-contracting roofers to wait, it is easier for the surveyor to make it clear to the builder that he expects temporary coverings so that the carcassing timbers and boarding or underlay are kept as dry as can reasonably be expected. On inspecting work of this kind the surveyor is well advised to direct his attention to awkward angles and details such as the abutments to chimney stacks, particularly those to party walls, verges, gable details and valleys. Any shortcomings or lack of thought on the part of the roofer normally shows up at such points. On one occasion that is recalled the roofing foreman and the general foreman of works had a loud argument on the site, the roofing foreman finally walking off in a huff. The surveyor, who happened to be present, was informed that the reason was that the roofing foreman did not consider the alignment of the rafters and the firring that was necessary at one point to be satisfactory, and the surveyor, when asked to adjudicate, could not find any fault. It was evident that the two foremen had merely had a row since no extra work was carried out by the general contractor and shortly afterwards the roofing foreman came once more with his men and meekly carried out the work without argument.

The trade of plasterer has at least the merit that the work is carried out indoors under cover, in conditions where often a pleasant and correct temperature can be maintained. As can be seen in the Chapter dealing with plastering, the present-day materials that are obtainable are highly sophisticated in their make-up and the manufacturer's instructions for each have to be followed to the letter to ensure that success is achieved. If this is not done, the failure in the plastering is likely to be dramatic to say the least of it and the surveyor is not likely to achieve much by proffering advice unless he has had particular experience on his own account. The surveyor can however, even when inexperienced, object if the backing is loose or unsatisfactory or the materials, tools or water used are obviously dirty or impure.

Painting at the present time is subject to the same advantages and disadvantages of plastering in that while modern materials require careful handling and can achieve good results, failure to follow the exact instructions of the manufacturer can lead to a complete breakdown of the paint film. So far as outside painting is concerned, it is vital that time and care is taken since haste and scamped work can lead to failures in the paint film at vulnerable points with annoying results in 18 months' time. For this reason, the surveyor is well advised to pay particular attention to outside painting and to examine the whole operation from start to finish, insofar as his circumstances allow, from the vantage points provided by the scaffolding before this is dismantled. Adequate preparation is, of course, vital, and the surveyor will hope to see that the woodwork is washed down as well as being rubbed down while rust is effectively removed from metal surfaces. Knotting only assumes real importance if the wood exudes resin to an appreciable degree but this is not so likely in old houses. Adequate priming, however, is vital since subsequent paint films depend on this for their key. It has long been accepted practice and is still a good idea for the surveyor to specify the application of undercoats in different colours so that he can easily check if each one is adequately completed before the next is applied. Although this is helpful to some degree, the real test of his inspection is in items of detail such as sills, including the edges and undersides, the backs of rainwater pipes, the painting of casements and sashes prior to the application of linseed oil putty, the detailing at the edges and sides of windows and frames and the interiors of cast iron gutters and the like. The surveyor should always try to foresee conditions that are not normal and to vary his specification on the spot should the need arise. This is so with internal painting as well as external and if the surveyor discovers alkali salts in the plaster for example, he should specify an alkali resisting priming coat and ensure that this is applied. Some defects such as saponification are difficult to spot but if the painting foreman says that he is running into trouble, it is best if the work is stopped while a correct remedy is found. It is unnecessary to say that painting of external work should cease in conditions of continual drizzle or winter mist or fog, but it should also be remembered that painting should not be carried out in conditions of extreme heat whether internally or externally. With all decorative finishes, however, there is always a sudden desire for haste. Many contracts by this time are perhaps behind the clock or alternatively the building owner, seeing that the job is nearing completion, evinces a sudden and incessant interest and spurs everyone on to an early finish. This is often a pity as rushed paintwork can result in unsightly defects as can other signs of scamped work such as woodwork not being properly rubbed down. Poor paper hanging is evidenced by joints that do not butt but overlap or even at times show gaps. Graver than this are the defects that result from haste in application when the house is not dried out so that the paper peels from the wall, paint blisters, and mould growth appears in corners. Paint will always spread easily, particularly externally, if it is thinned, and if the painters are urged to get a move on and to finish in an unreasonably short time, they will achieve this by adding thinners. This cannot be detected at the time but two years after the paint film has been applied, the penalty for haste will be all too apparent.

So far as the specialist trades of electrician, gas fitter, plumber and heating engineer are concerned, the surveyor is, to a large degree, dependent on the specialists that he introduces for the quality and safety of the work. There are, however, steps that he can take to keep his eyes open and point out any matters that are obviously wrong. Enquiry will elicit if the right sort of conduit tubing is being used and if this has the appropriate fittings to go with it. The writer has seen conduit set up in an existing property prior to being covered up where certain bends were missing and the wiring was, at angles, merely laid over the joists. This type of scamped work has also been known to happen in plumbing and heating installations where the correct matching set of copper fittings has always been notoriously difficult to acquire at one and the same time.

It should always be borne in mind that the demarcation line between the specialist trades discussed in the last paragraph and the traditional trades is a notoriously difficult one. Thus the surveyor is advised to inspect, for example, timber supports and bearers for cold or hot water storage tanks and cisterns whether in the roof space or on a back addition roof since these instead of being constructed properly by a carpenter may have been knocked up in a crude manner by the plumber or heating engineer. The roof space is often a place there the surveyor may see short cuts in all their crude simplicity and pipes, whether a service pipe or overflow pipe, may undulate gently if tapped, indicating that a total support of two bent nails is scarcely adequate. Again, a plumber rarely sees frost precaution in the roof space or to a rising main as part of his province and work such as this that does not strictly fall into any trade category is often either neglected or forgotten about completely unless checked thoroughly by the surveyor.

The ability to supervise the running of a contract successfully from the technical point of view on the site is by no means an easy one and like most other things requires a certain amount of experience. The surveyor should always remember, however, that he represents a building owner and has the duty of ensuring that a large sum of money is spent wisely and well. This is a considerable responsibility and the surveyor should feel that he owes his client a duty to ensure that the work is properly carred out, even if this involves him asking the questions that may make him appear to look foolish or to take action to protect his client's interest even if this action involves an unpleasant exchange of words. In the last resort the surveyor is the only person left to protect his client from an unscrupulous builder and although mercifully such firms are very much in a minority, the surveyor will be unlikely to escape having to deal with some such firms during the course of his career.

INTERIM CERTIFICATES

As the work proceeds, the point will come where the contractor will apply for payment under the terms of the contract and he will ask the surveyor to issue what is known as an interim or "progress" certificate which he can present to the employer certifying that he is due a particular sum of money. It may be, of course, that a lump sum contract specifies that one payment only is to be made upon successful completion of the work but this applies only to small contracts for simple repairs or maintenance work, for example the exterior re-painting of a dwelling house, and most larger building contracts enable interim payments to be made as the work progresses, usually if the period for the completion of the work exceeds two months.

Interim or Progress Certificates are merely approximate estimates given by the surveyor to certify the value of work carried out to the property including unfixed materials already delivered to the site, less a specified percentage which is to be retained as a reserve and which is known as the Retention Sum.

It is most important to understand the difference between interim or "progress" certificates and the final certificate. Interim certificates in no way imply satisfaction with the quality of workmanship of materials nor do they infer that the sum changing hands is a correct one. They are subject to re-adjustment in the final settlement between the parties and an over-payment on an interim certificate does not prejudice the surveyor against adjustment when the final certificate is issued. This, however, does not mean that the surveyor need exercise no care, since in issuing interim certificates he is not acting in a judicial capacity as "quasi arbitrator" but purely as an agent of the employer to whom he would be liable in negligence.[1]

Thus if the surveyor overcertifies to a substantial degree on an interim payment and the builder goes bankrupt and is subsequently proved to be a man of straw, the employer is likely to seek his remedy for his loss against his surveyor. It should be emphasised, however, that the surveyor's position when he certifies interim payments as against when he certifies the final payment, is a different one. When issuing the final certificate he acts in a "quasi-judicial" capacity and is therefore not the agent of the employer and thus is not liable in negligence.

Although interim certificates include the value of the work executed so far, together with the value of unfixed materials on the site, less a specified retention sum, the surveyor often finds that individual contracts introduce borderline cases where applications for interim certificates include work or materials that are not strictly within the above definition. It may well be that some purpose-made joinery has been ordered and completed by the contractor, but is

---

[1] *Wisbech R.D.C. v. Ward* (1927) 2KB556; (1928) 2KB1.

still at his yard since it would be inconvenient for it to be delivered at the site at the particular stage that the contract has reached. Joinery may include large double doors, for example, and there may be simply no room to store such articles at the site while the contract is in its preliminary and rather untidy stage. The builder is probably justified in saying from his own point of view that he is entitled to interim payment since to strictly comply with the terms, he has merely to put the joinery on a lorry and deliver it to the property however inconvenient a proceeding this might be. On the other hand, however, the surveyor should remember that while the joinery items remain at the builder's yard, they are outside the physical control of the building owner and himself and should the builder unfortunately go bankrupt quite suddenly, the building owner would not be able to collect them, even although payment had been made. In actual fact situations like this are dealt with by some compromise being effected whereby both parties are left moderately contented, but difficulties of this sort are not altogether easy to solve.

COMPLETION OF THE CONTRACT

The exact day of the completion of a contract for the repair of a house may be of considerable importance for reasons that will be referred to later, but first one must have regard to what is meant by the term "completion". The Courts in construing conditions of contract such as those under consideration, will firstly consider them as a whole in their ordinary and popular sense, and secondly, in any peculiar sense that they may have acquired by usage in the trades concerned. What constitutes completion therefore depends on the terms of the contract and what might reasonably constitute fulfilment of it having regard to the intentions of the parties. It should be emphasised, however, that the Courts will pay attention to the true meaning of the words printed or written above the signatures to the contract and no evidence may be adduced, however strong this may be, to prove an unexpressed intention. Accordingly, where a contract is entered into under a standard R.I.B.A. form neither the employer nor the builder will be able to subsequently call evidence to show that some different arrangement was obvious at the outset of the contract to all parties concerned so far as completion was concerned, since the Court will turn its attention to interpreting the words laid down in the standard clause of the contract where these relate specifically to the question of completion. If any unusual arrangements are contemplated, the surveyor would presumably have specified them in the contract and varied the standard wording accordingly.

The word "completion" has been judicially interpreted on several occasions and may be said to arise on that day and at that moment when the surveyor or architect by inspection of the works decides that he may with all reasonableness certify completion with its resulting payment, regard being had to the number of days' latitude, if any, permitted by the contract and when he is satisfied that the amount of retention money held is adequate to its particular purpose.[1]

The R.I.B.A. form of contract uses the term "practical completion". These words are not defined in the conditions but the issue of a certificate on practical completion of the works is envisaged. Clause 15 of the R.I.B.A. form states as follows:

"When in the opinion of the architect the works are practically completed, he shall forthwith issue a certificate to that effect and Practical Completion of the Works shall be deemed for all the purposes of this contract to have taken place on the day named in such certificate."

Under the R.I.B.A. form in Clause 15 (2) the surveyor is given power to prepare a Schedule of Defects which he is bound to deliver to the contractor not later than 14 days after the end of the defects liability period. The term used in Clause 15 (2) is "any defects, shrinkages or other faults . . . " and are matters which it is envisaged that the contractor must make good at his own cost unless the surveyor instructs otherwise in the case of a doutbful item which might count as an extra. An interesting point arises should the surveyor forget to deliver his Schedule of Defects to the contractor within the time limit of 14 days from the end of the defects liability period. Under the terms of the R.I.B.A. contract this, presumably, would be invalid, but the employer is not disbarred from his right in common law to claim for damages against the contractor for his failure to complete a proper contract.

Accordingly it will now be seen that the date on which practical completion is certified is of considerable importance since the defects liability period runs strictly from this same day. The defects liability period agreed between the parties is normally inserted in the Appendix to the contract but six months is taken to be the period if no other date is stated.

Clause 15 (3) conflicts to some extent with the previous clause in the R.I.B.A. form of contract. This clause enables the surveyor to issue instructions for any defects to be made good other than those listed in the Schedule of Defects referred to in the previous clause.

[1] Emden & Gill's Building Contracts and Practice, 7th edition.

Clause 15 (3) is intended to give the surveyor power to ask the contractor to make good particular defects during the defects liability period itself, but there is nothing inconsistent in the previous clause to bar a surveyor from compiling his Schedule of Defects within the defects liability period, although this proceeding would be unwise, since once the Schedule of Defects is issued the surveyor is disbarred from making any further claims upon the contractor under Clause 15(3) as well as Clause 15(2). Under Clause 15(4) the surveyor is bound to certify to the building owner when the contractor has made good the defects, shrinkages or other faults that have been specified and once he has done so, final completion takes place on the same day that the certificate was issued so that the retention monies become due for payment.

Under Clause 16 of the R.I.B.A. standard form of contract, there is provision for what is called "sectional completion". This clause is interesting as it enables the contractor and the employer by agreement to complete part of the contract before the day fixed for practical completion of the whole contract. In order for this clause to take effect the employer, with the consent of the contractor, is allowed to take possession of part of the contract works and sectional completion might apply for example, in the case of a large repair contract for an estate of houses, the houses being released one by one as they are repaired so that they can be let to tenants. Other than an example such as this, however, sectional completion is not a usual proceeding. It will be noted however that sectional completion does not prevent the contract from still being defined as an Entire Contract.

One of the matters specifically referred to under the R.I.B.A. form of contract in Clause (15)5 is the question of frost damage. It should be noted that the contractor is not required to make good at his own cost any damage by frost which appears after practical completion of the works, unless the surveyor shall certify that such damage is due to injury which took place before practical completion of the work.

TIME FOR COMPLETION

The reader will recall that if no particular time is specified for completion of the work in the contract, it is inferred at law that the work must be completed within a reasonable time and if the builder drags his feet to an unacceptable degree, the employer is entitled to fix a date for completion which allows a sensible time for the work to be finished and then, if the contractor fails to complete, having been given due notice, the employer is entitled to dismiss him. What is reasonable depends upon each individual set of circumstances.

It should be borne in mind however, that not withstanding the fact that a particular time for completion is specified in the contract, the mere fact of non-completion within that time will not release the employer from the contract unless there are unusual circumstances. He would be, however, entitled to damages which he would have to show as being caused by the delay. If, however, time is specified as being of the essence of the contract so that completion within a stated time limit is expressly made a condition precedent to payment, the employer is released from the contract if the builder fails to complete within the stipulated period. It should, of course, be added that such a condition is unusual in building contracts for obvious reasons. There may well, however, be circumstances where time is stated as being of the essence, where for example certain works have to be completed to a house before some particular event occurs, but the circumstances would of course have to be out of the ordinary for contractors to take up the challenge to complete the work within the time under such a terrible penalty. The cost would clearly rise due to this risk element and the expense of making a building contract wholly subject to being completed within a specified time would be so expensive as to be unacceptable except under the most extreme conditions. It should be emphasised that for a surveyor to make time the essence of the contract, is an unusual and grave step. The builder has until midnight of the day fixed for completion to finish every part of the contract otherwise the employer is released from his obligations under it. This is such a basic and fundamental requirement that it must stand on its own and cannot conflict with any other parts of the contract and is not to be confused with any lesser provisions such as the payment of a penalty for delay, the payments of bonuses for speedy work and otherwise where some possible postponement may be inferred as being tolerated by the parties under some other clause.

NON-COMPLETION

As we have seen earlier in the Chapter, every contract relies upon completion for its satisfaction and an employer, obviously, is only bound to pay for repair work if it has been satisfactorily completed. However, there will be occasions, although these will be rare, where completion will not take place. This will be due perhaps to the fact that the contract is impossible to perform owing, for example, to the fact that the house is burned to the ground by vandals after the contract has been entered into but before the works are commenced, and due to no fault or lack of care on the part of either the employer or the contractor. Alternatively, the contract entered into may be illegal for one reason or another, or, a more likely reason for non-completion, the fact that the employer or his representatives may prevent completion from taking place. This may be where the surveyor fails to supply the necessary drawings as the work proceeds, where these are of such a fundamental nature that they are necessary for completion of the work, or where the employer has a fit of insanity and refuses to allow the workmen access to the site. Finally the contract might be waived when a new contract is substituted for it either before or after the commencement of the work.

The duty of a contractor to fulfill the terms of a building contract that he has entered into cannot be lightly turned aside by excuses. It is his duty before submitting a tender to inform himself of all particulars concerning the works proposed and also as to the practicability of executing the work. He is not excused from performing his obligations by ignorance of what is entailed by the work and matters of difficulty, even where these involve increased expenditure, will not relieve him of his duty to carry the work through to completion. If, however, there was an impossible bar to completion and the surveyor knew at the time of entering into the contract that performance was impossible, these circumstances would be rather different. If the contractor did not know that performance was impossible the employer cannot anticipate his performance under such circumstances and since the minds of the parties are not "ad idem", neither party could sue upon the contract. Alternatively, if the contract becomes impossible and it could be proved by the contractor that he had no means of ascertaining this fact at the outset, the Court may release him from his duty to complete.

Most excuses for non-completion submitted by contractors are due to circumstances such as strikes, the failure of other contractors to carry out certain work, or due to exceptionally bad weather. The law frowns on all such excuses and none of them in the absence of exceptional circumstances, are sufficient to enable a contractor to be released from his duty to complete the work. Reasonable latitude for delay would be allowed under certain circumstances either under the terms of the contract or by the Court but it is interesting that in an early case dated 1611[1] where a man covenanted to build a house before a certain day and the plague broke out, the breach was

---

[1] *Lawrence v. Twentiman.*

admitted as being excusable at the time because the law did not compel the builder to risk his life, but he was expected to complete the work afterwards as soon as he possibly could!

The point was made early in this Chapter that specific performance of a building or engineering contract is seldom required by the Courts. If the employer refuses his builder access to the site, or turns the men away, the builder's remedy is to recover payment for the work he has done and damages for the loss that he has sustained by not being allowed to complete the work. Alternatively, he can treat the contract as being rescinded and sue for the reasonable value of the work carried out. It should be emphasised however, that the builder must show that he has been completely prevented from carrying out the work. A mere difference of opinion on the site and the builder walking away accompanied by his men, does not come within this category. If, however, the employer fails to nominate a surveyor or architect under the terms of a contract where this is a condition precedent to the contractor's obligation to do the work or if such a surveyor or architect is nominated but fails to provide the necessary drawings, the contractor is likely to be able to claim effective grounds for non-completion of the work. Again if delay or prevention is caused by a surveyor or architect acting in his capacity as agent of the employer, the employer becomes liable for the consequences but the position where a surveyor or architect acts in a quasi-judicial function under the terms of the contract and causes delay or total prevention of the construction of the works is an interesting one. Here it would appear that the contractor has no remedy against the employer.

It might again be emphasised that where sub-contractors or specialists are employed by the contractor under the terms of the contract, even where these have been selected by the employer, the employer is not liable to the contractor for their failure, but if the employer, on the other hand, employs specialists direct, he will be responsible to the contractor for any difficulty caused by their default.

THE FINAL CERTIFICATE

Where a building contract provides that work is to be completed to the approval or satisfaction of the surveyor, such approval or satisfaction, if final, is a condition precedent to payment for the work. We have already seen that in granting interim certificates the surveyor acts in the capacity of agent to the employer but the big difference between interim certificates and the final certificate is that in the latter case the surveyor acts as quasi-arbitrator between the parties and his opinion is binding. His opinion cannot be set aside by the employer or the contractor on the grounds that it is unreasonable, but only on the grounds of fraud or collusion. The contractor must obey all reasonable directions given to him by the surveyor and it might be added that if he has expressly contracted to carry out work in accordance with the directions of a surveyor, he is still bound to carry out the instructions of that surveyor even if these might count as being unreasonable since the employer gives no warranty that his surveyor will only give directions that are strictly reasonable, thus the refusal of the surveyor to issue his final certificate before certain work is properly completed to his satisfaction carries a good deal of weight and the contractor will be at pains to see that the surveyor is satisfied however unreasonable he may consider the demands to be.

Under normal circumstances the approaching completion of the work will have resulted in a number of interim certificates having been issued by the surveyor. Under these certificates, a certain sum, usually 5 per cent or sometimes 10 per cent of the work carried out will have been withheld as a retention fund for various purposes specified in the contract documents. When possession is taken by the employer, half the outstanding retention fund may be certified and on the expiration of the period of maintenance, the outstanding defects having been made good, the surveyor will issue his final certificate certifying the balance due to the builder. Where the R.I.B.A. Standard Form of Contract is in use, the surveyor issues a "certificate of practical completion" which marks the commencement of the defects liability period and at the end of this period the surveyor issues his final certificate. Although the surveyor acts as quasi-arbitrator in issuing his final certificate and must conduct himself with impartiality between the parties and give each side a hearing if necessary his certificate is not an award. The surveyor is not an arbitrator and the importance between the surveyor's role as agent to his employer, as quasi-arbitrator, and the distinction between an actual reference to arbitration under the terms of the R.I.B.A. contract, were considered in the recent case of Hosiery and Dickinson Ltd. v. P. & M. Kaye (1971).[1] In this case the contractors carried out work which led to a dispute but they then halted proceedings against the employers pending an informal settlement that they would put right certain defects. They were unable to carry out the work because no convenient time could be found by the employer to enable them to enter the premises and the matter went to Court. The architect issued his final certificate but

[1] Estates Gazette, March 11th 1972, page 1327.

the employers refused to pay, alleging that the work was defective. In the Court of Appeal the contractors argued that the counter claim for bad work was barred by the final certificate issued by the architect. This was "conclusive evidence" that the work had been properly carried out under the terms of Clause 30 (7) of the standard R.I.B.A. contract form. This provides that an architect's final certificate "shall be conclusive evidence in any proceedings arising out of the contract . . . that the works have been properly carried out". The employers disputed this submission and asked for the matter to be referred to arbitration but the Master of the Rolls, Lord Denning, in giving judgment said that "as the employers had not requested arbitration before the issue of the final certificate, Clause 30 (7), on the face of it, came into operation". Accordingly, the employers were barred by the final certificate from alleging that the work was not properly carried out. They had relied on the rule that once an arbitration clause is "waived" by allowing the Courts to decide a dispute, it cannot be afterwards maintained that those Courts have no jurisdiction. If the employers had wished to rely on an arbitration clause, they should have taken "no step in the action" but once they had done so, clause 30 (7) came into operation and this clause means exactly what it says. The final certificate is conclusive in any proceedings, whether already commenced or to be commenced and is then evidence that the works have been properly carried out.

In this case the architect's position as quasi-arbitrator was discussed and reference made to other case law on the subject. However, the judgment turned on the action taken by the parties in that under the terms of the contract the contractors were given 14 days in which to apply for arbitration after a final certificate was issued, whereas the employers were under a duty to apply for arbitration before the certificate was issued. The employers in fact did not follow this procedure. Under these particular circumstances and, it must be emphasised in this particular case, it was said that the architect remains the employer's agent, and, as such, he owes him a duty of care to see that the work has been properly carried out and cannot cover up his mistakes, if he were negligent, by giving a final certificate. There was no suggestion that the architect was, in fact, negligent, but it is evident that his position as quasi-arbitrator cannot be used to override his duty to his employer purely to cover up mistakes that he might have made.

Quite apart from other considerations, however, the case underlines the need for the surveyor to exercise care when he issues his final certificate. He should be perfectly satisfied in his own mind that the works are properly completed to his own satisfaction and since there is such a heavy onus upon him, he should not hesitate to ask the builder to put matters right even if this seems a matter of some inconvenience. Only then can he feel certain that he has fulfilled his duty and be in a position to deal with his employer who may have a number of quibbles or dissatisfied comments to make which the surveyor does not feel to be justified.

Printed certificates are bound and sold in pads by both the Royal Institution of Chartered Surveyors and the Royal Institute of British Architects. The certificate is signed by the surveyor and indentifies the name of the contract, the name of the contractor and employer and gives the amount certified as being due and the date on which the certificate is drawn. The certificates should have a serial number so that the surveyor's records can keep accurate trace of it. Provision is made on the forms for the amounts for nominated sub-contractors to be inserted and once the certificate is despatched to the contractor, he can present it to the building owner for payment. A second copy in the R.I.B.A. pad is kept for the architect's records. In the books of certificates prepared by the R.I.C.S. the surveyor's record of the issue of a certificate is maintained by the retention of the counterfoil.

In issuing a final certificate the surveyor should ensure that it is drawn up in the appropriate form. For example, it should he signed by the person named in the contract and if he himself is that person, he should not leave the certificate to be signed by an assistant. He should also be sure that he has exercised his correct quasi-judicial function in allowing the various parties to the contract to be heard in connection with any disputes before he decides the matter and he must ensure that he takes no action that might conflict with his impartiality so that he would appear to be prejudiced nor must he submit to pressure from one or other of the parties.[1] The reader should note that once a certificate is given and is drawn up in valid form, the surveyor cannot, unless so provided in the contract, withdraw it for the purpose of correcting statements of fact or value contained in it. He can only make another certificate if the first certificate is invalid. Finally it should be stated that if the surveyor refuses to certify or unreasonably delays the issue of his certificate, the builder can recover the money due from the building owner, notwithstanding that the contract may make a certificate a condition precedent to payment.

[1] *Roberts v. Hickman* (1909) 1913 A.C. 229.

THE FINAL ACCOUNT

It is hoped in the case of a lump sum contract that when the final account arrives, it will contain no unexpected shocks to the surveyor. The contract sum should be set out and omissions from it specified in detail including, of course, not only savings on the work as it proceeds, but also the deduction of prime cost and provisional sums. Against these items are set down the additions to the contract and here the surveyor will look down the list to ensure that the variations are authorised. In a properly run contract, every item should be backed by a variation order and the price previously agreed either by direct agreement between the surveyor and the contractor or alternatively valued by the quantity surveyor and agreed with the builder. In theory therefore, this means that the surveyor has simply to sit down and verify every item against the information that he already has in his file in order to discharge his duty to his employer. It will come as no surprise to learn that this rarely happens and there will always be extra items of which the surveyor has no knowledge perhaps ordered directly by the client, and which have to be looked into and examined, variations where the exact cost is not ascertained beforehand, savings where the amount placed against them is inadequate in the surveyor's opinion, and on some occasions savings omitted altogether.

There is little doubt in the writers' view that correct running of the contract from the financial point of view as the work proceeds so that every extra and omission is authorised and every variation in cost is priced should be the surveyor's aim. It is extremely difficult for the surveyor to deal adequately with a final account some time after works have been completed where the contract has been run in a sloppy way and variations have not been properly recorded or priced. The surveyor will be at an extreme disadvantage to the contractor who has much better records and who has the word of mouth evidence of his men to back up every extra with formidable feats of memory while being a little less zealous to perform feats of total recall where savings are concerned.

In day-work accounts the previously agreed rates for labour should be shown clearly with any price adjustments that may be agreed under the terms of the contract. Similarly trade invoices should be referred to and set down in detail so that these can be checked at the contractor's office if necessary and the appropriate adjustments made should profit be allowed under the terms of the contract.

The Royal Institution of Chartered Surveyors has issued a definition of Prime Cost of Day-Work carried out under a building contract and under these rules, if adopted, vouchers specifying the time and materials spent will have been submitted for verification to the surveyor or his representative not later than the end of the week following that on which the work is executed. These are mainly for the benefit of a clerk of works should there be one, but otherwise these will be sent direct to the surveyor who signs them and forwards them to the quantity surveyor should one be employed.

DEFECTS LIABILITY

The builder is liable to make good defects that occur within the defects liability period stated in the contract. Clearly, however, he is not responsible for matters that may occur where the causes for these lie outside the contract, nor is he liable to make good the effects of ordinary wear and tear. There will, however, be occasions where defects fail to be resolved simply within the defects liability period and some disputes might occur as a result of this. It appears that the position is that the builder's obligation extends to cover defects discovered within the defects liability period although the cause of the defect may not be ascertained until after the expiration of that period. On the other hand, a defect appearing outside the defects liability period is not, generally, the liability of the builder.

The contract may contain a provision that if the builder does not remedy the defects or execute the repairs he has undertaken to perform, the employer may engage another builder to do the work and charge the defaulting builder with the cost. Even if this right is stated in the contract, it must be used with extreme care and the surveyor is well advised to see to it that the contractor is given every opportunity to complete the work satisfactorily and only in the event of his total failure and upon due notice having been given should the surveyor employ another firm to complete the work. Before the contractor can be charged with a breach of duty he must be notified that the time for doing it has arrived so as to give him an opportunity to fulfill his obligation and if no notice is served upon him, he could, with some justice, allege that he was never clear as to what was finally expected of him.

In the case of a small maintenance contract there is often no defects liability period whatsoever. In the Form of Agreement for minor building works the period stated is 3 months but in larger contracts 6 months is usual and this is normally the period inserted in the Appendix to the R.I.B.A. Standard Form of Contract.

BREACH OF CONTRACT

If a breach of contract by the employer occurs during the progress of the work, it depends upon the particular circumstances of the case whether the breach goes to the root of the contract or not. If it does, the contractor is entitled to abandon the work and seek his remedy in damages but on the other hand if the breach does not go to the root of the contract he must continue with the work and complete it and then subsequently sue for damages as an addition to the contract price. If the employer gives notice to the contractor not to do any more work, that amounts to a total breach and the contractor is entitled to treat the contract as rescinded. The notice, however, must be final and not a mere postponement of the works. What constitutes a breach by the employer which goes to the root of the contract is a matter of fact depending upon each particular case. It has been held for example that the exclusion of two of the contractor's workmen from the building site by an employer did not repudiate the contract on the part of the employer. Clearly, however, the exclusion of all the contractor's workmen from the site would be a different matter.

If the contractor on his part abandons the work, the employer is justified in treating the contract as having been repudiated by the contractor.

The remedy for a breach of contract in a building matter is invariably damages. The measure of damages for failure by a contractor to complete a building contract includes firstly the difference between the price of the work as agreed in the contract and the cost that the employer is actually called upon to pay to complete it and secondly any loss of rent or use and occupation of the building which the employer has suffered in consequence of the delay in obtaining completion of the works. If, however, the employer intended to use the building for a special purpose which was unknown to the contractor, he is not entitled to base his claim for damages upon this fact. The Court will adopt as the measure of damages, the loss of the use of the building for the purpose for which the contractor might have reasonably supposed it was to be used.

Where defects in the builder's work remain undiscovered for some time, owing to the negligence of persons employed by the building owner to supervise the running of the contract, the utmost to which he is entitled to recover damages against the builder is the sum which it would have cost to remedy the defects at the time when they might have been discovered by the exercise of reasonable care.

PENALTIES AND LIQUIDATED DAMAGES

A common practice in building contracts is to insert a clause stating that in the event of the works not being completed by a particular date, a sum of money shall be payable by the contractor to the employer. This clause is known as a Penalty Clause and if an exact sum or sums are stated in the contract as being payable under specific conditions, the monetary amounts are known as Liquidated Damages. Usually where such a clause is employed in a building contract, Liquidated Damages are named as a certain sum for each day of delay after the expiry of the original completion date and the surveyor should be careful in the event of employing such a clause to state whether the days are working days or not since otherwise there will be doubt as to whether Saturdays, Sundays and Public Holidays are included.

Whether the sum or sums of money payable by the contractor in case of delay are to be treated as Liquidated Damages or as a Penalty, is not as simple as it appears. This will be a question for the Court to decide having regard to the intention of the parties when the contract was drawn up. A Penalty Clause is more likely to be a single sum named to frighten the other side into the realisation of the consequences of delay. It might be extravagent in amount and quite unrelated to the actual damage involved. Liquidated Damages on the other hand are the result of a genuine attempt by both parties to the contract to decide beforehand what sum or sums of money compensate the injured party for the genuine loss involved by delay.

It is of course essential that a day is stipulated in the contract from which Liquidated Damages or Penalties are to run. It is also usual for contracts to contain provision for the contractor to avoid the payment of Liquidated Damages due to some unforeseen causes or some act or default of the employer or his surveyors. For example the R.I.B.A. Standard Form of Contract sets out various reasons in Clause 23 and gives a procedure to be followed so that the surveyor or architect may agree an extension of time for completion.

BANKRUPTCY

If the contractor should go bankrupt, the trustee in bankruptcy would be responsible for the debts and duties of the bankrupt, but if the contract was a personal one with the bankrupt, the trustee could not continue the work on his behalf. The fundamental question in such cases is whether the particular contract is a personal one with the bankrupt or not. The trustee of a bankrupt builder for example, might decide to carry on the building contract to completion, except of course where the contract specifically provides that it is to be terminated in the event of bankruptcy, but the position where the surveyor goes bankrupt is more complicated as the trustees in bankruptcy would not be able to continue with his work if his contract was a personal one with the employer.

It is not unusual for a provision to be incorporated in the building contract empowering the employer to forefeit the contract on the bankruptcy of the contractor so as to prevent a contractor's trustee in bankruptcy from electing to complete the contract. This provision is valid if it is stated that the contract between the employer and the contractor is a personal one. Since the contractor has mere licence to enter on to the employer's property (which cannot therefore be defined as an interest in property), revocation of that licence can be properly conditional upon bankruptcy. A trustee in bankruptcy, however, has the right to enter upon a site to move any property of the bankrupt which cannot be claimed by the employer.

In matters of contract the trustee in bankruptcy normally has the right to disclaim a contract or to carry it out according to which course of action is to the benefit of the bankrupt. If the trustee decides to adopt the contract he becomes bound by its terms, but if he disclaims the contract it comes to an end and the employer then, if he suffers injury by the disclaimer, must seek his remedy in damages against the estate of the contractor. If the bankrupt continues to perform the work after his bankruptcy, the value of it becomes payable to his trustee.

In the event of the employer becoming bankrupt, the contractor is not bound to continue to supply materials or to carry out work on credit. He is entitled to proceed against the estate of the bankrupt for damages that occur due to the breach of contract.

DEATH

(a) *Death of the Employer or Building Owner*

If the building owner dies during the execution of the contract, his personal representatives, either executors or administrators, are entitled to the benefit of the contract and to ask that it be completed. On the other hand, however, they are not entitled to revoke the contract since this is highly unlikely to be a personal one, and they are liable for not only the price, but for the fees of the professional advisers as well.

(b) *Death of the Contractor*

If the contractor dies during the execution of the contract, his personal representatives are entitled to perform the contract and recover payment for it. If a personal representative enters into a supplementary contract in that capacity, he will then become personally liable under the terms of it. Today most firms of builders or contractors are capable of fulfilling building contracts, notwithstanding the death of the principal, but if, on the other hand, the employer has engaged a contractor who may be on his own with perhaps a single assistant for some special skill that he has, for example, skill in making and setting up wrought ironwork or skill in laying out a garden, the personal representatives of the deceased are hardly likely to be able to complete the contract, nor can they insist on doing so. They are entitled to be paid any instalments of the price which will have accrued due for work carried out by the deceased prior to his death or they may submit a claim on a basis of quantum meruit for work completed up until the date of death.

(c) *Death of the Surveyor*

If the surveyor dies during the execution of his contract his affairs pass into the hands of his personal representatives and their liability for the execution of the contract depends very much on the particular circumstances concerned. If the contract was essentially a personal one, for example, where the surveyor was engaged in business on his own account and perhaps worked from his home address with his wife acting as his secretary, it is probable that the client selected him on a personal basis for his individual skill and clearly the surveyor's executors could not be expected to carry on his contract, which therefore comes to an end. The position, however, is quite different where the surveyor is one of a number of partners in a large firm. Here the contract is far less likely to be a personal one and the employer would presumably be able to ask for the contract to be completed by one or other of the surveyor's partners. It will be appreciated however, that this may not invariably be the case since the employer may have made a personal choice of a particular building surveyor partner in a firm for his special skill and it may well be that the other partners specialise in other aspects of the profession such as valuation or agency. Under circumstances such as these, the appointment may well rank as a personal one and presumably the partners of the deceased surveyor could ask for it to be terminated. So far as the building contract is concerned, provision may or may not be made for the death of the surveyor or architect. The R.I.B.A. Form places a duty on the employer to nominate a successor.

ARBITRATION

The building contract may well provide that in the event of a dispute or difference occurring between the parties, that this will be referred for determination to an Arbitrator. This means that the submission of both sides to the dispute will be heard in a judicial manner by a person appointed by the parties to the dispute and who is referred to as the Arbitrator. The Arbitrator, unlike a solicitor or barrister, is not an officer of the Court but is purely a private person who, because of his special qualifications, is appointed to hear the evidence, often highly technical in nature, and decide the matter between the parties.

Although an arbitration is not a Court of Law, the Arbitrator nevertheless follows the ordinary rules of Court procedure relating to attendance and evidence and the Arbitrator will be well versed in such procedure. The reader might reasonably ask why, if this procedure is followed in the same manner as in a Court of Law, the parties do not apply to the Courts in the first case, but in fact the advantages of arbitration are very marked in that not only is the process of deciding the matter much quicker, which is extremely important in complicated building disputes, but there is also a saving in the cost of the arbitration hearing as against that entailed at a Court of Law. Perhaps, however, the biggest advantage of an arbitration is that the dispute can be heard before a man who is an expert in the field of the subject matter under consideration so that the parties can feel that he is equipped to grasp the various complicated points at issue. Perhaps the main weakness of the arbitration system however is that it is dependent very much on the personal qualities of the Arbitrator. The conditions can often be extremely exacting since not only has the Arbitrator to be an expert in his own field, but he must have a wide knowledge of quasi-judicial procedure as well and most important of all, be a man of considerable independence of mind and judgment. There are many excellent Arbitrators who can be appointed in such cases and most arbitrations are effective in deciding the point at issue, but it should be remembered that the hearing may turn not only a technical point, but perhaps a point of procedure or even prejudice and it is possible that the Arbitrator may not be fully equipped to deal with the matter and may arrive as a result at a poor Award. If this should happen, one of the parties at least would wish that they had applied to the Courts of Law for a decision but having elected to go to arbitration they must stand by the results unless the Award is, for example, bad in law and would be set aside by the Courts.

Arbitration agreements are governed by the provisions of the Arbitration Act, 1950. The Act lays down a number of rules, for example, that an agreement to submit a dispute to arbitration must be in writing and that it must be stamped. Other provisions, for example, are that the agreement must be in precise terms and it must be contained in a single document. One of the most important aspects of the matter, however, is that the agreement must specify clearly what type of disputes are to be the subject of the Arbitrator's Award. In some cases all disputes may be specified, but in others only certain areas of dispute are set down as being the possible subject of arbitration since others will be agreed between the parties as being best settled by the surveyor or architect in charge of the work acting in a quasi-judicial capacity. Until recent years it was the custom to insert a clause in the contract giving the surveyor or architect in charge of the work the right to decide disputes that might arise, his decision being final. This, however, led to a number of difficulties and a good deal of case law concerning the exact position held by the surveyor or architect. It is now the custom for the arbitrator to be named in the contract as being a completely independent person unconnected with any of the parties or alternatively for a clause to be drawn up stating that in the event of a dispute occurring, the Arbitrator will be appointed in some pre-determined manner, for example by the President of the R.I.B.A. in the case of the R.I.B.A. Standard Form of Building Contract.

MAINTENANCE PROCEDURES

Up to this point in this Chapter, consideration has been confined in the main to the surveyor's duties *vis-à-vis* his client or clients in regard to a contract for the repair and maintenance of a single building or perhaps a group of houses but on the assumption that he is not permanently appointed as a managing agent to look after his client's interests on a continuing basis. In other words the surveyor's instructions are limited to a particular task over a fairly limited period. Once this task is accomplished his appointment usually ceases but there are occasions when a surveyor having supervised the repair works will be asked to look after the property subsequently and to arrange as necessary for those routine items of repair and maintenance which are of a continuing nature but which are so vital to the preservation of the fabric.

Whereas on the completion of the repairs carried out for a client on the basis of the R.I.B.A. Conditions of Engagement the surveyor has a duty to "provide scale drawings showing the main lines of drainage and obtain drawings of other services as executed and give initial guidance on maintenance" something a little more than this in the way of information is required on the building if continuing attention is being considered. In the circumstances envisaged above there are strong grounds for employing the surveyor or whoever was in charge of the main contract, to prepare a Maintenance Manual. In view of the increasing complexity of the fittings in many houses, for example thermostatically controlled heating and hot water systems, there are almost equally strong grounds for arranging the preparation of such a manual at the end of any reasonably large-sized contract which involves the reconditioning of premises. Such a manual properly prepared in regard to an owner-occupied property would enable the householder to have readily available all the detailed information necessary for him to operate and maintain the fittings and services, to clean the various surfaces correctly and, if the need should arise, to effect minor repairs. At certain times it will be useful for him to have a document which he can hand to a contractor to enable a more serious fault to be diagnosed and corrected without unnecessary investigation into facts which can so easily be recorded.

Even with the largest of owner-occupied properties where much of the cleaning and routine maintenance may be supervised by the owner's managing agent there is still a case for a smaller manual being kept at the property with the necessary information for use, perhaps, by domestic staff on the day-to-day running of the property and for times of emergency when it is necessary to summon assistance. In these circumstances the manual might well be divided into two parts, a "housekeeping" section and a "maintenance" section, the surveyor keeping the second and probably much larger part complete with records of inspections and work carried out. There might also be a need for a clear division of responsibilities with such an arrangement.

Of course, where there is a managing surveyor acting on behalf of an owner occupying only part of a house or one house on an estate then the owner will be in the same position as a tenant in respect of the contents of his "Maintenance Manual". In these circumstances the tenant's manual will be limited to information on housekeeping, cleaning and operating as outlined above together with the location of stop-cocks, valves etc., and any restrictions imposed on the tenant by the nature of the construction regarding the fixing of any fittings or the carrying out of any alterations. An important part of the information will comprise the names, addresses and telephone numbers of the services to contact in case of emergency and in particular for reporting defects or other matters which require the attention of the managing surveyors. It is clearly sensible to include a statement of the respective responsibilities of both owner and tenant in this respect. Maintenance manuals of this nature are a sensible provision for tenants of rented accommodation whether the owners be private landlords, local authorities, housing associations, private companies or state corporations and whether those responsible for the management are surveyors in private practice employed for the purpose or employees on the permanent staff of the owners.

The contents of suitable maintenance manuals depend of course to a great extent on the size and type of buildings being dealt with, on the complexity of their fittings and on the degree of responsibility of tenants and owners where rented accommodation is involved. The main headings for the sections considered necessary when dealing with housing work are:

Section 1. Contract and Legal Details
   e.g. Tenure, lease details, easements, public authorities and if works recently carried out details of contract, maintenance period, etc.

Section 2. Housekeeping
   e.g. Schedules of finishes, routine cleaning and maintenance, precautions for fixings, fire precautions, avoidance of condensation etc.

Section 3. Operating
   e.g. heating and hot water, electricity, gas and cold water installation, operating manuals, routine inspections and cleaning, draining down, etc.

Section 4. Maintenance and Repair
   e.g. Details of the construction and finishings of the building, particularly hidden features and their location.

Section 5. Record of Maintenance Executed
   This should take the form of a log to record items of repair and re-decoration both as to the extent of the work carried out and its timing and details of any alterations, guarantees, etc.

Section 6. Plans and Drawings
   For use by both house owner and maintenance contractor and if necessary for the tenant as well. Plans and sections, plumbing, drainage, electrical and gas installations to be shown.

Section 7. Emergency Information
   e.g. The necessary contacts in the event of serious emergency for fire, theft, electrical failures, gas leaks, plumbing leaks, etc., and the shut down valve and stop cock control positions.

1004

The maintenance of records forms an essential part of any organisation responsible for the management of residential estates and where these estates are new or arise out of the repair and rehabilitation of older property the additional expense of preparing Maintenance Manuals as described above is adequately recompensed by the information now readily available both to owners, their staff or managing agents and the tenants at that very critical time before all parties become fully familiar with details of construction etc. It would seem logical for each tenant to have a Manual based on information derived from Sections 2, 3 and 7 as a matter of course with additional material from Sections 1, 4 and 6 as indicated by the circumstances of each case. The estate manager's Manual must obviously be complete in every respect and in as much detail as possible. Whether it will be necessary to have a separate Manual for each property will obviously depend on the character of the estate, but it will usually be necessary to have a number of copies made of each separate Manual for distribution to the various parties responsible for different aspects of the work likely to arise.

The managerial and technical problems of running an estate of any real size can be very demanding. There are the legal problems involved in the owner's responsibility for common parts which are by no means solely connected with the preservation of amenities but are concerned primarily with safety. There are innumerable law cases in connection with unlit staircases, slippery and broken steps, broken handrails and balustrades, defective lifts, etc., and those responsible for management must bear in mind the protection of people from risk and of the possibility of criminal proceedings arising out of a breach of the law in this respect, even apart from the aspect of heavy damages as a result of civil proceedings. If this were not enough there are the contractual liabilities which arise out of the relevant repairing responsibilities of owners in respect of the structure and exterior of premises and in addition the statutory obligations in regard thereto and in respect of the services.

Unfortunately in all except a few enlightened examples the spirit of parsimony pervades the field of maintenance and it has authoritatively been estimated that by 1970 an eight-year back-log in housing maintenance alone existed. The parsimony has to some extent been encouraged by legislation but the effect produced is depressing in appearance and wasteful of resources. It results in a lack of forward planning, a proper consideration of alternatives and *ad hoc* expenditure when there is money to spare rather than when it should be spent. However with the increasing realisation that the assets comprised in the older buildings are of value, there is a greater appreciation among owners that neglect, run-down and demolition is not the inevitable fate of old houses, despite the general acceptance of this viewpoint held until comparatively recently in post-Second World War Britain. As a result many surveyors are now faced with the problem of organising the administration of large residential estates and although the basic principles are the same, the methods of dealing with the repair and maintenance aspect may vary from those suitable when dealing with single buildings and it may be necessary to adopt slightly different contractual arrangements in order to secure the satisfactory performance of the work in an economic fashion.

Initially a consideration of objectives must be put in hand by the estate manager in conjunction with the owners as it is only by deciding these in advance that the correct basis for recording information can be taken and eventually a suitable system evolved for carrying out the necessary work, both on a planned basis and in any emergencies that may arise. In the field of housing very often a social consideration is paramount in that the aim of the maintenance organisation will be to maximise the economic life of the asset and to maintain tenant's satisfaction within the limitations of realistic financial budgets. While these considerations may seem obvious and may well be paramount in the mind of the maintenance manager he will become a very frustrated character if he has not ascertained that these are also the objectives of the owners. Often quite conscious decisions are taken to allow a run down of assets purely for a short-term gain, even apart from reasonable decisions involving future plans for the site occupied by the buildings in question. Similarly tenant's satisfaction may well be very low on the list of the aims of some organisations who may consider themselves better served without residential tenants at all. Economies and financial "squeezes" at regular intervals are a familiar pattern and it is all too easy to save money by putting off the repairs and redecoration for another couple of years. All these attitudes are regularly encountered and they are by no means confined to either the private or the public sector. On rare occasions the managing agent or maintenance director will have a say in overall policy and will be putting into effect his own recommendations. Matters might then proceed more smoothly but in the more frequently found situations where the agent or manager is to some extent kept in the dark on over-all policy or where, on the other hand, there is little policy or it is well known to fluctuate wildly, then the manager or agent should certainly do his best to ascertain what policy there is and only in the last resort evolve his own. At least this would be better than nothing and when it runs into difficulties it may at least bring others to a sense of reality and force them, if not into thinking, at least into communicating.

The objectives established, consideration can then be given to producing the information and evolving the techniques necessary to achieve those objectives efficiently with the minimum use of resources. The first essential for any property manager is a physical record of the estate which is to be managed. Without such records he will merely flounder and will be incapable of producing the necessary information on which to base his policy on estimates or budget his expenditure. There are many different ways of maintaining the appropriate records and it does not really matter how the information is stored provided it is readily available when required. Maintenance Manuals have already been referred to in respect of property being newly managed and if an arrangement is made to produce these at the time of new building or major rehabilitation it is probable that much of the necessary information will be available already. Although detailed inspections of every property on an estate can be a time consuming and expensive operation, it may be the only way to assemble what is required if there are no records already in existence. It may however be possible to spread such inspection over a period of years or to tackle groups of properties at a time when it is necessary to decorate the exterior, for example.

Vital to all systems of recording are details of the maintenance items carried out and the expenditure and from this it can be decided whether properties are being under maintained or, on rare occasions, over maintained. Furthermore from this information one can deduce whether previous maintenance has been satisfactory or not, whether the current rent is economic or whether there are substantial disadvantages with the use of certain materials or fittings. Often it is useful to record maintenance and total running costs against each individual property and then analyse them to show costs by age group or type of construction or even just location. Coupled with the keeping of adequate records, inspection cycles form another important part of maintenance organisation particularly where there are mechanical fittings which have a limited life due to the effects of heat and friction. Much of the work in relation to electrical and mechanical services can be arranged through maintenance contracts with the installers who will for an annual charge, inspect, renew in good time elements which are near the end of their useful life and report on what they have done. Particularly in the case of lifts these annual (and sometimes bi-annual) inspections and reports are the managing agent's or manager's evidence that he has taken all reasonable care to ensure the component's safe working.

In regard to the fabric of a building more difficulty is presented. While a Maintenance Manual will define the tenant's obligations on the "housekeeping" side and a lot, of course, will depend on the scope of these obligations, it is still usually necessary to arrange for inspections of the fabric at intervals, even apart from a certain amount of routine maintenance. It is all very well expecting tenants to clean out gutters and keep rainwater pipes clear of obstruction and also to flush out gullies, drains and inspection chambers but very few will do it. Similarly tenants can be requested to report the first sign of any unusual occurrence that may lead to a defect, but very few will bother to do so unless very severely discomfited. One can hardly envisage a full structural survey being carried out every six months but it is wise to have maintenance staff to deal with those items in regard to gutters, rainwater pipes, gullies and drains referred to above at this periodic time interval, coupled with an inspection of the exterior in sufficient detail to note any major trouble likely to arise. Internal inspections can be made at less frequent intervals, perhaps related to the period when there is some upheaval such as the external redecoration cycle every four to five years. It must be remembered however that quite serious defects in buildings can be surprisingly difficult to detect in the early stages so that although careful inspections are made, it is still possible for major faults to arise between the inspections and to require immediate attention. The more experienced the surveyor employed on this task the less likely it is that the slight indications of major faults will be missed, since the experienced man will know from the age and character of the building where to concentrate his examination.

In the previous paragraph mention has been made of cyclic inspections of the internal fabric of buildings and it is over the same number of years, say five, that forward estimating and budgetary control should be arranged if at all possible. Year to year budgetting is not satisfactory in the field of maintenance for the simple reason that the time is insufficient to arrange for many of the major items to be scheduled or specified, priced, ordered, put in hand and paid for where there is a large estate of buildings. It is, of course, accepted that the prediction of maintenance requirements and costs over a period of five years cannot be infallible. There will always be unpredictable demands caused by external factors or unexpected failures even apart from the difficulty of estimating costs over such a period in times of rapid materials' price and wage increases. Furthermore, a commitment over such a period may be unacceptable to owners so that the managing agent or estate manager may well have to settle for a period of between one and five years on medium to large estates and even, if he is unfortunate, for one year on the smaller estates.

The forward estimating of expenditure requires at this stage that the proper decisions are taken in regard to the repair or renewal of items. In the past these decisions have often been based on the technical knowledge and experience of individual managers, qualities which can vary substantially between individuals and which do not necessarily guarantee a capacity for sound judgment. The application of appropriate economic analysis can improve the quality of repair or renew decisions and the technique of discounted cash flow is a useful tool to this end. A comparison can be made between the cost of renewing an item or repairing it at intervals over the anticipated life of the building. In order that the comparison should be financially valid these costs must be related to the present time and each expressed in terms of the discount values. The comparison may show that the unexpected may indeed be the cheaper solution, but of course such techniques take no account of convenience or appearance and, since housing is so much a social field, the cheapest solution may not be the best on all counts if a feeling for people and their needs is brought into the reckoning.

It must be acknowledged that much maintenance work is repetitious. The great majority of small individual repairs could be described by standard specification clauses while many of the larger maintenance projects are made up of a number of small standard operations. Standard specification clauses, including standards of materials and workmanship, can therefore eliminate the continual writing of the same wordy descriptions. A complete standard maintenance specification covering all work which can reasonably be anticipated on an estate could be lodged with all the selected contractors on the managing agent's or manager's list for routine maintenance. Coupled with a deposited Schedule of Rates, it is already apparent that here is one method of arranging for works to be carried out which provides a saving in time and labour for both the owner's agent and the contractors, since the whole operation can be simplified both as to ordering, the supervision of the work and the rendering and passing of an account. Both sides of the contract know fully where they stand and a spirit of confidence can be developed in these circumstances.

A National Building Specification is in course of preparation but it is not known at the time of writing whether this will be sufficiently comprehensive and suitable for the field of maintenance. If not, it would be a logical step to utilise work already carried out towards the preparation of Standard Specifications so as to formulate a

"National Maintenance Specification" from which clauses could be extracted or referred to by number.

It has long been a tradition to employ a direct labour staff for routine maintenance and for the large estate in both the public and private sectors this method has many advantages. Among these advantages are the degree of flexibility, facilitating quick response to urgent demands, a standard of workmanship from known and tested workmen who enjoy a continuity of employment, the availability of a known complement of workmen ready to be deployed and the possibility for suitable incentive schemes to be evolved by management. Against these advantages however are the costs involved in providing and administering the support facilities in the form of accommodation, stores, workshops, transport, accounting and pay services in order to make the most efficient and economic use of the directly employed labour. Furthermore, resources have to be deployed in close supervision to ensure economic programming, productivity and quality. In respect of the latter item, there is no redress as there may be with the employment of contractors and no argument on costs if it is considered that the job has taken longer than it should. The final disadvantage is that yet more managerial staff have to be engaged on dealing with questions of working conditions, pay, the settlement of grievances and all the other difficulties that can arise in labour relationships.

In considering whether to employ contractors or to set up a direct labour organisation various factors need to be taken into account. There may be a case for the employment of particular skills on an estate which can only be provided by specially trained staff, there may be questions of security involved but much more likely there are the economic merits. The all-in costs of a wide sample of maintenance work done by direct labour and executed by contractors may need to be compared (perhaps on other estates within the same organisation). Another factor is the reaction time. Quite a lot of maintenance work is of an urgent nature and it is often thought that a direct labour organisation can respond more rapidly to such demands if it is of sufficient size. Experience indicates, however, that this is not necessarily a superior system than the use of outside contractors in this particular respect. The desire of outside contractors to maintain good relations with employers who provide them with regular work is such that they will switch labour with some alacrity should the urgency of the need be emphasised.

Private contractors can be engaged to carry out work by various methods. These methods are really no different from those which often arise in regard to a single house, with the exception of the second method, which is usually confined to estate work.

The first method is where a contractor is given a direct order and is provided with a brief description or specification of the work required. On the work being completed the account is rendered on a time and materials basis with agreed percentage additions for overheads and profit. It is usually considered best for ease of certification and payment that this method be confined to small easily defined jobs. It is particularly appropriate to isolated locations, where there is real urgency and also where it may not be entirely possible to set out exactly what should be done, so that a tradesman has to use his discretion as to an immediate solution.

The second method is by direct order as above, giving a similar description or perhaps the appropriate numbers from a standard specification but here, on completion, the account is settled on the basis of agreed measurements and in accordance with a previously agreed schedule of prices. This method is usually referred to as the measured term contract. The contractor on this basis is usually assured of a steady flow of work of a consistent volume over a specific period and accordingly is able to offer good service as well as continuity of employment to his operatives. The terms, however, must be strictly defined, particularly the schedules setting out items and unit prices. Many estate managers compile such schedules and operate this scheme and a schedule prepared by the former Ministry of Public Building and Works can be purchased and used by anyone as the basis for a measured term contract.

The final method is the lump sum offer based on a specification, perhaps a bill of quantities, and drawings if necessary, invited from selected tenderers. This method is appropriate to the larger, well-defined maintenance project, particularly those involving a substantial proportion of specialist work. Ideally there should, of course, be a minimum of provisional items and contractors should be selected with great care, although it may of course be necessary to seek tenders by public advertisement in certain circumstances.

Any of the above methods should satisfy the requirements of good practice in securing the satisfactory execution of maintenance works on an economic basis. Within a very large organisation all three methods may be used according to circumstances, but it is desirable that the estate manager should decide in advance the criteria for selection of one method as against another, even though this may seem to be obvious on many occasions.

Appendix

SCHEDULES OF AVERAGE WEIGHTS
OF MATERIALS

Note

In these Schedules where the figures are expressed in British units the traditional term pounds per square foot (lb./ft.²) etc. has been used which is strictly speaking a measurement of mass per unit area. Correctly the term should be pound force per square foot (lbf./ft.²) as expressing a load (weight) in force units, as explained in Chapter 5, but in practice there is no difference. Where, however, the figures are expressed in SI metric units both mass per unit area in kilogrammes per square metre (kg/m²) and force units in newtons per square metre (N/m²) are shown. The weights are grouped in four Schedules corresponding to the elements of construction and an additional Schedule 5 has been included to show the average density of various materials in both British and SI metric units. Where possible in the first four Schedules the figures have been checked with those given in British Standard 648:1964 to which acknowledgment is made, but in Schedule 5 figures have been rounded off in both British and SI metric units.

Schedule 1. Floors

Component	Material	Thickness in inches	lb./ft.² pounds per square foot	Thickness in millimetres	kg/m² kilogrammes per sq. metre	N/m² newtons per square metre
Wood boards (finished thickness)	Softwood	7/8	2·3	22·2	11·2	110·1
	Softwood	1 1/8	2·8	28·6	13·7	134·1
	Pitchpine	7/8	3·0	22·2	15·1	143·6
	Pitchpine	1 1/8	3·8	28·6	19·0	181·9
	Oak	7/8	3·3	22·2	16·1	158·0
	Oak	1 1/8	4·3	28·6	21·0	205·8
Coverings	P.C. Screed (1:3)	1/2	6·0	12·7	29·3	287·3
	Terrazzo	1	11·0	25·4	53·7	526·7
	Granolithic	1	12·5	25·4	61·0	598·5
	Rubber	1/4	2·2	6·4	10·7	105·3
	Clay tiles	1/2	5·6	12·7	27·3	268·1
	Compressed Cork	1/4	0·5	6·4	2·4	23·9
	P.V.C., vinyl asbestos	1/8	1·4	3·2	6·8	67·0
	Pitchmastic	1	12·0	25·4	58·6	574·5
	Asphalt	1	12·0	25·4	58·6	574·5
	Linoleum	1/8	0·9	3·2	4·4	43·1
Joists	Softwood per 1 inch (25·4mm) in depth at 14 inch (356mm) centres	2	0·43	50·8	2·1	20·6
Ceilings	Wood laths	3/4	1·3	—	6·3	62·2
	Lime plaster	—	7·5	19·1	36·6	359·1
	Plasterboard and setting coat	—	3·0	—	14·6	143·6

Schedule 2. Flat Roofs

Component	Material		Thickness in inches	lb./ft.² pounds per square foot	Thickness in millimetres	kg/m² kilogrammes per sq. metre	N/m² newtons per square metre
Boarding	Softwood		¾	2·0	19·1	9·8	95·8
Insulation	Woodwool		2	6·0	50·8	29·3	287·3
	Compressed Straw		2	4·0	50·8	19·6	191·5
Coverings	Asphalt 2 layers		¾	8·6	19·1	41·9	411·8
	Zinc 12 gauge		—	0·9	—	4·4	43·1
	14 gauge		—	1·2	—	5·9	57·4
	16 guage		—	1·6	—	7·8	76·6
	Lead	6 lb.	—	8·0	—	39·0	383·0
	(to include laps	7 lb.	—	9·0	—	43·9	430·9
	and rolls)	8 lb.	—	11·0	—	53·7	526·7
	Copper 24SWG		—	1·0	—	4·9	47·9
	18SWG		—	2·2	—	10·8	105·3
	Bituminous felt as laid		—	1·5	—	7·3	71·8
	Patent Glazing including lead bars at 24 inch (610mm) centres		¼	6·0	6·4	29·3	287·3

Schedule 3. Pitched Roofs (*weights per unit of roof area measured on slope*)

Materials	lb./ft.² pounds per square foot	kg/m² kilogrammes per sq. metre	N/m² newtons per square metre
Slating:			
Welsh thin	5·0	24·4	239·4
Welsh thick	10·0	48·8	478·8
Westmorland thin	10·0	48·8	478·8
Westmorland thick (including 3-inch (76·2mm) laps and nails)	16·0	78·1	766·0
Clay Tiling:			
Plain machine made to 4 inch (101·6mm) gauge	13·0	63·5	622·4
Hand made to 4 inch (101·6mm) gauge	14·5	70·8	694·3
Single lap interlocking and pantiles	7½–9	36·6–43·9	359·1–430·9
Concrete Tiling:			
Slate aggregate to 12 inch (305mm) gauge	9·0	43·9	430·9
Stone aggregate:			
3 inch (76·2mm) gauge	19·0	92·8	909·7
4 inch (101·6mm) gauge	14·0	68·4	670·3
4·5 inch (114·3mm) gauge	12·5	61·0	598·5
Interlocking single lap	11·5	56·0	550·6
Asbestos Cement Sheets:			
Large corrugations (including fixings)	3·4	16·6	162·8
Small corrugations (including fixings)	3·4	16·6	162·8
Slates	4·5	21·9	215·5
Slating and Tiling Battens: 1½ inch by ¾ inch (38·1mm × 19·1mm) softwood at 4 inch (101·6mm) gauge	0·7	3·4	33·5
Reed Thatching (including battens) 12 inches (305mm) thick	8·5	41·5	407·0
Underfelt (sarking) for tiling and slating	0·5	2·4	23·9
Common rafters 4 inch by 2 inch (102mm by 51mm) at 14 inch (356mm) centres	2·0	9·8	95·8
Purlins:			
wood	2·0	9·8	95·8
steel	4·0	19·5	191·5
Trusses, allow for:			
40 foot (12m) span	5·0	24·4	239·4
40 to 60 foot (12 to 18m) span	6·0	29·3	287·3
60 to 80 foot (18 to 24m) span	7·0	34·2	335·2
Shingles, cedar wood	1·5	7·3	71·8

Schedule 4. Walls and Partitions

Component	Material	Thickness in inches	lb./ft.² pounds per square foot	Thickness in millimetres	kg/m² kilogrammes per sq. metre	N/m² newtons per square metre
Brickwork	Clay, solid, low density, common and stock	1	10·4	25·4	50·8	498·0
	Medium density	1	11·2	25·4	54·7	537·2
	High density, engineering	1	12·1	25·4	59·1	579·3
	Clay, perforated, depending on density and proportion of voids	1	7·9–10·0	25·4	38·6–48·8	378·2–478·8
	Concrete	1	12·0	25·4	58·6	574·5
	Sand lime	1	10·4	25·4	50·8	498·0
Blockwork	Clay, hollow	1	5·3	25·4	25·9	253·8
	,, perforated 50%	1	5·8–6·7	25·4	28·3–32·7	277·7–320·8
	Concrete, depending on type of concrete and aggregate and proportion of voids, if any	1	3·0–11·2	25·4	14·6–54·7	143·6–537·2
	Glass, hollow					
	8 inch (203·2mm)	3⅞	17·0	98·4	83·0	813·9
	6 inch (152·4mm)	3⅞	20·0	98·4	97·6	957·6
	Render and set	¾	8·0	19·1	39·0	383·0
Weather Boarding	Softwood	¾	1·5	19·1	7·3	71·8
	Softwood	1	1·8	25·4	8·8	86·2

Walls and Partitions (continued)

Component	Material	Thickness inches in	lb./ft.² pounds per square foot	Thickness in millimetres	kg/m² kilogrammes per sq. metre	N/m² newtons per square metre
Partitions	4 by 2 inch (102 by 51mm) stud partition with ¾ inch (19mm) lath and plaster both sides	6	17·0	152	83·0	813·9
	Gypsum, building panels	3	9·0	76·2	43·9	430·9
		4	10·0	101·6	48·8	478·8
		5	12·0	127·0	58·6	574·5
		6	13·0	152·4	63·5	622·4
	Neat gypsum setting coat	1/5	1·4	5·1	6·8	67·0
	Gypsum, dry partition panels	2¼	4·2	57·2	20·5	201·1
		2½	5·3	63·5	25·9	253·8

Schedule 5. Mass Densities of Materials

Material	Pounds per cubic foot lb./ft.³	Kilogrammes per cubic metre kg/m³
Aerated Concrete	30–100	480–1600
Aggregates: Coarse	80–100	1280–1600
Fine	90–110	1440–1760
Aluminimum	173	2771
Anthracite, broken	50	805
Asbestos cement	120–130	1920–2082
Ashes	43	688
Asphalt: natural	63	1009
paving	130	2082
Ballast, river	112	1792
Beech	48	769
Birch	44	705
Bitumen: natural	68	1089
prepared	85	1362
emulsion	70	1120
Books in bulk	60	960
Boots and shoes in cases	24	384
Bottled goods cases	56	897
Bottles empty, crates	26	416
Brass	519	8304
Bricks:		
Common clay	100–120	1600–1920
Sand cement	115	1840
Sand lime	130	2080
Brickwork	120	1920
Bronze, phosphor	558	8938
Cast Stone	90	1442
Cedar, Western red	24	384
Chalk, broken	100–170	1602–2723
Cheese, cases	32	512
Chestnut, sweet	35	560
Cigarettes, cases	15	240
Clay damp	128	2048
Coke–Coal (loose)	30–56	480–896
Columbian pine	33	529
Concrete, cement plain:		
Brick aggregate	115–135	1842–2162
Natural aggregate	144	2307
Concrete, cement reinforced	150	2400
Concrete, breeze	90	1440
Copper (wrought)	558	8938
Cork, granular	7·5	120
Cotton (piece goods)	30	48
Deal	27	432
Delta metal	537	8600

Mass Densities of Materials (continued)

Material	Pounds per cubic foot lb./ft.^{3}	Kilogrammes per cubic metre kg/m^3
Douglas Fir	33	528
Earth, dry loose	80	1280
moist compact	115	1840
Ebony	83	1330
Elm	36	576
Felt, insulating	12	192
Files, cases	56	896
Fir, Douglas	33	528
Fish, boxes	45	720
Flint	160	2560
Flour, sacks	40	640
Freestone:		
masonry dressed	150	2400
Freestone:		
rubble	140	2240
Glass, plate	176	2784
Gold	1208	19318
Grain: Barley	39	624
Oats	26	416
Rye	45	720
Granite, chippings	90	1442
dressed	140	2240
Granolithic	140	2240
Gravel: loose	100	1600
compact	135	2162
Greenheart	66	1056
Gurjun/keruing	45	720
Gyplith	28	448
Hardcore	120	1920
Hemlock, Western	31	496
Hosiery, cased	14	224
Ice	57	912
Iroko	41	656
Iron: cast	450	7208
wrought	480	7689
Ironmongery,		
packages	56	896
Ivory	115	1842
Jute, bales compressed	40	640
Larch, wood	37	592
Lead, cast	707	11325
Leather:		
hides, compressed	23	368
rolls	10	160
Lime mortar, dry	103	1650
Lime wood	35	560
Linen, piece goods	35	560

Mass Densities of Materials (continued)

Material	Pounds per cubic foot lb./ft.³	Kilogrammes per cubic metre kg/m³
Linoleum, rolls	30	480
Loam, sandy clay, dry, loose	75	1200
wet compact	120	1920
Logwood	57	912
Macadam	130	2080
Mahogany:		
African	35	561
Honduras	34	545
Spanish	43	689
Maple:		
Canadian	46	737
English	43	689
Mercury	846	13536
Mica	36–55	577–881
Mortar, cement, set	120–130	1920–2080
lime, set	100–106	1600–1700
Mud	110–120	1760–1920
Nails, wire, bags	75	1200
Nickel	551	8816
Nickel Silver	545	8730
Oak	45–55	720–880
Oil	55–60	880–960
Oregon Pine	33	529
Padauk	349	785
Paint: red lead	195	3120
white lead	175	2800
Paper:		
blotting, bales	25	400
printing, reels	56	896
wall, rolls	24	384
writing	60	960
Perspex	84	1346
Petrol, in cans	50	800
Pine:		
American red	33	529
British Columbian	33	529
Columbian	33	529
Danzig	36	577
Memel	34	545
Kauri, Queensland	30	481
New Zealand	38	609
Oregon	33	529
Pitch	41	657
Pipes:		
cast iron, stacked	60–80	960–1280
salt glazed, stacked	25	400
Pitch	68	1088

Mass Densities of Materials (continued)

Material	Pounds per cubic foot lb,/ft.³	Kilogrammes per cubic metre kg/m³
Plaster of Paris, set	80	1280
Platinum	1341	21465
Plywood	30–40	480–640
Plywood, resin bonded	45–90	720–1440
Polystyrene	66	1056
P.V.C. acetate	75–84	1200–1344
Poplar	28	448
Porcelain	145	2320
Portland cement in bags or drums	80	1280
Potatoes	40	640
Pulp, wood:		
dry	35	560
wet	45	720
Pumice	30–57	480–912
Quicklime, ground dry	64	1025
Quilt, eel grass	5	80
Redwood:		
American	33	529
Baltic	31	497
Roman cement	60	960
Rope, in coils	32	512
Salt, bulk	60	960
Sand, dry	105	1680
saturated	120	1920
Satinwood	60	960
Sawdust	13	208
Screws, iron, packages	100	1600
Sea water	64	1024
Shingle	89	1424
Silk, bales	22	352
Silver, pure	656	10492
Slag, coarse	90	1440
granulated	60	960
Slag wool	14–18	224–288
Slate, Welsh	175	2800
Westmorland	187	2995
Snow, fresh	6	96
wet compact	20	320
Soap, boxed	57	912
Soda, bags	41	656
Spruce:		
Canadian	29	465
Norway	29	465
Sitka	28	449
Stationery, cases	32	513
Steel, cases	490	7849

Mass Densities of Materials (*continued*)

Material	Pounds per cubic foot lb./ft.^{3}	Kilogrammes per cubic metre kg/m^3
Stone:		
Ancaster	156	2499
Bath	130	2082
Caen	125	2000
Darley Dale	145	2320
Forest of Dean	152	2432
granite, medium	165	2643
Ham Hill	135	2162
Hoptonwood	158	2531
Kentish Rag	167	2675
Mansfield Red	150	2403
marble	170	2723
millstone grit	145	2323
Portland	140	2243
Purbeck	169	2707
York	140	2243
Woolton	137	2195
Stone, cramps for	5	80
Straw: pressed	6	96
compressed bales	19	304
Sugar	46	736
Sycamore	38	609
Tar, barrels	50	800
Tarpaulins, bundles	45	720
Tea (in chests)	25	400
Teak	41	657
Terracotta (solid)	132	2114
Timber	see species headings	
Tinned goods, in cases	30–40	480–640
Tools, hand cases	56	897
Tyres, rubber	11–16	176–256
Varnish, barrels	37	592
tins in cases	45	720
Vermiculite:		
exfoliated for loose fill	4–5	64–80
Walnut	41	656
Waste paper	22	352
pressed and packed	28–32	449–513
Water, fresh	62	1000
salt	63–75	1110–1200
Wheat	46	736
Willow:		
American	36	577
English	28	450
Wine:		
bulk	61	977

Mass Densities of Materials (continued)

Materials	Pounds per per cubic foot lb./ft.^{3}	Kilogrammes per cubic metre kg/m^3
Wine:		
bottles in cases	37	593
Wire rope in coils	90	1440
Wolfram	460	7368
Wool, uncompressed	13	208
compressed bales	48	769
piece goods	28	448
Yew	42–50	672–800
Zinc, cast	425	6804
rolled	449	7192

Schedule 6. Weights of Miscellaneous Items

Item	lb. pounds	kg kilogrammes
Pianos:		
Upright approx.	630	285
Baby grand approx.	600	272
Full size grand approx.	1040	471

Selected Bibliography

The Architect in Practice, Arthur J. Willis and W. N. B. George in collaboration with Christopher J. Willis (Crosby Lockwood & Son Ltd., 1970)

Architectural Building Construction, W. R. Jaggard and F. E. Drury (Cambridge University Press, 1916)

The Black Death, Phillip Ziegler (Collins, 1969)

Brickwork and Masonry, C. F. Mitchell (B. T. Batsford Ltd., 1904)

Building Construction (18th and 19th editions), G. A. and A. M. Mitchell (B. T. Batsford Ltd., 1947)

Building Construction (four volumes, various editions), W. B. and J. K. McKay (Longmans, Green & Co. Ltd., 1968)

Building in England down to 1540, a documentary history, L. F. Salzman (Oxford University Press, 1952)

Builders Materials, Bernard H. Knight and Rena G. Knight (Edward Arnold Ltd., 1963)

Building Materials, Cecil C. Handisyde (The Architectural Press, 1967)

Building Repairs and Renovations, Harry Bryant Newbold (Caxton Publishing Co. Ltd., 1951)

Carpentry and Joinery. Advanced examples, Frank Keeling (Cleaver Hume Press Ltd., 1965)

Constructional Carpentry (2nd edition), Frank Keeling (Macmillan and Co. Ltd., 1966)

Constructive Sanitary Work, W. Frost (Caxton Publishing Co. Ltd.,)

Damp Walls, R. W. Castle (The Technical Press Ltd.)

Dampness in Buildings, R. T. Gratwick (Crosby Lockwood & Son Ltd., 1966)

The Development of Carpentry 1200–1700, An Essex Study, Cecil Alec Hewett (David and Charles, 1969)

Domestic Hot Water Supplies and Central Heating, David H. Beattie (Crosby Lockwood & Son Ltd., 1966)

Domestic Sanitation, F. G. Goodin and J. Downing (Estates Gazette Ltd., 1959)

Drainage and Sanitation, E. H. Blake and W. R. Jenkins (B. T. Batsford Ltd., 1956)

Drainage Details, Leslie Woolley (Aquarius), (Northwood Industrial Publications)

Economics for Students, J. L. Hanson (MacDonald and Evans, 1949)

Electric Wiring (Domestic), A. J. Coker (Newnes–Butterworths, 1969)

Emden and Gills Building Contracts and Practice (Seventh Edition), William H. Gill (Butterworths, 1969)

England in the Nineteenth Century 1815–1914, David Thomson (Penguin Books Ltd., 1967)

The English House through Seven Centuries, Olive Cook (Thomas Nelson and Sons Ltd., 1968)

Framed buildings of the Weald, R. T. Mason (Coach Publishing, 1964)

A Future for the Past, Moultrie R. Kelsall and Stuart Harris (Oliver and Boyd, 1961)

The Genesis of Modern British Town Planning, William Ashworth (Routledge and Kegan Paul Ltd., 1965)

Georgian London, John Summerson (Pleiades Books, 1948)

An Historical Outline of Architectural Science, Henry J. Cowan (Elsevier Publishing Company, 1966)

A History of Architecture on The Comparative Method, Sir Banister Fletcher (B. T. Batsford Ltd., 1948)

A History of Britain, E. H. Carter and R. A. F. Mears (Clarendon Press, Oxford, 1943)

A History of the Regulation of Building in London and of District Surveyors 1189–1954, C. C. Knowles (The Blackheath Press Ltd., 1955)

House Drainage, W. M. Spinks and E. H. Blake (Biggs and Co., 1903)

Houses, Margaret and Alexander Potter (John Murray)

Illustrated English Social History, G. M. Trevelyan (Penguin Books Ltd., 1968)

The Making of Classical Edinburgh 1750–1840, A. J. Youngson (University Press, Edinburgh 1966).

Old Churches and Modern Craftsmanship, Alban D. R. Caroe (Oxford University Press Ltd., 1949)

The Origins of Modern Town Planning, Leonardo Benevolo (Routledge and Kegan Paul, 1967)

Our Building Inheritance, Walter H. Godfrey (Faber and Faber Ltd., 1944)

The Pattern of English Building, Alec Clifton–Taylor (B. T. Batsford Ltd., 1965)

The Practical Painter and Decorator, (Various), (Odhams Press Ltd.)

Practical Sanitary Engineering, Francis Wood (Charles Griffin and Company Ltd., 1906)

Repair of Ancient Buildings, A. R. Powys (J. M. Dent and Sons Ltd., 1929)

The Restoration of Old Houses, Hugh Braun (Faber and Faber Ltd., 1954)

The Smaller English House 1500–1939, Reginald Turnor (B. T. Batsford Ltd., 1952)

Timber Building in England, Fred H. Crossley (B. T. Batsford Ltd., 1951)

The Timber Framed House in England, Trudy West (David and Charles, 1970)

The Timber Framed Houses of Essex, Harry Forrester (Published Privately, 1959)

Victorian Cities, Asa Briggs (Penguin Books Ltd., 1958)

The Weathering of Natural Building Stones, R. J. Schaffer (H.M.S.O., 1932)

The Publications of
The Building Research Establishment
The Department of the Environment
The British Standards Institution
The Timber Research and Development Association.

Index

Italics indicate that the subject forms part of an illustration or is discussed in the notes thereto.

1039